Algebra, Structure and Method, Book 1, New Edition

Key ideas and **guidelines** are outlined in red for easy reference, pp. 53, 185.

Exercise sets are graded in difficulty to meet the needs of a wide range of student abilities; word problems are frequently included, pp. 119–121.

Extra practice and **word problems** at the end of the student book provide additional opportunities for students to practice important algebraic skills, pp. 491–513, 514–524.

A **Plan For Solving A Word Problem** is introduced in Chapter 1 and used throughout the text to help students attack word problems systematically, pp. 22–23, 74, 82 . . . .

Students are taught to **organize information** in chart form when solving word problems. In doing this, students see the similarity of different types of problems, pp. 134, 140, 142 . . . .

Calculator Key-In and **Computer Key-In** sections give students the opportunity to apply new technology in a meaningful way, pp. 128, 157.

Multiple-Choice Chapter Reviews not only review skills and concepts but also prepare students for the type of questions that appear on college entrance examinations, p. 108.

Cumulative Reviews and **Maintaining Skills** at the ends of chapters provide constant reinforcement of skills, pp. 316–317.

A **wide-format Teacher's Edition** provides all of the support needed to teach the daily lesson, p. T10.

Permission-to-reproduce pages provide additional review, evaluation, and enrichment, pp. T12– T41.

Topical Reviews give students the opportunity to review skills in an integrated format, pp. T32.

A **Resource Book** accompanies the Teacher's Edition and provides practice, review, and evaluation in blackline master form.

TEACHER'S EDITION

ALGEBRA

STRUCTURE AND METHOD

Book 1   new edition

Mary P. Dolciani

Richard G. Brown

Frank Ebos

William L. Cole

EDITORIAL ADVISERS
Robert H. Sorgenfrey
William Wooton

TEACHER CONSULTANTS
William T. Stanford
Lois B. Whitman

HOUGHTON MIFFLIN COMPANY · BOSTON
Atlanta   Dallas   Geneva, Ill.   Hopewell, N.J.   Palo Alto   Toronto

THE AUTHORS

Mary P. Dolciani, Professor of Mathematical Sciences, Hunter College of the City University of New York.

Richard G. Brown, Mathematics Teacher, The Phillips Exeter Academy, Exeter, New Hampshire.

Frank Ebos, Professor of Mathematics Education, University of Toronto.

William L. Cole, Associate Professor of Mathematics Education, Michigan State University.

EDITORIAL ADVISERS

Robert H. Sorgenfrey, Professor of Mathematics, University of California, Los Angeles.

William Wooton, former Professor of Mathematics, Los Angeles Pierce College.

TEACHER CONSULTANTS

William T. Stanford, Coordinator of Mathematics, Waco Independent School District, Waco, Texas.

Lois B. Whitman, Mathematics Teacher, James Monroe High School, Sepulveda, California.

The authors of ALGEBRA, STRUCTURE AND METHOD BOOK 1 NEW EDITION, wish to thank **Lois B. Whitman** for her valuable contribution to this Teacher's Edition.

ISBN: 0-395-34093-4

CONTENTS

Student Text with Annotations and Teaching Aids

A facsimile (ninety percent of full size) of each student page with answers to exercises provided. Side columns present chalkboard examples; additional exercises; quick quizzes; comments on the Extras; suggested assignments; and references to the Extra Practice section, the Teacher's Edition manual, and the supplementary materials.

ORGANIZATION

The text consists of twelve chapters, making it easy to teach the course in both a semester and a trimester system. Each chapter is divided into numbered sections. Groups of sections are organized into sub-units of chapters indicated by displayed headings. Following Chapter 12 is a section entitled *Looking Ahead,* which gives students a feeling for some of the basic properties of geometry they will be studying in future courses.

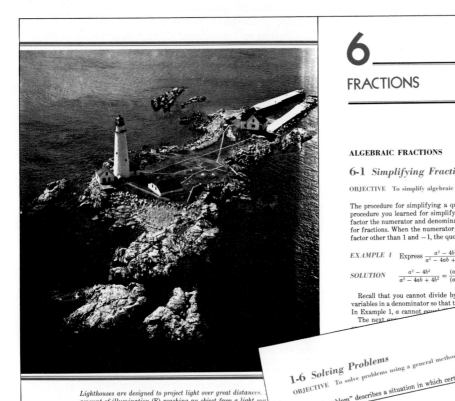

Lighthouses are designed to project light over great distances. The amount of illumination (E) reaching an object from a light source depends on the power of the light source (I) and its distance (s) from the object according to the formula $E = \frac{I}{s^2}$.

200

The content of the inset book page reads:

6

FRACTIONS

ALGEBRAIC FRACTIONS

6-1 Simplifying Fractions

OBJECTIVE To simplify algebraic fractions.

The procedure for simplifying a quotient of polynomials is the same procedure you learned for simplifying a quotient of monomials. Just factor the numerator and denominator and apply the cancellation rule for fractions. When the numerator and denominator have no common factor other than 1 and −1, the quotient is said to be in *simplest form.*

EXAMPLE 1 Express $\frac{a^2 - 4b^2}{a^2 - 4ab + 4b^2}$ in simplest form.

SOLUTION $\frac{a^2 - 4b^2}{a^2 - 4ab + 4b^2} = \frac{(a+2b)(a-2b)}{(a-2b)(a-2b)} = \frac{a+2b}{a-2b}$ $(a \neq 2b)$

Recall that you cannot divide by zero. Thus, you must
variables in a denominator so that the den
In Example 1, *a* cannot equa
The next ex

1-6 Solving Problems

OBJECTIVE To solve problems using a general method.

A "word problem" describes a situation in which certain numbers are related to each other. If
then you can solve the
Here are two simple
show you a general me

EXAMPLE 1
Maria bought a hit reco
of the same music. If the
was the cost of the cass

SOLUTION
Step 1 Read the pro
What numbers
Step 2 Choose a varia
the given facts
number(s) des
problem

9-2 The Slope-Intercept Form of a Linear Equation

OBJECTIVE To use the slope-intercept form of a linear equation.

The table shows the coordinates of a few of the points in the graph of the linear equation $y = 2x$.

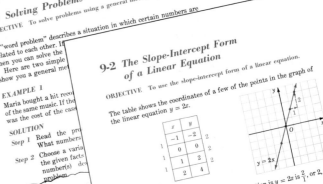

x	y
−1	−2
0	0
1	2
2	4

$y = 2x$

Notice that the slope of the line whose equation is $y = 2x$ is $\frac{2}{1}$, or 2, and that the line passes through the origin.

The graph of the equation $y = -\frac{1}{3}x$ is a line that has slope $-\frac{1}{3}$ and passes through the origin.

THE LESSONS

The lessons are designed to meet a wide range of pedagogical needs. Each Chapter Opener illustrates an application of a mathematical idea covered in that chapter. Every section begins with a stated objective for that section. The lessons are presented in a careful step-by-step development. Numerous detailed examples offer students additional guidelines. Equations and other material to be emphasized are displayed for clarity. Important properties are highlighted for easy reference by red double rules.

EXERCISES

Oral Exercises

For each trinomial, state the factors of the constant term whose sum is equal to the coefficient of the linear term.

SAMPLE $x^2 - 7x - 8$ *SOLUTION* $1, -8$

1. $a^2 + 3a - 4$ 4, −1   **2.** $x^2 + 2x - 3$ 3, −1   **3.** $t^2 + 5t - 6$ 6, −1

4. $y^2 + y - 6$ 3, −2   **5.** $y^2 - y - 6$ −3, 2   **6.** $b^2 - 8b - 9$ −9, 1

7. $b^2 + 8b - 9$ 9, −1   **8.** $u^2 - 3u - 10$ −5, 2   **9.** $r^2 + 5r - 14$ 7, −2

Written Exercises

Factor each expression. Check by multiplying the factors. If the expression is not factorable, write "prime."

A   **1.** $a^2 + 4a - 5$ **2.** $x^2 - 2x - 3$ **3.** $y^2 - 5y - 6$

   4. $b^2 + 2b - 15$ **5.** $c^2 - 11c - 10$ **6.** $r^2 + 6r - 16$

   7. $x^2 - 6x - 18$ **8.** $y^2 - 10y - 24$ **9.** $a^2 + 2a - 35$

   10. $k^2 - 2k - 20$ **11.** $z^2 + 5z - 36$ **12.** $r^2 - 3r - 40$

   13. $p^2 - 4p - 21$ **14.** $a^2 + 3a - 54$ **15.** $y^2 - 5y - 30$

   16. $z^2 - z - 72$ **17.** $a^2 - ab - 20b^2$ **18.** $y^2 - 2yz - 3z^2$

   19. $p^2 - 5pq - 50q^2$ **20.** $a^2 - 4ab - 77b^2$ **21.** $k^2 - 11kd - 60d^2$

   22. $s^2 + 14st - 72t^2$ **23.** $x^2 - 9xy - 22y^2$ **24.** $p^2 - pq - 72q^2$

B   **25.** $1 - 8ab - 20a^2b^2$ **26.** $1 - 7pq - 60p^2q^2$ **27.** $1 - ab - 56a^2b^2$

   28. $n^2 - 13nm + 48m^2$ **29.** $r^2 - 18r - 144$ **30.** $a^2 + 19a - 150$

   31. $800 - 20b - b^2$ **32.** $a^2 + 3a - 270$ **33.** $320 - 32x - x^2$

Find all the integral values of k for which the given polynomial can be factored.

34. $x^2 + kx - 12$ **35.** $y^2 + ky - 20$ **36.** $15 - kz - z^2$

1, 4, 11, −1, −4, −11   1, 8, 19, −1, −8, −19   2, 14, −2, −14

Find two negative values for k for which the given trinomial can be factored. Answers may vary for Exs. 37–42.

−12, −5

C   **37.** $x^2 - 3x + k$ −4, −10   **38.** $y^2 + 2y + k$ −3, −8   **39.** $z^2 + 4z + k$

   40. $k - 6x - x^2$ −5, −8   **41.** $n^2 + 11n + k$ −12, −26   **42.** $k + 4m - m^2$ −3, −4

Factor.

43. $(x + 1)^2 - 2(x + 1) - 15$ **44.** $(a + b)^2 - 3(a + b) - 70$

45. $(2x - y)^2 + 16(2x - y) + 60$ **46.** $4(a^2 - 1) - x^2(a^2 - 1)$

47. $x^4 - 8x^2 - 9$ **48.** $2x^4 - 34x^2 + 32$

49. $3a^4 - 63a^2 - 300$ **50.** $(3a + b)^4 - (a + b)^4$

Each section is followed by an ample set of exercises. Special emphasis is placed on providing practice with word problems. Written Exercises and Problems are graded A, B, and C. Enough B and C exercises are included to give students of all ability levels a challenge. Samples often are contained within exercise sets as a support for students when working on their own.

Problems

Solve.

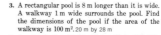
6 cm by 12 cm   Ex. 1

A   **1.** A rectangle is twice as long as it is wide. If its length and width are both increased by 2 cm, the area of the rectangle is increased by 40 cm². Find the dimensions of the original rectangle.

   2. A photo is 10 cm longer than it is wide. It is mounted in a frame 3 cm wide. The area of the frame is 156 cm². Find the dimensions of the picture. 5 cm by 15 cm

   3. A rectangular pool is 8 m longer than it is wide. A walkway 1 m wide surrounds the pool. Find the dimensions of the pool if the area of the walkway is 100 m². 20 m by 28 m

Ex. 2

   4. A poster is three times as long as it is wide. It is mounted on a piece of cardboard so that there is a strip 10 cm wide all around the poster. If the area of this bordering strip is 2800 cm², find the dimensions of the poster. 30 cm by 90 cm

B   **5.** A page of a book is 6 cm longer than it is wide. By increasing the length by 3 cm and the width by 2 cm, the book designer can increase the area of the page by 68 cm². Find the dimensions of the page. 10 cm by 16 cm

   6. An instrument is mounted on a rectangular base twice as long as it is wide. A design engineer must reduce the length of the base by 3 cm and the width by 1 cm to fit the instrument into the space available on a space vehicle. This change will reduce the area of the base by 27 cm². Find the original dimensions of the base. 6 cm by 12 cm

   7. A circular pool is surrounded by a walkway 2 m wide. Find the radius of the pool if the area of the walkway is 176 m². (*Hint:* The formula for the area of a circle with radius r is $A = \pi r^2$. Use $\frac{22}{7}$ as an approximation for π.) 13 m

   8. When the radius of a circular ripple in a pond increases by 4 cm, the area it encloses increases by 352 cm². Find the radius of the ripple after the increase. (See the hint for Exercise 7.) 16 cm

Ex. 7

Ex. 8

EXTRA PRACTICE

CHAPTER 1

Simplify.

   1. $4 + (3 \times 6)$ 22   **2.** $(4 + 3) \times 6$ 42   **3.** $(20 + 2) \times (7 + 3)$ 220

   4. $(20 \div 2) - (7 - 3)$ 6   **5.** $(20 - 2) \div (7 + 2)$ 2   **6.** $(20 \times 2) + (7 \times 3)$ 61

Evaluate each expression if $a = 1$, $b = 2$, $c = 3$, and $d = 4$.

   7. $ab + cd$ 14   **8.** $(b + c)(c + d)$ 35   **9.** $a(b + c - d)$ 1

   10. $\frac{c + d}{a + 3b}$ 1   **11.** $5a - 2a$ 3   **12.** $5c - 2c$ 9

   13. $\frac{ab + 2c}{a + c}$ 2   **14.** $2(a + bc)$ 14   **15.** $2a + 2bc$ 14

   16. $d[a + b(c + d)]$ 60   **17.** $\frac{2c + b}{2a} - \frac{(a + b)(c + d)}{3b + a}$ 1

Solve each equation if $x \in \{2, 4, 6, 8, 10\}$. If there is no solution over the given domain, write "no solution."

   18. $2 + x = 8$ {6}

Additional exercises and problems for each chapter are given in an Extra Practice section at the back of the book.

TESTS AND REVIEWS

Groups of sections conclude with a Self-Test that corresponds to the section objectives. Each chapter concludes with a brief Chapter Summary, a multiple-choice Chapter Review, and a Chapter Test. Both the Chapter Review and Chapter Test are keyed to the sections in the text for easy reference. Beginning with Chapter 3, each chapter contains a Cumulative Review that covers material presented in all of the preceding chapters. The Maintaining Skills pages at the ends of Chapters 1–11 provide practice with basic arithmetic and algebraic skills. Samples with complete solutions are included on all Maintaining Skills pages for students working by themselves.

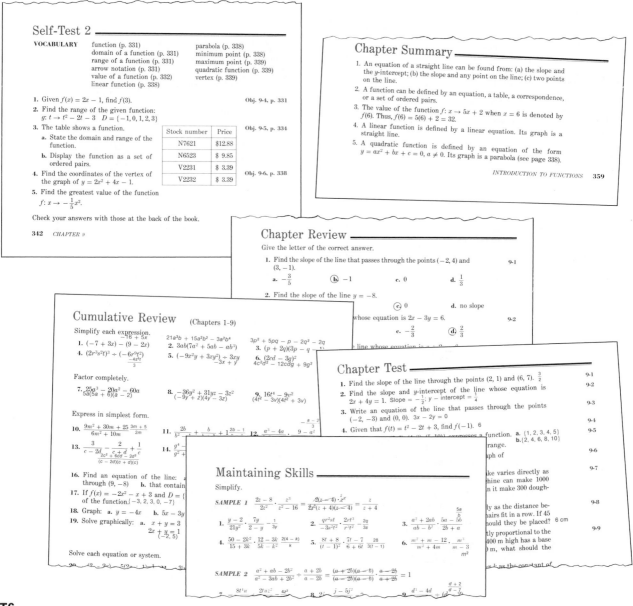

Self-Test 2

VOCABULARY function (p. 331)
domain of a function (p. 331)
range of a function (p. 331)
arrow notation (p. 331)
value of a function (p. 332)
linear function (p. 338)

parabola (p. 338)
minimum point (p. 338)
maximum point (p. 339)
quadratic function (p. 339)
vertex (p. 339)

1. Given $f(x) = 2x - 1$, find $f(3)$.   Obj. 9-4, p. 331
2. Find the range of the given function:
   $g: t \rightarrow t^2 - 2t - 3$ $D = \{-1, 0, 1, 2, 3\}$
3. The table shows a function.   Obj. 9-5, p. 334
   a. State the domain and range of the function.
   b. Display the function as a set of ordered pairs.

Stock number	Price
N7621	$12.88
N6523	$ 9.85
V2231	$ 3.39
V2232	$ 3.39

4. Find the coordinates of the vertex of the graph of $y = 2x^2 + 4x - 1$.   Obj. 9-6, p. 338
5. Find the greatest value of the function
   $f: x \rightarrow -\frac{1}{5}x^2$.

Check your answers with those at the back of the book.

342 CHAPTER 9

Chapter Summary

1. An equation of a straight line can be found from: (a) the slope and the y-intercept; (b) the slope and any point on the line; (c) two points on the line.
2. A function can be defined by an equation, a table, a correspondence, or a set of ordered pairs.
3. The value of the function $f: x \rightarrow 5x + 2$ when $x = 6$ is denoted by $f(6)$. Thus, $f(6) = 5(6) + 2 = 32$.
4. A linear function is defined by a linear equation. Its graph is a straight line.
5. A quadratic function is defined by an equation of the form $y = ax^2 + bx + c = 0, a \neq 0$. Its graph is a parabola (see page 338).

INTRODUCTION TO FUNCTIONS **359**

Chapter Review

Give the letter of the correct answer.

1. Find the slope of the line that passes through the points $(-2, 4)$ and $(3, -1)$.   9-1
   a. $-\frac{3}{5}$ b. -1 c. 0 d. $\frac{1}{3}$
2. Find the slope of the line $y = -8$.
   c. 0 d. no slope

   whose equation is $2x - 3y = 6$.   9-2
   c. $-\frac{2}{3}$ d. $\frac{2}{3}$

Cumulative Review (Chapters 1-9)

Simplify each expression.
1. $(-7 + 3x) - (9 - 2x)$ $-16 + 5x$
2. $3ab(7a^2 + 5ab - ab^3)$ $21a^3b + 15a^2b^2 - 3a^2b^4$
3. $(p + 2q)(3p - q - 1)$ $3p^2 + 5pq - p - 2q^2 - 2q$
4. $(2r^3s^2t)^3 \div (-6r^9t^2)$ $\frac{-4s^6t}{3}$
5. $(-9x^2y + 3xy^2) \div 3xy$ $-3x + y$
6. $(2ed - 3g)^2$ $4c^2d^2 - 12cdg + 9g^2$

Factor completely.
7. $25g^3 - 20a^2 - 60a$ $5a(5a + 6)(a - 2)$
8. $-36y^2 + 31yz - 3z^2$ $(-9y^2 + z)(4y - 3z)$
9. $16t^4 - 9y^2$ $(4t^2 - 3v)(4t^2 + 3v)$

Express in simplest form.
10. $\frac{9m^2 + 30m + 25}{6m^2 + 10m}$ $\frac{3m + 5}{2m}$
11. $\frac{2b}{b^2} + \frac{b}{\_} + 1 \frac{2b - 1}{\_}$
12. $a^3 - 4a$ $\frac{9 - a^2}{\_}$ $\frac{-a - 2}{3}$
13. $\frac{3}{c - 2d} + \frac{2}{\_} + \frac{1}{c}$ $\frac{2c^2 + 6cd + 2d^2}{(c - 2d)(c + d)(c)}$
14. $g^4 -$ $g^2 +$

16. Find an equation of the line: through $(9, -8)$ b. that contain
17. If $f(x) = -2x^2 - x + 3$ and $D = \{$ of the function.$\{-3, 2, 3, 0, -7\}$
18. Graph: a. $y = -4x$ b. $5x - 3y$
19. Solve graphically: a. $x + y = 3$ $2x + y = 1$ $(-2, 5)$

Solve each equation or system.

Chapter Test

1. Find the slope of the line through the points $(2, 1)$ and $(6, 7)$. $\frac{3}{2}$ 9-1
2. Find the slope and y-intercept of the line whose equation is $2x + 4y = 1$. Slope $= -\frac{1}{2}$; y-intercept $= \frac{1}{4}$ 9-2
3. Write an equation of the line that passes through the points $(-2, -3)$ and $(0, 0)$. $3x - 2y = 0$ 9-3
4. Given that $f(t) = t^2 - 2t + 3$, find $f(-1)$. 6   9-4

expresses a function. a. $\{1, 2, 3, 4, 5\}$ b.$\{2, 4, 6, 8, 10\}$ 9-5

range.   9-6

aph of   9-7

ke varies directly as
hine can make 1000
n it make 300 dough-   9-8

ly as the distance be-
hairs fit in a row. If 45
hould they be placed? 6 cm

tly proportional to the
400 m high has a base   9-9
0 m, what should the

or k as the constant of

Maintaining Skills

Simplify.

SAMPLE 1 $\frac{2z - 8}{2z^2} \cdot \frac{z^3}{z^2 - 16} = \frac{2(z - 4) \cdot z^3}{2z^2(z + 4)(z - 4)} = \frac{z}{z + 4}$

1. $\frac{y - 2}{21y^2} \cdot \frac{7y}{2 - y} - \frac{1}{3y}$
2. $\frac{qr^2st}{-3s^2t^2} \cdot \frac{2rt^3}{r^3t^2} - \frac{2q}{3s}$
3. $\frac{a^2 + 2ab}{ab - b^2} \cdot \frac{5a - 5b}{2b + a}$ $\frac{5a}{b}$
4. $\frac{50 - 2k^2}{15 + 3k} \cdot \frac{12 - 3k}{5k - k^2} \cdot \frac{2(4 - k)}{k}$
5. $\frac{8t + 8}{(t - 1)^2} \cdot \frac{7t - 7}{6 + 6t} \cdot \frac{28}{3(t - 1)}$
6. $\frac{m^2 + m - 12}{m^2 + 4m} \cdot \frac{m^3}{m - 3}$ m^2

SAMPLE 2 $\frac{a^2 + ab - 2b^2}{a^2 - 3ab + 2b^2} \div \frac{a + 2b}{a - 2b} = \frac{(a + 2b)(a - b)}{(a - 2b)(a - b)} \cdot \frac{a - 2b}{a + 2b} = 1$

7. $\frac{8t^4u}{\_}$ $\frac{2tuz^2}{\_}$ $\frac{4z^3}{\_}$
8. 2^j $\frac{j - 5j^7}{\_}$
9. $\frac{d^3 - 4d}{\_} \div (d^2 -)$ $\frac{d + 2}{d - 3}$

FEATURES

By placing calculator and computer topics in the text as optional features, special consideration is given to both of these important subjects without hindering the development of algebraic skills. The Computer Key-In features offer practical experience in using a computer to solve basic algebra problems. The Calculator Key-In features suggest how students can use a calculator to investigate ideas in algebra.

---

11. What is the area of a triangle whose sides are 8 cm, 9 cm, and 11 cm long? 35.5 cm²

Computer Key-In

If you have access to a computer that will accept BASIC, you can use the program below to print successive stages of the divide-and-average method of computing the square root of a positive integer. BASIC also has a built-in square root function which will give a positive square root directly. Before running the long program, try this:

```
10 PRINT SQR(16), SQR(17), SQR(18)
20 END
```

The last line of the following program prints the positive square root as given by the built-in function for comparison.

```
10  PRINT "INPUT A POSITIVE INTEGER";
20  INPUT N
30  IF N <= 0 THEN 10
40  PRINT "WHAT FACTOR WOULD YOU LIKE TO TRY";
50  INPUT F
60  IF F <= 0 THEN 40
70  LET Q=N/F
80  PRINT F,Q
90  IF ABS(F-Q)<.00001 THEN 120
100 LET F=(F+Q)/2
110 GOTO 70
120 PRINT "CHECK:";SQR(N)
130 END
```
3.87298

1. Run the program to find $\sqrt{15}$ by trying 1 as the factor. (Note: Input 15 as the positive integer.) Repeat, trying 2, 3, 4, and then 5 as factors.

2. Compare the print-out for the five parts of Exercise 1.

Experiment with other numbers and factors.

The closer the factor tried is to the actual square root, the shorter the print-out is.

RATIONAL AND IRRATIONAL NUMBERS 421

Calculator Key-In

You can use the calculator to evaluate a polynomial for a given value of the variable. One way is to evaluate the polynomial term by term using the calculator's memory to store the partial sums.

Another way is to express the polynomial in a form that suggests a sequence of steps on the calculator. For example, to evaluate $3x^2 - 4x + 5$, you could first rewrite it as follows:

$$3x^2 - 4x + 5 = (3x - 4)x + 5$$

To evaluate the polynomial for a particular value, you can just work through the rewritten expression from left to right substituting the appropriate value for x.

Evaluate the polynomial for the given value of the variable.

1. $4x^2 + 3x - 8$; 2 14
2. $6z^2 - 3z - 5$; 4 79
3. $2x^2 + 5x + 9$; -3 12
4. $y^2 - 2y - 3$; 1.5 -3.75
5. $15k^2 - 35k + 90$; 10 1240
6. $40v^2 - 20v + 80$; 17 11,300
7. $14x^2 - 15x - 5$; $\frac{1}{101}$ 8
8. $4y^2 + 4y - 5$; 0.4 -2.76
9. $10z^2 - 5z + 5$; -0.5 10

FACTORING POLYNOMIALS 157

---

e num
ts the
abe f
es f
$7c -$
e to school.
nutes less than the trip to school.
$- 3) = 75$

$$80(\tfrac{1}{2}t) + 100(\tfrac{1}{2}t) = 600$$

eled at 80 km/h for half of the time
half of the time. (Time of the trip)
ngular lot is 11 m less than twice the
hird side is 7 m longer than the first
235 m. (Length of the second side)
$s - 11) + s + ((2s - 11) + 7) = 235$

Career Note Programmer

$x_1 = 1$
$x_2 = (x_1 + 2)^2 = (1 + 2)^2 = 9$
$x_3 = (x_2 + 3)^2 = (9 + 3)^2 = 144$
$x_4 = (x_3 + 4)^2 = (144 + 4)^2 = 21,904$
$x_5 = (x_4 + 5)^2 = (21,904 + 5)^2 = 480,004,281$

How long would it take you to find x_{100}? Would you be likely to make a mistake? A computer can find x_{100} and do more complicated calculations accurately in just a fraction of a second. A computer cannot think for itself, however. It must be given detailed, step-by-step instructions in a computer language.

The primary task of the programmer is to write programs or instructions for a computer to follow. Then, after the program has been written, the programmer must check that the desired result will be obtained. A check is made by running the program with a set of typical data for which the results are known. Flowcharts which outline schematically the way in which the program works are sometimes used by programmers to plan their work and explain it to others.

A college degree with either a major or extensive course work in computer science is the usual requirement for a job in this field.

20 *CHAPTER 1*

The remaining features provide interesting and informative insights into the study of algebra. They may be used as short assignments or as bases for class discussions.

Biography Annie Jump Cannon

Annie Jump Cannon (1863–1941), by examining astronomical plates photographed through a prism, classified almost 400,000 [stars according to their stellar] spectra or temperatures [... Welles]ley College and did [work in ... physics, and astronomy [...
In 1896 she began [work ... classifying stars and d[eveloping a ... classification. She gro[uped ... cies to which the vas[t ... proved that these spe[... continuous series. In 1[... to receive an honorar[y degree from] Oxford University.

First factor out the greatest monomial factor. Then complete the factoring.

SAMPLE 3 $3x^3 - 75x = 3x(x^2 - 25) = 3x(x - 5)(x + 5)$

41. $2x^2 - 50$
$2(x + 5)(x - 5)$

42. $3y^2 - 48$
$3(y + 4)(y - 4)$

43. $45 - 5a^2$
$5(3 + a)(3 - a)$

44. $36x^2 - 81y^2$
$9(2x + 3y)(2x - 3y)$

45. $x^3 - 9x$
$x(x + 3)(x - 3)$

46. $2xy - 72x^3y$
$2xy(1 + 6x)(1 - 6x)$

47. $324 - 4k^4$
$4(9 + k^2)(3 + k)(3 - k)$

48. $\pi R^2 - \pi r^2$
$\pi(R + r)(R - r)$

Factor, assuming that n is a positive integer.

SAMPLE 4 $x^{2n} - y^{2n} = (x^n)^2 - y^2 = (x^n - y)(x^n + y)$

49. $x^{2n} - y^{2n}$
$(x^n + y^n)(x^n - y^n)$

50. $a^{2n} - 9$
$(a^n + 3)(a^n - 3)$

51. $b^{2n} - c^{4n}$
$(b^n + c^{2n})(b^n - c^{2n})$

52. $2x^{2n} - 98$
$2(x^n + 7)(x^n - 7)$

C **53.** $a^{4n} - b^{6n}$
$(a^{2n} + b^{3n})(a^{2n} - b^{3n})$

54. $x^{2n+1} - x$
$x(x^n + 1)(x^n - 1)$

55. $y^{2n+3} - y^3$
$y^3(y^n + 1)(y^n - 1)$

56. $ab^{4n} - a$
$a(b^{2n} + 1)(b^n + 1)(b^n - 1)$

EXTRA

Sums and Differences of Cubes

The following factoring patterns indicate that both sums and differences of cubes can be factored.

$$x^3 + y^3 = (x + y)(x^2 - xy + y^2)$$
$$x^3 - y^3 = (x - y)(x^2 [...]$$

EXAMPLE Factor $a^3 + 8$.

SOLUTION $a^3 + 8 = (a + 2)(a^2 - 2[...]$

1. Verify the factoring pattern for the sum [...]
$(x + y)(x^2 - xy + y^2)$.

2. Verify the factoring pattern for the differ[...]
ing $(x - y)(x^2 + xy + y^2)$.

Factor.

3. $n^3 + 27$
$(n + 3)(n^2 - 3n + 9)$

4. $a^3 - 8$
$(a - 2)(a^2 + 2a + 4)$

5. $x^3 [...]$
$(x + [...]$

7. **a.** Factor $z^6 - 1$ as a difference of cu[bes.]
$z^6 - 1 = (z - 1)(z + [...]$

b. Factor $z^6 - 1$ as a difference of sq[uares.]
$z^6 - 1 = (z - 1)(z + 1)(z^2 [...]$

c. Show that the factorizations given in [...]
$[...]^2 + 1 = (z^4 + [...]$
[...]he difference of [...]

Just for Fun

1, 3, 6, 10, 15, . . . are called triangular numbers because they can be represented by dots arranged to form triangles.

1   3   6   10   15   and so on

1. Draw diagrams for the next five triangular numbers.
2. If n represents the number of the triangular number in the list ($n = 1$ for 1, $n = 2$ for 3, and so on), verify for the first ten triangular numbers that the n[th tri...] $\dfrac{n(n + 1)}{[...]}$

Historical Note The Equals Sign

The symbols shown were all used in the sixteenth and seventeenth centuries to denote equality. It was not until the eighteenth century that the current equals sign $=$ was universally adopted.

The Englishman Robert Recorde is credited with the invention of the symbol $=$. He published a mathematics book in 1557 in which he used $=$ "to avoid the tedious repetition of the words 'is equal to.'" He said that he chose a pair of line segments of the same length because "no two things could be more equal." With the passage of time, the segments were shortened until the symbol became $=$.

Application Optics

The curved pieces of glass or plastic in a magnifying glass or a pair of eyeglasses are examples of *lenses*. When light passes through a lens, it is bent. The most common type of lens is the *converging lens,* which is used in cameras, movie projectors, and eyeglasses. Converging lenses cause parallel rays of light to converge to a point, as shown in the photo below.

The point at which the rays converge is called the *principal focus* of the lens. The distance from the principal focus to the center of the lens is called the *focal length* of the lens.

When you look through a converging lens, the size of the image you see will be determined by the distance from the object to the lens (d_o), the distance from the image to the lens (d_i), and the focal length of the lens (f).

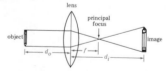

The relationship between d_o, d_i, and f is given by the following formula:

$$\frac{1}{d_o} + \frac{1}{d_i} = \frac{1}{f}$$

The apparent change in the size of an object viewed through a lens is called magnification. The magnification (M) of the image is given by the formula:

$$M = \frac{d_i}{d_o}$$

SUPPLEMENTARY MATERIALS

The Supplementary Materials on duplicating masters include Progress Tests, Practice Masters, and Computer Activities. All sets of masters are keyed to the text. The Progress Tests offer a simple way to measure achievement and keep track of performance. Practice Masters provide additional practice for students who may need extra help. Answers to the Progress Tests and Practice Masters are overprinted on the masters in nonreproducible ink. Computer Activities are self-contained worksheets that students can use to explore algebra by learning how to program a computer in BASIC. Complete answers are provided.

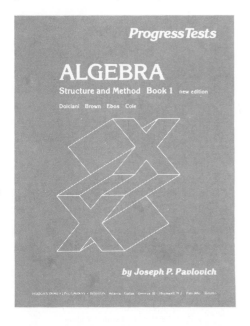

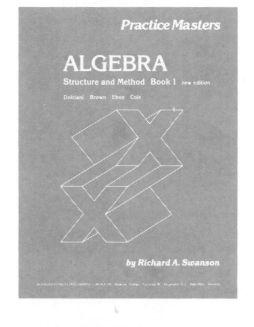

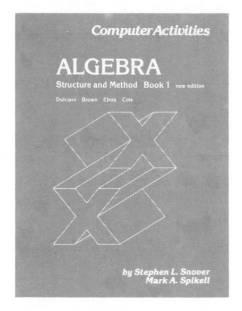

The Solution Key includes complete solutions to all exercises and problems.

USING THE TEACHER'S EDITION

The Teacher's Edition incorporates a nearly full-sized annotated student text with time-saving suggestions and additional materials right in the margins where they are most helpful.

Featured are references for Teaching Suggestions and Suggested Extensions at the front of the Teacher's Edition,

Chalkboard Examples for illustrating each lesson,

Supplementary Materials indexes that include references for reinforcing the lesson,

Suggested Assignments for various levels of ability,

references for Extra Practice Problems at the back of the student text,

---

Teaching Suggestions p. T47

Suggested Extensions p. T48

Chalkboard Examples
Solve.
1. $5y + 2y - 2 = 19$ 3
2. $\frac{x}{3} - 7 = 5$ 36
3. $3(x - 5) = -21$ -2
4. $12 - 2(z - 2) = 12$ 2
5. $-\frac{1}{3}x + 4 = 9$ -15
6. $-21 = 3 - 2x$ 12
7. $-16 = -4(2 - t)$ -2

Supplementary Materials
Practice Master 12

Computer Activity 8
Break-Even Point
 Using elementary algebra and a computer program that generates an easy-to-read chart, students are introduced to an important business idea, the break-even point. Various problems are included that provide practice in running the program and analyzing the results.

Suggested Assignments
Minimum
Day 1:   97/1-43 odd
    R 94/*Self-Test 2*

Day 2:   97/42, 44
      98/*P:* 1-9 odd
Average
Day 1:   97/1-47 odd
    R 94/*Self-Test 2*

Day 2:   98/*P:* 1-7 odd, 8,
        10, 11, 13, 15
Maximum
Day 1:   97/1-49 odd
    R 94/*Self-Test 2*

Day 2:   98/*P:* 1, 8, 9,
        12-18, 21, 24, 25

Extra Practice Problems
 p. 515

96

TRANSFORMING EQUATIONS

3-7 *Using Several Transformations*

OBJECTIVE   To use several transformations to solve an equation.

To solve the equation $3x + 8 = 20$, you transform it into an equivalent equation which has x alone as one side. Look at the side with x in it: $3x + 8$. To get x alone, first subtract 8 and then divide by 3, as follows.

$$3x + 8 = 20$$
$$3x + 8 - 8 = 20 - 8 \quad \leftarrow \text{Subtract 8.}$$
$$3x = 12$$
$$\frac{3x}{3} = \frac{12}{3} \quad \leftarrow \text{Divide by 3.}$$
$$x = 4$$

To "undo" the *addition* of a number, you use the *subtraction* of that number. Addition and subtraction are called **inverse operations.** Multiplication and division are also inverse operations.

The following steps are usually helpful when you solve an equation in which all the variables are on the same side.

---

1. Simplify each side of the equation.
2. If there are still indicated additions or subtractions, use the inverse operations to undo them.
3. If there are indicated multiplications or divisions involving the variable, use the inverse operations to undo them.

EXAMPLE 1   Solve $8x + 5x - 3 = 23$.

SOLUTION
$$8x + 5x - 3 = 23$$
$$(8 + 5)x - 3 = 23 \quad \left\{ \begin{array}{l} \text{Use the distributive axiom} \\ \text{to simplify the left side.} \end{array} \right.$$
$$13x - 3 = 23$$
$$13x - 3 + 3 = 23 + 3 \quad \leftarrow \text{Add 3 to each side.}$$
$$13x = 26$$
$$\frac{13x}{13} = \frac{26}{13} \quad \leftarrow \text{Divide each side by 13.}$$
$$x = 2$$

CONDENSED $8x + 5x - 3 = 23$ *Check:* $8x + 5x - 3 = 23$
SOLUTION $13x - 3 = 23$ $8(2) + 5(2) - 3 \overset{?}{=} 23$
         $13x = 26$ $16 + 10 - 3 \overset{?}{=} 23$
         $x = 2$ $23 = 23$ √
                         ∴ the solution is 2. *Answer*

96   CHAPTER 3

Oral Exercises

Describe how you would solve each equation.

SAMPLE $\frac{1}{3}x + 1 = -2$ **SOLUTION** First subtract 1 from each side;
then multiply each side by 3.

1. $4x + 1 = 5$ 2. $3x - 2 = 8$ 3. $\frac{1}{2}x - 3 = -1$

4. $-\frac{1}{5}x + 8 = 4$ 5. $6 + \frac{x}{2} = 7$ 6. $-2 + \frac{x}{-3} = 4$

7. $5x + x = 18$ 8. $4y - y = 12$ 9. $z - 4z = 6$

10. $-5t + 7t = -20$ 11. $6s + s - 2 = 5$ 12. $3m - m + 1 = -7$

Written Exercises

Solve.

A
1. $3x + 5 = 14$ 2. $2y - 5 = 17$ 3. $-13 + 4t = -37$
4. $12 + 5s = -78$ 5. $\frac{a}{2} - 4 = 8$ 6. $\frac{b}{3} + 6 = 9$
7. $\frac{c}{5} + 20 = -15$ 8. $\frac{-d}{4} - 2 = -1$ 9. $9 = 5 - 2m$
10. $12 = -3 - 5n$ 11. $-6w + 3w = 21$ 12. $3k - k = -8$
13. $5t + 3t = -32$ 14. $2p - 5p = -15$ 15. $3q + 4q = 0$
16. $7s - 11s = 0$ 17. $2k + 42 = 0$ 18. $4w + 80 = 0$
19. $5q - 3q + 10 = 0$ 20. $3w - w - 2 = 0$ 21. $x - 4x + 2 = 5$
22. $r - 7 - 4r = -4$ 23. $0 = m - 14 - 3m$ 24. $0 = u + 15 + 4u$
25. $x + 2x + 3x = 24$ 26. $3y - 2y + y = 36$ 27. $5(a - 2) = -35$
28. $6(b + 9) = -30$ 29. $-3(r - 3) = 12$ 30. $-8(s + 5) = 56$

B
31. $3(x + 1) + 2 = -7$ 32. $2(y - 1) - 7 = 5$
33. $4(w + 8) - 13 = -1$ 34. $5(z - 2) + 8 = 3$
35. $8 + 3(x + 1) = -4$ 36. $13 + 4(y + 5) = -3$
37. $4 - 3(a - 1) = -2$ 38. $7 - 4(b + 1) = -1$
39. $-4 - 3(2y + 1) = -13$ 40. $-5 + 4(3d - 6) = 7$
41. $(a - 10) + (a - 2) + a = 0$ 42. $(3 - b) + (4 - b) + (5 - b) = 0$
43. $3(r + 4) - 2r = -5$ 44. $2(s - 3) - s = -2$

C
45. $x - 2[6 - (1 - 2x)] = 0$ 46. $\frac{1}{2}[3(m + 2) - (2 - m)] = 6$
47. $-2[y + 3(5 - y)] - 5(y - 7) = 0$ 48. $5z + 2[3(1 - z) - 2(1 + z)] = 22$
49. $2|x| - (|x| - 1) = 7$ 50. $7(|y| - 2) - 3|y| - 16 = 2$

SOLVING EQUATIONS **97**

Additional Answers
Oral Exercises

7. Add x to $5x$; then divide each side by 6.

8. Subtract y from $4y$; then divide each side by 3.

9. Subtract $4z$ from z; then divide each side by -3.

10. Add $7t$ to $-5t$; then divide each side by 2.

11. Add s to $6s$; then add 2 to each side; then divide each side by 7.

12. Subtract m from $3m$; then subtract 1 from each side; then divide each side by 2.

Additional A Exercises

Solve.
1. $6x + 5 = 29$ 4
2. $3a - 2 = 13$ 5
3. $\frac{1}{2}m + 7 = 2$ -10
4. $\frac{1}{5}c - 3 = -5$ -10
5. $2n + 5n = 56$ 8
6. $5y - y = -28$ -7

97

Additional Answers to supplement the annotations,

Additional A Exercises to assure that students can proceed with the Written Exercises on their own,

and a Quick Quiz for each page on which a Self-Test appears, to check students' understanding. For example, the quiz below accompanies Self-Test 5 on page 195.

Quick Quiz

Solve.
1. $w(w + 3)(w - 1) = 0$
   $0, -3, 1$
2. $x^2 - 12x + 36 = 0$ 6
3. $a^2 - 9a = 52$ $13, -4$
4. $4d^3 - 36d = 0$ $0, 3, -3$
5. The squares of two consecutive positive integers differ by 31. Find the integers. 15, 16

Permission-to-reproduce pages, including Alternate Chapter Tests, Trimester Cumulative Reviews, Cumulative Topical Reviews, and Optional Enrichment Activities, are located in the front of the Teacher's Edition. Also included are Answers to the Tests, Reviews, and Activities, an Assignment Guide, a Supplementary Materials Chart of program supplements, and a section-by-section Lesson Commentary.

CHAPTER TESTS _____

Chapter 1 Test

1. Simplify $(40 - 8) \div (4 \times 2)$.

2. Evaluate $\dfrac{st}{s-t} - \dfrac{r+s}{r}$ if $r = 5$, $s = 10$, and $t = 6$.

3. Simplify $13 + 8 - 7 \times 2 + 4 \div 2$.

4. Evaluate $c\left[a(b-c) + \dfrac{b}{a+c}\right]$ if $a = 6$, $b = 18$, and $c = 3$.

5. Find the solution set of $3x = 5x - 14$ if $x \in \{1, 3, 5, 7, 9\}$.

6. If x represents the first number, write an expression for the sum of three consecutive odd numbers.

7. An adult one-way bus ticket and a child's one-way ticket together cost $2.40. The adult fare is twice the child's fare. If c represents the child's fare, write an equation that represents the given facts.

Solve.

8. During a sale, if you buy one record at the local department store, you get another record for half price. The half price record costs $2.65. If all records are the same price, what is the regular price of a record?

Chapter 2 Test

1. Graph the numbers 0, 3.5, $^-2$, and $^-0.5$ on a number line.

Replace the __?__ with one of the symbols $<$ or $>$ to make a true statement.

2. $^-8$ __?__ $^-7$

3. $40 - 4(2 \times 3)$ __?__ $30 - 3(1 + 4)$

4. Write the numbers 0, 3, $^-2$, $^-2.5$, and 3.5 in order from least to greatest.

Name the axiom that justifies each step.

5. $(20 \times 3.5) \times 5 = (3.5 \times 20) \times 5$ __?__

6. $\qquad\qquad\quad = 3.5 \times (20 \times 5)$ __?__

7. $\qquad\qquad\quad = 3.5 \times 100$ __?__

8. $\qquad\qquad\quad = 350$ __?__

9. Write the opposite of $-x$.

10. Simplify $3 - (-2)$.

11. Simplify $|-5| + |5|$.

12. Simplify $-(|-7| + |3|)$.

Solve.

13. At the beginning of the academic year at a university, 3068 students were enrolled. During the year, 795 students graduated, 351 students transferred in, 292 students transferred out, and 217 students failed courses and left school. How did the enrollment at the end of the year compare to that of the beginning of the year?

14. Simplify $36\left(\dfrac{1}{3} + \dfrac{1}{4}\right)$.

15. Simplify $4(x + 2y) + 11(3x + y)$.

16. Simplify $(-2)(-5)(-1)$.

17. Simplify $-r + 3r + 2[5 + (-3)r] + (-7)$.

18. Simplify $\dfrac{1}{xy}(3xyz)$, assuming $x \neq 0$ and $y \neq 0$.

19. Simplify $-2\left[\dfrac{1}{5}(10x + 3) + \left(-\dfrac{2}{5}\right)\right]$.

Chapter 3 Test

Solve.

1. $x + (-8) = 15$

2. $5 + (-a) = -3$

Simplify.

3. $t - (t - 3) - 1$

4. $12 - (x - 5) - [2x - (x - 1)]$

Solve.

5. $s + 74 = 210$

6. $-3 - (r - 5) = -2$

7. $-\frac{1}{5}z = 5$

8. $-1.5x = -3.0$

9. Simplify $24 \div \left(-\frac{1}{3}\right)$.

10. Evaluate $\dfrac{2x - y}{z}$ if $x = -3$, $y = -1$, and $z = \dfrac{1}{5}$.

Solve.

11. $6y = -42$

12. $-5u = -455$

13. $2x - 6x + 7 = -41$

14. $2 - 3(2x - 1) = 15$

15. $3p - 14 = 2 - p$

16. $7(m + 1) = 12 - 2(5 - m)$

17. Find a number which is nine less than twice its opposite.

Write the missing reasons.

	$3x - 5x = 22$	Given
18.	$(3 - 5)x = 22$	_?_
19.	$-2x = 22$	_?_
20.	$-\frac{1}{2}(-2x) = -\frac{1}{2}(22)$	_?_

Chapter 4 Test

1. Write "Four less than the cube of the sum of a and b" in exponential form.

2. Evaluate $7(x^3 - 1) + 3y^2 - (2x)^2$ if $x = 3$ and $y = 2$.

Simplify.

3. $3x^2y + 2xy^2 - 5x^2y - xy - xy^2$

4. $(3x - 2y + 5z) - (2x - 4z)$

5. Solve $3 - (a^2 - 2a + 5) = 6 - a^2$.

Simplify.

6. $x \cdot 2x^3 \cdot (2x)^4$

7. $x^{n+1} \cdot 3x^{2n-1} \cdot (2x)^2$

8. $-2(y^3)^3$

9. $(2x)^4 (3x^2) \left(\dfrac{1}{6}x\right)^3$

10. Multiply $-\dfrac{1}{2}x^2(6x^3 - 4x^2 + 2x)$.

11. Solve $2(n - 6) - (3 - 5n)n = 5n^2 - (2n - 12)$.

Multiply.

12. $(x - 4)(x + 3)$

13. $(3p - 2q)(9p^2 + 6pq + 4q^2)$

14. Solve $(x - 3)(x - 2) - x(x + 1) = 18$.

15. Laura has x quarters and three more dimes than quarters. Write an expression to describe the value in cents of the dimes.

16. Solve the equation $\dfrac{a - x + b}{2} = c$ for x.

Solve.

17. Fletcher earns \$4.50 an hour at his dad's office and \$3.75 an hour at a garage. Last week he worked six hours more at the garage than at the office, and his total earnings were \$55.50. How many hours did he work at the office?

18. Two planes left an airport at the same time, headed in the same direction. One plane traveled 100 km/h faster than the other. The faster plane took 6 h and the slower plane took 7 h to arrive at the same destination. What was the rate of each plane?

19. A rectangular pool is 5 m longer than it is wide. A walkway 2 m wide is to be added around three sides of the pool, the two shorter sides and one of the longer sides. If the area of the new walkway is 159 m², what is the length of the pool?

Chapter 5 Test

1. Write the prime factorization of 308.
2. Find the greatest common factor of 252 and 270.

Simplify, assuming no denominator equals 0.

3. $\dfrac{-8x^3y}{32xy^2z}$

4. $\dfrac{(2x^2)^3\,(3xy)^2}{6x^2yz^5}$

5. Divide: $\dfrac{5r^2s^3 + 15rs^5 - 35r^2s^4}{5rs^3}$

6. Factor $6x^2y^2 - 12x^3y + 18x^3y^2$ as a product of its greatest monomial factor and another polynomial.
7. Multiply $(a - 2b)(3a - 5b)$.
8. Solve $(x - 3)(x - 1) = (x + 3)(x - 15)$.
9. Multiply $(2a^2 - 3b)(2a^2 + 3b)$.
10. Factor $16x^4 - 1$.
11. Multiply $(x^2 - 3y)^2$.
12. Factor $x^2y^2 - 14xy + 49$.

Factor.

13. $x^2 - 7x + 10$
14. $a^2 + 11ab + 24b^2$
15. $r^2 - 7r - 18$
16. $x^2 + xy - 20y^2$
17. $12b^2 + b - 1$
18. $2x^2 + 5xy - 3y^2$
19. $4x^2 - 9y^2$
20. $(x + 1) - y(x + 1)$
21. $3x^2 - 3x + xy - y$
22. $-a^2 - a + 12$
23. $3ax^2 - 18axy + 27ay^2$
24. $a(x - y) + (y - x)$
25. $3(a^2 - b^2) - a(b - a)$

Solve.

26. $x(x - 1) = 0$
27. $2n(n - 13)(n + 5) = 0$
28. $x^2 - 12x + 35 = 0$
29. $y^2 - 8y + 16 = 25$

30. A mat board is 20 cm wide and 24 cm long. A photo is placed on the mat board so that a uniform border of width x cm is left. If the photo covers two thirds of the area of the mat board, what are the dimensions of the photo?

Chapter 6 Test

Simplify.

1. $\dfrac{ax^2 - ay^2}{y - x}$

2. $\dfrac{r^2 - 2r - 15}{5 - 6r + r^2}$

3. $\left(\dfrac{2}{3}\right)^3 \cdot \dfrac{45}{12}$

4. $\dfrac{4 - y^2}{y} \cdot \dfrac{2x^2y}{2x - xy}$

5. $\left(\dfrac{2x^2yz^3}{3}\right)^3$

6. $\dfrac{3x}{2} \div \dfrac{(6x)^2}{5}$

7. $\dfrac{x^2 - 9}{3x} \div (x + 3)$

8. $\dfrac{3(a^2 + 2ab + b^2)}{a^2 - b^2} \div \dfrac{9a^2}{a^2 + ab - 2b^2}$

9. $\dfrac{(2x^2)^3}{4xy^2} \div \left(\dfrac{2x^3}{(2y)^2} \div \dfrac{y}{2x}\right)$

10. Find the least common denominator for $\dfrac{1}{6ab}$, $\dfrac{2}{9a^2}$, and $\dfrac{3}{2b}$.

11. Express each of $\dfrac{y}{4x}$, $\dfrac{x - y}{2(x + y)}$, and $\dfrac{1}{2x^2}$ by using their LCD.

Simplify.

12. $\dfrac{3}{x} + \dfrac{5}{x} - \dfrac{4}{x}$

13. $\dfrac{2a}{3b^2} - \dfrac{b}{2a} + \dfrac{1}{4ab}$

14. $\dfrac{3}{x - 1} - \dfrac{4}{1 - x}$

15. $\dfrac{x + 1}{2x - 1} + \dfrac{x}{2x + 1} - \dfrac{2(2 - x)}{4x^2 - 1}$

16. $\dfrac{7}{2n} + 3n$

17. $\dfrac{4}{y} - 1 - \dfrac{5}{y^2}$

18. $2\left(\dfrac{a + b}{a}\right) \div \left(\dfrac{a^2 - b^2}{b}\right)$

19. Divide $(6x^2 + 11x - 10)$ by $(3x - 2)$.

20. Divide $(x^3 - 1)$ by $(x - 1)$.

Chapter 7 Test

State each ratio in simplest form.

1. 6 cm to 2.5 m

2. $(6ab)^2 : 9a^2b$

3. Find the ratio of x to y if $6x + 18y = 2(x + y)$.

Solve.

4. Three partners are to receive the profits from their business in the ratio of $1:2:4$. If the profit for one month is \$21,000, how much does each partner receive?

Solve for x.

5. $\dfrac{3x}{10} = \dfrac{9}{2}$

6. $\dfrac{2}{x} = \dfrac{3}{2(x - 1)}$

7. $\dfrac{a}{b} = \dfrac{x}{c}$

8. $\dfrac{x}{3} + \dfrac{x}{2} = 5$

9. $\dfrac{4x}{5} - \dfrac{3(x - 3)}{2} = 1$

10. $\dfrac{5}{x} = \dfrac{x + 1}{x + 12}$

11. $\dfrac{1}{x - 4} + \dfrac{4}{4x - x^2} = 1$

12. What is 115% of \$30?

13. What percent of 75 is 60?

14. A \$250 desk is on sale for \$162.50. What is the percent of discount?

15. The Allens received \$74,806 for their house after paying their broker a 6% commission on the selling price. What was the selling price?

16. A butcher grinds together 15 kg of beef that is 72% lean and 20 kg of beef that is 86% lean. What is the percent of lean meat in the resulting mixture?

17. One variety of coffee beans sells for \$6.90 per kilogram. Another variety sells for \$5.90 per kilogram. How many kilograms of each variety must be blended to make a mixture of coffee beans that sells for \$6.30 per kilogram?

18. John can wash a car in 1 h, Julie can wash the same car in 0.75 h, and Vicki can wash it in 1.25 h. How long will it take them to wash the car if they all work together?

Chapter 8 Test

Plot the graph of each ordered pair in a coordinate plane. Name the quadrant in which each graph is located.

1. $(2, -5)$ 2. $(-3, 1)$

3. Solve the equation $2x - 3y = 15$ for y in terms of x.

4. Find the solution set of $x - 2y = 8$ if both x and y are members of $\{-4, -2, 0, 2, 4\}$.

Graph in a coordinate plane.

5. $x + 4y = 12$ 6. $x = -2$

7. Solve by the graphic method: $x - y = 5$
                                         $2x + 5y = 3$

8. Solve by the substitution method: $x - 2y = 2$
                                         $3x + 2y = 0$

9. Use a system of two equations in two variables and the substitution method to solve the following problem: Jan and Sue each work a three-hour shift, but at different rates of pay. If Jan works 1 shift and Sue works 2 shifts, their total pay is $40. If Jan works 3 shifts and Sue works 2 shifts, their total pay is $60. What is each paid for a three-hour shift?

Solve each system by the addition-or-subtraction method.

10. $2x - y = -2$ 11. $2x - 3y = 21$
     $3x - y = -1$ $3x - 2y = 19$

Solve by using a system of two equations in two variables.

12. The sum of the digits of a two-digit number is 10. When the digits are reversed, the new number is one less than twice the original number. Find the original number.

13. A canoeist paddles downstream for 6 h and travels a distance of 93 km. But when paddling upstream, the same canoeist travels only 42 km in 4 h. What is the rate of the current?

Chapter 9 Test

1. Find the slope of the line through the points $(3, 5)$ and $(-3, 1)$.

2. The points $(-2, 7)$, $(1, 3)$, and $(4, c)$ all lie on the same line. Find the value of c.

3. Write in standard form the equation of a line that has a slope of $-\frac{2}{3}$ and a y-intercept of -1.

4. Write an equation of the line having the same y-intercept as the graph of $x - 2y = 6$ and the same slope as the graph of $3y - x = 2$.

5. Write an equation of the line with slope $\frac{5}{2}$ that passes through the point $(0, 7)$.

6. Write an equation of the line that passes through the points $(2, 5)$ and $(-3, 5)$.

7. Given that $f(x) = x^2 - 3x + 4$, find $\frac{1}{2}f(-1)$.

8. State the domain and range of the function described by the set of ordered pairs $\{(-3, 3), (5, 5), (-1, 1), (4, 4), (0, 0)\}$.

9. Given the equation $y = x^2 - 4x + 7$,

   a. write the coordinates of the vertex of the graph of the equation;

   b. sketch the graph, using at least three points; and

   c. state whether the vertex is a maximum or minimum point of the graph of the function defined by the equation.

10. The number of cookies Alan can bake is directly proportional to the amount of time available for baking. If he can bake two and one-half dozen cookies in a half hour, how long will it take him to bake six dozen cookies?

11. (m_1, d_1) and (m_2, d_2) are ordered pairs of the same inverse variation. Find m_2 if $m_1 = 10$, $d_1 = 75$, and $d_2 = 25$.

12. The area of a circle varies directly as the square of the radius, according to the formula $A = \pi r^2$.

   a. What is the constant of proportionality?

   b. If the radius of a circle is tripled, how is the area affected?

13. The distance a car travels from rest varies jointly as its acceleration and the square of the time it is in motion. How long will it take a car to go 4000 m from rest at an acceleration of 18 m/sec^2 if it can go 400 m from rest in 3 s at an acceleration of 20 m/sec^2?

Chapter 10 Test

1. Find the solution set of $3x + 2 \geq 1$ if $x \in \{-2, -1, 0, 1, 2\}$.

2. Graph the solution set of $-3 \leq k < 2$ if the domain is the set of real numbers.

Solve each inequality and graph the solution set on a number line.

3. $2(x - 3) < 3 - x$

4. $2 - 3x \leq 5$

5. The sum of three consecutive positive even integers is greater than 27 and less than 37. Find all possible combinations of such numbers.

Graph each solution set if the domain is the set of real numbers.

6. $x \geq 2$ or $x + 1 < 0$

7. $3 \leq 1 - k < 5$

8. Solve $|2 - x| = 5$.

9. Solve $|2x - 3| < 13$ and graph the solution set.

10. Graph the inequality $3x - 5x < 15$ in a coordinate plane.

11. Graph the solution set of the system: $x \geq 4$
$$2x - y < 7$$

Chapter 11 Test

1. Find the rational number halfway between $-\dfrac{7}{8}$ and $-\dfrac{8}{9}$.

2. Express $\dfrac{13}{11}$ as a decimal.

3. Express $5.3\overline{24}$ as a fraction in simplest form.

Find the indicated square roots.

4. $\sqrt{\dfrac{900}{67600}}$

5. $\sqrt{0.0121}$

Use the Table of Square Roots on page 526 to approximate to the nearest tenth.

6. $\sqrt{396}$

7. $\sqrt{0.4}$

8. Simplify: $\sqrt{\dfrac{81ab^2c^5}{4abd^4}}$

9. Solve $x^2 = 81$.

10. Each side of a square measures 17 cm in length. Find the length of a diagonal of the square to the nearest hundredth.

11. Are 7, 23, and 25 the lengths of the sides of a right triangle?

Express in simplest form.

12. $5\sqrt{450}$

13. $\sqrt{\dfrac{2x^2}{5}}$

14. $2\sqrt{5} + 3\sqrt{3} - \sqrt{5}$

15. $3\sqrt{18} - \sqrt{242} + 2\sqrt{50}$

16. $(\sqrt{2} + 3\sqrt{5})^2$

17. $(2\sqrt{3} + 5\sqrt{6})(4\sqrt{3} - 3\sqrt{6})$

18. Rationalize the denominator: $\dfrac{\sqrt{3}}{1 - 2\sqrt{3}}$

Solve.

19. $\sqrt{x+3} = 8$

20. $1 + 2\sqrt{3x^2 + 1} = 15$

Chapter 12 Test

Solve.

1. $2x^2 = 128$

2. $(x - 3)^2 + 4 = 9$

Solve by completing the square.

3. $x^2 + 4x - 2 = 0$

4. $2x^2 + 5x - 2 = 0$

Solve by the quadratic formula.

5. $r^2 + 6r + 4 = 0$

6. $2x^2 = 1 - 2x$

State the number of real-number roots.

7. $p^2 + 5p + 6 = 0$

8. $4x^2 - 4x + 1 = 0$

Solve by the most convenient method.

9. $3x^2 - 8x + 5 = 0$

10. $10x^2 - 65x = 0$

Solve. Approximate irrational roots to the nearest tenth.

11. The length of a rectangular swimming pool is 5 m more than its width. If the area of the pool is 500 m², what are the dimensions of the pool?

12. A rectangular garden is 10 m wide and 13 m long. One long side of the garden is against a permanent fence. If the garden is to be doubled in area next year by adding a uniformly wide strip on the other three sides, how wide should the strip be?

CUMULATIVE REVIEWS _____

Review for Chapters 1–4

Simplify.

1. $(66 + 11 \div 11 - 4) \div (9 - 6)$

2. $-(-3) + 2 - (-0)$

3. $9 - (|-2| + |2|)$

4. $21 + (-33) + 71 + (-45) + (-15) + 125$

5. $\frac{1}{8}(9) + \frac{1}{8}(15)$

6. $-15a + 4 + 6a + (-9) + a$

7. $3[7x + 2(3x + 4)] + (-11x) + (-5)$

8. $(-2)(-3)(-4) + (-3)(5) + (-1)(-7) + (2)(-4)$

9. $-4[3x + (-2x) + 10x]$

10. $\left(-\frac{1}{5}\right)5xy$

11. $\left(-\frac{1}{2}\right)[14a + (-2)b]$

12. $2x - 3y + 5x - y - (x - y)$

13. $\dfrac{-10}{\frac{1}{7}}$

14. $6(4^2 - 1) + 3^3 - (24 \div 2^3)$

15. $4a^2 - 3ab + b^2 + ab - a^2$

16. $(2x^3 - 5x^2 + 7x - 1) - (x^3 - 4x^2 + 2)$

17. $3p \cdot p^2 \cdot (-p)^5$

18. $x^{2m+1} \cdot 3x^{m-1} \cdot (2x)^2$

19. $\frac{1}{3}(-x^4)^5$

20. $x^2(xy^2)^3 + x^3(-xy)^2$

21. $2m(3m - 1) - 3m(2m - 5)$

22. $x^2(3x + 1) + x(2x - 3x^2)$

Evaluate the following if $x = 3$, $y = 5$, $z = \frac{1}{6}$, $a = 12$, $b = -2$, and $c = 2$.

23. $(2x + 3y)(3x - y) \div [x(y - x)]$

24. $\dfrac{a - 3b}{az}$

25. $4(c^2 - x) - (2x)^2 + 3(c^3 - 2x^3)$

26. $\dfrac{(c - b)^2 - (y - x)^2}{4xz}$

27. The sum of two numbers is 18. If one number is $3a$, write an expression for the other number.

28. If n represents a number, write an expression for five less than twice the number.

29. Write an expression for the volume of a rectangular box with width $2a$, length $5a$, and height $3a$.

30. What is the value of n nickels and three times as many dimes?

31. Write the numbers 0, 4.7, -1.8, 4.75, -1.6, and -1.5 in order from least to greatest.

32. If x is a negative number, then $|x| = \underline{\ ?\ }$.

Multiply.

33. $(x - 1)(x + 5)$

34. $(x - 2y)(3x^2y - 4xy^2 + 5y^3)$

Name the axiom that guarantees each of the following for real numbers a and b, assuming $a \neq b$.

35. $a + b = b + a$

36. $\dfrac{1}{a - b} \cdot (a - b) = 1$

Name the axiom that justifies each step.

37. a. $x + 15 + (22 + y) = x + (15 + 22) + y$ $\underline{\ ?\ }$

   b. $\qquad\qquad\quad = x + 37 + y$ $\underline{\ ?\ }$

   c. $\qquad\qquad\quad = x + y + 37$ $\underline{\ ?\ }$

38. a. $4 + [-(4 + x)] = 4 + [-4 + (-x)]$ $\underline{\ ?\ }$

   b. $\qquad\qquad\quad = [4 + (-4)] + (-x)$ $\underline{\ ?\ }$

   c. $\qquad\qquad\quad = 0 + (-x)$ $\underline{\ ?\ }$

   d. $\qquad\qquad\quad = -x$ $\underline{\ ?\ }$

39. Solve $5y = 2y + 12$ if $y \in \{0, 1, 2, 3, 4, 5, 6\}$.

40. The sum of three consecutive odd integers is 93. If x is the smallest of the integers, write an equation that represents the given facts.

Solve.

41. $3x + (-1.3) = -0.4$

42. $-\dfrac{1}{x} = 3$

43. $-22 + r = 51$

44. $34 = -17 + [-(x + 1)]$

45. $|x| - 1 = 4$

46. $3s - (2 - s) = 10$

47. $-\dfrac{2}{3}t = 12$

48. $0 = -2k$

49. $0 = \dfrac{a}{3} + 4$

50. $p - 3(p - 3) = 17$

51. $1 - 3x - 2(4 - x) = -(x - 1)$

52. $(3 - 2t) - (t - 5) = t - (13 + 2t)$

53. $3x(x^2 + 1) - 3x^2(x - 5) + 3x - 15x^2 = 0$

54. $(2a - 1)(a + 5) - a(2a - 3) = 7$

55. Solve for h: $V = \frac{1}{3}Bh$.

56. The length of Maki's rectangular pool is twice the width. If the perimeter of the pool is 36 m, what is the length?

57. Julie had four coins, all the same. She used two of the coins for a purchase and received 16¢ change. The amount of money she has now is 34¢ less than the amount she had originally. What type of coin did she have originally?

58. The junior class sold 15 more reflectors than coaster sets, with each product selling for $1.50. If the total receipts were $136.50, how many reflectors were sold?

59. Leslie gets a ride to the movies at 35 km/h, but walks home at 7 km/h. If her total travel time is 12 minutes, how long does it take her to walk home?

60. Removing the 1 m wide hedge from all sides of the Mahoneys' rectangular yard increased its area by 200 m². The width of the usable lot had been 15 m less than its length before the hedge was removed. What are the dimensions of the yard with the hedge gone?

Review for Chapters 5–8

1. Write the prime factorization of 460.
2. Write the GCF of 12, 30, and 42.

Factor.

3. $20a^3b^2 + 50a^2b^3 - 30ab^4$

4. $25a^2 - 9b^4$

5. $4x^2 - 12xy + 9y^2$

6. $y^2 + 11y + 30$

7. $x^2 - 11xy + 24y^2$

8. $x^2 + 3x - 10$

9. $a^2 + ab - 30b^2$

10. $6k^2 - 19k + 3$

11. $6x^2 - 5x - 6$

12. $25x^2y^2 - 1$

13. $7x(y + 1) - (y + 1)$

14. $2a^2 - 6ab - a + 3b$

15. $-x^2 - 3x + 10$

16. $4x^2 - 10xy - 24y^2$

17. $2(b - a) - 5c(a - b)$

18. $x(x - y) + y^2 - x^2$

Multiply.

19. $(x - 3y^3)(x - 2y^3)$

20. $(a^2 + 2b)(4a - 3b^2)$

21. $(3x^2 - 1)(3x^2 + 1)$

22. $(ab - 5c)^2$

23. Find the LCD for $\dfrac{3a}{2a - 2b}$, $\dfrac{b^2}{2a^2 - 3ab + b^2}$, and $\dfrac{ab}{4}$.

24. Express $\dfrac{2}{3(x + 7)}$, $\dfrac{1}{2(x - 7)}$, and $\dfrac{x}{4(x + 7)^2}$ with their LCD.

Simplify.

25. $\dfrac{35xy^3z^5}{-7x^2y^3z}$

26. $\dfrac{(-2a)^2(-3ab^2)^2}{(4ab)(3b^2)}$

27. $\dfrac{\pi r^2h + 2\pi r^2}{\pi r}$

28. $\dfrac{3a^2 - 3b^2}{b - a}$

29. $\dfrac{4x^3 - x}{2x^2 - 5x - 3}$

30. $\dfrac{90}{75} \cdot \left(-\dfrac{5x}{6y}\right)^3$

31. $\dfrac{(a - b)^2}{3b} \cdot \dfrac{2ab^2}{b^2 - a^2}$

32. $\left(\dfrac{5x^2y}{3z}\right)^3$

33. $\dfrac{3a^2}{b} \div \dfrac{(2a)^2}{b^3}$

34. $\dfrac{x + 1}{x - 1} \div \dfrac{x^2 - 1}{(x - 1)^2}$

35. $\dfrac{6x}{x^2 + 3xy + 2y^2} \div \dfrac{3x^3}{x^2 - xy - 2y^2}$

36. $\dfrac{18x^3y}{5z^2} \div \left(\dfrac{3x^2}{2z^3} \div \dfrac{5xz}{2y}\right)$

Simplify.

37. $\dfrac{3}{a} - \dfrac{1}{a} + \dfrac{4}{a}$

38. $\dfrac{3x}{x^2 - y^2} + \dfrac{3y}{x^2 - y^2}$

39. $\dfrac{2}{a - b} - \dfrac{3}{b - a}$

40. $\dfrac{c}{c^2 - 4} - \dfrac{1}{c^2 - c - 6}$

41. $3 - \dfrac{2}{x}$

42. $\left(4 - \dfrac{x}{3}\right) \div \left(3 - \dfrac{x}{4}\right)$

Divide.

43. $(3n^2 + 23n + 14)$ by $(3n + 2)$

44. $(a^3 + 1)$ by $(a + 1)$

State each ratio in simplest form.

45. 5 h 6 min to 4 h 30 min

46. x to y if $2(x - 3) = 3(y - 2)$

Solve for x.

47. $3x(x + 5) = 0$

48. $x(x - 7)(x + 6) = 0$

49. $x^2 - x - 12 = 0$

50. $x^2 + 6x + 9 = 25$

51. $\dfrac{2}{m} = \dfrac{n}{5x}$

52. $\dfrac{x}{a} = \dfrac{a}{c}$

53. $\dfrac{2x}{3} - \dfrac{x}{5} = 7$

54. $\dfrac{2x + 3}{12} - \dfrac{3(x - 1)}{8} = 5$

55. $\dfrac{3 - x}{x} = 2$

56. $\dfrac{x}{x - 2} - \dfrac{5}{x^2 - 4} = \dfrac{2}{x + 2}$

57. A ball is thrown upward with an initial velocity of 44.1 m/s. If its motion is described by the formula $h = vt - 4.9t^2$, when will it be 98 m high?

58. Three numbers whose sum is 230 are in the ratio 2:5:3. What are the numbers?

59. What is 2.5% of $114?

60. What percent of 150 is 108?

61. There were 5,106,000 people unemployed last month. The new figures show a 0.7% rise in unemployment this month. How many people are currently unemployed?

62. A blazer is on sale at one-fourth off its regular price. The reduced price of the blazer, including a 5% sales tax, is $40.95. What was the original price of the blazer?

63. With 50 kg of an alloy that is 70% iron, a metallurgist must mix a second alloy that is 82% iron to get a new alloy that is 80% iron. How much of the 82% iron alloy should be used to make the new alloy?

64. One clerk can straighten the shelves in 45 min working alone, and the other clerk can do the job alone in 30 min. How long will it take them if they work together?

65. Plot $A(-5, -4)$, $B(3, -2)$, and $C(-1, 4)$ on a coordinate plane.

66. Solve the equation $x - 5y = 5$ for y in terms of x. For what values of x will the y-coordinate be an integer?

Graph each in a separate coordinate plane.

67. $2x - 3y = 12$ **68.** $y = -5$

69. Solve by the graphic method: $2x + 3y = 11$
$x - 2y = 2$

70. Solve by the substitution method: $x - 2y = 5$
$3x - 2y = 13$

71. Solve by substitution: Seventy-five people attended the Saturday matinee. Admission prices were \$1.50 for children and \$3.50 for adults. If the total receipts were \$176.50, how many children were at the matinee?

Solve by the addition-or-subtraction method.

72. $x + 2y = -14$
$5x + 2y = -6$

73. $7x - 3y = 9$
$8x + 5y = -15$

Solve by using two equations in two variables.

74. Twice the numerator of a given fraction is one less than the denominator. If the denominator were increased by one, the numerator would be one third the new denominator. What is the original fraction?

75. It takes a jet 3 h to travel 1800 km with a tail wind. The return trip against the wind takes 5 h. What is the rate of the jet in still air, and what is the rate of the wind?

Review for Chapters 9–12

1. Find the slope of the line through $(-2, 5)$ and $(7, -8)$.

2. Write the slope and y-intercept of the line whose equation is $3x - 2y = 7$.

3. Write an equation of the line containing the points $(3, 0)$ and $(-5, -5)$.

4. Given that $f(t) = t + 3$ and $g(t) = 2t^2$, find $f(3) + g(3)$.

5. State the domain and range of the function described by the ordered pairs $(7, -6)$, $(-20, 15)$, $(2, -6)$, and $(100, 15)$.

6. Find the maximum value of the function $y: x \rightarrow -3x^2 - 6x + 12$.

7. If y varies directly as x, and y is 21 when x is 5, find x when y is 30.

8. The law of the lever is an example of inverse variation. How far from the fulcrum should a 10 g mass be placed to balance a 15 g mass 20 cm from the fulcrum?

9. Given that y varies inversely as the square of x, and y is 8 when x is 5, find x when y is 2.

10. Translate the statement into a formula, using k as the constant of variation: The resistance, R, of a wire to an electrical current varies directly as the length, l, of the wire and inversely as the square of the diameter, d, of the wire.

Solve and graph the solution set on a number line.

11. $5 - 2x < 3$, if $x \in \{-2, -1, 0, 1, 2\}$.

12. $2 - \frac{1}{3}x \geq 5$

13. $7 \geq 3 - 2m \geq 1$

14. $x < -2$ or $x \geq 1$

15. $|2x - 5| > 9$

16. Find the smallest possible values for two consecutive odd integers whose average is greater than five.

Graph each in a separate coordinate plane.

17. $7x - 2y \leq 6$

18. $|y| < 2$
$x + y \geq 1$

19. Find the number halfway between $\frac{11}{12}$ and $\frac{10}{11}$.

20. Express $\frac{13}{33}$ as a decimal.

21. Express $10.1\overline{17}$ as a fraction in simplest form.

22. Approximate $\sqrt{0.05}$ to the nearest tenth. Use the Table of Square Roots on page 526 as needed.

23. Rationalize the denominator: $\dfrac{1 - \sqrt{3}}{3 + 2\sqrt{2}}$

Express in simplest form.

24. $\sqrt{\dfrac{486}{576}}$ **25.** $\sqrt{0.0036}$ **26.** $\sqrt{\dfrac{9x^{10}}{4y^6}}$ **27.** $2\sqrt{1575}$

28. $\dfrac{\sqrt{18}}{\sqrt{5x^2}}$ **29.** $15\sqrt{7} + 2\sqrt{7} - 4\sqrt{6}$

30. $4\sqrt{75} + 2\sqrt{432} - 10\sqrt{48}$ **31.** $(10 - 7\sqrt{7})^2$

32. $(2\sqrt{3} - 5\sqrt{6})(8\sqrt{3} + 2\sqrt{6})$ **33.** $(\sqrt{3} + \sqrt{5})(\sqrt{3} - \sqrt{5})$

Solve.

34. $\left| 2 - \dfrac{k}{3} \right| = 5$ **35.** $\sqrt{2x} = \dfrac{1}{10}$ **36.** $4y^2 = 49$

37. $2 + \sqrt{5x + 6} = 8$ **38.** $x^2 - 25 = 0$ **39.** $2(x - 1)^2 - 2 = 30$

40. Find the length to the nearest hundredth of a diagonal of a rectangle with sides 7 and 10. Use the Table of Square Roots on page 526 as needed.

41. State the number of real roots of $\dfrac{1}{2}x^2 - 3x + 5 = 0$.

42. Without drawing the graph of $16x^2 - 8x + 1 = 0$, determine how many points the parabola has in common with the x-axis.

Solve by completing the square.

43. $x^2 + 2x - 7 = 0$ **44.** $3x^2 - \dfrac{15}{2}x = 0$

Solve by the quadratic formula.

45. $3x^2 - 4x - 7 = 0$ **46.** $4a^2 = 20a - 13$

Solve by the most convenient method.

47. $3(b - 1)^2 - 135 = 0$ **48.** $10x^2 - 23x + 12 = 0$

49. The width of a rectangle is 5 m less than its length. If the area is 300 m², find the dimensions.

50. Abby and Hugo are laying out a garden in a plot of land that is 5 m wide and 6 m long. The area of the garden is to be two thirds of the area of the whole plot, and there will be a gravel path of uniform width bordering the garden. What should be the dimensions of the garden?

TOPICAL REVIEWS

Review of Factoring Polynomials

Factor completely.

1. $x^2 + 13x - 14$
2. $3p^2 - 12q^2$
3. $m^2 + 16m - 192$
4. $-4p^2 + 25q^2$
5. $22x^2 - 7x - 2$
6. $36r^2 - 16$
7. $4cx + 6cy - 3ay - 2ax$
8. $6x^2 - 73x + 12$
9. $1 - 81w^8x^4$
10. $4acz - 4bcz + 3ay - 3by$
11. $6x^2 + 15x - 21$
12. $200c^2 + 80c + 8$
13. $9 + 18y - 16y^2$
14. $3 + 20x^2 - 16x$
15. $76x^2y - 19y^5$
16. $4x^2 + 8x - 12$
17. $0.16ax^4 - 0.09ay^2$
18. $4 - 4x - 3x^2$
19. $12x^2 + 57xy - 21y^2$
20. $6(3 - x) + y(x - 3)$
21. $32x^2 - 44x + 5$
22. $14a^3 - 29a^2 - 15a$
23. $30fg - 5fk + 12gh - 2hk$
24. $14x^4 + 21x^3 - 35x^2$
25. $-x^2 - x + 2$
26. $2p^3 - 3p^2 - 8p + 12$
27. $(a - b)^2 + 4ab$
28. $32x^4 - 32x^2 + 2$
29. $2(c - d)^2 - 8$
30. $5c^2d^2 + 30cd + 45$
31. $9 - (a + b)^2$
32. $-p^2 - q^2 - 2pq$
33. $m^4 - 23m^2 - 50$
34. $63x^2y - 28x^2y^3$
35. $-30x^2 - 61x - 30$
36. $4ax - 5mx + 12am - 15m^2$
37. $2a^3 + 2a^2 + a + 1$
38. $(3x - 5)(x + 3) - 4(x + 3)$
39. $(x + 1)(x + 2) - 12$
40. $2x^3 - 12x^2 + x - 6$
41. $(x - 2)(x^2 - 7) + 3(x - 2)$
42. $a^{14} + 4a^{13} - 5a^{12}$
43. $4c^2 - 4c + 1 - 9d^2$
44. $x^4 - 2x^2 + 1$
45. $(x + 1)^2 + 6(x + 1) + 8$
46. $m^2 - n^2 - (m - n)^2$
47. $a(b - c) - (b - c)^2$
48. $x^2 - 6xy + 9y^2 - 1$

Challenge Problems

49. $2a^2 + a - 2 - a^3$
50. $x^4 - (x - 1)^4$

Review of Simplifying Expressions

Simplify. Rationalize denominators where appropriate.

1. $(5x^7)(-23x^{17})$
2. $(4\sqrt{18})(-2\sqrt{20})$
3. $\dfrac{3x^2 - 12}{x^2 - 2x - 8}$
4. $\dfrac{a^2 - b^2}{2a^3} \div \dfrac{4b - 4a}{a^3 + a^2b}$
5. $\dfrac{4a - 7}{12} + \dfrac{a + 1}{9} - \dfrac{a + 2}{6}$
6. $(x^7)^3$
7. $\sqrt{\dfrac{14}{5}} \cdot \sqrt{\dfrac{35}{2}}$
8. $\dfrac{2x^3 + 7x^2 + 16}{x + 4}$
9. $\left(\dfrac{3x}{7}\right)^2$

10. $\left(1 + \dfrac{3}{x}\right)\left(1 + \dfrac{4}{x-4}\right)$

11. $5\sqrt{8}(8\sqrt{3} - 6\sqrt{2})$

12. $\dfrac{-32x^7y^4z^9}{18xy^{10}z^{10}}$

13. $\dfrac{cd}{c^2 - 4cd + 4d^2} + \dfrac{c}{3c - 6d}$

14. $\left(\dfrac{a}{-6c^2}\right)^3$

15. $\dfrac{3x^2 + xy - 24y^2}{2x^2 - 18y^2}$

16. $(y - 5)(2y^2 + 4y - 3)$

17. $\dfrac{2}{3 - \sqrt{5}}$

18. $(4a)^2\left(\dfrac{1}{2}a\right)(-a)^3$

19. $\dfrac{4x - 1}{x^2 - 9} \cdot \dfrac{x^2 - 3x}{2 - 8x}$

20. $\dfrac{m - 3}{m^2 + 7m} - \dfrac{m + 7}{m^2 - 3m}$

21. $\dfrac{p^3 - 4p^2}{4p^4} \div \dfrac{48 - 3p^2}{6p^2 + 24p}$

22. $(-3x^2)^4$

23. $\dfrac{6x^2 + x - 2}{2x^2 + 9x - 5}$

24. $\dfrac{4ab^2}{4a - 2b} \cdot \dfrac{4a^2 - b^2}{4a^3 + 4a^2b + ab^2}$

25. $\left(\dfrac{4a^2}{3b}\right)^2$

26. $\dfrac{1}{a + 4} + 2 - \dfrac{1}{a - 4}$

27. $\dfrac{15x^4 - 4x^3 + 13x + 4}{3x + 1}$

28. $(5 - 7\sqrt{2})^2$

29. $-2(x^6)^4$

30. $\dfrac{1}{y + 3} + \dfrac{4}{y}$

31. $\dfrac{(-6a)^3}{-6a^3}$

32. $(4x + 7)(x + 1)(x + 2)$

33. $\dfrac{x^2 + 3x - 28}{2x - 4x^2} \div \dfrac{2x^2 - 7x - 4}{1 - 4x^2}$

34. $\dfrac{xy^2 - x^3}{2x^2 - 9xy + 7y^2}$

35. $3\sqrt{\dfrac{4}{7}} + \dfrac{2}{3}\sqrt{28}$

36. $\dfrac{5 - 2x}{2x^2 + 4x + 3} + \dfrac{7x}{4x^2 + 16x + 15}$

37. $\dfrac{3}{4x^2 + 4x + 1} - \dfrac{2}{2x^2 - x - 1}$

38. $\left(x - 5 + \dfrac{6}{x}\right) \div \left(x - \dfrac{9}{x}\right)$

39. $\dfrac{(x + 3y)^3}{3x^2 + xy - 24y^2} \cdot \dfrac{8xy - 3x^2}{x^2 + 6xy + 9y}$

40. $(4\sqrt{3x})^2 \sqrt{9x}$

41. $\dfrac{2a^3 + a^2 - 17a + 5}{2a - 5}$

42. $\left(\dfrac{5c}{2d^5}\right)^4$

43. $(12a^2 - 2a) \div \dfrac{108a^3 - 3a}{6a^2 - 35a - 6}$

44. $\dfrac{a}{2a - 3} + \dfrac{a + 1}{a + 2}$

45. $c^{2n}(c^{3n})^2c^4$

46. $(2x^3 - 3y)^2$

47. $(-4p^2q^3)(3pq^5)(3p^7q)^2$

48. $\dfrac{2}{3p + 1} - \dfrac{1}{3p + 2} - 4$

49. $\dfrac{(4x^3)^3x^2y^2}{22x^7y^5}$

50. $7\sqrt{\dfrac{27}{8}}$

51. $\dfrac{8}{4 - 3x} + \dfrac{6x}{3x - 4}$

52. $a^{m+6} \cdot a^m \cdot a^{2m-1}$

53. $\dfrac{4x^4 - 14x^2 + 3x^3 - 9x + 6}{4x^2 + 3x - 2}$

54. $\dfrac{a^2 - ab - ac + bc}{a^2 - 2ab + b^2}$

55. $\left(\dfrac{3a^2c}{2d}\right)^3$

56. $\dfrac{5\sqrt{6}}{1 - \sqrt{2}}$

57. $\dfrac{4x^2 - 21x - 18}{2x^2 - 72} \div \dfrac{12x^2 - 7x - 12}{x^2 + 7x + 6}$

58. $(3xy^2)^3 \cdot 2(x^2y)^2$

59. $\dfrac{12x - 3}{x^3 - 5x^2} \cdot \dfrac{2x^2 - 10x}{2 - 32x^2}$

60. $4\sqrt{32} - 5\sqrt{98} + \sqrt{162}$

61. $(a - 5)^3$

62. $\dfrac{x - 5}{10 - 2x} + \dfrac{5}{3x + 15}$

63. $\dfrac{(7x^2y^5z^7)^5}{(7x^2y^5z^7)^3}$

64. $\dfrac{4a - 4c}{6c^3} \cdot \dfrac{a^2c + 4ac^2 + 4c^3}{a^2 + ac - 2c^2}$

65. $\left(\dfrac{4x}{7y}\right)^2 \div \dfrac{(3x^2)^2}{-7y^3}$

66. $3c(4c^2c)^3\left(\dfrac{1}{2}c^3\right)^2$

67. $\left(a - \dfrac{4}{a+3}\right) \div \left(2a + \dfrac{a+3}{a-3}\right)$

68. $\dfrac{4 - x^2}{x^2 + 3x - 10} \cdot \dfrac{2x^2 - 9x + 7}{2x^2 - 3x - 14}$

69. $\dfrac{3}{p^2 - 6p + 5} + \dfrac{4}{p^2 - 25}$

70. $3(2 + 3\sqrt{2})^2$

71. $\dfrac{4x + 2y}{6y} \div \dfrac{2x^2 + xy}{4}$

72. $\dfrac{15x^3 + 38x - 14 - 41x^2}{7 - 5x}$

73. $(\sqrt{2x^3})(5\sqrt{8x^6})$

74. $\dfrac{2x - 7}{3x^2 + 4x + 1} + \dfrac{x + 4}{9x^2 - 1}$

75. $\dfrac{16x^3 - 36x}{-4x^2 - 12x - 9} \div (6 - 4x)$

76. $\left(\dfrac{x^2}{3} - x\right)\left(1 + \dfrac{7}{x}\right)$

77. $\dfrac{3\sqrt{2} - 7}{3\sqrt{2} + 7}$

78. $\dfrac{4x - y}{8xy + 2y^2} \cdot \dfrac{16x^2 + 8xy + y^2}{y^2 - 16x^2}$

79. $\dfrac{3x}{x^2 - 1} - \dfrac{1}{5 - 5x}$

80. $\dfrac{3\sqrt{2} - \sqrt{3}}{\sqrt{8}} - \sqrt{\dfrac{3}{2}}$

81. $5^{2n} \cdot 5^{4n+2} \cdot 5$

82. $(2\sqrt{6} + 3\sqrt{7})(2\sqrt{6} - 3\sqrt{7})$

83. $\sqrt{\dfrac{6}{5}} + \sqrt{\dfrac{5}{6}} - \dfrac{\sqrt{120}}{15}$

84. $(3a)^2(2a^2b^4)^3 - (-3a^4b)^2(b^2)^5$

Challenge Problems

85. $\dfrac{\dfrac{1}{a^2} + \dfrac{1}{ab}}{\dfrac{1}{ab} + \dfrac{1}{b^2}}$

86. $\dfrac{\dfrac{c}{d} - 3 + \dfrac{2d}{c}}{\dfrac{4d}{c} - \dfrac{c}{d}}$

87. $\dfrac{x^3 - y^3}{x^4 + xy^3} \cdot \dfrac{6x^3 - 6xy^2}{4x^2 + 4xy + 4y^2}$

Review of Solving Equations, Inequalities, and Systems

Solve the following equations, inequalities, and systems. If a problem has no solution, write "no solution." Graph the solution sets for Exercises 8, 25, 40, 58, and 69, which are marked with a ᵍ.

1. $5a - 1 - 3(a + 7) = 2(a - 6)$

2. $4 + 6(2x - 3) \le (1 - 3x)2 + x$

3. $\dfrac{3}{x^2 - 7x + 6} + \dfrac{1}{x^2 - 1} = \dfrac{x + 3}{x^2 - 5x - 6}$

4. $4\left(\dfrac{1}{2}x + 7\right) - 3x = \dfrac{1}{3}(9 - 6x) + 23$

5. $2x + \dfrac{2}{3}(4 - x) = \dfrac{1}{6}(4x + 5) + \dfrac{9}{2}$

6. $\dfrac{5}{2}(1 - 4a) \le \dfrac{3}{2} - \dfrac{7}{5}(6a + 5)$

7. $\sqrt{3x - 2} = x - 2$

ᵍ8. $|3x - 8| \ge 4$

9. $0.5y + 0.1 = y^2$

10. $4x - y = 7$
$x - 5y = -3$

11. $0.1y - 0.02x = 0.02$
$0.1x - 0.16y = 0.24$

12. $y = 6 - 3x$
$5x - 4y = 10$

13. $\dfrac{3}{x^2 - 9} + \dfrac{2}{x + 3} = \dfrac{7}{x - 3}$

14. $\dfrac{a + b}{c} = d$ (Solve for a.)

15. $3 - \dfrac{2}{3x} = x$

16. $\dfrac{7x + 2}{4} = \dfrac{5}{x - 3}$

17. $\dfrac{5}{4a - 4} + \dfrac{3}{6a - 6} - 2 = \dfrac{1}{a - 1}$

18. $\sqrt{\dfrac{5a + 4}{2}} = 4$

19. $x - 4x^2 = 1 - 7x$

20. $3\,|x - 2| = 6$

21. $3 + 5(x - 7) > 3x + 7$

22. $\dfrac{3(2x - 7)}{11} - \dfrac{2 - 3x}{3} = \dfrac{17}{33}$

23. $\dfrac{x + 1}{x^2 - x} - \dfrac{13}{2x} = 2$

24. $\dfrac{3}{a + 5} - \dfrac{2}{2a + 3} = 0$

ᵍ25. $|-3 - 2a| \le 11$

26. $3cx - a = c(5 - x)$ (Solve for x.)

27. $7 - 2x^2 = 0$

28. $x^2 + 6x - 2 = 0$

29. $\sqrt{2w^2 + 7} = 6$

30. $6(5 - \frac{1}{3}x) \le 3 - x$

31. $\dfrac{4x - 5}{x + 2} = \dfrac{1 - 5x}{x + 6}$

32. $\dfrac{x}{x - 1} + \dfrac{12}{x + 1} = \dfrac{2}{x^2 - 1}$

33. $\dfrac{9}{4x + 1} - \dfrac{2}{2x - 3} = -1$

34. $m^3 + 4m^2 - 9m - 36 = 0$

35. $(a - 5)(2a + 3) = -11$

36. $2\sqrt{x - 3} = 5$

37. $\dfrac{m - n}{3} = 5$

$\dfrac{m + n}{3} = -1$

38. $4a + 4 = 7b$

$\dfrac{a}{3} + b + 2 = 0$

39. $y = -\dfrac{5}{2}x + 3$

$x = -\dfrac{2}{5}y + 1$

ᵍ40. $|2x + 1| < 7$

41. $2x^2 - 4x = 3$

42. $81p^4 - 18p^2 + 1 = 0$

43. $\dfrac{5}{2x} - \dfrac{4}{3x} = \dfrac{7}{12}$

44. $\dfrac{3}{5x + 3} = \dfrac{1}{3x - 7}$

45. $\dfrac{1}{x + 3} + \dfrac{2}{x^2(x + 3)} = \dfrac{2}{x^2}$

46. $\dfrac{cx - a}{2c} = d$ (Solve for x.)

47. $3 - 2(c + 1) + 3c = 28 - 8c$

48. $\dfrac{x^2}{3x - 2} = -2$

49. $2\sqrt{t} = 2\sqrt{3} - 6$

50. $|5x - 2| = 0$

51. $10x^2 - 6 = 7x$

52. $-\dfrac{3x - 1}{8} \ge \dfrac{x}{3} + \dfrac{71}{24}$

53. $\dfrac{4}{x} = \dfrac{x}{3}$

54. $\dfrac{3}{x - 4} + \dfrac{1}{2x - 8} = -1$

55. $\dfrac{x}{3} - \dfrac{3}{x} = 3$

56. $\dfrac{2x}{x - 2} - \dfrac{3}{x + 2} = \dfrac{7}{x^2 - 4}$

57. $\dfrac{1}{x - 4} - \dfrac{1}{x} = 2$

ᵍ58. $|4 - y| > |-2 - 4|$

59. $0.02x^2 + 0.2x - 2 = 0$

60. $\sqrt{3x^2 + 4x} = 8$

61. $s = vt - \frac{1}{2}gt^2$ (Solve for v.)

62. $\dfrac{3w - 1}{7} + \dfrac{5 - 2w}{2} = -\dfrac{15}{14}$

63. $\dfrac{4}{3} - \dfrac{3c + 1}{2} > 12$

64. $t = \dfrac{1 - 6s}{5}$

$s = \dfrac{2 - 6t}{7}$

65. $\frac{1}{5}(3x - 5y) = 5$

$x = -2y - 10$

66. $y = \frac{1}{6}(x - 5)$

$3x - 18y = 15$

67. $3c^3 + 48c = 24c^2$

68. $\sqrt{2x + 3} = \sqrt{x^2 - 5}$

ᵍ69. $\left|-\dfrac{4x}{7}\right| \le 3$

Challenge Problems

70. $\dfrac{4x + 1}{3x^2 - 12x} + \dfrac{x}{16 - 4x} = \dfrac{1}{12x} - \dfrac{1}{4}$

71. $\dfrac{8}{2x^2 + 9x - 5} + \dfrac{3x - 1}{1 - 4x^2} = \dfrac{x + 1}{2x^2 + 11x + 5}$

72. $\sqrt{3x - 5} = \sqrt{x - 2} + 1$

73. $\sqrt{2x - 2} = \sqrt{x} + 1$

Review of Solving Word Problems

Use the Table of Square Roots on page 526 where applicable.

1. Four brothers decided to buy a color television set that cost $392. Their contributions were in the ratio 4:2:3:5. How much did each contribute?

2. Marie and Tony went shopping together. Marie bought 2 L of milk and 10 oranges for $3.44. Tony bought 3 L of milk and 8 oranges for $3.69. What was the cost of one liter of milk? of one orange?

3. The hypotenuse of a right triangle is 3 cm longer than twice the length of the shorter side. The longer side measures 12 cm. Find the lengths of the shorter side and the hypotenuse.

4. Electric card reader A can read decks of punched cards in half the time it takes electric card reader B. Together they can read a certain deck in eight minutes. How long would it take each reader alone to read the deck?

5. How many grams of a 5% antiseptic solution must be added to 300 g of a 10% solution to produce an 8% solution?

6. Anthony has $6.10 in coins. He has six more quarters than nickels and half as many dimes as quarters. He also has three half dollars. How many coins of each type does he have?

7. Harry Truman's picture appears on 8% of Pedro's collection of presidential campaign buttons. If he has 34 Harry Truman buttons, how many buttons are in the collection?

8. Two years ago Seth was one third as old as his father. If he is now 22 years younger than his father, how old is Seth now?

9. A square and a rectangle have the same area. If the length of the rectangle is 4 cm greater and the width is 3 cm less than the length of a side of the square, what are the dimensions of the rectangle?

10. Colin and Maureen receive $3.50 per hour and $4.00 per hour respectively for working in Brendan's garden. Colin works on Saturdays and Maureen works on Sundays. How much money did each one earn if they received $42 between them for a total of 11 hours' work one weekend?

11. The ratio of the lengths of the sides of two squares is 3:7. The sum of their areas is 522 cm². Find the area of each square.

12. Find the three smallest consecutive odd integers whose sum is at least 99.

13. The volume of a cylinder varies directly as the square of the radius of the base. If the volume is 18 cm³ when the radius is 3 cm, find the volume when the radius is 4 cm.

14. Heather paid $650 for some stock in Newcar, Inc. If she sold the stock for $728, what was the percent gain on her original investment?

15. The width of a rectangle is 5 cm less than half its length. Its area is 72 cm². Find the length and the width of the rectangle.

16. The denominator of a fraction is 1 more than twice the numerator. If 1 is subtracted from the numerator, the resulting fraction is equivalent to $\frac{1}{3}$. Find the original fraction.

17. The first cyclist in a two-leg relay race rode at a speed of 40 km/h. The second cyclist rode at 30 km/h. If they completed the 170 km course in 4 h 50 min, how far did each cyclist ride?

18. A quilt is made from 150 small squares. It is possible to make a quilt of the same size using 100 squares, 1 cm longer on each side than the smaller squares. What is the length of a side of each smaller square?

19. Inge invested part of her $6000 savings in common stock and the rest in rare stamps. At the end of the year, she realized a gain of 9% on the stock and 12% on the stamps. If her savings now amount to $6615, how much did she invest in stamps?

20. A 3 m by 5 m rectangular wall hanging is hung in the center of a wall. The uncovered part of the wall is a border strip of uniform width. How wide is the border strip if the area of the wall hanging is three sevenths of the area of the entire wall?

21. A tea merchant prepares a blend of 30 kg of tea to sell at $2.95 per kilogram. The merchant blends two types of tea, one selling at $2.70 per kilogram, the other at $3.00 per kilogram. How much of each type should the merchant use?

22. The sum of the digits of a two-digit number is 11. If the digits are reversed, the new number is 7 more than twice the original number. Find the original number.

23. Paula leaves her house at 1:20 P.M. to get to the ball park by 2:00 P.M. Malcolm, who is to meet her there, leaves his house at 1:30 P.M. Paula lives 2 km further away from the ball park than Malcolm, but can walk 2 km/h faster. How fast can Paula walk?

Challenge Problems

24. Louise can trim the shrubbery in 6 h working alone. Her father can do it in 5 h. They worked together until dinner but trimmed only $\frac{11}{15}$ of the shrubbery. How long did they work?

25. On their way to a campsite, Edie and Wilma walked 5 km west and 8 km north. After lunch they walked 3 more km west and 7 km north, arriving at the campsite at 5 P.M. How far would they have walked had they taken the more dangerous, straight-line route through the forest?

Review of Graphing

Graph each pair of lines on the same set of axes. How are the lines related to each other?

1. $5x - 2y = 4$

   $y = \frac{5}{2}x + 1$

2. $y = 3x - 7$

   $2x + y = 4$

3. $y = -\frac{2}{3}x + 3$

   $4x + 6y = 18$

Write in standard form an equation of the line that passes through the given points.

4. $(-3, 6), (4, -1)$ 5. $(0, 3), (-2, -2)$ 6. $(7, -4), (11, -10)$ 7. $(4, -3), (4, 0)$
8. $(1, 8), (4, 7)$ 9. $(-5, -1), (7, -1)$ 10. $(6, -2), (2, -6)$ 11. $(-4, 5), (-6, 1)$

Solve each open sentence and graph each solution set which is not empty.

12. $4 < 2x \le 8$

13. $-2x \le 4$ and $x < 3.5$

14. $-4x > 2$ and $x + 1 > 6$

15. $2 - 3x < 5$ or $2x - 5 < -3$

16. $5a - 1 \le 9$ or $7 - 3a \ge -2$

17. $|1 - 2x| > 3$

Write an equation for each line whose graph is shown.

18. 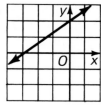   19. 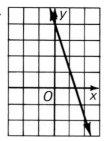   20. 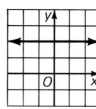   21.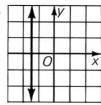

Find the coordinates of the vertex of the graph of each equation. Use the vertex and four other points to graph each equation on a separate coordinate plane.

22. $y = x^2 - 2x$ 23. $y = -2x^2 + 5x - 3$ 24. $y = x^2 + 4x + 1$

Graph each pair of inequalities and indicate the solution set of the system with crosshatching or shading.

25. $y \ge x + 3$

    $y > -2x - 1$

26. $x + 2y > 4$

    $x \ge 3$

27. $3x - 5y < 5$

    $x - 3y \ge 0$

Write in standard form an equation of the line that has the given slope and passes through the given point.

28. $m = \frac{4}{3}$; $(0, 4)$

29. $m = \frac{2}{3}$; $(-3, -3)$

30. $m = -\frac{1}{4}$; $(6, 0)$

31. $m = \frac{3}{8}$; $(1, -3)$

32. $m = -5$; $(5, -2)$

33. $m = 0$; $(6, 4)$

34. The points $(3, -4)$ and $(-2, a)$ lie on a line with slope $\frac{3}{5}$. Find the value of a.

Write an equation in standard form for the line that passes through the given point and has the slope described.

35. $(2, 3)$; the same slope as the graph of $3x - y = 2$

36. $(-1, 4)$; the same slope as the graph of $x + 2y = 5$

Draw the graph of each line on a separate coordinate plane.

37. $m = -3$, $b = -1$

38. $\frac{x}{2} + \frac{y}{4} = 1$

39. $x = 2\frac{1}{2}$

40. $y = \frac{1}{2}x + 3$

41. $m = -\frac{2}{3}$, $b = 3$

42. $4y - 3x = 4$

Use slope to determine whether the points lie on the same line.

43. $(4, 7)$, $(2, -1)$, $(-6, -33)$, $(-1, -13)$

44. $(3, -7)$, $(-1, -4)$, $(6, -10)$, $(-9, 2)$

Challenge Problems

Solve each open sentence and graph each solution set which is not empty.

45. $-1 \leq t \leq 3$ and $|t| \geq 2$

46. $\frac{1}{2}|3x - 6| + 3 < 2$

47. $x > 3\frac{1}{2}$ or x is an integer.

ENRICHMENT ACTIVITIES

Around in Circles

GAME 1

You will need eight game markers such as beads, beans, or pennies. The objective is to fill all but one of the circles in the figure above. To put a marker in a circle, you place it in an empty circle and slide it along a straight line path to another empty circle on the opposite side, where it will remain. Continue filling the board in this manner until all but one of the circles contain a marker.

GAME 2

Again the objective is to fill all but one of the circles. In this game you start in an empty circle and move your marker three jumps clockwise around the board. You then leave your marker in the circle where you land after the three jumps.

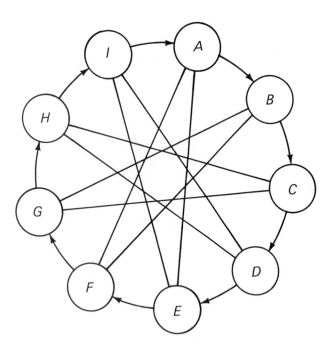

What's Next?

2, 4, 6, 8, 10, ... is a *sequence* of numbers. The next three numbers would be 12, 14, 16. A rule that describes this sequence is the following. Start with the number 2 and add 2 to get the next term, then continue adding 2 to each term to get the following term.

Think about the sequence 2, 6, 18, 54, ... To determine the next term you need to discover the rule. Begin with the number 2 and multiply by 3 to get the next term, 6. Now multiply 6 by 3. Do you get 18? Is the next term, 54, equal to 3×18? What are the next two terms?

Not all sequences use numbers. For example, the sequence A, B, C, D, ... is the letters of the alphabet. It simply repeats after all 26 letters have been used.

For each sequence, find the next three terms.

1. 1, 5, 9, 13, ...
2. 3, 6, 12, 24, ...
3. 8, 5, 2, −1, ...
4. 16, 8, 4, 2, ...
5. 2, 3, 5, 7, 11, ...
6. 1, 4, 3, 6, 5, ...
7. 1, 4, 9, 16, ...
8. 3, 7, 15, 31, ...
9. 1, 1, 2, 3, 5, ...
10. 18, 38, 58, 78, ...
11. 17, 27, 37, 47, ...
12. 3, 33, 63, 93, 123, ...

Imagine taking a piece of paper that is 0.3 mm thick. Folding it in half makes the thickness 0.6 mm. Folding it again gives a thickness of 1.2 mm. Consider folding the paper 30 times.

13. Write the first 6 terms of the sequence of thicknesses.

The Meaning of the Message

Many secret codes have been developed to camouflage messages. One simple code consists of separating a sentence into groups of five letters. For example, the sentence GO INSIDE BEFORE IT RAINS would become GOINS IDEBE FOREI TRAIN S. Another code, called an alphabet circle, involves replacing each letter in a message with the next letter in the alphabet. For example, GO INSIDE BEFORE IT RAINS becomes HP JOTJEF CFGPSF JU SBJOT. A third code can be obtained by combining the alphabet circle and the grouping code. This would give HPJOT JEFCF GPSFJ USBJO T.

In this message the letters of the alphabet have been scrambled and regrouped into five-letter segments.

KFJPP	HJPHR	PJVLQ	KJQBL
DBQJV	BNOCV	SICBP	BHVQL
ISHHS	QHRSV	KVWBK	SFDPB
KVHJP	HRPJV	LQKDB	QALQF
VWBAL	RQOJK	SHJQS	VWFBV
SHLDB	QJVSL	IK	

The table below gives the frequency of each letter in the original message. Determine the frequency of each letter in the coded message and work backward to decode the words.

Letter	Frequency	Letter	Frequency
A	10	N	3
B	2	O	8
C	10	P	4
D	1	Q	0
E	11	R	11
F	2	S	8
G	0	T	12
H	3	U	4
I	9	V	0
J	0	W	0
K	0	X	0
L	8	Y	2
M	4	Z	0

Stopping Point

Suppose you counted on the fingers of one hand as follows:

1 thumb
2 index finger
3 middle finger
4 ring finger
5 little finger (reverse direction)
6 ring finger
7 middle finger

and so on as shown in the figure.

What finger would you land on if you counted up to:

100?
200?
741?
5000?
1,000,000?

(*Hint:* Notice the pattern of numbers every time you land on the thumb.)

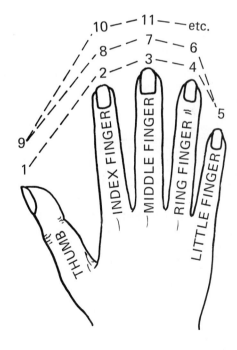

ANSWERS

Chapter Tests

CHAPTER 1 TEST

1. 4 **2.** 12 **3.** 9 **4.** 276 **5.** 7
6. $x + (x + 2) + (x + 4)$ or $3x + 6$ **7.** $c + 2c = 2.40$
8. \$5.30

CHAPTER 2 TEST

1. **2.** $<$ **3.** $>$

4. $-2.5, -2, 0, 3, 3.5$ **5.** Commutative axiom for mult.
6. Associative axiom for mult. **7.** Substitution principle
8. Substitution **9.** x **10.** 5 **11.** 10 **12.** -10
13. There were 953 fewer students at the end of the year.
14. 21 **15.** $37x + 19y$ **16.** -10 **17.** $-4r + 3$
18. $3z$ **19.** $-4x \ -\dfrac{2}{5}$

CHAPTER 3 TEST

1. 23 **2.** 8 **3.** 2 **4.** $-2x + 16$ **5.** 136 **6.** 4
7. -25 **8.** 2 **9.** -72 **10.** -25 **11.** -7 **12.** 91
13. 12 **14.** $-\dfrac{5}{3}$ **15.** 4 **16.** -1 **17.** -3
18. Distributive axiom **19.** Substitution principle
20. Multiplication property of equality

CHAPTER 4 TEST

1. $(a + b)^3 - 4$ **2.** 158 **3.** $-2x^2y + xy^2 - xy$
4. $x - 2y + 9z$ **5.** 4 **6.** $32x^8$ **7.** $12x^{3n+2}$ **8.** $-2y^9$
9. $\dfrac{2}{9}x^9$ **10.** $-3x^5 + 2x^4 - x^3$ **11.** 24 **12.** $x^2 - x - 12$
13. $27p^3 - 8q^3$ **14.** -2
15. $10(x + 3)$, or $10x + 30$, cents **16.** $x = a + b - 2c$
17. 4 h **18.** slower, 600 km/h; faster, 700 km/h
19. 28.5 m

CHAPTER 5 TEST

1. $2^2 \cdot 7 \cdot 11$ **2.** 18 **3.** $-\dfrac{x^2}{4yz}$ **4.** $\dfrac{12x^6y}{z^5}$
5. $r + 3s^2 - 7rs$ **6.** $6x^2y(y - 2x + 3xy)$
7. $3a^2 - 11ab + 10b^2$ **8.** -6 **9.** $4a^4 - 9b^2$
10. $(2x - 1)(2x + 1)(4x^2 + 1)$ **11.** $x^4 - 6x^2y + 9y^2$
12. $(xy - 7)^2$ **13.** $(x - 5)(x - 2)$ **14.** $(a + 8b)(a + 3b)$

15. $(r - 9)(r + 2)$ **16.** $(x + 5y)(x - 4y)$
17. $(4b - 1)(3b + 1)$ **18.** $(2x - y)(x + 3y)$
19. $(2x - 3y)(2x + 3y)$ **20.** $(x + 1)(1 - y)$
21. $(x - 1)(3x + y)$ **22.** $(-a + 3)(a + 4)$ **23.** $3a(x - 3y)^2$
24. $(x - y)(a - 1)$ **25.** $(a - b)(4a + 3b)$ **26.** $\{0, 1\}$
27. $\{0, 13, -5\}$ **28.** $\{5, 7\}$ **29.** $\{9, -1\}$
30. 20 cm by 16 cm

CHAPTER 6 TEST

1. $-a(x + y)$ **2.** $\dfrac{r + 3}{r - 1}$ **3.** $\dfrac{10}{9}$ **4.** $2x(2 + y)$
5. $\dfrac{8x^6y^3z^9}{27}$ **6.** $\dfrac{5}{24x}$ **7.** $\dfrac{x - 3}{3x}$ **8.** $\dfrac{(a + b)(a + 2b)}{3a^2}$
9. $2xy$ **10.** $18a^2b$ **11.** $\dfrac{xy(x + y)}{4x^2(x + y)}, \dfrac{2x^2(x - y)}{4x^2(x + y)}, \dfrac{2(x + y)}{4x^2(x + y)}$
12. $\dfrac{4}{x}$ **13.** $\dfrac{8a^2 - 6b^3 + 3b}{12ab^2}$ **14.** $\dfrac{7}{x - 1}$ **15.** $\dfrac{2x + 3}{2x + 1}$
16. $\dfrac{6n^2 + 7}{2n}$ **17.** $\dfrac{-y^2 + 4y - 5}{y^2}$ **18.** $\dfrac{2b}{a(a - b)}$
19. $2x + 5$ **20.** $x^2 + x + 1$

CHAPTER 7 TEST

1. $3:125$ **2.** $4b:1$ **3.** $\dfrac{x}{y} = \dfrac{-4}{1}$
4. \$3000, \$6000, \$12,000 **5.** 15 **6.** 4 **7.** $\dfrac{ac}{b}$ **8.** 6
9. 5 **10.** $\{10, -6\}$ **11.** 1 **12.** \$34.50 **13.** 80%
14. 35% **15.** \$79,581 **16.** 80% **17.** 80 kg of the
\$6.90/kg beans and 120 kg of the \$5.90/kg beans **18.** 0.32 h

CHAPTER 8 TEST

1. IV **2.** II **3.** $y = \dfrac{2x - 15}{3}$

4. $\{(0, -4), (4, -2)\}$

5. **6.** **7.**

8. $\left(\dfrac{1}{2}, -\dfrac{3}{4}\right)$ **9.** Jan, \$10/shift; Sue, \$15/shift
10. $(1, 4)$ **11.** $(3, -5)$ **12.** 37 **13.** 2.5 km/h

T42

CHAPTER 9 TEST

1. $\dfrac{2}{3}$ **2.** -1 **3.** $2x + 3y = -3$ **4.** $y = \dfrac{1}{3}x - 3$ or

$x - 3y = 9$ **5.** $y = \dfrac{5}{2}x + 7$ or $5x - 2y = -14$ **6.** $y = 5$

7. 4 **8.** D: $\{-3, -1, 0, 4, 5\}$; R: $\{0, 1, 3, 4, 5\}$ **9. a.** $(2, 3)$

b. 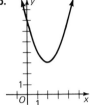 **c.** minimum **10.** 1.2 h

11. 30 **12. a.** π **b.** The area is 9 times larger. **13.** 10 s

CHAPTER 10 TEST

1. $\{0, 1, 2\}$ **2.**

3. $x < 3$ **4.** $x \ge -1$

5. 8, 10, 12; 10, 12, 14 **6.**

7. **8.** $\{-3, 7\}$

9. $-5 < x < 8$

10.   **11.**

CHAPTER 11 TEST

1. $-\dfrac{127}{144}$ **2.** $1.\overline{18}$ **3.** $\dfrac{1757}{330}$ **4.** $\dfrac{3}{26}$ **5.** 0.11 **6.** 19.9

7. 0.6 **8.** $\dfrac{9c^2}{2d^2}\sqrt{bc}$ **9.** $\{9, -9\}$ **10.** 24.04 cm **11.** No

12. $75\sqrt{2}$ **13.** $\dfrac{|x|}{5}\sqrt{10}$ **14.** $\sqrt{5} + 3\sqrt{3}$ **15.** $8\sqrt{2}$

16. $47 + 6\sqrt{10}$ **17.** $-66 + 42\sqrt{2}$ **18.** $-\dfrac{\sqrt{3} + 6}{11}$

19. 61 **20.** $\{4, -4\}$

CHAPTER 12 TEST

1. $\{8, -8\}$ **2.** $\{3 + \sqrt{5}, 3 - \sqrt{5}\}$

3. $\{-2 + \sqrt{6}, -2 - \sqrt{6}\}$ **4.** $\left\{\dfrac{-5 + \sqrt{41}}{4}, \dfrac{-5 - \sqrt{41}}{4}\right\}$

5. $\{-3 + \sqrt{5}, -3 - \sqrt{5}\}$ **6.** $\left\{\dfrac{-1 + \sqrt{3}}{2}, \dfrac{-1 - \sqrt{3}}{2}\right\}$

7. 2 **8.** 1 **9.** $\left\{\dfrac{5}{3}, 1\right\}$ **10.** $\left\{0, \dfrac{13}{2}\right\}$ **11.** 20 m by 25 m

12. 3.3 m

Cumulative Reviews

REVIEW FOR CHAPTERS 1–4

1. 21 **2.** 5 **3.** 5 **4.** 124 **5.** 3 **6.** $-8a - 5$
7. $28x + 19$ **8.** -40 **9.** $-44x$ **10.** $-xy$
11. $-7a + b$ **12.** $6x - 3y$ **13.** -70 **14.** 114
15. $3a^2 - 2ab + b^2$ **16.** $x^3 - x^2 + 7x - 3$ **17.** $-3p^8$
18. $12x^{3m+2}$ **19.** $-\dfrac{1}{3}x^{20}$ **20.** $x^5y^6 + x^5y^2$ **21.** $13m$
22. $3x^2$ **23.** 14 **24.** 9 **25.** -170 **26.** 6
27. $18 - 3a$ **28.** $2n - 5$ **29.** $30a^3$ **30.** $35n$
31. $-1.8, -1.6, -1.5, 0, 4.7, 4.75$ **32.** $-x$
33. $x^2 + 4x - 5$ **34.** $3x^3y - 10x^2y^2 + 13xy^3 - 10y^4$
35. Commutative axiom for add. **36.** Axiom of reciprocals
37. a. Associative axiom for addition **b.** Substitution
c. Commutative axiom for addition
38. a. Property of the opposite of a sum
b. Associative axiom for addition **c.** Axiom of opposites
d. Identity axiom for addition **39.** 4
40. $x + (x + 2) + (x + 4) = 93$ **41.** 0.3 **42.** $-\dfrac{1}{3}$
43. 73 **44.** -52 **45.** $\{5, -5\}$ **46.** 3 **47.** -18
48. 0 **49.** -12 **50.** -4 **51.** No solution **52.** $\dfrac{21}{2}$
53. 0 **54.** 1 **55.** $h = \dfrac{3V}{B}$ **56.** 12 m **57.** quarters
58. 53 reflectors **59.** 10 min **60.** 58.5 m by 43.5 m

REVIEW FOR CHAPTERS 5–8

1. $2^2 \cdot 5 \cdot 23$ **2.** 6 **3.** $10ab^2(2a - b)(a + 3b)$
4. $(5a - 3b^2)(5a + 3b^2)$ **5.** $(2x - 3y)^2$ **6.** $(y + 6)(y + 5)$
7. $(x - 8y)(x - 3y)$ **8.** $(x + 5)(x - 2)$
9. $(a + 6b)(a - 5b)$ **10.** $(k - 3)(6k - 1)$
11. $(2x - 3)(3x + 2)$ **12.** $(5xy - 1)(5xy + 1)$
13. $(y + 1)(7x - 1)$ **14.** $(2a - 1)(a - 3b)$
15. $(-x + 2)(x + 5)$ **16.** $2(2x + 3y)(x - 4y)$
17. $(b - a)(2 + 5c)$ **18.** $y(y - x)$ **19.** $x^2 - 5xy^3 + 6y^6$
20. $4a^3 - 3a^2b^2 + 8ab - 6b^3$ **21.** $9x^4 - 1$
22. $a^2b^2 - 10abc + 25c^2$ **23.** $4(a - b)(2a - b)$
24. $\dfrac{8(x + 7)(x - 7)}{12(x + 7)^2(x - 7)}, \dfrac{6(x + 7)^2}{12(x + 7)^2(x - 7)}, \dfrac{3x(x - 7)}{12(x + 7)^2(x - 7)}$
25. $-\dfrac{5z^4}{x}$ **26.** $3a^3b$ **27.** $r(h + 2)$ **28.** $-3(a + b)$

29. $\dfrac{x(2x - 1)}{x - 3}$ **30.** $-\dfrac{25x^3}{36y^3}$ **31.** $-\dfrac{2ab(a - b)}{3(a + b)}$

32. $\dfrac{125x^6y^3}{27z^3}$ **33.** $\dfrac{3b^2}{4}$ **34.** 1 **35.** $\dfrac{2(x - 2y)}{x^2(x + 2y)}$

36. $6x^2z^2$ **37.** $\dfrac{6}{a}$ **38.** $\dfrac{3}{x - y}$ **39.** $\dfrac{5}{a - b}$

40. $\dfrac{c^2 - 4c + 2}{(c + 2)(c - 2)(c - 3)}$ **41.** $\dfrac{3x - 2}{x}$ **42.** $\dfrac{4}{3}$

43. $n + 7$ **44.** $a^2 - a + 1$ **45.** 17:15 **46.** $\dfrac{3}{2}$

47. $\{0, -5\}$ **48.** $\{0, 7, -6\}$ **49.** $\{4, -3\}$ **50.** $\{-8, 2\}$

51. $\dfrac{mn}{10}$ **52.** $\dfrac{a^2}{c}$ **53.** 15 **54.** -21 **55.** 1

56. $\{1, -1\}$ **57.** 4 s and 5 s **58.** 46, 115, 69 **59.** $2.85

60. 72% **61.** 5, 141, 742 **62.** $52 **63.** 250 kg

64. 18 min **65.**

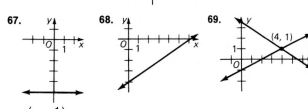

66. $y = \dfrac{x - 5}{5}$; multiples of 5

67. **68.** **69.**

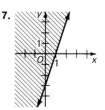
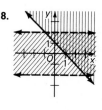

70. $\left(4, -\dfrac{1}{2}\right)$ **71.** 43 children **72.** $(2, -8)$ **73.** $(0, -3)$

74. $\dfrac{2}{5}$ **75.** jet, 480 km/h; wind, 120 km/h

REVIEW FOR CHAPTERS 9–12

1. $-\dfrac{13}{9}$ **2.** slope, $\dfrac{3}{2}$; y-intercept, $-\dfrac{7}{2}$

3. $y = \dfrac{5}{8}x - \dfrac{15}{8}$ or $5x - 8y = 15$ **4.** 24

5. D: $\{-20, 2, 7, 100\}$; R: $\{-6, 15\}$ **6.** 15 **7.** $\dfrac{50}{7}$

8. 30 cm **9.** $\{10, -10\}$ **10.** $R = \dfrac{kl}{d^2}$

11. 2; ───┼┼┼┼┼──
　　　　-1 0 1 2

12. $x \le -9$; ──┼┼┼──
　　　　　　　-10 -8

13. $-2 \le n \le 1$ ──┼┼┼┼┼──
　　　　　　　　　-2 0 2

14. ──┼○┼┼┼┼──
　　　-2 0 2

15. $x > 7$ or $x < -2$ ──┼┼○┼┼┼┼○┼┼──
　　　　　　　　　-4 -2 0 2 4 6 8

16. 5 and 7

17.

18.

19. $\dfrac{241}{264}$ **20.** $0.\overline{39}$ **21.** $\dfrac{5008}{495}$ **22.** 0.2

23. $3 - 2\sqrt{2} - 3\sqrt{3} + 2\sqrt{6}$ **24.** $\dfrac{3}{8}\sqrt{6}$ **25.** 0.06

26. $\dfrac{3|x|^5}{2|y|^3}$ **27.** $30\sqrt{7}$ **28.** $\dfrac{3\sqrt{10}}{5|x|}$ **29.** $17\sqrt{7} - 4\sqrt{6}$

30. $4\sqrt{3}$ **31.** $443 - 140\sqrt{7}$ **32.** $-12 - 108\sqrt{2}$

33. -2 **34.** $\{-9, 21\}$ **35.** $\dfrac{1}{200}$ **36.** $\left\{\dfrac{7}{2}, -\dfrac{7}{2}\right\}$

37. 6 **38.** $\{5, -5\}$ **39.** $\{5, -3\}$ **40.** 12.21 **41.** 0

42. 1 **43.** $\{-1 + 2\sqrt{2}, -1 - 2\sqrt{2}\}$ **44.** $\left\{0, \dfrac{5}{2}\right\}$

45. $\left\{\dfrac{7}{3}, -1\right\}$ **46.** $\left\{\dfrac{5 + 2\sqrt{3}}{2}, \dfrac{5 - 2\sqrt{3}}{2}\right\}$

47. $\{1 + 3\sqrt{5}, 1 - 3\sqrt{5}\}$ **48.** $\left\{\dfrac{3}{2}, \dfrac{4}{5}\right\}$ **49.** 20 m by 15 m

50. 4 m wide and 5 m long

Topical Reviews

REVIEW OF FACTORING POLYNOMIALS

1. $(x + 14)(x - 1)$ **2.** $3(p + 2q)(p - 2q)$

3. $(m + 24)(m - 8)$ **4.** $(5q + 2p)(5q - 2p)$

5. $(11x + 2)(2x - 1)$ **6.** $4(3r + 2)(3r - 2)$

7. $(2x + 3y)(2c - a)$ **8.** $(6x - 1)(x - 12)$

9. $(1 + 9w^4x^2)(1 + 3w^2x)(1 - 3w^2x)$ **10.** $(a - b)(4cz + 3y)$

11. $(6x + 21)(x - 1)$ **12.** $8(5c + 1)^2$

13. $(3 + 8y)(3 - 2y)$ **14.** $(10x - 3)(2x - 1)$

15. $19y(2x + y^2)(2x - y^2)$ **16.** $4(x + 3)(x - 1)$

17. $a(0.4x^2 + 0.3y)(0.4x^2 - 0.3y)$ **18.** $(2 - 3x)(2 + x)$

19. $(3x - y)(4x + 21y)$ **20.** $(x - 3)(y - 6)$

21. $(4x - 5)(8x - 1)$ **22.** $a(7a + 3)(2a - 5)$

23. $(6g - k)(5f + 2h)$ **24.** $7x^2(2x + 5)(x - 1)$

25. $(x + 2)(1 - x)$ **26.** $(2p - 3)(p + 2)(p - 2)$

27. $(a + b)^2$ **28.** $2(16x^4 - 16x^2 + 1)$

29. $2(c - d + 2)(c - d - 2)$ **30.** $5(cd + 3)^2$

31. $(3 + a + b)(3 - a - b)$ **32.** $-(p + q)^2$

33. $(m + 5)(m - 5)(m^2 + 2)$ **34.** $7x^2y(3 + 2y)(3 - 2y)$

35. $-(6x + 5)(5x + 6)$ **36.** $(4a - 5m)(x + 3m)$

37. $(2a^2 + 1)(a + 1)$ **38.** $3(x + 3)(x - 3)$

39. $(x + 5)(x - 2)$
41. $(x - 2)^2(x + 2)$
43. $(2c + 3d - 1)(2c - 3d - 1)$
45. $(x + 3)(x + 5)$
47. $(b - c)(a - b + c)$
49. $(a + 1)(a - 2)(1 - a)$

40. $(x - 6)(2x^2 + 1)$
42. $a^{12}(a + 5)(a - 1)$
44. $(x - 1)^2(x + 1)^2$
46. $2n(m - n)$
48. $(x - 3y + 1)(x - 3y - 1)$
50. $(2x^2 - 2x + 1)(2x - 1)$

47. $-36p^{10}q^{10}$
48. $\dfrac{-36p^2 - 33p - 5}{(3p + 1)(3p + 2)}$
49. $\dfrac{32x^4}{11y^3}$
50. $\dfrac{21\sqrt{6}}{4}$
51. 2
52. a^{4m+5}
53. $x^2 - 3$
54. $\dfrac{a - c}{a - b}$
55. $\dfrac{27a^6c^3}{8d^3}$
56. $-5\sqrt{6} - 10\sqrt{3}$
57. $\dfrac{x + 1}{2(3x - 4)}$
58. $18x^7y^8$
59. $-\dfrac{3}{x(4x + 1)}$
60. $-10\sqrt{2}$
61. $a^3 - 15a^2 + 75a - 125$
62. $\dfrac{-3x - 5}{6(x + 15)}$
63. $49x^4y^{10}z^{14}$
64. $\dfrac{2(a + 2c)}{3c^2}$
65. $\dfrac{-16y}{63x^2}$
66. $48c^{16}$
67. $\dfrac{(a + 4)(a - 3)}{(2a - 3)(a + 3)}$
68. $\dfrac{1 - x}{x + 5}$
69. $\dfrac{7p + 11}{(p - 1)(p + 5)(p - 5)}$
70. $66 + 36\sqrt{2}$
71. $\dfrac{4}{3xy}$
72. $-3x^2 + 4x - 2$
73. $20x^4\sqrt{2x}$
74. $\dfrac{7x^2 - 18x + 11}{(3x + 1)(3x - 1)(x + 1)}$
75. $\dfrac{2x}{2x + 3}$
76. $\dfrac{(x - 3)(x + 7)}{3}$
77. $\dfrac{42\sqrt{2} - 67}{31}$
78. $-\dfrac{1}{2y}$
79. $\dfrac{16x + 1}{5(x + 1)(x - 1)}$
80. $\dfrac{6 - 3\sqrt{6}}{4}$
81. 5^{6n+3}
82. -39
83. $\dfrac{7\sqrt{30}}{30}$
84. $63a^8b^{12}$
85. $\dfrac{b}{a}$
86. $\dfrac{d - c}{2d + c}$
87. $\dfrac{3(x - y)^2}{2(x^2 - xy + y^2)}$

REVIEW OF SIMPLIFYING EXPRESSIONS

1. $-115x^{24}$
2. $-48\sqrt{10}$
3. $\dfrac{3x - 6}{x - 4}$
4. $-\dfrac{(a + b)^2}{8a}$
5. $\dfrac{10a - 29}{36}$
6. x^{21}
7. 7
8. $2x^2 - x + 4$
9. $\dfrac{9x^2}{49}$
10. $\dfrac{x + 3}{x - 4}$
11. $80\sqrt{6} - 120$
12. $-\dfrac{16x^6}{9y^6z}$
13. $\dfrac{c^2 + cd}{3(c - 2d)^2}$
14. $-\dfrac{a^3}{216c^6}$
15. $\dfrac{3x - 8y}{2(x - 3y)}$
16. $2y^3 - 6y^2 - 23y + 15$
17. $\dfrac{3 + \sqrt{5}}{2}$
18. $-8a^6$
19. $-\dfrac{x}{2x + 6}$
20. $\dfrac{-20m - 40}{m(m + 7)(m - 3)}$
21. $-\dfrac{1}{2}p$
22. $81x^8$
23. $\dfrac{3x + 2}{x + 5}$
24. $\dfrac{2b^2}{2a + b}$
25. $\dfrac{16a^4}{9b^2}$
26. $\dfrac{2a^2 - 40}{(a + 4)(a - 4)}$
27. $5x^3 - 3x^2 + x + 4$
28. $123 - 70\sqrt{2}$
29. $-2x^{24}$
30. $\dfrac{5y + 12}{y(y + 3)}$
31. 36
32. $4x^3 + 19x^2 + 29x + 14$
33. $\dfrac{x + 7}{2x}$
34. $\dfrac{-x(y + x)}{2x - 7y}$
35. $\dfrac{46\sqrt{7}}{21}$
36. $\dfrac{3x^2 + 7x + 25}{(2x + 3)(x + 1)(2x + 5)}$
37. $\dfrac{-x - 5}{(2x + 1)^2(x - 1)}$
38. $\dfrac{x - 2}{x + 3}$
39. $-x$
40. $144 \times \sqrt{x}$
41. $a^2 + 3a - 1$
42. $\dfrac{625c^4}{16d^{20}}$
43. $\dfrac{2(a - 6)}{3}$
44. $\dfrac{3a^2 + a - 3}{(2a - 3)(a + 2)}$
45. c^{8n+4}
46. $4x^6 - 12x^3y + 9y^2$

REVIEW OF SOLVING EQUATIONS, INEQUALITIES, AND SYSTEMS

1. No solution
2. {all real numbers less than or equal to $\frac{16}{17}$}
3. $\{0, 2\}$
4. -2
5. 4
6. {all real numbers greater than or equal to 5}
7. 6
8. {all real numbers greater than or equal to 4 or less than or equal to $\frac{4}{3}$}
9. $\left\{\dfrac{5 + \sqrt{65}}{20}, \dfrac{5 - \sqrt{65}}{20}\right\}$

10. (2, 1)   **11.** (4, 1)   **12.** (2, 0)   **13.** $\dfrac{-24}{5}$ **14.** $cd - b$

15. $\left\{\dfrac{9 + \sqrt{57}}{6}, \dfrac{9 - \sqrt{57}}{6}\right\}$ **16.** $\left\{-1, \dfrac{26}{7}\right\}$ **17.** $\dfrac{11}{8}$

18. $\dfrac{28}{5}$ **19.** $\left\{\dfrac{2 + \sqrt{3}}{2}, \dfrac{2 - \sqrt{3}}{2}\right\}$ **20.** $\{0, 4\}$

21. $\left\{\text{all real numbers greater than } \dfrac{39}{2}\right\}$ **22.** 2   **23.** $\left\{-3, \dfrac{5}{4}\right\}$

24. $\dfrac{1}{4}$ **25.** $\{-7, 4, \text{ and all real numbers between}$

$-7 \text{ and } 4\}$ **26.** $\dfrac{5c + a}{4c}$ **27.** $\left\{\dfrac{\sqrt{14}}{2}, -\dfrac{\sqrt{14}}{2}\right\}$

28. $\{3 + \sqrt{11}, 3 - \sqrt{11}\}$ **29.** $\left\{\dfrac{\sqrt{58}}{2}, -\dfrac{\sqrt{58}}{2}\right\}$

30. $\{$all real numbers greater than or equal to 27$\}$

31. $\left\{-4, \dfrac{8}{9}\right\}$ **32.** -14 **33.** $\{2, -2\}$ **34.** $\{-4, -3, 3\}$

35. $\left\{4, -\dfrac{1}{2}\right\}$ **36.** $\dfrac{37}{4}$ **37.** $(6, -9)$ **38.** $(-3, -1)$

39. No solution
40. $\{$all real numbers between -4 and $3\}$

41. $\left\{\dfrac{2 + \sqrt{10}}{2}, \dfrac{2 - \sqrt{10}}{2}\right\}$ **42.** $\left\{-\dfrac{1}{3}, \dfrac{1}{3}\right\}$ **43.** 2   **44.** 6

45. $\{1 + \sqrt{5}, 1 - \sqrt{5}\}$ **46.** $\dfrac{2cd + a}{c}$ **47.** 3

48. $\{-3 + \sqrt{13}, -3 - \sqrt{13}\}$ **49.** $12 - 6\sqrt{3}$ **50.** $\dfrac{2}{5}$

51. $\left\{\dfrac{6}{5}, -\dfrac{1}{2}\right\}$

52. $\{$all real numbers less than or equal to $-4\}$

53. $\{2\sqrt{3}, -2\sqrt{3}\}$ **54.** $\dfrac{1}{2}$ **55.** $\left\{\dfrac{9 + 3\sqrt{13}}{2}, \dfrac{9 - 3\sqrt{13}}{2}\right\}$

56. $\left\{-1, \dfrac{1}{2}\right\}$ **57.** $\{2 + \sqrt{6}, 2 - \sqrt{6}\}$

58. $\{$all real numbers greater than 10 or less than $-2\}$

(number line: -2 0 2 4 6 8 10 12)

59. $\{-5 + 5\sqrt{5}, -5 - 5\sqrt{5}\}$ **60.** $\left\{4, -\dfrac{16}{3}\right\}$

61. $\dfrac{2s + gt^2}{2t}$

62. 6   **63.** $\left\{\text{all real numbers less than } -\dfrac{67}{9}\right\}$ **64.** $(-4, 5)$

65. $(0, -5)$ **66.** Infinite set of solutions   **67.** $\{0, 4\}$

68. 4

69. $\left\{-\dfrac{21}{4}, \dfrac{21}{4} \text{ and all real numbers between } -\dfrac{21}{4} \text{ and } \dfrac{21}{4}\right\}$

70. $-\dfrac{8}{3}$ **71.** $\left\{\dfrac{1 + \sqrt{281}}{10}, \dfrac{1 - \sqrt{281}}{10}\right\}$

72. $\{2, 3\}$ **73.** 9

REVIEW OF SOLVING WORD PROBLEMS

1. $112, $56, $84, $140
2. 1 L milk, $.67; 1 orange, $.21
3. side = 5 cm, hyp. = 13 cm
4. Reader A, 12 min; Reader B; 24 min
5. 200 g
6. 8 nickels, 14 quarters, 7 dimes, 3 half dollars
7. 425 buttons
8. 13 years
9. 9 cm by 16 cm
10. Colin, $14.00; Maureen, $28.00
11. 81 cm², 441 cm²
12. 31, 33, 35 (Divide 99 by 3 to find the middle number)
13. 32 cm³
14. 12%
15. 4 cm by 18 cm

16. $\dfrac{4}{9}$

17. first cyclist, 100 km; second cyclist, 70 km
18. about 4.45 cm
19. $2500
20. 1 m
21. 5 kg at $2.70, 25 kg at $3.00
22. 38
23. 6 km/h
24. 2 h
25. 17 km

REVIEW OF GRAPHING

1. 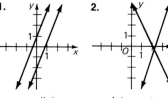   **2.**   **3.**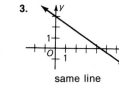

parallel   intersect   same line

4. $x + y = 3$
5. $5x - 2y = -6$ **6.** $3x + 2y = 13$ **7.** $x = 4$
8. $x + 3y = 25$ **9.** $y = -1$ **10.** $x - y = 8$
11. $2x - y = -13$
12. $\{4, \text{ and all real numbers between 2 and } 4\}$

(number line: 0 1 2 3 4)

13. $\{-2, \text{ and all real numbers between } -2 \text{ and } 3.5\}$

(number line: -2 0 2 4)

14. No solution   **15.** $\{$all real numbers$\}$

(number line: -1 0 1 2)

16. $\{$all real numbers less than or equal to $3\}$

(number line: 0 1 2 3 4)

17. {all real numbers greater than 2 or less than -1}

18. $2x - 3y = -6$ **19.** $3x + y = 4$ **20.** $y = 2$

21. $x = -\dfrac{3}{2}$ **22.**

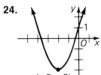

23.

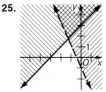

24.

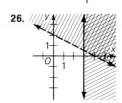

25.

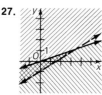

26.

 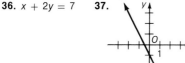

27.

28. $4x - 3y = 12$

29. $2x - 3y = 3$ **30.** $x + 4y = 6$ **31.** $3x - 8y = 27$

32. $5x + y = 23$ **33.** $y = 4$ **34.** -7 **35.** $3x - y = 3$

36. $x + 2y = 7$ **37.**

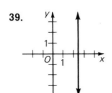

38.

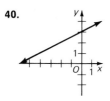

39.

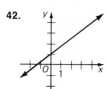

40.   **41.**

42.

43. Yes; $m = 4$ **44.** No

45. {2, 3 and all real numbers between 2 and 3}

46. No solution

47. {all real numbers greater than 3.5 or all integers less than or equal to 3}

Enrichment Activities

AROUND IN CIRCLES

Game 1: answers may vary

Start Move in Zone:	Land on Zone:
F	A
B	F
G	B
C	G
H	C
D	H
I	D
E	I

Zone E is left empty.

Game 2: answers may vary

Start Move in Zone:	Land on Zone:
H	A
F	H
D	F
B	D
I	B
G	I
E	G
C	E

Zone C is left empty.

WHAT'S NEXT?

1. 17, 21, 25   **2.** 48, 96, 192   **3.** $-4, -7, -10$

4. $1, \dfrac{1}{2}, \dfrac{1}{4}$ **5.** 13, 17, 19   **6.** 8, 7, 10   **7.** 25, 36, 49

8. 63, 127, 255   **9.** 8, 13, 21   **10.** 98, 118, 138

11. 57, 67, 77   **12.** 153, 183, 213   **13.** 0.3 mm; 0.6 mm;
1.2 mm; 2.4 mm; 2.8 mm; 9.6 mm

THE MEANING OF THE MESSAGE

Small calculators are operated by tiny electronic circuits. The simplest calculators perform the four basic arithmetic operations.

STOPPING POINT

The pattern of numbers when landing on the thumb is 1, 9, 17, 25, 33, . . . , which can be described algebraically by the expression $1 + 8r$, where r is the number of times that you have gone through the cycle. To answer the first example, find out what number you reach at the thumb just before 100. Since $1 + 8r$ becomes $1 + 8(12)$, that number is 97. Continue counting from the thumb and you will reach 100 at the ring finger. The others are done similarly.

$1 + 8(24) = 193$, so you will reach 200 at the index finger.

$1 + 8(92) = 737$, so you will reach 741 at the little finger.

$1 + 8(624) = 4993$, so you will reach 5000 at the index finger.

$1 + 8(124,999) = 999,993$, so you will reach 1,000,000 at the index finger.

ASSIGNMENT GUIDE

The following guide offers suggestions for planning separate minimum, average, and maximum courses which you can adapt as necessary to fit the needs of your particular classes.

Because students' interests and backgrounds differ so widely from class to class, most of the optional features are not listed. You will want to choose those features which best suit your individual classes. If you have access to a computer that accepts BASIC, you may wish to allow some time to show your students how to use it. Please note, however, that in order to use the Computer Activities, students need not learn the BASIC language.

All the assignments refer to written exercises, with the letter "P" indicating word problems. The letter "S" indicates the spiraled portion of the assignment, which reviews earlier work. The letter "R" indicates a review built into the text. "EP" refers the teacher to the Extra Practice section, which contains extra A and B exercises and problems to be used as needed.

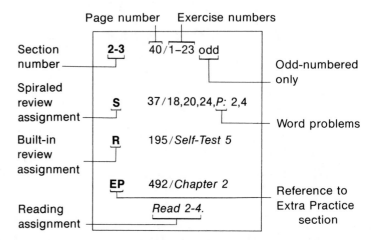

Summary Time Schedule for the Assignments

Chapter	1	2	3	4	5	6	7	8	9	10	11	12	Looking Ahead	Total
Minimum Course	11	14	14	15	24	15	16	15	13	10	13	0	0	160
Average Course	9	14	14	15	22	12	13	15	13	10	13	10	0	160
Maximum Course	8	12	12	14	22	9	10	13	13	10	13	11	13	160

LESSON	MINIMUM COURSE		AVERAGE COURSE		MAXIMUM COURSE	
1	**1-1**	3/1–17, 21, 23, 26, 33	**1-1**	3/1–37 odd	**1-1**	3/1–33 odd, 34–38
2	**1-2**	6/1–18, 19–29 odd	**1-2**	6/1–33 odd	**1-2**	6/5–17 odd, 20–24,
	S	4/22, 28, 34	**S**	4/20, 26, 32, 34		25–35 odd
3	**1-3**	10/1–27 odd	**1-3**	10/1–27 odd	**1-3**	10/1–31 odd
	S	7/20–30 even	**S**	7/20, 22, 24, 32	**S**	7/32, 34, 36

LESSON	MINIMUM COURSE		AVERAGE COURSE		MAXIMUM COURSE	
4	**1-4**	14/1–14	**1-4**	14/1–6, 7–35 odd	**1-4**	14/1–37 odd
	R	11/*Self-Test 1*	**R**	11/*Self-Test 1*	**R**	11/*Self-Test 1*
5	**1-4**	14/15–33 odd	**1-5**	18/1–15 odd	**1-5**	18/1–19 odd
			S	15/24, 28, 30, 36	**S**	15/32–38 even
6	**1-5**	18/1–13	**1-6**	23/*P:* 1–7 odd	**1-6**	23/*P:* 1–11 odd
			S	19/17–25 odd	**S**	19/20–26
7	**1-5**	19/14–24	**1-6**	24/*P:*9–15 odd	**1-6**	24/*P:*13, 15, 16
			R	25/*Self-Test 2*	**R**	25/*Self-Test 2*
8	**1-6**	23/*P:*1–7	*Prepare for Chapter Test*		*Prepare for Chapter Test*	
			R	26/*Chapter Review*		
			EP	491/*Chapter 1*		
9	**1-6**	24/*P:* 8–14	*Administer Chapter 1 Test*		*Administer Chapter 1 Test*	
	R	25/*Self-Test 2*	*Test, page T12*		*Test, page T12*	
			R	27/*Maintaining Skills*		*Read 2-1*
					2-1	31/1–43 odd
10	*Prepare for Chapter Test*		**2-1**	31/1–41 odd	**2-2**	34/1–31 odd
	R	26/*Chapter Review*				35/33–40
	EP	491/*Chapter 1*			**S**	32/42, 44
11	*Administer Chapter 1 Test*		**2-2**	34/1–31 odd, 32	**2-3**	39/1–15 odd, 17–19
	Test, page T12		**S**	32/43	**S**	34/32
	R	27/*Maintaining Skills*				
12	**2-1**	31/1–11 odd	**2-2**	35/33–39 odd	**2-4**	42/1–27 odd, 28–31
		32/13–20	**2-3**	39/1–15 odd	**R**	39/*Self-Test 1*
13	**2-1**	32/21–42	**2-3**	39/17, 18	**2-5**	45/1–35 odd
			R	39/*Self-Test 1*	**S**	42/32–34
14	**2-2**	34/1–12, 13–31 odd	**2-4**	42/1–19 odd, 20–31	**2-6**	49/5–25 odd
						50/*P:* 1–15 odd
					S	45/37–41
15	**2-3**	39/1–16	**2-5**	45/1–35 odd	**2-6**	49/12, 20–26 even
	S	34/32				51/*P:* 8–16 even
16	**2-4**	42/1–30	**2-6**	49/1–23 odd	**2-7**	55/1–37 odd, 38–42
	R	39/*Self-Test 1*		50/*P:* 1–13 odd	**R**	52/*Self-Test 2*
			S	45/37		
17	**2-5**	45/1–28	**2-6**	49/12–22 even	**2-8**	59/1–41 odd
	S	42/31		50/2–14 even	**S**	56/43, 44
18	**2-6**	49/1–22	**2-7**	55/1–43 odd	**2-9**	63/1–25 odd, 26–32
	S	45/29–36	**R**	52/*Self-Test 2*		
19	**2-6**	50/*P:* 1–11 odd, 14	**2-8**	59/1–37 odd	*Prepare for Chapter Test*	
					R	64/*Self-Test 3*

LESSON	MINIMUM COURSE		AVERAGE COURSE		MAXIMUM COURSE	
20	**2-7**	55/1–39 odd	**2-9**	63/1–29 odd	*Administer Chapter 2 Test*	
	R	52/*Self-Test 2*	**S**	60/39, 40	*Test, page T13*	
					Reading or Review	
					Assignment	
21	**2-8**	59/1–39 odd	**2-9**	63/22–32 even	**3-1**	73/1–39 odd
	S	56/38, 40	**R**	64/*Self-Test 3*		75/*P:* 1–11 odd
22	**2-9**	63/1–25 odd	*Prepare for Chapter Test*		**3-2**	78/13–43 odd
	S	60/38, 40	**R**	67–68/*Chapter*		79/*P:* 1–9 odd
				Review		
			EP	492/*Chapter 2*		
23	**2-9**	63/20–26 even	*Administer Chapter 2 Test*		**3-3**	82/1–25 odd,
	R	64/*Self-Test 3*	*Test, page T13*			*P:* 1–11 odd
			R	69/*Maintaining Skills*		
24	*Prepare for Chapter Test*		**3-1**	73/1–37 odd	**3-4**	86/1–25 odd, 26–
	R	67–68/*Chapter*		75/*P:* 1–11 odd		28, *P:* 2–8, 10
		Review			**R**	83/*Self-Test 1*
	EP	492/*Chapter 2*				
25	*Administer Chapter 2 Test*		**3-2**	78/1–41 odd	**3-5**	90/1–31 odd
	Test, page T13					
	R	69/*Maintaining Skills*				
26	**3-1**	73/1–35 odd	**3-2**	79/*P:* 1–10	**3-6**	93/1–23 odd, *P:* 1–
		75/*P:* 1–9 odd	**S**	75/*P:* 10, 12		9 odd, 10
					S	91/32
27	**3-2**	78/1–41 odd	**3-3**	82/1–25 odd, *P:* 1–	**3-7**	97/1–49 odd
				11 odd	**R**	94/*Self-Test 2*
28	**3-2**	79/*P:* 1–4, 9	**3-4**	86/1–27 odd, *P:* 1–	**3-7**	98/*P:* 1, 8, 9, 12–
	S	75/*P:* 8, 10, 12		9 odd		18, 21, 24, 25
			R	83/*Self-Test 1*		
29	**3-3**	82/1–17, 19, 21, 23,	**3-5**	90/1–31 odd	**3-8**	101/1–39 odd
		P: 1–9 odd				102/*P:* 3, 4, 6, 7, 9,
						10
30	**3-4**	86/1–23 odd,	**3-6**	93/1–23 odd, *P:* 1–	**3-9**	105/1–11 odd
		P: 1, 3, 5, 8		9 odd	**S**	103/*P:* 16, 19, 20
	R	83/*Self-Test 1*				
31	**3-5**	90/1–25, 27, 29	**3-7**	97/1–47 odd	*Prepare for Chapter Test*	
			R	94/*Self-Test 2*	**R**	107/*Self-Test 3*
32	**3-6**	93/1–24, *P:* 1, 3, 4	**3-7**	98/*P:* 1–7 odd, 8,	*Administer Chapter 3 Test*	
				10, 11, 13, 15	*Test, page T14*	
					Reading or Review	
					Assignment	

LESSON	MINIMUM COURSE		AVERAGE COURSE		MAXIMUM COURSE	
33	3-7 R	97/1–43 odd 94/*Self-Test 2*	3-8 S	101/1–39 odd 99/*P:* 17	4-1	115/1–37 odd, 38–40
34	3-7	97/42, 44 98/*P:* 1–9 odd	3-8	102/*P:* 2–4, 7, 9, 10, 16	4-2	119/1–55 odd, 56
35	3-8	101/1–23 odd, 25–30, 35	3-9 R	105/1–7 odd 107/*Self-Test 3*	4-2 R	120/*P:* 2–4, 6, 7, 9, 10, 13–16 121/*Self-Test 1*
36	3-8	102/*P:* 1–6, 10	*Prepare for Chapter Test* R EP	108–109/*Chapter Review* 495/*Chapter 3* 514/*Problems*	4-3	123/1–43 odd
37	3-9 R	105/1–5 107/*Self-Test 3*	*Administer Chapter 3 Test* *Test, page T14* R	110/*Cumulative Review*	4-4 S	127/1–41 odd 123/34, 38
38	*Prepare for Chapter Test* R EP	108–109/*Chapter Review* 495/*Chapter 3* 514/*Problems*	4-1	115/1–39 odd	4-5 S	129/1–47 odd 124/40, 42
39	*Administer Chapter 3 Test* *Test, page T14* R	111/*Maintaining Skills*	4-2	119/1–55 odd	4-6 S	132/1–49 odd 130/36, 44
40	4-1	115/1–18, 19–35 odd	4-2 R	120/*P:* 1, 3, 4, 6, 7, 9 121/*Self-Test 1*	4-7 R	136/1–27 odd 133/*Self-Test 2*
41	4-2	119/1–55 odd	4-3 S	123/1–37 odd 121/*P:* 13, 14	4-7 4-8	138/*P:* 2, 4, 6, 8, 9, 11, 12 140/*P:* 1, 2, 4, 5, 8, 10
42	4-2 R	120/*P:* 1, 3, 4, 5, 7 121/*Self-Test 1*	4-4 S	127/1–27 odd, 29–40 123/32, 34	4-9 S	144/*P:* 1–9 odd, 10, 12–14 132/6, 10, 42
43	4-3	123/1–28, 29–35 odd	4-5 S	129/1–45 odd 124/39	4-10	147/*P:* 1–7 odd
44	4-4 S	127/1–20, 21–39 odd 123/36, 37	4-6 S	132/1–43 odd 130/36, 44	4-10 R	147/*P:* 8–10 148/*Self-Test 3*

LESSON	MINIMUM COURSE	AVERAGE COURSE	MAXIMUM COURSE
45	**4-5** 129/1–43 odd **S** 123/30, 32, 34	**4-7** 136/1–27 odd **R** 133/Self-Test 2	Prepare for Chapter Test
46	**4-6** 132/1–41 odd **S** 130/36, 40	**4-7** 138/P: 1–9 odd **4-8** 140/P: 1, 2, 4, 5, 7	Administer Chapter 4 Test Test, page T15 Read Extra, pages 124–125 125/1–13 odd, 14, 15
47	**4-7** 136/1–8, 11–19 odd **R** 133/Self-Test 2	**4-9** 144/P: 1–5, 8 **S** 141/P: 9	**5-1** 157/1–45 odd
48	**4-7** 138/P: 1, 3, 5 **4-8** 140/P: 1–3, 5, 6	**4-9** 144/P: 9, 10, 12–14 **S** 132/8, 10, 40	**5-2** 160/1–45 odd
49	**4-9** 144/P: 1–4, 7 **S** 141/P: 8	**4-10** 147/P: 1–3, 5, 7	**5-3** 163/1–49 odd **S** 160/38, 44
50	**4-9** 144/P: 9, 10, 13, 14 **S** 132/2, 8, 38	**4-10** 147/P: 6, 8, 9 **R** 148/Self-Test 3	**5-3** 164/P: 1–8 **R** 165/Self-Test 1
51	**4-10** 147/P: 1–4	Prepare for Chapter Test **R** 149–150/Chapter Review **EP** 497/Chapter 4 516/Problems	**5-4** 167/1–39 odd **S** 133/38, 40, 46, 48
52	**4-10** 147/P: 5, 7 **R** 148/Self-Test 3	Administer Chapter 4 Test Test, page T15 **R** 152/Cumulative Review	**5-5** 169/1–39 odd **S** 167/30, 38, 40
53	Prepare for Chapter Test **R** 149–150/Chapter Review **EP** 497/Chapter 4 516/Problems	**5-1** 157/1–45 odd	**5-5** 169/26–40 even, 41–55 odd
54	Administer Chapter 4 Test Test, page T15 **R** 153/Maintaining Skills	**5-2** 160/1–45 odd	**5-6** 172/1–45 odd
55	**5-1** 157/1–10, 11–45 odd	**5-3** 163/1–43 odd	**5-6** 173/47–57 odd, 59–61 **R** 174/Self-Test 2
56	**5-2** 160/1–43 odd	**5-3** 164/45, 47, 49, P: 1–7 odd **S** 130/10, 12	**5-7** 176/1–49 odd
57	**5-3** 163/1–25 odd **S** 160/42, 44	**5-4** 167/1–39 odd **R** 165/Self-Test 1 **S** 133/38, 42, 46, 48	**5-8** 179/1–49 odd **S** 177/42–50 even

LESSON	MINIMUM COURSE		AVERAGE COURSE		MAXIMUM COURSE	
58	**5-3** **S**	164/27–43 odd, P: 1, 3 130/10, 12	**5-5**	169/1–39 odd	**5-9** **S**	181/1–35 odd, 37–41 179/44–50 even
59	**5-4** **R**	167/1–33 odd 165/Self-Test 1	**5-5**	169/26–40 even, 41–53 odd	**5-10** **R**	184/1–47 odd 182/Self-Test 3
60	**5-4** **S**	167/18, 22, 26, 30, 32, 35, 37, 39 133/40, 42, 47, 49	**5-6** **S**	172/1–41 odd 170/42–54 even	**5-11** **S**	186/1–43 odd 184/49, 51, 53
61	**5-5**	169/1–31 odd	**5-6** **R**	173/47–57 odd, P: 59, 60 174/Self-Test 2	**5-11** **S**	186/44–51 184/52, 54
62	**5-5**	169/22-32 even, 33–49 odd	**5-7**	176/1–45 odd	**5-12** **R**	188/1–11 186/Self-Test 4
63	**5-6**	172/1–41 odd	**5-8** **S**	179/1–47 odd 176/34, 36, 42	**5-13** **S**	190/1–47 odd 188/12, 13
64	**5-6** **R**	173/43–57 odd, P: 59 174/Self-Test 2	**5-9** **S**	181/1–39 odd 179/44, 46	**5-13** **5-14**	190/49–55 odd 192/P: 2, 4–6, 8–11
65	**5-7**	176/1–37 odd	**5-10** **R** **S**	184/1–35 odd 182/Self-Test 3 169/6, 8, 22, 24	**5-14** **S**	193/P: 13–20 190/38–46 even
66	**5-8** **S**	179/1–35 odd 176/32, 34, 36	**5-10** **S**	184/37–51 odd 182/36, 38, 40	**5-14** **R**	194/P: 23–27 195/Self-Test 5
67	**5-9** **S**	181/1–35 odd 179/22–32 even	**5-11** **S**	186/1–43 odd 184/53	*Prepare for Chapter Test*	
68	**5-10** **R** **S**	184/1–35 odd 182/Self-Test 3 169/6, 8, 34, 38, 40	**5-12** **R** **S**	188/1–11 186/Self-Test 4 186/45, 47, 48	*Administer Chapter 5 Test* *Test, page T16* *Read Extra, page 170* 170/1–7	
69	**5-10** **5-11**	184/37–45 odd 186/1–18	**5-13** **S**	190/1–43 odd 188/12	**6-1** **S**	202/1–41 odd 160/22, 24, 46
70	**5-11** **S**	186/19–43 odd 184/47, 49, 51	**5-14** **S**	192/P: 1–13 odd 190/42, 44, 47	**6-1** **6-2**	203/43–48 205/7–49 odd
71	**5-12** **R** **S**	188/1–10 186/Self-Test 4 186/36, 38, 40	**5-14**	193/P: 16, 18, 20–23	**6-3** **S**	209/1–39 odd 206/51, 53, 55
72	**5-13** **S**	190/1–25 188/11, 12	**5-14** **R**	194/P: 24–26 195/Self-Test 5	**6-4** **R**	214/1–43 odd 210/Self-Test 1

LESSON	MINIMUM COURSE	AVERAGE COURSE	MAXIMUM COURSE
73	**5-13** 190/27–41 odd	*Prepare for Chapter Test* R 195–197/*Chapter Review* EP 498/*Chapter 5* 517/*Problems*	**6-4** 215/45, 46, 48 **6-5** 217/5–49 odd
74	**5-14** 192/P: 1, 3, 6–8 S 190/36, 40	*Administer Chapter 5 Test* Test, page T16 R 198/*Cumulative Review*	**6-6** 221/1–25 odd R 219/*Self-Test 2* S 218/48, 50, 51
75	**5-14** 193/P: 10–12, 14, 15, 20	**6-1** 202/1–37 odd S 160/16, 18, 22, 24	**6-7** 223/1–37 odd S 221/27, 28
76	**5-14** 194/P: 21–23, 26 R 195/*Self-Test 5*	**6-1** 203/39–45 odd **6-2** 205/1–23 odd	*Prepare for Chapter Test* R 225/*Self-Test 3*
77	*Prepare for Chapter Test* R 195–197/*Chapter Review* EP 498/*Chapter 5* 517/*Problems*	**6-2** 206/27, 28, 29–51 odd	*Administer Chapter 6 Test* Test, page T17 Read Extra, page 225 226/1–15 odd
78	*Administer Chapter 5 Test* Test, page T16 R 199/*Maintaining Skills*	**6-3** 209/1–35 odd	**7-1** 237/1–25 odd 238/P: 1–15 odd
79	**6-1** 202/1–26 S 160/12, 16	**6-4** 214/1–31 odd R 210/*Self-Test 1*	**7-2** 241/1–31 odd 242/P: 1–11 odd S 238/P: 14, 16
80	**6-1** 202/27–41 odd S 160/18, 22	**6-4** 215/33–46 S 209/36, 37, 39	**7-3** 244/7–33 odd 245/P: 1–11 odd R 243/*Self-Test 1* S 242/32
81	**6-2** 205/1–15 odd, 17–24	**6-5** 217/1–47 odd	**7-4** 248/1–11 odd, 13–15, 17–29 odd S 245/28, 30, 32
82	**6-2** 206/25, 26, 29–49 odd	**6-6** 221/1–10 R 219/*Self-Test 2* S 218/28, 30	**7-5** 253/1–17 odd, 23–29 odd, 37–41 odd 254/P: 1–3, 6, 8, 9, 11, 12 R 250/*Self-Test 2*
83	**6-3** 209/1–11 odd, 13–18	**6-6** 221/11–25 odd **6-7** 223/1–19 odd	**7-6** 257/P: 1–13 odd S 248/31, 32, 34
84	**6-3** 209/19–35 odd	**6-7** 224/21–35 odd R 225/*Self-Test 3*	**7-7** 261/P: 1–19 odd, 20, 21 R 258/*Self-Test 3* S 258/P: 14

LESSON	MINIMUM COURSE			AVERAGE COURSE			MAXIMUM COURSE		
85	6-4	214/1–23 odd		*Prepare for Chapter Test*			7-8	265/P: 1–19 odd	
	R	210/*Self-Test 1*		R	228–230/*Chapter Review*				
				EP	500/*Chapter 6*				
86	6-4	214/25–43 odd		*Administer Chapter 6 Test*			*Prepare for Chapter Test*		
				Test, page T17			R	268/*Self-Test 4*	
				R	232/*Cumulative Review*				
87	6-5	217/1–9 odd, 11–21, 23–29 odd		7-1	237/1–25 odd		*Administer Chapter 7 Test*		
					238/P: 1, 3, 4		*Test, page T18*		
							S	226/16–19, 21, 23, 25, 26, 27–31 odd	
88	6-5	218/31–43 odd		7-1	238/P: 5, 6, 9, 12, 15		8-1	278/1–35 odd	
	R	219/*Self-Test 2*		7-2	241/1–21 odd				
89	6-6	221/1–24		7-2	242/23–31 odd, P: 1, 3, 5, 9, 11, 12		8-2	281/9–39 odd	
				S	102/36, 38		S	278/30, 32, 34	
90	6-7	223/1–19 odd		7-3	244/7–31 odd		8-3	285/1–35 odd	
				R	243/*Self-Test 1*		S	282/34–40 even	
91	6-7	224/21–31 odd		7-3	245/P: 1, 3, 4, 7, 10, 12		8-4	289/1–23 odd, 25–28	
	R	225/*Self-Test 3*		7-4	248/1–29 odd		R	286/*Self-Test 1*	
92	*Prepare for Chapter Test*			7-5	253/1–41 odd		8-5	292/7–29 odd, 30, 31	
	R	228–230/*Chapter Review*		R	250/*Self-Test 2*				
	EP	500/*Chapter 6*							
93	*Administer Chapter 6 Test*			7-5	254/P: 1, 3, 8–11		8-6	294/P: 1–13 odd	
	Test, page T17						S	292/32	
	R	233/*Maintaining Skills*							
94	7-1	237/1–24		7-6	257/P: 1–13 odd		8-7	297/5–23 odd	
				S	255/P: 12			298/P: 1, 5, 7	
							S	292/10, 12, 14	
95	7-1	238/P: 1–4, 6, 7, 9		7-7	261/P: 1–13 odd, 14		8-8	301/1–31 odd	
				R	258/*Self-Test 3*		S	298/P: 6, 8	
96	7-2	241/1–31 odd		7-7	262/P: 16, 18, 20		8-8	302/P: 1, 4, 6, 7, 10	
	S	101/20, 22, 24, 31, 33		7-8	265/P: 1, 2, 4, 5		8-9	306/P: 4–7, 11	
97	7-2	242/P: 2, 4–6, 8, 12		7-8	266/P: 8, 9, 11, 12, 16, 17, 19		8-9	307/P: 13, 14, 16, 20, 21	
				R	268/*Self-Test 4*		8-10	310/P: 1, 3, 5	
							R	303/*Self-Test 2*	

LESSON	MINIMUM COURSE		AVERAGE COURSE		MAXIMUM COURSE	
98	**7-3** **R**	244/7–18, 19–25 odd 243/Self-Test 1	*Prepare for Chapter Test* **R** **EP**	269–271/Chapter Review 502/Chapter 7 517/Problems	**8-10** **R** **S**	311/P: 9, 12, 15, 18 312/Self-Test 3 308/23
99	**7-3**	245/P: 1, 3, 4, 7, 9	*Administer Chapter 7 Test* *Test, page T18* **R**	272/Cumulative Review	*Prepare for Chapter Test*	
100	**7-4**	248/1–29 odd	**8-1**	278/1–33 odd	*Administer Chapter 8 Test* *Test, page T19* **S**	226/17–31 odd
101	**7-5** **R**	253/1–41 odd 250/Self-Test 2	**8-2** **S**	281/1–37 odd 278/22–34 even	**9-1** **S**	322/1–41 odd 286/32, 34, 36
102	**7-5**	254/P: 1–3, 6–9	**8-3** **S**	285/1–31 odd, 35 281/18, 28, 34, 36, 39	**9-2** **S**	326/1–29 odd 323/40, 42
103	**7-6**	257/P: 1–13 odd	**8-4** **R**	289/1–27 odd 286/Self-Test 1	**9-3** **S**	329/1–29 odd, 31–33 326/26
104	**7-7** **R**	261/P: 1–11 odd 258/Self-Test 3	**8-5** **S**	292/1–29 odd 289/16, 20, 24	**9-4** **R**	333/1–35 odd 330/Self-Test 1
105	**7-7** **7-8**	262/P: 14, 16, 17, 19 265/P: 1–3, 5	**8-6** **S**	294/P: 1–11 odd 292/24, 30	**9-4** **9-5**	333/37–41, 43 336/1, 3, 5, 6
106	**7-8**	266/P: 7, 11–13	**8-7** **S**	297/1–23 odd 295/P: 12, 14	**9-6**	341/1–25 odd, 26
107	**R** **S**	268/Self-Test 4 266/16, 17	**8-7**	298/P: 1–7 odd	**9-7** **R**	345/1–19 odd, 20–23 342/Self-Test 2
108	*Prepare for Chapter Test* **R** **EP**	269–271/Chapter Review 502/Chapter 7 517/Problems	**8-8** **S**	301/1–25 odd, 29 298/P: 4, 8	**9-8** **S**	350/1–13 odd 351/P: 1–7 odd 346/P: 1–7 odd, 8, 10
109	*Administer Chapter 7 Test* *Test, page T18* **R**	273/Maintaining Skills	**8-8** **8-9**	302/P: 1–7 odd 306/P: 2–5	**9-9** **S**	354/P: 1, 2, 5–7 352/P: 10–14
110	**8-1**	278/1–20, 21–31 odd	**8-9** **R** **S**	307/P: 7–15 odd, 19, 22 303/Self-Test 2 302/P: 9	**9-10** **S**	357/P: 1, 4, 5, 7, 9 355/P: 8, 9, 11

LESSON	MINIMUM COURSE	AVERAGE COURSE	MAXIMUM COURSE
111	**8-2** 281/1–31 odd **S** 278/22–30 even	**8-10** 310/P: 1–11 odd **S** 308/P: 23	**9-10** 358/P: 10 **R** 359/Self-Test 3 **S** 341/12, 14, 22
112	**8-3** 285/1–31 odd **S** 281/14, 16, 18, 28	**8-10** 311/P: 14, 15, 17 **R** 312/Self-Test 3	Prepare for Chapter Test
113	**8-4** 289/1–4, 5–23 odd **R** 286/Self-Test 1	Prepare for Chapter Test **R** 313–315/Chapter Review **EP** 503/Chapter 8 520/Problems	Administer Chapter 9 Test Test, page T20 **S** 207/55 **S** 308/P: 24, 25
114	**8-5** 292/1–6, 7–21 odd **S** 289/14, 16, 18, 22	Administer Chapter 8 Test Test, page T19 **R** 316/Cumulative Review	**10-1** 367/1–31 odd, 32–35
115	**8-6** 294/P: 1–3, 5, 6 **S** 289/20, 23, 25	**9-1** 322/1–39 odd **S** 286/32–34, 36	**10-2** 373/9–63 odd
116	**8-7** 297/1–8, 9–23 odd **S** 295/P: 7, 9	**9-2** 326/1–29 odd **S** 323/41	**10-3** 376/9, 11, P: 1–19 odd **S** 373/48–62 even
117	**8-7** 297/18, 22 298/P: 1–7 odd	**9-3** 329/1–31 odd **S** 326/24, 26	**10-4** 384/1–37 odd **R** 378/Self-Test 1 **S** 377/P: 20, 22
118	**8-8** 301/1–25 odd **S** 298/P: 8	**9-4** 333/1–35 odd **R** 330/Self-Test 1	**10-5** 387/1–37 odd **S** 385/39, 40
119	**8-8** 302/P: 1–3, 6 **8-9** 306/P: 1, 4, 5	**9-4** 333/37–41 **9-5** 336/3, 4	**10-6** 391/1–33 odd, 34 **R** 388/Self-Test 2 **S** 388/39, 40
120	**8-9** 307/P: 7–9, 13, 15, 21 **R** 303/Self-Test 2	**9-6** 341/1–25 odd, 26	**10-7** 394/1–23 odd **S** 392/35
121	**8-10** 310/P: 1–3, 6, 7, 9	**9-7** 345/1–21 odd, 22 **R** 342/Self-Test 2	**10-7** 395/24–27 **R** 396/Self-Test 3
122	**8-10** 311/P: 10, 12, 15 **R** 312/Self-Test 3	**9-8** 350/1–13 odd 351/P: 1, 3, 5 **S** 346/P: 1–7 odd	Prepare for Chapter Test
123	Prepare for Chapter Test **R** 313–315/Chapter Review **EP** 503/Chapter 8 520/Problems	**9-9** 354/P: 1–3, 5–7 **S** 351/P: 4, 6, 7, 10	Administer Chapter 10 Test Test, page T21 Read Extra, page 380 380/1–29 odd

LESSON	MINIMUM COURSE		AVERAGE COURSE		MAXIMUM COURSE	
124		*Administer Chapter 8 Test* *Test, page T19*	9-10 S	357/P: 1–9 odd 355/P: 10	11-1	406/1–35 odd
	R	317/*Maintaining Skills*				
125	9-1 S	322/1–33 odd 286/32, 33, 36	9-10 R S S	358/6, 8 359/*Self-Test 3* 322/30, 34 341/12, 16, 24	11-2 S	410/1–41 odd 406/26, 34
126	9-2 S	326/1–25 odd 322/35–38	R EP	*Prepare for Chapter Test* 360–361/*Chapter Review* 504/*Chapter 9* 521/*Problems*	11-3 S	414/1–43 odd 411/43
127	9-3 S	329/1–4, 5–29 odd 326/26, 27	R	*Administer Chapter 9 Test* *Test, page T20* 362/*Cumulative Review*	11-4 R	418/1–19 odd 415/*Self-Test 1*
128	9-4 R	333/1–31 odd 330/*Self-Test 1*	10-1	367/1–29 odd, 30–34	11-5	420/1–35 odd, P: 1–9 odd
129	9-4 9-5	333/33–39 odd 336/2, 5	10-2	373/9-55 odd	11-6 S	424/1–25 odd 425/P: 1–5 421/P: 10
130	9-6	341/1–25 odd	10-3 S	375/1–11 odd 376/P: 1, 2, 5, 7, 8 373/57–63 odd	11-7 R S	429/1–35 odd 426/*Self-Test 2* 425/P: 6–9
131	9-7 R	345/1–23 odd 342/*Self-Test 2*	10-4 R S	384/1–27 odd 378/*Self-Test 1* 376/P: 9, 14	11-8 S	430/1–33 odd 429/37–40
132	9-8 S	350/1–13 odd 346/P: 1, 3, 5	10-5 S	387/1–27 odd 384/29–37 odd	11-9 S	432/1–41 odd 431/30, 32, 34
133	9-9 S	354/P: 1, 2, 5-7 351/P: 1, 3, 5, 6	10-6 S	391/1–33 odd 388/29–37 odd	11-10 S	435/1–37 odd 433/38, 40, 42
134	9-10 S	357/P: 1, 4, 5, 7 355/P: 9	10-7 R S	394/1–21 odd 388/*Self-Test 2* 392/34	11-10 R	435/34, 38, 39, P: 1–7, 9 437/*Self-Test 3*
135	9-10 R S S	358/P: 8 359/*Self-Test 3* 322/30, 32, 34 341/10, 18, 24, 26	10-7 R S	395/23–25 396/*Self-Test 3* 377/P: 17, 19		*Prepare for Chapter Test*

LESSON	MINIMUM COURSE			AVERAGE COURSE			MAXIMUM COURSE	
136	*Prepare for Chapter Test*	R	360–361 / *Chapter Review*	*Prepare for Chapter Test*	R	398–399 / *Chapter Review*	*Administer Chapter 11 Test Test, page T22 Read Extra, pages 426–427*	
		EP	504 / *Chapter 9* 521 / *Problems*		EP	507 / *Chapter 10* 522 / *Problems*	427 / 1–13 odd	
137	*Administer Chapter 9 Test Test, page T20*	R	363 / *Maintaining Skills*	*Administer Chapter 10 Test Test, page T21*	R	400 / *Cumulative Review*	**12-1**	445 / 1–51 odd
138	**10-1**		367 / 1–10, 11–31 odd	**11-1**		406 / 1–33 odd	**12-1** **12-2**	445 / 52–58 448 / 1–17 odd
139	**10-2**		372 / 1–8, 9–35 odd	**11-2**		410 / 1–41 odd	**12-2**	448 / 19–35 odd, 37–39
140	**10-3** S		375 / 1–11 odd 376 / *P: 1, 3, 7* 373 / 37–43 odd	**11-3** S		414 / 1–43 odd 411 / 42	**12-3**	450 / 1–23 odd, 24 *Read Extra, page 451*
141	**10-4** R S		384 / 1–25 odd 378 / *Self-Test 1* 376 / *P: 9, 13*	**11-4** R		418 / 1–19 odd 415 / *Self-Test 1*	**12-4** S S	454 / 1–19 odd 282 / 30, 32 451 / 25
142	**10-5** S		387 / 1–21 odd 384 / 27–33 odd	**11-5**		420 / 1–35 odd, *P: 1, 3, 5*	**12-5** R S	457 / 1–31 odd 455 / *Self-Test 1* 455 / 20
143	**10-6** S		391 / 1–29 odd 388 / 23–33 odd	**11-6** S		424 / 1–25 odd 425 / *P: 1–4* 420 / *P: 4, 6, 7*	**12-6** S	460 / *P: 3–5, 7–10* 458 / 24–30 even *Read Extra, page 462*
144	**10-7** R		394 / 1–21 odd 388 / *Self-Test 2*	**11-7** R S		429 / 1–35 odd 426 / *Self-Test 2* 425 / *P: 5, 6, 8*	**12-6** **Extra**	460 / *P: 6, 11–14* 462 / 1–5
145	**10-7** R		394 / 12–22 even 396 / *Self-Test 3*	**11-8** S		430 / 1–29 odd, 33 429 / 37, 39	**Extra** R	462 / 6–8 461 / *Self-Test 2*
146	*Prepare for Chapter Test*	R	398–399 / *Chapter Review*	**11-9** S		432 / 1–37 odd 431 / 30–32	*Prepare for Chapter Test*	
		EP	507 / *Chapter 10* 522 / *Problems*					
147	*Administer Chapter 10 Test Test, page T21*	R	401 / *Maintaining Skills*	**11-10** S		435 / 1–37 odd 433 / 39, 40	*Administer Chapter 12 Test Test, page T23 Reading or Review Assignment*	
148	**11-1**		406 / 1–33 odd	**11-10** R S		435 / *P: 1, 2, 5–7* 437 / *Self-Test 3* 421 / *P: 9*	**Looking Ahead**	470 / 1–21

LESSON	MINIMUM COURSE		AVERAGE COURSE		MAXIMUM COURSE	
149	**11-2**	410/1–37 odd	*Prepare for Chapter Test* R 438–439/*Chapter Review* EP 508/*Chapter 11* 522/*Problems*		**Looking Ahead** 472/1–11 odd S 424/8, 10, 12	
150	**11-3** S	414/1–39 odd 411/41	*Administer Chapter 11 Test* *Test, page T22* R 440/*Cumulative Review*		**Looking Ahead** 475/1–11 odd, 13–17, 19, 21 S 473/10, 12	
151	**11-4** R	418/1–19 odd 415/*Self-Test 1*	**12-1**	445/1–45 odd	**Looking Ahead** 476/*P:* 1, 3–5, 8, 9	
152	**11-5**	420/1–31 odd, *P:* 1, 3	**12-1** **12-2**	445/47–57 odd 448/1–11 odd	**Looking Ahead** 478/1–11	
153	**11-6** S	424/1–9 odd, 10–13, 17, 19 425/*P:* 1, 2 420/*P:* 4, 5	**12-2**	448/13–35 odd	**Looking Ahead** 479/*P:* 1–6	
154	**11-7** R S	429/1–33 odd 426/*Self-Test 2* 425/*P:* 3	**12-3** S	450/1–23 odd, 24 448/37, 39	**Looking Ahead** 482/1–13	
155	**11-8** S S	430/1–27 odd 425/*P:* 4, 6 429/35	**12-4** S	454/1–17 odd 282/30, 32	**Looking Ahead** 484/1–24	
156	**11-9** S	432/1–29 odd 431/22–28 even	**12-5** R S	457/1–27 odd 455/*Self-Test 1* 455/19	**Looking Ahead** 487/1–17 odd	
157	**11-10** S	435/1–33 odd 433/31, 33	**12-6** S	460/*P:* 1, 2, 5, 7-10 458/29	**Looking Ahead** 487/*P:* 1–15 odd	
158	**11-10** R	435/34, 35, *P:* 1, 3, 5, 6 437/*Self-Test 3*	**12-6** R	460/*P:* 6, 11–14 461/*Self-Test 2*	**Looking Ahead** 488/*P:* 8, 12 R 490/*Review*	
159	*Prepare for Chapter Test* R 438–439/*Chapter Review* EP 508/*Chapter 11* 522/*Problems*		*Prepare for Chapter Test* R 464–465/*Chapter Review* EP 512/*Chapter 12* 523/*Problems*		*Prepare for Chapter Test*	
160	*Administer Chapter 11 Test* *Test, page T22*		*Administer Chapter 12 Test* *Test, page T23*		*Administer Looking Ahead Test*	

SUPPLEMENTARY MATERIALS GUIDE

For use after Section	Practice Masters	Progress Tests	Computer Activities
1-2	Sheet 1		
1-3		Test 1	
1-4	Sheet 2		
1-6	Sheet 3	Test 2	
Chapter 1		Test 3	Activities 1, 2, and 3
2-1			Activities 4 and 5
2-2	Sheet 4		
2-3		Test 4	
2-5	Sheet 5		
2-6		Test 5	Activity 6
2-7	Sheet 6		
2-9	Sheet 7	Test 6	
Chapter 2		Test 7	
3-1	Sheet 8		
3-3	Sheet 9	Test 8	
3-4	Sheet 10		
3-6	Sheet 11	Test 9	
3-7	Sheet 12		Activity 7
3-8	Sheet 13		Activity 8
3-9		Test 10	Activity 9
Chapter 3		Test 11	
Cumulative Review	Sheets 14 and 15		
4-1	Sheet 16		Activity 10
4-2	Sheet 17		Activity 11
4-4	Sheet 18		
4-5	Sheet 19		

For use after Section	Practice Masters	Progress Tests	Computer Activities
4-6	Sheet 20	Test 12	
4-7			Activity 12
4-8	Sheet 21		
4-10	Sheet 22	Test 13	
Chapter 4		Test 14	
Cumulative Review		Test 15	
5-1			Activity 13
5-2	Sheet 23		
5-3	Sheet 24		
5-4	Sheet 25		
5-5	Sheet 26		Activity 14
5-6	Sheet 27	Test 16	
5-7	Sheet 28		Activity 15
5-8	Sheet 29		
5-9	Sheet 30		
5-11	Sheet 31	Test 17	
5-13	Sheet 32		
5-14	Sheet 33	Test 18	
Chapter 5		Test 19	
6-1	Sheet 34		
6-3	Sheet 35	Test 20	
6-4			Activity 16
6-5	Sheet 36		Activity 17
6-7	Sheet 37	Test 21	Activity 18
Chapter 6		Test 22	
Cumulative Review	Sheets 38 and 39	Test 23	

For use after Section	Practice Masters	Progress Tests	Computer Activities
7-1			Activity 19
7-2	Sheet 40		
7-4	Sheet 41	Test 24	Activity 20
7-5			Activity 21
7-6	Sheet 42		
7-8	Sheet 43	Test 25	
Chapter 7		Test 26	
8-1	Sheet 44		
8-2			Activity 22
8-3	Sheet 45	Test 27	
8-4			Activity 23
8-5	Sheet 46		
8-6	Sheet 47	Test 28	
8-8	Sheet 48		Activity 24
8-9	Sheet 49		
8-10	Sheet 50	Test 29	
Chapter 8		Test 30	
Cumulative Review		Test 31	
9-1			Activity 25
9-2	Sheet 51		Activity 26
9-3	Sheet 52	Test 32	
9-5	Sheet 53		Activity 27
9-6	Sheet 54	Test 33	
9-8	Sheet 55		
9-10	Sheet 56	Test 34	
Chapter 9		Test 35	
Cumulative Review	Sheets 57 and 58		
10-2	Sheet 59		

For use after Section	Practice Masters	Progress Tests	Computer Activities
10-3		Test 36	
10-4	Sheet 60		Activity 28
10-5	Sheet 61		Activity 29
10-7	Sheet 62	Test 37	Activity 30
Chapter 10		Test 38	
11-2	Sheet 63		Activity 31
11-3		Test 39	
11-4	Sheet 64		
11-6	Sheet 65	Test 40	
11-7	Sheet 66		
11-8	Sheet 67		Activity 32
11-9	Sheet 68		
11-10	Sheet 69	Test 41	Activity 33
Chapter 11		Test 42	
12-2	Sheet 70		
12-3	Sheet 71		
12-4		Test 43	Activity 34
12-5	Sheet 72		Activity 35
12-6	Sheet 73	Test 44	Activity 36
Chapter 12		Test 45	
Cumulative Review	Sheets 74, 75, and 76	Test 46 or Test 47	
Pairs of Angles	Sheet 77		
Similar Triangles	Sheet 78		
Trigonometric Tables	Sheet 79		
Numerical Trigonometry	Sheet 80		

LESSON COMMENTARY

1 *Introduction to Algebra*

This chapter presents the mathematical vocabulary and some of the basic skills that are essential to solving simple word problems. Students solve equations by inspection, with systematic methods postponed until later chapters. A careful presentation of the translation of words into mathematical symbols leads students to a general method for problem solving that will be used throughout the text.

1-1 *(pages 1–4)*

KEY MATHEMATICAL IDEAS

- simplifying numerical expressions
- evaluating variable expressions

TEACHING SUGGESTIONS

Tables listing related quantities can help students understand the idea of using a variable expression to represent a large amount of information. The table shown here leads to a variable expression for the number of cents in x quarters.

Number of quarters	1	2	3	. . .	x
Number of cents	25	50	75	. . .	$25x$

You may wish to present the idea visually. The following presentation leads students to an expression for the number of faces on n blocks. You will need a box containing a number of blocks. Display one block and ask the class how many faces are on that block. (6 faces) Then display two blocks and ask the class how many faces there are in all. (12 faces) Continue with three, four, and five blocks, recording the results in a table on the chalkboard. (18, 24, and 30 faces) Then say, "There are a number of blocks in the box, but I don't know how many there are." Discuss how to express the unknown number of blocks. (Choose a variable, say n.) Have the class develop an expression for the total number of faces on the blocks in the box. ($6n$ faces)

In this section, parentheses indicate which calculation comes first in expressions that use more than one operation. Other grouping symbols and conventions for order of operations are presented in Section 1-2.

Students may be interested in the development of the equals sign, described in the Historical Note on page 75.

SUGGESTED EXTENSIONS

1. Challenge students to write as many different numerical expressions for a particular number, say 12, as they can in a given time limit. (For example, 3×4, $60 \div 5$, $1 + 2 + 3 + 4 + 2$, $(6 \times 3) - (12 \div 2)$, and so on) The class might enjoy comparing expressions, classifying them on the basis of numerals used and operations involved, and compiling a master list of the expressions, organized according to some logical scheme.

2. Ask students to write a numerical expression for each number from 0 to 9. Each expression should include four different numerals from 0 to 9 and involve three of the operations addition, subtraction, multiplication, and division. For example,

$$0 = (3 \times 2) - (5 + 1)$$
$$1 = (2 + 3) - (4 \times 1)$$
$$2 = (0 + 1) \times (8 - 6)$$

and so on.

1-2 *(pages 5–8)*

KEY MATHEMATICAL IDEAS

- simplifying expressions containing more than one grouping symbol
- simplifying expressions when grouping symbols are omitted

TEACHING SUGGESTIONS

One way to clarify the use of parentheses in algebra and to provide an introduction to this section is to read the expression $12 - 6 + 2$ aloud in three different ways, "twelve minus (pause) six plus two," "twelve minus six (pause) plus two,'' and "twelve-minus-six-plus-two (no pauses),'' while writing the corresponding expressions $12 - (6 + 2)$, $(12 - 6) + 2$, and $12 - 6 + 2$ on the chalkboard. Do the same for the expressions $12 + 6 + 2$, $12 - 6 - 2$, $12 + 6 \times 2$, and $12 \div 6 \times 2$ to form a table with pause-before-6, pause-after-6, and no-pause columns. Ask students to simplify the expressions in the first two columns. After a discussion of the different answers obtained and the need to agree upon the order of operations in expressions without grouping symbols, introduce students to the conventions for order of operations listed on page 6. Do note that the rules are simply *conventions*, accepted by general agreement to avoid confusion. Then return to the table and ask students to use these conventions to simplify the expressions in the third column.

Students with calculators may wish to investigate the rules used by their calculators to simplify numerical expressions. This topic is explored in the Calculator Key-In on page 8.

SUGGESTED EXTENSIONS

1. Challenge students to write numerical expressions for as many numbers from 0 to 100 as they can, using four numerals (not necessarily different) from 1 to 4; one or more of the operations addition, subtraction, multiplication, and division; and appropriate grouping symbols. For example,

$$0 = 2 - 2 + (3 - 3)$$
$$1 = 3 + 2 - 4 \times 1$$
$$2 = (3 + 1) \div (4 \div 2)$$
$$3 = (1 + 1 + 1) \div 1$$
$$4 = (3 - 1) \times (4 \div 2)$$

and so on.

2. Write these expressions on the chalkboard and ask students to place grouping symbols so that each expression has the given value.
   a. $5 \times 8 \div 2 + 6$; 5 $\quad 5 \times 8 \div (2 + 6)$
   b. $7 \times 4 - 3 \div 1 + 6$; 1 $\quad 7 \times (4 - 3) \div (1 + 6)$
   c. $2 \div 2 + 2 \div 2 \times 2 + 2$; 4
      $\quad 2 \div [(2 + 2) \div (2 \times 2)] + 2$

1-3 (pages 9–10)

KEY MATHEMATICAL IDEAS

- using the vocabulary and symbols related to equations
- finding solution sets of open sentences

TEACHING SUGGESTIONS

You may wish to review the last lesson and introduce the concepts in this section by writing the following statements on the chalkboard and asking, "Which are true and which are false?''

$$8 \div 4 + 3 = 5 \quad \text{True}$$
$$6 + 3 \times 3 = 27 \quad \text{False}$$
$$16 - 8 - 2 = 10 \quad \text{False}$$

Then write the statements

$$n + 8 = 12 \text{ and } 1 + x = x + 1$$

on the chalkboard and ask, "What about these?'' (Responses may vary from "You can't tell,'' "Sometimes true, sometimes false,'' or "It depends on what number you replace the variable with'' to "The first one is true when $n = 4$ and false when n is replaced by any other number, but the second one is true no matter what number replaces x.'') Direct the discussion toward the concepts presented in this section.

Students may have learned synonyms for some of the terms introduced in this section, such as *element*, rather than member, *of a set* and *member*, rather than side, *of an equation*. This text avoids referring to *members* of an equation because of possible confusion with *members* of a set. For convenience, refer to the *left side* and the *right side* of an equation.

The set-notation symbols used in the text to indicate the domain (sometimes called *replacement set*) of a variable may be new to some students. "$x \in \{1, 2, 3\}$'' may be read "x belongs to the set whose elements are the numbers 1, 2, and 3'' or "the domain of x consists of the values 1, 2, and 3.'' Recall from Section 1-1 that the numbers represented by a variable are the *values* of the variable.

SUGGESTED EXTENSIONS

1. Challenge students to write five equations whose solution set is the set of *all* numbers. For example, $x + 0 = x$, $3 + x = x + 3$, $x = x$, $4x = x \cdot 4$, and so on.

2. Challenge students to write five equations that have *no* solution. For example, $x + 1 = x + 3$, $x = x - 2$, $0 \cdot x = 15$, and so on.

1-4 (pages 12–15)

KEY MATHEMATICAL IDEAS

- translating words into variable expressions and equations

TEACHING SUGGESTIONS

Point out that mathematical symbols form a special language, one that is used throughout the world. Translating mathematical symbols into words (and vice versa) is essential to representing and then solving word problems such as those found in the next two sections and throughout the text.

Mention should be made of the fact that one equation, such as $2 + 5 = 7$, can be translated in a variety of ways. For example,

1. Two plus five is equal to seven.
2. Five greater than two is seven.
3. The sum of two and five represents the same number as seven.
4. Five added to two has the value of seven.
5. If two is increased by five, the result is seven.

You may wish to work with your class to develop a list of the different ways symbols such as "$+$," "$-$," and "$=$" can be verbalized.

SUGGESTED EXTENSIONS

1. Students with knowledge of other languages can be asked to read "$2 + 5 = 7$" in those languages. They may also read or write the chalkboard examples in other languages.
2. The metric system provides a good example of mathematical symbols as an international language. Ask students to explore the history of the development of the metric system, the history of metric-system conversion in various countries, or the translation in various languages of symbols such as "2 cm," "100 mL," and "35 kg."

1-5 (*pages 17–20*)

KEY MATHEMATICAL IDEA

- representing problem situations by variable expressions and equations

TEACHING SUGGESTIONS

You may wish to introduce this section by having a class discussion focusing on the ways in which your students and their families and friends use formulas in their daily activities, such as measuring a floor for carpeting, figuring out the worth of a handful of change or the distance traveled in a car, and deciding how much or many of a given item can be purchased with funds available. Some students may claim that they never use formulas, but you can point out that they probably use formulas without realizing it. Some of the situations described should lend themselves to chalkboard examples patterned after the examples in the text.

The fact that a large variety of verbal sentences can be represented by one equation (see Teaching Suggestions, Section 1-4) makes it possible to apply algebra to a great number of situations. Sometimes, however, it is difficult to know just which equation is represented by a given problem situation. Caution your students to read word problems very carefully, since overlooking or misreading even one word could change the meaning of the entire problem.

SUGGESTED EXTENSIONS

1. Ask each student to write a simple equation containing a variable. Then challenge them to describe at least three different problem situations that could be represented by that equation. For example, suppose the equation is $7x = 42$. If x represents the number indicated by the words in parentheses, the situations could be

   a. The heat wave lasted 42 days. (Number of weeks the heat wave lasted)

   b. Eduardo's 42-year-old father is seven times as old as Eduardo. (Eduardo's age now)

   c. It costs $42 to buy seven tickets. (Cost of one ticket)

2. Ask students to write formulas similar to those at the top of page 17. For example,

   $A = \pi r \cdot r$ Area of circle $= \pi \times$ radius $\times$ radius

   $V = s \cdot s \cdot s$ Volume of cube $=$ side $\times$ side $\times$ side

   $D = \pi dn$ Distance covered by bicycle $= \pi \times$ wheel diameter $\times$ number of wheel revolutions

   $W = rh$ Weekly wage $=$ hourly rate $\times$ hours worked per week

   and so on.

1-6 (*pages 22–24*)

KEY MATHEMATICAL IDEAS

- using a general plan to solve word problems

Since the five-step method for solving word problems will be used throughout the text, you may find it useful to prepare a large chart listing the five steps. The chart could be mounted at one end of the chalkboard and used for general classroom reference and as a guide for writing out solutions at the chalkboard during discussions and recitations (each step under the preceding one and aligned with the corresponding step on the chart).

A common error is made by students who check answers by substituting the solution obtained in Step 4 into the equation written in Step 3. Emphasize that substitution in the equation checks *only* the work done in Step 4, and that the equation itself may be incorrect. Students should check answers in the original problem. Some students may need several reminders to identify the unit when choosing a variable and to give the answer in words ("Let n = cost of cassette in dollars" and "The cassette costs \$5" rather than "Let n = cost" and "5").

2 *Working with Real Numbers*

The development of this chapter focuses on two major mathematical ideas, the real number line and the algebraic properties of real numbers.

The number line provides a visual model for the real numbers and their operations. For example, the order of points on the number line can also be used to compare any two numbers, and the distance between any point and the origin can be used to relate numbers and their absolute values. The operations of addition and subtraction can be demonstrated by arrows which illustrate movement along the number line.

The associative, commutative, and distributive properties strengthen the development of the rules for addition, subtraction, multiplication, and in the next chapter, for division of positive and negative numbers. These properties also support the relationships between the four basic operations, and real number opposites and reciprocals.

2-1 *(pages 29–32)*

KEY MATHEMATICAL IDEAS

• graphing real numbers on a number line

TEACHING SUGGESTIONS

A review of some common uses of positive and negative numbers leads naturally to a discussion of number lines. Use examples like temperature above and below zero, asset and debt, altitude above and below sea level, and gain and loss of points in a game.

Take the time to make the first number line with the class. Draw a horizontal line and ask a student to choose a point and label it "0" (zero) for the origin. Ask another student to select some small object in the room whose

length can be used as a unit distance. Emphasize the fact that the location of the origin and the unit distance can vary but only from number line to number line. Locate the point corresponding to "1." You may need to mention that it is a convention to place positive numbers to the right of the origin. Locate several more positive integers and a few negative ones. Remind students that although the "+" may be omitted when writing positive numbers, the "−" must always be written to indicate a negative number.

Introduce the meanings of graph and coordinate using a finite set such as $\{^-2, ^-1, 0\}$. On a second number line expand the example to illustrate the graph of an infinite set.

$\{^-2, ^-1, 0\}$
$^-3\ ^-2\ ^-1\ \ 0\ \ 1\ \ 2\ \ 3\ \ 4$

$\{^-2, ^-1, 0, ..\}$
$^-3\ ^-2\ ^-1\ \ 0\ \ 1\ \ 2\ \ 3\ \ 4$

SUGGESTED EXTENSIONS

Using a number line, pair the letter *A* with the point whose coordinate is $^-11$, *B* with the point whose coordinate is $^-10$, and so on, so that *L* has coordinate 0 (zero), M has coordinate $^+1$, and *Z* has coordinate $^+14$. (See Chalkboard Examples 2-1 on page 30.) For each list of coordinates that follows, have students name the points and unscramble the letters to spell various breeds of dogs.

1. $^-8, ^-7, 0, 3, 3, 4$ **2.** $^-9, ^-7, ^-3, 0, 0, 3$

3. $^-7, ^-7, ^-3, 6, 6, 6, 8$ **4.** $^-11, ^-10, ^-7, ^-7, ^-5, 0$

5. $^-10, ^-7, 3, 5, 12$ **6.** $^-4, ^-1, 7, 9, 13$

1. Poodle   **2.** Collie   **3.** Terrier
4. Beagle   **5.** Boxer   **6.** Husky

2-2 (pages 33–35)

KEY MATHEMATICAL IDEAS

• showing order relations of real numbers

TEACHING SUGGESTIONS

Prepare several number lines on the chalkboard for the lesson. (If available, a music staff liner is convenient for marking off unit distances on each line.) You can begin by providing students with examples of comparing numbers on the number line. Then ask students to write down any integer between, for instance, $^-10$ and $^+10$, without revealing their choices. Choose two students to write their numbers on the chalkboard and graph them on one of the number lines. Ask the class to give two statements that express the order relationship between the two numbers. After several times, erase the number lines and repeat the exercise.

You might ask students to name various methods of remembering the meanings of the symbols "$<$" and "$>$." For example,

a. The words "less" and "left" sound similar.
b. The symbol "$<$" looks more like an "L" than "$>$."
c. Both symbols point toward the smaller number.

SUGGESTED EXTENSIONS

List the following statements and ask students to rewrite them using negative numbers. This exercise will help prepare students for multiplication by $^-1$.

1. $15 > 13$	**2.** $5 > 1$	**3.** $10 < 15$
4. $5 < 6$	**5.** $10 > 9$	**6.** $20 < 21$
7. $18 < 21$	**8.** $16 > 14$	**9.** $10 < 19$
10. $2 > 1$	**11.** $15 < 16$	**12.** $18 > 17$
1. $^-15 < ^-13$	**2.** $^-5 < ^-1$	**3.** $^-10 > ^-15$
4. $^-5 > ^-6$	**5.** $^-10 < ^-9$	**6.** $^-20 > ^-21$
7. $^-18 > ^-21$	**8.** $^-16 < ^-14$	**9.** $^-10 > ^-19$
10. $^-2 < ^-1$	**11.** $^-15 > ^-16$	**12.** $^-18 < ^-17$

2-3 (pages 36–39)

KEY MATHEMATICAL IDEAS

• using commutative and associative properties to simplify expressions.

TEACHING SUGGESTIONS

The properties in this section will be a review for most of your students. It is a good idea, however, to begin by giving an example of each property. Although addition and multiplication of negative numbers will be presented later in the chapter, you should emphasize that the properties hold for all real numbers. You can demonstrate the associative axiom by asking students to add (or multiply) sequences of numbers using different arrangements of parentheses. For example, $5 + 4 + 3 + 2 =$
$$(5 + 4) + (3 + 2) = (5 + 4 + 3) + 2 =$$
$$5 + (4 + 3 + 2) = 5 + (4 + 3) + 2 = 14$$

SUGGESTED EXTENSIONS

Ask your students to consider the following relations and tell which are reflexive, which are symmetric, and which are transitive. Have students make up relations of their own to add to the list.

1. "is the sister of"   Symm., trans.

2. "is the ancestor of"   Trans.

3. "is parallel to"   Symm., trans.

4. "is not equal to"   Symm.

2-4 (pages 40–42)

KEY MATHEMATICAL IDEAS

• adding numbers with a number line

TEACHING SUGGESTIONS

Introduce the lesson with this example of a game where each player can gain or lose points on each play, as recorded in the positive and negative scores below.

Player	First turn	Second turn
A	$^+4$	$^+3$
B	$^-4$	$^-3$
C	$^+4$	$^-3$
D	$^-3$	$^+4$
E	$^-3$	$^+3$
F	$^+4$	$^-4$
G	$^+3$	$^-4$

Ask your students to find the total score for each player at the end of two plays (turns), and verify the results on a number line. For instance, player A starts with "0," gains 4, and then gains 3 more points.

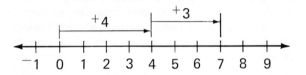

The first arrow starts at the origin and the second arrow starts at the number where the first arrow ended. Ask the class which axiom guarantees that players C and D are tied.

SUGGESTED EXTENSION

Ask students to name several situations which can be described by the addition of 5 and ⁻3. For example, "The temperature rose 5 degrees then dropped 3 degrees."

2-5 (pages 43–46)

KEY MATHEMATICAL IDEAS

• using opposites and absolute values

TEACHING SUGGESTIONS

The number line can be very useful in presenting this lesson. Draw a number line on the chalkboard and ask several students to graph various numbers. Locate the opposite of each number, pointing out that each number and its opposite are the same distance from the origin but are in opposite directions (hence the name "opposite"). Be sure your students understand, for example, that "the opposite of 3" or "−3" and "negative 3" or "⁻3" are the same number. Explain that the lowered minus sign will be used to mean both.

Students will probably have less trouble understanding the notion of absolute value if you emphasize that the absolute value of a number is the distance of the graph of that number from the origin on a number line. Give several examples of absolute value using a number line. You might mention that since "distance" can never be negative, the absolute value of a number will always be positive.

T68

SUGGESTED EXTENSIONS

Ask students to name the following.
1. A number whose absolute value is 7.
2. A number whose absolute value is 10.
3. The opposite of a number whose absolute value is 6.
4. The opposite of the opposite of ⁻4.

1. 7 or ⁻7   2. 10 or ⁻10   3. 6 or ⁻6   4. ⁻4

2-6 (pages 47–52)

KEY MATHEMATICAL IDEAS

• using rules to add real numbers
• applying addition to solving problems

TEACHING SUGGESTIONS

Begin this lesson by listing the following addition problems on the chalkboard. Ask the students to state whether each names a positive number, a negative number, or zero. Answers can be verified on a number line.

$$-7 + 8 \quad \text{(Positive)}$$
$$-7 + (-8) \quad \text{(Negative)}$$
$$7 + 8 \quad \text{(Positive)}$$
$$7 + (-8) \quad \text{(Negative)}$$
$$-7 + 8 + (-1) \quad \text{(Zero)}$$

Instruct your students to find the sum of a sequence of numbers first by adding from left to right and then by grouping the negative numbers. (For example, given the sequence 7, −9, 2, −1, −5, 0, 8, $7 + (-9) + 2 + (-1) + (-5) + 0 + 8 = 2$ and $[(-9) + (-1) + (-5)] + 7 + 2 + 0 + 8 = -15 + 17 = 2$.) Point out that the process of grouping the negative numbers first is based upon the property of the opposite of a sum, $-(a + b) = -a + (-b)$.

SUGGESTED EXTENSIONS

Ask your students to explain why the following statements are true.
1. $|-4 + 3| \neq |-4| + |3|$
2. $|5 + (-6)| \neq |5| + |-6|$

1. $|-4 + 3| = |-1| = 1$; $|-4| + |3| = 4 + 3 = 7$; $1 \neq 7$
2. $|5 + (-6)| = |-1| = 1$; $|5| + |-6| = 5 + 6 = 11$; $1 \neq 11$

2-7 (pages 53–56)

KEY MATHEMATICAL IDEAS

• using the distributive axiom to simplify expressions

TEACHING SUGGESTIONS

The distributive axiom can be demonstrated visually as follows. Write down the multiplication problem 3×15 on the chalkboard. Take a piece of squared graph paper that has been cut into a rectangle measuring 3 squares by 15 squares. Cut the rectangle into two rectangles, as shown below, to illustrate $3 \times 15 = 3(10 + 5) =$
$$(3 \times 10) + (3 \times 5).$$

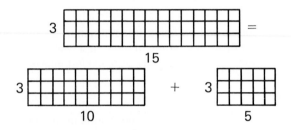

To illustrate $3 \times 15 = 3(14 + 1) = (3 \times 14) + (3 \times 1)$, simply regroup the squares.

You will probably need to stress the importance of the common factor in the distributive property.

SUGGESTED EXTENSIONS

Ask students to determine whether the following statements are true or false.

1. $2(28 - 12) = 2(28) - 2(12)$ True

2. $(28 - 12)2 = 28(2) - 12(2)$ True

3. $\left(28 - 12\right)\frac{1}{2} = 28\left(\frac{1}{2}\right) + 12\left(\frac{1}{2}\right)$ False

4. $2(28 - 0) = 2(28) + 2(0)$ True

5. $(28 - 12)\frac{1}{2} = \frac{28}{2} - \frac{12}{2}$ True

6. $0(28 - 12) = 0(28) + 0(12)$ True

2-8 (pages 57–60)

KEY MATHEMATICAL IDEAS

• multiplying real numbers

TEACHING SUGGESTIONS

Identify 1, 0, and −1 as three special numbers and ask the class to complete the multiplication table below. Point out that the last two entries can be determined by using the fact that multiplication by −1 produces the opposite of a number.

×	1	0	−1
2	2	0	−2
1	1	0	−1
0	0	0	0
−1	−1	0	1
−2	−2	0	2

Be sure your students understand why the product of two negative numbers is a positive number. Examples such as the following will be helpful. Remind your students of the associative axioms.

$(-10)(-10) = (-1)(10)(-1)(10) = (-1)(-1)(10)(10) =$
$(-1)(-1)(100) = (1)(100) = 100$

$(-a)(-b) = (-1)(a)(-1)(b) = (-1)(-1)(a)(b) =$
$(-1)(-1)(ab) = (1)(ab) = ab$

SUGGESTED EXTENSIONS

Ask students to state whether the following products will be positive or negative.

1. $-4(5 + 2)$ **2.** $-4(2 + 5)$ **3.** $3(-6 + 1)$

4. $-3(-6 + 1)$ **5.** $-3(1 + 0)$ **6.** $(0 + 1)(-4)$

1. Negative   **2.** Negative   **3.** Negative
4. Positive   **5.** Negative   **6.** Negative

2-9 (pages 61–65)

KEY MATHEMATICAL IDEAS

• using reciprocals

TEACHING SUGGESTIONS

Because the notion of reciprocals is a relatively simple one, most of your students will have little difficulty with this section. You might begin this lesson by asking students to name pairs of numbers whose product is 1.

Be sure to stress that 0 has no reciprocal because the

product of 0 and any number is 0 and not 1. This will prepare students for the idea that division by zero has no meaning in the real numbers, which is presented in Chapter 3.

SUGGESTED EXTENSIONS

Ask your students to give the reciprocal of each of the following.

1. $-\dfrac{1}{abc}$, $a \neq 0$, $b \neq 0$, $c \neq 0$ $-abc$

2. $\dfrac{1}{-abc}$, $a \neq 0$, $b \neq 0$, $c \neq 0$ $-abc$

3. the reciprocal of 3 $\dfrac{1}{3}$

4. the reciprocal of $\dfrac{1}{3}$ 3

5. the reciprocal of -3 $-\dfrac{1}{3}$

6. the reciprocal of $\dfrac{1}{ab}$, $a \neq 0$, $b \neq 0$ ab

3 *Solving Equations*

Subtraction and division of real numbers are presented in this chapter in terms of addition and multiplication, respectively. Addition and subtraction, and multiplication and division are described as inverse operations which can be used to transform and solve equations. Two or more transformations are combined to solve more complex equations, including equations with no solution and those with infinitely many solutions.

The concluding section presents the style of two-column proofs for verifying theorems.

3-1 *(pages 71–75)*

KEY MATHEMATICAL IDEAS

• using addition to solve equations

TEACHING SUGGESTIONS

When explaining the expression $(a + b) + (-b) = a$, you can use the associative axiom; for example, $(5 + 4) + (-4) = 5 + (4 + (-4)) = 5 + (0) = 5$. Keep in mind that the goal for this chapter is to teach students how to solve equations. Be sure that your students know how to choose transformations that will leave the variable alone on one side of the equation. To do this, ask your students to give the fastest way to transform the following equations.

$x + (-5) = 7$ Add 5 to both sides
$x + 4 = 5$ Add -4 to both sides
$-6 + s = 4 + 2$ Add 6 to both sides
$-6 = s + 4$ Add -4 to both sides

Since students will be using transformation by substitution frequently in their study of algebra, it will be a good idea to stress it here as a way of checking answers.

SUGGESTED EXTENSIONS

Have your students match the equations on the left with their equivalent equations on the right.

1. $x + 7 = 14$ **a.** $x = 10$
2. $50 + x = 40$ **b.** $x = 14$
3. $-50 + x = -40$ **c.** $x = -10$
4. $2 = x + (-12)$ **d.** $x = 7$
5. $16 = 7 + x$ **e.** $x = 0$
6. $6 + (-x) = 6$ **f.** $x = 9$

1. d   **2.** c   **3.** a   **4.** b   **5.** f   **6.** e

3-2 *(pages 76–80)*

KEY MATHEMATICAL IDEAS

• simplifying expressions involving differences

TEACHING SUGGESTIONS

Provide several examples of the rule for subtraction, such as the following.

$19 - 13 = 19 + (-13) = 6$
$6 - 10 = 6 + (-10) = -4$
$6 - (-4) = 6 + (- (-4)) = 6 + 4 = 10$
$-19 - (-18) = -19 + (- (-18)) = -19 + 18 = -1$

Some of your students will probably notice that when two minus signs appear consecutively in an expression, they can be replaced by a single plus sign.

At this point you can summarize the three ways that a minus sign can be used in algebra: as a subtraction sign, as a sign for the opposite of a number, and as a sign for a negative number.

SUGGESTED EXTENSIONS

Ask your students to state whether the following are true or false.

1. $|5 - 4| = |4 - 5|$ True

2. $|-5 - 4| = |-4 - 5|$ True

3. $|2 - (3 - 1)| = |(2 - 3) - 1|$ False

4. $|2(4 - 1)| = |2(4) - 2(1)|$ True

5. $|(3 - 2)6| = |3(6) - 2(6)|$ True

6. $|-2 - (3 - 1)| = |(-2 - 3) - 1|$ False

3-3 (pages 81–83)

KEY MATHEMATICAL IDEAS

• solving equations and problems by using addition or subtraction

TEACHING SUGGESTIONS

To begin with, provide your students with several examples like the following. Encourage students to use the condensed method illustrated in the text.

$$
\begin{array}{ll}
x + 5 = 7 & x - 5 = 7 \\
x + 5 - 5 = 7 - 5 & x - 5 + 5 = 7 + 5 \\
x = 2 & x = 12
\end{array}
$$

Stress the idea of "adding the opposite" to isolate the variable on one side of the equation.

Remind students that the actual solution of an equation is a number and not another equation. In the example above, for instance, the solution to $x + 5 = 7$ is 2, not the equation "$x = 2$."

SUGGESTED EXTENSIONS

Ask your students to solve the following equations.

1. $z + |3 - (-3)| = 6$ 0

2. $z + |-3 - 6| = 3$ -6

3. $z + |6 - 3| = -3$ -6

4. $-3 + |3 - 6| = z$ 0

5. $-3 + |z - 6| = 3$ 0 or 12

6. $-3 + |z - 3| = 6$ -6 or 12

7. $3 + |z - 6| = -3$ No solution

8. $3 + |z - (-3)| = 6$ 0 or -6

3-4 (pages 84–87)

KEY MATHEMATICAL IDEAS

• using multiplication to solve equations

TEACHING SUGGESTIONS

Ask the class how each of the following equations is obtained from the equation $x = 3$. Make a list of their answers on the chalkboard.

a. $-5x = -15$ **b.** $7x = 21$

c. $\dfrac{1}{3} x = 1$ **d.** $\dfrac{2}{7} x = \dfrac{6}{7}$

e. $1.5x = 4.5$ **f.** $5.1x = 15.3$

Now ask your students how to transform each of the six equations above back into the equation $x = 3$ using multiplication. Compare their answers with the list on the chalkboard. Emphasize that every nonzero real number has a reciprocal so that every equation of the form $ax = b$ (a not zero) can be solved by multiplying by $\dfrac{1}{a}$. Remind students that since zero has no reciprocal, the term $\dfrac{1}{0}$ is meaningless.

SUGGESTED EXTENSIONS

Have your students match the equations on the left with their equivalent equations on the right.

1. $7x = 14$ **a.** $x = 3\dfrac{1}{3}$

2. $-6x = -20$ **b.** $x = 3$

3. $33 = 11x$ **c.** $x = -1$

4. $-49x = 7$ **d.** $x = 1$

5. $3x - 3 = 0$ **e.** $x = 2$

6. $3x + 3 = 0$ **f.** $x = -\dfrac{1}{7}$

1. e   **2.** a   **3.** b   **4.** f   **5.** d   **6.** c

3-5 (pages 88–91)

KEY MATHEMATICAL IDEAS

- simplifying expressions involving quotients

TEACHING SUGGESTIONS

The rule for division follows directly from the previous section, so your students should have little difficulty. Students will appreciate the parallelism if you write the rule for division under the rule for subtraction as indicated below.

"To subtract a number b, add the opposite of b."

"To divide by a number b, multiply by the reciprocal of b."

Point out that the statements about quotients of positive and negative numbers are the same as those for multiplication of positive and negative numbers.

Be sure that your students do not confuse the expressions $\frac{1}{0}$ and $\frac{0}{1}$.

SUGGESTED EXTENSION

Ask your students to show that $a \div b$ can be defined as the number x such that $bx = a$, by solving the equation $bx = a$ for x.

$$bx = a$$
$$\frac{1}{b}(bx) = \frac{1}{b}(a)$$
$$\frac{1}{b}(bx) = a\left(\frac{1}{b}\right)$$
$$x = a \cdot \frac{1}{b} = a \div b$$

3-6 (pages 92–95)

KEY MATHEMATICAL IDEAS

- solving equations and problems using multiplication or division

TEACHING SUGGESTIONS

Show your students the relationship between solving an equation using division and solving an equation using multiplication by reciprocals, with the following example.

$$5x = 20 \qquad\qquad 5x = 20$$
$$\frac{1}{5}(5x) = \frac{1}{5}(20) \qquad \frac{5x}{5} = \frac{20}{5}$$
$$x = 4 \qquad\qquad x = 4$$

Encourage students once again to use transformation by substitution to check their work.

SUGGESTED EXTENSIONS

Ask your students to solve equation **a**, and predict the answers to equations **b** through **f**.

a. $25x = 1875$ 75

b. $2.5x = 187.5$ 75

c. $0.25x = 18.75$ 75

d. $0.025x = 1.875$ 75

e. $25x = 1875$ 75

f. $2.5x = 1875$ 750

3-7 (pages 96–99)

KEY MATHEMATICAL IDEAS

- solving equations and problems by using several transformations

TEACHING SUGGESTIONS

Write the equation $3x + 6 = 18$ on the chalkboard twice and show students the following two methods to solve it.

$$3x + 6 = 18$$
Multiply by $\frac{1}{3}$ $\frac{1}{3}(3x + 6) = \frac{1}{3}(18)$
$$x + 2 = 6$$
Subtract 2 $x + 2 - 2 = 6 - 2$
$$x = 4$$

$$3x + 6 = 18$$
Subtract 6 $3x + 6 - 6 = 18 - 6$
$$3x = 12$$
Divide by 3 $x = 4$

Point out that in some cases it is often easier to add or subtract first.

SUGGESTED EXTENSIONS

1. Have your students solve the equation $0.05(x - 1) = 10.15$ by using the distributive property first. $x = 204$

2. Have students solve the equation $0.05(x - 1) = 10.15$ by dividing by 0.05 first.

3. Have students solve the equation $0.05(x - 1) = 10.15$, transforming it first by multiplying both sides by 100.

3-8 (pages 100–103)

KEY MATHEMATICAL IDEAS

• solving equations when the variable appears in both sides

TEACHING SUGGESTIONS

Be sure that your students understand that variables represent numbers. Caution students that in order to divide by a variable, they must state that the variable cannot be zero.

Explain that while most of the equations in this chapter have one solution, in this section there will be equations with no solution (or whose solution is the empty set) and equations that are satisfied by every real number. Another way of describing the possibilities is to say,

a. the equation has a unique root,

b. the equation has no root, or

c. the equation is an identity.

SUGGESTED EXTENSION

Have each student write three equations: one with one root, one with no root, and one that is an identity. Instruct several students to write their equations on the chalkboard. Ask the other students to guess which equations have one root, which have no root, and which are identities.

3-9 (pages 104–107)

KEY MATHEMATICAL IDEAS

• proving theorems in algebra

TEACHING SUGGESTIONS

A good way to begin this lesson is to summarize the properties learned thus far. For the most part, students will be asked in this section to fill in the reasons for proofs, rather than complete the entire proof. In any case, encourage your students to become familiar with the two column, statement and reason, format. When writing proofs on the chalkboard, explain each statement and reason as you write it.

SUGGESTED EXTENSION

Ask your students to fill in the missing statements in the following proof of the multiplication property of zero.

Prove $a \cdot 0 = 0$.

Proof:

STATEMENTS	REASONS
1. $0 + 0 = 0$	**1.** Identity axiom for addition
2. $\underline{?}$	**2.** Multiplication property of equality
3. $\underline{?}$	**3.** Distributive axiom
4. $\underline{?}$	**4.** Identity axiom for addition
5. $a \cdot 0 = 0$	**5.** Rule for subtraction and addition property of equality

2. $a(0 + 0) = a \cdot 0$
3. $a \cdot 0 + a \cdot 0 = a \cdot 0$
4. $a \cdot 0 + a \cdot 0 = a \cdot 0 + 0$

4 Polynomials and Problem Solving

This chapter presents the use of exponents in numerical expressions and variable expressions. A carefully sequenced development leads through the basic operations on polynomials. The last portion of the chapter concentrates on techniques for problem solving, so that the skills from earlier portions can be applied.

4-1 (pages 113–116)

KEY MATHEMATICAL IDEAS

• simplifying expressions with exponents

TEACHING SUGGESTIONS

Write the following words on the chalkboard:

base   exponent   factor   power

along with the five expressions:

a. 5^2 **b.** 3^4 **c.** x^2 **d.** 10^3 **e.** $(y + 1)^5$

Ask students to use the four words in four statements for each expression. For example, typical statements for **b** are "The base is 3," "the exponent is 4," "there are four factors of 3," and "this is the fourth power of 3."

Explain that raising to a power is a new operation and that $(5x)^2$ and $5(x^2)$ have different meanings. Tell students that the parentheses are usually omitted in the second expression because raising to a power will always be done before multiplications and divisions. Be sure your students learn the Summary of Order of Operations on page 114. Give examples like the following.

$2(3 + 4)^2 + 6 = 2(7)^2 + 6 = 2(49) + 6 = 98 + 6 = 104$

$2(3) + 4^2 + 6 = 6 + 16 + 6 = 28$

SUGGESTED EXTENSIONS

Ask your students to answer the following questions.

1. Is $3^{15} = 15^3$?   no

2. Is $(3^2)^3 = 3^{(2^3)}$?   no

3. Find an integer n such that $3^n = 3$. $n = 1$

4. Is $(3 + 1)^2 = 3^2 + 1^2$?   no

5. Is $(3 - 1)^2 = 3^2 - 1^2$?   no

6. Find an integer n such that $a^n = 1$ for any real number a.

$n = 0$

of a polynomial is to write all of the powers in factored form; for example,

$$-4x^2yz^3 = -4 \cdot x \cdot x \cdot y \cdot z \cdot z \cdot z$$

$$\text{or } -4xxyzzz$$

Explain that the degree of the monomial will be the length of the "word" that is "spelled" by the variables. Point out that the degree of each term of a polynomial can be thought of as a tool for organizing the work in this chapter.

Demonstrate both the horizontal and vertical forms of addition and subtraction when presenting the examples on the chalkboard. Errors in subtraction are very common, so students should be warned to work carefully and to check their work. One alternative is to think of a subtraction problem as "multiplying the second polynomial by (-1) and finding the sum."

SUGGESTED EXTENSIONS

Instruct your students to find the missing polynomial P for each of the following.

1. $x^2 + 3x + 2 + P = 0$

2. $4y^4 - 3y + 6 + P = 0$

3. $17y - 4y^2 + 6y^3 + P = 0$

4. $9x^4 + 3x^2 + 3 - P = 0$

5. $2x^5 + 3 - P = 0$

6. $17y - 14y^2 + y^3 - P = 0$

1. $-x^2 - 3x - 2$ **2.** $-4y^4 + 3y - 6$

3. $-6y^3 + 4y^2 - 17y$ **4.** $9x^4 + 3x^2 + 3$

5. $2x^5 + 3$ **6.** $y^3 - 14y^2 + 17y$

4-2 (pages 117–121)

KEY MATHEMATICAL IDEAS

• addition and subtraction of polynomials

TEACHING SUGGESTIONS

Write two binomials and two trinomials on the chalkboard; for example, $5t + u$, $x^2 - 1$, $7r + r^2 - 1$, $2a + 7 + 2c$. To demonstrate the need for clear definitions for monomial and polynomial, ask the class to identify which are binomials and to explain why. Emphasize the number of terms and the degree of a polynomial.

Tell your students that one way to determine the degree

4-3 (pages 122–125)

KEY MATHEMATICAL IDEAS

• multiplication of monomials

TEACHING SUGGESTIONS

Write these three problems on the chalkboard and apply the commutative and associative properties to simplify as shown.

$$(2x)(3x) \quad = (2 \cdot 3)(x \cdot x) = 6x^2$$

$$(-5x)(2y) = (-5 \cdot 2)(x \cdot y) = -10xy$$

$$(2x^2)(kx) \quad = (2 \cdot k)(x^2 \cdot x) = 2kx^3$$

The last product challenges the students to remember the definition of an exponent. Use this definition to show the following.

$(a^4)(a) = a^5$ $\qquad$ $(b^7)(b) = b^8$ $\qquad$ $(c^{20})(c) = c^{21}$

Next, discuss the product, $(d^4)(d^7)$, and relate it to the rule of exponents. Finally write $(e^{20})(f^3)$ and note that the answer is simply $e^{20}f^3$.

SUGGESTED EXTENSIONS

Explore several possible distributive properties by asking your students to tell whether the following statements are true or false.

1. $5^{2\cdot3} = 5^2 \cdot 5^3$ $\quad$ False

2. $5^{(2+3)} = 5^2 + 5^3$ $\quad$ False

3. $(5 \cdot 4)^2 = 5^2 \cdot 4^2$ $\quad$ True

4. $(5 + 4)^2 = 5^2 + 4^2$ $\quad$ False

4-4 (pages 126–128)

KEY MATHEMATICAL IDEAS

• finding powers of monomials

TEACHING SUGGESTIONS

It may be a good idea to begin your lesson with the following concrete examples.

$(2^2)^3 = 2^2 \cdot 2^2 \cdot 2^2 = 2^{2+2+2} = 2^{2\cdot3} = 2^6$

$(4^2)^5 = 4^2 \cdot 4^2 \cdot 4^2 \cdot 4^2 \cdot 4^2 = 4^{2+2+2+2+2} = 4^{2\cdot5} = 4^{10}$

$(6^3)^2 = 6^3 \cdot 6^3 = 6^{3+3} = 6^{3\cdot2} = 6^6$

$(3^3)^4 = 3^3 \cdot 3^3 \cdot 3^3 \cdot 3^3 = 3^{3+3+3+3} = 3^{3\cdot4} = 3^{12}$

You can use the associative axiom to explain the rule of exponents for a power of a product.

$(2 \cdot 3)^3 = (2 \cdot 3)(2 \cdot 3)(2 \cdot 3) = (2 \cdot 2 \cdot 2)(3 \cdot 3 \cdot 3) = 2^3 \cdot 3^3$

$(6 \cdot 7)^2 = (6 \cdot 7)(6 \cdot 7) = (6 \cdot 6)(7 \cdot 7) = 6^2 \cdot 7^2$

Be sure your students know the difference between the expressions $(ab)^m$ and ab^m.

SUGGESTED EXTENSIONS

Have your students tell whether the following expressions are positive or negative if both a and b are positive numbers.

1. $(-2a)^2(b)(3ab)(-6a)$ $\quad$ −

2. $(a^2)(b^2)^3(-b)^2b^4$ $\quad$ +

3. $(6ab)^2(-6ab)(-6a)^2(-b)^3$ $\quad$ +

4. $(-a)^3(-b)^2(6a)$ $\quad$ −

5. $(-ab)^4(ab)(-5ab)^5$ $\quad$ −

6. $(-a)^{21}(-ab)^5$ $\quad$ +

4-5 (pages 129–130)

KEY MATHEMATICAL IDEAS

• multiplication of a polynomial by a monomial

TEACHING SUGGESTIONS

This lesson provides students with a review of both the distributive law and order of operations. Begin with a few simple examples like the following.

$$a(a^2 + 1 + 3a) = a^3 + a + 3a^2$$
$$b(b + b^2) = b^2 + b^3$$

You might show a simple example using the vertical form.

$$\begin{array}{r} b \;+\; b^2 \\ b \\ \hline b^2 + b^3 \end{array}$$

Instruct your students to work carefully from left to right.

SUGGESTED EXTENSIONS

Write the following statement on the chalkboard.

$$321 \times 20 = [3(100) + 2(10) + 1] \times 2(10)$$

Ask your students to write the right side of the statement in polynomial form using the variable t and letting $t = 10$.

Solution: $(3t^2 + 2t + 1) \times 2t$

Have students write other polynomial products using t which correspond to the following.

1. 123×30 $\qquad$ **1.** $(t^2 + 2t + 3) \times 3t$

2. 3214×20 $\qquad$ **2.** $(3t^3 + 2t^2 + t + 4) \times 2t$

3. 143×2 $\qquad$ **3.** $(t^2 + 4t + 3) \times 2$

4-6 (pages 131–133)

KEY MATHEMATICAL IDEAS

• multiplication of a polynomial by a polynomial

TEACHING SUGGESTIONS

Draw a rectangle on the chalkboard as shown whose area can represent the product

$$(4x + 1)(5x + 3).$$

Apply the distributive axiom to simplify as follows.

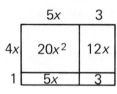

$$4x(5x + 3) + 1(5x + 3)$$
$$= 20x^2 + 12x + 5x + 3$$
$$= 20x^2 + 17x + 3$$

One way to describe this process is to say that each of the terms in the first polynomial is distributed to each of the terms in the second polynomial.

SUGGESTED EXTENSION

Instruct your students to examine the pattern shown below, for multiplying a product of the form $(a + b)(a + c)$.

$$(a + b)(a + c) = a^2 + ab + ac + bc$$
$$= a^2 + (b + c)a + bc$$

Have students apply this method to some of the written exercises.

4-7 *(pages 134–139)*

KEY MATHEMATICAL IDEAS

• using charts and formulas in solving problems

TEACHING SUGGESTIONS

Write on the chalkboard:

Step 2 Choose a variable and use it with the given facts to represent the number(s) described in the problem.

Tell the students that Step 2 can be organized in chart form in many cases. Use Written Problem 11 on page 104 in Section 3-8 to illustrate this idea.

"Cycles, Inc., manufactures ten-speed and three-speed bicycles. The profit on a ten-speed is three times the profit on a three-speed. If the profit on each kind of bicycle is increased by $15, then the profit on the ten-speed will be twice the profit on the three-speed. What is the current profit on each?"

Step 2

	Profit Now	Profit Will Be
Ten Speed	$3x$	$3x + 15$
Three Speed	x	$x + 15$

Step 3 $3x + 15 = 2(x + 15)$

Explain that many problems contain variables that are related to various formulas from mathematics, science, or business. Examples are:

$$A = \frac{1}{2}bh \quad \text{(Area of a triangle)}$$

$$s = \frac{1}{2}gt^2 \quad \text{(Falling body)}$$

$$I = Prt \quad \text{(Simple interest)}$$

SUGGESTED EXTENSIONS

Using the numbers from 1 to 12 consecutively to represent the months of the year, give your students the following instructions. "Multiply the number representing the month you were born in by 5, add 3, multiply your answer by 2, subtract 6, and divide by 10." Ask several students what their answers are. Students' answers will correspond to the month in which they were born.

4-8 *(pages 140–141)*

KEY MATHEMATICAL IDEAS

• solving money problems

TEACHING SUGGESTIONS

Write these three formulas on the chalkboard and explain their meanings.

a. $C = np$

b. $I = hw$

c. $T = nv$

a. Cost equals number of items times price;

b. Income equals number of hours times hourly wage; and

c. Total value equals number of coins (or bills) times the value of each.

Ask part of the class to write a simple problem using formula **a**, another part to write one for **b**, and the remainder for **c**.

Allow students to read these problems and have the class solve some of them.

The common theme in these three types of problems can be emphasized using the following generalization.

(number of units) · (unit value) = (total value)

Clarify this by posing these three problems.

"What is the cost of 6 cassettes at $5 each?"

"How much income is earned in 6 hours at $5 per hour?"

"What is the value of 6 five-dollar bills?"

In all of the problems in this section emphasize the need for uniformity in choice of units (for example, cents or dollars).

SUGGESTED EXTENSION

Discuss the practice of unit pricing for groceries and write the following formula on the chalkboard.

$$u = \frac{p}{n} \text{ (unit price equals price divided by the number of liters, etc.)}$$

Tell your students to solve this formula for p and use it to solve the following problem. Solution: $p = nu$

A one liter can of juice costs twenty cents per liter less than the 750 ml can. Find the unit price of the smaller can if the prices are equal.

	number of liters	×	unit price	=	price
first can	1		$x - 20$		$1 \cdot (x - 20)$
second can	0.750		x		$0.750x$

Let x = unit price of 750 ml can
$$x - 20 = 0.750x$$
$$0.250x = 20$$
$$x = 80$$

Check: 80 cents per liter times 0.750 is 60¢
80 − 20 is also 60¢ per liter
∴ Unit price of small can is 80¢ per liter.

4-9 (pages 142–145)

KEY MATHEMATICAL IDEAS

• solving uniform motion problems

TEACHING SUGGESTIONS

You may wish to compare the formula $D = rt$ with the formula for income (hourly rate times number of hours). The charts used in this section are quite similar to those in Section 4-8. One difference is that a sketch accompanies each chart to help the student complete Steps 2 and 3 in the problem. Some students will enjoy drawing pictures of the vehicles in the sketches for the problems.

Before doing the chalkboard examples solve the formula $D = rt$ first for r and then for t. Use all three formulas for quick solutions. This procedure will show students the value of knowing how to solve a formula for the different variables.

It may be necessary to discuss approximate values for some of the answers in this section. For instance, in Example 3 on page 143 the answer given is approximately 3.3 km.

SUGGESTED EXTENSION

Have your class compose one or more word problems involving rate, time, and distance. Let the first student give the first word of a sentence, the second student the second word, and so on until an entire sentence of the problem is composed. Ask students to solve the problems.

4-10 (pages 146–148)

KEY MATHEMATICAL IDEAS

• solving area problems involving rectangles and circles

TEACHING SUGGESTIONS

Emphasize the need for sketches in solving problems involving area. Students will need to know the following two basic area formulas for this section.

RECTANGLES $A = lw$

CIRCLES $A = \pi r^2$

Point out that charts will be useful for all problems involving more than one rectangle or circle.

Since many of the exercises use the idea of a uniform border, you may wish to spend some time working simple exercises involving borders. Draw a rectangle 20 units by 40 units with a uniform border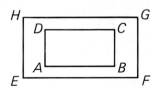

4 units wide surrounding the rectangle. Ask the students to suggest methods for finding the area of the strip. (There are various ways of dissecting it into rectangles or rectangles and squares.) If none of them suggest the method of subtracting the inner area from the total area, ask them to

a. Find the area of *ABCD*.

b. Find the length and width of *EFGH*.

c. Find the area of *EFGH*.

d. Find the area of the border by subtraction.

SUGGESTED EXTENSIONS

Ask your students to solve the following.

1. Find the area of a playing field that is formed by a rectangle with semicircles on each end. The width is 50 meters and the maximum length is 150 meters. (Use $\pi = 3.14$.)

Area of rectangle is $50(100) = 5000$

Area of two ends is area of one complete circle of radius 25 m, or $3.14(25^2) = 1962.5$

Total area is approximately 6960 m².

2. A circle is inscribed in a square as shown. If the side of the square is 14 cm, find the shaded area. (Use $\pi = \frac{22}{7}$.)

Area of square: $14^2 = 196$

Area of circle: $\frac{22}{7} \cdot 7^2 = 154$

Shaded area is $196 - 154$ or 42 cm².

5 *Factoring Polynomials*

This chapter uses division and factoring to find missing numbers or expressions in a known product. Beginning with the factorization of integers, the chapter proceeds to division by monomials and encompasses factoring a wide variety of polynomials. Each of the major factoring patterns is presented as the product of appropriate binomials.

The last part of the chapter includes the key technique used for solving polynomial equations and its application to problem solving.

5-1 *(pages 155–157)*

KEY MATHEMATICAL IDEAS

• factoring integers

TEACHING SUGGESTIONS

Before discussing prime numbers, be sure your students understand the concept of factoring over the set of integers. Stress the idea of finding factors by dividing. (If the remainder is zero, the divisor is a factor.)

When finding the prime factorization of an integer, encourage your students to try the prime numbers, in order, as divisors. The following tests for factors will be helpful.

a. If the one's digit of an integer is even, then 2 is a factor of the integer.

b. If the sum of the digits is divisible by 3, then 3 is a factor.

c. If the one's digit is 0 or 5, then 5 is a factor.

d. If the one's digit is taken off, doubled, and subtracted from what's left and the answer is divisible by 7, then 7 is a factor.

SUGGESTED EXTENSIONS

Remind your students that the product of a number and an integer is called a multiple of the number. (For example, 2, 4, 6, 8, etc., are all multiples of 2.) Then ask them to make a list of prime numbers less than 150 as follows. "On squared paper, write the numbers in a column six squares wide. Cross out 1 since it is not a prime. Circle 2 because it is the first prime. Cross out all the multiples of 2. Circle the next prime, 3, and cross out all of its multiples. Circle each successive prime and look for a pattern to find the multiples."

✗	②	③	4	5	6
7	8	9	10	11	12
13	14	15	16	17	18
19	20	21	22	23	24
25	26	etc. to 150			

5-2 (pages 158–161)

KEY MATHEMATICAL IDEAS

• dividing and factoring monomials

TEACHING SUGGESTIONS

Write the property of quotients on the chalkboard along with the following examples of its use.

$$\frac{6y}{12x} = \frac{(6)}{(6)} \cdot \frac{(y)}{(2x)} \qquad \frac{k^5}{4k^2} = \frac{(k^2)}{(k^2)} \cdot \frac{k^3}{4} \qquad \frac{2r^3}{r^5} = \frac{(r^3)}{(r^3)} \cdot \frac{2}{r^2}$$

Point out the cancellation rule for fractions which reduces the above fractions to $\frac{y}{2x}$, $\frac{k^3}{4}$, and $\frac{2}{r^2}$. Show how the last two examples lead to the rule of exponents for division. Use this opportunity to review the rules for exponents from Sections 4-3 and 4-4 (pages 122 and 126).

You may extend the method of prime factorization to find the GCF of two monomials by introducing the following rules.

1. For each monomial, find the prime factorization of the numerical coefficients. Multiply it by the variables listed in alphabetical order.

2. Find the smallest power of each prime factor that appears in both monomials and find the smallest power of each variable that appears in both monomials.

3. Form the product of the smallest powers.

Use the following example.
Find the GCF of $24x^5yz$ and $32x^3y^8$.

Solution: $24x^5yz = 2^3 \cdot 3 \cdot x^5 \cdot y \cdot z$
$\qquad\qquad 32x^3y^8 = 2^5 \cdot x^3 \cdot y^8$
$\qquad\qquad$ GCF is $2^3 \cdot x^3 \cdot y$ or $8x^3y$

SUGGESTED EXTENSIONS

Show your students the following example of dividing two numbers written in scientific notation. (See the EXTRA on page 124.)

$$\frac{2.26 \times 10^5}{1.13 \times 10^8} = \left(\frac{2.26}{1.13}\right)\left(\frac{10^5}{10^8}\right) = \frac{2}{(10^{8-5})} =$$

$$\frac{2}{(10^3)} = \frac{2}{1 \times 10^3} \quad \text{or} \quad \frac{2}{1000}$$

Instruct students to simplify each expression.

1. $\dfrac{6.24 \times 10^{10}}{8.0 \times 10^3}$ $\quad 7.8 \times 10^6$

2. $\dfrac{4.86 \times 10^6}{1.62 \times 10^{17}}$ $\quad \dfrac{3}{1 \times 10^{11}}$

3. $\dfrac{1.35 \times 10^7}{2.25 \times 10^6}$ $\quad 6$

5-3 (pages 162–165)

KEY MATHEMATICAL IDEAS

• dividing a polynomial by a monomial
• finding the greatest monomial factor of a polynomial

TEACHING SUGGESTIONS

When presenting this lesson, be certain that you explain the importance of learning how to divide a polynomial by a monomial before learning how to factor a polynomial. It may be helpful to have students keep in mind that each polynomial is the sum of monomials. Suggest that they find the greatest monomial factor of two monomials at a time in each polynomial. Encourage them to work in order from left to right.

Give your students the following problems.

1. Use factoring to find the total area of all five rectangles shown. The base of each is 5 cm and the heights are 8 cm, 12 cm, 18 cm, 10 cm, and 6 cm.

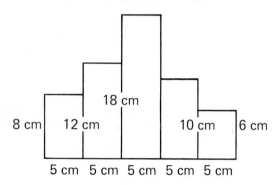

2. a. Find the area of the shaded region and factor your answer.

   b. Use the result in part **a** to evaluate the area when $a = 173$, $b = 312$, and $c = 112$.

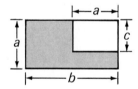

1. $5(8) + 5(12) + 5(18) + 5(10) + 5(6) =$
   $5(8 + 12 + 18 + 10 + 6) = 280$; 280 cm^2

2. a. $ab - ca = a(b - c)$
   b. $173(312 - 112) = 173(200) = 34{,}600$

5-4 (pages 166–167)

KEY MATHEMATICAL IDEAS

• using a short method to find the product of binomials

TEACHING SUGGESTIONS

Write the first two chalkboard examples on the board in vertical form and have two students complete the multiplication. Now write the first example horizontally and demonstrate the short method. Ask the class to help you do the second one horizontally. Emphasize the use of the distributive axiom.

T80

A device for remembering the short method is "FOIL" (first times first, outer plus inner, last times last). Students may find it helpful to draw "arcs" for each product as it is completed. For example $(3x + 4)(5x - 2) = 15x^2 + 14x$, etc.

SUGGESTED EXTENSIONS

Ask your students to multiply the following mentally. You will probably need to give the example below.

$(x + 2)(x^2 + 3x + 4)$

Step 1 $(x + 2)(x^2 + 3x + 4)$

Write: x^3.

Step 2 $(x + 2)(x^2 + 3x + 4)$

Write: $+5x^2$.

Step 3 $(x + 2)(x^2 + 3x + 4)$

Write: $+10x$.

Step 4 $(x + 2)(x^2 + 3x + 4)$

Write: $+8$.

Solution: $x^3 + 5x^2 + 10x + 8$

1. $(x + 1)(x^2 + x + 1)$ $x^3 + 2x^2 + 2x + 1$
2. $(x + 4)(x^2 + 2x + 7)$ $x^3 + 6x^2 + 15x + 28$
3. $(2x + 1)(x^2 + x + 1)$ $2x^3 + 3x^2 + 3x + 1$

5-5 (pages 168–170)

KEY MATHEMATICAL IDEAS

• finding products of binomials which result in the difference of two squares
• factoring the difference of two squares.

TEACHING SUGGESTIONS

Write the example below on the chalkboard.

$$
\begin{array}{r}
y + 7 \\
y - 7 \\
\hline
y^2 + 7y \\
- 7y - 49 \\
\hline
y^2 \quad\quad - 49
\end{array}
$$

Point out that the "middle term" is always zero when two of the products are opposites.

Encourage students to check polynomials for their greatest monomial factor before looking for patterns like the one presented here.

Instruct students to use the methods of this section to simplify **a.** 51×49, **b.** 199×201, and **c.** $17^2 - 15^2$.

a. $51 \times 49 = (50 + 1)(50 - 1) = 2500 - 1 = 2499$

b. $199 \times 201 = (200 - 1)(200 + 1)$

$$= 40{,}000 - 1 = 39{,}999$$

c. $17^2 - 15^2 = (17 - 15)(17 + 15) = 2(32) = 64$

5-6 (pages 171–174)

KEY MATHEMATICAL IDEAS

- squaring binomials
- factoring trinomial squares

TEACHING SUGGESTIONS

Ask students to find the following products using the short method.

$$(a + b)(a + b) = a^2 + 2ab + b^2$$
$$(a - b)(a - b) = a^2 - 2ab + b^2$$
$$(y + 6)(y + 6) = y^2 + 12y + 36$$
$$(k - 3m)(k - 3m) = k^2 - 6km + 9m^2$$

Use the last two examples to point out that the first two can be memorized as general rules. Alert students to the fact that $(a + b)^2$ is the same as $(a + b)(a + b)$ and is *not* equal to $a^2 + b^2$. Compare this with $(a \cdot b)^2 = a^2 \cdot b^2$ and $\left(\dfrac{a}{b}\right)^2 = \dfrac{a^2}{b^2}$.

Explain that a trinomial square is any trinomial that is equal to the square of a binomial.

SUGGESTED EXTENSIONS

Have your students complete the following exercises.

1. The formula for the square of $(a + b)$ can be demonstrated by drawing this diagram. Explain how.

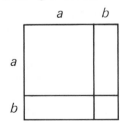

2. Use graph paper to prove the following. Let $a = 10$ and $b = 3$.

a. $(a + b)^2 = a^2 + 2ab + b^2$
b. $(a + b)(a - b) = a^2 - b^2$

1. The areas of the four sections are a^2, ab, ba, and b^2. Since the entire area is $(a + b)^2$, the sum $a^2 + 2ab + b^2 = (a + b)^2$.

2. a. Use the same type of diagram as above.
b.

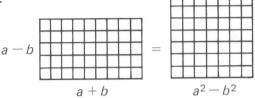

5-7 (pages 175–177)

KEY MATHEMATICAL IDEAS

- factoring quadratic trinomials whose quadratic coefficient is 1 and whose constant term is positive

TEACHING SUGGESTIONS

Demonstrate how to find the following products using the short method.

$$(x + 5)(x + 2) = x^2 + 7x + 10$$
$$(x + 4)(x + 6) = x^2 + 10x + 24$$
$$(x - 3)(x - 4) = x^2 - 7x + 12$$

Show how $x^2 - 11x + 24$ can be factored by listing negative values of r and s whose product is 24. Ask the class to explain why negative values of r and s, rather than positive values, are in the list.

$r \cdot s$	r	s	$r + s$
24	-1	-24	-25
24	-2	-12	-14
24	-3	-8	-11
24	-4	-6	-10
24	-6	-4	-10
24	-8	-3	-11
24	-12	-2	-14
24	-24	-1	-25

Point out that the only possible factors exist when $r = -3$ and $s = -8$ or $r = -8$ and $s = -3$. Therefore, the answer is $(x - 3)(x - 8)$. Your students can check using the short method.

Ask your students to factor $x^2 + 19x + 78$ by listing positive values of r and s whose sum is 19, and finding any pairs whose product is 78.

$$x^2 + 19x + 78 = (x + 6)(x + 13)$$

$r + s$	r	s	$r \cdot s$
19	1	18	18
19	2	17	34
19	3	16	48
19	4	15	60
19	5	14	70
19	6	13	78
19	7	12	84
19	8	11	88
19	9	10	90
19	10	9	90

5-8 (pages 178–179)

KEY MATHEMATICAL IDEAS

• factoring quadratic polynomials whose quadratic coefficient is 1 and whose constant term is negative

TEACHING SUGGESTIONS

Ask students to find the following products by the short method.

$$(x + 5)(x - 2) = x^2 + 3x - 10$$
$$(x - 5)(x + 2) = x^2 - 3x - 10$$
$$(x + 6)(x - 4) = x^2 + 2x - 24$$
$$(x + 3)(x - 4) = x^2 - x - 12$$

Explain that it is possible to use the same technique as before; that is, $(x + r)(x + s) = x^2 + (r + s)x + rs$. Point out that r and s must have opposite signs if the third term is negative.

SUGGESTED EXTENSION

Tell your students to factor $x^2 + 12x - 64$ by listing pairs of numbers, one positive and one negative, whose sum is 12.

$$x^2 + 12x - 64 = (x + 16)(x - 4)$$

$r + s$	r	s	$r \cdot s$
12	13	−1	−13
12	14	−2	−28
12	15	−3	−45
12	16	−4	−64
12	17	−5	−85
12	18	−6	−108

5-9 (pages 180–182)

KEY MATHEMATICAL IDEAS

• factoring trinomials when the quadratic coefficient is a positive integer greater than 1

TEACHING SUGGESTIONS

Write the following polynomials on the chalkboard and ask the students to factor them. (This is review.)

1. $4x^2 - y^2$ $(2x + y)(2x - y)$
2. $4x^2 + 4xy + y^2$ $(2x + y)^2$
3. $x^2 + 2xy - 3y^2$ $(x + 3y)(x - y)$
4. $x^2 - 3xy + 2y^2$ $(x - 2y)(x - y)$
5. $2x^2 + 3xy + y^2$ (see below)

After a few minutes hint that they should reverse the terms in 5. Then they can factor $y^2 + 3xy + 2x^2$ into $(y + 2x)(y + x)$. Explain that the purpose of this lesson is to learn to factor trinomials, regardless of the value of the first coefficient. Make a list of hints:

1. If the last coefficient is 1, reverse the terms.
2. If the first coefficient is −1, begin by factoring a common monomial factor of −1.
3. Factor out common factors.
4. Decide whether the binomial factors will be sums or differences.
5. Use knowledge of even and odd numbers to eliminate some of the possibilities.

SUGGESTED EXTENSION

Ask your students to state which of the following are prime polynomials and why.

1. $x^2 + 3x + 5$ Prime
2. $b^2 + 4b + 3$ Not prime

3. $4t^2 - t + 2$ Prime   **4.** $-x^2 + 3x - 1$ Prime
5. $17x^2 + 34x + 17$ Not prime
6. $5s^2 - 3s + 1$ Prime

5-10 (*pages 183–184*)

KEY MATHEMATICAL IDEAS

• factoring polynomials using the distributive axiom

TEACHING SUGGESTIONS

In order to help students recognize which terms of a polynomial they can group, give them the following examples.

$$x^2 + 2x - 3 + y^2 = (x^2 + 2x - 3) + y^2$$
$$= (x + 3)(x - 1) + y^2$$
$$4(2a - b) + 3(b - 2a) = 4(2a - b) - 3(2a - b)$$
$$= 2a - b$$
$$ra - 3t + tr - 3a = (ra - 3a) + (rt - 3t) =$$
$$a(r - 3) + t(r - 3) = (a + t)(r - 3)$$

Ask your students if they can find a different way to group the terms in $ra - 3t + tr - 3a$. Solution:
$(-3t + tr) + (ra - 3a) = t(-3 + r) + a(r - 3) =$
$(t + a)(r - 3)$.

SUGGESTED EXTENSION

Give your students the following instructions.

"Factor $x^2 + 2x - 3$. Then factor $(x^2 + 2x + 1) - (4)$ using the difference of two squares. Compare your answers. Repeat with $x^2 - 8x - 48$ and $(x^2 - 8x + 16) - (64)$. Create some more examples using this method."

$$x^2 + 2x - 3 = (x^2 + 2x + 1) - (4) = (x + 3)(x - 1);$$
$$x^2 - 8x - 48 = (x^2 - 8x + 16) - (64)$$
$$= (x - 12)(x + 4)$$

5-11 (*pages 185–186*)

KEY MATHEMATICAL IDEAS

• factoring polynomials completely

TEACHING SUGGESTIONS

Once your students learn how to recognize terms which can be grouped and factored, they should have little diffi-

culty in factoring polynomials completely. You might write an example on the chalkboard, such as $9t^3 + 18t^2 + 9t$, and factor it step by step using the guidelines on page 185.

Solution: $9t^3 + 18t^2 + 9t = 9t(t^2 + 2t + 1) = 9t(t + 1)^2$

SUGGESTED EXTENSION

Refer your students to the EXTRA on page 170 before asking them to factor the following.

1. $a^3 + 125$ **2.** $a^3 - 216$
3. $5a^3 + 40$ **4.** $a^3 - 27$
5. $a^{27} + 729$ **6.** $a^3t + 27t + a^3 + 27$

1. $(a + 5)(a^2 - 5a + 25)$
2. $(a - 6)(a^2 + 6a + 36)$
3. $5[(a + 2)(a^2 - 2a + 4)]$
4. $(a - 3)(a^2 + 3a + 9)$
5. $(a^3 - 9)(a^6 + 9a^3 + 81)$
6. $(t + 1)(a + 3)(a^2 - 3a + 9)$

5-12 (*pages 187–188*)

KEY MATHEMATICAL IDEAS

• using the zero-product property to solve equations

TEACHING SUGGESTIONS

In this section your students will be asked to solve simple equations which are already in factored form. Since the zero-product property is straightforward, most students should have little difficulty. You might suggest that each factor containing a variable be considered as a separate equation set equal to zero. Encourage students to write each factor in a separate column.

SUGGESTED EXTENSION

The following is a proof of the statement "If $a = 0$ or $b = 0$, then $ab = 0$." Instruct your students to supply the missing reasons.

Case 1: $a = 0$

STATEMENTS	REASONS
1. $a = 0$	**1.** _?_
2. $ab = 0 \cdot b$	**2.** _?_
3. $ab = 0$	**3.** _?_

Case 2: $b = 0$

STATEMENTS	REASONS
1. $b = 0$	**1.** ?
2. $ab = a \cdot 0$	**2.** ?
3. $ab = 0$	**3.** ?

Case 1: **1.** Given **2.** Mult. prop. of equality **3.** Mult. prop. of zero

Case 2: **1.** Given **2.** Mult. prop. of equality **3.** Mult. prop. of zero

5-13 (pages 189–190)

KEY MATHEMATICAL IDEAS

• using factoring to solve polynomial equations

TEACHING SUGGESTIONS

Use this opportunity to review the meaning of the term "degree of a polynomial." Synonyms can be used as follows.

linear—first degree
quadratic—second degree
cubic—third degree

You may relate the degree of a polynomial to the number of roots. (If double roots are counted twice, triple roots three times, etc., the degree is equal to the "number" of roots.)

Make certain that all students are aware of the fact that "standard form" means that one side is zero. This cannot be emphasized too much. It is a common mistake for students to factor $x^2 + 2x = 3$, for example, into $x(x + 2) = 3$ and apply the zero-product property.

Encourage your students to check their answers by substituting them in the original equation.

SUGGESTED EXTENSIONS

Have your students complete the following exercises.

1. Solve $x^3 - x^2 = 6x$, if x is a positive integer, by dividing both sides by x. (This is permissible since $x \neq 0$.)

2. Solve $x^3 - x^2 = 6x$ if x is any real number.

1. $x^2 - x = 6$; $x^2 - x - 6 = 0$; $(x - 3)(x + 2) = 0$;
$x - 3 = 0$ or $x + 2 = 0$; $x = 3$ or $x = -2$; since -2 is not a positive integer, $x = 3$

2. $x^3 - x^2 - 6x = 0$; $x(x^2 - x - 6) = 0$;
$x(x - 3)(x + 2) = 0$; $x = 0$ or $x = 3$ or $x = -2$;
$\{-2, 0, 3\}$

5-14 (pages 191–195)

KEY MATHEMATICAL IDEAS

• using factoring to solve problems involving quadratic equations

TEACHING SUGGESTIONS

It is always a good idea to tell your students to begin each word problem by identifying the question asked. Next, they should draw a picture when possible and define each variable needed.

Inform the class that an essential part of solving problems involving quadratic equations is checking each member in the solution set by seeing if it answers the original question. Remind students to label their answers.

SUGGESTED EXTENSIONS

Have your students explore Example 1 on page 191 with these questions.

1. Why does $x = 12$ satisfy the equation?

2. Imagine that Jason programmed a computer to mow his lawn. Both solutions were used and the robot was set to mow every Monday with $x = 2$ and every Friday with $x = 12$. What will happen? How many square meters are mowed each time?

1. The width is $12 - 2x$ or $12 - 24 = -12$.
The length is $16 - 2x$ or $16 - 24 = -8$.
The product of -12 and -8 is $+96$ and this is exactly one-half the area of the lawn Jason is mowing.

2. On Mondays the lawn will be half mowed in a strip 2 m wide, mowing 96 m². On Fridays the lawn will be mowed two and one-half times with the center strip mowed the extra half, for a total of 240 m².

6 Fractions

This chapter presents various ways of simplifying numerical and algebraic fractions. The basic rules for multiplication, division, addition, and subtraction of fractions are introduced. The last two sections are reserved for division of polynomials. Emphasis is placed on writing mixed expressions in simplified form and dividing polynomials using the long division form.

6-1 (pages 201–203)

KEY MATHEMATICAL IDEAS

- reducing algebraic fractions to simplest form

TEACHING SUGGESTIONS

It will be beneficial to begin this lesson with a review of greatest common factors. Tell your students that in general, whenever a fraction is expressed in the form $\frac{a \cdot c}{b \cdot c}$ where c is the greatest common factor of the numerator and denominator, the equivalent fraction $\frac{a}{b}$ is in simplest form.

Tell the students to write fractions with the least number of minus signs, using just one in front of the fraction whenever possible. For example,

$$\frac{-4}{6} = -\frac{2}{3} \qquad \frac{-4}{-5} = \frac{4}{5} \qquad \frac{4}{-5} = -\frac{4}{5} \qquad \frac{x-2}{2-x} = -1.$$

In the last example it will not be obvious that $2 - x = -1(x - 2)$.

One common error is for students to cancel single terms of binomial factors; for example, $\frac{a+b}{a+2b} \neq \frac{b}{2b}$. Remind students that they should be dividing when they cancel, not subtracting. When this error occurs, reinforce the fact that any binomial factor must be kept intact.

SUGGESTED EXTENSION

Have your students complete the chart in the next column showing the numerator, the denominator, and the reduced value of the fraction $\frac{x-2}{x^2-4}$ for integral values of x from -3 to 3. Instruct them to use the results to answer the questions.

x	$x - 2$	$x^2 - 4$	reduced value
3	1	5	$\frac{1}{5}$
2	0	0	–
1	-1	-3	$\frac{1}{3}$
0	-2	-4	$\frac{1}{2}$
-1	-3	-3	1
-2	-4	0	–
-3	-5	5	-1

1. Guess the value of x that will make the reduced value $-\frac{1}{2}$.

2. Explain why the value $\frac{1}{4}$ does not appear in the last column.

3. Write a formula that will give the reduced value for any value of x.

1. -4 **2.** When $x = 2$, the denominator equals zero.

3. $\frac{1}{x+2}$

6-2 (pages 204–207)

KEY MATHEMATICAL IDEAS

- finding products of fractions

TEACHING SUGGESTIONS

Write the multiplication problem $\frac{3}{12} \cdot \frac{4}{5} = \frac{12}{60}$ on the chalkboard and reduce the answer to $\frac{1}{5}$. Ask the class to suggest short cuts. Some students might suggest reducing the $\frac{3}{12}$ before multiplying; for example, $\frac{1}{4} \cdot \frac{4}{5} = \frac{4}{20}$ which reduces to $\frac{1}{5}$. Others might suggest cancelling the fours as well. You may wish to prove this cancellation:

$$\frac{e}{cf} \cdot \frac{cx}{y} = \frac{ex}{fy}.$$

SUGGESTED EXTENSIONS

Have your students use the fact that $\frac{a}{b} = a \cdot \frac{1}{b}$ ($b \neq 0$) to solve the following.

1. Use the associative and commutative properties of multiplication to prove the multiplication rule for fractions.

$$\frac{c}{d} \cdot \frac{x}{y} = \left(c \cdot \frac{1}{d}\right)\left(x \cdot \frac{1}{y}\right) = (c \cdot x)\left(\frac{1}{d} \cdot \frac{1}{y}\right) = cx\left(\frac{1}{dy}\right) = \frac{cx}{dy}$$

2. Use the distributive property to show that fractions with a common denominator can be added by adding the numerators.

$$\frac{c}{b} + \frac{a}{b} = \left(c \cdot \frac{1}{b}\right) + \left(a \cdot \frac{1}{b}\right) = (c + a)\frac{1}{b} = \frac{(c + a)}{b}$$

6-3 (pages 208–211)

KEY MATHEMATICAL IDEAS

• finding quotients of fractions

TEACHING SUGGESTIONS

Since most students have learned to divide fractions before they have had much experience with negative numbers, take this opportunity to point out these parallels.
Subtraction is accomplished by adding an opposite.
Division is accomplished by multiplying by a reciprocal.
Reinforce the rule by allowing students to read the symbol "÷" as "times the reciprocal of," just as they can read "$a - b$" as "a plus the opposite of b."

   One short cut that students may use with long problems is to factor in the first step, while they are changing division to multiplication by the reciprocal.

SUGGESTED EXTENSION

Ask students to change each quotient to an equation to be solved, using the fact that $a \div b = x$ is equivalent to $bx = a$. Have them solve using the multiplication property of equality.

1. $\dfrac{2}{3} \div \dfrac{8}{3}$ $\qquad \dfrac{8}{3}x = \dfrac{2}{3}$

$$\left(\frac{3}{8}\right)\left(\frac{8}{3}\right)x = \frac{2}{3}\left(\frac{3}{8}\right)$$

$$x = \frac{1}{4} \quad \text{The quotient is } \frac{1}{4}.$$

2. $\dfrac{8}{3} \div \dfrac{2}{3}$ $\quad$ 4

3. $\dfrac{5}{6} \div \dfrac{2}{3}$ $\quad \dfrac{5}{4}$

4. $\dfrac{2}{3} \div \dfrac{5}{6}$ $\quad \dfrac{4}{5}$

5. $\dfrac{p}{q} \div \dfrac{n}{m}$ $\quad \dfrac{pm}{qn}$

6-4 (pages 212–215)

KEY MATHEMATICAL IDEAS

• changing fractions to have least common denominators

TEACHING SUGGESTIONS

Write a few numerical multiplication problems on the board and ask the class to find both the reduced and "unreduced" forms of the answers. Discuss the fact that there are times when the "unreduced" form is needed; for example, adding fractions when common denominators are needed.

   In doing the examples students may wish to leave space for a multiplier to be written. For example, $\dfrac{2}{3} \cdot \dfrac{?}{?} = \dfrac{?}{12}$.
This procedure works very well when changing a group of fractions to have their LCD.

SUGGESTED EXTENSION

Have students find the LCD of any two fractions and the GCF of their denominators. Ask students to find the LCD by using the GCF. Suggest that they might try using numerical examples.

Multiply the two denominators together and divide by the GCF.

6-5 (pages 216–219)

KEY MATHEMATICAL IDEAS

• adding and subtracting algebraic fractions

TEACHING SUGGESTIONS

In this section, the most common student error is made when subtracting fractions with binomial numerators. Try highlighting the minus sign in a few examples to make certain that the signs of both terms are changed to their opposites. Another error is that students become so involved when adding and subtracting numerators that they neglect to write a denominator in the answer. This error becomes even more commonplace after students have learned to solve algebraic equations. Emphasize the fact that the sum, difference, product, or quotient of two fractions is a fraction. In rare cases, the denominator reduces to just "1," in which case it is not written. (You may wish to compare this with other situations in algebra where the "1" is not written, for example, coefficients and exponents.)

SUGGESTED EXTENSIONS

Challenge students to spot the error in each of the following simplifications.

1. $\dfrac{x}{3} - \dfrac{x+1}{6} = \dfrac{2x}{6} - \dfrac{x+1}{6}$

$= \dfrac{2x - x + 1}{6}$ $\leftarrow$ Error is here. It should read $\dfrac{2x - x - 1}{6}$

$= \dfrac{x+1}{6}$ which equals $\dfrac{x-1}{6}$.

2. $\dfrac{a-1}{4} - \dfrac{2a-3}{12}$

$= \dfrac{3(a-1)}{12} - \dfrac{2a-3}{12}$

$= \dfrac{3a - 3 - 2a - 3}{12}$ $\leftarrow$ Error here. Should be $\dfrac{3a - 3 - 2a + 3}{12} = \dfrac{a}{12}$

$= \dfrac{a-6}{12}$

6-6 (pages 220–221)

KEY MATHEMATICAL IDEAS

• changing mixed expressions to fractions and vice versa

TEACHING SUGGESTIONS

Ask students to evaluate $x + y$ and xy for $x = 6$ and $y = \dfrac{2}{3}$.

Solutions: $6 + \dfrac{2}{3} = 6\dfrac{2}{3}$ $6\left(\dfrac{2}{3}\right) = 4$

Point out that the notation used in arithmetic for mixed numbers is different from that used in algebra because the "missing operation" in $6\dfrac{2}{3}$ is addition. This is understood when we read it "six and two-thirds."

Write $\dfrac{a}{b} + \dfrac{c}{d}$ on the chalkboard and evaluate it when $a = 6$, $b = 1$, $c = 2$, and $d = 3$. Write

$$\dfrac{6}{1} + \dfrac{2}{3} = \dfrac{6}{1} \cdot \dfrac{3}{3} + \dfrac{2}{3} = \dfrac{18 + 2}{3} = \dfrac{20}{3}.$$

Ask students to compare this with other methods they have used for changing $6\dfrac{2}{3}$ to $\dfrac{20}{3}$. Remind them that this procedure for changing a mixed number to a single fraction is useful when multiplying and dividing. Encourage students to write a denominator of "1" in the first step.

SUGGESTED EXTENSIONS

Have students complete each table and explain the results.

1.

	value at $x = 0$	$x = 1$	$x = 2$	$x = 3$
$x - 2 + \dfrac{4-x}{x+2}$	0	0	$\dfrac{2}{4}$	$\dfrac{6}{5}$
$\dfrac{x(x-1)}{x+2}$	0	0	$\dfrac{2}{4}$	$\dfrac{6}{5}$

The values are the same in both rows because the two expressions are equal for all x except -2.

2.

	value at $x = 0$	$x = -1$	$x = -2$	$x = -3$
$\dfrac{8x+3}{4-x} - x$	$\dfrac{3}{4}$	0	$-\dfrac{1}{6}$	0
$\dfrac{(x+1)(x+3)}{4-x}$	$\dfrac{3}{4}$	0	$-\dfrac{1}{6}$	0

The values are the same in both rows because the two expressions are equal for all x except 4.

6-7 (pages 222–227)

KEY MATHEMATICAL IDEAS

• dividing by a polynomial

TEACHING SUGGESTIONS

Emphasize the parallels between long division with numbers and with polynomials. Point out that the two examples on page 222 are identical if you let $x = 10$, except for the following minor difference. In Step 1 with numbers the first digit, 2, of the quotient is written over the 5 and in Step 1 with polynomials the first term of the quotient, $2x$, is written over the first term $6x^2$. Emphasize the relationship used for checking:

Dividend = Quotient × Divisor + Remainder

SUGGESTED EXTENSION

A more intricate example of dividing polynomials is simplifying complex fractions. (Assign the Extra on page 225.)

Ask your students to write the following as complex fractions and simplify. Suggest that your students begin by writing down the least common denominator of all the simple fractions for easy reference. Assume that $a \neq 0$ and $b \neq 0$.

1. $\left(\dfrac{6}{a} - \dfrac{a}{6}\right) \div \left(\dfrac{3}{4a} + \dfrac{3}{24}\right)$ $\dfrac{4}{3}(6 - a)$

2. $\left(\dfrac{1}{b} + \dfrac{1}{a}\right) \div \left(1 + \dfrac{a}{b}\right)$ $\dfrac{1}{a}$

3. $\left(a + \dfrac{2}{b}\right) \div \left(b + \dfrac{2}{a}\right)$ $\dfrac{a}{b}$

4. $\left(\dfrac{2}{ab} + ab\right) \div \left(\dfrac{b}{a} + \dfrac{ab}{2}\right)$ $\dfrac{2(2 + a^2b^2)}{b^2(2 + a^2)}$

7   *Applying Fractions*

This chapter expands problem solving skills to a wide variety of problems involving algebraic fractions. The opening sections include discussions of ratio and proportion. The five-step method for problem solving first presented in Chapter 1 is utilized in the sections on percentages. The chapter ends with more difficult problems on mixtures and rates of work which involve equations with both fractional coefficients and variable denominators.

7-1 (*pages 235–239*)

KEY MATHEMATICAL IDEAS

• solving problems involving ratios

TEACHING SUGGESTIONS

In many applications, the most common way of expressing ratios is with the symbol ":", read "is to." (For example, 9:5 is read "9 is to 5.") Make sure your students understand that expressions such as 9:5, $9 \div 5$, $\dfrac{9}{5}$, and 1.8 are equivalent. Some students may have difficulty thinking of 1.8, for instance, as a ratio.

Emphasize the importance of expressing the measures of two quantities in a ratio, in the same unit. Remind your students to answer the question asked in a word problem.

SUGGESTED EXTENSION

Introduce the following method for solving ratio problems. Since most students will find actually solving the problem difficult without knowing the material in the next three sections, you need not present Steps 4 and 5.

The ratio of oil to vinegar in one liter of a salad dressing is 3:2. How much oil is there in the dressing?

Step 1   The problem asks for the amount of oil in the dressing.

Step 2   Let $x =$ the amount of oil and $1 - x$ the amount of vinegar.

Step 3 $\dfrac{x}{1 - x} = \dfrac{3}{4}$ *Step 4* $4x = 3(1 - x)$

$4x = 3 - 3x$

$7x = 3$

$x = \dfrac{3}{7}$

Step 5   There is about 0.4 L of oil in the dressing.

7-2 (*pages 240–243*)

KEY MATHEMATICAL IDEAS

• finding solution sets of proportions
• using proportions to solve problems

TEACHING SUGGESTIONS

Place dots on a large piece of clear plastic to represent the proportion $\frac{2}{3} = \frac{4}{6}$. Rotate and flip the plastic in a variety of ways so that the array of dots represents $\frac{2}{4} = \frac{3}{6}$, $\frac{3}{2} = \frac{6}{4}$, etc. Write each new proportion as it is found. Ask

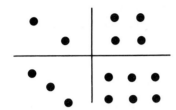

the class to verify the fact that each of them is true by reducing both sides to lowest terms. Point out that the products of the extremes and means will be 12, no matter how the plastic is turned.

In applying the means-extremes property of proportions, point out the fact that these products can be left in factored form until after dividing.

SUGGESTED EXTENSIONS

Ask your students to complete the following exercises.
1. Prove the converse of the "means-extremes" property.

$$\text{If } ad = bc \text{ then } \frac{a}{b} = \frac{c}{d}.$$

That is, "If the product of two numbers is equal to the product of two other numbers, the first two can be made the extremes in a proportion whose means are the other two."

2. Use the converse in 1. to find the ratio of x to y if $8x = 13y$.

1. Use the division property, dividing by bd.

2. $\frac{x}{y} = \frac{13}{8}$

7-3 (pages 244–246)

KEY MATHEMATICAL IDEAS

• solving equations with fractional coefficients

TEACHING SUGGESTIONS

Review solving equations which involve a single fraction with these examples.

$$\frac{x}{3} = 7 \qquad\qquad \frac{2x}{7} = 6$$

Mult. by 3   Mult. by 7

$$x = 21 \qquad\qquad 2x = 42$$

$$x = 21$$

Present the following solutions to $\frac{x}{3} + \frac{2x}{7} = 13$.

Method 1   Write $\frac{1}{3}x + \frac{2}{7}x = 13$

$$\left(\frac{1}{3} + \frac{2}{7}\right)x = 13$$

$$\frac{13}{21}x = 13$$

$$x = 21$$

Method 2   Multiply by 21, the LCD of the two fractions.

$$21\left(\frac{x}{3} + \frac{2x}{7}\right) = 21 \cdot 13$$

$$7x + 6x = 273$$

$$13x = 273$$

$$x = 21$$

Generalize that fractional equations may be transformed by multiplying both sides by the LCD of all of the fractions in the equation.

SUGGESTED EXTENSION

Tell your students to solve for x in $\frac{x+3}{3} + \frac{x}{5} = \frac{11}{3k}$ if $k + 3 = 4$. You can give them a hint to use substitution. $x = 5$

7-4 (pages 247–250)

KEY MATHEMATICAL IDEAS

• solving fractional equations

TEACHING SUGGESTIONS

Ask students to solve and check $\frac{5}{x} = 1 + \frac{10}{2x}$.

Solution: LCD 2x, multiply by 2x; $10 = 2x + 10$

Students should obtain zero as an answer, which will not check when substituted in the original equation. Explain that this can happen in solving equations with variables in the denominator because there are some numbers that are not permissible in each equation. (In the above equation, for instance, $x \neq 0$.) Instruct your students to carefully list these values before starting each problem to be certain that they are not dividing by zero. Encourage them to check all values to insure that they have not included answers which are not permissible.

SUGGESTED EXTENSION

Have your students solve the equation $\dfrac{4}{a^2 - 4a} - \dfrac{1}{a} =$

$\dfrac{a - 3}{a - 4}$ twice, first by multiplying by the LCD and second by writing both sides of the equation as a single fraction in reduced form.

Method 1 $\quad \dfrac{4}{a^2 - 4a} - \dfrac{1}{a} = \dfrac{a - 3}{a - 4}$

$\dfrac{4}{a(a - 4)} - \dfrac{1}{a} = \dfrac{a - 3}{a - 4}$

$4 - (a - 4) = a^2 - 3a$

$8 - a = a^2 - 3a$

$a^2 - 2a - 8 = 0$

$(a - 4)(a + 2); \ a = 4, \ -2$

Since 4 is not permissible, $a = -2$.

Method 2 $\quad \dfrac{4}{a^2 - 4a} - \dfrac{1}{a} = \dfrac{a - 3}{a - 4}$

$\dfrac{4 - (a - 4)}{a(a - 4)} = \dfrac{a - 3}{a - 4}$

$\dfrac{8 - a}{a - 4} = \dfrac{a^2 - 3a}{a - 4}$

$(8 - a)(a - 4) = (a^2 - 3a)(a - 4)$

$8 - a = a^2 - 3a$

$a^2 - 2a - 8 = 0; \ a = -2$

7-5 (pages 251–255)

KEY MATHEMATICAL IDEAS

• solving problems involving percentages

TEACHING SUGGESTIONS

Make certain that students can readily express decimals and fractions as percents and vice versa. Allow time for review as needed.

Some of your students may find it easier at first to solve the problems in this section by writing proportions. Stress that the word "of" means "times" (multiplication) and the word "is" means "equals." Tell your students to think of writing an equation as deciphering a message. For example, "78 is 40% of what number?" can be translated into

$78 = \dfrac{40}{100} \cdot x$.

SUGGESTED EXTENSIONS

Ask your students to determine which is the better investment for the given annual simple interest rate.

1. $1200 at 6% or $1100 at 8%? $1100 at 8%
2. $10,000 at 15% or $11,000 at 14%? $11,000 at 14%
3. $600 at 12% or $700 at 10%? $600 at 12%
4. $350 at 6% or $400 at 5%? $350 at 6%
5. $1250 at 8% or $1300 at 7.5%? $1250 at 8%
6. $540 at 6% or $500 at 6.5%? $500 at 6.5%

7-6 (pages 256–258)

KEY MATHEMATICAL IDEAS

• solving problems involving percent decrease and increase

TEACHING SUGGESTIONS

Emphasize the fact that the percent increase or decrease is always based upon the original amount. Encourage your students to follow the five step method for solving problems. Stress the importance of checking answers by substituting them in the original equation.

SUGGESTED EXTENSION

Explain compound interest to your students. (Interest is periodically added to the principal and interest is then paid on the new principal.) Give them the following formula for finding the amount A of money in an account.

$A = P\left(1 + \dfrac{R}{N}\right)^{NT}$ where P = principal, R = rate, N = times a year, and T = number of years.

Ask students to compute the amount of money to the nearest cent, accumulated at the end of one year for a $1000 investment if the interest is 10% and it is compounded **a.** annually, **b.** semiannually, and **c.** quarterly.

a. $1100   **b.** $1102.50   **c.** $1103.81

7-7 (pages 259–262)

KEY MATHEMATICAL IDEAS

• solving mixture problems

TEACHING SUGGESTIONS

To begin this lesson, ask your students to list things that are made up of different mixtures. A few suggestions are recipes, air, cement, etc.

Your students will find making a chart for Step 2 of the procedure for solving problems very helpful. Remind students to carefully read through each problem and identify all of the essential information given.

SUGGESTED EXTENSION

Have your students solve a mixture problem involving percentages in two ways, based on a different ingredient each time. For instance, in Example 2 on page 260, let x = number of grams of water to be added, but change the chart as shown below.

	Total amount	× % water =	amount of water
original solution	60	65%	0.65(60)
new solution	60 + x	80%	0.80(60 + x)

Then $0.65(60) + x = 0.80(60 + x)$; $39 + x = 48 + 0.80x$ and $x = 45$

7-8 (pages 263–268)

KEY MATHEMATICAL IDEAS

• solving problems involving rate of work

TEACHING SUGGESTIONS

Continue the idea of using a formula with a chart to organize the information in these problems. Compare the relationship "Work rate × time = amount of work done" with the formula for uniform motion, $D = rt$.

The most difficult concept here involves the calculation of the work rate. This idea can be clarified if the abstract unit of work is presented in terms of some unit of measurement. For example, suppose the garage walls cover 60 square meters in Example 1 in the text (page 263). Then your rate of work is 30 square meters per day and your friend's rate of work is 20 square meters per day. If you work together for x days to paint the entire 60 square meters, the equation is $20x + 30x = 60$ and $x = 1.2$. Demonstrate that this analysis is equivalent to

$$60\left(\frac{1}{2}\right) \text{ for your rate,}$$

$$60\left(\frac{1}{3}\right) \text{ for your friend's rate,}$$

$$\text{and } 60\left(\frac{1}{2}\right)x + 60\left(\frac{1}{3}\right)x = 60.$$

Dividing by 60 produces $\frac{1}{2}x + \frac{1}{3}x = 1$. Point out that the equation would be exactly the same, independent of the size of the garage. Remind the students that there are three "ones" in the equation (representing the whole job divided by two and by three on the left side).

You may wish to spend some time reviewing the relationships between hours and minutes and minutes and seconds so that fractional answers can be expressed in smaller units of time.

SUGGESTED EXTENSION

Suggest that your students solve some of the problems using the relationship $\frac{1}{t_1} + \frac{1}{t_2} = \frac{1}{t}$, where $\frac{1}{t_1}$ is the first rate, $\frac{1}{t_2}$ is the second rate, and $\frac{1}{t}$ is the combined rate. For instance, Example 1 on page 263 becomes

$$\frac{1}{2} + \frac{1}{3} = \frac{1}{r}$$

$$\frac{3}{6} + \frac{2}{6} = \frac{1}{r}$$

$$\frac{5}{6} = \frac{1}{r} \quad \text{and} \quad r = \frac{6}{5}$$

8 Linear Equations and Systems

This chapter includes the basic tools for working with more than one variable in linear relationships. By extending the number line to the two-dimensional "number plane," problems involving two variables are represented graphically. Several methods of solving pairs of linear equations in two variables provide the basis for using systems of linear equations to solve puzzle problems and problems involving uniform motion.

8-1 (pages 275–279)

KEY MATHEMATICAL IDEAS

- graphing points in a coordinate plane

TEACHING SUGGESTIONS

Have students use coordinate paper with about two squares per centimeter (4 or 5 per inch) for the exercises in this chapter. If available, a music staff liner can be used to draw grids on the chalkboard.

Emphasize the significance of the *order* of the coordinates in locating a point in the coordinate plane. For example, have the students compare the coordinates $(-3, 4)$ with the coordinates $(4, -3)$. Also, ask them to compare the graph of $(2, -3)$ with that of $(-3, 2)$. Some students may observe the symmetry and be able to predict the location of (b, a) from the location of (a, b).

SUGGESTED EXTENSION

Have students connect the following dots in sequence and identify the resultant figure.

$(0, 7)$, $(-2, 4)$, $(-1, 4)$, $(-3, 1)$, $(-2, 1)$, $(-4, -2)$, $(-3, -2)$, $(-5, -5)$, $(-1, -5)$, $(-1, -7)$, $(1, -7)$, $(1, -5)$, $(5, -5)$, $(3, -2)$, $(4, -2)$, $(2, 1)$, $(3, 1)$, $(1, 4)$, $(2, 4)$, $(0, 7)$

a fir tree

8-2 (pages 280–282)

KEY MATHEMATICAL IDEAS

- solving equations in two variables over given domains

TEACHING SUGGESTIONS

The material in this section may be completely new to some students, so the basic idea of an equation in two variables should be explained carefully. Emphasize that if an equation has two variables, the solution set must be made up of ordered pairs. Demonstrate the meaning of the phrase "solve the equation for y in terms of x" with several examples. Point out that unless otherwise specified, the value of x is written first in the ordered pair, regardless of the appearance of the variable x in the equation. For instance, the solutions of the equation $y - x = -4$ are written in the form (x, y).

SUGGESTED EXTENSION

Ask students to create examples of applied problems for the given equations below. Solutions must be whole numbers.

1. $x + 3y = 9$
2. $2x + y = 15$
3. $5x + y = 18$

An example for Equation 1 would be, "If a group of people spent \$9 to attend a movie, how many people with \$1 discount tickets and how many with regular \$3 tickets were in the group?"

8-3 (pages 283–286)

KEY MATHEMATICAL IDEAS

- graphing linear equations in two variables

TEACHING SUGGESTIONS

You may wish to introduce the word "intercept" when finding the point where a line crosses an axis.

Students can check the validity of the sentence on page 283, "In fact, when x and y are real numbers, each solution of $x + 2y = 6$ gives the coordinates of a point on the line shown above. . ." by

a. checking some points on the line in the graph on the right other than those shown in the graph on the left, to see whether their coordinates satisfy the equation $x + 2y = 6$ (for example, the point $(-2, 4)$), and
b. checking some other solutions of the equation (for example, $(1, 2.5)$), to see whether they are coordinates of points on the line shown.

Since the students will be using other standard forms later in the course, it may be helpful to use a more specific phrase in referring to the "standard form" of an equation, such as "standard linear form."

SUGGESTED EXTENSION

Ask your students to rewrite each of several equations from the standard form $Ax + By = C$ by dividing both sides by C. Have them compare the result with the points where the line crosses each of the axes.

Samples:

a. $x + 2y = 6$ Line crosses the x-axis at
$\dfrac{x}{6} + \dfrac{y}{3} = 1$ (6, 0) and the y-axis at (0, 3).

b. $3x + 8y = 27$ Line crosses the x-axis at
$\dfrac{x}{9} + \dfrac{8y}{27} = 1$ (9, 0) and the y-axis at $\left(0, \dfrac{27}{8}\right)$

c. $3x - y = 5$ Line crosses x-axis at $\left(\dfrac{5}{3}, 0\right)$
$\dfrac{3x}{5} - \dfrac{y}{5} = 1$ and the y-axis at (0, −5).

If a line crosses the x-axis at $(a, 0)$ and the y-axis at $(0, b)$, an equation of the line is $\dfrac{x}{a} + \dfrac{y}{b} = 1$ or $\dfrac{1}{a}x + \dfrac{1}{b}y = 1$.

8-4 (pages 287–289)

KEY MATHEMATICAL IDEAS

• using graphs to solve systems of linear equations

TEACHING SUGGESTIONS

Introduce the idea of a *system* of two linear equations by emphasizing the words "two" and "and" in the following puzzle: "I am thinking of *two* numbers whose sum is ten *and* whose difference is four."
Explain that the word "two" suggests that we can solve the problem with two variables and that the word "and" suggests we can write two equations. Have the class suggest two equations.
Answer: $x + y = 10$ and $x - y = 4$
Graph both equations on the chalkboard and determine the point of intersection (7, 3). Show that the solution checks in *both* equations.
   Point out that a system of equations may have one solution (just one ordered pair), no solution, or an infinite set of solutions.

SUGGESTED EXTENSIONS

Ask your students to tell whether the following systems of linear equations have no solution, an infinite set of solutions, or one solution.

1. $x - y = 4$ **2.** $x + y = 7$
    $2x + y = 8$ $x + y = 0$

3. $x + y = 8$ **4.** $3x - y = 5$
   $-x + y = 6$ $6x - 2y = 10$

1. one solution   **2.** no solution   **3.** one solution
4. infinite set of solutions

8-5 (pages 290–292)

KEY MATHEMATICAL IDEAS

• solving systems of linear equations by substitution

TEACHING SUGGESTIONS

Point out that the equation in Step 3 of the Substitution Method on page 291 should never have two variables. Explain that the solutions obtained by substitution are more accurate than those obtained by graphing. You may wish to add that the Substitution Method can be used for many types of equations in combination with one linear equation.
   The idea of equivalent systems can be tied to the four steps in the Substitution Method as follows.
a. The equations in Steps 1 and 3 form a system which is equivalent to the given system, and
b. The equations in Steps 3 and 4 form a system which is equivalent to the given system.

These statements can be verified graphically for one of the examples.

SUGGESTED EXTENSIONS

For each of the following systems tell your students to
a. apply the Substitution Method to solve,
b. state whether they think the graphs are intersecting, parallel, or coincident lines, and
c. check their answers by graphing the equations.

1. $x + y = 1$ $2 - y + y = 1$
    $x = 2 - y$ $2 = 1$ Parallel

2. $2x - 2y = 2$ $2x - 2(x - 1) = 2$
    $y = x - 1$ $2x - 2x + 2 = 2$
                     $2 = 2$ Coincident

8-6 *(pages 293–295)*

KEY MATHEMATICAL IDEAS

• using two variables to solve problems

TEACHING SUGGESTIONS

As you begin this lesson, it will be helpful to review the plan for solving word problems first introduced on page 23, and adapt it to use for problems involving two variables. Point out that problems which can be solved using a system of linear equations often ask for two different solutions.

SUGGESTED EXTENSION

Have your students select some of the problems on pages 98 and 102 which ask for two numbers and solve them using two variables and the method of substitution. Ask students to compare this method with the method used in Chapter 3.

8-7 *(pages 296–298)*

KEY MATHEMATICAL IDEAS

• solving systems of linear equations using addition or subtraction

TEACHING SUGGESTIONS

Review the addition property of equality since this is the basis for the addition-or-subtraction method. Instruct students to write equations in standard form before deciding whether to add or subtract. Suggest that they try to choose the *simpler* equation to use in Step 3 on page 297.

   To demonstrate the validity of the addition-or-subtraction method, solve Example 1 on page 296 using both the graphic method and the substitution method. Encourage your students to check their answers to the problems in this section by using either the graphic or the substitution method.

SUGGESTED EXTENSIONS

For each of the following systems ask your students to
a. apply the addition-or-subtraction method to solve,
b. state whether they think the graphs are intersecting, parallel, or coincident lines, and
c. check their answers by graphing the equations.

1. $x + y = 7$ By subtraction, $0 = 1$
  $x + y = 6$ Parallel; no solution
2. $x + y = 6$ By addition, $0 = 0$
  $-x - y = -6$ Coincident; infinite set of solutions

8-8 *(pages 299–303)*

KEY MATHEMATICAL IDEAS

• using multiplication with the addition-or-subtraction method to solve systems of linear equations

TEACHING SUGGESTIONS

You may begin this lesson with the following demonstration of how to solve the system $\begin{matrix} 4x - 6y = 14 \\ 5x + 2y = 8 \end{matrix}$ by using addition three times.

$4x - 6y = 14$	$5x + 2y = 8$	$5x + 2y = 8$
$5x + 2y = 8$	$9x - 4y = 22$	$14x - 2y = 30$
$9x - 4y = 22$	$14x - 2y = 30$	$19x = 38$
		$x = 2, y = -1$

Then ask your students to find a short cut by using the multiplication property of equality for the equation $5x + 2y = 8$ in the original system. Emphasize the need to transform equations to standard form before deciding how to proceed.

SUGGESTED EXTENSION

Have the students graph all of the lines obtained in the process of solving the system $\begin{matrix} 4x - 6y = 14 \\ 5x + 2y = 8 \end{matrix}$ by using addition three times, demonstrated in the TEACHING SUGGESTIONS above.

8-9 *(pages 304–308)*

KEY MATHEMATICAL IDEAS

• solving puzzle problems using systems of equations in two variables

TEACHING SUGGESTIONS

Emphasize the suggestion of making a chart to organize the information given in a problem. Remind your students once again, to check their answers with the question asked in the original problem.

It may be helpful to give the following examples of writing two-digit decimal numerals in the form $10t + u$ where $t \in \{1, 2, 3, 4, 5, 6, 7, 8, 9\}$ and $u \in \{0, 1, 2, 3, 4, 5, 6, 7, 8, 9\}$.

$$98 = 90 + 8 = 9 \cdot 10 + 8 \qquad 63 = 60 + 3 = 6 \cdot 10 + 3$$
$$47 = 40 + 7 = 4 \cdot 10 + 7$$

SUGGESTED EXTENSION

Have your students solve the problem below.

"The sum of the digits in a three-digit number is 9. The new number obtained when the digits are reversed is 198 more than the original number. If the one's digit in the original number is 3, what is the original number?" 153

8-10 (pages 309–312)

KEY MATHEMATICAL IDEAS

• solving uniform motion problems using systems of equations in two variables.

TEACHING SUGGESTIONS

Begin this lesson by stating that an object that moves without changing its speed is said to be in uniform motion. Ask your students to give several examples of uniform motion, such as a plane flying 1300 km/h in still air. Be sure your students learn the formula

$$\text{Distance} = \text{rate} \times \text{time}.$$

SUGGESTED EXTENSIONS

Give your class the following problem.

An airplane takes off to fly north at 120 km/h. The pilot ignores the fact that the wind is blowing from the west at 50 km h. Use a coordinate plane to represent the motion during the first six minutes as follows.

a. Draw an arrow from the origin to the point (0, 12) to represent the motion due to the engine.

b. Draw an arrow from the origin to the point (5, 0) to represent the motion due to the wind.

c. Draw an arrow from the origin to the point (5, 12) to represent the actual motion. Use the edge of a second piece of graph paper as a ruler to measure the length of this arrow.

1. How far will the plane actually travel in six minutes? in one hour? 13 km; 130 km

2. How far will the pilot be from the expected location at the end of six minutes? at the end of one hour? 5 km east; 50 km east

9 Introduction to Functions

Students have gained experience with the graphs of linear equations in Chapter 8. This chapter follows with a thorough analysis of linear functions, focusing on the idea of slope and leading to the introduction of the general concept of a function. Several notational features employed may be new to the students. The section on quadratic functions provides a preview of Chapter 12, including a technique for finding the vertex of a parabola.

9-1 (pages 319–323)

KEY MATHEMATICAL IDEAS

• using the definition of slope

TEACHING SUGGESTIONS

Write the following equations on the chalkboard and ask the class to help you graph them on a single grid.

$$x - y = 5 \qquad 2x - y = 4 \qquad 3x - y = 3$$

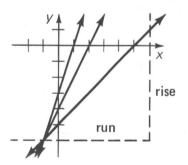

Point out that the lines do not have the same "steepness." Present *slope* as a way to describe steepness; that is, slope $= \dfrac{\text{rise}}{\text{run}}$. Starting at the point of intersection, $(-1, 6)$, show that the three lines have slopes $\dfrac{6}{6}, \dfrac{6}{3}$, and $\dfrac{6}{2}$, respectively, by determining the rise and the run to the x-axis. Explain that the slopes are simply 1, 2, and 3.

In order to give students a "feeling" for slopes, draw several reference grids, each with a line of known slope (such as $+2, -2, +1, -1, 0$) through the origin. Then hold up a meter stick in various positions on the grids and ask the class to estimate the slope of the stick in each position.

SUGGESTED EXTENSIONS

Ask your students to complete the following.
1. Through any point in a plane
   a. draw lines whose slopes are $+1, +2, +4, +8, +16$;
   b. draw lines whose slopes are $-1, -2, -4, -8, -16$.
   Answers may vary
2. What happens to the definition
   slope $= \dfrac{\text{difference between } y\text{-coordinates}}{\text{difference between } x\text{-coordinates}}$ for vertical lines?

   The difference between x-coordinates is always zero so the slope is undefined.

9-2 (pages 324–327)

KEY MATHEMATICAL IDEAS

• using the slope-intercept form of a linear equation

TEACHING SUGGESTIONS

Begin this lesson by graphing the linear equations $y = 2x$ and $y = 2x + 3$ on the same set of axes. Ask your students to compare the graphs by finding the slope of each line.

Answer: slope of $y = 2x$ is 2; slope of $y = 2x + 3$ is 2.

Define the term y-intercept and point out that the y-intercept of $y = 2x$ is 0 and the y-intercept of $y = 2x + 3$ is 3. Introduce the forms $y = mx$ and $y = mx + b$. Explain that m is the slope of the line and b is the y-intercept as shown in the given equations.

Some of your students may notice that the lines $y = 2x$ and $y = 2x + 3$ are parallel. Make the general statement that parallel lines have the same slope.

SUGGESTED EXTENSIONS

Have your students do the following.
1. Using the equation $y = 2x + 1$, **a.** write an expression for y when $x = k$, **b.** write an expression for y when $x = (k + 1)$, and **c.** find the change in y as x changes from k to $(k + 1)$.

2. Repeat the instructions in Exercise 1 using the equation $y = mx + b$.

1. **a.** $2k + 1$ **b.** $2k + 3$ **c.** 2
2. **a.** $mk + b$ **b.** $m(k + 1) + b$ **c.** m

9-3 (pages 328–330)

KEY MATHEMATICAL IDEAS

• finding an equation of a line given the slope and one point on the line, or two points on the line

TEACHING SUGGESTIONS

Ask the class to use slopes to help you draw the graphs of the following three lines.
1. A line with slope 3 passing through the point $(0, 3)$
2. A line with slope 3 passing through the point $(3, 7)$
3. A line with slope $-\dfrac{1}{3}$ passing through the point $(3, 7)$

Have the class estimate the values of the y-intercepts from the graphs. Then show them how to use the slope-intercept form of an equation to find the values of b for each of the lines. It is helpful to use the idea that the set of all lines with slope 3 can be represented by the equation $y = 3x + b$. Reinforce the fact that the x and y coordinates of every point on the line must satisfy the equation.

SUGGESTED EXTENSIONS

Tell your students to find the equation of the line passing through $(3, 7)$ if the line is of the given form.
1. $Ax + 3y = 6$ $A = -5$; $-5x + 3y = 6$
2. $-2x + By = 1$ $B = 1$; $-2x + y = 1$
3. $4x - 3y = C$ $C = -9$; $4x - 3y = -9$
4. $y = 5x + b$ $b = -8$; $-5x + y = -8$
5. $y = mx + 10$ $m = -1$; $x + y = 10$

9-4 (pages 331–333)

KEY MATHEMATICAL IDEAS

- understanding what a function is and how to find its values

TEACHING SUGGESTIONS

There are several important ideas in this section that you will want to stress. One is the idea of an equation assigning values to y, given certain values of x. Another is that every function must have two parts: a domain and a range. Be sure that your students understand that every function assigns each member of the domain to exactly one member of the range, and that each member of the range must be assigned to at least one member of the domain. Point out that equations are rules that define functions.

SUGGESTED EXTENSION

The idea of a function machine may help to clarify the meaning of functions. For example, the diagram below represents the function $f: x \rightarrow (x + 1)^2$. Copy the diagram on the chalkboard. Let your students choose a domain which they can "put into" the machine. Tell them to record the resulting range.

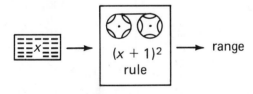

9-5 (pages 334–337)

KEY MATHEMATICAL IDEAS

- extending the idea of a function to any set of ordered pairs
- displaying functions by means of tables, bar graphs, and line graphs.

TEACHING SUGGESTIONS

The chart below gives the results when a liquid is heated. Draw the chart on the chalkboard and ask your students if they can think of a rule that assigns values in the Time-elapsed column to values in the Temperature column.

Time elapsed (minutes)	Temperature (deg. C)
0	6°
0.5	7°
1.0	8°
1.5	10°
2.0	12°
2.5	15°
3.0	20°

After a few guesses, tell students that the data given in the chart cannot be expressed by a simple rule. Explain that the data does represent a function, however, since each member of the left column can be paired with exactly one member of the right column. Discuss how to define the function using ordered pairs.

SUGGESTED EXTENSIONS

Ask your students to tell which of the following are functions.

1. {(blue, green), (yellow, red), (pink, blue)}
2. {(3,4), (2, 3), (4, 5) (6, 10)}
3. {(200, 5), (300, 4), (200, 3)}
4. {(1, 1), (2, 2), (3, 3), (4, 4)}
5. {(heads, tails), (tails, heads), (heads, heads)}
6. {(0, 1), (−5, 7), (−6, 1), (−7, 1)}

1. a function   2. a function   3. not a function
4. a function   5. not a function   6. a function

9-6 (pages 338–342)

KEY MATHEMATICAL IDEAS

- graphing quadratic functions

TEACHING SUGGESTIONS

It may be helpful to graph the quadratic equation $y = x^2 - 2x - 3$, given on page 338, on the chalkboard. Take the time to carefully plot each point given in the table. Point out the minimum point of the parabola. Draw the graph of $y = -x^2 + 2x + 3$ on the same set of axes and ask your students to compare both parabolas. Point out the maximum point of $y = -x^2 + 2x + 3$.

Draw the graph of $y = 3x - x^2$ shown below and ask students to estimate the coordinates of the vertex.

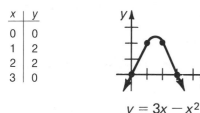

x	y
0	0
1	2
2	2
3	0

$$y = 3x - x^2$$

Have your students determine the actual coordinates with the formula $x = \dfrac{-b}{2a}$ and compare their answers with their estimates.

The vertex is the point $\left(\dfrac{3}{2}, \dfrac{9}{4}\right)$.

SUGGESTED EXTENSIONS

Ask your students to do the following.

1. Show that these five points lie on the graph of $y = \dfrac{1}{4a}x^2$:

   (0, 0) (2a, a) (−2a, a) (4a, 4a) (−4a, 4a).

2. Use the results from Exercise 1 to draw the graphs of

   a. $y = \dfrac{1}{4}x^2$ **b.** $y = \dfrac{1}{8}x^2$

   c. $y = \dfrac{1}{12}x^2$ **d.** $y = -\dfrac{1}{4}x^2$

   (Hint: $a = -1$)

9-7 (*pages 343–347*)

KEY MATHEMATICAL IDEAS

• solving problems involving direct variation

TEACHING SUGGESTIONS

Remind students that the graph of an equation of the form $y = kx$ is a line whose slope is k. Point out, too, that although the definition of a linear direct variation specifies only that the constant $k \neq 0$, in most practical situations, the constant is a positive number. You may need to explain the use of subscripts in this section. Stress that each variable with a subscript represents a particular value of the variable.

When using the proportion method review the methods of solving proportions on page 240 in Section 7-2.

SUGGESTED EXTENSIONS

For each formula given below, ask your students to write and solve a problem involving direct variation.
1. Cost = price × number
2. Distance = rate × time
3. Area of a rectangle = length × width

9-8 (*pages 348–353*)

KEY MATHEMATICAL IDEAS

• solving problems involving inverse variation

TEACHING SUGGESTIONS

You can introduce the concept of inverse variation by using the following table showing the values of various coins and the number of coins needed to equal the value of one dollar. Emphasize that one value increases as the other decreases.

coin	value in cents	number needed to equal $1
penny	1	100
nickel	5	20
dime	10	10
quarter	25	4
half-dollar	50	2
dollar	100	1

Be sure your students do not confuse the formula for direct variation with the formula for inverse variation.

SUGGESTED EXTENSIONS

Tell your students that the law of the lever given on page 349 can be extended to include four masses as follows.
$$m_1d_1 + m_2d_2 = m_3d_3 + m_4d_4$$
Propose the following problem to your class.
"A see-saw, 4 meters long, is balanced at a point 1.5 m from one end when the following persons are seated.

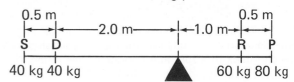

Phil is 80 kg and sits at an end. Rosa is 60 kg and sits 0.5 m from that end. Sue is 40 kg and sits at the other end. Dom is 40 kg and sits 0.5 m from that end. Prove that this possible.'' $40(2.5) + 40(2) = 60(1) + 80(1.5)$

$$180 = 180$$

9-9 (pages 353–355)

KEY MATHEMATICAL IDEAS

• solving problems involving quadratic variation
• solving problems involving inverse square variation

TEACHING SUGGESTIONS

Write the following chart on the chalkboard. Review the formula for the area of a square of side s: Area $= s^2$.

Area of a Square	
Side	Area
1	1
2	4
3	9
4	16

Explain that another way of describing this relationship is to say that the area of a square varies directly as the square of the side. Generalize to any relationship of the form $y = kx^2$.

A flashlight or another light source may be used to illustrate that illumination decreases as the surface is moved away from the light source. Other examples of inverse variation as the square include the following.

1. the weight of an object at or above the earth's surface varies inversely as the square of the object's distance from the center of the earth; and
2. the electrical resistance of a wire of fixed length varies inversely as the square of the diameter of the wire.

SUGGESTED EXTENSIONS

Ask your students to consider the functions

$F: x \rightarrow x^2$ and $G: x \rightarrow \dfrac{1}{x}$.

Ask them to **a.** find $G[F(x)]$ (Hint: first find $F(x)$.), **b.** find $F[G(x)]$, and **c.** describe the functions in **a** and **b** in terms of variation.

a. $\dfrac{1}{x^2}$ **b.** $\left(\dfrac{1}{x}\right)^2$ **c.** Both are inverse square variations.

9-10 (pages 356–359)

KEY MATHEMATICAL IDEAS

• solving problems involving joint and combined variation

TEACHING SUGGESTIONS

Make certain that students understand that the word ''jointly'' implies that all of the variations are direct. In other combinations the words ''directly'' and ''inversely'' are specified.

In doing the examples, point out that the two methods of solving problems described on page 345 can be used here also. To demonstrate this, solve Example 1 on page 356 using the alternate method as follows.

Example 1 $V = khr^2$ Therefore, $V = \pi hr^2$
$\qquad\qquad 160\pi = k(10)(4)^2$ $\qquad\quad V = \pi(8)(3)^2$
$\qquad\qquad 160\pi = 160k$ $\qquad\qquad\quad V = 72\pi$
$\qquad\qquad\quad \pi = k$

SUGGESTED EXTENSIONS

Instruct your students to study the graph below which was prepared for drivers and answer the following question.

If the ''thinking distance'' varies directly as the speed, find the missing values.

Stopping Distance

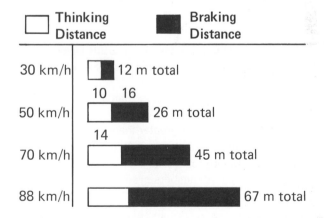

At 30 km/h, thinking distance $=6$ m and braking distance $=6$ m.
At 70 km/h, braking distance $=31$ m.
At 88 km/h, thinking distance $=17.6$ m and braking distance $=49.4$ m.

10 *Inequalities*

The introduction to inequalities presented in Chapter 2 provides the background for this chapter. Here the student will perform the basic transformations on linear inequalities with one and two variables. Most of the solution sets are exhibited on graphs.

In the last part of the chapter, disjunctions and conjunctions of statements are applied to open sentences. Equations and inequalities containing absolute values are solved.

2. Draw the graph of
a. $(-6, -2]$

b. $\left(3, 4\frac{1}{2}\right)$

c. $[-1, 1]$

10-1 *(pages 365–368)*

KEY MATHEMATICAL IDEAS

- reviewing the concept of order of real numbers
- solving inequalities by substitution

TEACHING SUGGESTIONS

Review the material presented in Section 2-2. First, draw a number line on the chalkboard. Ask your students to compare pairs of numbers using the symbols $<$ and $>$. Introduce statements such as $-1 < x < 1$, using the number line to solve for x. Be sure that your class knows the difference between $<$ and $\leq$, and $>$ and $\geq$.

SUGGESTED EXTENSIONS

Introduce the following definitions to your class.

$[a, b]$ = {all real numbers greater than or equal to a and less than or equal to b}

$(a, b]$ = {all real numbers greater than a and less than or equal to b}

(a, b) = {all real numbers greater than a and less than b}

Have your students complete the following.

1. Write the meaning of
a. $[3, 7]$ {all real numbers greater than or equal to 3 and less than or equal to 7}

b. $\left(-5, \frac{1}{2}\right]$ {all real numbers greater than -5 and less than or equal to $\frac{1}{2}$}

c. $(-2, 3)$ {all real numbers greater than -2 and less than 3}

10-2 *(pages 369–373)*

KEY MATHEMATICAL IDEAS

- transforming inequalities to find solution sets

TEACHING SUGGESTIONS

Write the following chart on the board and tell students to observe what happens to $x - 2$, $2x$, etc. when given the fact that $x \geq 4$.

x	$x - 2$	$2x$	$\dfrac{x}{2}$	$-2x$
4	2	8	2	-8
5	3	10	2.5	-10
6	4	12	3	-12
7	5	14	3.5	-14
8	6	16	4	-16

Complete the chart through $x = 8$ and ask the class what conclusions can be drawn.

If $x \geq 4$, then $x - 2 \geq 2$.
If $x \geq 4$, then $2x \geq 8$.
If $x \geq 4$, then $\dfrac{x}{2} \geq 2$.
If $x \geq 4$, then $-2x \leq -8$.

Generalize to the transformations in the text. Emphasize the parallels with the properties of equality, highlighting the special cases of multiplication or division by a negative number.

T100

Draw the graph of $0 \leq r \leq 2$ on the chalkboard.

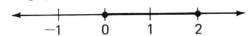

For each of the following inequalities ask your students to
a. draw the graph, **b.** describe how the graph would have to be changed to match the graph of $0 \leq r \leq 2$, and **c.** describe the transformation.

1. $1 \leq s \leq 3$

a.

b. Move the graph one unit to the left.

c. Subtract 1.

2. $0 \leq w \leq 1$

a.

b. The graph stretches to twice its size.

c. Multiply by 2.

3. $0 \geq x \geq -2$

a.

b. The graph is reflected over the origin.

c. Multiply by -1.

10-3 *(pages 374–381)*

KEY MATHEMATICAL IDEAS

• solving problems involving inequalities

TEACHING SUGGESTIONS

Remind your students of the plan for solving word problems on page 23. Before assigning any of the exercises in this section, give your students practice in translating phrases involving inequalities into mathematical terms using inequality symbols.

For example:

a height of no less than 3 m: $h \geq 3$

a height of less than 3 m: $h < 3$

a height of at least 3 m: $h \geq 3$

a height of at most 3 m: $h \leq 3$

a height of no more than 3 m: $h \leq 3$

a height of more than 3 m: $h > 3$

SUGGESTED EXTENSION

Provide the class with various solution sets and have the class create inequalities to fit the solution sets. For example, if you give them {all positive integers equal to or less than 11}, they might write:

$$x \leq 11$$
$$2x \leq 22$$
$$2x + 30 \leq 52$$

10-4 *(pages 382–385)*

KEY MATHEMATICAL IDEAS

• finding solution sets of combined inequalities

TEACHING SUGGESTIONS

Suggest that your students rewrite inequalities of the form $a < x < b$ using the word "and;" for example, $a < x$ and $x < b$. Stress that the word "and" means that the values chosen for the variable must solve both open sentences. Likewise, stress that the word "or" means that the values chosen for the variable can solve either one or the other open sentence. Encourage your students to draw number line graphs for each open sentence so they can visualize what the solution set is.

SUGGESTED EXTENSIONS

Have your students use the notation for intervals defined in the SUGGESTED EXTENSIONS for Section 10-1 to simplify the conjunctions and disjunctions.

1. (2, 8] and (5, 10]   (5, 8]

2. (2, 8] or (5, 10]   (2, 10]

3. $(-5, -2]$ and $(-2, 2)$ $\emptyset$

4. $(-5, -2]$ or $(-2, 2)$ $(-5, 2)$

10-5 *(pages 386–388)*

KEY MATHEMATICAL IDEAS

• solving open sentences involving absolute value

TEACHING SUGGESTIONS

Review the definition of absolute value on page 44 and the property that the absolute value of any real number is the distance on a number line between that number and the origin. Explain that $|x| = 2$ is equivalent to the disjunction $x = 2$ or $x = -2$, that $|x| > 2$ is equivalent to the disjunction $x < -2$ or $x > 2$, and that $|x| < 2$ is equivalent to $-2 < x < 2$.

Write $|x - 4| \leq 2$ on the chalkboard. Ask students to tell you what is known about the quantity $(x - 4)$.

Answer: $-2 < (x - 4) < 2$

Then solve to obtain the conjunction $2 \leq x \leq 6$. Encourage your students to draw number line graphs for each open sentence.

SUGGESTED EXTENSIONS

Tell your students that for all real numbers a and b, the solution set of $|x - a| = b$ can be represented geometrically as the set of real numbers whose distance from the graph of a on a number line equals b. Ask the class to solve the following using this interpretation.

1. $|x - 1| = 3$

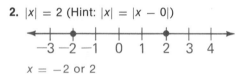

$x = -2$ or 4

2. $|x| = 2$ (Hint: $|x| = |x - 0|$)

$x = -2$ or 2

3. $|2x - 1| = 1$

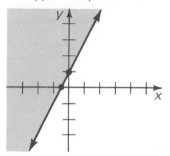

The distance between $2x$ and 1 must be equal to 1. Therefore, $2x$ is either 0 or 2 so $x = 0$ or 1.

10-6 (*pages 389–392*)

KEY MATHEMATICAL IDEAS

• graphing linear inequalities in two variables

TEACHING SUGGESTIONS

Write $y \geq 2x + 1$ on the chalkboard and tell the class that you wish to find all points in the coordinate plane for which this open sentence is true. Graph the boundary line $y = 2x + 1$ by plotting the points in the chart.

T102

$$\text{If } x = 0, y = 1; \quad (0, 1)$$

$$\text{If } y = 0, x = -\frac{1}{2}; \quad \left(-\frac{1}{2}, 0\right)$$

Choose a point above and a point below the boundary line to determine which coordinates satisfy the open sentence. Shade the upper half plane.

Answer:

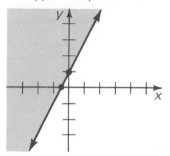

Be certain that students note the difference between a dashed and a solid line in a graph.

SUGGESTED EXTENSIONS

Ask your students to graph the set of all points in the coordinate plane that satisfy the following.

1. $|x| < 2$ **2.** $|y| > 3$

1.

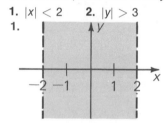

2.

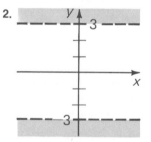

10-7 (*pages 393–397*)

KEY MATHEMATICAL IDEAS

• graphing the solution set of a system of two linear inequalities in two variables

TEACHING SUGGESTIONS

It will be helpful to give students an example such as graphing the solution set of $\begin{array}{l} x + y < 4 \\ x - 2y \leq 4 \end{array}$.

Answer:

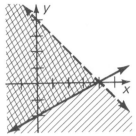

Point out that the solution set contains both a dashed and a solid line.

SUGGESTED EXTENSION

Ask your students to graph the solution set of $y \leq x^2$.

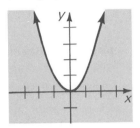

11 *Rational and Irrational Numbers*

After introducing rational numbers in terms of fractions and decimals, the chapter continues with a discussion of rational square roots. Irrational numbers are then presented in terms of irrational square roots. Finding the square roots of variable expressions leads to the Pythagorean theorem.

The second part of the chapter is devoted to working with expressions involving radicals. The chapter ends with the solution of simple radical equations.

11-1 (pages 403–407)

KEY MATHEMATICAL IDEAS

- finding the greater of two rational numbers
- finding a number between two rational numbers

TEACHING SUGGESTIONS

Draw a number line on the chalkboard with integers from -5 to $+5$. Ask the class to help you locate the points whose coordinates have the following values:

$$\frac{1}{2}, \frac{5}{2}, \frac{5}{3}, \frac{-5}{3}, \frac{-3}{4}, \frac{28}{-7}, \frac{-72}{-16}, \frac{0}{-8}.$$

Designate the points A, B, C, D, E, F, G, H, respectively.

```
        F       D E  H A    C   B        G
    ←──┼──●──┼──┼──●┼─●┼─●●─┼──●●┼──┼──●──┼──→
      -5 -4 -3 -2 -1  0  1  2  3  4  5
```

Explain that those real numbers which are quotients of

two integers are called rational numbers. Point out that the quotient of two integers will have a position on the number line, whenever the quotient is defined (denominator not zero).

Challenge the class to find the greater of two rational numbers, e.g. $\frac{14}{3}$ and $\frac{9}{2}$, without using a number line. Try some of the methods which are suggested. (For example, write them with a common denominator, i.e. $\frac{28}{6}$ and $\frac{27}{6}$. Thus, the first one is greater, $\frac{14}{3}$.)

Ask the class to name some numbers which are between $\frac{9}{2}$ and $\frac{14}{3}$. $\left(\text{For example, since } \frac{9}{2} = 4.50 \text{ and } \frac{14}{3} > 4.66, \text{ the number } 4.60 \text{ is between } \frac{9}{2} \text{ and } \frac{14}{3}.\right)$

SUGGESTED EXTENSION

Tell your students that to determine the greater of two rational numbers having the same sign, they can write them with the same positive numerators, find the lesser denominator, and reverse the order to compare the fractions. Instruct them to use this method to compare:

a. $\frac{5}{4}$ and $\frac{5}{3}$ $3 < 4$ so $\frac{5}{4} < \frac{5}{3}$

b. $\frac{3}{4}$ and $\frac{2}{3}$

  Change to $\frac{6}{8}$ and $\frac{6}{9}$. Since $8 < 9$, $\frac{3}{4} > \frac{2}{3}$.

11-2 (pages 408–411)

KEY MATHEMATICAL IDEAS

- expressing rational numbers as decimals or fractions

TEACHING SUGGESTIONS

Most students have had experience converting terminating decimals to fractions. One device which is helpful is to have students write, for example, $0.83 = 83(0.01) = \dfrac{83}{100}$.

The following is a slight variation on the procedure in the text for changing repeating decimals to fractions. This method eliminates the decimal from the numerator of the fraction produced.

Express $0.2\overline{45}$ as a common fraction.

Solution Multiply the given number N by 10^k where k is the number of digits after the decimal point and before the repeating block. In this case $k = 1$, $10\,N = 2.\overline{45}$.

Then, multiply the resulting number by 10^n, where n is the number of digits in the repeating block. In this case $n = 2$. $100(10\,N) = 100(2.\overline{45})$ or $1000\,N = 245.\overline{45}$. Subtract the first result from the second.

$$1000\,N = 245.\overline{45}$$
$$\underline{10\,N = 2.\overline{45}}$$
$$990\,N = 243$$

$$N = \frac{243}{990} \quad \text{or} \quad \frac{27}{110}$$

$$0.2\overline{45} = \frac{27}{110}$$

SUGGESTED EXTENSIONS

Ask your class to solve the following.

1. Find these prices to the nearest cent.
   a. 3 for 25¢ 8¢
   b. 4 for 25¢ 6¢
   c. 6 for $1.00 $0.17
   d. 3 for $1.99 $0.66

2. Use the method in the text to express each of the following as a fraction in lowest terms.
   a. $1.4\overline{9}$ $\dfrac{3}{2}$
   b. $3.\overline{9}$ $\dfrac{4}{1}$

c. $(1.4\overline{9})(3.\overline{9})$ $\dfrac{6}{1}$

d. $1.4\overline{9} + 3.\overline{9}$ $\dfrac{11}{2}$

11-3 (pages 412–415)

KEY MATHEMATICAL IDEAS

- finding square roots which are rational

TEACHING SUGGESTIONS

Be sure your students learn the Product Property of Square Roots. It may be helpful to review the methods for factoring presented in Chapter 5. Emphasize the need to look for factors with known square roots like 4, 9, 25, etc. You may also wish to review the divisibility tests for 4, 9, and 25. Tell students that it is most efficient to concentrate on the squares of prime numbers.

SUGGESTED EXTENSION

Have your students compare the product and quotient properties of square roots with the rule of exponents for power of a product (Section 4-4). Write a rule for the power of a quotient.

$$\left(\frac{a}{b}\right)^m = \frac{a^m}{b^m}$$

11-4 (pages 416–418)

KEY MATHEMATICAL IDEAS

- finding approximations to irrational square roots

TEACHING SUGGESTIONS

Write the following square roots on the chalkboard.

$$\sqrt{36} \qquad \sqrt{50} \qquad \sqrt{64}$$

Begin to simplify them as follows.

$$\sqrt{36} = 6$$
$$\sqrt{50} = \sqrt{25 \cdot 2} = \sqrt{25} \cdot \sqrt{2}$$
$$\sqrt{64} = 8$$

Point out that since 50 is exactly half-way between 36 and 64, the square root of 50 is approximately 7. Ask, "Is 7 too large or too small?" (It is too small because $7^2 = 49$.)

Ask the class to try 7.1 by squaring it. (Answer: 50.41 so 7.1 is too large.)

Refer to the proof on page 416 that shows that $\sqrt{50}$ cannot be rational unless it is an integer. State that since $\sqrt{50}$ must be between 7.0 and 7.1 it cannot be an integer. Explain that any real number which is not rational is called *irrational,* so $\sqrt{50}$ is irrational.

Refer to the Property of Completeness and Table of Square Roots (page 526) to find the $\sqrt{50}$ to three decimal places (7.071). Have students multiply $(7.071)^2$ to show that this value for the square root of fifty is still too small. Indicate on a number line that $\sqrt{50}$ is at a point just past 7.071 but well before 7.072.

SUGGESTED EXTENSION

Have your students solve for x and approximate any answers which are not integers to three decimal places.

a. $2^x = 4$ 2

b. $2^x = 8$ 3

c. $x^2 = 8$ ±2.828

d. $3^x = 9$ 2

11-5 (*pages 419–421*)

KEY MATHEMATICAL IDEAS

• finding square roots of variable expressions
• using square roots to solve equations

TEACHING SUGGESTIONS

Write the chart below on the chalkboard with the first column filled in. Ask the class to help you complete the chart.

y	$\|y\|$	y^2	$\sqrt{y^2}$
0	0	0	0
1	1	1	1
2	2	4	2
3	3	9	3
−2	2	4	2
−3	3	9	3

Point out the fact that columns 2 and 4 are identical. Generalize that $\sqrt{y^2} = |y|$.

An alternate to the Property of Square Roots of Equal Numbers which you may wish to use, is the statement $r^2 = s^2$ if and only if $|r| = |s|$.

SUGGESTED EXTENSION

Ask your students to graph the parabola $y = x^2$ and show values of x for which $y = 9$, $y = 6$, $y = 3$, and $y = 1$. There will be positive and negative values for every positive value of y.

If $y = 9$, $x = +3$ or -3.

If $y = 6$, x is about $+2.45$ or -2.45.

If $y = 3$, x is about $+1.73$ or -1.73.

If $y = 1$, $x = +1$ or -1.

11-6 (*pages 422–427*)

KEY MATHEMATICAL IDEAS

• applying the Pythagorean theorem and its converse

TEACHING SUGGESTIONS

Most likely your students are already familiar with the Pythagorean theorem. Draw the diagram below on the chalkboard. You may wish to present the following alternate statement of the theorem, which is most appropriate to the diagram. "In any right triangle, the area of the square on the hypotenuse equals the sum of the areas of the squares on the legs." Have students count the squares to verify the theorem, $c^2 = a^2 + b^2$.

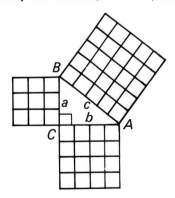

SUGGESTED EXTENSION

Ask your students to explain why the converse of the Pythagorean theorem can be extended to:

a. If the square of the longest side of a triangle is greater than the sum of the squares of the other two sides, then the angle opposite the longest side is greater than a right angle.

b. If the square of the longest side of a triangle is less than the sum of the squares of the other two sides, then the angle opposite the longest side is less than a right angle.

11-7 *(pages 428–429)*

KEY MATHEMATICAL IDEAS

- simplifying products and quotients of radicals

TEACHING SUGGESTIONS

Review the product and quotient properties of square roots. Compare the idea of a square-root radical in simplest form with the idea of a fraction in simplest form. (Fractions must have no common factors in the numerator and the denominator. Radicals must have no perfect square factors in the numerator and no denominators under radicals.)

Ask the class to compare approximating the quotient $\dfrac{2\sqrt{15}}{5\sqrt{12}}$ by simplifying it first, with approximating the quotient without simplifying it. Tell students to use the Table of Square Roots on page 526 and long division.

Answer: $\dfrac{2\sqrt{15}}{5\sqrt{12}} = \dfrac{2\sqrt{5\times 3}}{10\sqrt{3}} = \dfrac{1}{5}\sqrt{5}$; 0.447

SUGGESTED EXTENSIONS

Have the class solve the following.

1. Find the length of the altitude of a triangle if all of the sides are of length 10.

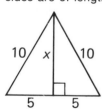

$5^2 + x^2 = 10^2$

$x^2 = 75$

$x = 5\sqrt{3}$

2. Find the ratio of the length of the side of a square to the length of the diagonal.

$\dfrac{s}{s\sqrt{2}} = \dfrac{1}{\sqrt{2}}$ or $\dfrac{\sqrt{2}}{2}$

11-8 *(pages 430–431)*

KEY MATHEMATICAL IDEAS

- simplifying sums and differences of radicals

TEACHING SUGGESTIONS

Point out that an expression such as $13\sqrt{2} + 5\sqrt{8}$ can be simplified since $5\sqrt{8} = 10\sqrt{2}$. Therefore, $13\sqrt{2} + 10\sqrt{2} = (13 + 10)\sqrt{2} = 23\sqrt{2}$.

When simplifying expressions involving quotients the following technique will clarify the application of the distributive property.

$$\sqrt{12} + \sqrt{\dfrac{25}{3}} = 2\sqrt{3} + \dfrac{5\sqrt{3}}{3} = 2\sqrt{3} + \dfrac{5}{3}\sqrt{3} =$$
$$\left(2 + \dfrac{5}{3}\right)\sqrt{3} = \dfrac{11}{3}\sqrt{3}$$

SUGGESTED EXTENSION

Challenge your students to prove that, if a, b, c, d, e, and f are positive integers, $a\sqrt{b} + c\sqrt{d}$ can be simplified to $e\sqrt{f}$ if and only if $\sqrt{bd}$ is an integer.

Square both sides, $a^2b + 2ac\sqrt{bd} + c^2d = e^2f$. Now $\sqrt{bd} = \dfrac{e^2f - c^2d - a^2b}{2ac}$ so the Closure Property for integers implies that e^2f will be an integer. Therefore, the left side will be an integer if and only if $\sqrt{bd}$ is an integer.

11-9 *(pages 432–433)*

KEY MATHEMATICAL IDEAS

- multiplying binomials containing square-root radicals

TEACHING SUGGESTIONS

Begin this lesson by reviewing methods of multiplying binomials. You can use the examples below.

$(a + b)(a - b) = a^2 - b^2$

$(a + b)(a + b) = a^2 + 2ab + b^2$

$(a - b)(a - b) = a^2 - 2ab + b^2$

$(x + r)(x + s) = x^2 + (r + s)x + rs$

$(x + r)(y + s) = xy + ry + xs + rs$

Point out the similarity between multiplying conjugates and the example $(a + b)(a - b) = a^2 - b^2$ above.

Instruct your class to use conjugates to simplify each of the following fractions.

1. $\dfrac{5}{\sqrt{3} + \sqrt{2}}$ $5\sqrt{3} - 5\sqrt{2}$

2. $\dfrac{8}{\sqrt{14} - \sqrt{10}}$ $2\sqrt{14} + 2\sqrt{10}$

3. $\dfrac{2\sqrt{3}}{2\sqrt{7} + 3\sqrt{3}}$ $4\sqrt{21} - 18$

11-10 *(pages 434–437)*

KEY MATHEMATICAL IDEAS

• solving equations involving radicals

TEACHING SUGGESTIONS

Refer to Section 3-7 on page 96 for the general method of solving equations by means of inverse operations. Point out that we can square both sides of an equation to "undo" a square root. Review the Property of Square Roots of Equal Numbers (page 419) to explain why squaring both sides does not always result in an equivalent equation. (If $a = b$ then $a^2 = b^2$, and if $a^2 = b^2$ then $a = b$ or $a = -b$.) Be sure your class understands the importance of checking every apparent root in the original equation.

SUGGESTED EXTENSION

Write the following example on the chalkboard.

$$\sqrt{16a^2 - 3} = 2a$$
$$16a^2 - 3 = 4a^2$$
$$12a^2 = 3$$
$$4a^2 = 1$$
$$a = \frac{1}{2} \ \text{ or } \ -\frac{1}{2}$$

Point out that $-\dfrac{1}{2}$ cannot be a root because $-\dfrac{1}{2}$ makes the right side negative while the left side must be positive. Have your class apply this idea to analyze the examples on page 434.

12 *Quadratic Functions*

This chapter concentrates on various methods of solving quadratic equations. Factoring and finding square roots are extended to include completing the square and the quadratic formula. Guidelines assist the student in selecting the most appropriate method.

The techniques for solving quadratic equations are applied to a variety of problems and to a thorough analysis of quadratic functions.

12-1 *(pages 443–445)*

KEY MATHEMATICAL IDEAS

• solving quadratic equations using perfect squares

TEACHING SUGGESTIONS

Review the Property of Square Roots of Equal Numbers on page 419. Remind students that this property makes it possible to solve any equation of the form $x^2 = k$, where k is nonnegative. There will be either one solution if k is zero, or two solutions if k is not zero.

Write the equations below on the chalkboard and ask your students to tell, without solving, whether each equation has one solution, two solutions, or no solution.

$x^2 = -5$ no solution
$x^2 + 6 = 0$ no solution
$(x + 2)^2 = -6$ no solution
$(x - 1)^2 = 1$ two solutions
$x^2 + 5 = 5$ one solution

SUGGESTED EXTENSION

Tell your students to imagine that $\sqrt{-1}$ and $-\sqrt{-1}$ are numbers. Instruct them to use $\sqrt{-1}$ and $-\sqrt{-1}$ to solve **a.** $x^2 = -5$ and   **b.** $x^2 + 6 = 0$.   (Hint: $-5 = (-1)(5)$)

a. $x = +\sqrt{-1}\sqrt{5}$ or $-\sqrt{-1}\sqrt{5}$
b. $x = +\sqrt{-1}\sqrt{6}$ or $-\sqrt{-1}\sqrt{6}$

12-2 (pages 446–448)

KEY MATHEMATICAL IDEAS

- using the method of completing the square

TEACHING SUGGESTIONS

Write the following statements on the chalkboard:

$$(x + a)^2 = x^2 + 2ax + a^2$$
$$(x - a)^2 = x^2 - 2ax + a^2$$

Review the fact that the square of any binomial is a trinomial whose first and last terms are squares and whose middle term is exactly twice the product of the two numbers which are squared. Demonstrate the technique of completing the square on the chalkboard with the example below.

$$x^2 + 6x + \underline{\ ?\ }$$

$$\frac{1}{2}(6) = 3$$

$$3^2 = 9$$

so $x^2 + 6x + 9$ is the answer.

Remind your students that if they add a value to one side of an equation they must add the same value to the other side of the equation.

SUGGESTED EXTENSION

Use the method of completing the square as shown below, to demonstrate that the distance from the point $(-4, 3)$ to every point (x, y) on the graph of $x^2 + 8x + y^2 - 6y = 0$ is equal to 5. Have your students read the EXTRA on page 426.

$$x^2 + 8x + \underline{\ \ } + y^2 - 6y + \underline{\ \ } = 0$$
$$x^2 + 8x + 16 + y^2 - 6y + 9 = 0 + 16 + 9$$
$$(x + 4)^2 + (y - 3)^2 = 25$$
$$\sqrt{(x + 4)^2 + (y - 3)^2} = 5$$

12-3 (pages 449–451)

KEY MATHEMATICAL IDEAS

- using the quadratic formula

TEACHING SUGGESTIONS

Explain that the quadratic formula should be memorized and used only when both factoring and completing the

square seem unreasonable.

There is one step in the derivation of the formula that your students may find hard to follow. Since

$$\sqrt{4a^2} = 2|a|,$$

the denominator of

$$\pm\sqrt{\frac{b^2 - 4ac}{4a^2}}$$

will be $2a$ if a is positive and $-2a$ if a is negative. Point out that this does not affect the final result because of the "$\pm$" sign.

SUGGESTED EXTENSION

Challenge your students to write a quadratic equation whose roots are $1 + \sqrt{2}$ and $1 - \sqrt{2}$ by reversing the steps in completing the square.

$$x = 1 \pm \sqrt{2}$$
$$x - 1 = \pm \sqrt{2}$$
$$(x - 1)^2 = 2$$
$$x^2 - 2x + 1 = 2$$
$$x^2 - 2x - 1 = 0$$

12-4 (pages 452–455)

KEY MATHEMATICAL IDEAS

- using the discriminant to analyze quadratic equations and functions

TEACHING SUGGESTIONS

Draw the graph of $y = x^2 - 4x$ on the chalkboard by substituting values for x as shown below.

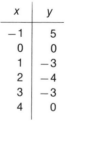
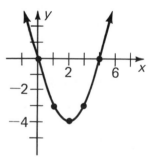

x	y
-1	5
0	0
1	-3
2	-4
3	-3
4	0

Show that the x-intercepts are the solutions of the quadratic equation $0 = x^2 - 4x$. Generalize that the x-intercepts of $y = x^2 - 4x + c$ are the solutions of the quadratic equation $0 = x^2 - 4x + c$.

Explain that the number $b^2 - 4ac$ is a critical value in the quadratic formula, since it determines the number of roots of an equation.

Refer to the chart on page 453 and describe all three cases. Point out that "$b^2 - 4ac$" is referred to as the *discriminant*.

SUGGESTED EXTENSION

Demonstrate how to use completing the square to find the vertex of the parabola $y = 2x - 3 - x^2$:

$$y + 3 = -x^2 + 2x$$
$$y + 3 = -1(x^2 - 2x + \underline{?})$$
$$y + 3 + (-1)(1) = -1(x^2 - 2x + 1)$$
$$y + 2 = -1(x - 1)^2$$

Explain that the vertex is the point where both $y + 2$ and $-1(x - 1)^2$ are zero. The vertex is $(1, -2)$.

12-5 (*pages 456–458*)

KEY MATHEMATICAL IDEAS

• choosing the best method for solving a quadratic equation

TEACHING SUGGESTIONS

Divide the class into three groups: a "factoring" group, a "completing the square" group, and a "quadratic formula" group. Give all three groups the following equations to solve as quickly as possible by their appointed methods. Ask the class to determine which method is best for solving each equation.

1. $2x^2 + 4x - 3 = 0$ $x = -1 \pm \dfrac{\sqrt{10}}{2}$

2. $x^2 + 4x + 3 = 0$ $x = -1$ or -3

3. $x^2 + 4x + 1 = 0$ $x = -2 \pm \sqrt{3}$

SUGGESTED EXTENSION

Have your class solve $ax^2 - c = 0$ by the method of completing the square.

$$x^2 = \frac{c}{a}$$
$$x^2 + 0x = \frac{c}{a}$$
$$x^2 + 0x + 0^2 = \frac{c}{a} + 0^2$$

$$(x + 0)^2 = \frac{c}{a}$$
$$x + 0 = \pm\sqrt{\frac{c}{a}}$$
$$x = 0 \pm \sqrt{\frac{c}{a}}$$

The solution set is $\left\{ \sqrt{\dfrac{c}{a}}, -\sqrt{\dfrac{c}{a}} \right\}$.

12-6 (*pages 459–463*)

KEY MATHEMATICAL IDEAS

• solving problems involving quadratic equations

TEACHING SUGGESTIONS

Review the five-step method of solving problems. Make certain that students check their answers to each verbal problem with the words of the problem so that they can reject inappropriate roots.

SUGGESTED EXTENSION

Tell your students that a formula for the number of pairs of people who can converse at a party is $\dfrac{n(n - 1)}{2}$. This can be proved with the diagram below for the case when $n = 5$. Person A can talk with 4 different persons. Person B can talk with 4 persons, etc. Point out that 5(4) will count all possible conversations twice. The number of pairs, then, is $\dfrac{5(4)}{2}$ or 10.

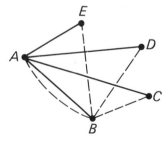

Have students use this formula to solve: "How many people are present at a party where 78 pairs of people can converse?"   13

Looking Ahead

Looking Ahead offers an introduction to geometry with some related applications of algebra. The first few sections explore the properties of lines, rays, and angles. The subsequent sections are devoted to the properties of general triangles and special triangles such as right, isosceles, equilateral, and similar triangles. The final three sections introduce the trigonometric ratios, the use of trigonometric tables, and applications of trigonometry to right triangles.

LINES AND ANGLES
(*pages 468–470*)

KEY MATHEMATICAL IDEAS

- representing points, lines, planes, and angles
- measuring and classifying angles

TEACHING SUGGESTIONS

The purpose of this section is to present some of the basic ideas that students will need in order to study geometry. Most of your students will probably be familiar with some, if not all, of the vocabulary. Ask your class to name a few objects in the classroom that can be used to represent some of the terms discussed. Examples are given below.

Term	Representation
a point	a pencil point
a line	the edge of a wall
a segment	a pencil
a ray	a pointer
an angle	the edge of an opened book
a plane	a wall

Remind students that geometric terms are abstract concepts that have no thickness.

SUGGESTED EXTENSION

Extend the interval notation defined in the SUGGESTED EXTENSIONS for Section 10-4 to include:

$[a, \infty)$ = {all numbers greater than or equal to a}

$(-\infty, c]$ = {all numbers less than or equal to c}

Ask your students to associate each of the following with a point, line, segment, or ray. (For more examples, introduce the ideas of open ray, closed ray, open segment, etc.)

a. $[2, 3]$ segment
b. $(-\infty, 1]$ ray
c. $[-3, 5]$ and $[4, 6]$ segment
d. $[-3, 5)$ or $[5, \infty)$ ray
e. $(-\infty, 0]$ or $[0, \infty)$ line
f. $(-\infty, 0]$ and $[0, \infty)$ point

PAIRS OF ANGLES
(*pages 471–473*)

KEY MATHEMATICAL IDEAS

- solving problems involving vertical angles
- solving problems involving complementary and supplementary pairs of angles

TEACHING SUGGESTIONS

Draw the following diagrams on the chalkboard, with x and y representing the measures of the angles shown.

1.
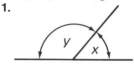

2.

3.
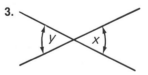

Ask students to write equations relating x and y.

1. $x + y = 180$ **2.** $x + y = 90$ **3.** $x = y$

State that Diagram 1 shows a pair of supplementary angles, Diagram 2 shows a pair of complementary angles, and Diagram 3 shows a pair of equal angles called vertical angles.

Ask your students to state whether the given pairs of angles are complementary, supplementary, or equal.

1. An angle of 35° and an angle whose complement is 35°

2. An angle whose supplement is 92° and an angle whose complement is 2°

3. An angle whose complement is 30° and an angle whose supplement is 60°

4. The complement of the supplement of a 130° angle and the complement of a 40° angle

1. complementary   2. equal
3. supplementary   4. complementary

TRIANGLES (*pages 474–476*)

KEY MATHEMATICAL IDEAS

• using properties of triangles

TEACHING SUGGESTIONS

Begin this lesson by drawing several kinds of labeled triangles on the chalkboard. Ask students to identify various parts of each triangle. Include diagrams of a right triangle, an isosceles triangle, and an equilateral triangle.

As suggested on page 474, instruct the class to make a triangle out of paper, tear off the corners, and fit them together to form a straight angle of 180°.

SUGGESTED EXTENSION

Define a "golden" triangle to be an isosceles triangle whose angles are such that the measure of each base angle is twice the measure of the third angle. Tell your class to draw a golden triangle with a base angle of 72°. Have them divide both of the base angles in half with lines and use the lines to draw a five-pointed star. Ask them to find the measure of the angle at each of the five points.

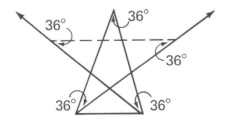

SIMILIAR TRIANGLES (*pages 477–479*)

KEY MATHEMATICAL IDEAS

• using similar triangles

TEACHING SUGGESTIONS

Photographic enlargements offer an ideal example of similiar figures. A classroom demonstration of this idea would be to project a simple figure on a large piece of white paper at two different distances from the projector. After focusing each time, allow a student to trace the figure onto the paper. If a very simple figure has been used, students will be able to show that the corresponding angles have equal measures and that the corresponding sides are proportional.

SUGGESTED EXTENSION

Have students draw a grid over a small picture using lines 5 mm apart. Tell them to copy the drawing one square at a time on a piece of graph paper (any size) to form similar figures.

TRIGONOMETRIC RATIOS (*pages 480–482*)

KEY MATHEMATICAL IDEAS

• finding the sine, cosine, and tangent of an acute angle

TEACHING SUGGESTIONS

To complete the exercises in this section, students will need to learn the definitions of sine, cosine, and tangent given on page 480.

You can explain that the values of the trigonometric ratios of an angle depend only upon the measure of the angle, by using similar right triangles. Draw the triangles below on the chalkboard.

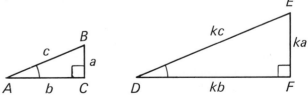

Tell your students that $\angle A = \angle D$ so the triangles are similar. Point out that k can be any positive real number. Have students compare the sine, cosine, and tangent ratios for $\angle A$ and $\angle D$. (The ratios are the same.)

SUGGESTED EXTENSIONS

Draw the triangle below on the chalkboard and ask students to find the following.

1. If $a = 4$ and $\sin A = \dfrac{8}{10}$, find c. 5

2. If $a = 4$ and $\sin A = \dfrac{4}{5}$, find b. 3

3. If $a = 3$ and $\tan B = \dfrac{2}{3}$, find b. 2

4. If $c = 10$ and $\cos A = \dfrac{8}{10}$, find a. 6

USING TRIGONOMETRIC TABLES *(pages 483–484)*

KEY MATHEMATICAL IDEAS

• using a trigonometric table to find ratios and angles

TEACHING SUGGESTIONS

Point out the table on page 527 and explain that the values have been approximated to four decimal places. Tell students that the table can be used to find trigonometric ratios given the angle measure of an acute angle, or to find the measure of an acute angle given a trigonometric ratio.

SUGGESTED EXTENSION

Instruct students to draw a graph of a sine curve for acute angles as follows.
"Let one unit on the x-axis represent 10° and one unit on the y-axis represent 0.100. Use the table of trigonometric ratios to find values of x and y."

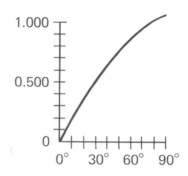

NUMERICAL TRIGONOMETRY *(pages 485–489)*

KEY MATHEMATICAL IDEAS

• using trigonometric ratios to solve problems

TEACHING SUGGESTIONS

Remind your students of the plan for solving word problems given on page 23. You will probably need to go over the terms "angle of elevation" and "angle of depression" with your students. You may wish to use the following alternate definitions.

An angle formed by a horizontal ray and another ray above the horizontal is called an angle of elevation.

An angle formed by a horizontal ray and another ray below the horizontal is called an angle of depression.

SUGGESTED EXTENSION

Draw the diagram below on the chalkboard and ask students to prove that $\dfrac{\sin A}{a} = \dfrac{\sin C}{c}$.

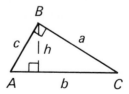

$\sin \angle A = \dfrac{h}{c}$ and $\sin C = \dfrac{h}{a}$ so $\dfrac{\sin A}{a} = \dfrac{h}{ac}$ and $\dfrac{\sin C}{c} = \dfrac{h}{ca}$ which means that $\dfrac{\sin A}{a} = \dfrac{\sin C}{c}$.

ALGEBRA

STRUCTURE AND METHOD

Book 1   new edition

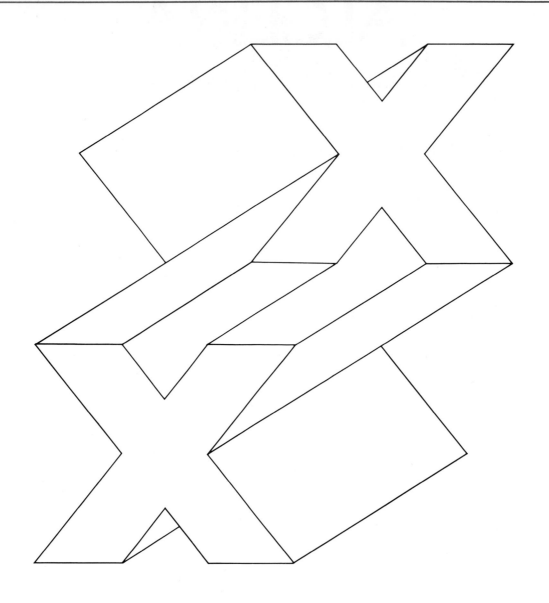

ALGEBRA

STRUCTURE AND METHOD

Book 1   new edition

Mary P. Dolciani

Richard G. Brown

Frank Ebos

William L. Cole

EDITORIAL ADVISERS
Robert H. Sorgenfrey
William Wooton

TEACHER CONSULTANTS
William T. Stanford
Lois B. Whitman

HOUGHTON MIFFLIN COMPANY · BOSTON

Atlanta   Dallas   Geneva, Ill.   Hopewell, N.J.   Palo Alto   Toronto

THE AUTHORS

Mary P. Dolciani, Professor of Mathematical Sciences, Hunter College of the City University of New York.

Richard G. Brown, Mathematics Teacher, The Phillips Exeter Academy, Exeter, New Hampshire.

Frank Ebos, Professor of Mathematics Education, University of Toronto.

William L. Cole, Associate Professor of Mathematics Education, Michigan State University.

EDITORIAL ADVISERS

Robert H. Sorgenfrey, Professor of Mathematics, University of California, Los Angeles.

William Wooton, former Professor of Mathematics, Los Angeles Pierce College.

TEACHER CONSULTANTS

William T. Stanford, Coordinator of Mathematics, Waco Independent School District, Waco, Texas.

Lois B. Whitman, Mathematics Teacher, James Monroe High School, Sepulveda, California.

Copyright © 1984, 1981 by Houghton Mifflin Company

Printed in U.S.A.

ISBN: 0-395-34092-6

CONTENTS

3 *Solving Equations*

4 *Polynomials and Problem Solving*

5 *Factoring Polynomials*

6 *Fractions*

7 *Applying Fractions*

8 *Linear Equations and Systems*

9 *Introduction to Functions*

10 *Inequalities*

11   *Rational and Irrational Numbers*

12   *Quadratic Functions*

Looking Ahead

SYMBOLS

		Page
$\cdot$	$\times$ (times)	1
$=$	equals, is equal to	2
$\neq$	is not equal to	2
( )	parentheses—a grouping symbol	5
[ ]	brackets—a grouping symbol	5
π	pi, a number approximately equal to $\frac{22}{7}$	7
$\therefore$	therefore	9
$\in$	is a member of, belongs to	10
$-$	negative	29
$+$	positive	29
$<$	is less than	33
$>$	is greater than	33
$-a$	opposite or additive inverse of a	43
$\|a\|$	absolute value of a	44
$\frac{1}{b}$	reciprocal or multiplicative inverse of b	61
$\stackrel{?}{=}$	is this statement true?	73
$\emptyset$	empty set, null set	100
$a:b$	ratio of a to b	235
(a, b)	ordered pair whose first component is a and second component is b	275
$f(x)$	f of x, the value of f at x	332
$\cap$	the intersection of	380
$\cup$	the union of	380
$\geq$	is greater than or equal to	385
$\leq$	is less than or equal to	385
$\approx$	is approximately equal to	410
$\sqrt{\ }$	principal square root	412
$\overleftrightarrow{AB}$	line AB	468
$\overline{AB}$	segment AB	468
AB	the length of $\overline{AB}$	468
$\overrightarrow{AB}$	ray AB	468
$\angle$	angle	468
$^\circ$	degree(s)	469
$\triangle$	triangle	474
$\sim$	is similar to	477
$\cos A$	cosine of A	480
$\sin A$	sine of A	480
$\tan A$	tangent of A	480

Metric Units of Measure

Length:

cm	centimeter
m	meter
km	kilometer

Area:

cm^2	square centimeter
m^2	square meter
km^2	square kilometer
ha	hectare

Time:

s	second
min	minute
h	hour

Speed:

m/s	meters per second
km/h	kilometers per hour

Mass:

g	gram
kg	kilogram

Volume:

cm^3	cubic centimeter
mL	milliliter
L	liter

Temperature: °C degrees Celsius

WHY STUDY ALGEBRA?

The study of algebra can help you in two ways:
(1) It will help you organize your thoughts to solve mathematical problems that you will meet in your everyday life.
(2) It will prepare you to continue your studies in mathematics and the sciences.

Whatever you choose to do in the future—from teaching children to running a business to doing scientific or social research—you will need to use mathematics.

Information about some possible careers appears throughout the book in the Career Notes: Programmer (page 20); Carpenter (page 35); Nutritionist (page 139); Meteorologist (page 182); Accountant (page 231); Bilingual Math Teacher (page 267); Drafter (page 279); Agricultural Engineer (page 323); Darkroom Technician (page 385); Architect (page 458).

You may think that calculators and computers will do all your problem solving for you, but they can only help. Machines do not think; *you* must do the thinking. If you know what steps to take—what numbers and operations to use—then calculators and computers can be made to do a great deal of the work for you.

The study of physics, biology, astronomy, and social sciences requires mathematics. The caption that accompanies the photograph at the opening of each chapter suggests one of the scientific, natural, or social phenomena that are studied using mathematics. Although an understanding of some applications requires a thorough study of advanced concepts, there are many applications that you can understand. For example, see the Applications about Electrical Energy (page 94), Optics (page 249), Gear Ratios (page 268), Nutrition Labeling (page 397), and Newton's Law of Motion (page 463).

About the Photo

The table on page 1 lists specific cases of the formula $v = 9.8n$, where v is the velocity, or speed, of the diver after n seconds. Note that the formula does not account for air resistance and becomes less accurate as the skydivers' speed increases. The number 9.8 is called the "gravitational constant." Different gravitational constants are associated with different extraterrestrial objects.

   Your students may be interested in examining the following hypothetical situation: Suppose the skydivers were approaching the moon instead of Earth. The applicable formula would be $v = 1.6n$. Since the moon has less mass than Earth, its gravitational constant, 1.6, is less than 9.8. Thus the skydivers would accelerate more slowly, as shown by the table below. Because the lack of atmosphere at the moon's surface eliminates air resistance, the formula $v = 1.6n$ gives an accurate measure of the speed of skydivers approaching the moon.

Seconds	Speed in m/s
1	1.6×1
2	1.6×2
3	1.6×3
4	1.6×4

Sky divers must be aware of the distance they can fall before having to open their parachutes in order to land safely. See the chart on the facing page that shows the speed at which a sky diver falls in the first several seconds after jumping.

1

INTRODUCTION TO ALGEBRA

Teaching References

Lesson Commentary,
   pp. T63–T66

Assignment Guide,
   pp. T48–T49

Supplementary Materials

   Practice Masters 1–3

   Progress Tests 1–3

   Computer Activities
   1 *Secret Codes*
   2 *Generating Sequences*
   3 *Sum of Odd Numbers*

Extra Practice, pp. 491–492

Alternate Test, p. T12

VARIABLES AND EQUATIONS

1-1 *Variables*

OBJECTIVE To simplify numerical expressions and evaluate variable expressions.

A skydiver fell for several seconds before the parachute opened. The table below shows the downward speed one, two, three, and four seconds after the start of the fall.

Number of seconds of fall	Speed in meters per second
1	9.8×1
2	9.8×2
3	9.8×3
4	9.8×4

Each of the expressions for speed fits the pattern

$$9.8 \times n$$

where the letter n stands for 1, 2, 3, or 4. We call n a *variable*.

A **variable** is a symbol used to represent one or more numbers. The numbers are called the **values of the variable.**

1

An expression, such as $9.8 \times n$, which contains a variable is called a **variable expression.** Expressions, such as 9.8×2, which name a particular number are called **numerical expressions** or **numerals.**

When you write a product that contains a variable, you usually omit the multiplication symbol.

$$9.8 \times n \text{ is usually written } 9.8n.$$

$$y \times z \text{ is usually written } yz.$$

In numerical expressions for products like 9.8×2, you must use a multiplication symbol to avoid confusion. The raised dot $\cdot$ is also used as a multiplication sign.

$$9.8 \times 2 \text{ can be written } 9.8 \cdot 2.$$

The number named by a numerical expression is called the **value of the expression.** Since the expressions $2 + 5$ and 7 name the same number, they have the same value. To show that these expressions have the same value, you use the *equals sign,* $=$. You write

$$2 + 5 = 7$$

and say "two plus five *equals* (or *is equal to*) seven." Of course, 7 is the *simplest,* or most common, name for the number seven.

The symbol $\neq$ means "is *not* equal to." You write $2 + 5 \neq 8$ to show that the expressions $2 + 5$ and 8 do not have the same value.

Replacing a numerical expression by the simplest name of its value is called **simplifying the expression.** In simplifying a numerical expression, you use the following principle.

SUBSTITUTION PRINCIPLE

Changing the numeral by which a number is named in an expression does not change the value of the expression.

EXAMPLE 1   Simplify.   **a.** $(48 \div 6) + 2$ **b.** $48 \div (6 + 2)$

SOLUTION   The parentheses ( ) show how the numerals in the expression are to be grouped.

  a. $(48 \div 6) + 2 = 8 + 2 = 10$ **b.** $48 \div (6 + 2) = 48 \div 8 = 6$

Replacing each variable in a variable expression by a given value and simplifying the result is called **evaluating the expression** or **finding its value.**

2   CHAPTER 1

EXAMPLE 2 Find the value of $(9x) - (4 + y)$ if $x = 3$ and $y = 5$.

SOLUTION Replace x with 3 and y with 5, and insert the necessary multiplication symbol. Then simplify the result.

$$(9x) - (4 + y) = (9 \times 3) - (4 + 5)$$
$$= 27 - 9$$
$$= 18$$

Oral Exercises

State whether or not each statement is true. Give a reason for your answer.

SAMPLE 1 $3 \times 4 = 6 + 6$ **SOLUTION** True, because 3×4 and $6 + 6$ both name the number 12.

SAMPLE 2 $2 \times 5 = 2 + 5$ **SOLUTION** False, because $2 \times 5 = 10$, whereas $2 + 5 = 7$.

1. $8 \times 6 = 6 \times 8$ True; $48 = 48$

2. $7 \times 0 = 0 \times 5$ True; $0 = 0$

3. $6 \div 1 = 1 \div 6$ False; $6 \neq \frac{1}{6}$

4. $100 \times \frac{1}{5} = 100 \times 0.2$ True; $20 = 20$

5. $3 \times (7 \times 2) = (3 \times 7) \times 2$ True; $42 = 42$

6. $(9 - 2) - 2 = 9 - (2 - 2)$ False; $5 \neq 9$

7. $0.25 \times 36 = 2.5 \times 3.6$ True; $9 = 9$

8. $\frac{(6 - 3)}{3} = 6 - 1$ False; $1 \neq 5$

Simplify each expression.

9. $6 + (4 \times 3)$ 18

10. $(6 + 4) \times 3$ 30

11. $18 - (2 \times 5)$ 8

12. $(18 - 2) \times 5$ 80

13. $\frac{(22 - 10)}{4}$ 3

14. $\frac{(15 + 3)}{(8 - 2)}$ 3

State the value of each expression if $x = 1$, $y = 2$, and $z = 3$.

15. $6y$ 12

16. $8x$ 8

17. $z - 3$ 0

18. $7 - z$ 4

19. $\frac{4}{y}$ 2

20. $(yz) + x$ 7

21. $z + (xy)$ 5

22. $(4y) - 5$ 3

23. $2 \cdot (y + 1)$ 6

24. $3 \cdot (2 - x)$ 3

25. $\frac{(x + y)}{z}$ 1

26. $\frac{x}{(z - y)}$ 1

Written Exercises

Simplify each expression.

A **1.** $(9 - 4) + 5$ 10

2. $7 + (19 - 2)$ 24

3. $4 \times (12 + 3)$ 60

4. $(15 - 7) \times 8$ 64

5. $(9 + 18) \div 3$ 9

6. $9 + (18 \div 3)$ 15

7. $6 - (0 \times 2)$ 6

8. $4 - (15 \div 5)$ 1

9. $(7 \times 18) + (3 \times 18)$ 180

10. $(14 \times 9) - (4 \times 9)$ 90

11. $(22 + 8) \div (60 \div 4)$ 2

12. $(70 \div 10) \div (7 \times 1)$ 1

INTRODUCTION TO ALGEBRA   **3**

Supplementary Material

Computer Activity
Secret Codes
  Using a computer program either to decode a message or to create original secret-coded messages is one example of a computer's ability to handle systematically a non-numerical process.

Suggested Assignments

Minimum
  3/1–17, 21, 23, 26, 33
Average
  3/1–37 odd
Maximum
  3/1–33 odd, 34–38

Additional A Exercises

Simplify each expression.

1. $(5 + 2) \times 3$ 21

2. $(4 \times 7) - 8$ 20

3. $\frac{(10 + 29)}{3}$ 13

State the value of each expression if $a = 2$, $b = 3$, and $c = 5$.

4. $(a \times b) + c$ 11

5. $c - (a + b)$ 0

6. $(a + b) \div c$ 1

Evaluate each expression if $r = 2, s = 5, t = 7, u = 0, v = 1,$ and $w = 8$.

13. rs 10

14. tu 0

15. $w - (vr)$ 6

16. $v + (ts)$ 36

17. $(3r) + (3s)$ 21

18. $(3s) - (2r)$ 11

19. $(wt) - (5s)$ 31

20. $(sw) + (vr)$ 42

21. $(4v) \cdot (r + t)$ 36

22. $(5t) \cdot (w + u)$ 280

23. $\dfrac{(w + r)}{(t - r)}$ 2

24. $\dfrac{(w + v)}{(s - r)}$ 3

B 25. $s \cdot (w - t) \cdot \dfrac{ur}{v}$ 0

26. $(r + w) - \dfrac{(vt)}{(s + r)}$ 9

27. $\dfrac{(r + s)}{(tv)} + (rwu)$ 1

28. $(rw) + (rs) - (t + u + v)$ 18

Simplify the expression on each side of the _?_. Then make a true statement by replacing the _?_ with the symbol $=$ or $\neq$.

29. $(7 + 5) \times (7 - 5)$ _?_ $(7 \times 7) - (5 \times 5)$ $=$

30. $(8 + 4) \times (8 + 4)$ _?_ $(8 \times 8) + (4 \times 4)$ $\neq$

31. $(6 - 1) \times (6 - 1)$ _?_ $(6 \times 6) - (1 \times 1)$ $\neq$

32. $(9 + 2) \times (9 - 2)$ _?_ $(9 \times 9) - (2 \times 2)$ $=$

Evaluate each expression shown in color for the given values of the variables.

33. lw (Area of a rectangle)   336
    if $l = 28$ and $w = 12$

34. $(2l) + (2w)$ (Perimeter of a rectangle)   130
    if $l = 40$ and $w = 25$

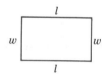

35. $a + b + c$ (Perimeter of a triangle)   40
    if $a = 8, b = 15,$ and $c = 17$

36. $\dfrac{1}{2}ab$ (Area of a right triangle)   96
    if $a = 12$ and $b = 16$

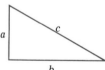

C 37. Prt (Simple interest on a loan of P dollars) $720
    if $P = 6000$ (dollars), $r = 12\%$ (per year), and $t = 1$ (year)

38. $P + (Prt)$ (Amount of an investment of P dollars at simple interest) $3700
    if $P = 2500$ (dollars), $r = 8\%$ (per year), and $t = 6$ (years)

1-2 *Grouping Symbols*

OBJECTIVE To simplify expressions with and without grouping symbols.

Parentheses have been used to show you how to group the numerals in an expression. Different groupings may produce expressions that name different numbers.

$$(48 \div 6) + 2 \text{ means } 8 + 2, \text{ or } 10.$$
$$48 \div (6 + 2) \text{ means } 48 \div 8, \text{ or } 6.$$

A **grouping symbol** is a device, such as parentheses, used to enclose an expression. Brackets [ ] are also used.

Multiplication symbols are often omitted from expressions with grouping symbols. For example,

$$5 \times (4 - 1) = 5(4 - 1) = 5(3) = 15.$$

Note that 5(3) stands for 5×3. Other ways to write this product using parentheses are (5)3 and (5)(3).

In a fraction such as $\dfrac{12 + 8}{6 - 2}$ the bar is a grouping symbol as well as a division symbol.

$$\frac{12 + 8}{6 - 2} = \frac{20}{4} = 20 \div 4 = 5$$

Throughout your work in algebra you will use these symbols:

GROUPING SYMBOLS		
Parentheses	Brackets	Fraction Bar
$5(4 - 1)$	$5[4 - 1]$	$\dfrac{12 + 8}{6 - 2}$

If an expression contains more than one grouping symbol, first simplify the numeral in the innermost grouping symbol. Then work toward the outermost grouping symbol until the simplest expression is found.

EXAMPLE 1 Simplify $9 - [21 \div (3 + 4)]$.

SOLUTION $9 - [21 \div (3 + 4)] = 9 - [21 \div 7] = 9 - 3 = 6$

INTRODUCTION TO ALGEBRA **5**

Teaching Suggestions p. T63

Suggested Extensions p. T64

Chalkboard Examples

Simplify.

1. $10 - [24 \div (3 + 5)]$
$10 - [24 \div 8] =$
$10 - 3 = 7$

2. $(5 - 3) \times [(8 \times 2) - 4]$
$(5 - 3) \times [16 - 4] =$
$2 \times 12 = 24$

3. $10 - 4 \times 2$
$10 - 8 = 2$

4. $8 + 13 - 8 \div 2$
$8 + 13 - 4 = 21 - 4 = 17$

5. $8 \div 4 \div 2 \quad 2 \div 2 = 1$

6. $\dfrac{2 + 24 \div 4}{64 \div 8}$
$\dfrac{2 + 6}{8} = \dfrac{8}{8} = 1$

If $a = 2$, $b = 6$, and $c = 20$, evaluate each of the following.

7. $5a + 2b - c$
$5(2) + 2(6) - 20 =$
$10 + 12 - 20 =$
$22 - 20 = 2$

8. $\dfrac{2a + c}{b - a}$
$\dfrac{2(2) + 20}{6 - 2} = \dfrac{4 + 20}{4} =$
$\dfrac{24}{4} = 6$

When there are no grouping symbols, you take the following steps to simplify an expression.

Step 1 Do all multiplications and divisions in order from left to right.

Step 2 Do all additions and subtractions in order from left to right.

$$8 + \underline{5 \times 6}$$
$$\underline{8 + \quad 30}$$
$$38$$

$$9 + 4 - \underline{6 \times 2} \div 4$$
$$9 + 4 - \underline{\quad 12 \quad \div 4}$$
$$\underline{9 + 4 - \quad\quad 3}$$
$$\underline{13 \quad - \quad\quad 3}$$
$$10$$

EXAMPLE 2 Evaluate $\dfrac{3r + 7s}{5r - s}$ if $r = 2$ and $s = 6$.

SOLUTION Replace r with 2 and s with 6, and insert the necessary multiplication symbols. Then simplify the result.

$$\frac{3r + 7s}{5r - s} = \frac{3\,(2) + 7\,(6)}{5\,(2) - 6}$$
$$= \frac{6 + 42}{10 - 6}$$
$$= \frac{48}{4} = 12$$

Oral Exercises

In Exercises 1–8, the given expression indicates one or more operations to be performed. Describe the operation(s) for each expression.

SAMPLE $4(x + 2)$ **SOLUTION 1** "Multiply 4 by the sum of x and 2."

  SOLUTION 2 "Add x and 2, and then multiply the sum by 4."

1. $5x$ **2.** $y - 4$ **3.** $3 + 2x$ **4.** $5z - 8$

5. $7(z + 6)$ **6.** $4(9x - 2)$ **7.** $\dfrac{y - x}{z}$ **8.** $\dfrac{y}{z + x}$

9–16. In Exercises 1–8, evaluate each expression if $x = 3$, $y = 15$, and $z = 2$.

9. 15 **10.** 11 **11.** 9 **12.** 2
13. 56 **14.** 100 **15.** 6 **16.** 3

Written Exercises

Evaluate each expression if $a = 1$, $b = 3$, $c = 5$, $x = 0$, $y = 1$, and $z = 6$.

A **1.** $bx + y$ 1 **2.** $cy + a$ 6 **3.** $z - ab$ 3 **4.** $ac - y$ 4

  5. $6z + by$ 39 **6.** $x(a - y) + c$ 5 **7.** $(z - y)c + a$ 26 **8.** $9c - bz$ 27

9. $(2c - 3b)(z + y)$ 7

10. $(c - 4a)(4y - b)$ 1

11. $\dfrac{ab + c}{y + 3}$ 2

12. $\dfrac{cz - 4y}{15 - 2a}$ 2

13. $b(z - c) + \dfrac{yz}{b}$ 5

14. $c(b + y) - az$ 14

Simplify each expression.

15. $\dfrac{6 \times 3 + 5 \times 3 \times 3}{10 - 2 - 1}$ 9

16. $\dfrac{32 \div 8 + 3}{2 + 5}$ 1

17. $(25 - 4 + 9 \div 3) \div (12 \div 6)$ 12

18. $12(11 - 7) - 30 \div (6 - 3)$ 38

Evaluate each expression shown in color for the given values of the variables.

19. $2(a + b)$ (Perimeter of a parallelogram) 61.4
if $a = 5.5$ and $b = 25.2$

20. $2a + b + c$ (Perimeter of an isosceles trapezoid) 254
if $a = 54$, $b = 98$, and $c = 48$

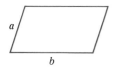
Ex. 19

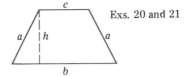
Exs. 20 and 21

21. $\frac{1}{2}h(b + c)$ (Area of a trapezoid) 937.5
if $h = 25$, $b = 50$, and $c = 25$

22. $(\pi r)r$ (Area of a circle) 616
if $r = 14$. Use $\dfrac{22}{7}$ as an approximate value for π.

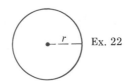
Ex. 22

B 23. $2(r + h) + \pi r$ (Perimeter of a Norman window) 11.14
if $r = 1.00$ and $h = 3.00$. Use 3.14 as an
approximate value for π.

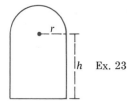
Ex. 23

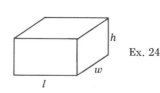
Ex. 24

24. $2(lw + wh + lh)$ (Surface area of a rectangular solid) 1256
if $l = 18$, $w = 16$, and $h = 10$

INTRODUCTION TO ALGEBRA   7

Simplify the expression on each side of the __?__. Then make a true statement by replacing the __?__ with the symbol = or ≠.

25. $\dfrac{12 \times 4}{6 + 2}$ __?__ $\dfrac{6 \times 2}{3 + 1}$ ≠

26. $\dfrac{39 + 6}{15 \times 3}$ __?__ $(24 \div 8) - 2$ =

27. $3[2(2 + 3)]$ __?__ $(6 \times 6) - 6$ =

28. $4[24 \div (6 + 2)]$ __?__ $4[(24 \div 6) + 2]$ ≠

29. $\dfrac{(8 \times 6) \div 12}{4 - (6 \div 2)} + 1$ __?__ $25 - \dfrac{38 + 4}{10 - 8}$ ≠

30. $1 + \dfrac{30 - 3}{5 + 4}$ __?__ $\dfrac{(8 \times 6) - 8}{(54 \div 3) + 2} + 2$ =

C 31. $([(2 \times 3) + 5]3)3 - 6$ __?__ $2 \times 3 \times 3 \times 3 + 5 \times 3 \times 3 - 6$ =

32. $([(5 \times 2) - 3]2)2 + 9$ __?__ $5 \times 2 \times 2 - 3 \times 2 \times 2 + 9$ ≠

33. $(1 \times 1) + (2 \times 2) + (3 \times 3) + (4 \times 4)$ __?__ $\dfrac{4(4 + 1)[(2 \times 4) + 1]}{6}$ =

34. $[(3 \times 1) + 1] + [(3 \times 2) + 1] + [(3 \times 3) + 1]$ __?__ $2(3 \times 3) + 3$ =

35. $\dfrac{[7 - (3 \times 2)] + (4 \times 6)}{[(24 \div 4) + 2] - 3}$ __?__ $[2 + (2 \times 2) - (30 \div 6)] \times \dfrac{12 - 2}{5 - 2}$ ≠

36. $\dfrac{78 - [(11 \times 18) \div 3]}{[(8 \times 3) + 8] - (4 \times 5)}$ __?__ $\dfrac{(16 \times 6) \div 3}{(32 \times 2) \div 8} - \dfrac{20 - 4}{2 \times 4}$ ≠

Calculator Key-In _____

Does your calculator follow the steps for simplifying an expression stated on page 6? Experiment with your calculator by entering the following example exactly as it appears here:

$$5 + 2 \times 3 =$$

If your calculator displays the answer 11, it followed the order of operations you learned for simplifying expressions: multiplication before addition. Your calculator has an algebraic operating system. The answer 11 is correct.

If your calculator displays the answer 21, it performed the addition and the multiplication in the order in which you pressed the keys. One way to get the correct answer on your calculator is to multiply 2 and 3 first and then add 5, just as you would if you were using pencil and paper.

Use a calculator to simplify each expression.

1. $17 - 2.5 \times 6.8$ 0

2. $1.8 + 0.6 \div 0.3$ 3.8

3. $0.25 \div 0.5 \times 0.6 - 0.2$ 0.1

4. $369 \times 0.75 + 369 \times 0.25$ 369

5. $308 \div 11 \times 15873 - 7 \times 5291 \times 3$ 333,333

1-3 *Equations*

OBJECTIVE To find solution sets of open sentences.

Here are three equations:

$$8 - 2 = 6 \qquad 3x + 1 = 7 \qquad y + 2 = 2 + y$$
$$\text{the two sides} \qquad \text{the two sides} \qquad \text{the two sides}$$

An **equation** is formed by placing an equals sign between two numerical or variable expressions, called the **sides** of the equation.

Equations containing variables are called **open sentences.** The given set of numbers that a variable may represent is called the **domain** of the variable. When you replace each variable in an open sentence by one of the numbers in its domain, you obtain a true statement or a false statement.

You may use *braces* { } to show a set of numbers. A short way to write "the set whose members are 1, 2, and 3" is $\{1, 2, 3\}$.

EXAMPLE 1 The domain of x is $\{1, 2, 3\}$. Find any values in the domain of x for which $3x + 1 = 7$ becomes a true statement.

SOLUTION Replace x in turn by 1, 2, and 3.

$$3x + 1 = 7$$
$$3(1) + 1 = 7 \quad \text{False}$$
$$3(2) + 1 = 7 \quad \text{True}$$
$$3(3) + 1 = 7 \quad \text{False}$$

$\therefore$ (read "therefore") the required value of x is 2. *Answer*

Any value of a variable that converts an open sentence into a true statement is called a **solution** or **root** of the sentence, and is said to **satisfy** the sentence.

The set of *all* solutions of an open sentence is called the **solution set** of the sentence. Finding the solution set is called **solving** the sentence.

You may use braces to show a solution set. Thus, for Example 1, you may say either

"The solution is 2" or "The solution set is {2}."

You can see that the solution set of the equation $x + 2 = 2 + x$ is the set of *all* numbers, because the sentence is true no matter what number is substituted for x. If you are asked to solve this equation *over the domain* $\{0, 1, 2, 3\}$, however, you should state that the solution set is $\{0, 1, 2, 3\}$.

INTRODUCTION TO ALGEBRA   9

Teaching Suggestions p. T64

Suggested Extensions p. T64

Chalkboard Examples

1. Solve the equation $n + 8 = 12$ if the domain of n is $\{1, 2, 3, 4, 5\}$. $\{4\}$

2. Solve the equation $1 + x = x + 1$ if $x \in \{1, 2, 3\}$. $\{1, 2, 3\}$

3. Solve the equation $y - 2 = 7 - y$ if the domain of y is $\{3, 4, 5\}$. No solution

4. Solve the equation $\frac{1}{2}x = 1$ if $x \in \{0, 1, 2, 3\}$. $\{2\}$

5. Solve the equation $7 - z = 2$ if the domain of z is $\{4, 5, 6, 7\}$. $\{5\}$

6. Solve the equation $n \div n = 1$ if $n \in \{2, 4, 6\}$. $\{2, 4, 6\}$

Supplementary Materials

Progress Test 1

Computer Activity 3
Sum of Odd Numbers
  By rapidly performing lengthy or tedious arithmetic operations, the computer frees the student to look for generalizations and possibly derive formulas concerning the results.

Suggested Assignments

Minimum
  10/1–27 odd
  7/20–30 even

Average
  10/1–27 odd
  7/20, 22, 24, 32

Maximum
  10/1–31 odd
  7/32, 34, 36

Additional A Exercises

Solve each equation if
$x \in \{0, 1, 2, 3, 4, 5, 6\}$. If
there is no solution, write
"no solution."

1. $x + 2 = 5$ {3}

2. $2x = 2$ {1}

3. $15 + x = 15$ {0}

4. $x - 3 = x - 3$
  {0, 1, 2, 3, 4, 5, 6}

5. $x + 3 = x + 1$
  No solution

6. $14 \div x = 7$ {2}

EXAMPLE 2 Solve the equation $y(3 - y) = 2$ if $y \in \{0, 1, 2, 3\}$ (read "y *is a member of* (or *belongs to*) the set whose members are 0, 1, 2, and 3").

SOLUTION Replace y in turn by 0, 1, 2, and 3.

$$y(3 - y) = 2$$
$0(3 - 0) = 2$ False
$1(3 - 1) = 2$ True
$2(3 - 2) = 2$ True
$3(3 - 3) = 2$ False

∴ the solution set is $\{1, 2\}$. *Answer*

Oral Exercises

Solve each equation if $x \in \{0, 1, 2, 3, 4, 5, 6\}$. If there is no solution over the given domain, state "no solution."

1. $x + 1 = 5$ {4}   **2.** $x - 1 = 3$ {4}   **3.** $3x = 6$ {2}   **4.** $x \div 2 = 1$ {2}

5. $x - 2 = 4$ {6}   **6.** $x + 3 = 6$ {3}   **7.** $x + 1 = 1 + x$ **8.** $x + 1 = x$

9. $2x = x + x$ **10.** $3x = x + 2$ {1}   **11.** $x + x = 0$ {0}   **12.** $(6 - x)x = 0$
                                                                              {0, 6}

7. {0, 1, 2, 3, 4, 5, 6}   **8.** No solution   **9.** {0, 1, 2, 3, 4, 5, 6}

Written Exercises

Solve each equation if $x \in \{0, 1, 2, 3, 4, 5, 6\}$.

A **1.** $x + 4 = 9$ {5}   **2.** $7 + x = 9$ {2}   **3.** $x - 1 = 4$ {5}   **4.** $x - 3 = 1$ {4}

5. $4 - x = 3$ {1}   **6.** $5 - x = 2$ {3}   **7.** $2x = 10$ {5}   **8.** $3x = 12$ {4}

9. $3x = 9$ {3}   **10.** $2x = 12$ {6}   **11.** $x \div 2 = 1$ {2}   **12.** $x \div 2 = 2$ {4}

13. $\frac{1}{2}x = 3$ {6}   **14.** $\frac{1}{3}x = 1$ {3}   **15.** $x - x = 0$ **16.** $x \cdot x = 1$
                                                                   {0, 1, 2, 3, 4, 5, 6}   {1}

Solve each equation over the domain $\{0, 1, 2, 3, 4, 5, 6, 7, 8, 9\}$.

B **17.** $2a + 7 = 15$ {4}   **18.** $3b - 2 = 13$ {5}   **19.** $12 = 8c - 4$ {2}

20. $14 = 6d - 4$ {3}   **21.** $7 + 7r = 49$ {6}   **22.** $4 + 4s = 40$ {9}

23. $2x = x + 4$ {4}   **24.** $4t = t(4)$ {0, 1, 2, ..., 9}   **25.** $3z = z(z)$ {0, 3}

26. $x(9 - x) = 0$ {0, 9}   **27.** $(9 - t)(8 + t)t = 0$ {0, 9}   **28.** $8s = (2s)(2s)(2s)$
                                                                           {0, 1}

Write an equation for which the solution set over the domain $\{0, 1, 2, 3, 4\}$ is the given set. Answers may vary for Exercises 29–32.

C **29.** {2}   **30.** {0}   **31.** {0, 1, 2, 3, 4}   **32.** {0, 4} $x(x) = 4x$
     $x + 3 = 5$ $9 - x = 9$ $2x = x + x$

10   *CHAPTER 1*

Self-Test 1

VOCABULARY   variable (p. 1)
variable (p. 1)
value of a variable (p. 1)
variable expression (p. 2)
value of a numerical
  expression (p. 2)
simplify an expression (p. 2)
substitution principle (p. 2)
evaluate an expression (p. 2)
grouping symbol (p. 5)

equation (p. 9)
open sentence (p. 9)
domain of a variable (p. 9)
solution (p. 9)
root (p. 9)
satisfy an open sentence (p. 9)
solution set (p. 9)
solve an open sentence (p. 9)

Evaluate each expression if $x = 6$, $y = 3$, and $z = 5$.

1. $(2x + 1) + (3y - z)$ **2.** $\dfrac{x}{y} \cdot z$ Obj. 1-1, p. 1

3. $x - 2(z - y)$ **4.** $\dfrac{3(x + 4)}{5y - z}$ Obj. 1-2, p. 5

Solve each equation if $x \in \{0, 1, 2, 3, 4\}$.

5. $x + 1 = 3$ **6.** $12 - 2x = 4$ Obj. 1-3, p. 9

Check your answers with those at the back of the book.

Quick Quiz

Evaluate each expression if $a = 7$, $b = 2$, and $c = 4$.

1. $(3a - 5) + (4b - c)$ 20

2. $\dfrac{c}{b} \cdot a$ 14

3. $a - 3(c - b)$ 1

4. $\dfrac{2(a + b)}{5b - c}$ 3

Solve each equation if $x \in \{0, 1, 2, 3, 4\}$

5. $x + 4 = 6$ 2

6. $11 - 3x = 2$ 3

฀istorical ฀ote

Why We Call It "Algebra"

In ninth-century Baghdad, the mathematician and as-tronomer Muhammed ibn-Musa al-Khwarizmi wrote a mathematical treatise entitled *hisab al-jabr w'al muqabalah*, which means "the science of reduction and comparison" and which probably refers to the solving of equations. For the first time, algebra was systematically discussed as a distinct branch of mathematics. Al-Khwarizmi's book made its way to Europe and in the twelfth century was translated into Latin, the common language of European scholars. As the book was stud-ied throughout Europe, the word "al-jabr" in the title grew into "algebra," which is what this branch of math-ematics is called today.

INTRODUCTION TO ALGEBRA   **11**

Chalkboard Examples

Represent each word phrase by a variable expression.

1. Four times the number
$4n$

2. The number increased by six $n + 6$

3. Thirteen decreased by the number $13 - n$

Represent each expression by a word phrase.

4. $6 + 4 \times 2$
Six increased by the product of four and two

5. $5(4 + n)$
The product of five and the sum of four and a number

Represent each word sentence by an equation.

6. Seven less than a number is three.
$n - 7 = 3$

7. Twice a number increased by three is fifteen.
$2n + 3 = 15$

Represent each equation by a word sentence.

8. $n + 8 = 12$
A number increased by eight is twelve.

9. $17 - 2n = 5$
Seventeen decreased by twice a number is five.

(continued)

APPLICATIONS

1-4 *Words into Symbols:*
Numerical Relationships

OBJECTIVE   To represent numerical relationships stated in words by mathematical expressions or equations.

To apply algebra, you must often translate word phrases into numerical or variable expressions, and word sentences into equations.

Suppose you think of two numbers, one five more than the other. If x stands for the smaller number, then the greater number is represented by

$$x + 5.$$

EXAMPLE 1   Represent each word phrase by a variable expression.

    a. Five less than a number x

    b. Five times a number x

SOLUTION   **a.** $x - 5$ **b.** $5x$

EXAMPLE 2   Represent each word sentence by an equation.

    a. The sum of the number n and eight is thirty-three.

    b. Three is seven less than twice the number n.

SOLUTION   **a.** $n + 8 = 33$ **b.** $3 = 2n - 7$

The numbers

$$0, 1, 2, 3, 4, \ldots$$

are called the **whole numbers.** The three dots are read "and so on" and indicate that the list continues without end. When you count by *ones* from any whole number, you obtain **consecutive numbers.** For example, 7, 8, and 9 are three consecutive numbers.

EXAMPLE 3   A whole number is represented by n.

    a. Write the next three whole numbers after n.

    b. Write an equation which states that the sum of four consecutive numbers is 70, given that the first number is n.

SOLUTION   **a.** $n + 1, \quad n + 2, \quad n + 3$

              b. $n + (n + 1) + (n + 2) + (n + 3) = 70$

12   *CHAPTER 1*

Six is called an *even* number because $6 = 2 \times 3$. The numbers which are the product of 2 and any whole number are the **even whole numbers:**

$$0, 2, 4, 6, 8, \ldots$$

The **odd whole numbers** are those which are not even:

$$1, 3, 5, 7, 9, \ldots$$

If you count by *twos* from any even number, you obtain **consecutive even numbers.** If you count by *twos* from any odd number, you obtain **consecutive odd numbers.**

Three consecutive even numbers: 10; $10 + 2$, or 12; $12 + 2$, or 14

Three consecutive odd numbers: 11; $11 + 2$, or 13; $13 + 2$, or 15

Thus,

$$n, \quad n + 2, \quad n + 4$$

are consecutive even numbers if n is even, and consecutive odd numbers if n is odd.

Oral Exercises

Represent each word phrase by a variable expression. Use n to represent the number referred to.

SAMPLE Five less than twice the number   *SOLUTION* $2n - 5$

1. Four times the number $4n$
2. One third of the number $\frac{1}{3}n$
3. Six greater than the number $n + 6$
4. The product of six and the number $6n$
5. The number decreased by three $n - 3$
6. The number increased by nine $n + 9$
7. Five less than half the number $\frac{1}{2}n - 5$
8. Seven more than twice the number $2n + 7$

Represent each sentence by an equation. Use n to represent the number.

9. Five more than the number is fifty-four. $n + 5 = 54$
10. Eight less than the number is twenty-six. $n - 8 = 26$
11. The sum of nine and twice the number is thirty-one. $9 + 2n = 31$
12. If one is subtracted from five times the number, the difference is fourteen. $5n - 1 = 14$

Represent the required numbers in terms of the given variables.

13. If w is a whole number, what is the next consecutive whole number? $w + 1$ the next consecutive whole number after that one? $w + 2$
14. If v is an even whole number, what is the even whole number just before v? the even whole number just before that one? $v - 2; v - 4$
15. If n is a whole number, is $2n$ even or odd? Is $2n + 1$ even or odd? Is $2n + 2$ even or odd? Even; odd; even

INTRODUCTION TO ALGEBRA **13**

10. **a.** Write the next two whole numbers after x.
    $x + 1$, $x + 2$

    b. Write an equation which states that the sum of three consecutive whole numbers is 30, given that the first number is x.
    $x + (x + 1) + (x + 2) = 30$

11. **a.** Write the next two odd whole numbers after x, assuming that x is odd.
    $x + 2$, $x + 4$

    b. Write an equation which states that the sum of three consecutive odd whole numbers is 39, given that the first odd whole number is x.
    $x + (x + 2) + (x + 4) = 39$

Supplementary Material

Practice Master 2

Suggested Assignments

Minimum
Day 1: 14/1–14
     R 11/*Self-Test 1*
Day 2: 14/15–33 odd

Average
     14/1–6, 7–35 odd
     R 11/*Self-Test 1*

Maximum
     14/1–37 odd
     R 11/*Self-Test 1*

Represent each word phrase by a variable expression. Use n to represent the number.

1. Five times the number $5n$

2. Ten less than the number $n - 10$

3. Four more than half the number $\frac{1}{2}n + 4$

Represent each sentence by an equation. Use n to represent the number.

4. Six more than the number is fifteen. $n + 6 = 15$

5. Two less than three times the number is seven. $3n - 2 = 7$

6. One fourth of the number is eleven. $\frac{1}{4}n = 11$

Written Exercises

Match the word sentence in Column I with the corresponding open sentence in Column II. (You will not use all the open sentences.)

Column I

Column II

A   **1.** Ten less than half a number is seven. **g.**

2. Three times the sum of a number and two is fifteen. **e.**

3. Nine decreased by twice a number is one. **f.**

4. The product of six and one less than a number is eighteen. **c.**

5. The sum of three times a number and two is fifteen. **a.**

6. If twice a number is decreased by five, the difference is three. **i.**

a. $3x + 2 = 15$

b. $2x - 9 = 1$

c. $6(x - 1) = 18$

d. $\frac{1}{2}(x - 10) = 7$

e. $3(x + 2) = 15$

f. $9 - 2x = 1$

g. $\frac{1}{2}x - 10 = 7$

h. $6x - 1 = 18$

i. $2x - 5 = 3$

j. $2(x - 5) = 3$

Represent each word phrase by a variable expression.

7. Eight times the number t $8t$

8. Five times the number s $5s$

9. Half the number n $\frac{1}{2}n$

10. One third of the number g $\frac{1}{3}g$

11. Seven greater than the number a $a + 7$

12. Five less than the number k

13. Two less than the number b $b - 2$

14. Nine more than the number m

12. $k - 5$ **14.** $m + 9$

Represent the required numbers in terms of the given variables.

15. What number is one more than twice the number q? $2q + 1$

16. What number is two less than half the number w? $\frac{1}{2}w - 2$

17. If t is a whole number, what is the whole number just before t? the whole number just before that one? $t - 1$; $t - 2$

18. If s is an odd whole number, what is the next consecutive odd whole number? the next consecutive odd whole number after that one? $s + 2$; $s + 4$

19. The sum of two numbers is fifteen. One number is y. What is the other number? $15 - y$

20. The sum of two numbers is eight. One number is n. What is the other number? $8 - n$

B   **21.** The difference between two numbers is six. The greater number is x. What is the smaller number? $x - 6$

22. The difference between two numbers is ten. The smaller number is s. What is the greater number? $s + 10$

23. Does $2n + 5$ represent an even number or an odd number? What is the next greater even number? the next greater odd number?
Odd; $2n + 6$; $2n + 7$

24. Does $2k + 4$ represent an even number or an odd number? What is the next greater odd number? the next greater even number?

Even; $2k + 5$; $2k + 6$

Represent each sentence by an equation.

25. One half of the number r is thirty-four. $\frac{1}{2}r = 34$
26. One sixth of the number t is forty. $\frac{1}{6}t = 40$
27. Fifteen is three more than twice the number z. $15 = 2z + 3$
28. Twenty is seven less than one half of the number h. $20 = \frac{1}{2}h - 7$
29. When you increase one third of the number x by five, you obtain nine. $\frac{1}{3}x - 5 = 9$
30. When you decrease nine times the number y by six, you obtain four. $9y - 6 = 4$
31. Three times the sum of four and the number t is forty-two. $3(4 + t) = 42$
32. If five is subtracted from the number y, six times the difference is ninety. $6(y - 5) = 90$
33. Twice the number x is eight more than x itself. $2x = x + 8$
34. Half the number a is ten less than a itself. $\frac{1}{2}a = a - 10$
35. The first of three consecutive whole numbers is x, and the sum of the three numbers is one hundred fifty-three. $x + (x + 1) + (x + 2) = 153$
36. The first of three consecutive even numbers is y, and the sum of the three numbers is twenty-four. $y + (y + 2) + (y + 4) = 24$

C 37. The first of three consecutive odd numbers is d, and the sum of the first and second exceeds the third by nine. $d + (d + 2) = (d + 4) + 9$
38. The first of three consecutive even numbers is x, and the sum of the three numbers is three tenths of the product of the first two. $x + (x + 2) + (x + 4) = 0.3x(x + 2)$

Just for Fun

1, 3, 6, 10, 15, . . . are called triangular numbers because they can be represented by dots arranged to form triangles.

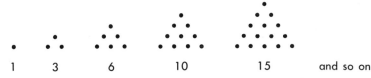

1   3   6   10   15   and so on

1. Draw diagrams for the next five triangular numbers.
2. If n represents the number of the triangular number in the list ($n = 1$ for 1, $n = 2$ for 3, and so on), verify for the first ten triangular numbers that the nth triangular number $= \dfrac{n(n + 1)}{2}$.

Additional Answers

Just for Fun

1.

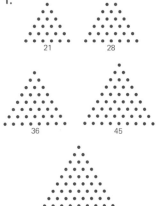

21   28

36   45

55

Calculator Key-In

1. Solve each equation if the domain of n is $\{1, 2, 3, 4\}$.

   a. $\dfrac{n(n+1)}{2} = 1$

   b. $\dfrac{n(n+1)}{2} = 1 + 2$

   c. $\dfrac{n(n+1)}{2} = 1 + 2 + 3$

   d. $\dfrac{n(n+1)}{2} = 1 + 2 + 3 + 4$

2. First guess what value of n in the set of whole numbers satisfies each equation. Then use a calculator to check your guess.

   a. $\dfrac{n(n+1)}{2} = 1 + 2 + 3 + 4 + \cdots + 10$ (The three dots indicate that all the whole numbers between 4 and 10 are to be included in the sum.)

   b. $\dfrac{n(n+1)}{2} = 1 + 2 + 3 + 4 + \cdots + 15$

   c. $\dfrac{n(n+1)}{2} = 1 + 2 + 3 + 4 + \cdots + 26$

Biography   Annie Jump Cannon

Annie Jump Cannon (1863–1941), by examining astronomical plates photographed through a prism, classified almost 400,000 stars according to their stellar spectra or temperatures. She was a graduate of Wellesley College and did graduate work in mathematics, physics, and astronomy there and at Radcliffe College.

In 1896 she began her lifelong career at Harvard classifying stars and developing a new system for this classification. She greatly reduced the number of species to which the vast majority of stars belong and proved that these species, for the most part, form a continuous series. In 1925 she became the first woman to receive an honorary Doctor of Science degree from Oxford University.

16   *CHAPTER 1*

1-5 *Words into Symbols: Problem Situations*

OBJECTIVE   To represent problem situations by mathematical expressions or equations.

To apply algebra, you often use *formulas*. **Formulas** are equations that state rules about measurements. Here are four formulas:

$A = lw$ Area of rectangle = length of rectangle × width of rectangle
$P = 2l + 2w$ Perimeter of rectangle = (2 × length) + (2 × width)
$D = rt$ Distance traveled = rate × time traveled
$C = np$ Cost = number of items × price per item

EXAMPLE 1
Using the given variable, write an expression for the measure required to complete each statement.

1. A rectangle has length 8 units and width w units.
   The area is __?__ square units

2. A rectangle has length 6 cm (centimeters) and width x cm.
   The perimeter is __?__ cm.

3. You travel for $(x + 2)$ hours at 70 km/h (kilometers per hour).
   The distance you travel is __?__ km.

4. You buy 2 pens at x cents each and 3 notebooks at y cents each.
   The total cost is __?__ cents.

SOLUTION
1. Area = length × width $= 8w$
2. Perimeter = (2 × length) + (2 × width) $= 2(6) + 2x = 12 + 2x$
3. Distance = rate × time $= 70(x + 2)$
4. Cost of pens $= 2x$; cost of notebooks $= 3y$; total cost $= 2x + 3y$

The next examples show how you can choose a variable to represent a number and then write an equation to represent the facts in a given situation.

EXAMPLE 2
Jan paid two dollars less than Bob at the pizza parlor. Together, they paid $3.90.

   a. Choose a variable to represent the amount Bob paid and use it to write an expression for the amount Jan paid.

   b. Write an equation that represents the given facts.

SOLUTION
   a. Let x = amount Bob paid; then $x - 2$ = amount Jan paid.
   b. $x + (x - 2) = 3.90$

INTRODUCTION TO ALGEBRA   **17**

Chalkboard Examples
Using the given variable, write an expression for the measure required to complete the sentence.

1. An airplane flies 800 km/h for t hours. It travels a distance of __?__ km. $800t$

2. One ticket costs 25¢. n tickets will cost __?__ ¢. $25n$

Let x represent the number indicated by the words in parentheses. Write a equation to represent the given facts.

3. A rectangle is 12 cm long and has an area of 60 cm². (width of the rectangle)
   $12x = 60$

4. Jennifer is twice as old now as she was eight years ago. (Jennifer's age now)
   $x = 2(x - 8)$

5. Joan and Steve had lunch together. Steve paid $2 less than Joan. The total bill came to $5.

   a. Choose a variable to represent the amount Joan paid and use it to write an expression for the amount Steve paid.
   $x, x - 2$

   b. Write an equation that represents the given facts.
   $x + (x + 2) = 5$
   (continued)

6. The length of a garden is twice the width. It takes 18 m of fence to enclose it.

a. Choose a variable to represent the width and use it to write an expression for the length. *w, 2w*

b. Draw a sketch to represent the relationships given.

c. Write an equation that represents the given facts.

$w + 2w + w + 2w = 18$
or $2w + 4w = 18$
or $6w = 18$

Additional A Exercises

Give a variable expression for the measure required to complete each statement.

1. In *x* days there are _?_ hours. *24x*

2. A rectangle has a length of *r* cm and a width of 4 cm. It has an area of _?_ cm². *4r*

3. Jane is *y* years old. Sally is 4 years older. Sally is _?_ years old. *y + 4*

4. You travel 3 h at *s* km/h. The distance traveled is _?_ km. *3s*

5. A baseball costs *z* dollars. Five baseballs cost _?_ dollars. *5z*

6. Susan jogs for 2h. If she jogs at *q* km/h, she has traveled _?_ km. *2q*

EXAMPLE 3

The length of a rectangular rug is 1 m (meter) more than the width. It takes 14 m of fringe to go around the edges of the rug.

a. Choose a variable to represent the width in meters and use it to write an expression for the length.

b. Write an equation that represents the given facts.

SOLUTION

a. Let w = width in meters.
Then $w + 1$ = length in meters.

b. Draw a sketch to help you see the relationships given.

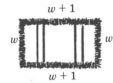

$2(w + 1) + 2w = 14$ *Answer*

Oral Exercises

Give a variable expression for the measure required to complete each statement.

1. A rectangle has width 4 units and length $(x + 5)$ units. Its area is _?_ square units. *4(x + 5)*

2. You travel for $(t - 1)$ hours at 60 km/h. The distance traveled is _?_ km. *60(t − 1)*

3. You buy $(n + 2)$ hamburgers at 85 cents each. The cost is _?_ cents. *85(n + 2)*

4. Lanette earns $(w + 2)$ dollars per hour. In *h* hours, she earns _?_ dollars. *h(w + 2)*

5. Joe is two years older than Fred. The sum of their ages is 30.
a. Choose a variable for Fred's age and use it to express Joe's age. *f, f + 2*
b. State an equation that represents the given facts. *f + (f + 2) = 30*

Written Exercises

Using the given variable, write an expression for the measure required to complete each statement.

A **1.** Dick is *y* years old. Bill is three years older than Dick. Bill is _?_ years old. *y + 3*

2. Mary is *t* cm tall. Marcia is 5 cm shorter than Mary. Marcia is _?_ cm tall. *t − 5*

3. A book costs *x* dollars. Six copies of the book cost _?_ dollars. *6x*

4. John is *m* years old. Five years ago he was _?_ years old. *m − 5*

5. In x weeks there are __?__ days. $7x$

6. In y hours there are __?__ minutes. $60y$

7. Kelley bicycles at a rate of 15 km/h. In t hours she bicycles a distance of __?__ km. $15t$

8. Jay walks at a rate of x km/h. In half an hour he walks a distance of __?__ km. $\frac{1}{2}x$

9. The length of a rectangular lot is 18 m less than twice its width, w m. The length is __?__ m. The perimeter is __?__ m. $2w - 18$; $6w - 36$

10. The width of a rectangular field is 2 km more than half the length, l km. The width is __?__ km. The perimeter is __?__ km. $\frac{1}{2}l + 2$; $3l + 4$

In Exercises 11–22:

a. Choose a variable to represent the number indicated by the words in parentheses.

b. Write an equation that represents the given facts.

11. The perimeter of a square is 28 m   (Length of a side) $4s = 28$

12. The perimeter of an equilateral triangle (a triangle with three equal sides) is 42 cm.   (Length of a side) $3s = 42$

13. Four identical tires cost \$120 altogether.   (Cost of one tire) $4x = 120$

14. Six bus passengers paid a total fare of \$5.40.   (Fare for one passenger) $6y = 5.40$

15. Four years ago Rhoda was 11 years old.   (Rhoda's age now) $x - 4 = 11$

16. Max has read all but the last 16 pages of a 250-page book.   (Number of pages Max has read) $y + 16 = 250$

B 17. The Science Museum gives students a dollar off the price of admission. Fran, a high school freshman, paid \$1.50.   (Admission price) $x - 1 = 1.50$

18. A mail-order firm charges \$1.52 for shipping charges on a pair of field glasses. Paulo ordered a pair and sent a check for \$34.99.   (Price of the field glasses) $x + 1.52 = 34.99$

19. A soccer field has a perimeter of 348 m. The length is 37 m more than the width.   (Width) $2w + 2(w + 37) = 348$

20. A football team that played 13 games won five times as many games as it lost, and finished one game in a tie.   (Number of games lost) $l + 5l + 1 = 13$

21. There were five more men than women on a grand jury of 23 people.   (Number of women) $w + (w + 5) = 23$

22. There were twice as many dark chocolates as milk chocolates in a box of two dozen.   (Number of milk chocolates) $m + 2m = 24$

Suggested Assignments

Minimum
Day 1: 18/1–13
Day 2: 19/14–24

Average
18/1–15 odd
S 15/24, 28, 30, 36

Maximum
18/1–19 odd
S 15/32–38 even

In Exercises 23–26:

a. Choose a variable to represent the number indicated by the words in parentheses.

b. Write an equation that represents the given facts.

23. On a 1200 km trip, the Watanabe family traveled by car and by plane. They traveled seven times farther by plane than by car. (Distance traveled by car) $c + 7c = 1200$

24. The coach drove from her home to school and back in 75 minutes. The return trip took three minutes less than the trip to school. (Time to drive to school) $t + (t - 3) = 75$

C 25. On a trip of 600 km, a van traveled at 80 km/h for half of the time and at 100 km/h for the other half of the time. (Time of the trip) $80(\frac{1}{2}t) + 100(\frac{1}{2}t) = 600$

26. The length of one side of a triangular lot is 11 m less than twice the length of the second side. The third side is 7 m longer than the first side. The perimeter of the lot is 235 m. (Length of the second side) $(2s - 11) + s + ((2s - 11) + 7) = 235$

Career Note Programmer

$$x_1 = 1$$
$$x_2 = (x_1 + 2)^2 = (1 + 2)^2 = 9$$
$$x_3 = (x_2 + 3)^2 = (9 + 3)^2 = 144$$
$$x_4 = (x_3 + 4)^2 = (144 + 4)^2 = 21,904$$
$$x_5 = (x_4 + 5)^2 = (21,904 + 5)^2 = 480,004,281$$

How long would it take you to find x_{100}? Would you be likely to make a mistake? A computer can find x_{100} and do more complicated calculations accurately in just a fraction of a second. A computer cannot think for itself, however. It must be given detailed, step-by-step instructions in a computer language.

The primary task of the programmer is to write programs or instructions for a computer to follow. Then, after the program has been written, the programmer must check that the desired result will be obtained. A check is made by running the program with a set of typical data for which the results are known. Flowcharts which outline schematically the way in which the program works are sometimes used by programmers to plan their work and explain it to others.

A college degree with either a major or extensive course work in computer science is the usual requirement for a job in this field.

Computer Key-In

How does a computer work? A computer is made up of several connected electronic parts. It works according to the instructions given to it by programs that can be stored in it.

A person called a *programmer* writes programs that tell the computer how to perform various tasks. Such programs are generally written in a programming language, such as BASIC (which is used for the programs shown in this book) or FORTRAN or COBOL. In order for one of these languages to be used, there must be a program stored in the computer that will translate the program instructions into commands that will control the computer circuits.

To get the computer to perform a particular task, the programmer must break the task down into the kinds of steps that the computer can do. These steps must be carefully arranged in the proper order. Sometimes "decision steps" are included to change the order as necessary. The programmer must also consider the numbers and words (*data*) that the computer is to work with (*process*) for them to be *input* as needed. (The work that computers do is sometimes called *data processing*.) The programmer must also arrange for the results to be *output* in a convenient form.

A commonly used business program is one that handles the payroll. Such a program stores payroll records (names of employees, their salaries or wages, and the deductions) and computes and prints the payroll checks.

Other kinds of programs are used to store information in libraries and to retrieve portions of such information on request.

To obtain correct results, a program must be correct in every detail and data must be input correctly. The writing of a successful computer program is a very exciting accomplishment.

INTRODUCTION TO ALGEBRA **21**

1-6 *Solving Problems*

OBJECTIVE   To solve problems using a general method.

A "word problem" describes a situation in which certain numbers are related to each other. If you can state the relationship in an equation, then you can solve the problem by solving the equation.

Here are two simple examples (which you could solve mentally) to show you a general method for solving word problems.

EXAMPLE 1

Maria bought a hit record album for $10. Her friend bought a cassette of the same music. If the album cost twice as much as the cassette, what was the cost of the cassette?

SOLUTION

Step 1 Read the problem carefully. What numbers are asked for?

This problem asks for the number of dollars in the cost of the cassette.

Step 2 Choose a variable. Use it with the given facts to represent the number(s) described in the problem.

Let n = cost of cassette in dollars. Then $2n$ = cost of album in dollars.

Step 3 Write an equation based on the given facts.

The cost of the album is $10.
$$2n \quad\quad = 10$$

Step 4 Solve the equation.

From arithmetic, you know that 5 is the number whose product with 2 is 10.

$$n = 5$$

Step 5 Check your results with the statement of the problem. Give the answer.

Is the cost of the album ($10) twice the cost of the cassette?

$$10 \overset{?}{=} 2 \times 5$$
$$10 = 10 \;\checkmark$$

∴ the cost of the cassette was $5.

Answer

EXAMPLE 2

The approximate height of Yudaki Falls in Japan is 100 m. That is 4 m more than six times the approximate height of Minnehaha Falls in Minnesota. What is the approximate height of Minnehaha Falls?

SOLUTION

Step 1 The problem asks for the number of meters in the approximate height of Minnehaha Falls.

Step 2 Let h = approximate height of Minnehaha Falls in meters. Then $6h + 4$ = approximate height of Yudaki Falls in meters.

Solve each problem by using the five-step method given on page 23.

1. The total number of students in the chess club is twelve. If there are seven girls in the club, how many boys are there?
   Step 1 The problem asks for the number of boys in the club.
   Step 2 Let b = the number of boys. Then $b + 7$ = total number of boys and girls.
   Step 3 $b + 7 = 12$
   Step 4 $b = 5$
   Step 5 Is the number of girls (7) and boys (5) equal to 12?
   $7 + 5 \overset{?}{=} 12$,
   $12 = 12 \;\checkmark$
   ∴ There are 5 boys in the club.

2. The perimeter of a square is 72 cm. Find the measure of one side of the square.
   Step 2 Let s = measure of one side. Then $4s$ = perimeter.
   Step 3 $4s = 72$
   Step 4 $s = 18$
   ∴ The measure of one side is 18 cm.

   (continued)

Step 3 The approximate height of Yudaki Falls is 100 m.

$$\underset{6h + 4}{\downarrow} \qquad \underset{= 100}{\downarrow \ \downarrow}$$

Step 4 The sketch shows that $6h = 96$. From arithmetic, you know that 16 is the number whose product with 6 is 96.

$$h = 16$$

Step 5 Checking the result of Step 4 is left to you.

∴ the approximate height of Minnehaha Falls is 16 m.

Answer

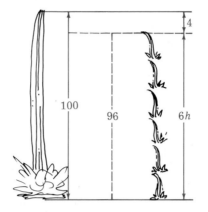

The five steps used to solve the problems in Examples 1 and 2 form a plan that usually helps in solving any word problem.

PLAN FOR SOLVING A WORD PROBLEM

Step 1 Read the problem carefully and decide what numbers are asked for.

Step 2 Choose a variable and use it with the given facts to represent the number(s) described in the problem. Making a sketch may be helpful.

Step 3 Write an open sentence based on the given facts.

Step 4 Solve the open sentence and find the required numbers.

Step 5 Check your results with the words of the problem. Give the answer.

Problems

Solve each problem by writing out the five steps.

A **1.** Last year Hal scored three times as many touchdowns as Bryce. If Hal scored 15 touchdowns, how many did Bryce score? 5 touchdowns

2. A truck driver is traveling at a constant rate of 100 km/h. How long will it take her to reach Oklahoma City, which is 200 km away? 2 h

3. Ruby Francis bought a used car for $2400. Her friend Lillian Chen bought a new moped. The car cost six times as much as the moped. What was the cost of Lillian's moped? $400

INTRODUCTION TO ALGEBRA **23**

---

3. There are 54 steps up to Sam's apartment. This is three times as many as there are up to Sarah's apartment. How many steps are there up to Sarah's apartment?

Step 2 Let s be the number of steps up to Sarah's apartment. Then, the number of steps up to Sam's apartment is $3s$.

Step 3 $3s = 54$

Step 4 $s = 18$

∴ There are 18 steps up to Sarah's apartment.

4. Jim is 19 years old. He was 15 when his brother Bill was born. How old is Bill?

Step 2 Let $a = $ Bill's age. Then $a + 15 = $ Jim's age.

Step 3 $a + 15 = 19$

Step 4 $a = 4$

∴ Bill is 4 years old.

Supplementary Materials

Practice Master 3

Progress Test 2

Additional A Exercises

Solve each problem by writing out the five steps.

1. Emily has 36 coins. Twelve of the coins are nickels, 11 are dimes, and the rest are quarters. How many quarters does Emily have? 13 quarters

2. During the baseball season, Elwood had 21 hits. He had one home run, 2 triples, and 13 singles. How many doubles did Elwood hit? 5 doubles

(continued)

3. In a pet store there are 3 times as many birds as dogs. If there are 11 dogs, how many birds are there? 33 birds

4. A train makes 6 stops between Barrytown and Mid City, which are 56 km apart. If the stops are equally spaced, and Mid City is the seventh and last stop, how far does the train travel between stops? 8 km

Suggested Assignments

Minimum
Day 1: 23/P:1–7
Day 2: 24/P: 8–14
    R 25/Self-Test 2

Average
Day 1: 23/P: 1–7 odd
    S 19/17–25 odd
Day 2: 24/P:9–15 odd
    R 25/Self-Test 2

Maximum
Day 1: 23/P: 1–11 odd
    S 19/20–26
Day 2: 24/P: 13, 15, 16
    R 25/Self-Test 2

4. For $8.00 Jim and his friends can get 16 pieces of pizza if they buy whole pizza pies and share them. Find the cost per piece of pizza. $0.50

5. Senior citizens pay a dollar less than the general admission price to the Museum of Science. Anna Raciti, a senior citizen, paid $2.50. What is the general admission price? $3.50

6. Including the tip, the cost of a meal was $5.00. The tip was $.75. What was the cost of the meal before the tip? $4.25

7. The number of students enrolled in Massapoag High School is 150 less today than it was ten years ago when 1800 students were enrolled. How many are enrolled today? 1650 students

8. In one year 218,899 poodles were registered with the Kennel Club. This was 117,500 more than the number of German shepherds registered in that year. How many German shepherds were registered? 101,399 German shepherds

B 9. a. If a number is decreased by 6, the result is 30. Find the number. 36
    b. If four times another number is decreased by 6, the result is 30. Find the number. 9

10. a. If a number is increased by 15, the result is 25. Find the number. 10
    b. If one half of another number is increased by 15, the result is 25. Find the number. 20

11. Jane dives from a platform that is 10 m high. Joe dives from a springboard. The height of the platform is 1 m more than three times the height of the springboard. What is the height of the springboard? 3 m

12. Fourteen-year-old Manuel is two years older than twice the age of his brother Juan. How old is Juan? 6 years old

13. A ski jacket costing $60 is priced $20 less than twice the cost of a matching pair of ski pants. How much are the ski pants? $40

14. The total height of the Sutherland Falls in New Zealand is 580 m. That is 20 m less than ten times the approximate height of Niagara Falls (between New York State and Ontario, Canada). What is the approximate height of Niagara Falls? 60 m

C 15. Dorothy Lee will authorize her bank to transfer a fixed amount each month from her checking account to a savings account. She has $125 in the savings account now. In six months she wishes to have $1325 in the savings account to pay her real estate tax. What fixed amount should she have transferred each month? (Do not consider the amount of interest her account may draw during this time.) $200

16. At the beginning of a seven-week speed reading course, Ted read at the rate of 250 words per minute (wpm). At the end of the course, his reading speed was 1020 wpm. What was the average weekly increase in his reading speed over the course? 110 wpm

24   *CHAPTER 1*

Self-Test 2

VOCABULARY whole numbers (p. 12)   consecutive even number
consecutive numbers (p. 12)   (p. 13)
even number (p. 13)   consecutive odd number (p. 13)
odd number (p. 13)   formula (p. 17)

Represent each sentence by an equation.

1. The sum of the number n and three is five.

2. If one is subtracted from twice the number t, the difference is eleven.

3. Five years ago, Gina was nine years old.

  a. Choose a variable to represent Gina's age now and use it to write an expression for Gina's age five years ago.

  b. Write an equation that represents the given facts.

4. Use the five-step method to solve this problem: Noriko sold twice as many tickets to the school play as Lou. If Noriko sold 10 tickets, how many did Lou sell?

Obj. 1-4, p. 12

Obj. 1-5, p. 17

Obj. 1-6, p. 22

Check your answers with those at the back of the book.

Chapter Summary

1. A numerical expression represents a particular number. Replacing a numerical expression by the simplest name of the number represented by the expression is called simplifying the expression.

2. A variable expression is evaluated by replacing each variable with its value and simplifying the resulting numerical expression.

3. Grouping symbols are used to show the order in which operations are to be performed to simplify an expression. If no grouping symbols appear, the steps listed on page 6 are followed.

4. Replacing each variable in an open sentence by each of its values, in turn, is a way to find solutions of the open sentence.

5. A problem can often be solved by writing an open sentence based on the given facts and solving the open sentence.

INTRODUCTION TO ALGEBRA **25**

Chapter Review

Give the letter of the correct answer.

1. Simplify $(84 \div 7) \div (10 + 2)$.

   a. 0   **b.** 1   **c.** 24   **d.** 144

   1-1

2. Evaluate $(3a) - (b - c)$ if $a = 2$, $b = 5$, and $c = 1$.

   a. 0   **b.** 1   **c.** 2   **d.** 3

3. Simplify $\dfrac{19 \times 5 - 7 \times 5}{3 \times 3 + 1}$.

   a. 5   **b.** 6   **c.** 19   **d.** 44

   1-2

4. Evaluate $\dfrac{r}{2} + (4s - 1)t$ if $r = 6$, $s = 3$, and $t = 4$.

   a. 11   **b.** 14   **c.** 47   **d.** 56

5. Solve the equation $2x + 9 = 15$ if $x \in \{0, 1, 2, 3, 4, 5, 6\}$.

   a. 3   **b.** 4   **c.** 5   **d.** 6

   1-3

6. Which equation represents the word sentence "Five more than twice the number n is nineteen"?

   a. $2(n + 5) = 19$ **b.** $2(n - 5) = 19$ **c.** $2n - 5 = 19$ **d.** $5 + 2n = 19$

   1-4

7. A rectangle is 4 cm longer than it is wide. If it is y cm wide, then what is the number of centimeters in its perimeter?

   a. $4y + 4$ **b.** $y(y + 4)$ **c.** $y + (y + 4)$ **d.** $2y + 2(y + 4)$

   1-5

8. Alma has four times as much money as Wally. Together they have $40. How much money does Wally have?

   a. $8   **b.** $10   **c.** $36   **d.** $160

   1-6

Chapter Test

1. Simplify $(18 + 3) \div (56 \div 8)$. 3

   1-1

2. Evaluate $(xy) - (5x)$ if $x = 4$ and $y = 7$. 8

3. Simplify $9 \times 8 \div 4 \times 2 \div 36 + 1$. 2

   1-2

4. Evaluate $\dfrac{4q - w + 5}{3q - p}$ if $p = 1$, $q = 2$, and $w = 3$. 2

5. Find the solution set of $4z - 1 = 19$ if $z \in \{1, 2, 3, 4, 5, 6, 7\}$. $\{5\}$

   1-3

6. Represent this word sentence by an equation: Twelve less than half the number n is twenty. $\frac{1}{2}n - 12 = 20$

   1-4

7. The sum of two test scores is 178. If x represents one score, represent the other score in terms of x. $178 - x$

   1-5

8. The novel has twice as many pages as the poetry book. If the novel has 512 pages, how many pages does the poetry book have? 256 pages

   1-6

26   CHAPTER 1

Maintaining Skills

Perform the indicated operations.

SAMPLE 1
```
  112
 1025
   37
  429
+ 856
 2347
```

SAMPLE 2
```
   115
 3982̷5
- 7406
 32419
```

SAMPLE 3
```
   5133
 ×  407
  35931
      0
  20532
 2089131
```

SAMPLE 4
```
       86 R2
 72)6194
    576
    434
    432
      2
```

1.
```
   7702
   1946
     57
 +  813
  10518
```

2.
```
  12898
  26065
 + 3442
  42405
```

3.
```
      4
    521
     98
 + 6376
   6999
```

4.
```
  50483
  39017
 +  646
  90146
```

5.
```
   9250
     28
    774
 + 3216
  13268
```

6.
```
   4025
 - 3917
    108
```

7.
```
   8610
 -  218
   8392
```

8.
```
   5376
 - 5193
    183
```

9.
```
  19401
 -  795
  18606
```

10.
```
  68224
 -46808
  21416
```

11.
```
   1273
 ×   56
  71288
```

12.
```
    4095
 ×   710
 2907450
```

13.
```
    8162
 ×   348
 2840376
```

14.
```
   30146
 ×    98
 2954308
```

15.
```
    59281
 ×    612
 36279972
```

16. 24)7260
    302 R12

17. 57)4854
    85 R9

18. 108)4428
    41

19. 371)35616
    96

Round each number (a) to the nearest ten; (b) to the nearest thousand.

SAMPLE 5   14,325

SOLUTION   (a) The ones' digit, 5, is greater than or equal to 5; round up to 14,330.   (b) The hundreds' digit, 3, is less than 5; round down to 14,000.

20. 6184
6180; 6000

21. 70,569
70,570; 71,000

22. 39,752
39,750;
40,000

23. 87,918
87,920;
88,000

24. 104,055
104,060;
104,000

Estimate each answer to the nearest hundred.

SAMPLE 6
```
  2813
 + 952
```
SOLUTION
```
  2800
 +1000
  3800
```

25.
```
   837
 + 651
  1500
```

26.
```
   382
 - 179
   200
```

27.
```
   2091
 -  509
   1600
```

28.
```
    419
    682
 +  904
   2000
```

29.
```
    2055
    7996
 + 5247
  15,300
```

About the Photo

The vents depicted in the photograph were found at the mouth of the Gulf of California. Others occur just to the east of the Galápagos Islands. New ocean crust is being formed in both places. The vents, sometimes called "black smokers," resemble two- to five-meter–high chimneys spewing forth zinc, copper, iron, and sulphur, which precipitate upon encountering the much colder (2°C) sea water near the ocean floor. These discoveries mark the first human observance of the formation of metallic ore.

Your students may be interested in the following numerical facts: The temperature of the water from the California vents (which melted the explorer ship's heat probe) was estimated at between 350°C and 400°C. The most interesting vents were found where the ocean ridge spreads at the rapid rate of 6 cm per year. It has been estimated that the entire ocean recycles through Earth's crust once every 8,000,000 years.

Limpets, crabs, seaworms, an unknown variety of fish, and large tube worms were photographed near an undersea vent at −2800 m. Hot currents rich in dissolved minerals enter the ocean floor at these vents and nourish an abundance of animal life.

28

2

WORKING WITH
REAL NUMBERS

Teaching References

Lesson Commentary,
　pp. T66–T70

Assignment Guide,
　pp. T49–T50

Supplementary Materials

　Practice Masters 4–7

　Progress Tests 4–7

　Computer Activities
　4 *Arithmetic Expressions in*
　　BASIC
　5 *Dividing a Segment*
　6 PRINT *Statements in*
　　BASIC

Extra Practice, pp. 492–495

Alternate Test, p. T13

BASIC PROPERTIES

2-1 *Real Numbers*

OBJECTIVE　**To graph real numbers on a number line.**

To show how numbers relate to each other, you may represent them as points on a line, called a *number line*. To construct a number line:

1. Choose a starting point on a line and label it "0" (zero). This point is called the **origin.** The origin separates the line into two sides, the **positive side** and the **negative side.** If the line is horizontal, the side to the right of the origin is usually taken to be the positive side.

2. Mark off equal units of distance on both sides of the origin. On the positive side, pair the endpoints of successive units with the **positive integers**

$$1, 2, 3, 4, 5, \ldots .$$

On the negative side, pair the endpoints with the **negative integers**

$$^-1, \ ^-2, \ ^-3, \ ^-4, \ ^-5, \ldots .$$

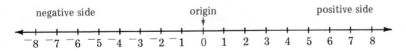

You read $^-1$ as "negative one." You usually read 1 as "one." You may also read 1 as "positive one," and you may write it as $^+1$.

29

Chalkboard Examples

1. Using a number line, pair the letter *A* with the point whose coordinate is ⁻11, *B* with the point whose coordinate is ⁻10, and so on, so that *L* has coordinate 0 (zero), *M* has coordinate ⁺1, and *Z* has coordinate ⁺14.

   a. Name the coordinates of the points *K, O, A, L, A.*
   ⁻1, 3, ⁻11, 0, ⁻11

   b. Name the points with the coordinates ⁻7, 9, ⁻9, ⁻11, 0, 13, 4, 8, 9, 7.
   E, U, C, A, L, Y, P, T, U, S

2. Name the coordinates of the points shown.

   ```
   +--+--•--•--+--•--+--•--+--•--+
   ⁻5 ⁻4 ⁻3 ⁻2 ⁻1  0  1  2  3  4  5
   ```

   ⁻3, $\frac{-3}{2}$, 0, $\frac{5}{2}$, 4

Graph the given numbers on a number line. Draw a separate line for each exercise.

3. ⁻5, ⁻4, 2

   ```
   +--•--•--+--+--+--+--+--•--+--+
   ⁻7 ⁻6 ⁻5 ⁻4 ⁻3 ⁻2 ⁻1  0  1  2  3
   ```

4. ⁻3, $\frac{-3}{2}$, 0, $2\frac{1}{2}$

   ```
   +--+--•--+--•--•--+--+--•--+--+
   ⁻5 ⁻4 ⁻3 ⁻2 ⁻1  0  1  2  3  4  5
   ```

Name a positive or negative number for each measurement.

5. Bank deposit of $23.50
   ⁺23.50

6. 3 under par   ⁻3

The positive integers, the negative integers, and zero make up the set of **integers.** The integers which are the product of 2 and any integer are the *even* integers.

$$\{\text{the integers}\} = \{\ldots, ^-3, ^-2, ^-1, 0, 1, 2, 3, \ldots\}$$

$$\{\text{the even integers}\} = \{\ldots, ^-6, ^-4, ^-2, 0, 2, 4, 6, \ldots\}$$

$$\{\text{the odd integers}\} = \{\ldots, ^-5, ^-3, ^-1, 1, 3, 5, \ldots\}$$

In general, a **positive number** is a number paired with a point on the positive side of a number line. A **negative number** is a number paired with a point on the negative side of a number line. For example:

P is $1\frac{1}{3}$ units from 0 on the *positive* side. The *positive* number $1\frac{1}{3}$ is paired with *P.*

Q is $1\frac{1}{3}$ units from 0 on the *negative* side. The *negative* number $^-1\frac{1}{3}$ is paired with *Q.*

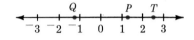

On a number line, the point paired with a number is called the **graph** of the number. The number paired with a point is called the **coordinate** of the point. On the number line above, point *T* is the graph of 2.5, and 2.5 is the coordinate of *T.*

Any number which is either a positive number, a negative number, or zero is called a **real number.** When you graph real numbers, you take the following facts for granted:

1. Each real number is paired with exactly one point on a number line.
2. Each point on a number line is paired with exactly one real number.

Thus, the graphs of *all* the real numbers make up the entire number line:

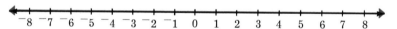

The arrowheads indicate that the number line and the graphs go on indefinitely in both directions.

Because positive and negative numbers suggest opposite directions, they are sometimes called *directed numbers.* You use them for measurements that have *direction* as well as *size.* For example:

A *profit* of $75: 75

6 km *north:* 6

A temperature *rise* of 2.5°C (degrees Celsius): 2.5

The charge on a proton: ⁺1

A *loss* of $75: ⁻75

6 km *south:* ⁻6

A temperature *drop* of 2.5°C: ⁻2.5

The charge on an electron: ⁻1

Oral Exercises

Exercises 1-16 refer to the number line below.

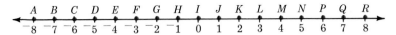

Name the point that is the graph of the given number.

SAMPLE 1 ⁻5   **SOLUTION** Point D

1. 3 *L*   **2.** 0 *I*   **3.** ⁻2 *G*   **4.** ⁻1 *H*   **5.** 7 *Q*   **6.** ⁻7 *B*

State the coordinate of the given point.

7. *K* 2   **8.** *F* ⁻3   **9.** *I* 0   **10.** *Q* 7   **11.** *C* ⁻6   **12.** *R* 8

SAMPLE 2 The point halfway between L and M **SOLUTION** 3.5

13. The point halfway between J and K 1.5
14. The point halfway between C and D ⁻5.5
15. The point one fourth of the way from P to Q 6.25
16. The point one third of the way from I to H $-\frac{1}{3}$

For each exercise, state the temperature if the mercury in the thermometer shown has reached the level indicated.

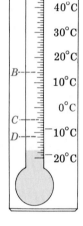

17. *A* 46°C   **18.** *B* 14°C   **19.** *C* ⁻5°C   **20.** *D* ⁻12°C

Written Exercises

Write a positive number for each measurement. Then write the opposite of that number and describe the measurement indicated by that opposite.

A   **1.** Two floors up   **2.** One step to the right
     3. 250 m above sea level   **4.** Five degrees above freezing (0°C)
     5. A gain of 6 points   **6.** Three wins
     7. 8 km east   **8.** Latitude 44° north
     9. One second after liftoff **10.** 2 above par
     11. Receipts of $28.09   **12.** A bank deposit of $5.75

Suggested Assignments
Minimum
Day 1: 31/1–11 odd
        32/13–20
Day 2: 32/21–42
Average
        31/1–41 odd
Maximum
        31/1–43 odd

Additional A Exercises
Write the number that indicates the same measurement in the opposite direction.

1. 4 ⁻4
2. 13 ⁻13
3. $\frac{3}{4}$ $\frac{-3}{4}$
4. ⁻2 2
5. ⁻42 42
6. ⁻9 9

Additional Answers
Written Exercises

1. 2; ⁻2; 2 floors down
2. 1; ⁻1; 1 step to the left
3. 250; ⁻250; 250 m below sea level
4. 5; ⁻5; 5° below freezing
5. 6; ⁻6; a loss of 6 points
6. 3; ⁻3; 3 losses
7. 8; ⁻8; 8 km west
8. 44; ⁻44; latitude 44° south
9. 1; ⁻1; 1 s before liftoff
10. 2; ⁻2; 2 below par
11. 28.09; ⁻28.09; payments of $28.09
12. 5.75; ⁻5.75; a bank withdrawal of $5.75

Name the coordinates of the points shown in color.

13.
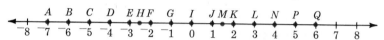
$^-3$ $^-2$ $^-1$ 0 1 2 3
$^-1$, 0, 1

14.
$^-3$ $^-2$ $^-1$ 0 1 2 3
$^-2$, 0, 2

15.
$^-1$ 0 1 2 3 4 5
$^-1$, 2, 5

16.
$^-2$ $^-1$ 0 1 2 3 4
$^-2$, 2, 4

17.
$^-6$ $^-5$ $^-4$ $^-3$ $^-2$ $^-1$ 0
$^-5$, $^-3$, $^-1$, 0

18.
0 1 2 3 4 5 6
1, 3, 5, 6

19.
$^-3$ $^-2$ $^-1$ 0 1 2 3
$-\frac{1}{2}$, $\frac{1}{2}$

20.
$^-3$ $^-2$ $^-1$ 0 1 2 3
$-1\frac{1}{2}$, $2\frac{1}{2}$

List the letters for the points whose coordinates are given.

A   B   C   D   E HF   G   I   J MK   L   N   P   Q
$^-8$ $^-7$ $^-6$ $^-5$ $^-4$ $^-3$ $^-2$ $^-1$ 0 1 2 3 4 5 6 7 8

21. $^-3$, 4 *E, N*   **22.** $^-1$, 5 *G, P*   **23.** 0, $^-7$ *I, A*   **24.** 2, $^-5$ *K, C*
25. $^-6$, 6 *B, Q*   **26.** $^-4$, 3 *D, L*   **27.** $^-2$, $^-2.5$ *F, H*   **28.** 1, 1.5 *J, M*

Additional Answers
Written Exercises

29.
$^-4$ $^-3$ $^-2$ $^-1$ 0 1 2 3 4

30.
$^-4$ $^-3$ $^-2$ $^-1$ 0 1 2 3 4

31.
$^-2$ $^-1$ 0 1 2

32.
$^-4$ $^-3$ $^-2$ $^-1$ 0 1 2 3 4

33.
$^-2$ $^-1$ 0 1 2

34.
$^-2$ $^-1$ 0 1 2

35.
$^-3$ $^-2$ $^-1$ 0 1

36.
0 1 2

Graph the given numbers on a number line. Draw a separate line for each exercise.

29. $^-3$, $^-1$, 1, 3   **30.** 2, 4, $^-2$, $^-4$

31. 1, $\frac{1}{2}$, 0, $^-2$ **32.** $^-3$, $^-2.5$, $^-2$, 0

B 33. $^-2$, $^-1\frac{2}{3}$, $^-1\frac{1}{3}$, 0   **34.** $^-1$, $^-0.5$, 0, 0.5

35. $^-2\frac{1}{4}$, $\frac{^-1}{4}$, $\frac{1}{4}$, $\frac{3}{4}$ **36.** $\frac{^-1}{3}$, $\frac{1}{3}$, $\frac{4}{3}$, $\frac{7}{3}$

On a horizontal number line, point P has coordinate $^-2$ and point Q has coordinate 2. Write the coordinate of each point described.

37. 3 units to the right of Q 5   **38.** 3 units to the left of P $^-5$
39. 3 units to the left of Q $^-1$ **40.** 3 units to the right of P 1
41. Halfway between P and Q 0   **42.** One fourth of the way from P to Q $^-1$

C 43. On a number line, point A has coordinate 3, and point D has coordinate 6. What is the coordinate of the point between A and D that is half as far from A as it is from D? 4

44. On a number line, point X has coordinate $^-1$, and point Y has coordinate 5. What is the coordinate of the point between X and Y that is twice as far from X as it is from Y? 3

32   *CHAPTER 2*

32

2-2 Comparing Real Numbers

OBJECTIVE To show the order of real numbers.

You know that 2 is less than 6 and that 6 is greater than 2. **Inequality symbols** can be used to show the *order* of pairs of real numbers as follows.

$$< \text{ means "is less than": } \quad 2 < 6$$

$$> \text{ means "is greater than": } \quad 6 > 2$$

To avoid confusing the symbols $>$ and $<$, notice that the name of the greater number is placed at the greater (or open) end of the inequality symbol. The statements $2 < 6$ and $6 > 2$ give the same information.

The graphs of real numbers on a number line show the order of the numbers. Compare the graphs of 2 and 6 below. The graph of the smaller number, 2, lies to the left of the graph of the greater number, 6.

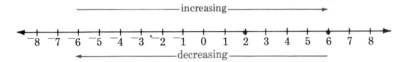

On a horizontal number line, such as the one above, the numbers increase from left to right and decrease from right to left. By studying the number line, you can see that the following statements are true.

$$-6 < -4 \qquad -6 < 0 \qquad -6 < 2$$
$$-4 > -6 \qquad 0 > -6 \qquad 2 > -6$$

EXAMPLE Graph the numbers 3, -1, 5.5, 0, -2, -4 on a number line, and then name them in order from least to greatest.

SOLUTION

From least to greatest, the numbers are -4, -2, -1, 0, 3, 5.5.

Oral Exercises

Translate the following statements into words.

1. $2 < 7$ **2.** $0 < 1$ **3.** $0 > -1$ **4.** $-2 > -6$

5. $-4 > -10$ **6.** $\dfrac{1}{10} < \dfrac{1}{4}$ **7.** $0.35 < 0.4$ **8.** $-0.5 > -2.5$

WORKING WITH REAL NUMBERS 33

Teaching Suggestions p. T67

Suggested Extensions p. T67

Chalkboard Examples

1. Graph the numbers

$$3, \ -1\tfrac{1}{2}, \ -4, \ 0, \ \tfrac{1}{2}, \text{ and } 5$$

on a number line. Then name the numbers in order from least to greatest.

$$-4, \ -1\tfrac{1}{2}, \ 0, \ \tfrac{1}{2}, \ 3, \ 5$$

2. Write another inequality that gives the same information as $-3 < 4$.

$$4 > -3$$

Replace each ? with one of the symbols $<$ or $>$ to make a true statement.

3. $-7 \ \underline{?} \ 5$ **4.** $4 \ \underline{?} \ 3$

    $<$ $>$

5. $\dfrac{1}{100} \ \underline{?} \ \dfrac{1}{5}$ **6.** $-\dfrac{1}{3} \ \underline{?} \ \dfrac{1}{10}$

    $<$ $<$

7. $\dfrac{3}{5} \ \underline{?} \ \dfrac{7}{10}$

    $<$

8. $0.025 \ \underline{?} \ 0.205$

    $<$

Translate into symbols.

9. Negative one is greater than negative two.

$$-1 > -2$$

Additional Answers
Oral Exercises

1. 2 is less than 7.

2. 0 is less than 1.

3. 0 is greater than -1.

4. -2 is greater than -6.

5. -4 is greater than -10.

6. $\dfrac{1}{10}$ is less than $\dfrac{1}{4}$.

7. 0.35 is less than 0.4.

8. -0.5 is greater than -2.5.

Supplementary Material

Practice Master 4

Suggested Assignments

Minimum
        34/1–12, 13–31 odd
Average
Day 1: 34/1–31 odd, 32
        S 32/43
Day 2: 35/33–39 odd
        39/1–15 odd
NOTE: Day 2 finishes Sec.
        2-2 and starts Sec.
        2-3.

Maximum
        34/1–31 odd
        35/33–40
        S 32/42, 44

Additional A Exercises

Translate into words.

1. $3 < 8$
   Three is less than eight.

2. $^-4 > ^-7$
   Negative four is greater
   than negative seven.

3. $^-7 < 2$
   Negative seven is less
   than two.

Translate into symbols.

4. Six is less than thirteen.
   $6 < 13$

5. Negative nine is less than
   negative four.
   $^-9 < ^-4$

6. One third is greater than
   negative one.
   $\frac{1}{3} > ^-1$

In Exercises 9–16, tell whether or not the given statement is true. Give a reason for your answer.

SAMPLE $8 \times 4 > 8 + 4$ **SOLUTION** True, because $8 \times 4 = 32$, $8 + 4 = 12$, and $32 > 12$.

9. $^-3 < 0 + \frac{3}{5}$ True; $^-3 < \frac{3}{5}$ **10.** $\frac{3}{4} \times \frac{1}{4} < \frac{3}{4} + \frac{1}{4}$ True; $\frac{3}{16} < 1$

11. $4 \times 3 < 3 \times 4$ False; $12 \not< 12$ **12.** $18 + (1 + 19) > (18 + 1) + 19$
                                                                        False; $38 \not> 38$
13. $\frac{7+1}{4} > \frac{7-1}{3}$ False; $2 \not> 2$ **14.** $\frac{10+2}{4+8} > ^-1$ True; $1 > ^-1$

15. $4(6 - 3) < 3(6 - 4)$ False; $12 \not< 6$ **16.** $7(0 + 6) < (7 \times 0) + (7 \times 6)$
                                                                        False; $42 \not< 42$

Written Exercises

Translate each statement into symbols.

A   **1.** Five is greater than negative two. $5 > ^-2$

   2. Negative seven is less than negative one. $^-7 < ^-1$

   3. Negative ten is greater than negative fifteen. $^-10 > ^-15$

   4. Nine is greater than six. $9 > 6$

   5. Four is less than four and five tenths. $4 < 4.5$

   6. Zero is greater than negative five tenths. $0 > ^-0.5$

   7. Negative twelve is less than zero. $^-12 < 0$

   8. One fourth is less than seven. $\frac{1}{4} < 7$

Replace each __?__ with one of the symbols $<$ or $>$ to make a true statement.

   9. $^-7 \underline{\ ?\ } 0 <$ **10.** $0 \underline{\ ?\ } ^-9 >$ **11.** $5 \underline{\ ?\ } 4 + 3 <$ **12.** $2 - 1 \underline{\ ?\ } ^-6 >$

   13. $7 \times 9 \underline{\ ?\ } 8 \times 6 >$ **14.** $1 \times 3 \underline{\ ?\ } 2 \times 2 <$ **15.** $1 \times 1 \underline{\ ?\ } ^-1 >$ **16.** $^-1.23 \underline{\ ?\ } ^-1.24 >$

   17. $49 - 7 \times 7 \underline{\ ?\ } 2(24 \div (5 + 3)) <$ **18.** $(7 \times 7) - 7 \underline{\ ?\ } (4 + 3)(4 - 3) >$

   19. $7.2 - 2.2 \underline{\ ?\ } \frac{7.2 + 2.2}{2} >$ **20.** $\frac{4.5 + 3.5}{4} \underline{\ ?\ } (4.5 - 3.5)5 <$

Write the given numbers in order from least to greatest.

B 21. $0, ^-4, 7, ^-6$ $^-6, ^-4, 0, 7$ **22.** $^-5, ^-7, 0, ^-9$ $^-9, ^-7, ^-5, 0$ **23.** $^-1, 3, ^-5, 2$

24. $^-8, 9, ^-9, 1$ $^-9, ^-8, 1, 9$ **25.** $\frac{^-1}{2}, \frac{^-1}{5}, \frac{^-1}{3}, \frac{^-1}{4}$ $\frac{^-1}{2}, \frac{^-1}{3}, \frac{^-1}{4}, \frac{^-1}{5}$ **26.** $\frac{^-2}{3}, \frac{^-3}{4}, \frac{^-1}{6}, \frac{^-1}{9}$

27. $1.5, ^-1.4, ^-0.6, 0.8$ $^-1.4, ^-0.6, 0.8, 1.5$ **28.** $2.6, ^-3.4, ^-2, 3$ $^-3.4, ^-2, 2.6, 3$

29. $3.142, 3.14, 3.1416$ $3.14, 3.1416, 3.142$ **30.** $^-6\frac{1}{3}, ^-6\frac{1}{7}, ^-6\frac{1}{2}$ $^-6\frac{1}{2}, ^-6\frac{1}{3}, ^-6\frac{1}{7},$

31. $^-2\frac{1}{4}, ^-2\frac{1}{6}, ^-2\frac{1}{2}$ $^-2\frac{1}{2}, ^-2\frac{1}{4}, ^-2\frac{1}{6}$ **32.** $1.414, 1.4, 1.41$ $1.4, 1.41, 1.414$

23. $^-5, ^-1, 2, 3$

26. $\frac{^-3}{4}, \frac{^-2}{3}, \frac{^-1}{6}, \frac{^-1}{9}$

34   *CHAPTER 2*

Let x be any positive number and y any negative number. State whether or not the given sentence is true.

C 33. $x < y$ False   34. $y < 0$ True   35. $x > y$ True   36. $0 > x$ False

37. Some value of x is equal to zero. False

38. No value of y is equal to zero. True

39. On a number line, the graphs of x and y are on opposite sides of the origin. True

40. On a number line, the graph of x is on the same side of the origin as the graph of 1. True

Career Note Carpenter

Have you ever used a miter box, a level, a try square, a vise, or a bevel? If you have, then you were probably doing some carpentry work, because these are all hand tools used by carpenters.

Skilled carpenters are involved in almost every aspect of construction. They construct scaffolding, temporary buildings on construction sites, partitions, rafters, sub-floors, and molds for concrete. This work would all be called "rough" carpentry.

Carpenters also do "finish" work. They make cabinets, doors, and stairs. They install floors, paneling, and molding.

To become a skilled carpenter, a student is advised to finish high school or vocational school and then enroll in an apprenticeship program. An apprenticeship program generally includes four years of on-the-job training in carpentry techniques and 144 hours of classroom instruction each year in drafting, blueprint reading, and mathematics.

35

Chalkboard Examples

Simplify.

1. 2 + (28 + 7)   37

2. 3 × 11 × $\frac{1}{3}$ × 2   22

3. 5 + 3y + 1   3y + 6

4. (37 × 25) × 4   3700

Name the axiom illustrated in each example below.

5. (3)(4 × w) = (3 × 4)(w)
   Associative axiom for multiplication

6. Since $\frac{1}{3}$ and $\frac{1}{4}$ are real

   numbers, $\left(\frac{1}{3} + \frac{1}{4}\right)$ must

   be a real number.
   Closure axiom for addition

7. $\frac{1}{5}(5x) = \left(\frac{1}{5} \cdot 5\right)(x)$

   Associative axiom for multiplication

8. 25 + 9 = 9 + 25
   Commutative axiom for addition

Supplementary Material

Progress Test 4

2-3 *Using Basic Properties*

OBJECTIVE   **To use number properties to simplify expressions.**

Addition and multiplication of real numbers have several basic properties that you are asked to take for granted. For example, you may accept the following statements as facts.

1. Every pair of real numbers has a unique (one and only one) sum which is also a real number.

2. Every pair of real numbers has a unique product which is also a real number.

3. When you add two real numbers, you get the same sum no matter what order you use in adding them.

$$7 + 5 = 5 + 7 \qquad\qquad 1.2 + 0.4 = 0.4 + 1.2$$

4. When you multiply real numbers, you get the same product no matter what order you use in multiplying them.

$$0 \times 13 = 13 \times 0 \qquad\qquad \frac{1}{3} \times \frac{2}{5} = \frac{2}{5} \times \frac{1}{3}$$

Statements that are assumed to be true are called **axioms**, or **postulates**. Statements (1) and (2) above may be stated more formally as follows.

AXIOMS OF CLOSURE

For all real numbers a and b:

$a + b$ is a unique real number.

ab is a unique real number.

Statements (3) and (4) above may be stated as follows.

COMMUTATIVE AXIOMS

For all real numbers a and b:

$$a + b = b + a$$

$$ab = ba$$

---

36   *CHAPTER 2*

In the sum $a + b$, a and b are called **terms.** In the product ab, a and b are called **factors.**

You find a sum or a product by working with two numbers at a time. To find the sum of several numbers, such as

$$87 + 75 + 25,$$

you usually do the additions in order from left to right:

$$(87 + 75) + 25 = 162 + 25 = 187.$$

This example would be easier to compute if the terms were grouped as follows:

$$87 + (75 + 25) = 87 + 100 = 187.$$

Note that the sum is 187 no matter which way the terms of $87 + 75 + 25$ are grouped. When you add three or more real numbers, you get the same sum no matter how you group, or *associate,* the numbers.

Similarly, products of three or more real numbers do not depend on the way you group the factors. For example, you can verify that

$$\left(7 \times \tfrac{1}{2}\right) \times 20 = 7 \times \left(\tfrac{1}{2} \times 20\right).$$

ASSOCIATIVE AXIOMS

For all real numbers a, b, and c:

$$(a + b) + c = a + (b + c)$$

$$(ab)c = a(bc)$$

The commutative and associative axioms permit you to add or multiply numbers *in any order* and *in any groups of two.* Thoughtful use of these axioms can sometimes help you simplify expressions.

EXAMPLE 1   Simplify $3 \times 25 \times 42 \times 4$.

SOLUTION $\begin{aligned}
3 \times 25 \times 42 \times 4 &= (3 \times 42)(25 \times 4) \\
&= 126 \times 100 \\
&= 12{,}600
\end{aligned}$

EXAMPLE 2   Simplify $3 + 7x + 2$.

SOLUTION $\begin{aligned}
3 + 7x + 2 &= 7x + 3 + 2 \\
&= 7x + 5
\end{aligned}$

You use the sign $=$ to show that two expressions name the same number (page 2). In your work, you will usually use the following properties of equality without mention.

For all real numbers a, b, and c:

Reflexive Property $a = a$

Symmetric Property   If $a = b$, then $b = a$.

Transitive Property   If $a = b$ and $b = c$, then $a = c$.

Throughout the rest of this book, the domain of all variables is the set of real numbers unless otherwise specified.

Oral Exercises

Name the axiom or property illustrated.

SAMPLE $6 + 5 = 5 + 6$ *SOLUTION*   Commutative axiom for addition

1. $7 \times 8 = 8 \times 7$ Comm. ax. for $\times$ 2. $(65 + 99) + 1 = 65 + (99 + 1)$ Assoc. ax. for $+$

3. $\frac{1}{2} + 3 = 3 + \frac{1}{2}$ Comm. ax. for $+$ 4. $(9)(6 \times 0) = (9 \times 6)(0)$ Assoc. ax. for $\times$

5. $y + 2.5 = 2.5 + y$ Comm. ax. for $+$ 6. If $8y = 56$, then $56 = 8y$. Symmetric prop.

7. $\frac{1}{2}(4t) = \left(\frac{1}{2} \cdot 4\right)t$ Assoc. ax. for $\times$ 8. If $r + 3 = 7$, then $7 = r + 3$. Symmetric prop.

9. $(12 + x) + 3 = (x + 12) + 3$ Comm. ax. for add.

10. There is only one real number that is the sum of 3.9 and 0.7. Closure ax. for add.

11. Every real number is equal to itself. Reflexive prop.

12. If $x + 4 = 5$ and $5 = 1 + 4$, then $x + 4 = 1 + 4$. Transitive prop.

13. $x + 26 + 14 + y = x + (26 + 14) + y$ Assoc. ax. for add.

Name the axiom that justifies each step. A check ($\checkmark$) shows that the step is justified by the substitution principle (page 2).

14. $49 + (28 + 11) = 49 + (11 + 28)$ (1) _?_ Comm. ax. for add.
$\qquad\qquad\qquad = (49 + 11) + 28$ (2) _?_ Assoc. ax. for add.
$\qquad\qquad\qquad = 60 + 28$ (3) _$\checkmark$_
$\qquad\qquad\qquad = 88$ (4) _$\checkmark$_

15. $(25 \times 93) \times 4 = 4 \times (25 \times 93)$ (1) _?_ Comm. ax. for mult.
$\qquad\qquad\qquad = (4 \times 25) \times 93$ (2) _?_ Assoc. ax. for mult.
$\qquad\qquad\qquad = 100 \times 93$ (3) _$\checkmark$_
$\qquad\qquad\qquad = 9300$ (4) _$\checkmark$_

38   CHAPTER 2

Suggested Assignments

Minimum
39/1–16
S 34/32

Average
NOTE: Day 2 of Sec. 2-2 finishes Sec. 2-2 and starts Sec. 2-3.
39/17, 18
R 39/Self-Test 1

Maximum
39/1–15 odd, 17–19
S 34/32

Written Exercises

In each of Exercises 1-16, simplify the expression.

A
1. $329 + 45 + 71 + 5$ 450
2. $422 + 36 + 78 + 14$ 550
3. $2 \times 33 \times 5 \times 3$ 990
4. $50 \times 11 \times 11 \times 20$ 121,000
5. $25 \times 57 \times 2 \times 2$ 5700
6. $4 \times 19 \times 7 \times 25$ 13,300
7. $7\frac{1}{2} + 5\frac{1}{3} + 1\frac{1}{2} + \frac{2}{3}$ 15
8. $99\frac{6}{7} + 1\frac{2}{5} + \frac{1}{7} + \frac{3}{5}$ 102
9. $0.1 + 1.5 + 7.9 + 0.5$ 10.0, or 10
10. $6.75 + 8.95 + 1.05 + 3.25$ 20.00, or 20

SAMPLE $x + 1 + y + 15 = x + y + 1 + 15 = x + y + 16$

B
11. $x + 2 + y + 9 + z + 4$ $x + y + z + 15$
12. $t + 3 + 8 + s + 16 + r$ $t + s + r + 27$
13. $(5k)(3p)(2q)$ 30kpq
14. $(4x)(10y)(7z)$ 280xyz
15. $(75a)(3b)(10c)(2)$ 4500abc
16. $(25t)(25p)(25q)(4)(8)$ 500,000tpq

In each of Exercises 17-19, an operation $*$ is defined over the set of positive integers.

a. Find $2 * 3$.
b. State whether or not $*$ has a commutative property.
c. State whether or not $*$ has an associative property.

C
17. $a * b = a + (b + 1)$
   a. 6   b. Yes   c. Yes
18. $a * b = a + 2b$
   a. 8   b. No   c. No
19. $a * b = 2(a + b)$
   a. 10   b. Yes   c. No

Self-Test 1

VOCABULARY

origin (p. 29)
positive side (p. 29)
negative side (p. 29)
integers (p. 30)
positive number (p. 30)
negative number (p. 30)
graph (p. 30)
coordinate (p. 30)

real number (p. 30)
inequality symbols (p. 33)
axiom (p. 36)
axioms of closure (p. 36)
commutative axioms (p. 36)
terms (p. 37)
factors (p. 37)
associative axioms (p. 37)

1. Graph the given numbers on the same number line: Obj. 2-1, p. 29
   $^-4, ^-1, 0, 2$

2. Translate the given statement into words: $^-3 < 2$.   Obj. 2-2, p. 33

3. Write the given numbers in order from least to greatest:
   $5, 0, ^-6, ^-1$

Simplify.

4. $25 \times 89 \times 4$
5. $5 + 2x + 6$ Obj. 2-3, p. 36

Check your answers with those at the back of the book.

WORKING WITH REAL NUMBERS   **39**

Chalkboard Examples

1. Using arrows along a number line, draw a diagram to represent the sum $^-6 + 4$.

2. Give an addition statement illustrated by the diagram.

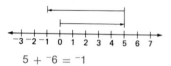

$5 + {}^-6 = {}^-1$

Find the sums mentally. Verify the answers on a number line, if necessary.

3. $^-3 + {}^-2$ $^-5$

4. $^-7 + 7$ 0

5. $(2 + {}^-6) + {}^-3$ $^-7$

6. $^-1.5 + ({}^-0.3 + 2)$ 0.2

7. Solve the equation $^-4 + y = 3$ by using a number line.

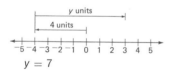

$y = 7$

ADDING REAL NUMBERS

2-4 *Addition on a Number Line*

OBJECTIVE   To use a number line to add real numbers.

You can use a horizontal number line to help you find the sum of two real numbers. To find the sum of $^-3$ and $^-5$, draw a number line and follow these directions. Starting at the origin, move your pencil along your number line 3 units to the left. Then, from that position, move your pencil 5 units to the left. Moves to the *left* represent *negative* numbers. Together, the two moves amount to a move of 8 units to the left from the origin. The arrows in the diagram below show the moves.

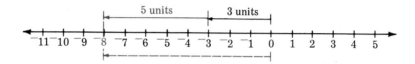

Thus, $^-3 + {}^-5 = {}^-8$.

To find the sum $^-3 + 5$, first move 3 units to the left from the origin. Then, from that position, move 5 units to the right. Moves to the *right* represent *positive* numbers. The two moves amount to a move of 2 units to the right, as shown below.

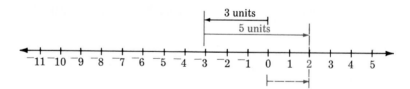

Thus, $^-3 + 5 = 2$

The next diagram shows how to find the sum $3 + {}^-5$.

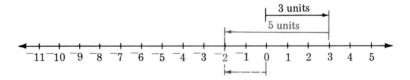

Thus, $3 + {}^-5 = {}^-2$.

40   *CHAPTER 2*

You can use a number line to help you find the sum of any two real numbers. Can you visualize $^-3 + 0$ on a number line? Interpret "add 0" to mean "move no units." Then you can see that

$$^-3 + 0 = ^-3 \quad \text{and} \quad 0 + ^-3 = ^-3.$$

These equations illustrate the special property of zero for addition of real numbers: When 0 is added to any given number, the sum is *identical* to the given number. We call 0 the **identity element for addition.**

IDENTITY AXIOM FOR ADDITION

There is a unique real number 0 such that for every real number a,

$$\boldsymbol{a + 0 = a} \quad \text{and} \quad \boldsymbol{0 + a = a.}$$

Oral Exercises

Give an addition statement illustrated by each diagram.

1.
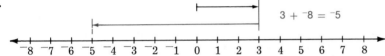
$$3 + ^-8 = ^-5$$

2.
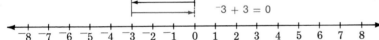
$$^-3 + 3 = 0$$

3.
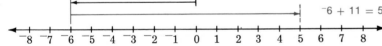
$$^-6 + 11 = 5$$

4.
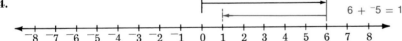
$$6 + ^-5 = 1$$

Simplify each expression. If necessary, think of moves along a number line.

5. $^-7 + 0$ $^-7$	**6.** $0 + ^-4$ $^-4$	**7.** $^-6 + 6$ 0	**8.** $5 + ^-5$ 0
9. $^-4 + ^-5$ $^-9$	**10.** $^-9 + ^-1$ $^-10$	**11.** $3 + ^-1$ 2	**12.** $^-4 + 7$ 3
13. $^-8 + 6$ $^-2$	**14.** $5 + ^-3$ 2	**15.** $17 + ^-20$ $^-3$	**16.** $^-1 + ^-99$ $^-100$
17. $101 + ^-1$ 100	**18.** $^-100 + 1$ $^-99$	**19.** $^-10 + 0$ $^-10$	**20.** $^-59 + 59$ 0

Suggested Assignments

Minimum
42/1–30
R 39/Self-Test 1

Average
42/1–19 odd, 20–31

Maximum
42/1–27 odd, 28–31
R 39/Self-Test 1

Additional A Exercises

Simplify each expression. If necessary, use a number line.

1. $12 + {}^-7$ 5

2. ${}^-17 + 5$ ${}^-12$

3. ${}^-13 + {}^-22$ ${}^-35$

4. $(3 + 9) + {}^-14$ ${}^-2$

5. $6 + ({}^-7 + {}^-9)$ ${}^-10$

6. $({}^-3 + 8) + {}^-5$ 0

Written Exercises

Simplify each expression. If necessary, draw a number line such as the one below to help you.

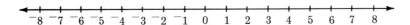

A **1.** $({}^-2 + 5) + {}^-3$ 0
2. $(7 + {}^-4) + {}^-11$ ${}^-8$

3. $(15 + {}^-21) + 5$ ${}^-1$
4. $({}^-10 + {}^-17) + 10$ ${}^-17$

5. ${}^-71 + ({}^-14 + 21)$ ${}^-64$
6. $(48 + {}^-8) + (1 + {}^-1)$ 40

7. $({}^-45 + {}^-25) + (0 + 2)$ ${}^-68$
8. $43 + (6 + {}^-12)$ 37

9. ${}^-3 + {}^-2 + {}^-6 + {}^-7$ ${}^-18$
10. ${}^-12 + {}^-8 + {}^-22 + {}^-2$ ${}^-44$

11. ${}^-3.2 + 1.6 + 1.2$ ${}^-0.4$
12. $4.8 + {}^-1.5 + {}^-2.3$ 1.0

13. $\frac{{}^-2}{3} + 4\frac{1}{3} + ({}^-6) + \left({}^-1\frac{1}{3}\right)$ ${}^-3\frac{2}{3}$
14. ${}^-6\frac{1}{2} + \left({}^-1\frac{1}{2}\right) + 5 + 2\frac{1}{2}$ $\frac{{}^-1}{2}$

15. $5.50 + ({}^-2.25) + ({}^-1)$ 2.25
16. $3.1 + ({}^-2.8) + ({}^-8)$ ${}^-7.7$

In Exercises 17–34, solve each equation. Use a number line as needed.

SAMPLE ${}^-3 + y = 4$

SOLUTION

The equation states that ${}^-3$ plus a certain number is 4. To arrive at 4 from ${}^-3$ on a number line, you move 7 units to the right.

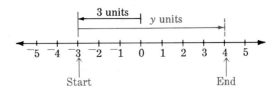

∴ the solution is 7. *Answer*

B **17.** ${}^-4 + y = {}^-5$ $y = {}^-1$ **18.** ${}^-2 + x = 17$ $x = 19$ **19.** $0 = 12 + z$ $z = {}^-12$

20. $v + 0 = {}^-8$ $v = {}^-8$ **21.** ${}^-13 + k = {}^-9$ $k = 4$ **22.** ${}^-1 + r = {}^-6$ $r = {}^-5$

23. ${}^-20 = 4 + d$ $d = {}^-24$ **24.** $11 = {}^-3 + m$ $m = 14$ **25.** ${}^-3.5 + n = {}^-4$ $n = {}^-0.5$

26. ${}^-1.25 + t = {}^-2$ $t = {}^-0.75$ **27.** ${}^-4 + q = {}^-4$ $q = 0$ **28.** $0 = {}^-50 + w$ $w = 50$

C **29.** $r + {}^-2 = {}^-3 + 5$ $r = 4$ **30.** ${}^-8 + a = {}^-3 + {}^-10$ $a = {}^-5$ **31.** $a + a = 0$ $a = 0$

32. $b + b = {}^-12$ $b = {}^-6$ **33.** $9 = 2y + {}^-1$ $y = 5$ **34.** $6x + {}^-3 = 0$ $x = \frac{1}{2}$

42   CHAPTER 2

2-5 Opposites and Absolute Values

OBJECTIVE   To use opposites and absolute values.

The diagram below shows pairings of points on a number line. The paired points are at the same distance from the origin but on opposite sides of the origin. The origin is paired with itself.

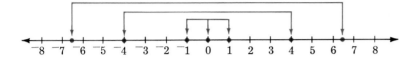

The coordinates of the paired points can also be paired:

0 with 0   ⁻1 with 1   ⁻4 with 4   ⁻6.5 with 6.5

The sum of the numbers in such a pair is 0. You can think of adding ⁻4 and 4 on a number line to check that

$$^-4 + 4 = 0.$$

Each number in a pair such as 4 and ⁻4 is called the **opposite,** or **additive inverse,** of the other number. The symbol for the opposite, or additive inverse, of a number a is

$-a$ (note the lowered position of the minus sign).

For example:

$-4 = {}^-4$, read "The opposite of four equals negative four."
$-(^-1) = 1$, read "The opposite of negative one equals one."
$-0 = 0$. read "The opposite of zero equals zero."

The following axiom is a formal way of saying that every real number has one and only one opposite and that the sum of a number and its opposite is always zero.

AXIOM OF OPPOSITES

For every real number a, there is a unique real number $-a$ such that

$$a + (-a) = 0 \quad \text{and} \quad -a + a = 0.$$

Note that the numerals -4 (lowered minus sign) and ⁻4 (raised minus sign) name the same number. Thus -4 can mean "negative 4" as well as "the opposite of 4."

WORKING WITH REAL NUMBERS   43

Chalkboard Examples
Simplify.
1. $-(-2.4)$ 2.4
2. $-(5 + 3)$ -8
3. $-\left(-7 + \dfrac{1}{3}\right)$
   $\dfrac{20}{3}$, or $6\dfrac{2}{3}$
4. $|-8|$ 8
5. $-|1|$ -1
6. $-|-3.5|$ -3.5
7. $-(-0)$ 0
8. $-x - (-x)$ 0
9. $5(|2|) + 3(|-1|)$ 13
10. $-(-6) + (-4)$ 2
11. $-|-6| + |-4|$ -2

*To simplify notation, lowered minus signs will be used in the numer-
als for negative numbers throughout the rest of this book.*

Be sure you understand the meaning of a variable expression like
$-a$. If a represents -7, then $-a$ is the positive number 7. In general:

1. If a is a positive number, then $-a$ is a negative number;
   if a is a negative number, then $-a$ is a positive number;
   if a is 0, then $-a$ is 0.

2. The opposite of $-a$ is a; that is, $-(-a) = a$.

EXAMPLE 1 Simplify.

$$\textbf{a.}\ -(7+5) \qquad \textbf{b.}\ -(-2.5) \qquad \textbf{c.}\ -0 \qquad \textbf{d.}\ -(-n)$$

SOLUTION   **a.** -12 **b.** 2.5 **c.** 0 **d.** n

EXAMPLE 2 $-(-10) + (-14) = 10 + (-14) = -4$

In any pair of nonzero opposites, such as -4 and 4, one number is
negative and the other is positive. The positive number of any pair of
opposite nonzero real numbers is called the **absolute value** of each
number in the pair.

The absolute value of a number a is denoted by $|a|$. For example,

$$|-4| = 4 \quad \text{and} \quad |4| = 4.$$

The absolute value of a number may be thought of as the distance of
the graph of the number from the origin on a number line. The graphs
of both -4 and 4 are 4 units from the origin.

The absolute value of 0 is defined to be 0 itself: $|0| = 0$.

EXAMPLE 3 $8|-2| + |-5| = (8 \times 2) + 5 = 16 + 5 = 21$

Oral Exercises

Name the opposite of each number.

   1. 8 $_{-8}$ **2.** 5 $_{-5}$ **3.** -1 $_1$ **4.** -3 $_3$ **5.** 1000 $_{-1000}$

   6. -101 $_{101}$ **7.** 0 $_0$ **8.** 0.5 $_{-0.5}$ **9.** 2.4 $_{-2.4}$ **10.** $-1\frac{1}{2}$ $1\frac{1}{2}$

Simplify.

   11. $-(-6)$ $_6$ **12.** $-(-14)$ $_{14}$ **13.** $-\left[-\left(-\frac{1}{2}\right)\right]$ $_{-\frac{1}{2}}$

   14. $-[-(-0)]$ $_0$ **15.** $(-3+6)+(-6)$ $_{-3}$ **16.** $(8+2)+(-8)$ $_2$

   17. $5+[-(-1)]$ $_6$ **18.** $-(-4)+4$ $_8$ **19.** $|2.1|$ $_{2.1}$

20. $|-32|$ 32   **21.** $6 + |6|$ 12   **22.** $6 + |-6|$ 12

23. $-8 + |-8|$ 0   **24.** $-|9| + |-9|$ 0   **25.** $-(-|2| + |1|)$ 1

Complete.

26. If r is a negative number, then $-r$ is a __?__ number. positive

27. If r is a positive number, then $-r$ is a __?__ number. negative

28. The absolute value of every real number is __?__ than zero or equal to greater
zero.

Written Exercises

Simplify.

A   **1.** $-(-6) + 12$ 18   **2.** $-(-8) + 2$ 10   **3.** $-7 + [-(-3)]$ −4

    4. $5 + [-(-1)]$ 6   **5.** $-(8 + 9)$ −17   **6.** $-(-5 + 6)$ −1

    7. $-(-10) + 10$ 20   **8.** $-(31 + 49)$ −80   **9.** $-20 + [-(-15)]$ −5

   10. $-[8 + (-3)]$ −5   **11.** $-[-3 + (-3)]$ 6   **12.** $-[11 + (-9)]$ −2

   13. $7 + |-8|$ 15   **14.** $|-6| + |0|$ 6   **15.** $|-7| + |10|$ 17

   16. $|1.2| + |-1.2|$ 2.4   **17.** $|3 + (-2)| + 6$ 7   **18.** $|9 + (-3)| + (-6)$ 0

   19. $-|-13 + 5|$ −8   **20.** $-|8 + (-10)|$ −2   **21.** $3|-1| + |-4|$ 7

   22. $5\left|-\dfrac{1}{5}\right| + |-2|$ 3   **23.** $-(2|6|) + (-|6|)$ −18   **24.** $-[5|-2| + (-8)]$ −2

In Exercises 25–36, let the domain of the variable be $\{-2, -1, 0, 1, 2\}$.
For each number in the given domain, tell whether the open sentence is
true or false. Then solve the open sentence.

   SAMPLE $-x < 1$ *SOLUTION* $-(-2) < 1$;   that is, $2 < 1$;   false
                                         $-(-1) < 1$;   that is, $1 < 1$;   false
                                         $-(0) < 1$;   that is, $0 < 1$;   true
                                         $-(1) < 1$;   that is, $-1 < 1$;   true
                                         $-(2) < 1$;   that is, $-2 < 1$;   true
                          The solution set is $\{0, 1, 2\}$.

B   **25.** $-y = 2$ {−2}   **26.** $-1 = -a$ {1}   **27.** $-2 + b = 0$ {2}

   28. $x + (-1) = 1$ {2}   **29.** $1 - [-(-z)] = -1$ {2} **30.** $-(-s) + 2 = 0$ {−2}

   31. $|x| = 1$ {−1, 1}   **32.** $|-x| = 2$ {−2, 2}   **33.** $|y| + 1 = 3$ {−2, 2}

   34. $-6 + |n| = -4$ **35.** $-z > 1$ {−2}   **36.** $-t < 0$ {1, 2}
         {−2, 2}

In Exercises 37–40, suppose that a can be any nonzero real number.
State whether the given sentence is always true, only sometimes true,
or never true.

C   **37.** $|-a| > 0$ **38.** $|-a| < 0$ **39.** $|a| > -a$ **40.** $|a| < -a$
     Always   Never   Sometimes   Never

WORKING WITH REAL NUMBERS   **45**

Suggested Assignments

Minimum
   45/1–28
S 42/31

Average
   45/1–35 odd

Maximum
   45/1–35 odd
S 42/32–34

Additional A Exercises

Simplify.

1. $-(-9)$ 9

2. $-3 + [-(-6)]$ 3

3. $-(-7) + (-4)$ 3

4. $-[-3 + -(-1)]$ 2

5. $|7.3|$ 7.3

6. $|-4.5|$ 4.5

41. Explain why the following statement is true.

If a is a real number, then

$|a| = a$ if $a > 0$;

$|a| = a$ if $a = 0$;

$|a| = -a$ if $a < 0$.

By definition, $|a|$ is the positive number of the pair of opposites a and $-a$, which is a if $a > 0$ and is $-a$ if $a < 0$. If $a = 0$, then $|a| = |0| = 0 = a$, since the abs. val. of 0 is defined to be 0 itself.

Computer Key-In _____

If you type the following program into a computer that accepts the language BASIC, the computer will then be ready to add any two numbers that you give it.

```
10  PRINT "TYPE IN TWO NUMBERS TO BE ADDED."
20  INPUT A
30  INPUT B
40  PRINT "SUM =";A+B
50  END
```

Now type RUN. When the computer prints a question mark, type in any positive or negative integer or decimal and then press the RETURN key.

To add more than two numbers (except zero), try the following program. This program uses zero to indicate the end of your list of numbers to be added.

```
10  PRINT "TYPE IN A NUMBER AFTER EACH QUESTION MARK."
20  PRINT "TO END INPUT AND PRINT SUM, TYPE ZERO."
30  LET S=0
40  INPUT N
50  IF N=0 THEN 80
60  LET S=S+N
70  GOTO 40
80  PRINT "SUM=";S
90  END
```

Just for Fun _____

Find the sum of each row, column, and diagonal in the table at the right.

For example, in the first row:
$[3 + (-4)] + 1 = \underline{}$ 0

Each sum is 0.

3	−4	1	?
−2	0	2	?
−1	4	−3	?
?	?	?	?

?

2-6 Rules for Addition

OBJECTIVE   To add real numbers.

The expression $-(4 + 3)$ represents the opposite of the sum of 4 and 3. Since $4 + 3 = 7$,

$$-(4 + 3) = -7.$$

The expression $-4 + (-3)$ represents the sum of the opposite of 4 and the opposite of 3. As you saw earlier, you can use a number line to find $-4 + (-3)$ as shown below.

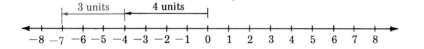

Thus, $-4 + (-3) = -7.$

Since $-(4 + 3) = -7$ and $-4 + (-3) = -7$, the following equation is true.

$$-(4 + 3) = -4 + (-3)$$

Using a number line, you can show that the following equations are also true.

$$-[-5 + (-2)] = 5 + 2 \qquad -[9 + (-4)] = -9 + 4 \qquad -(-7 + 6) = 7 + (-6)$$

These equations suggest the following property.

PROPERTY OF THE OPPOSITE OF A SUM

The opposite of a sum of real numbers is equal to the sum of the opposites of the numbers. That is, for all real numbers a and b,

$$-(a + b) = -a + (-b).$$

Using the property of the opposite of a sum along with axioms you have learned and the familiar addition facts for positive numbers, you can compute sums of any real numbers without thinking of a number line.

EXAMPLE 1   Simplify $-9 + (-5)$. 　　　SOLUTION 　　　$-9 + (-5) = -(9 + 5)$
$$= -14$$

WORKING WITH REAL NUMBERS   47

Teaching Suggestions p. T68

Suggested Extensions p. T68

Chalkboard Examples
Simplify.
1. $-7 + (-8)$ -15
2. $8 + (-7)$ 1
3. $(-8) + 7$ -1

Simplify.
4. $7 + (-9) + 2 + (-1) + 5$
   4
5. $28 + (-30) + (-17) + 45$
   26
6. Add:　-209
　　　　　578
　　　　　396
　　　　-181
　　　　　589

Supplementary Materials

Progress Test 5

Computer Activity 5
Dividing a Segment
   A short computer program divides a segment with given endpoint coordinates into any specified number of equal parts. Practice is given in finding midpoint coordinates and in finding the distance between two of the subdivision points.

EXAMPLE 2   Simplify $12 + (-7)$.

SOLUTION
$$12 + (-7) = (5 + 7) + (-7)$$
$$= 5 + [7 + (-7)]$$
$$= 5 + 0$$
$$= 5$$

   After computing many sums by using either a number line or the methods of Examples 1 and 2, you would probably discover the short-cut methods permitted by the following rules.

RULES FOR ADDITION OF POSITIVE AND NEGATIVE NUMBERS

1. If a and b are both positive, then $a + b = |a| + |b|$.
   Example. $2 + 6 = 8$

2. If a and b are both negative, then $a + b = -(|a| + |b|)$.
   Example. $-4 + (-5) = -(4 + 5) = -9$

3. If a is positive and b is negative and a has the greater absolute value, then $a + b = |a| - |b|$.
   Example. $7 + (-3) = 7 - 3 = 4$

4. If a is positive and b is negative and b has the greater absolute value, then $a + b = -(|b| - |a|)$.
   Example. $6 + (-9) = -(9 - 6) = -3$

5. If a and b are opposites, then $a + b = 0$.
   Example. $4 + (-4) = 0$

The following examples show how to add more than two real numbers.

EXAMPLE 3   Simplify $6 + (-10) + 12 + (-5)$.

SOLUTION 1   Add the numbers in order from left to right.
$$6 + (-10) = -4; \quad -4 + 12 = 8; \quad 8 + (-5) = 3 \quad \textbf{\textit{Answer}}$$

SOLUTION 2

Add positive numbers.	Add negative numbers.	Add the sums.
6	-10	18
12	-5	-15
18	-15	**3** *Answer*

48   *CHAPTER 2*

EXAMPLE 4   Add. -142
263
184
-357

SOLUTION   *Step 1*   *Step 2*   *Step 3*

Step 1	*Step 2*	*Step 3*
-142	263	-499
-357	184	447
-499	447	-52
		Answer

Oral Exercises

Add.

1. 7
    $\underline{7}$ 14

2. -3
    $\underline{-2}$ -5

3. -9
    $\underline{5}$ -4

4. $\overset{\neg}{}$ 7
    $\underline{-11}$ -4

5. -13
    $\underline{-27}$ -40

6. -1
    $\underline{9}$ 8

7. -15
    $\underline{6}$
    -9

8. -12
    $\underline{-5}$
    -17

9. -14
    $\underline{34}$
    20

10. 55
    $\underline{-75}$
    -20

11. -89
    $\underline{24}$
    -65

12. 55
    $\underline{-39}$
    16

Simplify.

13. $-8 + (-2)$ -10

14. $-17 + 9$ -8

15. $12 + (-12)$ 0

16. $13 + (-4)$ 9

17. $2 + (-11)$ -9

18. $-7 + 15$ 8

19. $7 + (-1) + (-6)$ 0

20. $-1 + (-3) + 3$ -1

21. $-5 + (-6) + 11$ 0

Written Exercises

Add.

A

1. 7
    6
    -1
    $\underline{3}$
    15

2. -4
    -7
    5
    $\underline{2}$
    -4

3. 43
    -23
    52
    $\underline{-10}$
    62

4. -35
    31
    48
    $\underline{-70}$
    -26

5. 148
    -72
    -26
    $\underline{-9}$
    41

6. -137
    241
    -85
    $\underline{-66}$
    -47

Simplify.

7. $-19 + 6 + (-10) + 41$ 18

8. $-14 + (-7) + 12 + 24$ 15

9. $111 + (-58) + (-93) + 28$ -12

10. $-310 + (-90) + 275 + 65$ -60

11. $-[35 + (-7)] + [-(-3 + 8)]$ -33

12. $[-5 + (-3)] + [-(3 + 5)]$ -16

13. $33 + (-44) + (-23) + 0 + 64 + 128$ 158

14. $-70 + 114 + (-81) + (-92) + 4$ -125

15. $29 + 41 + (-15) + 13 + (-57) + 5 + (-38) + (-18)$ -40

16. $48 + (-31) + 16 + 0 + (-95) + (-4) + (-36)$ -102

Replace each __?__ with a numeral to make a true statement.

B

17. __?__ $+ (-8) = 2$ 10

18. $-11 +$ __?__ $= 4$ 15

19. $6 +$ __?__ $= -5$ -11

20. __?__ $+ (-7) = 2$ 9

21. $0.4 +$ __?__ $= -1$ -1.4

22. __?__ $+ 0.75 = -0.25$ -1.00

Suggested Assignments

Minimum
Day 1: 49/1–22
    S 45/29–36
Day 2: 50/P: 1–11 odd, 14

Average
Day 1: 49/1–23 odd
      50/P: 1–13 odd
    S 45/37
Day 2: 49/12–22 even
      50/2–14 even

Maximum
Day 1: 49/5–25 odd
      50/P: 1–15 odd
    S 45/37–41
Day 2: 49/12, 20–26 even
      51/P: 8–16 even

Additional A Exercises

Add.

1. 16
    -12 25
    21

2. -23
    14 -28
    -19

3. 84
    -16 77
    9

4. 61
    -42 -8
    -27

5. -40
    -22 -125
    -63

6. 7
    2 12
    -5
    8

23. $-8 + (-x + x + 8)$
$= -8 + [(-x + x) + 8]$
$= -8 + [0 + 8]$
$= -8 + 8$
$= 0$

24. $-(-a + b) + b$
$= [-(-a) + (-b)] + b$
$= -(-a) + [-b + b]$
$= -(-a) + 0$
$= -(-a)$
$= a$

25. $a + b + [-(a + b + c)]$
$= (a + b) +$
$\quad [-(a + b) + (-c)]$
$= [(a + b) + (-(a + b))] +$
$\quad\quad\quad\quad\quad (-c)$
$= 0 + (-c)$
$= -c$

26. $m + [-(m + p)]$
$= m + [-m + (-p)]$
$= [m + (-m)] + (-p)$
$= 0 + (-p)$
$= -p$

In Exercises 23–26, write equations leading to the given equation. Justify each step.

SAMPLE $(a + b) + [-a + (-b)] = 0$

SOLUTION

$(a + b) + [-a + (-b)] = [a + (-a)] + [b + (-b)]$ Commutative and associative
axioms

$= 0 + 0$ Axiom of opposites

$= 0$ Identity axiom for addition

C **23.** $-8 + (-x + x + 8) = 0$ **24.** $-(-a + b) + b = a$

   25. $a + b + [-(a + b + c)] = -c$ **26.** $m + [-(m + p)] = -p$

Problems

a. Name a positive or a negative number to represent each measurement given in the problem.

b. Compute the sum of the numbers.

c. Answer the question.

SAMPLE

During a period of unsettled weather, the temperature fell 9°C, rose 3°C, fell 4°C, and then rose 6°C. How did the temperature at the end of the period compare with the temperature at the beginning?

SOLUTION

  a. $-9, 3, -4, 6$

  b. $-9 + 3 + (-4) + 6 = -4$

  c. At the end, the temperature was 4°C lower than at the beginning.

A   **1.** On one play a football team gained 5 yards. On the next play it lost 7 yards but then gained 9 yards on the third play. What was the team's net gain on the three plays? 7 yards

    2. An elevator starts at the 16th floor. It then goes down nine floors and up five floors. At what floor is the elevator then located? 12th floor

    3. Henry LeBlanc has $237 in his checking account. He deposits $63 and then writes a check for $28. How much is then in the checking account? $272

    4. The stock of Acme Rotors opened in the morning at $38 per share. By noon it had lost $5, but during the afternoon it gained $3. What was its closing value? $36

    5. A jet plane flying at an altitude of 7800 m dropped 900 m and then rose 750 m. What was its new altitude? 7650 m

50   *CHAPTER 2*

6. A submarine dove to a level 240 m below the surface of the ocean. Later it climbed 80 m and then dove 45 m. What was the new depth of the submarine? 205 m below the surface

7. A helicopter was flying in Death Valley at an altitude of 13 m below sea level. If it climbed 37 m and then dropped 29 m, at what altitude was it then flying? 5 m below sea level

8. A submarine 38 m below the ocean surface descended 15 m and then fired a rocket which rose 265 m. How far above the ocean surface did the rocket rise? 212 m

9. During their first year after opening a restaurant, the Taylors had a loss of $12,760. During their second and third years of operation, they had gains of $19,350 and $25,180. What was the restaurant's net gain or loss over the three-year period? Net gain of $31,770

10. During a four-day period, Milville Hospital received 24 new patients and discharged 6, received 8 and discharged 11, received 12 and discharged 21, and received 9 and discharged 13. How did the number of patients in the hospital at the end of the fourth day compare with the number at the start of the four-day period? There were 2 more patients.

B 11. A passenger on a train traveling at 133 km/h walks toward the back of the train at the rate of 7 km/h. What is the passenger's rate of travel with respect to the ground? 126 km/h

12. Departing from Center City at noon, Sandra flew to Westville. The flight took 3.5 hours, but the time in Westville is 2 hours earlier than it is in Center City. What time was it in Westville when Sandra landed? 1:30 P.M.

13. A golfer played six rounds of golf with the following scores: 2 under par, 4 over par, par, 3 over par, 1 under par, 5 over par. How did she finish with respect to par? 9 over par

14. On opening a revolving charge account, Jim Halloran bought $168.40 worth of clothing, and $88.20 worth of garden equipment. He then made two monthly payments of $35.00 each. If the interest charges for the two-month period totaled $6.50, what did Jim then owe on the account? $193.10

C 15. During a training exercise, an astronaut's heart rate rose 33 beats per minute, then fell 18 beats per minute, then rose 21 beats per minute, and after the exercise was completed, fell 30 beats per minute. If the rate was 74 beats per minute after the exercise was completed, what was it at the beginning? 68 beats per minute

16. During a ten-year period, the population of Windham increased by 2500. Over the next three ten-year periods, the population grew by 1500, decreased by 3000, and then decreased again by 2000. What was the population at the beginning of the forty-year period if the population was 15,000 at the end of the period? 16,000 people

Quick Quiz

Simplify.

1. $-4 + {}^-3$ -7

2. $-3 + 20 + {}^-5$ 12

3. $-(-6) + 4$ 10

4. $-|-8 + 2|$ -6

5. $-12 + (-4)$ -16

6. $-24 + 0 + (-12) + 6$
-30

Self-Test 2

VOCABULARY   identity element for addition   absolute value (p. 44)
(p. 41)   opposite of a sum (p. 47)
opposite (p. 43)

Simplify.

1. ${}^-3 + {}^-2$ **2.** ${}^-5 + 17 + {}^-6$ Obj. 2-4, p. 40

3. $-(-8) + 5$ **4.** $-|-7 + 3|$ Obj. 2-5, p. 43

5. $-11 + (-1)$ **6.** $-16 + 0 + (-12) + 8$ Obj. 2-6, p. 47

Check your answers with those at the back of the book.

Calculator Key-In

Use a calculator to add.

1.	2.	3.
$50.00	-3679	0.1000
$-$ 19.99	5153	-0.0100
$-$ 6.59	-2768	0.0010
3.25	4627	-0.0001
$26.67	3333	0.0909

Historical Note Plus and Minus

In one Egyptian papyrus dated around 1550 B.C., a pair of legs drawn walking in one direction was used to indicate addition and a pair of legs drawn walking in the opposite direction was used to indicate subtraction.

The symbols $+$ and $-$ that are used today for addition and subtraction were not used universally until the eighteenth century, although variations of these two symbols were in common use in Europe at about the time Columbus explored the Americas.

During the nineteenth century, as mathematicians turned to the foundations of algebra, they tried various ways of differentiating between "plus and minus" and "positive and negative." At about the beginning of the twentieth century, the small raised symbols, $+$ for positive and $-$ for negative, that are used in the early work with integers in this book came into general use in the United States.

52   *CHAPTER 2*

MULTIPLYING REAL NUMBERS

2-7 *The Distributive Axiom*

OBJECTIVE: To use the distributive axiom to simplify expressions.

The fare on the ferry from Port Alice to Seagate was $5 for each motorbike and $4 for the rider. Therefore, the total fare in dollars for three friends and their bikes was

$$3(5 + 4) = 3 \times 9 = 27.$$

The total fare was also the sum of the fares for the bikes and the fares for the riders:

$$(3 \times 5) + (3 \times 4) = 15 + 12 = 27.$$

Either way you compute it, the total fare is the same. That is,

$$3(5 + 4) = (3 \times 5) + (3 \times 4).$$

Teaching Suggestions p. T69

Suggested Extensions p. T69

Chalkboard Examples

Use the distributive axiom to simplify.

1. $40\left(\dfrac{1}{5} + \dfrac{3}{8}\right)$ 23

2. $12(3.25)$ 39

3. $14(21)$ 294

4. $22(25) + 13(25)$ 875

5. $22x + 13x$ 35x

6. $-3x + 5 + 6x + (-2)$
   $3x + 3$

Supplementary Material

Practice Master 6

Note that 3 is *distributed* as a multiplier of each term of $5 + 4$. This example illustrates another axiom that we use in working with real numbers: multiplication is *distributive with respect to addition*.

DISTRIBUTIVE AXIOM OF MULTIPLICATION WITH
RESPECT TO ADDITION

For all real numbers a, b, and c,

   $a(b + c) = ab + ac$ and $(b + c)a = ba + ca.$

By applying the symmetric property of equality, you can also state the distributive axiom in the following form.

For all real numbers a, b, and c,

   $ab + ac = a(b + c)$ and $ba + ca = (b + c)a.$

For example, the diagram below illustrates that

$$(4 \times 3) + (4 \times 2) = 4(3 + 2).$$

Area:
4 × 3

Area:
4 × 2

Area:
4 × (3 + 2)

 + =

The following examples show some uses of the distributive axiom.

EXAMPLE 1   **a.** $45\left(\frac{1}{3} + \frac{1}{5}\right) = \left(45 \times \frac{1}{3}\right) + \left(45 \times \frac{1}{5}\right) = 15 + 9 = 24$

b. $8(7.5) = 8(7 + 0.5) = (8 \times 7) + (8 \times 0.5) = 56 + 4 = 60$

c. $28 \times 7 = (20 + 8) \times 7 = (20 \times 7) + (8 \times 7) = 140 + 56 = 196$

d. $(25 \times 9) + (75 \times 9) = (25 + 75)9 = (100)9 = 900$

EXAMPLE 2   Show that $5x + 8x = 13x$ for every real number x.

SOLUTION $5x + 8x = (5 + 8)x$ Distributive axiom
$ = 13x$ Substitution principle

Because properties of real numbers and equality guarantee that for all values of the variable

$$5x + 8x \quad \text{and} \quad 13x$$

represent the same number, the two expressions are said to be **equivalent.** The expression $5x + 8x$ has two terms. The expression $13x$ has one term. Replacing an expression containing a variable by an equivalent expression with as few terms as possible is called **simplifying the expression.**

EXAMPLE 3   Simplify $5y + 1 + (-3)y + 19$.

SOLUTION $5y + 1 + (-3)y + 19 = [5y + (-3)y] + (1 + 19)$
$ = [5 + (-3)]y + 20$
$ = 2y + 20$

Oral Exercises

Use the distributive axiom to simplify each expression.

1. $2(50 + 1)$ 102

2. $3(40 + 2)$ 126

3. $5(20 + 7)$ 135

4. $4(30 + 5)$ 140

5. 4×2.5 10

6. $6 \times 1\frac{1}{3}$ 8

7. $10\left(3\frac{1}{2}\right)$ 35   **8.** $12(2.25)$ 27   **9.** $(25 + 75)\left(\frac{1}{5}\right)$ 20

10. $(49 + 77)\left(\frac{1}{7}\right)$ 18   **11.** $\left(\frac{1}{3} \times 16\right) + \left(\frac{1}{3} \times 2\right)$ 6   **12.** $\left(17 \times \frac{1}{4}\right) + \left(3 \times \frac{1}{4}\right)$ 5

Simplify.

13. $3x + 11x$ 14x   **14.** $10y + 18y$ 28y   **15.** $x + 7x$ 8x

16. $4r + r$ 5r   **17.** $(-2)t + (-4)t$ (−6)t   **18.** $(-3)s + (-7)s$ (−10)s

19. $5b + (-2)b$ 3b   **20.** $7a + (-3)a$ 4a   **21.** $3(2 + x) + 5$
  11 + 3x

Written Exercises

Simplify.

A 1. $80\left(\frac{1}{4} + \frac{1}{5}\right)$ 36   **2.** $3\left(1\frac{1}{3}\right)$ 4   **3.** $\frac{1}{6}(13) + \frac{1}{6}(11)$ 4

4. $(0.25)(9) + (0.75)(9)$ 9.00,   **5.** $(4 \times 37) + (6 \times 37)$ 370   **6.** $(33 \times 89) + (67 \times 89)$
      or 9   8900
7. $2x + 13x$ 15x   **8.** $20y + 14y$ 34y   **9.** $z + 29z$ 30z

10. $99w + w$ 100w   **11.** $45t + (-30)t$ 15t   **12.** $-16s + 36s$ 20s

13. $3x + 2x + 8$ 5x + 8   **14.** $5 + 7y + 4y$ 5 + 11y   **15.** $2(a + 1) + 5$ 2a + 7

16. $9(b + 7) + 7$ 9b + 70   **17.** $8c + (-5)c + 16$ 3c + 16   **18.** $21 + (-4)d + 12d$
                                                                             21 + 8d

19. $6a + 1 + 7a + 3$ 13a + 4   **20.** $4 + 11c + 4c + 11$ 15c + 15

21. $10x + (-3) + (-3)x + 5$ 7x + 2   **22.** $-9y + 7 + 18y + (-6)$ 9y + 1

23. $-12 + 12x + 12 + (-1)x$ 11x   **24.** $16y + 8 + (-8)y + (-8)$ 8y

25. $8b + (-2)b + (-4)b$ 2b   **26.** $(-9)c + (-2)c + 22c$ 11c

B 27. $3m + 5k + (-1)m + 12k$ 2m + 17k   **28.** $5h + (-2)g + 4h + 7g$ 9h + 5g

29. $7x + 9y + 3 + x + y$ 8x + 10y + 3   **30.** $8r + s + (-6)r + 2 + 4s$ 2r + 5s + 2

SAMPLE $2(x + y + z) + 3(2x + 3y)$

SOLUTION $2(x + y + z) + 3(2x + 3y) = (2x + 2y + 2z) + (6x + 9y)$
                                       $= (2x + 6x) + (2y + 9y) + 2z$
                                       $= 8x + 11y + 2z$

31. $7(n + r) + 13(n + r)$ 20n + 20r   **32.** $3(u + v) + 17(u + v)$ 20u + 20r

33. $8(x + 3) + 9(4 + x) + x$ 18x + 60   **34.** $6(y + 2) + 9(4 + y) + y$ 16y + 48

35. $5(z + 2x + 4) + 3(2z + 8)$ **36.** $16(k + 2) + 4(3p + 5k + 4)$ 36k + 12p + 48
  11z + 10x + 44

Suggested Assignments
Minimum
  55/1–39 odd
  R 52/*Self-Test 2*
Average
  55/1–43 odd
  R 52/*Self-Test 2*
Maximum
  55/1–37 odd, 38–42
  R 52/*Self-Test 2*

Additional A Exercises
Simplify.
1. $7a + (-2a)$ 5a
2. $-8x + 3x$ −5x
3. $-4c + (-9c)$ −13c
4. $5(x + 2) + 3x$ 8x + 10
5. $7 + 3[r + (-10)]$
    3r + (−23)
6. $10\left(\frac{1}{2} + \frac{1}{5}\right)$ 7

Represent each word expression by a variable expression. Then simplify it.

37. Six times the sum of x and y, increased by twice the sum of $3x$ and $2y$. $12x + 10y$

38. Twice the sum of seven and m, increased by three times the sum of eleven and m. $5m + 47$

39. Ten more than the sum of negative seven and x, increased by one half the sum of $10x$ and $12y$. $6x + 6y + 3$

40. Three more than twice the sum of p and q, increased by the product of negative five and q. $2p + (-3)q + 3$

Simplify.

C **41.** $9[7x + 5(4 + 3x)] + (-16)x + (-8)$ $182x + 172$

42. $-21 + (-1)y + 2[6y + 3(5y + 12)]$ $41y + 51$

43. $10(2q + p) + 17[2q + 4(3q + 9p + 5)]$ $622p + 258q + 340$

44. $8[9(3v + 4w + 1) + 14(v + 7)] + 5(8v + 3w)$ $368v + 303w + 856$

Biography John Cunningham McLennan

Sir John Cunningham McLennan (1867–1935) was born in Ingersoll, Ontario. He graduated from the University of Toronto in 1892 and was professor of physics there from 1907 to 1931. His major contributions in physics were made in the study of the flow of electricity in metals at very low temperatures.

McLennan's research in other areas included work in radioactivity and the use of radium in treating cancer. During World War I, he aided in the development of magnetic detection devices for submarines. He and another physicist were able to obtain a spectrum similar to that of the aurora by passing electrons through thin oxygen. Another achievement was his success in liquefying helium in 1932.

2-8 Rules for Multiplication

OBJECTIVE   To multiply real numbers.

When you multiply any given real number by 1, the product is identical to the given number. For example,

$$3 \times 1 = 3 \quad \text{and} \quad 1 \times 3 = 3.$$

The **identity element for multiplication** is 1.

> IDENTITY AXIOM FOR MULTIPLICATION
>
> There is a unique real number 1 such that for every real number a,
>
> $$a \cdot 1 = a \quad \text{and} \quad 1 \cdot a = a.$$

The equations

$$3 \times 0 = 0 \quad \text{and} \quad 0 \times 3 = 0$$

illustrate the *multiplicative property of zero:* When one of the factors of a product is zero, the product itself is zero.

> MULTIPLICATIVE PROPERTY OF ZERO
>
> For every real number a,
>
> $$a \cdot 0 = 0 \quad \text{and} \quad 0 \cdot a = 0.$$

Would you guess that $3 \times (-1) = -3$? You can verify this product by noticing that

$$3 \times (-1) = (-1) + (-1) + (-1) = -3.$$

Multiplying *any* real number by -1 produces the opposite of the number.

> MULTIPLICATIVE PROPERTY OF -1
>
> For every real number a,
>
> $$a(-1) = -a \quad \text{and} \quad (-1)a = -a.$$

WORKING WITH REAL NUMBERS   57

Teaching Suggestions p. T69

Suggested Extensions p. T69

Chalkboard Examples

State whether each expression below names a positive number, a negative number, or zero. Then simplify the expression.

1. $(-3)(12)(-1)$
   Positive; 36

2. $(-7)(0)\left(\frac{1}{2}\right)$
   Zero; 0

3. $(3)(-13)\left(\frac{1}{3}\right)$
   Negative; -13

4. $(-1)(2)(-3)(4)(-5)$
   Negative; -120

Simplify.

5. $(-5x)(2y)$ $-10xy$

6. $(-1)(6a)(3b)$
   $-18ab$

7. $(-1)(-1)(-1)$ -1

8. $(-2)(-6 + 10)$ -8

9. $(-3)(-7) + (-2)(13)$
   -5

A special case of the multiplicative property of -1 occurs when the value of a is -1:

$$(-1)(-1) = 1.$$

Using the multiplicative property of -1 with the familiar multiplication facts for positive numbers and axioms that you have learned, you can compute the product of *any* two real numbers. Here are some examples:

1. $3(4) = 12$
2. $(-3)(4) = (-1)(3)(4) = (-1)(12) = -12$
3. $3(-4) = 3(-1)(4) = (-1)(12) = -12$
4. $(-3)(-4) = (-1)(3)(-1)(4) = (-1)(-1)(12) = (1)(12) = 12$

Similarly, the following property can be shown.

PROPERTY OF OPPOSITES IN PRODUCTS

For all real numbers a and b:

$$-a(b) = -ab \qquad a(-b) = -ab \qquad -a(-b) = ab$$

Practice in computing products will lead you to discover the following rules.

RULES FOR MULTIPLICATION OF POSITIVE AND NEGATIVE NUMBERS

1. The product of a positive number and a negative number is a negative number.
2. The product of two positive numbers or of two negative numbers is a positive number.
3. The absolute value of the product of two real numbers is the product of the absolute values of the numbers:

$$|ab| = |a| \times |b|.$$

By pairing the negative numbers in a product of more than two factors, you will find that

the product of an *even* number of negative numbers is *positive;*

the product of an *odd* number of negative numbers is *negative.*

58 *CHAPTER 2*

EXAMPLE 1 State whether the expression names a positive number, a negative number, or zero. Then simplify the expression.

      a. $-8(-4)(-3)$ **b.** $15(-73)(0)$ **c.** $4(-3)(-2)$

SOLUTION   **a.** Negative; -96 **b.** 0   **c.** Positive; 24

EXAMPLE 2 Simplify.   **a.** $(-3x)(-12y)$ **b.** $7t + (-8t)$

SOLUTION   **a.** $(-3x)(-12y) = (-3)(-12)(x)(y) = 36xy$

             b. $7t + (-8t) = 7t + (-8)t = [7 + (-8)]t = (-1)t = -t$

Oral Exercises

Simplify.

  1. $(-8)(-1)$ 8   **2.** $10(-9)$ -90 **3.** $(-3)(-7)$ 21

  4. $(-9)(-5)$ 45   **5.** $(-1)(3)(-3)$ 9   **6.** $2(-5)(-1)$ 10

  7. $(-1)(-3)(-5)$ -15 **8.** $(-2)(-4)(-6)$ -48 **9.** $15(0)(-21)$ 0

  10. $-8(-12)(0)$ 0   **11.** $(-7)(-10x)$ $70x$ **12.** $(-6)(11y)$ $-66y$

  13. $(-2a)(-3b)$ $6ab$ **14.** $(4x)(-6y)$ $-24xy$ **15.** $(-7w)(11z)$ $-77wz$

  16. $5t + (-4t)$ t **17.** $8u + (-8u)$ 0   **18.** $-9xy + 8xy$ $-xy$

  19. $-4mn + (-6mn)$ **20.** $-a + 12a$ $11a$ **21.** $(-39k) + (-k)$ $-40k$
           $-10mn$

Written Exercises

Simplify.

A   **1.** $(-30)(-4)$ 120   **2.** $21(-4)$ -84 **3.** $(-4)(12)(-10)$ 480

    4. $(-6)(-11)(20)$ 1320   **5.** $(-7)(-3)(-5)$ -105 **6.** $(-8)(-4)(-2)$ -64

    7. $(-18)(-19)(0)$ 0   **8.** $(-45)(55)(0)$ 0   **9.** $4(-2)(-10)(-5)$ -400

  10. $(-6)(15)(-2)(-10)$ -1800 **11.** $(-4)(-1)(-6)(-10)$ 240   **12.** $(-8)(-5)(-1)(-\frac{3}{120})$

  13. $-2[-1 + (-8)]$ 18   **14.** $(-6 + 15)(-1)$ -9 **15.** $(9 \times 1) + 9(-11)$ -90

  16. $(-3 \times 8) + (-3 \times 2)$ -30 **17.** $(-6 \times 8) + (-6 \times 2)$ -60 **18.** $21(-1) + 21(11)$ 210

  19. $6(-r + 7t)$ $-6r + 42t$ **20.** $-7[2x + (-y)]$ $-14x + 7y$

  21. $-3[-a + (-5)b]$ $3a + 15b$ **22.** $-2(3m + 4k)$ $-6m + (-8k)$

  23. $-m + 3 + 3m + (-4)$ $2m + (-1)$ **24.** $3 + (-b) + (-7) + (-2b)$ $-3b + (-4)$

  25. $15q + (-4p) + (-7q) + (-8p)$ **26.** $n + (-5k) + 3n + (-4n) + k$ $-4k$
             $8q + (-12p)$

B **27.** $2.3a + 0.5b + (-1.7a) + (-2.5b)$ **28.** $-0.1m + 3.1n + (-3.9m) + (-2.3n)$
                 $0.6a + (-2.0b)$ $-4.0m + 0.8n$

  29. $-x + \frac{3}{4}x + \frac{1}{2}y + \frac{5}{2}y$ $-\frac{1}{4}x + 3y$ **30.** $-3v + (-\frac{1}{2}t) + 2\frac{1}{2}v + (-\frac{1}{2}t)$

  31. $2(a + 3b) + (-3)(3a + b)$ $-7a + 3b$ **32.** $6[x + (-y)] + 5(3y + x)$
                         30. $-\frac{1}{2}v + (-t)$ **32.** $11x + 9y$

Suggested Assignments

Minimum
  59/1–39 odd
S 56/38, 40

Average
  59/1–37 odd

Maximum
  59/1–41 odd
S 56/43, 44

Additional A Exercises

Simplify.

 1. $(-4)(-7)$ 28

 2. $(15)(2k)$ $30k$

 3. $(-4)(16s)$ $-64s$

 4. $(-9)(-11)(0)$ 0

 5. $(6ab)(-3c)$ $-18abc$

 6. $(-2)(-6)(-4)(3)$ -144

Simplify.

33. $-2(3t + s) + 7[t + (-s)]$ **34.** $-3(6a + c) + (-2)(a + 10c)$

35. $-4(-d + 2e) + (-3)[d + (-5e)]$ **36.** $-6[q + (-3t)] + (-5)(3q + t)$

37. $2[-3(m + 4n) + (-n)] + (-m)$ **38.** $3[2(-3k + g) + (-k)] + (-6g)$

39. $-10 + (-3)[2(-1 + w) + (-2w)]$ **40.** $3r + (-2)[3(-r + 1) + r]$

C 41. To show that $a(-1)$ is the opposite of a for every real number a, you can show that the sum of $a(-1)$ and a is zero as follows. Name the axiom or property that justifies each step.

$$a(-1) + a = a(-1) + a(1)$$
$$= a[(-1) + 1]$$
$$= a(0)$$
$$= 0$$

(1) __?__ Identity axiom for multiplication
(2) __?__ Distributive axiom
(3) __?__ Substitution principle
(4) __?__ Multiplicative property of zero

Calculator Key-In

Use a calculator to simplify each expression.

1. $34(-34)$ -1156 **2.** $(-334)334$ $-111,556$ **3.** $(-3334)(-3334)$ $11,115,556$

4. $3(-5)(-37)$ 555 **5.** $2(-3)(-4)(-37)$ -888 **6.** $-3(-3)(-3)(-37)$ 999

7. $(1234)(8) + 4$ 9876 **8.** $(-12345)(8) - 5$ $-98,765$ **9.** $(-123456)(-8) + 6$ $987,654$

Just for Fun

Copy the diagram and write the products in the boxes. (Use a calculator if you like.) Do you see a pattern in the results?

$142857 \times 1 =$ __?__
$142857 \times 2 =$ __?__
$142857 \times 3 =$ __?__
$142857 \times 4 =$ __?__
$142857 \times 5 =$ __?__
$142857 \times 6 =$ __?__

1	4	2	8	5	7		

	2	8	5	7	1	4

	4	2	8	5	7	1

5	7	1	4	2	8

7	1	4	2	8	5

8	5	7	1	4	2

2-9 *The Reciprocal of a Real Number*

OBJECTIVE To use reciprocals.

Two numbers whose product is 1 are called **reciprocals,** or **multiplicative inverses,** of each other. For example:

1. 3 and $\frac{1}{3}$ are reciprocals because $3 \times \frac{1}{3} = 1$.
2. -1.25 and -0.8 are reciprocals because $(-1.25)(-0.8) = 1$.
3. $\frac{2}{3}$ and $\frac{3}{2}$ are reciprocals because $\frac{2}{3} \cdot \frac{3}{2} = 1$.
4. 1 is its own reciprocal because $1 \times 1 = 1$.
5. -1 is its own reciprocal because $(-1)(-1) = 1$.
6. 0 has no reciprocal because the product of 0 and *any* real number is 0, *not* 1.

The symbol for the reciprocal, or multiplicative inverse, of a nonzero real number a is $\frac{1}{a}$.

Every real number except 0 has a reciprocal. This fact is stated as an axiom.

AXIOM OF RECIPROCALS

For every nonzero real number a, there is a unique real number $\frac{1}{a}$ such that

$$a \cdot \frac{1}{a} = 1 \quad \text{and} \quad \frac{1}{a} \cdot a = 1.$$

You know that -3 and $-\frac{1}{3}$ are reciprocals because $(-3)\left(-\frac{1}{3}\right) = 1$.
You can show in general that $(-a)\left(-\frac{1}{a}\right) = 1$ for $a \neq 0$ as follows:

$$(-a)\left(-\frac{1}{a}\right) = (-1 \cdot a)\left(-1 \cdot \frac{1}{a}\right) = [(-1)(-1)]\left(a \cdot \frac{1}{a}\right) = 1 \times 1 = 1.$$

Therefore, for every nonzero real number a,

$$\frac{1}{-a} = -\frac{1}{a}, \text{ read "The reciprocal of } -a \text{ is } -\frac{1}{a}."$$

Teaching Suggestions p. T69

Suggested Extensions p. T70

Chalkboard Examples

Simplify.

1. $(5 \times 7)\left(\frac{1}{5} \times \frac{1}{7}\right)$ 1

2. $\frac{1}{a} \cdot \frac{1}{-c}$ $-\frac{1}{ac}$

3. $3 \cdot \frac{1}{5} \cdot \frac{1}{-3}$ $-\frac{1}{5}$

4. $\left(-\frac{1}{8}\right)(-40)$ 5

5. $\frac{1}{s}(12st)$ 12t

6. $-36ab\left(-\frac{1}{6}\right)$ 6ab

7. $\frac{1}{3}(15a + 9)$ 5a + 3

8. $\left(-\frac{1}{3}\right)[9x + (-3y)]$
   $-3x + y$

Supplementary Materials

Practice Master 7

Progress Test 6

EXAMPLE 1 Simplify each expression.

$$\textbf{a. } (8 \times 9)\left(\frac{1}{8} \times \frac{1}{9}\right)$$

$$\textbf{b. } (ab)\left(\frac{1}{a} \cdot \frac{1}{b}\right), \ a \neq 0, \ b \neq 0$$

SOLUTION **a.** $(8 \times 9)\left(\frac{1}{8} \times \frac{1}{9}\right) = \left(8 \times \frac{1}{8}\right)\left(9 \times \frac{1}{9}\right) = 1 \times 1 = 1$

b. $(ab)\left(\frac{1}{a} \cdot \frac{1}{b}\right) = \left(a \cdot \frac{1}{a}\right)\left(b \cdot \frac{1}{b}\right) = 1 \times 1 = 1$

Example 1(b) shows that the product of ab and $\frac{1}{a} \cdot \frac{1}{b}$ is 1. Therefore, $\frac{1}{a} \cdot \frac{1}{b}$ is the reciprocal of ab. This fact can be stated as follows.

PROPERTY OF THE RECIPROCAL OF A PRODUCT

The reciprocal of a product of nonzero real numbers is the product of the reciprocals of the numbers. That is, for all nonzero real numbers a and b,

$$\frac{1}{ab} = \frac{1}{a} \cdot \frac{1}{b}.$$

EXAMPLE 2 Simplify the product $\frac{1}{3} \cdot \frac{1}{-5}$.

SOLUTION $\frac{1}{3} \cdot \frac{1}{-5} = \frac{1}{3(-5)} = \frac{1}{-15} = -\frac{1}{15}$

Oral Exercises

State the reciprocal of each number.

1. $7 \quad \frac{1}{7}$ **2.** $1 \quad 1$ **3.** $-1 \quad -1$ **4.** $\frac{1}{6} \quad 6$

5. $-2 \quad -\frac{1}{2}$ **6.** $\frac{3}{4} \quad \frac{4}{3}$, or $1\frac{1}{3}$ **7.** $0.25 \quad 4$ **8.** $-\frac{1}{8} \quad -8$

9. $-\frac{5}{6}$ **10.** $d, d \neq 0 \quad \frac{1}{d}$ **11.** $\frac{a}{5}, a \neq 0 \quad \frac{5}{a}$ **12.** $-\frac{1}{t}, t \neq 0 \quad -t$

$-\frac{6}{5}$, or $-1\frac{1}{5}$

Simplify.

13. $\frac{1}{6} \cdot \frac{1}{7} \quad \frac{1}{42}$ **14.** $\frac{1}{-3} \cdot \frac{1}{-2} \quad \frac{1}{6}$ **15.** $\frac{1}{4} \cdot \frac{1}{-5} \quad -\frac{1}{20}$ **16.** $\frac{1}{-x} \cdot \frac{1}{y} \quad -\frac{1}{xy}$

62   *CHAPTER 2*

Written Exercises

Simplify each expression.

SAMPLE 1 $\quad -63xy\left(-\dfrac{1}{7}\right) = (-1 \cdot 63)xy\left(-1 \cdot \dfrac{1}{7}\right)$

$$= [(-1)(-1)]\left(63 \cdot \dfrac{1}{7}\right)xy$$

$$= 1 \cdot \left(9 \cdot 7 \cdot \dfrac{1}{7}\right)xy$$

$$= 1 \cdot (9 \cdot 1)xy = 9xy$$

A 1. $\dfrac{1}{5}(-20)$ -4

2. $-\dfrac{1}{12}(36)$ -3

3. $-100\left(\dfrac{1}{10}\right)$ -10

4. $-60\left(-\dfrac{1}{6}\right)$ 10

5. $96\left(-\dfrac{1}{8}\right)\left(-\dfrac{1}{12}\right)$ 1

6. $-51\left(-\dfrac{1}{3}\right)\left(-\dfrac{1}{17}\right)$ -1

7. $\dfrac{1}{-4}(48)\left(\dfrac{1}{3}\right)$ -4

8. $-90\left(\dfrac{1}{2}\right)\left(\dfrac{1}{-3}\right)$ 15

9. $6xy\left(-\dfrac{1}{6}\right)$ $-xy$

10. $22kt\left(-\dfrac{1}{11}\right)$ $-2kt$

11. $\dfrac{1}{x}(7xy)$, $x \neq 0$ $7y$

12. $(3mn)\dfrac{1}{n}$, $n \neq 0$ $3m$

SAMPLE 2 $\quad \dfrac{1}{4}[28t + (-4s)] = \dfrac{1}{4}(28t) + \dfrac{1}{4}(-4s)$

$$= \left(\dfrac{1}{4} \times 28\right)t + \left[\dfrac{1}{4}(-4)\right]s$$

$$= 7t + (-1)s$$

$$= 7t + (-s)$$

13. $\dfrac{1}{2}(-10x + 6)$ $-5x + 3$

14. $\dfrac{1}{3}[12y + (-27)]$ $4y + (-9)$

15. $-\dfrac{1}{7}(-21c + 14d)$
$3c + (-2d)$

16. $-\dfrac{1}{9}(45u + 81v)$
$-5u + (-9v)$

17. $[16a + (-24b)]\left(-\dfrac{1}{8}\right)$
$-2a + 3b$

18. $[-26p + (-39)q]\left(-\dfrac{1}{13}\right)$
$2p + 3q$

B 19. $\dfrac{1}{2}(6x + 4y) + \dfrac{1}{3}(-3x + 15y)$ $2x + 7y$

20. $\dfrac{1}{5}(-5z + 10w) + \dfrac{1}{2}(-8w + 2z)$ $-2w$

21. $12\left[\dfrac{1}{3}a + \left(-\dfrac{1}{2}b\right)\right] + 21\left[\dfrac{1}{7}b + \dfrac{1}{3}a\right]$
$11a + (-3b)$

22. $-8\left[\dfrac{1}{8}d + \left(-\dfrac{1}{8}e\right)\right] + \dfrac{1}{3}[6d + (-9e)]$
$d + (-2e)$

23. $-\dfrac{1}{6}[48r + (-6)] + \left(-\dfrac{1}{4}\right)(64r + 4)$
$-24r$

24. $-4\left(\dfrac{1}{2}p + 4\right) + \dfrac{1}{5}(-30p + 5)$
$-8p + (-15)$

25. $-3\left[\dfrac{1}{4}(8w + 1) + \left(-\dfrac{1}{4}\right)\right] + 7w$ w

26. $5h + \left(-\dfrac{1}{2}\right)\left[8 + 40\left(-\dfrac{1}{5} + \dfrac{1}{4}h\right)\right]$ 0

Use the definition of reciprocals to find the value of x.

C 27. $-\dfrac{1}{3}x = 1$ -3

28. $-0.5x = 1$ -2

29. $x \cdot \dfrac{1}{\pi} = 1$ π

30. $\dfrac{1}{x} = 3$ $\dfrac{1}{3}$

31. $\dfrac{1}{\frac{1}{x}} = 3$ 3

32. $\dfrac{1}{\frac{1}{x}} = -2$ -2

WORKING WITH REAL NUMBERS   **63**

Suggested Assignments

Minimum
Day 1: 63/1–25 odd
S 60/38, 40
Day 2: 63/20–26 even
R 64/Self-Test 3

Average
Day 1: 63/1–29 odd
S 60/39, 40
Day 2: 63/22–32 even
R 64/Self-Test 3

Maximum
63/1–25 odd, 26–32

Additional A Exercises

Simplify.

1. $\dfrac{1}{4} \cdot \dfrac{1}{9}$ $\dfrac{1}{36}$

2. $\left(\dfrac{1}{-3}\right)\left(\dfrac{1}{8}\right)$ $-\dfrac{1}{24}$

3. $\left(\dfrac{1}{-6}\right)\left(\dfrac{1}{-10}\right)$ $\dfrac{1}{60}$

4. $\left(\dfrac{1}{2}\right)(2)$ 1

5. $\left(\dfrac{1}{7}\right)(49)$ 7

6. $\left(\dfrac{1}{-5}\right)(40)$ -8

Calculator Key-In

Use the reciprocal key on a calculator to find the reciprocal of each number.

1. 0.125 8   **2.** −8 −0.125   **3.** −0.0625 −16   **4.** 15625 0.000064

5. For each number in Exercises 1–4, press the reciprocal key twice. Your results illustrate the property: The reciprocal of the reciprocal of a number is __?__. the original number

6. a. Copy and complete the table.

a	b	$\dfrac{1}{ab}$	$\dfrac{1}{a} \cdot \dfrac{1}{b}$	$\dfrac{1}{ab} = \dfrac{1}{a} \cdot \dfrac{1}{b}$
4	8	?	?	0.03125
0.678	0.789	?	?	1.8693615
−64	−0.5	?	?	0.03125
999	888	?	?	0.00000113

b. What property does your completed table illustrate? The reciprocal of the product of two nonzero numbers is equal to the product of the reciprocals of the numbers.

7. If you have not done Exercises 27–32 on page 63, you may wish to try them now and to check your answers using the reciprocal key on a calculator. To check Exercise 29, you will also need to use the key labeled ''π.''

Exercises 27–32 on page 63

Quick Quiz

Simplify.

1. $-3x + 14x + 8$
   $11x + 8$

2. $4(a - 3) + 8$
   $4a - 4$

3. $7(-9)$ -63

4. $y(-1) + (-4)(-1)$
   $-y + 4$

5. $\dfrac{1}{5} \cdot 5c$ c

6. $-\dfrac{1}{3}[15x + (-9)y]$
   $-5x + 3y$

Self-Test 3

VOCABULARY   distributive axiom (p. 53)
                  equivalent expressions (p. 54)
                  simplify a variable expression (p. 54)
                  identity element for multiplication (p. 57)
                  reciprocals (p. 61)
                  reciprocal of a product (p. 62)

Simplify.

1. $-7x + 12x + 5$ **2.** $3(y - 2) + 1$ Obj. 2-7, p. 53

3. $6(-7)$ **4.** $a(-1) + (-2)(-3)$ Obj. 2-8, p. 57

5. $\dfrac{1}{8} \cdot 8x$ **6.** $-\dfrac{1}{2}[12a + (-2)b]$ Obj. 2-9, p. 61

Check your answers with those at the back of the book.

64   *CHAPTER 2*

Application Balancing a Checkbook

The amount of a check or a deposit and the date written are recorded in a checkbook register or on a check stub. To calculate the new balance, subtract the amount of a check from the previous balance or add the amount of a deposit to the previous balance.

CHECK NO.	DATE	CHECK ISSUED TO	AMOUNT OF CHECK		√	DATE OF DEP.	AMOUNT OF DEPOSIT		BALANCE	
		BALANCE BROUGHT FORWARD →							904	21
319	3/15	Zelkova Stationery	12	43					891	78
320	3/21	Phoenix Realty	205	00					691	78
321	4/11	Short's Sports, Inc.	21	50					670	28
						4/12	793	81	1464	09

Banks send each customer a monthly statement, which is accompanied by the canceled checks. The customer then balances the checkbook by comparing his or her records with the bank statement.

As a preliminary step in balancing your checking account, you indicate in your records all checks that have been canceled and all deposits that have been recorded. On a separate sheet of paper, you do the following:

1. Write down the current balance according to your records.
2. Add the amount of any check not yet canceled.
3. Subtract any deposits not yet credited to your account.
4. Subtract any service charges.
5. Compare the last amount with the closing balance on the bank statement. They should agree.

If the balances do not agree, search for the error. First, go over the arithmetic so far. If the error is not discovered, add the sum of the deposits to the previous correct balance and subtract the total of the amounts of the checks written. If this result agrees with the corrected bank balance, then there is simply an error in computing the running balances. If this result does not agree, then find the difference between the balances. Does it suggest a check or a deposit that was not recorded?

Balance the checkbook register shown above with the bank statement at the right. Be sure to check for arithmetic errors.

OPENING DATE THRU CLOSING DATE	
3/13/8X	4/12/8X
PREVIOUS BALANCE	NEW BALANCE
904.21	1480.59

DATE	CHECKS PAID	DEPOSITS
3/16	12.43	
4/3	205.00	
4/12		793.81

To make them balance, correct the error in subtracting Check 320 from the balance in the checkbook register.

Chapter Summary

1. The positive numbers, the negative numbers, and zero make up the real numbers and can be paired with the points on a number line, thereby showing their order.

2. A number line can be used to find the sum of two real numbers.

3. Opposites and absolute values are used in the rules for adding real numbers (page 48) and multiplying real numbers (page 58).

4. Real number axioms are statements about numbers that are accepted as true and are the basis for computation in arithmetic and in algebra. The following statements are true for all real values of each variable except as noted.

Equality:	Reflexive property	$a = a$
	Symmetric property	If $a = b$, then $b = a$.
	Transitive property	If $a = b$ and $b = c$, then $a = c$.

	Addition	Multiplication
Axioms of closure	$a + b$ is a unique real number.	ab is a unique real number.
Commutative axioms	$a + b = b + a$	$ab = ba$
Associative axioms	$(a + b) + c = a + (b + c)$	$(ab)c = a(bc)$
Identity axioms	$a + 0 = 0 + a = a$	$a \cdot 1 = 1 \cdot a = a$
Axiom of opposites	$a + (-a) = (-a) + a = 0$	
Axiom of reciprocals		$a \cdot \dfrac{1}{a} = \dfrac{1}{a} \cdot a = 1; a \neq 0$
Distributive axiom	$a(b + c) = ab + ac$ and $(b + c)a = ba + ca$	

5. Other useful properties about addition or multiplication:

Property of the opposite of a sum:	$-(a + b) = -a + (-b)$
Multiplicative property of zero:	$a \cdot 0 = 0 \cdot a = 0$
Multiplicative property of -1:	$a(-1) = (-1)a = -a$
Property of opposites in products:	$-a(b) = -ab$; $a(-b) = -ab$; $-a(-b) = ab$
Property of the reciprocal of a product.	$\dfrac{1}{ab} = \dfrac{1}{a} \cdot \dfrac{1}{b}; a \neq 0, b \neq 0$

Chapter Review

Give the letter of the correct answer.

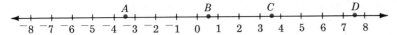

Extra Practice pp. 492–495

1. Refer to the number line above. Give the coordinate of the point halfway between the origin and $^-1$.   2-1

   a. 1   b. $^-2$ (c.) $\dfrac{^-1}{2}$ d. $\dfrac{1}{2}$

2. Refer to the number line above. Name the point that is the graph of $\dfrac{7}{2}$.

   a. A b. B (c.) C d. D

3. Which of the following statements is true?   2-2

   a. $^-5 > 0$ b. $^-5 > 5$ (c.) $^-5 < 2$ d. $2 < 0$

4. Name the axiom illustrated: $4n + 5 = 5 + 4n$.   2-3

   a. axiom of closure for addition

   (b.) commutative axiom for addition

   c. associative axiom for multiplication

   d. commutative axiom for multiplication

5. Simplify $7 + 5m + 2$.

   a. $12m + 2$ b. $7 + 7m$ c. $14m$ (d.) $5m + 9$

6. Simplify $^-2 + 0$.   2-4

   (a.) $^-2$ b. 0 c. 2 d. $^-1$

7.

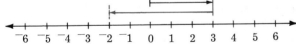

   The diagram above suggests that $3 + \underline{\ ?\ } = ^-2$.

   a. 5   (b.) $^-5$ c. $^-2$ d. $^-1$

8. Simplify $-(-7) + 3$.   2-5

   a. -4 b. 4 c. -10 (d.) 10

9. Simplify $-(-6 + |-3|)$.

   (a.) 3 b. -3 c. 9 d. -9

10. Simplify $-12 + (-10) + 14 + (-3)$.   2-6

    a. 11 b. -5 c. -39 (d.) -11

11. Simplify $4(a + 2) + 6$.   2-7

    (a.) $4a + 14$ b. $4a + 32$ c. $4a + 8$ d. $8a + 6$

1.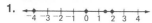

12. Simplify $7x + 1 + 9x + 5$.

    a. $8x + 14$ **b.** $79x + 6$ **c.** $63x + 6$ **d.** $16x + 6$

13. Simplify $(-3)(-1)(-2)(-6)$.   2-8

    a. -36 **b.** 36 **c.** -12 **d.** 12

14. Simplify $-6x + 2y + 5x + (-2y)$.

    a. $-xy$ **b.** $-4x + 3y$ **c.** $-x$ **d.** $-11x - 4y$

15. Simplify $8rs\left(-\dfrac{1}{8}\right)$.   2-9

    a. $-rs$ **b.** rs **c.** $-64rs$ **d.** $7\dfrac{7}{8}rs$

16. Simplify $\dfrac{1}{-p} \cdot \dfrac{1}{q}$.

    a. $-\dfrac{q}{p}$ **b.** $\dfrac{1}{-p+q}$ **c.** $-pq$ **d.** $-\dfrac{1}{pq}$

Chapter Test

1. Graph the numbers $^-4$, 0, 1.5, and 2 on a number line.   2-1

2. Name the greater of the two numbers 7 and $^-10$. 7   2-2

3. Replace the _?_ with one of the symbols $<$ or $>$ to make a true
statement: $(6 \times 6) + 6$ _?_ $(6 + 6)(6 + 6)$. $<$

4. Simplify $54 + 27 + 6 + 73$. 160   2-3

5. Name the two axioms that guarantee that for all real numbers $h, j,$
and k, Comm. ax. for addition; Assoc. ax. for addition
$$h + (j + k) = (h + k) + j.$$

6. The diagram below suggests that _?_ $+$ _?_ $=$ _?_. $-4 + 3 = -1$ 2-4

7. Simplify $-(-5) + 7$. 12   **8.** Simplify $|2| + |0| + |-3|$. 5   2-5

9. Simplify $8 + (-2) + 9 + (-7)$. 8   2-6

10. Simplify $(64 \times 271) + (36 \times 271)$. 27,100   2-7

11. Simplify $35 + (-8)x + 15x + (-10)$. $7x + 25$

12. Simplify $(-6)(-9) + (7)(-5)(0)$. 54   **13.** Simplify $-4[7v + (-w)]$. $-28v + 4w$ 2-8

14. Simplify $-\dfrac{1}{2}[14q + (-2q)]$. $-6q$ **15.** Simplify $\dfrac{1}{w} \cdot \dfrac{1}{-x}$. $-\dfrac{1}{wx}$ 2-9

68   *CHAPTER 2*

Maintaining Skills

Perform the indicated operations.

SAMPLE 1 $1.9 + 5.62 + 1.493$ *SAMPLE 2* $35.6 - 1.872$

SOLUTION
```
  1.900
  5.620
+ 1.493
  9.013
```

SOLUTION
```
  35.600
-  1.872
  33.728
```

SAMPLE 3 1.87×0.043 *SAMPLE 4* $12.04 \div 2.8$

SOLUTION
```
    1.87
  ×0.043
     561
     748
 0.08041
```

SOLUTION
```
          4.3
  2.8)12.0,4
       112
        84
        84
         0
```

1.
```
   37.5
   8.616
+  0.99
  47.106
```

2.
```
  0.0192
  1.7
  5.16
+ 3.057
  9.9362
```

3.
```
   57.12
  193.4
+   4.581
  255.101
```

4.
```
   47.03
    6.8
    0.46
+ 52.511
  106.801
```

5. $5.4 + 7.86 + 9.3$ 22.56   **6.** $12.2 + 6.051 + 4$ 22.251   **7.** $29.41 + 0.058 + 103.6$
133.068

8.
```
   204.91
 - 153.64
   51.27
```

9.
```
  70.038
-  7.129
  62.909
```

10.
```
   4.615
 - 0.28
   4.335
```

11.
```
  36.71
-  1.648
  35.062
```

12. $6.8 - 0.591$ 6.209   **13.** $34.227 - 12.4$ 21.827   **14.** $871.2 - 0.0391$ 871.1609

15.
```
   50.8
 ×1.26
 64.008
```

16.
```
   1.954
 × 0.31
 0.60574
```

17.
```
   62.15
 × 0.07
 4.3505
```

18.
```
    0.724
  ×0.015
  0.010860
```

19. $0.2107 \div 0.86$ 0.245   **20.** $3657.7 \div 0.79$ 4630   **21.** $327.68 \div 0.032$ 10,240

Estimate each answer by using rounded numbers. Then find the exact
product or quotient. Estimates may vary. Exact answers are given.

SAMPLE 5 0.39×7.12 *SOLUTION* $0.4 \times 7 = 2.8;\ 0.39 \times 7.12 = 2.7768$

SAMPLE 6 $0.039 \div 0.15$ *SOLUTION* $0.04 \div 0.2 = 0.2;\ 0.039 \div 0.15 = 0.26$

22. 0.29×0.73 0.2117   **23.** 1.4×0.077 0.1078   **24.** 3.85×1.68 6.4680   **25.** 49.2×0.93
45.756

26. $0.031)\overline{0.868}$ 28   **27.** $0.48)\overline{17.16}$ 35.75   **28.** $6.2)\overline{0.589}$ 0.095   **29.** $7.5)\overline{50.91}$
6.788

Since the dawn of civilization, people have pondered over their need to enclose space, first for basic shelter and later for large arenas, meeting halls, and places of worship. The large supporting columns used by the ancient Egyptians, though functional and decorative, decreased usable space in their buildings.

Advances in mathematics (calculus) and physics (laws governing stress and elasticity), which many of your students will encounter in high school or college, have played a role in developing modern construction methods. Also, the development of materials such as steel and reinforced concrete helped eliminate the need for post-and-beam construction.

Large major league baseball stadiums often have seemingly unsupported tiers of seats and overhanging roofs. Closer to home, your students may wish to take a more critical look at the school auditorium or gymnasium.

A gymnasium must provide adequate room overhead for people to jump and for balls to be thrown. To design a large roof that can be supported with a minimum number of beams and posts requires a knowledge of the mathematics of architecture and engineering.

70

3

SOLVING EQUATIONS

Teaching References

Lesson Commentary,
pp. T70–T73

Assignment Guide,
pp. T50–T51

Supplementary Materials

Practice Masters 8–15

Progress Tests 8–11

Computer Activities
7 *Solving Equations*
8 *Break-Even Point*
9 *Discovering Theorems*

Extra Practice, pp. 495–497,
514–515

Alternate Test, p. T14

USING ADDITION AND SUBTRACTION

3-1 *Transforming Equations: Addition*

OBJECTIVE   To solve equations using addition.

Two competing gymnasts are tied: 48.3 to 48.3. If each gymnast scores 12 points in the next event, then the score is still tied:

$$48.3 + 12 = 48.3 + 12$$

This example illustrates the **addition property of equality:** *If the same number is added to equal numbers, the sums are equal.*

ADDITION PROPERTY OF EQUALITY

If a, b, and c are any real numbers and $a = b$, then

$$a + c = b + c \quad \text{and} \quad c + a = c + b.$$

Another property of real numbers is suggested by the following calculation.

$$
\begin{aligned}
(8 + 9) + (-9) &= 8 + [9 + (-9)] \\
&= 8 + 0 \\
&= 8 \\
\therefore (8 + 9) + (-9) &= 8
\end{aligned}
$$

71

Teaching Suggestions p. T70

Suggested Extensions p. T70

Chalkboard Examples

State whether the given number is a root of the equation.

1. $z + 8 = 4;\ -4$ Yes
2. $2 + w = -6;\ 8$ No

Solve each equation.

3. $y + (-3) = 2$ 5
4. $4 = -5 + x$ 9
5. $-7 + m = 17$ 24
6. $16 + n = -29$ −45
7. $4 = x + 9$ −5
8. $0 = k + 4$ −4

Supplementary Material

Practice Master 8

The calculation suggests a useful idea: *To "undo" the addition of a number, add the opposite of that number to the sum.* This idea can be stated more formally as follows.

> For all real numbers a and b,
>
> $$(a + b) + (-b) = a.$$

You can use the idea of "undoing" an addition along with the addition property of equality to solve equations. Study the following equations.

$$\begin{aligned} &(1) & x + 7 &= 4 \\ &(2) & x + 7 + (-7) &= 4 + (-7) \\ &(3) & x &= -3 \end{aligned}$$

When you add -7 to each side of equation (1) and simplify the result, you obtain equation (3).

On the other hand, when you add 7 to each side of equation (3), you obtain equation (1), as shown below.

$$\begin{aligned} &(3) & x &= -3 \\ &(2') & x + 7 &= -3 + 7 \\ &(1) & x + 7 &= 4 \end{aligned}$$

The addition property of equality guarantees that any root, or solution, of equation (1) is also a root of equation (3), and any root of (3) is also a root of (1). Therefore the two equations have the same solution, namely -3.

Equations having the same solution set over a given domain are called **equivalent equations** over that domain. To solve an equation, you usually try to change, or *transform,* it into a simple equivalent equation whose solution or solutions can be seen at a glance.

> WAYS TO TRANSFORM AN EQUATION INTO AN EQUIVALENT EQUATION
>
> **Transformation by Substitution:** Substitute for any expression in a given equation an equivalent expression.
>
> **Transformation by Addition:** Add the same real number to each side of a given equation.

EXAMPLE 1 Solve $t + (-5) = 8$.

SOLUTION

$$\begin{aligned} t + (-5) &= 8 \\ t + (-5) + 5 &= 8 + 5 \\ t &= 13 \end{aligned}$$

To obtain t alone as the left side, add the opposite of -5, namely 5, to each side.

Because errors may occur in transforming equations, always check your work by showing that each root of the transformed equation satisfies the original equation.

Check: $t + (-5) = 8$ ← original equation
$13 + (-5) \overset{?}{=} 8$
$8 = 8$ ✓

∴ the solution is 13. *Answer*

EXAMPLE 2 Solve $-12 = 20 + z$.

SOLUTION

$$-12 = 20 + z$$
$$-20 + (-12) = -20 + 20 + z$$
$$-32 = z$$

To obtain z alone as the right side, add the opposite of 20, namely -20, to each side.

Check: $-12 = 20 + z$
$-12 \overset{?}{=} 20 + (-32)$
$-12 = -12$ ✓

∴ the solution is -32. *Answer*

Oral Exercises

State the number that must be added to each side of the given equation to produce an equivalent equation with the variable alone as one side. Then state this equivalent equation.

In each answer, the number to be added is given first.

SAMPLE $u + 8 = 12$ **SOLUTION** Add -8; $u = 4$

1. $x + 5 = 6$ -5; $x = 1$
2. $y + 4 = 13$ -4; $y = 9$
3. $v + (-1) = 6$

4. $w + (-11) = 3$ 11; $w = 14$
5. $z + 10 = 1$ -10; $z = -9$
6. $s + 8 = 6$

7. $5 + h = -5$ -5; $h = -10$
8. $-1 + q = 1$ 1; $q = 2$
9. $-1 + p = -1$

10. $16 + m = 16$ -16; $m = 0$
11. $4 = u + (-6)$ 6; $u = 10$
12. $-7 = y + (-10)$

13. $-8 = -2 + a$ 2; $a = -6$
14. $9 = -1 + t$ 1; $t = 10$
15. $0 = 0.6 + b$ -0.6; $b = -0.6$

16. $\frac{3}{5} = \frac{1}{5} + c$ $-\frac{1}{5}$; $c = \frac{2}{5}$
17. $\frac{9}{7} + y = \frac{5}{7}$ $-\frac{9}{7}$; $y = -\frac{4}{7}$
18. $-1.7 + d = -2.3$ 1.7; $d = -0.6$

Written Exercises

Use transformation by addition to solve each equation.

A
1. $t + (-11) = 14$ 25
2. $v + (-8) = 14$ 22
3. $x + 5 = 24$ 19

4. $m + 15 = 23$ 8
5. $-17 + a = 13$ 30
6. $-59 + m = 41$ 100

7. $z + (-3) = -19$ -16
8. $n + (-23) = -17$ 6
9. $k + 14 = -22$ -36

10. $a + 80 = -25$ -105
11. $28 + b = 0$ -28
12. $0 = x + (-13)$ 13

13. $x + (-27) = -54$ -27
14. $y + (-84) = -100$ -16
15. $9 + c = -18$ -27

SOLVING EQUATIONS   73

Suggested Assignments

Minimum
73/1–35 odd
75/P: 1–9 odd

Average
73/1–37 odd
75/P: 1–11 odd

Maximum
73/1–39 odd
75/P: 1–11 odd

Extra Practice Problems
p. 514

Additional Answers
Oral Exercises

3. 1; $v = 7$

6. -8; $s = -2$

9. 1; $p = 0$

12. 10; $y = 3$

Additional A Exercises

Solve.

1. $a + (-3) = 5$ 8
2. $c + (-8) = 4$ 12
3. $x + 7 = 13$ 6
4. $z + 12 = 19$ 7
5. $r + (-5) = -11$ -6
6. $t + 8 = -15$ -23

Use transformation by addition to solve each equation.

16. $16 + m = -36$ -52 **17.** $55 = t + 7$ 48   **18.** $46 = s + 5$ 41

19. $-17 + z = -21$ -4 **20.** $-30 + j = -80$ -50 **21.** $t + 6 = |-14|$ 8

22. $u + (-4) = |20|$ 24   **23.** $v + 5 = |2 - 7|$ 0   **24.** $q + (-6) = |8 - 14|$
 12

$$
\begin{array}{ll}
SAMPLE & -a + 12 = 3 \\
& -a + 12 + (-12) = 3 + (-12) \\
& -a = -9 \\
& \therefore a = 9 \quad \text{(By definition of the opposite of a number)}
\end{array}
$$

B 25. $-a + 7 = 5$ 2   **26.** $-x + 1 = 19$ -18 **27.** $20 + (-z) = 26$ -6

28. $-5 + (-b) = 11$ -16 **29.** $7 = 10 + (-s)$ 3   **30.** $10 = -s + 7$ -3

31. $(y + 2) + 5 = 3$ -4 **32.** $(r + 3) + 8 = 1$ -10 **33.** $1 = 11 + (-1 + x)$

34. $7 = 19 + (m + 1)$ -13 **35.** $-2 + (1 + x) = 8$ 9   **36.** $-3 + (1 + q) = 5$
 **33.** -9 **36.** 7

$$
\begin{array}{ll}
SAMPLE & |z| + 3 = 7 \\
& |z| + 3 + (-3) = 7 + (-3) \\
& |z| = 4 \\
& \therefore z = 4 \text{ or } z = -4 \quad \text{(By definition of absolute value)}
\end{array}
$$

C 37. $|x| + (-2) = 4$ **38.** $|y| + (-1) = 1$ **39.** $-5 + |r| = 0$ **40.** $6 + |w| = 2$
 {6, −6} {2, −2} {5, −5} No solution

Problems

Solve each problem by using an equation. (Though you may be able to solve some by mental arithmetic, using equations provides practice for more difficult problems later.)

SAMPLE

Sam has a temperature of 39°C. This is two degrees above normal body temperature. What is normal temperature?

SOLUTION

Step 1 The problem asks for the number of degrees in normal body temperature.

Step 2 Let n = normal temperature in degrees.
 Then $n + 2$ = Sam's temperature in degrees.

Step 3 $n + 2 = 39$

Step 4 $n + 2 + (-2) = 39 + (-2)$
 $n = 37$

Step 5 The check is left to you.
 ∴ normal temperature is 37°C. *Answer*

74 CHAPTER 3

A

1. Seven more than a number is 36. Find the number. 29

2. Nine more than a number is 67. Find the number. 58

3. A number increased by 5 is −2. Find the number. −7

4. A number increased by 3 is −11. Find the number. −14

5. In his final game of the season Tom scored two touchdowns, making his touchdown record for the season 11. How many touchdowns had he scored in that season before the final game? 9 touchdowns

6. The monthly rent for an apartment was increased by $16. If the new monthly rent is $279, what was the previous rent? $263

7. If the temperature of the water in the beaker rises three degrees Celsius above what it is now, the water will be at the boiling point (100°C). What is the temperature of the water now? 97°C

8. The temperature this morning is −4°C. How many degrees will the temperature have to rise to reach 4°C today? 8°C

B

9. The school principal arrived at school at 7:55 A.M. This is 25 minutes later than her usual time of arrival. At what time does she usually arrive? 7:30 A.M.

10. Fred sold a dozen magazine subscriptions during the last six days in January. During the whole month of January he sold 44 subscriptions. How many subscriptions had he sold during the first 25 days in January? 32 subscriptions

11. A factory hired 125 new employees during a year in which 17 employees retired. If there were 526 employees in the factory at the end of that year, how many were there at the beginning? 418 employees

12. After cashing a check for $75 and then spending $28.75, Jeanne LePage had $134 in her purse. How much did she have in her purse before she cashed the check? $87.75

Historical Note The Equals Sign

The symbols shown were all used in the sixteenth and seventeenth centuries to denote equality. It was not until the eighteenth century that the current equals sign = was universally adopted.

The Englishman Robert Recorde is credited with the invention of the symbol =. He published a mathematics book in 1557 in which he used ===== "to avoid the tedious repetition of the words 'is equal to.'" He said that he chose a pair of line segments of the same length because "no two things could be more equal." With the passage of time, the segments were shortened until the symbol became =.

SOLVING EQUATIONS 75

3-2 *Subtracting Real Numbers*

OBJECTIVE   **To subtract real numbers and to simplify expressions involving differences.**

If you pay for a 45-cent soda with a half dollar, the cashier may hand you a nickel and say,

"45 and 5 is 50."

The cashier is using addition,

$45 + 5 = 50,$

to do subtraction,

$50 - 45 = 5.$

In general, the **difference** $a - b$ is the number whose sum with b is a. Thus, the equations

$$a - b = x \quad \text{and} \quad b + x = a$$

have the same solution and are equivalent.

Using this definition, you can compute a difference such as $6 - 2$ by asking yourself, "What number *added* to 2 gives me 6?" The answer is 4.

EXAMPLE 1   Simplify $4 - (-3)$.

SOLUTION   Ask, "What number added to -3 gives 4?"
On the number line below, think of moving from the graph of -3 to the graph of 4.

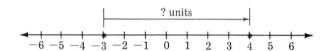

From -3 you move 7 units to the right to reach 4. Thus, $4 - (-3) = 7$.   ***Answer***

It would be helpful to find a way to simplify a difference such as $4 - (-3)$ without using a number line. In general, to compute $a - b$, you can ask, "What number added to b gives a?" and solve $b + x = a$ for x to find the answer. You can use transformation by addition and transformation by substitution as follows:

$$b + x = a$$
$$x + b = a$$
$$x + b + (-b) = a + (-b)$$
$$x + 0 = a + (-b)$$
$$x = a + (-b)$$

76   *CHAPTER 3*

Since $a + (-b)$ is the value of x that satisfies the last equation, it also satisfies the equations $b + x = a$ and $a - b = x$. The following rule can be stated.

RULE FOR SUBTRACTION

For all real numbers a and b,

$$a - b = a + (-b).$$

To subtract b, add the opposite of b.

EXAMPLE 2 Simplify.

        a. $4 - (-3)$ **b.** $-8 - 2$ **c.** $-5 - (-6)$ **d.** $x - (x + 7)$

SOLUTION   **a.** $4 - (-3) = 4 + 3 = 7$
                b. $-8 - 2 = -8 + (-2) = -10$
                c. $-5 - (-6) = -5 + 6 = 1$
                d. $x - (x + 7) = x + [-(x + 7)] = x + (-x) + (-7) = -7$

                      Note that the property of the opposite of a sum is used. The opposite of $(x + 7)$ is $-x + (-7)$.

Using the rule for subtraction, you may replace any difference with a sum. For example,

      $10 - 7 - 5 + 6$ means $10 + (-7) + (-5) + 6$.

You may evaluate this expression by grouping from left to right:

$$10 - 7 - 5 + 6$$
$$3$$
$$-2$$
$$4$$

This method is convenient if you are doing the work mentally or with a hand calculator. For written work, you may want to group positive terms and negative terms:

      $10 - 7 - 5 + 6 = (10 + 6) - (7 + 5) = 16 - 12 = 4$

Certain sums are usually replaced by differences. For example,

      $8 + (-3x)$ is usually written as $8 - 3x$.

Suggested Assignments

Minimum
Day 1: 78/1–41 odd
Day 2: 79/P: 1–4, 9
  S 75/P: 8, 10, 12

Average
Day 1: 78/1–41 odd
Day 2: 79/P: 1–10
  S 75/P: 10, 12

Maximum
  78/13–43 odd
  79/P: 1–9 odd

Extra Practice Problems
  p. 514

Additional A Exercises

Simplify.

1. $16 - (-7)$ 23
2. $-4 - 11$ -15
3. $x - (x + 5)$ -5
4. $a - (a - 3)$ 3
5. $47 - 105$ -58
6. $126 - (-184)$ 310

Here are some important questions and answers about subtraction of real numbers:

1. Is subtraction commutative? No, for example,
$$9 - 3 = 6 \quad \text{but} \quad 3 - 9 = -6.$$

2. Is subtraction associative? No, for example,
$$(5 - 4) - 8 = -7 \quad \text{but} \quad 5 - (4 - 8) = 9.$$

3. Is multiplication distributive with respect to subtraction? Yes. (See Exercise 43.) For all real numbers a, b, and c,
$$a(b - c) = ab - ac \quad \text{and} \quad (b - c)a = ba - ca.$$

Oral Exercises

Simplify.

1. $36 - 4$ 32   **2.** $18 - 11$ 7   **3.** $7 - 12$ -5 **4.** $9 - 29$ -20
5. $0 - 6$ -6 **6.** $0 - (-4)$ 4   **7.** $-15 - 0$ -15 **8.** $-8 - 2$ -10
9. $3 - (-1)$ 4   **10.** $8 - (-2)$ 10   **11.** $-9 - (-14)$ 5   **12.** $-7 - (-3)$
13. $x - (x + 1)$ -1 **14.** $v - (v + 3)$ -3 **15.** $a - (a - 2)$ 2   **16.** $b - (b - 5)$

12. -4 **16.** 5

Written Exercises

Simplify.

                                                                             4. 56   **8.** -98 **12.** 350

A   **1.** $42 - 212$ -170 **2.** $134 - 241$ -107 **3.** $29 - (-22)$ 51   **4.** $27 - (-29)$
    5. $-17 - (-3)$ -14 **6.** $-23 - (-9)$ -14 **7.** $-26 - 42$ -68 **8.** $-41 - 57$
    9. $153 - (-23)$ 176   **10.** $-201 - (-58)$ -143 **11.** $182 - (-103)$ 285   **12.** $195 - (-155)$

13. $123 - (65 - 59)$ 117   **14.** $265 - (90 - 75)$ 250
15. $342 - (72 - 85)$ 355   **16.** $193 - (35 - 60)$ 218
17. $(33 - 44) - (66 - 77)$ 0   **18.** $(53 - 60) - (82 - 90)$ 1
19. $(2 - 7) - (-14 + 17)$ -8 **20.** $(32 - 23) - (-7 + 9)$ 7
21. $1066 - 1492 - 1776$ -2202 **22.** $1914 - 1939 + 2001$ 1976
23. $13 - (-7) - [6 - (-5)]$ 9   **24.** $-10 - 8 - [-5 - (-7)]$ -20
25. $3 - 4 + 7 - 16 + 32$ 22   **26.** $19 - 15 + 13 + 6 - 23$ 0
27. $38x - 18x - 43x + 17x - 27x$ $-33x$ **28.** $43y - 18y + 11y - 23y - 35y$ $-22y$
29. $2x - (-3 + x)$ $x + 3$ **30.** $y - (-y + 5)$ $2y - 5$

B   **31.** $x + y - (x - y) - y$ y **32.** $u - v - (u + v) + v$ $-v$
    33. $2h + 9 - (-7 + h)$ $h + 16$ **34.** $-(10 - 3k) - (12 + k)$ $-22 + 2k$

Write each phrase using symbols of algebra. Then simplify.

35. -11 decreased by 7 $\quad -11 - 7 = -18$ **36.** -8 decreased by -3 $\quad -8 - (-3) = -5$

37. $(a - 4)$ less than a $\quad a - (a - 4) = 4$ **38.** $(7 + z)$ less than z $\quad z - (7 + z) = -7$

39. $(\pi + 1)$ subtracted from $(\pi - 6)$ $\quad (\pi - 6) - (\pi + 1) = -7$

40. $(8 - 2\pi)$ subtracted from $(5 - 2\pi)$ $\quad (5 - 2\pi) - (8 - 2\pi) = -3$

41. The sum of -8 and -9, decreased by -5 $\quad (-8 + (-9)) - (-5) = -12$

42. -32 decreased by the sum of -27 and 14 $\quad -32 - (-27 + 14) = -19$

C 43. Name the axiom, property, or rule that justifies each step.

$$a(b - c) = a[b + (-c)] \qquad (1) \ \underline{\ ?\ } \text{ Rule for subtraction}$$
$$= a(b) + a(-c) \qquad (2) \ \underline{\ ?\ } \text{ Distrib. ax. of mult. with respect to add.}$$
$$= ab + (-ac) \qquad (3) \ \underline{\ ?\ } \text{ Property of opposites in products}$$
$$= ab - ac \qquad (4) \ \underline{\ ?\ } \text{ Rule for subtraction}$$

Problems

Express the answer to each question as the difference between two real numbers. Compute the difference. Answer the question.

SAMPLE

The Qattara Depression in Egypt is about 133 m below sea level. The Dead Sea is about 396 m below sea level. How much higher is the Qattara Depression than the Dead Sea?

SOLUTION $-133 - (-396) = -133 + 396 = 263$

         The Qattara Depression is about 263 m higher.

A 1. One winter evening the temperature dropped from $-3°C$ to $-8°C$. How many degrees did the temperature drop? 5°C

2. The temperature was $19°C$ in the classroom and $-2°C$ outdoors. How much warmer was it in the classroom than outdoors? 21°C

3. In one round of a game, Mike's score dropped from 50 points to -25 points. How many points did he lose in that round? 75 points

4. Jan's team's score is 125 points. The other team's score is -175 points. How many points higher is Jan's team's score than the other team's score? 300 points

B 5. Winnipeg's latitude is about $50°N$. Rio de Janeiro's latitude is about $23°S$. What is the approximate difference in latitude between the two cities? 73°

6. The North Pole is located at latitude $90°N$. The South Pole is located at latitude $90°S$. What is the difference in latitude between the two poles? 180°

7. The town of Aucanquilcha, Chile, is about 5334 m above sea level. Several villages on the shores of the Dead Sea are about 396 m below sea level. About how many meters higher is Aucanquilcha than the Dead Sea villages? 5730 m

8. New Orleans, the lowest point in Louisiana, is 1.524 m below sea level. Driskill Mountain, the highest point in the state, is 163.068 m above sea level. What is the difference in elevation between the highest and lowest points in Louisiana? 164.592 m

9. The highest recorded weather temperature on earth is 58.0°C. The lowest is −88.3°C. What is the difference between these two extremes? 146.3°C

10. Mercury is a metallic element that melts at −38.87°C and boils at 356.9°C. How many degrees are there in the range between the melting and boiling points of mercury? 395.77°C

Calculator Key-In

Use a calculator to simplify each expression.

3. −693   **6.** 2596

1. 1332 − 369 963
2. 1332 + (−396) 936
3. −1332 − (−639)
4. 9265 − 12221 −2956
5. 9526 + (−12221) −2695
6. −9625 − (−12221)
7. 5296 − 5692 + (−5962) − (−5629) + 6925 + (−6529) − 6259 + 6592 0

Biography Andres Manuel del Río

Andres Manuel del Río (1764–1849) introduced modern mining techniques in Mexico. Born in Madrid, Spain, del Río studied the classics at the Colegio de San Isidro in Madrid. After winning a public competition in physics, he was subsidized first by King Charles III and later by the state to study mineralogy at the Mining Academy of Almadén and at mining centers in France, England, and Germany.

In 1794 he sailed to Mexico to become professor of mineralogy at Colegio de Minería, which had just been founded in Mexico City. He discovered the new chemical element vanadium in 1801, but it was not until some thirty years later that this discovery was verified.

3-3 Transforming Equations: Subtraction

OBJECTIVE To solve equations using addition or subtraction.

EXAMPLE 1 Solve $z - 4 = 13$.

SOLUTION

$$z - 4 = 13$$
$$z + (-4) = 13$$
$$z + (-4) + 4 = 13 + 4$$
$$z = 17$$

Check: $z - 4 = 13$
$$17 - 4 \overset{?}{=} 13$$
$$13 = 13 \;\checkmark$$

$\therefore$ the solution is 17. ***Answer***

CONDENSED $\quad z - 4 = 13$
SOLUTION $\quad z - 4 + 4 = 13 + 4$
$$z = 17$$

EXAMPLE 2 Solve $a + 8 = 1$.

SOLUTION

$$a + 8 = 1$$
$$a + 8 - 8 = 1 - 8$$
$$a = -7$$

Check: $a + 8 = 1$
$$-7 + 8 \overset{?}{=} 1$$
$$1 = 1 \;\checkmark$$

$\therefore$ the solution is -7. ***Answer***

The method used in Example 2 is called **transformation by subtraction,** because 8 is *subtracted* from each side of the equation. Of course, transformation by subtraction is just a special case of transformation by addition, since you can just as well add -8 to solve the equation in Example 2.

Oral Exercises

State the number that must be added to or subtracted from each side of the given equation to produce an equivalent equation with the variable alone as one side. Then state this equivalent equation.

SAMPLE 1 $\quad x + 6 = -1$ $\qquad$ **SOLUTION** $\quad$ Subtract 6; $x = -7$

SAMPLE 2 $\quad x - 10 = -4$ $\qquad$ **SOLUTION** $\quad$ Add 10; $x = 6$

1. $x + 3 = 11$ $\qquad$ 2. $y + 5 = -1$ $\qquad$ 3. $z - 2 = 8$

4. $t - 8 = 3$ $\qquad$ 5. $s + 6 = 21$ $\qquad$ 6. $r + 7 = 1$

7. $x - 9 = -4$ $\qquad$ 8. $y - 3 = -6$ $\qquad$ 9. $q - 14 = -18$

10. $z - \dfrac{1}{2} = \dfrac{1}{2}$ $\qquad$ 11. $w + 0.25 = -0.50$ $\qquad$ 12. $p - 1.5 = -3$

SOLVING EQUATIONS **81**

Solve.

1. $c + 8 = 16$ 8

2. $d - 9 = 27$ 36

3. $x - 5 = -19$ -14

4. $y + 16 = -18$ -34

5. $a + 2.1 = 2.1$ 0

6. $7 + b = -3$ -10

Written Exercises

Solve.

A

1. $x + 16 = 42$ 26   **2.** $y + 31 = 79$ 48   **3.** $-1 = a + 51$ -52

4. $-22 = b + 7$ -29 **5.** $1.5 + c = 1.5$ 0   **6.** $0.4 + d = 0.4$ 0

7. $p - 4 = 13$ 17   **8.** $q - 6 = 8$ 14   **9.** $s - 2 = 19$ 21

10. $t - 6 = 23$ 29   **11.** $18 = x - 1$ 19   **12.** $14 = y - 10$ 24

B

13. $34 - x = 10$ 24   **14.** $17 - y = -6$ 23   **15.** $(z + 8) - 3 = -2$ -7

16. $(w - 5) + 19 = 144$ 130   **17.** $(v - 4) + 6 = 11$ 9   **18.** $(h + 1) + 9 = 10$ 0

19. $y - 8 = |21 - 29|$ 16   **20.** $x - 9 = |7 - 16|$ 18   **21.** $b + |7 - 12| = -8$

22. $a + |3 - 5| = -1$ -3 **23.** $d - 4 = ||-3| - |6||$ 7   **24.** $c - 7 = ||-1| - |-7||$

21. -13 **24.** 13

C **25.** $2|a| - (|a| - 3) = 9$ $\{6, -6\}$ **26.** $4(|b| - 1) - 2|b| - 19 = 1$

$\{12, -12\}$

Problems

Solve each problem by using an equation. (Though you may be able to solve some by mental arithmetic, using equations provides practice for more difficult problems later.)

SAMPLE

Using a coupon that read "35¢ off," Jimmy paid $1.94 for a bag of dry dog food. What was the price of the dog food without the coupon?

SOLUTION

Step 1   The problem asks for the price of the dog food without the coupon.

Step 2   Let p = price of the dog food without the coupon in dollars. Then $p - 0.35$ = price of the dog food with the coupon.

Step 3 $p - 0.35 = 1.94$

Step 4 $p - 0.35 + 0.35 = 1.94 + 0.35$

$p = 2.29$

Step 5   The check is left to you.

∴ the price is $2.29.   *Answer*

A

1. Fifteen less than a number is 19. Find the number. 34

2. A number decreased by 9 is -10. Find the number. -1

3. A number decreased by 22 is 22. Find the number. 44

4. Eight less than a number is -7. Find the number. 1

5. Three students are absent from Homeroom 101 today. If 26 of the students assigned to the homeroom are present, how many are assigned to Homeroom 101? 29 students

82   CHAPTER 3

6. Five of the chorus members missed the last rehearsal. Twenty-eight of the members did attend the rehearsal. How many members does the chorus have in all? 33 members

7. Miguel's grade on today's biology test was 89. This grade was five points lower than his grade on last week's test. What was Miguel's grade on last week's test? 94

8. Mimi swam the length of the pool in 21 seconds. This was two seconds less than her previous time. What was her previous time? 23 seconds

B 9. A newspaper ad offers a dollar off the price of any album in the record store if a customer brings in the ad. Alicia brought in the ad and paid $9.99 for an album. What would the album have cost Alicia without the ad? $10.99

10. The last check Henri wrote was for $18.95. His next bank statement showed an overdraft of $7.64 on his account. How much did he have in his account before he wrote that last check? $11.31

11. A rocket landed 17 km from its launching pad. If it fell 1.5 km short of its target, how far was the target from the launching pad? 18.5 km

12. An astronaut spent 32.6 days in space. This was 2.4 days shorter than her previous record. What was her previous record? 35 days

Self-Test 1

VOCABULARY   equivalent equations (p. 72)   difference (p. 76)
transformation by substitution (p. 72)   transformation by sub-
transformation by addition (p. 72)   traction (p. 81)

Solve.

1. $x + 12 = 20$ 2. $-15 + y = 7$ Obj. 3-1, p. 71

Simplify.

3. $26 - 37$ 4. $-9 - 12$ Obj. 3-2, p. 76
5. $15 - (-5)$ 6. $x - (x + 6)$

Solve.

7. $18 + w = 59$ 8. $16 = z - 10$ Obj. 3-3, p. 81

9. This year the cross-country team has four more runners than last year. This year's team has 11 runners. Find out how many runners were on last year's team by writing an equation and solving it.

Check your answers with those at the back of the book.

SOLVING EQUATIONS **83**

Quick Quiz

Solve.

1. $y + 18 = 25$ 7
2. $-11 + x = 9$ 20

Simplify.

3. $18 - 27$ -9
4. $-8 - 15$ -23
5. $24 - (-6)$ 31
6. $y - (8 + y)$ -8

Solve.

7. $21 + k = 40$ 19
8. $24 = a - 9$ 33
9. The junior varsity football team has twelve more players than the varsity team. There are 46 players on the junior varsity team. Determine the number of players on the varsity team by writing and solving an equation.

34 players

USING MULTIPLICATION AND DIVISION

3-4 *Transforming Equations: Multiplication*

OBJECTIVE   To solve equations using multiplication.

Jim earned the same amount as Millie working at the supermarket on Friday. Each of them earned twice as much working on Saturday. From this information you can conclude that Jim earned the same amount as Millie on Saturday also.

This example illustrates the **multiplication property of equality:** *If equal numbers are multiplied by the same number, the products are equal.*

MULTIPLICATION PROPERTY OF EQUALITY

If a, b, and c are any real numbers and $a = b$, then

$$ca = cb \quad \text{and} \quad ac = bc.$$

This property guarantees another way to transform an equation into an equivalent equation:

Transformation by Multiplication: Multiply each side of a given equation by the same *nonzero* real number.

EXAMPLE 1   Solve $4x = 52$.

SOLUTION

$$4x = 52$$

$$\tfrac{1}{4}(4x) = \tfrac{1}{4}(52)$$

To obtain x alone as the left side, multiply each side by the reciprocal of 4, namely $\frac{1}{4}$.

$$x = 13$$

Check: $4x = 52$

$$4(13) \overset{?}{=} 52$$

$$52 = 52 \quad \checkmark$$

∴ the solution is 13.   *Answer*

EXAMPLE 2   Solve $-\frac{1}{5}v = 2$.

SOLUTION $-5\left(-\frac{1}{5}v\right) = -5(2)$ $\left\{ \begin{array}{l} \text{To obtain } v \text{ alone as the left side, multiply each} \\ \text{side by the reciprocal of } -\frac{1}{5}, \text{ namely } -5. \end{array} \right.$

$v = -10$

Check: $-\frac{1}{5}v = 2$

$-\frac{1}{5}(-10) \overset{?}{=} 2$

$2 = 2$ √

∴ the solution is -10. ***Answer***

Examples 1 and 2 suggest a useful idea: To "undo" multiplication by a number, multiply the product by the reciprocal of that number. This idea can be stated more formally as follows.

For every real number a and every *nonzero* real number b,

$$\frac{1}{b}(ba) = a.$$

EXAMPLE 3   Solve $\frac{2}{3}r = 18$.

SOLUTION $\frac{3}{2} \cdot \frac{2}{3}r = \frac{3}{2} \cdot 18$ $\left\{ \begin{array}{l} \text{To obtain } r \text{ alone as the left side, multiply each} \\ \text{side by the reciprocal of } \frac{2}{3}, \text{ namely } \frac{3}{2}. \end{array} \right.$

$r = 27$

Check: The check is left to you.

∴ the solution is 27. ***Answer***

Do you know why zero is not allowed as a multiplier in transforming an equation? Look at the following equations.

$$\begin{array}{ll} (1) & 3y = 18 \\ (2) & 0 \cdot 3y = 0 \cdot 18 \\ (3) & (0 \cdot 3)y = 0 \cdot 18 \\ (4) & 0 \cdot y = 0 \end{array}$$

Equation (1) has just one root, namely 6. Equation (4) is satisfied by *any* real number. Equations (1) and (4) are not equivalent (see page 72). *In transforming an equation, never multiply by zero.*

Supplementary Materials
Practice Master 10
Computer Activity 7
Solving Equations
   Solving linear equations of the form $Ax + B = C$ with a computer program requires the student to convert each equation algebraically to the specified form before "inputting" the values of A, B, and C.

Suggested Assignments

Minimum
  86/1–23 odd, P: 1, 3, 5, 8
R 83/Self-Test 1

Average
  86/1–27 odd, P: 1–9 odd
R 83/Self-Test 1

Maximum
  86/1–25 odd, 26–28,
    P: 2–8, 10
R 83/Self-Test 1

Extra Practice Problems
  p. 515

Additional A Exercises

Solve.

1. $\frac{1}{4}x = 6$ 24

2. $\frac{1}{7}a = 5$ 35

3. $-\frac{1}{4}c = 2$ −8

4. $-3y = 42$ −14
5. $-5z = 65$ −13
6. $-9b = -81$ 9

Oral Exercises

State the number by which each side of the given equation must be multiplied to produce an equivalent equation with the variable alone as one side. Then state the equivalent equation.

1. $\frac{1}{2}x = 5$ 2; $x = 10$ **2.** $\frac{1}{3}z = 8$ 3; $z = 24$ **3.** $\frac{1}{10}y = 7$ 10; $y = 70$ **4.** $\frac{1}{9}m = \frac{2}{9}$

5. $5v = 30$ $\frac{1}{5}$; $v = 6$ **6.** $4w = 24$ $\frac{1}{4}$; $w = 6$ **7.** $-3n = 12$ **8.** $-6p = -54$

9. $-\frac{1}{5}q = -3$ −5; $q = 15$ **10.** $\frac{1}{13}t = -1$ 13; $t = -13$ **11.** $\frac{3}{4}c = -\frac{1}{4}$ **12.** $-\frac{2}{7}z = \frac{1}{7}$

4. 9; $m = 2$ **7.** $-\frac{1}{3}$; $n = -4$ **8.** $-\frac{1}{6}$; $p = 9$ **11.** $\frac{4}{3}$; $c = -\frac{1}{3}$ **12.** $-\frac{7}{2}$; $z = -\frac{1}{2}$

Written Exercises

Solve each equation.

A **1.** $\frac{1}{8}x = 21$ 168 **2.** $\frac{1}{9}y = 14$ 126 **3.** $\frac{1}{12}r = -12$ −144 **4.** $\frac{1}{17}s = -101$ −1717

5. $13m = 91$ 7 **6.** $8v = -136$ −17 **7.** $-5t = 850$ −170 **8.** $-11a = 165$ −15

9. $-64 = -\frac{1}{8}x$ 512 **10.** $-\frac{1}{6}z = -36$ 216 **11.** $12p = -84$ −7 **12.** $-25q = 300$ −12

B 13. $\frac{1}{2}y = \frac{5}{2}$ 5 **14.** $\frac{1}{3}x = \frac{4}{3}$ 4 **15.** $-\frac{3}{5} = \frac{1}{5}b$ −3 **16.** $-\frac{5}{7} = -\frac{1}{7}a$ 5

17. $-\frac{3}{8} = -\frac{1}{16}d$ 6 **18.** $\frac{5}{6} = -\frac{1}{12}c$ −10 **19.** $-3y = \frac{6}{5}$ $-\frac{2}{5}$ **20.** $-2x = -\frac{8}{9}$ $\frac{4}{9}$

21. $9n = \frac{36}{11}$ $\frac{4}{11}$ **22.** $4x = -\frac{48}{23}$ $-\frac{12}{23}$ **23.** $-17m = \frac{1}{2}$ $-\frac{1}{34}$ **24.** $10r = -\frac{1}{5}$ $-\frac{1}{50}$

C 25. $0.5x = 1$ 2 **26.** $1.5t = -3$ −2 **27.** $-0.2y = 10$ −50 **28.** $-0.25z = -4$ 16

Problems

Solve using an equation.

A **1.** A dozen eggs cost $1.08. How much is one egg worth? $.09

2. Six tacos cost $5.70. How much does each taco cost? $.95

3. One eighth of a pizza pie is sold for 65¢. How much will be received when all the pieces of a pie have been sold at this price? $5.20

4. Nine-year-old Chico is one fifth as old as his aunt Sofia. How old is Sofia? 45 years

5. The perimeter of a square garden plot is 140 m. How long is each side of the plot? 35 m

6. The perimeter of an equilateral triangle (a triangle with all sides equal) is 7.5 cm. How long is each side of the triangle? 2.5 cm

B 7. A rectangular quilt is made up of 195 small squares. The quilt is 15 squares long. How many squares wide is it? 13 squares

8. A train traveled 448 km at the rate of 128 km/h. How long did it travel? 3.5 h

9. The Ecology Club has $18.25 in its treasury. This is one third the amount in the Computer Club treasury. How much is in the Computer Club treasury? $54.75

10. In a scale drawing of a kitchen, dimensions are shown $\frac{1}{100}$ of actual size. The width of the kitchen in the drawing is 3.5 cm. What is the actual width of the kitchen in centimeters? in meters? 350 cm; 3.5 m

Computer Key-In _____

The following computer program in BASIC will solve simple equations for you.

```
10  PRINT "TO SOLVE AN EQUATION OF THE FORM"
20  PRINT "    X  (SIGN)  A = B"
30  PRINT "INPUT SIGN,A,B";
40  INPUT S$,A,B
50  IF S$="+" THEN 110
60  IF S$="-" THEN 130
70  IF S$="*" THEN 150
80  IF S$="/" THEN 170
90  PRINT "WHAT DID YOU INTEND?"
100  GOTO 30
110  PRINT "X =";B-A
120  STOP
130  PRINT "X =";B+A
140  STOP
150  PRINT "X =";B/A
160  STOP
170  PRINT "X =";B*A
180  END
```

Here is an example of a RUN of this program which solves the equation $x + 4 = 10$.

```
RUN

TO SOLVE AN EQUATION OF THE FORM
    X  (SIGN)  A = B
INPUT SIGN,A,B?"+",4,10
X = 6

END
```

Notice that the operational sign must be typed in quotation marks, and that it and the two numerical values are typed on one line, separated by commas.

SOLVING EQUATIONS   **87**

Rewrite each quotient as a product and simplify.

1. $45 \div (-5)$

$$45 \cdot \left(-\frac{1}{5}\right) = -9$$

2. $-18 \div \left(-\frac{1}{2}\right)$

$$-18 \cdot (-2) = 36$$

3. $12d \div \frac{4d}{3}, \ d \neq 0$

$$12d \cdot \left(\frac{3}{4d}\right) = 9$$

Simplify.

4. $-108 \div 9$ -12

5. $24 \div \left(-\frac{1}{2}\right)$ -48

6. $\dfrac{-14}{-\frac{1}{2}}$ 28

7. $\dfrac{39x}{-13x}, \ x \neq 0$ -3

8. $-4 \cdot \dfrac{x}{4}$ $-x$

9. If $a = 6$, $b = -8$, and $c = 5$, evaluate $\dfrac{b^2 - 2c}{a}$.

10

3-5 *Dividing Real Numbers*

OBJECTIVE To divide real numbers and to simplify expressions involving quotients.

In arithmetic when you learned the multiplication fact $8 \times 6 = 48$, you found that you also knew the related division fact $48 \div 8 = 6$.

In general, if b is *not* zero, the **quotient** $a \div b$ is the number whose product with b is a. Thus, the equations

$$a \div b = x \quad \text{and} \quad bx = a$$

are equivalent equations.

A quotient is often represented by a fraction:

$$a \div b = \frac{a}{b}$$

When you studied fractions, you learned facts like these:

$$\frac{4}{9} = 4 \times \frac{1}{9} \qquad \frac{5}{3} = 5 \times \frac{1}{3} \qquad \frac{24}{8} = 24 \times \frac{1}{8}$$

These equations suggest the following rule.

RULE FOR DIVISION

For every real number a and every *nonzero* real number b,

$$a \div b = a \cdot \frac{1}{b}, \quad \text{or} \quad \frac{a}{b} = a \cdot \frac{1}{b}.$$

To divide by b, multiply by the reciprocal of b.

You can use the rule for division to replace any quotient by a product.

$$\frac{15}{3} = 15 \times \frac{1}{3} = 5 \qquad\qquad \frac{-15}{-3} = -15 \times \left(-\frac{1}{3}\right) = 5$$

$$\frac{-15}{3} = -15 \times \frac{1}{3} = -5 \qquad\qquad \frac{15}{-3} = 15 \times \left(-\frac{1}{3}\right) = -5$$

The quotient of two positive or two negative numbers is positive.

The quotient of a positive number and a negative number is negative.

The quotient when zero is divided by any nonzero number is zero.

---

88 CHAPTER 3

Here are some important questions and answers about division of real numbers:

1. Why can you never divide by zero? Suppose you allowed division by zero in the definition of $a \div b$. Then $a \div 0 = x$ would mean that $0 \cdot x = a$. If $a \neq 0$, no value of x can satisfy this equation, because $0 \cdot x = 0$ for each value of x. But if $a = 0$, then every value of x would satisfy $0 \cdot x = a$. A "quotient" $a \div 0$ would have either *no* value or *many* values! Therefore, *division by zero has no meaning in the set of real numbers.*

2. You cannot divide zero by zero, but can you divide zero by any other number? Look at these examples:

$$\frac{0}{5} = 0 \times \frac{1}{5} = 0 \qquad 0 \div (-2) = 0 \times \left(-\frac{1}{2}\right) = 0$$

When zero is divided by any nonzero number, the quotient is zero.

3. Is division commutative? *No*, for example,

$$8 \div 2 = 4 \quad \text{but} \quad 2 \div 8 = 0.25.$$

4. Is division associative? *No*, for example,

$$(12 \div 3) \div 2 = 4 \div 2 = 2 \quad \text{but} \quad 12 \div (3 \div 2) = 12 \div 1.5 = 8.$$

5. Is division distributive with respect to addition and with respect to subtraction? Yes. In Exercises 31 and 32 it will be shown that for all real numbers a, b, and c such that $c \neq 0$,

$$\frac{a+b}{c} = \frac{a}{c} + \frac{b}{c} \quad \text{and} \quad \frac{a-b}{c} = \frac{a}{c} - \frac{b}{c}.$$

Oral Exercises

Read each quotient as a product. Then simplify.

SAMPLE 1 $12 \div \left(-\frac{1}{4}\right)$ **SOLUTION** $12 \times (-4); \; -48$

SAMPLE 2 $\dfrac{16x}{-8}$ **SOLUTION** $16x \times \left(-\frac{1}{8}\right); \; -2x$

1. $0 \div 8$
2. $-3 \div (-3)$
3. $-1 \div (-1)$
4. $1 \div (-1)$
5. $50 \div (-10)$
6. $40 \div (-5)$
7. $-10 \div \frac{1}{2}$
8. $-1 \div \left(-\frac{1}{5}\right)$
9. $\dfrac{35}{-7}$
10. $\dfrac{-14}{14}$
11. $\dfrac{18}{-1}$
12. $\dfrac{-81}{-9}$
13. $y \div (-1)$
14. $\dfrac{-x}{-1}$
15. $\dfrac{-27r}{3}$
16. $\dfrac{-12a}{-4}$
17. $-3 \div \frac{1}{m}, \; m \neq 0$
18. $-1 \div \left(-\frac{1}{z}\right), \; z \neq 0$
19. $\dfrac{-a}{-a}, \; a \neq 0$
20. $\dfrac{b}{-b}, \; b \neq 0$

SOLVING EQUATIONS   89

Suggested Assignments

Minimum
90/1–25, 27, 29

Average
90/1–31 odd

Maximum
90/1–31 odd

Simplify.

SAMPLE 3 $\frac{z}{4} \cdot 4$ **SOLUTION** $\frac{z}{4} \cdot 4 = z \cdot \frac{1}{4} \cdot 4 = z \cdot 1 = z$

21. $5 \cdot \frac{x}{5}$ x **22.** $\left(-\frac{t}{8}\right)(-8)$ t **23.** $2\left(\frac{a}{-2}\right)$ $-a$ **24.** $-7 \cdot \frac{b}{7}$ $-b$

Written Exercises

Simplify.

A **1.** $-256 \div 32$ -8 **2.** $204 \div (-17)$ -12 **3.** $36 \div \left(-\frac{1}{3}\right)$ -108 **4.** $0 \div (-23)$ 0

5. $\dfrac{-25}{-\frac{1}{5}}$ 125 **6.** $\dfrac{7}{-\frac{1}{2}}$ -14 **7.** $\dfrac{-10}{\frac{1}{6}}$ -60 **8.** $\dfrac{0}{-\frac{1}{7}}$ 0

9. $\dfrac{165x}{-15}$ $-11x$ **10.** $\dfrac{192y}{-8}$ $-24y$ **11.** $\dfrac{-426a}{3a}$, $a \neq 0$ -142 **12.** $\dfrac{-108c}{-12c}$, $c \neq 0$ 9

13. $-\frac{z}{12}(-12)$ z **14.** $-9 \cdot \frac{t}{9}$ $-t$ **15.** $\frac{3x}{2} \cdot 2$ $3x$ **16.** $-\frac{5r}{3}(-3)$ $5r$

Find the average of the numbers given in Exercises 17–20. (The average is the sum of the numbers divided by the number of numbers.)

SAMPLE 1 $15, -7, -14, 2$

SOLUTION $\dfrac{15 + (-7) + (-14) + 2}{4} = \dfrac{17 - 21}{4} = \dfrac{-4}{4} = -1$

17. $-18, 5, -10, 3$ -5

19. $21, -2, -17, 3, -15$ -2

18. $9, -20, -6, 13$ -1

20. $23, -19, 0, -20, 11$ -1

Evaluate each expression if $x = -2$, $y = -1$, $z = 3$, and $w = 6$.

SAMPLE 2 $\dfrac{xzw}{x - y} = \dfrac{(-2)(3)(6)}{-2 - (-1)} = \dfrac{-6(6)}{-2 + 1} = \dfrac{-36}{-1} = 36$

B **21.** $\dfrac{4x + y}{z}$ -3

22. $\dfrac{5z + y}{w + 1}$ 2

23. $\dfrac{zw}{xy}$ 9

24. $\dfrac{z - w}{x + y}$ 1

25. $\dfrac{w - 7z}{y}$ 15

26. $\dfrac{z - 2w}{y - x}$ -9

27. $\dfrac{2z - w}{xyz}$ 0

28. $\dfrac{x - 2y}{yzw}$ 0

29. $\dfrac{(x + z)(x - z)}{w - y}$ $-\frac{5}{7}$

30. $\dfrac{(5x + w)(5x - w)}{y - z}$ -16

90   *CHAPTER 3*

In Exercises 31 and 32 assume that a, b, and c are any real numbers and $c \neq 0$.

C **31.** Name the axiom, property, or rule that justifies each numbered step.

$$\frac{a + b}{c} = (a + b) \cdot \frac{1}{c}$$ (1) __?__ Rule for division

$$= \left(a \cdot \frac{1}{c}\right) + \left(b \cdot \frac{1}{c}\right)$$ (2) __?__ Distrib. ax. of mult. with respect to add.

$$= \frac{a}{c} + \frac{b}{c}$$ (3) __?__ Rule for division

32. Using the fact that multiplication is distributive with respect to subtraction, show that $\frac{a - b}{c} = \frac{a}{c} - \frac{b}{c}$. (Hint: See Exercise 31.)

Calculator Key-In

Use the division key on a calculator to find a decimal equal to each expression.

SAMPLE $\frac{-3}{2}$ *SOLUTION* $\frac{-3}{2} = -3 \div 2 = -1.5$

1. $\frac{1}{4}$ 0.25
2. $\frac{-1}{8}$ −0.125
3. $\frac{1}{-16}$ −0.0625
4. $\frac{-1}{-25}$ 0.04
5. $\frac{1}{40}$ 0.025

6. $\frac{-7}{4}$ −1.75
7. $\frac{6}{-50}$ −0.12
8. $\frac{-5}{-8}$ 0.625
9. $\frac{31}{32}$ 0.96875
10. $\frac{37}{-64}$ −0.578125

11–20. Use the reciprocal key on a calculator to find a decimal equal to each expression in Exercises 1–10. Are your answers the same as before? Answers are the same.

SAMPLE $\frac{-3}{2}$ *SOLUTION* $\frac{-3}{2} = -3 \times \frac{1}{2} = -1.5$

Just for Fun

Find at least three numbers that satisfy all three conditions: Answers may vary.

there is a remainder of 1 when the number is divided by 2; Examples: 11, 23, 35
there is a remainder of 2 when the number is divided by 3;
there is a remainder of 3 when the number is divided by 4.

Chalkboard Examples

Solve each equation.

1. $-\dfrac{y}{5} = -2$ 10

2. $-12 = -\dfrac{k}{2}$ 24

3. $5q = 20$ 4
4. $-3x = 18$ -6

5. $\dfrac{3}{2}t = 15$ 10

6. $0 = 18w$ 0
7. $-8d = 64$ -8

Supplementary Materials

Practice Master 11

Progress Test 9

3-6 Transforming Equations: Division

OBJECTIVE To solve equations using multiplication or division.

EXAMPLE 1 Solve $-\dfrac{z}{4} = -13$.

SOLUTION
$$-\frac{z}{4} = -13$$
$$(-4)\left(-\frac{z}{4}\right) = (-4)(-13)$$
$$z = 52$$

$$\textit{Check: } -\frac{z}{4} = -13$$
$$-\frac{52}{4} \overset{?}{=} -13$$
$$-13 = -13 \quad \sqrt{}$$

$\therefore$ the solution is 52. **Answer**

EXAMPLE 2 Solve $-8a = 72$.

SOLUTION
$$-8a = 72$$
$$\frac{-8a}{-8} = \frac{72}{-8}$$
$$a = -9$$

$$\textit{Check: } -8a = 72$$
$$-8(-9) \overset{?}{=} 72$$
$$72 = 72 \quad \sqrt{}$$

$\therefore$ the solution is -9. **Answer**

The method used in Example 2 is called **transformation by division,** because each side of the equation is *divided* by -8. Of course, transformation by division is just a special case of transformation by multiplication, since you can just as well multiply by $-\dfrac{1}{8}$ to solve the equation in Example 2.

Oral Exercises

State the number by which each side of the given equation must be divided to produce an equivalent equation with the variable alone as one side. Then state this equivalent equation.

1. $12a = 72$ 12; $a = 6$ 2. $8b = -8$ 8; $b = -1$ 3. $7c = -21$ 7; $c = -3$
4. $-4x = 32$ -4; $x = -8$ 5. $-6y = -6$ -6; $y = 1$ 6. $-35z = -105$ -35; $z = 3$

92 *CHAPTER 3*

State the root of each equation.

7. $8t = 48$ 6

8. $2m = -22$ −11

9. $-5n = 60$ −12

10. $-6 = 6x$ −1

11. $0 = -3k$ 0

12. $-9r = -27$ 3

13. $y \div 3 = 9$ 27

14. $\frac{y}{2} = -4$ −8

15. $10 = x \div 5$ 50

16. $8 = -\frac{u}{3}$ −24

17. $-7v = -7$ 1

18. $11f = 99$ 9

Written Exercises

Solve.

A

1. $17s = 510$ 30

2. $30r = 450$ 15

3. $-1024 = 64t$ −16

4. $-351 = 27g$ −13

5. $-7f = 133$ −19

6. $15h = -255$ −17

7. $-14x = -364$ 26

8. $-5y = 435$ −87

9. $-9a = -216$ 24

10. $12b = -576$ −48

11. $8y = -344$ −43

12. $-11x = 154$ −14

13. $6d = 210$ 35

14. $2680 = 40z$ 67

15. $-374 = 34m$ −11

16. $-18k = 198$ −11

17. $5 = \frac{1}{74}p$ 370

18. $0 = -\frac{1}{89}t$ 0

19. $-\frac{q}{10} = -68$ 680

20. $-77 = -\frac{v}{7}$ 539

21. $27c = -675$ −25

22. $736 = -32d$ −23

23. $-37x = -962$ 26

24. $-26f = -858$ 33

Problems

Solve using an equation.

A

1. Twelve times a number is −348. Find the number. −29

2. Negative seven times a number is 259. Find the number. −37

3. Eric Danielle paid $86 for a series of four operas. How much is that for each opera? $21.50

4. Maria Brilla paid $418 for a season ticket to the 38 home basketball games. How much is that for each game? $11

5. A package of two AA batteries costs $1.18. How much is that for each battery? $.59

6. A half-dozen blueberry muffins cost $1.80. How much does one muffin cost? $.30

B

7. This week you can get 12 color prints developed for $2.88. How much is that for each print? $.24

8. A monthly commuter ticket costs $39. If it is used for 50 rides, how much does each ride cost? $.78

9. Four diesel-powered sedans cost a company $31,361.60. How much did each sedan cost? $7840.40

10. A corporation gained $820,000 from the sale of some property. This was a gain of $.25 for each share of stock in the corporation. How many shares of stock are there in the corporation? 3,280,000 shares

SOLVING EQUATIONS **93**

Suggested Assignments

Minimum
  93/1–24, P: 1, 3, 4

Average
  93/1–23 odd, P: 1–9 odd

Maximum
  93/1–23 odd, P: 1–9 odd, 10
S 91/32

Extra Practice Problems
  p. 515

Additional A Exercises

Solve.

1. $2r = 18$ 9

2. $5x = -55$ −11

3. $-7y = 42$ −6

4. $-6z = -18$ 3

5. $8c = 104$ 13

6. $-12b = -168$ 14

Solve.

1. $\frac{1}{3}x = 21$ 63

2. $-\frac{1}{4}y = 4$ -16

Simplify.

3. $\frac{28}{-7}$ -4

4. $-40 \div 10$ -4

5. $-36 \div (-9)$ 4

6. $-5y \div \frac{1}{5}$ $-25y$

Solve.

7. $6y = -54$ -9

8. $-3x = -39$ 13

9. Linda lost one third of her books when she changed dormitory rooms. She lost 21 books. By writing and solving an equation, determine how many books Linda had originally.

63 books

Self-Test 2

VOCABULARY   transformation by multiplication (p. 84)
quotient (p. 88)
transformation by division (p. 92)

Solve.

1. $\frac{1}{4}y = 16$ $\qquad$ **2.** $-\frac{1}{2}x = 10$ $\qquad$ Obj. 3-4, p. 84

Simplify.

3. $\frac{36}{-6}$ $\qquad$ **4.** $-42 \div 7$ $\qquad$ Obj. 3-5, p. 88

5. $-18 \div (-9)$ $\qquad$ **6.** $-2x \div \frac{1}{2}$

Solve.

7. $8x = -72$ $\qquad$ **8.** $-5z = -35$ $\qquad$ Obj. 3-6, p. 92

9. Half of the oranges that the coach brought were eaten on the way home from the game. Twelve of the coach's oranges were eaten. By writing an equation and solving it, find out how many oranges the coach brought.

Check your answers with those at the back of the book.

Application

Electrical Power and Energy

Power is associated with the flow of an electric current in a circuit. Electrical power is measured in watts (W). The amount of power that is used depends on the number of volts (V) of the source of electricity and on the current. Current is the rate of flow of electrical charge, measured in amperes (A). Most household appliances (with the exception of large ones, such as stoves or clothes dryers) operate at voltages between 115 V and 125 V. Look at some electrical appliances in your home. The voltage and power are usually labeled.

The watt, ampere, and volt are units in the metric system. Using these units of measurement, power (P) is related to voltage (V) and current (I) by the formula

$$P = VI.$$

EXAMPLE 1   If current from a 120 V source flows through a 100 W light bulb, find the amount of current flowing in the circuit.

94   *CHAPTER 3*

SOLUTION   You are given $V = 120$ and $P = 100$. Use the formula:

$$P = VI$$
$$100 = 120 \cdot I$$
$$I = \frac{100}{120} = \frac{5}{6}$$
$$I = \frac{5}{6}$$

$\therefore$ the amount of current is about 0.83 A.

When P watts of power are used for t hours, the energy (e) consumed, measured in watt-hours ($W \cdot h$), is

$$e = PT.$$

Electric companies base their charge to their customers on a larger unit, the kilowatt-hour ($kW \cdot h$), which is equal to one thousand watt-hours.

EXAMPLE 2   A room air conditioner uses about 860 W. If the average cost of electricity is 8.4¢ per $kW \cdot h$, how much does it cost to operate the air conditioner for six hours?

SOLUTION   Using the formula for energy, find the amount of energy consumed.

$$e = Pt$$
$$e = 860 \cdot 6$$
$$e = 5160$$

$\therefore$ the amount of energy consumed is 5160 $W \cdot h$ or 5.160 $kW \cdot h$.
To compute the cost:

$$cost = 8.4 \times 5.160$$
$$= 43.344$$

$\therefore$ the cost of energy is about 43¢.

1. A desk calculator operates at 115 V with a current of 0.14 A. How much power is used by the calculator? 16.1 W

2. A toaster uses about 1150 W. If it operates at 120 V, how much current flows through the wiring? 9.58 A

3. A 1000 W hair dryer operates on a current of 8.33 A. What is the voltage in the circuit? 120.05 V

4. A solid-state color television uses 200 W. Assuming the cost of electricity is 8.4¢ per $kW \cdot h$, how much does it cost to watch a three hour movie? 5¢

5. The oven in an electric range uses 12,200 W. At 8.4¢ per $kW \cdot h$, how much does it cost to roast a turkey for five hours? $5.12

Chalkboard Examples

Solve.

1. $5y + 2y - 2 = 19$ 3

2. $\dfrac{x}{3} - 7 = 5$ 36

3. $3(x - 5) = -21$ -2

4. $12 - 2(z - 2) = 12$ 2

5. $-\dfrac{1}{3}x + 4 = 9$ -15

6. $-21 = 3 - 2x$ 12

7. $-16 = -4(2 - t)$ -2

Supplementary Materials

Practice Master 12

Computer Activity 8
Break-Even Point
  Using elementary algebra and a computer program that generates an easy-to-read chart, students are introduced to an important business idea, the break-even point. Various problems are included that provide practice in running the program and analyzing the results.

Suggested Assignments

Minimum
Day 1: 97/1–43 odd
    R 94/Self-Test 2
Day 2: 97/42, 44
      98/P: 1–9 odd

Average
Day 1: 97/1–47 odd
    R 94/Self-Test 2
Day 2: 98/P: 1–7 odd, 8, 10,
      11, 13, 15

Maximum
Day 1: 97/1–49 odd
    R 94/Self-Test 2
Day 2: 98/P: 1, 8, 9, 12–18,
      21, 24, 25

Extra Practice Problems
    p. 515

TRANSFORMING EQUATIONS

3-7 *Using Several Transformations*

OBJECTIVE To use several transformations to solve an equation.

To solve the equation $3x + 8 = 20$, you transform it into an equivalent equation which has x alone as one side. Look at the side with x in it: $3x + 8$. To get x alone, first subtract 8 and then divide by 3, as follows.

$$3x + 8 = 20$$
$$3x + 8 - 8 = 20 - 8 \quad \leftarrow \text{Subtract 8.}$$
$$3x = 12$$
$$\frac{3x}{3} = \frac{12}{3} \quad \leftarrow \text{Divide by 3.}$$
$$x = 4$$

  To "undo" the *addition* of a number, you use the *subtraction* of that number. Addition and subtraction are called **inverse operations.** Multiplication and division are also inverse operations.
  The following steps are usually helpful when you solve an equation in which all the variables are on the same side.

---

1. Simplify each side of the equation.
2. If there are still indicated additions or subtractions, use the inverse operations to undo them.
3. If there are indicated multiplications or divisions involving the variable, use the inverse operations to undo them.

EXAMPLE 1 Solve $8x + 5x - 3 = 23$.

SOLUTION
$$8x + 5x - 3 = 23$$
$$(8 + 5)x - 3 = 23 \qquad \left\{ \begin{array}{l} \text{Use the distributive axiom} \\ \text{to simplify the left side.} \end{array} \right.$$
$$13x - 3 = 23$$
$$13x - 3 + 3 = 23 + 3 \quad \leftarrow \text{Add 3 to each side.}$$
$$13x = 26$$
$$\frac{13x}{13} = \frac{26}{13} \quad \leftarrow \text{Divide each side by 13.}$$
$$x = 2$$

CONDENSED $8x + 5x - 3 = 23$ *Check:* $8x + 5x - 3 = 23$
SOLUTION $13x - 3 = 23$ $8(2) + 5(2) - 3 \overset{?}{=} 23$
            $13x = 26$ $16 + 10 - 3 \overset{?}{=} 23$
            $x = 2$ $23 = 23$ $\checkmark$
            $\therefore$ the solution is 2.   ***Answer***

96   CHAPTER 3

Oral Exercises

Describe how you would solve each equation.

SAMPLE $\frac{1}{3}x + 1 = -2$ *SOLUTION* First subtract 1 from each side; then multiply each side by 3.

In Exs. 1–6, perform the indicated operations in the order shown.
1. $4x + 1 = 5$ -1; $\div 4$
2. $3x - 2 = 8$ $+2$; $\div 3$
3. $\frac{1}{2}x - 3 = -1$ $+3$; $\times 2$
4. $-\frac{1}{5}x + 8 = 4$ -8; $\times(-5)$
5. $6 + \frac{x}{2} = 7$ -6; $\times 2$
6. $-2 + \frac{x}{-3} = 4$ $+2$; $\times(-3)$
7. $5x + x = 18$
8. $4y - y = 12$
9. $z - 4z = 6$
10. $-5t + 7t = -20$
11. $6s + s - 2 = 5$
12. $3m - m + 1 = -7$

Written Exercises

Solve.

A 1. $3x + 5 = 14$ 3
2. $2y - 5 = 17$ 11
3. $-13 + 4t = -37$ -6
4. $12 + 5s = -78$ -18
5. $\frac{a}{2} - 4 = 8$ 24
6. $\frac{b}{3} + 6 = 9$ 9
7. $\frac{c}{5} + 20 = -15$ -175
8. $\frac{-d}{4} - 2 = -1$ -4
9. $9 = 5 - 2m$ -2
10. $12 = -3 - 5n$ -3
11. $-6w + 3w = 21$ -7
12. $3k - k = -8$ -4
13. $5t + 3t = -32$ -4
14. $2p - 5p = -15$ 5
15. $3q + 4q = 0$ 0
16. $7s - 11s = 0$ 0
17. $2k + 42 = 0$ -21
18. $4w + 80 = 0$ -20
19. $5q - 3q + 10 = 0$ -5
20. $3w - w - 2 = 0$ 1
21. $x - 4x + 2 = 5$ -1
22. $r - 7 - 4r = -4$ -1
23. $0 = m - 14 - 3m$ -7
24. $0 = u + 15 + 4u$
25. $x + 2x + 3x = 24$ 4
26. $3y - 2y + y = 36$ 18
27. $5(a - 2) = -35$
28. $6(b + 9) = -30$ -14
29. $-3(r - 3) = 12$ -1
30. $-8(s + 5) = 56$

24. -3 27. -5 30. -12

B 31. $3(x + 1) + 2 = -7$ -4
32. $2(y - 1) - 7 = 5$ 7
33. $4(w + 8) - 13 = -1$ -5
34. $5(z - 2) + 8 = 3$ 1
35. $8 + 3(x + 1) = -4$ -5
36. $13 + 4(y + 5) = -3$ -9
37. $4 - 3(a - 1) = -2$ 3
38. $7 - 4(b + 1) = -1$ 1
39. $-4 - 3(2y + 1) = -13$ 1
40. $-5 + 4(3d - 6) = 7$ 3
41. $(a - 10) + (a - 2) + a = 0$ 4
42. $(3 - b) + (4 - b) + (5 - b) = 0$ 4
43. $3(r + 4) - 2r = -5$ -17
44. $2(s - 3) - s = -2$ 4

C 45. $x - 2[6 - (1 - 2x)] = 0$ $-\frac{10}{3}$
46. $\frac{1}{2}[3(m + 2) - (2 - m)] = 6$ 2
47. $-2[y + 3(5 - y)] - 5(y - 7) = 0$ 5
48. $5z + 2[3(1 - z) - 2(1 + z)] = 22$ -4
49. $2|x| - (|x| - 1) = 7$ $\{7, -7\}$
50. $7(|y| - 2) - 3|y| - 16 = 2$ $\{8, -8\}$

SOLVING EQUATIONS   **97**

Additional Answers
Oral Exercises

7. Add x to $5x$; then divide each side by 6.

8. Subtract y from $4y$; then divide each side by 3.

9. Subtract $4z$ from z; then divide each side by -3.

10. Add $7t$ to $-5t$; then divide each side by 2.

11. Add s to $6s$; then add 2 to each side; then divide each side by 7.

12. Subtract m from $3m$; then subtract 1 from each side; then divide each side by 2.

Additional A Exercises
Solve.

1. $6x + 5 = 29$ 4
2. $3a - 2 = 13$ 5
3. $\frac{1}{2}m + 7 = 2$ -10
4. $\frac{1}{5}c - 3 = -5$ -10
5. $2n + 5n = 56$ 8
6. $5y - y = -28$ -7

Problems

SAMPLE

In the class elections Maria received 53 more votes than Annie. In all, 221 votes were cast for the two girls. How many votes were for Annie?

SOLUTION

Step 1   The problem asks for the number of votes for Annie.

Step 2   Let n = number of votes for Annie.
Then $n + 53$ = number of votes for Maria.

Step 3 $n + (n + 53) = 221$

Step 4 $2n + 53 = 221$

Complete the solution.

A   1. The sum of twice a number and 63 is 191. Find the number. 64

2. The sum of 17 and three times a number is 80. Find the number. 21

3. Four times a number, decreased by 43, is -11. Find the number. 8

4. Six times a number, increased by 9, is 123. Find the number. 19

5. Seventy, decreased by five times a number, is -100. Find the number. 34

6. Twice a number, decreased by 37, is -3. Find the number. 17

7. If you add to 8 the product of 3 and a number, you get 41. Find the number. 11

8. If you subtract 57 from the product of 4 and a number, you get -1. Find the number. 14

9. The perimeter of a rectangle is 32 and the length is 10. Find the width. 6

10. The perimeter of a rectangle is 44 and the width is 8. Find the length. 14

Drink, $.55; sandwich, $1.65

11. Together, a soft drink and a sandwich cost $2.20. What was the price of each if the sandwich cost three times as much as the drink?

12. Casey's Car Care Center sold 1864 L (liters) of gasoline today. Seven times as much gasoline was bought with credit cards as with cash. How much gasoline was bought on credit? 1631 L

13. Sally Chin has practiced law three years longer than her younger brother. Together, they have a total of 21 years of practice. How long has her brother practiced law? 9 years

14. The home team's score of 102 points was 60 points less than twice the visiting team's score. What was the visiting team's score? 81 points

B 15. One number is 17 greater than a second number. When the lesser number is subtracted from twice the greater number, the difference is 157. Find each number. 123 and 140

98   *CHAPTER 3*

16. Two numbers differ by 3. Four times the lesser diminished by three times the greater is 7. Find the numbers. 16 and 19

17. The side of a square is twice as long as the side of an equilateral triangle (a triangle with all sides equal). The perimeter of the square is 60 cm more than the perimeter of the triangle. What are the lengths of the sides of the square and the triangle? Square, 12 cm; triangle, 24 cm

18. In woodshop, Lisa cut a board 2 m long into two pieces. One piece is 10 cm shorter than the other. How long is each piece? 95 cm; 105 cm

19. Juan and Ingrid went selling magazine subscriptions. Ingrid sold four fewer subscriptions than twice as many as Juan sold. Together, they sold 23 subscriptions. How many subscriptions did each sell? Juan, 9 subscriptions; Ingrid, 14 subscriptions

20. With optional equipment, an automobile cost $7840. If the cost of the basic car was $165 more than four times the price of the optional equipment, what was the cost of the basic car? $6305

C 21. The record low temperature at one station in Antarctica is 3.1°C warmer than the record low at a second station. The average of the two record low temperatures is −86.75°C. What is the record low at the first station? −85.2°C

22. The total length of three wilderness trails is 20 km. The first trail is 1 km shorter than twice the length of the second trail. The third trail is 2 km longer than the first. Find the length of each trail. 1st, 7 km; 2nd, 4 km; 3rd, 9 km

23. There is a three-year age difference between each child in the Miller family and the next older child. If there are four children in the family and the sum of their ages is 34, how old is the oldest? 13 years

24. The perimeter of a rectangular lot is 260 m. The length exceeds the width by 20 m. Find the dimensions of the lot. 55 m by 75 m

25. Mac paid $8.55 for a table tennis set at a 10%-off sale. What was the price of the set before the sale? $9.50

Just for Fun _____

Philanthropic Philomena was trying to get people to contribute $10 to the scholarship fund. She knocked on the door of the first house and said, "Give me as much money as I have of my own in my pocket and I'll put $10 into the fund box in your name." It was done, and Philomena repeated the procedure at a second and a third house, after which she had no money of her own left in her pocket and $30 in the fund box. How much money of her own did Philomena start out with in her pocket? $8.75

3-8 Equations Having the Variable in Both Sides

OBJECTIVE   To solve equations having the variable in both sides.

The variable appears in both sides of the equation

$$4y = y + 12.$$

Are you allowed to transform the equation by subtracting y from both sides? The answer is Yes. Because variables represent numbers, you may transform an equation by adding a variable expression to each side or by subtracting a variable expression from each side.

EXAMPLE 1   Solve $4y = y + 12$.

SOLUTION
$$4y = y + 12$$
$$4y - y = y + 12 - y$$
$$3y = 12$$
$$\frac{3y}{3} = \frac{12}{3}$$
$$y = 4$$

CONDENSED $4y = y + 12$ *Check:* $4y = y + 12$
SOLUTION $3y = 12$ $4(4) \stackrel{?}{=} 4 + 12$
             $y = 4$ $16 = 16$ √

$\therefore$ the solution is 4.   ***Answer***

It is possible that an equation may have *no* roots, or that it may be satisfied by *every* real number. Study the next two examples.

EXAMPLE 2   Solve $5(1 - x) + 8x = 3(x + 2)$.

SOLUTION
$$5(1 - x) + 8x = 3(x + 2)$$
$$5 - 5x + 8x = 3x + 6$$
$$5 + 3x = 3x + 6$$
$$3x - 3x = 6 - 5$$
$$0 = 1$$

Since the given equation is equivalent to the false statement $0 = 1$, it has no root. ***Answer***

It is convenient to call the set with no members the **empty set,** or the **null set.** It is denoted by the symbol ∅. Thus, you may say that the solution set of the equation in Example 2 is ∅.

100   *CHAPTER 3*

EXAMPLE 3 Solve $\frac{1}{2}(8t - 18) + 16 = -5 + 4(t + 3)$.

SOLUTION
$$\frac{1}{2}(8t - 18) + 16 = -5 + 4(t + 3)$$
$$4t - 9 + 16 = -5 + 4t + 12$$
$$4t + 7 = 7 + 4t$$

The given equation is equivalent to $4t + 7 = 7 + 4t$, which is satisfied by every real number.

$\therefore$ the solution set is the set of real numbers. **Answer**

An equation which is true for every value of the variable(s) is called an **identity.** Thus, the equation in Example 2,

$$\frac{1}{2}(8t - 18) + 16 = -5 + 4(t + 3),$$

is an identity.

Oral Exercises

Solve.

1. $3x = 2x + 5$ $x = 5$
2. $y + 8 = 2y$ $8 = y$
3. $4t + 1 = 5t$ $1 = t$
4. $2u - 7 = 3u$ $-7 = u$
5. $x + 5 = 1 + x$ No root
6. $2a = 4 + 2a$ No root
7. $3x = x + 2x$ Identity
8. $2m = m$ $m = 0$
9. $3x = x + 2$ $x = 1$
10. $3b + 1 = 3b + 2$ No root
11. $2(x - 1) = 2x - 2$ Identity
12. $3(z + 1) = 3z$ No root

Written Exercises

Solve each equation. If the equation is an identity or if it has no root, state that fact.

A
1. $8u = 6u + 14$ 7
2. $13t = 40 + 8t$ 8
3. $x = 51 - 2x$ 17
4. $z = 84 - 6z$ 12
5. $11h - 91 = 4h$ 13
6. $4i + 49 = 1$ -12
7. $29j + 54 = 23j$ -9
8. $41k - 63 = 34k$ 9
9. $98 - 5x = 2x$ 14
10. $42 + 10s = 4s$ -7
11. $2p = 11p + 45$ -5
12. $11e = 15e + 96$ -24
13. $17x + 66 = 14x$ -22
14. $-6q = q - 35$ 5
15. $-3a = -8a - 30$ -6
16. $-4k - 18 = -13k$ 2
17. $5y = -2 + 5y$ No root
18. $7t = 126 - 7t$ 9
19. $7u + 5 = 5u - 7$ -6
20. $4r - 3 = r + 6$ 3
21. $6x - 2 = x + 13$ 3
22. $6c + 8 = -8 + 6c$ No root
23. $53 - 2d = 2 + d$ 17
24. $3 - f = 6f + 24$ -3

B
25. $3(x + 4) = 2x$ -12
26. $2(y - 5) = y - 1$ 9
27. $5(1 + n) = 2(7 + n)$ 3
28. $3(2 + m) = 2(3 - m)$ 0
29. $4b + 4(1 - b) = b - 9$ 13
30. $2(2 + a) - 3a = a + 10$ -3

SOLVING EQUATIONS   **101**

Suggested Assignments

Minimum
Day 1: 101/1–23 odd, 25–30, 35
Day 2: 102/P: 1–6, 10
Average
Day 1: 101/1–39 odd
     S 99/P: 17
Day 2: 102/P: 2–4, 7, 9, 10, 16
Maximum
     101/1–39 odd
     102/P: 3, 4, 6, 7, 9, 10

Extra Practice Problems
     p. 515

Additional A Exercises

Solve. If the equation is an identity or has no root, state that fact.

1. $5x = 2x + 12$ 4
2. $3n + 9 = 2n$ -9
3. $4(x - 2) = 4x - 8$ Identity
4. $a - 7 = 8a$ -1
5. $2y - 1 = 2 + 2y$ No root
6. $b + 24 = -3b - 4$ -7

Solve each equation. If the equation is an identity or if it has no root, state that fact.

Identity

31. $4(2y - 1) + 5 = 3y + 1$ 0

32. $3(x - 4) - x = 2(x - 6)$

33. $4s - 2(1 - s) = 2(3s - 1)$ Identity

34. $3z + 2(1 - z) = z - 2$

35. $4(g + 1) = 10 - 2(3 - 2g)$ Identity

36. $1 + 3(d + 2) = d + 2(d + 4)$

34. no root   **36.** no root

C **37.** $4[1 - 3(r + 2)] + 2r = 0$ −2

38. $2[3(c + 2) - (c + 1)] = 3(1 + c)$ −7

39. $2[3(2 + v) - (-v)] = 5(v + 3) - 2(1 - v)$ 1

40. $y - 1 - [2(3 - 2y) - 3(3 - y)] = 2(y + 1)$ Identity

Problems

Solve.

A **1.** Find a number which is 24 greater than its opposite. 12

2. Find a number which is 14 less than its opposite. −7

3. Find a number which is 15 greater than twice its opposite. 5

4. Find a number whose product with 6 is the same as its sum with 60. 12

5. The sum of two numbers is 76. One of the numbers is three times the other. Find the numbers. 19 and 57

6. Twice a number, increased by 11, is the same as three times the number, decreased by 12. Find the number. 23

7. The difference of two numbers is 16. Four times the smaller number is 13 less than three times the larger. What are the numbers? 35 and 51

8. The sum of two numbers is 64. Twice the lesser number is five more than the greater number. Find the numbers. 23 and 41

9. Karla has five steel balls of equal mass. If she puts four of them in one pan of a beam balance and one ball along with a mass of 30 g (grams) in the other pan, the pans balance each other. What is the mass of each steel ball? 10 g

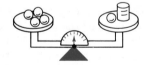

10. Sandy has six coins of the same kind. Two fifteen-cent stamps and three of the coins have the same total value as all six coins put together. What kind of coin does she have? Dime

11. Cycles, Inc., manufactures ten-speed and three-speed bicycles. The profit on a ten-speed is three times the profit on a three-speed. If the profit on each kind of bicycle is increased by $15, then the profit on the ten-speed will be twice the profit on the three-speed. What is the current profit on each? Three-speed, $15; ten-speed, $45

102   CHAPTER 3

12. During the passage of a cold front, the temperature dropped at the steady rate of 1°C per hour. The temperature at 6:00 P.M. was 3°C more than twice the temperature at midnight. What was the temperature at 6:00 P.M.? 9°C

B 13. On Friday, Mike and Steve shot baskets, and Mike made three times as many as Steve. On Saturday, Mike made seven fewer baskets than he did on Friday, while Steve made nine more than he did on Friday. If they tied on Saturday, how many baskets did each make on Friday? Steve, 8 baskets; Mike, 24 baskets

14. The combined length of the Panama and Suez Canals is 250 km. If the Suez Canal were 4 km shorter, it would be twice as long as the Panama Canal. How long is each canal? Panama, 82 km; Suez, 168 km

15. Angel Falls, the highest waterfall on earth, is 750 m higher than Niagara Falls. If each of the falls were 7 m lower, Angel Falls would be sixteen times as high as Niagara Falls. How high is Angel Falls? 807 m Niagara Falls? 57 m

16. A cup of coffee contains 20 more mg (milligrams) of caffeine than a cup of tea and 85 more mg of caffeine than the average cola drink. If one cup of tea and four cola drinks contain the same amount of caffeine as one cup of coffee, how many milligrams of caffeine are there in one cup of coffee? 90 mg

17. "Tom is two times as old as I am," said Dick. "On the other hand, I am four years younger than Harry while Tom is eight years older than Harry. How old are Harry, Tom, and I?" Harry, 16 y; Tom, 24 y; Dick, 12 y

18. Suppose that five plain hamburgers cost the same as three superburgers. Also, suppose that one superburger costs 30 cents more than one cheeseburger, while one plain hamburger costs 20 cents less than one cheeseburger. What would be the cost of one of each kind of burger? Hamburger, $.75; cheeseburger, $.95; superburger, $1.25

C 19. Television ratings showed that at nine o'clock on Monday night, 37% more of the city's TV audience watched a new situation comedy than watched an old hit movie. The percent watching the movie was 5% more than twice the percent watching a college football game. The percent watching the comedy was 2% more than six times the percent watching the game. What percent of the TV audience watched the game? the movie? the comedy? Game, 10%; Movie, 25%; Comedy, 62%

20. The three countries of greatest area in the world are the Soviet Union, Canada, and China, with a combined area of 41,939,000 km² (square kilometers). The area of Canada is 415,000 km² greater than that of China, while the combined area of Canada and China is 2,865,000 km² less than that of the Soviet Union. What is the area of each country? Canada, 9,976,000 km²; China, 9,561,000 km²; Soviet Union, 22,402,000 km²

SOLVING EQUATIONS **103**

Teaching Suggestions p. T73

Suggested Extensions p. T73

Chalkboard Examples

Write the missing reasons.

Prove: If $a + b = 0$, then $b = -a$.

Proof:

1. $a + b = 0$
   Given
2. $a + (-a) = 0$
   Ax. of opposites
3. $a + b = a + (-a)$
   Substitution
4. $-a + (a + b) = -a + [a + (-a)]$
   Add. prop. of equality
5. $(-a + a) + b = (-a + a) + -a$
   Assoc. ax. for add.
6. $0 + b = 0 + (-a)$
   Ax. of opposites
7. $b = -a$
   Identity ax. for add.

Supplementary Material

Progress Test 10

3-9 *Proving Statements*

OBJECTIVE To prove statements in algebra.

Many rules or number properties have been stated earlier in this book. Some of these are axioms, statements *assumed* to be true. Others are theorems. A **theorem** is a statement that is *shown* to be true by using axioms, definitions, and other theorems in a logical development.

Logical reasoning from known facts and axioms to a theorem is called a **proof.** The following example shows how a theorem is proved in algebra.

EXAMPLE Prove: For all real numbers a and b, $(a + b) + (-b) = a$.

PROOF

STATEMENTS	REASONS
1. $(a + b) + (-b) = a + [b + (-b)]$	1. Associative axiom for addition
2. $b + (-b) = 0$	2. Axiom of opposites
3. $a + [b + (-b)] = a + 0$	3. Substitution principle
4. $a + 0 = a$	4. Identity axiom for addition
5. $(a + b) + (-b) = a$	5. Transitive property of equality

Generally, a shortened form of proof is given, in which only the *key reasons* are stated. (The substitution principle and axioms of equality are usually not stated.)

The proof shown in the example above may be shortened to the three steps shown below.

STATEMENTS	REASONS
1. $(a + b) + (-b) = a + [b + (-b)]$	1. Associative axiom for addition
2. $= a + 0$	2. Axiom of opposites
3. $= a$	3. Identity axiom for addition

Once a theorem has been proved, it can be used as a reason in other proofs.

You may refer to the Chapter Summaries on pages 66 and 107 for listings of axioms and theorems that you can use as reasons in your proofs.

Oral Exercises

State the missing reasons.

1. Prove the *property of the opposite of a sum:* $-(a + b) = (-a) + (-b)$.

   Proof: Since $-(a + b)$ is the opposite of $a + b$, you can prove that
   $$-(a + b) = (-a) + (-b)$$
   by showing that $a + b + [(-a) + (-b)] = 0$.

			Assoc. and comm. axs. for add.
1. $a + b + [(-a) + (-b)] = [a + (-a)] + [b + (-b)]$		1. _?_ and _?_	
2.	$= 0 + 0$	2. _?_ Ax. of opposites	
3.	$= 0$	3. _?_ Identity ax.	

2. Prove the *addition property of equality:*

   If $a = b$, then $a + c = b + c$ and $c + a = c + b$.

   Proof:
   1. $a + c = a + c$ 1. _?_   Reflexive property
   2. $a = b$ 2. Given
   3. $a + c = b + c$ 3. _?_   Substitution principle
   4. $a + c = c + a$;   4. _?_   Commutative axiom for add.
      $b + c = c + b$
   5. $c + a = c + b$ 5. _?_   Substitution principle

Written Exercises

Write the missing reasons in Exercises 1-6.

A 1. a. Prove: If $b \neq 0$, then $\frac{1}{b}(ba) = a$.

   Proof:

   1. $\frac{1}{b}(ba) = \left(\frac{1}{b} \cdot b\right)a$ 1. _?_ Associative axiom for mult.
   2. $= 1 \cdot a$ 2. _?_ Axiom of reciprocals
   3. $= a$ 3. _?_ Identity axiom for mult.

b. From step 3 prove that $(ab)\frac{1}{b} = a$.

   3. $\frac{1}{b}(ba) = a$ (above)

   4. $(ba)\frac{1}{b} = a$ 4. _?_ Commutative axiom for mult.

   5. $(ab)\frac{1}{b} = a$ 5. _?_ Commutative axiom for mult.

   $\therefore$ if $b \neq 0$, $\frac{1}{b}(ba) = a$ and $(ab)\frac{1}{b} = a$.

SOLVING EQUATIONS **105**

Suggested Assignments

Minimum
105/1–5
R 107/*Self-Test 3*

Average
105/1–7 odd
R 107/*Self-Test 3*

Maximum
105/1–11 odd
S 103/*P*: 16, 19, 20

Additional A Exercises

Write the missing reasons.

Prove: For all real numbers a and b such that $a \neq 0$ and $b \neq 0$,
$$\frac{1}{ab} = \frac{1}{a} \cdot \frac{1}{b}.$$

Proof: Since $\frac{1}{ab}$ is the reciprocal of ab, we can prove that $\frac{1}{ab} = \frac{1}{a} \cdot \frac{1}{b}$ by showing that the product of ab and $\frac{1}{a} \cdot \frac{1}{b}$ is 1.

1. $(ab)\left(\frac{1}{a} \cdot \frac{1}{b}\right) = \left(a \cdot \frac{1}{a}\right)\left(b \cdot \frac{1}{b}\right)$
   Comm. and assoc. axs. for multiplication

2. $= 1 \cdot 1$
   Ax. of reciprocals

3. $= 1$
   Identity ax. for multiplication

7. Proof:

1. $a \neq 0$
   (Given)

2. $\dfrac{a}{a} = a \cdot \dfrac{1}{a}$

   (Rule for division)

3. $ = 1$
   (Ax. of reciprocals)

8. Proof: Since $\dfrac{1}{\frac{a}{b}}$ is the

reciprocal of $\dfrac{b}{a}$, you can

prove that $\dfrac{1}{\frac{a}{b}} = \dfrac{b}{a}$ by

showing that $\dfrac{b}{a}$ is the

reciprocal of $\dfrac{a}{b}$; that is,

$\dfrac{a}{b} \cdot \dfrac{b}{a} = 1.$

1. $a \neq 0,\ b \neq 0$
   (Given)

2. $\dfrac{a}{b} \cdot \dfrac{b}{a} = \left(a \cdot \dfrac{1}{b}\right)\left(b \cdot \dfrac{1}{a}\right)$

   (Rule for division)

3. $ = \left(a \cdot \dfrac{1}{a}\right)\left(b \cdot \dfrac{1}{b}\right)$

   (Assoc. and comm.
   axs. for mult.)

4. $ = (1)(1)$
   (Ax. of reciprocals)

5. $ = 1$
   (Ident. ax. for mult.)

9. Proof:

1. $a = b,\ c \neq 0$
   (Given)

2. $a \cdot \dfrac{1}{c} = b \cdot \dfrac{1}{c}$

   (Mult. prop. of equal.)

3. $\dfrac{a}{c} = \dfrac{b}{c}$

   (Rule for division)

---

2. Prove the *multiplication property of equality:*

$$\text{If } a = b, \text{ then } ca = cb \text{ and } ac = bc.$$

Proof:

1. $ca = ca$ 1. _?_   Reflexive property
2. $a = b$ 2. Given
3. $ca = cb$ 3. _?_   Substitution principle
4. $ca = ac;$ 4. _?_   Commutative axiom for mult.
   $cb = bc$
5. $ac = bc$ 5. _?_   Substitution principle

3. Prove: If $a + c = b + c$, then $a = b$.

Proof:

1. $ a + c = b + c$ 1. Given
2. $(a + c) + (-c) = (b + c) + (-c)$ 2. _?_ Addition prop. of equality
3. $ a = b$ 3. _?_ Theorem proved on p. 104

4. Prove: If $ac = bc$ and $c \neq 0$, then $a = b$.

Proof:

1. $ ac = bc$ 1. Given

2. $(ac) \cdot \dfrac{1}{c} = (bc) \cdot \dfrac{1}{c}$ 2. _?_ Multiplication prop. of equality

3. $ a = b$ 3. _?_ Theorem proved in Ex. 1, p. 105

B **5.** Prove: $-(a - b) = b - a$.

Proof:

1. $-(a - b) = -[a + (-b)]$ 1. _?_ Rule for subtraction
2. $ = -a + [-(-b)]$ 2. _?_ Prop. of the opposite of a sum
3. $ = -a + b$ 3. _?_ Def. of the opp. of a number
4. $ = b + (-a)$ 4. _?_ Commutative axiom for add.
5. $ = b - a$ 5. _?_ Rule for subtraction

6. Prove: $-(-a - b) = a + b$

Proof:

1. $-(-a - b) = -[-a + (-b)]$ 1. _?_ Rule for subtraction
2. $ = -(-a) + [-(-b)]$ 2. _?_ Prop. of the opp. of a sum
3. $ = a + b$ 3. _?_ Def. of the opp. of a number

Write proofs, including statements and reasons, for Exercises 7–11.

7. Prove: If $a \neq 0$, then $\dfrac{a}{a} = 1$.

8. Prove: If $a \neq 0$ and $b \neq 0$, then $\dfrac{\frac{1}{a}}{\frac{b}{b}} = \dfrac{b}{a}$. (Hint: Show that $\dfrac{a}{b} \cdot \dfrac{b}{a} = 1$.)

C 9. Prove: If $a = b$ and $c \neq 0$, then $\dfrac{a}{c} = \dfrac{b}{c}$.

10. Prove: If $c \neq 0$ and $\dfrac{a}{c} = \dfrac{b}{c}$, then $a = b$.

11. Prove: If $a \neq 0$ and $b \neq 0$, then $\dfrac{a + b}{ab} = \dfrac{1}{a} + \dfrac{1}{b}$.

Self-Test 3

VOCABULARY   inverse operations (p. 96)   theorem (p. 104)
empty set (p. 100)   proof (p. 104)
identity (p. 101)

Solve.

1. $4x - 3 = 21$ **2.** $y - 3y + 9 = 5$ Obj. 3-7, p. 96

3. $2z - 4 = z + 2$ **4.** $3(1 - t) + 2 = 2(t - 10)$ Obj. 3-8, p. 100

5. Fred is 6 years older than Liz.
This year he is twice as old as Liz.
How old is Liz this year?

6. Write the missing reasons.   Obj. 3-9, p. 104

1. $-a + (a + b) = (-a + a) + b$ 1. _?_
2. $= 0 + b$ 2. _?_
3. $= b$ 3. _?_

Check your answers with those at the back of the book.

Chapter Summary

1. Transforming an equation by substitution, or by addition or subtraction, or by multiplication or division (not by zero) produces an equivalent equation. These transformations are used in solving equations.
2. Inverse operations are used in solving equations.
3. The structure of algebra is built up of axioms and definitions and of theorems proved by using the axioms and definitions in a logical development.

SOLVING EQUATIONS   **107**

10. Proof:

1. $c \neq 0$, $\dfrac{a}{c} = \dfrac{b}{c}$ (Given)

2. $a \cdot \dfrac{1}{c} = b \cdot \dfrac{1}{c}$
(Rule for division)

3. $\left(a \cdot \dfrac{1}{c}\right) \cdot c = \left(b \cdot \dfrac{1}{c}\right) \cdot c$
(Mult. prop. of equal.)

4. $a \cdot \left(\dfrac{1}{c} \cdot c\right) = b \cdot \left(\dfrac{1}{c} \cdot c\right)$
(Assoc. ax. for mult.)

5. $a \cdot 1 = b \cdot 1$
(Ax. of reciprocals)

6. $a = b$
(Ident. ax. for mult.)

11. Proof:

1. $a \neq 0$, $b \neq 0$ (Given)

2. $\dfrac{a + b}{ab} = (a + b) \cdot \dfrac{1}{ab}$
(Rule for division)

3. $= a \cdot \dfrac{1}{ab} + b \cdot \dfrac{1}{ab}$
(Distributive axiom)

4. $= a \cdot \left(\dfrac{1}{a} \cdot \dfrac{1}{b}\right) +$
$\quad b \cdot \left(\dfrac{1}{a} \cdot \dfrac{1}{b}\right)$
(Prop. of the recip. of a product)

5. $= \left(a \cdot \dfrac{1}{a}\right) \cdot \dfrac{1}{b} +$
$\quad \left(b \cdot \dfrac{1}{b}\right) \cdot \dfrac{1}{a}$
(Comm. and assoc. axs. for mult.)

6. $= 1 \cdot \dfrac{1}{b} + 1 \cdot \dfrac{1}{a}$
(Ax. of reciprocals)

7. $= \dfrac{1}{b} + \dfrac{1}{a}$
(Ident. ax. for mult.)

8. $= \dfrac{1}{a} + \dfrac{1}{b}$
(Comm. ax. for add.)

(Quick Quiz next page)

Solve.

1. $3x - 2 = 19$ 7

2. $2x - 4x + 5 = 1$ 2

3. $3x - 5 = x + 3$ 4

4. $2(1 - y) + 3 = 3(y - 5)$
4

5. Carol is 3 years older than Jay. This year she is four times as old as Jay. How old is Jay this year?
1 year old

6. Write the missing reasons for each step in the proof.

1. $-b + (a + b)$
   $= (a + b) + (-b)$
   Comm. prop. for add.

2. $= a + [b + (-b)]$
   Assoc. prop. for add.

3. $= a + 0$
   Prop. of add. inverses

4. $= a$
   Add. identity

Supplementary Materials

Practice Masters 14, 15

Progress Test 11

Extra Practice pp. 495–497

Chapter Review

Give the letter of the correct answer.

1. Find the solution of $x + (-6) = -1$.   3-1
  a. -7 **b.** -5 **c.** 5 **d.** 6

2. Find the solution of $9 + y = 7$.
  a. 2 **b.** 16 **c.** -16 **d.** -2

3. Simplify $12 - (-6)$.   3-2
  a. -18 **b.** 18 **c.** -6 **d.** 6

4. Simplify $185 - (75 - 90)$.
  a. -200 **b.** 20 **c.** 170 **d.** 200

5. Find the solution of $w - 6 = 9$.   3-3
  a. -15 **b.** 15 **c.** -3 **d.** 3

6. Find the solution of $15 = 7 + z$.
  a. -22 **b.** -8 **c.** 8 **d.** 22

7. Find the solution of $\frac{1}{3}x = -12$.   3-4
  a. -36 **b.** -4 **c.** 36 **d.** 4

8. Find the solution of $-\frac{1}{2}t = -34$.
  a. -17 **b.** -68 **c.** 17 **d.** 68

9. Simplify $-100 \div (-50)$ 3-5
  a. $\frac{1}{2}$ **b.** 2 **c.** -5000 **d.** -2

10. Simplify $\frac{-96x}{8x}$, $x \neq 0$.
  a. -12 **b.** $-12x$ **c.** 12 **d.** $12x$

11. Find the solution of $27y = -81$.   3-6
  a. -54 **b.** -108 **c.** -3 **d.** $-\frac{1}{3}$

12. Find the solution of $-220 = -5t$.
  a. -1100 **b.** -44 **c.** 1100 **d.** 44

13. Find the solution of $4s - 2s - 2 = -42$.   3-7
  a. -42 **b.** -20 **c.** -22 **d.** 20

14. Find the solution of $29 - 3k = 1 + k$.   3-8
  a. -7 **b.** -4 **c.** 4 **d.** 7

108   *CHAPTER 3*

15. A statement assumed to be true is called: 3-9

    a. a theorem   **(b.)** an axiom   **c.** a definition   **d.** a proof

16. Which axiom guarantees that for every real number n,
$(n + 3) + 7 = n + (3 + 7)$?

    a. commutative axiom for multiplication

    b. axiom of closure for addition

    c. transitive property of equality

    (d.) associative axiom for addition

Chapter Test

Solve.

1. $y + (-4) = -15$ -11 **2.** $w + 12 = 33$ 21   3-1

Simplify.

3. $9 - (-1)$ 10   **4.** $218 - (14 - 59)$ 263   3-2

Solve.

5. $t - 15 = 2$ 17   **6.** $-7 = v + 8$ -15 3-3

7. $\frac{1}{3}u = -18$ -54 **8.** $-8 = -\frac{1}{8}a$ 64   3-4

Simplify.

9. $24 \div (-12)$ -2 **10.** $\frac{-56t}{-7t}$, $t \neq 0$ 8   3-5

Solve.

11. $4b = -32$ -8 **12.** $-9t = -108$ 12   3-6

13. $3q + 1 = -17$ -6 **14.** $p - 6 - 6p = 14$ -4 3-7

15. $3c + 2 = 4c - 9$ 11   3-8

16. Paula had four times as much money as her brother Larry, but after their aunt gave each of them four dollars, Paula had three times as much as Larry. How much did each have originally? Paula, $32; Larry, $8

Write the missing reasons.

17. $10x - 12 = 78$ 3-9

    $10x - 12 + 12 = 78 + 12$ __?__ Addition prop. of equality

18. $(\frac{1}{x} \cdot x)y = 1 \cdot y$ __?__ Axiom of reciprocals

20.

Cumulative Review (Chapters 1-3)

Simplify.

1. $7(18 \div 2) - 6$ 57

2. $\dfrac{72 \div 4}{5 + 2 \cdot 2}$ 2

3. $-15 + 22 + (-30)$ -23

4. $|0| + 2|-5|$ 10

5. $-[-10 - (-2)]$ 8

6. $-29 + [-(-5 + 8)]$ -32

7. $5(-r + 2) + 6r$ $r + 10$

8. $\dfrac{1}{10}(210xy)\left(-\dfrac{1}{7}\right)$ $-3xy$

9. $\dfrac{1}{3}[-27 + (-3t)]$ $-9 - t$

10. $(18 - 20) - (-2 + 5)$ -5

11. $(-4)(-2)(-1)$ -8

12. $(5a + 2) - (4 - 3a)$ $8a - 2$

13. $120z \div \left(-\dfrac{1}{5}\right)$ $-600z$

14. $-174 \div (-29)$ 6

15. $\dfrac{1}{4}(8m - 4n) + (-7m)$ $-5m - n$

Evaluate each expression if $a = 3$, $b = 7$, $c = \dfrac{1}{3}$, $d = -1$, and $e = -4$.

16. $3b - 4a$ 9

17. $\dfrac{2ac + b}{a}$ 3

18. $c(d - e)$ 1

19. $\dfrac{a - b}{de}$ -1

20. Graph the given numbers on one number line: $-1, 4, 0, -3$.

21. Write the numbers in order from least to greatest: $-2, 1, -3.5, 0.$
 $-3.5, -2, 0, 1$

Solve each equation if $x \in \{-6, -3, 0, 3, 6\}$.

22. $5x - 7 = 8$ 3

23. $x(x - 3) = 0$ $\{0, 3\}$

24. $-(-x) = -3$ -3

25. $|x| + 1 = 7$ $\{6, -6\}$

Solve. If the equation is an identity or has no root, state that fact.

26. $-1 = a + 5$ -6

27. $b - 7 = |-2|$ 9

28. $3 = -10 - c$ -13

29. $d - 11 = -4$ 7

30. $2.8 + e = 2.8$ 0

31. $f + 9 = 1$ -8

32. $-5 = -\dfrac{1}{3}g$ 15

33. $9h = 126$ 14

34. $\dfrac{1}{2}j = -\dfrac{7}{4}$ $-\dfrac{7}{2}$

35. $-15k = 795$ -53

36. $8 - 3m = -1$ 3

37. $9 = n + 3 - 2n$

38. $q - 3 = -(3 - q)$ Identity

39. $4(2 - r) = 2 + r$ $\dfrac{6}{5}$

40. $6(s + 5) = 4 + 6s$

37. -6 **40.** No root

Solve.

41. Nine less than a number is 2. Find the number. 11

42. The Farrens were driving to Palo Alto. They had driven 243.8 km when they had a flat tire 12.4 km from the city. How far do the Farrens live from Palo Alto? 256.2 km

43. Five pads of paper cost $4.15. What is the cost of three pads? $2.49

44. Half a number, increased by 2, is -5. Find the number. -14

110 *CHAPTER 3*

Maintaining Skills ━━━━━━━━━━━━━━

Express each fraction as a decimal to the nearest hundredth.

SAMPLE 1 $\frac{26}{25}$ **SOLUTION** $\frac{26}{25} = \frac{26}{25} \cdot \frac{4}{4} = \frac{104}{100} = 1.04$

SAMPLE 2 $\frac{3}{7}$ **SOLUTION** $\frac{3}{7} = 3 \div 7;$ $\underline{0.428}$; 0.43 ***Answer***

$$7\overline{)3.000}$$

1. $\frac{37}{50}$ 0.74   2. $\frac{13}{20}$ 0.65   3. $\frac{7}{4}$ 1.75 $\underline{28}$

 20

4. $\frac{5}{8}$ 0.63   5. $\frac{5}{6}$ 0.83   6. $\frac{25}{23}$ 1.09 $\underline{14}$

 60

Express each percent as a fraction in sim- $\underline{56}$
plest form.   4

SAMPLE 3 3.2%   **SOLUTION** $3.2\% = \frac{3.2}{100} = \frac{3.2}{100} \cdot \frac{10}{10} = \frac{32}{1000} = \frac{4}{125}$

7. 28% $\frac{7}{25}$ 8. 5% $\frac{1}{20}$ 9. 93% $\frac{93}{100}$ 10. 108% $\frac{27}{25}$ 11. 1.6% $\frac{2}{125}$ 12. 0.02% $\frac{1}{5000}$

Express each decimal as a percent.

SAMPLE 4 0.32   **SOLUTION 1** $0.32 = \frac{32}{100} = 32\%$

 **SOLUTION 2** $0.32 = 32\%$

SAMPLE 5 0.192   **SOLUTION** $0.192 = 19.2\%$

13. 0.37 37%   14. 0.04 4%   15. 0.3 30%   16. 2.56 256%   17. 0.075 7.5%   18. 0.003 0.3%

Find each number.

SAMPLE 6 15% of 18   **SOLUTION** $0.15 \times 18 = 2.7$

19. 4% of 135 5.4   20. 29% of 82 23.78   21. 0.5% of 450 2.25

22. 75.4% of 200 150.8   23. 120% of 40.8 48.96   24. 256% of 30 76.8

Find the value of x or of n to the nearest tenth.

SAMPLE 7 12% of $x = 3$ **SOLUTION** $0.12x = 3;$ $x = \frac{3}{0.12} = \frac{300}{12} = 25$

25. 15% of $x = 9$ 60   26. 10% of $x = 3.2$ 32   27. 4% of $x = 18$ 450

28. 0.8% of $x = 0.5$ 62.5 29. 120% of $x = 7$ 5.8   30. 45% of $x = 8$ 17.8

SAMPLE 8 $n\%$ of $6 = 3$ **SOLUTION** $\frac{n}{100} \times 6 = 3;$ $\frac{n}{100} = \frac{3}{6};$ $n = \frac{300}{6} = 50$

31. $n\%$ of $4 = 1$ 25   32. $n\%$ of $3 = 1$ 33.3   33. $n\%$ of $25 = 16$ 64

34. $5 = n\%$ of 18 27.8   35. $15 = n\%$ of 16 93.8   36. $48 = n\%$ of 40 120

SOLVING EQUATIONS   **111**

111

About the Photo

Carbon (C), in combination with other elements, is found in all living organisms. The most abundant type of carbon atom, carbon-12 (^{12}C), is not radioactive. A second type of carbon atom, carbon-14 (^{14}C), is radioactive and thus tends to decay. However, since ^{14}C is constantly being created in the upper atmosphere (by collisions between nitrogen atoms and cosmic rays), the total amount of ^{14}C in the atmosphere has remained essentially constant, at least for the past 4000 years. The ratio of ^{12}C to ^{14}C is about 10^{12} to 1.

Carbon dating is based on the fact that all *living* organisms contain ^{12}C and ^{14}C in the same ratio as that of the atmosphere. When an organism dies, the amount of ^{12}C it contains stays the same. However, the ^{14}C decays, thereby changing the ratio of ^{12}C to ^{14}C in the remains. The half-life of ^{14}C is about 5730 years. Thus, a piece of wood containing ^{12}C and ^{14}C in the ratio 10^{12} to 0.5 was a living part of a tree roughly 5730 years ago.

Due to changes in cosmic ray activity, corrections for variations in the original ratio of ^{12}C to ^{14}C must be made for organisms which lived more than 4000 years ago. These corrections, which are based largely on analyses of the ratios of ^{12}C to ^{14}C in the rings of the long-lived bristlecone pine, enable samples as old as 50,000 years to be dated accurately.

Archaeologists excavate an American Indian settlement in Wyoming. Carbon dating can be used to determine the ages of artifacts less than 4000 years old that are made of wood, leather, or other organic material. The formulas used in carbon dating involve expressions such as $A_0 e^{-kt}$.

4

POLYNOMIALS AND PROBLEM SOLVING

Teaching References

Lesson Commentary,
   pp. T73–T78

Assignment Guide,
   pp. T51–T52

Supplementary Materials
   Practice Masters 16–22

   Progress Tests 12–15

   Computer Activities
   10 *Using* LET *Statements*
   11 *Integer Problems*
   12 *Age Problems*

Extra Practice, pp. 497–498,
   516–517

Alternate Test and Review,
   pp. T15, T24–T26

ADDITION AND SUBTRACTION

4-1 *Exponents*

OBJECTIVE   To write and simplify exponential expressions.

The number 32 can be written as $2 \times 2 \times 2 \times 2 \times 2$ and is called a *power* of 2. Here is how other powers of 2 are defined and written:

First power of 2: $2^1 = 2$ (read "two to the first power")

Second power of 2: $2^2 = 2 \times 2$ (read "two to the second power," or "two squared," or "the square of two")

Third power of 2: $2^3 = 2 \times 2 \times 2$ (read "two to the third power," or "two cubed," or "the cube of two")

Fourth power of 2: $2^4 = 2 \times 2 \times 2 \times 2$ (read "two to the fourth power")

   In general, if b is any real number and n is any positive integer, the **nth power of b** is written b^n and is defined as follows:

$$b^n = \underbrace{b \cdot b \cdot b \cdot \ \ldots \ \cdot b}_{n \text{ factors}}$$

In b^n, the value of b is called the **base** and the value of the small raised symbol n is called the **exponent.**

$$\text{Exponent} \longrightarrow \quad b^n = \text{the } n\text{th power of } b \quad \longleftarrow \text{Base}$$

The exponent indicates the number of times the base occurs as a factor.

113

The third power of b can be written in the **exponential form** b^3 or in the **factored form** $b \cdot b \cdot b$.

EXAMPLE 1   Evaluate y^4 if $y = -7$.

SOLUTION   Replace y with -7, and simplify the result.
$$y^4 = (-7)^4 = (-7)(-7)(-7)(-7) = 2401$$

The expression $-2t^3$ represents $-2(t \cdot t \cdot t)$; that is, 3 is the exponent of the base t. On the other hand, $(-2t)^3$ stands for $(-2t)(-2t)(-2t)$. In this case, the parentheses show that the base is $-2t$. Study the following examples.

$5 \times 4^2 = 5(4 \times 4) = 80$ but $(5 \times 4)^2 = (5 \times 4)(5 \times 4) = 400$.

$-3^4 = -(3 \cdot 3 \cdot 3 \cdot 3) = -81$ but $(-3)^4 = (-3)(-3)(-3)(-3) = 81$.

$xz^3 = x(z \cdot z \cdot z)$ but $(xz)^3 = (xz)(xz)(xz)$.

$9 + a^2 = 9 + (a \cdot a)$ but $(9 + a)^2 = (9 + a)(9 + a)$.

The following steps are used to simplify numerical expressions which contain powers.

SUMMARY OF ORDER OF OPERATIONS

1. First simplify expressions within grouping symbols.
2. Then simplify powers.
3. Then simplify products and quotients in order from left to right.
4. Then simplify sums and differences in order from left to right.

EXAMPLE 2   Evaluate $\dfrac{(x+1)^3}{9} + 5(x - 8)^2 - 1$ if $x = 2$.

SOLUTION   Replace x with 2 and simplify the result.

$$\frac{(x+1)^3}{9} + 5(x - 8)^2 - 1 = \frac{(2+1)^3}{9} + 5(2 - 8)^2 - 1$$

$$= \frac{3^3}{9} + 5(-6)^2 - 1$$

$$= \frac{27}{9} + 5(36) - 1$$

$$= 3 + 180 - 1$$

$$= 182$$

114   *CHAPTER 4*

Oral Exercises

For each exercise state the power, the base of that power, and the exponent. Then state the expression with the power in factored form.

SAMPLE $7r^5$ **SOLUTION** Power r^5; base r; exponent 5; factored form $7 \cdot r \cdot r \cdot r \cdot r \cdot r$

1. 12^2 12^2; 12; 2; $12 \cdot 12$
2. c^5 c^5; c; 5; $c \cdot c \cdot c \cdot c \cdot c$
3. $4a^3$ a^3; a; 3; $4 \cdot a \cdot a \cdot a$
4. $-6b^4$ b^4; b; 4; $-6 \cdot b \cdot b \cdot b \cdot b$
5. $2(xy)^2$ $(xy)^2$; xy; 2; $2 \cdot xy \cdot xy$
6. $(u + v)^3$ $(u + v)^3$; $u + v$, 3; $(u + v)(u + v)(u + v)$

Simplify.

7. $(4 \times 5)^2$ 400
8. 2×3^2 18
9. $2 \times \left(\frac{1}{3}\right)^2$ $\frac{2}{9}$
10. $(12 - 2)^3$ 1000
11. $(2 \times 3)^2 - 4 + 1$ 33
12. $10 \times 2^2 \div 5$ 8
13. $2 \times 3^2 - 1 \times 3 + 7$ 22
14. $5(-2)^2 - 3(-2) - 10$ 16
15. $\left(\frac{6}{2} - 1\right)(2 + 3)^2$ 50
16. $(-1)^2$ 1
17. $(-1)^3$ -1
18. $(-1)^4$ 1

Complete each statement with the word *positive* or *negative*.

19. An even power of a negative number is a __?__ number. positive
20. An odd power of a negative number is a __?__ number. negative

Written Exercises

Write each expression in exponential form.

1. $x \cdot x \cdot x$ x^3
2. $m \cdot m \cdot m \cdot m$ m^4
3. z cubed z^3
4. y squared y^2
5. $7 \cdot b \cdot b$ $7b^2$
6. $-11 \cdot n \cdot n \cdot n$ $-11n^3$
7. $-5 \cdot r \cdot r \cdot s$ $-5r^2s$
8. $2 \cdot a \cdot b \cdot b \cdot b$ $2ab^3$
9. $6 \cdot y \cdot y \cdot y \cdot t \cdot t$ $6y^3t^2$
10. $\frac{1}{3} \cdot s \cdot s \cdot t \cdot t \cdot t$ $\frac{1}{3}s^2t^3$
11. $(a + b)(a + b)(a + b)$ $(a + b)^3$
12. $(x + y)(x - y)(x - y)$ $(x + y)(x - y)^2$
13. $(c - 2)$ squared $(c - 2)^2$
14. the fourth power of $5d$ $(5d)^4$
15. The product of 17 and the cube of $(m + p)$ $17(m + p)^3$
16. -47 divided by the square of $(c - d)$ $\frac{-47}{(c - d)^2}$
17. The sixth power of the sum of d and e $(d + e)^6$
18. The fifth power of the product of a and b $(ab)^5$

Simplify.

19. $2 + 2^2 + 6 \div 2 - 1$ 8
20. $2 + (2^2 + 6) \div 2 - 1$ 6
21. $(2 + 2^2 + 6) \div 2 - 1$ 5
22. $(2 + 2^2 + 6) \div (2 - 1)$ 12
23. $3 \times 4^2 - 5 \times 1 - 4$ 39
24. $3 \times 4^2 - (5 \times 1 - 4)$ 47

Supplementary Materials

Practice Master 16

Computer Activity 10
Using LET *Statements*
  Learning how a LET statement can be used in a computer program is the focus of this activity. Students are given the opportunity to rewrite algebraic expressions in BASIC and to evaluate these expressions for decimal and fractional values of the variables.

Suggested Assignments

Minimum
  115/1–18, 19–35 odd
Average
  115/1–39 odd
Maximum
  115/1–37 odd, 38–40

Additional A Exercises

Simplify.

1. $(4 \times 8)^2$ 1024
2. $9^2 \times 8^2 \div 2^4$ 324
3. $4^2 \times 2^3 - 5^3$ 3

Write each expression in exponential form.

4. $a \cdot a \cdot a \cdot a \cdot a$ a^5
5. $2 \cdot c \cdot c \cdot c$ $2c^3$
6. $-6 \cdot n \cdot n \cdot m \cdot m \cdot m$
   $-6n^2m^3$

Simplify.

B 25. $6^3 \div [5^2 - 3^2 - (-2)^2]$ 18

26. $(6^2 - 3 \times 2^2 + 1) \div [0 + (-5)^2]$ 1

27. $6(3^2 - 2^2) \div 3 + 4 \div (-4)$ 9

28. $7(3^2 - 1) + 2^4 \times 3 \div (-3)2^2$ -8

29. $8 \times (-1)^3 - 7(-1)^2 + 2(-1) + 4$ -13

30. $15(-2)^4 - 6(-2)^3 + 5(-2)^2 + 1$ 309

Evaluate each expression if $x = 4$ and $y = -3$.

31. $x^2 - 2xy + y^2$ 49

32. $(x - y)^3$ 343

33. $\dfrac{(x^2 + y^2)}{5^2}$ 1

34. $\dfrac{(x - 2y)^3}{x^3 + (2y)^2}$ 10

35. $\dfrac{3x + 2y}{3 - y^2}$ -1

36. $3x \div 6 + 2y^3 \div 18$ -1

Evaluate each expression for the given value of x.

C 37. $(x^2 + 4x - 5)(2x^2 - 7x + 1)$, $x = -5$ 0

38. $(3x^2 + 8x - 1)(x^2 + x - 6)$, $x = -2$ 20

39. $2(x - 1)^3 - 11(x - 1)^2 + 12(x - 1) + 9$, $x = 3$ 5

40. $4(x + 1)^3 - 2(x + 1)^2 - 8(x + 1) + 6$, $x = \dfrac{1}{2}$ 3

Calculator Key-In

Simplify each of the following mentally. Then use a calculator to check your answers.

1. $(0.1)^2$ 0.01   **2.** $(0.3)^2$ 0.09   **3.** $(0.4)^2$ 0.16   **4.** $(1.2)^2$ 1.44

5. $(0.12)^2$ 0.0144   **6.** $(0.05)^2$ 0.0025   **7.** $(0.03)^2$ 0.0009   **8.** $(0.011)^2$ 0.000121

9. $(0.2)^3$ 0.008   **10.** $(0.3)^3$ 0.027   **11.** $(0.5)^3$ 0.125   **12.** $(0.09)^3$ 0.000729

Just for Fun

Recall (page 15) that the triangular numbers are

1, 3, 6, 10, 15, and so on.

The square numbers are

1, 4, 9, 16, 25, and so on.

1. Verify that each square number from 4 to 100 is the sum of two consecutive triangular numbers.

2. Illustrate Exercise 1 by dividing the square array of dots shown at the right into two triangular arrays.

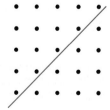

116 *CHAPTER 4*

4-2 Adding and Subtracting Polynomials

Teaching Suggestions p. T74

Suggested Extensions p. T74

OBJECTIVE To add and subtract polynomials.

Each of the expressions below is a *monomial*.

$$5 \qquad z \qquad \frac{1}{3}b \qquad -2xy^2$$

A **monomial** is an expression that is either a numeral, a variable, or a product of a numeral and one or more variables. A numeral, such as 5, is also called a **constant monomial,** or a **constant.**

A sum of monomials is called a **polynomial.** A polynomial such as $x^2 + (-5x) + (-6)$ is usually written as $x^2 - 5x - 6$. Some polynomials have special names:

Binomials (two terms): $3x + 7$ $4a^2 - 8b$
Trinomials (three terms): $x^2 - 5x - 6$ $3a^2 + 2ab - b^2$

A monomial may be thought of as a polynomial of one term.

In the monomial $-2xy^2$, the number -2 is called the **coefficient,** or **numerical coefficient.** Two monomials which are exactly alike or which differ only in their numerical coefficients are called **similar,** or **like.** The following monomials are all similar:

$$-2xy^2, \quad 5y^2x, \quad xy^2, \quad \text{and} \quad \tfrac{1}{2}xy^2.$$

The following monomials are *not* similar: $-2xy^2$ and $-2x^2y$.

A polynomial is **simplified,** or **in simplest form,** when no two of its terms are similar. You may use the distributive property to add similar terms.

EXAMPLE 1   Simplify $-2x^3 + 3x^2 + 5x^2 + 2x^3 - 6$.

SOLUTION
$$-2x^3 + 3x^2 + 5x^2 + 2x^3 - 6 = (-2 + 2)x^3 + (3 + 5)x^2 - 6$$
$$= 0x^3 + 8x^2 - 6$$
$$= 8x^2 - 6$$

The **degree of a monomial in a variable** is the number of times that variable occurs as a factor in the monomial. For example,

$$-4x^2yz^3 \text{ is of degree } \begin{cases} 2 \text{ in } x; \\ 1 \text{ in } y; \\ 3 \text{ in } z. \end{cases}$$

The **degree of a monomial** is the total number of times its variables occur as factors. Thus, the degree of $-4x^2yz^3$ is $2 + 1 + 3$, or 6. The degree of any nonzero constant monomial is 0.

POLYNOMIALS AND PROBLEM SOLVING   **117**

Chalkboard Examples

Simplify, if possible. Then state the number of terms and the degree of the resulting polynomial.

1. $x^2 + u^3$
   Cannot be simplified; two terms; degree three

2. $2x^2 + x + 5 + 3x$
   $2x^2 + 4x + 5$; three terms; degree two

3. $x^2 + 2xy^2 + 3x^2 + xy^2$
   $4x^2 + 3xy^2$; two terms; degree three

4. Add $x^2 + xy + z$ and $3x^2 - 4xy - 7$.
$$\begin{array}{r} x^2 + \ xy + z \quad\ \\ 3x^2 - 4xy \qquad - 7 \\ \hline 4x^2 - 3xy + z - 7 \end{array}$$

5. Subtract $-xy^2 + 6$ from $2xy^2 + x^2 + 4$.
$$\begin{array}{r} 2xy^2 + x^2 + 4 \\ -(-xy^2 \qquad\ + 6) \\ \hline 3xy^2 + x^2 - 2 \end{array}$$

6. Solve:
$$(k^2 - 3) - (6 - k^2) = 2k^2 + 3k$$
$$k^2 - 3 - 6 + k^2 = 2k^2 + 3k$$
$$2k^2 - 9 = 2k^2 + 3k$$
$$-9 = 3k$$
$$k = -3$$

Supplementary Materials

Practice Master 17

Computer Activity 11
Integer Problems
  To solve word problems involving consecutive, consecutive odd, and consecutive even integers, a computer program is used to check each guess made by the student.

Suggested Assignments

Minimum
Day 1: 119/1–55 odd
Day 2: 120/P: 1, 3, 4, 5, 7
    R 121/*Self-Test 1*

Average
Day 1: 119/1–55 odd
Day 2: 120/P: 1, 3, 4, 6, 7, 9
    R 121/*Self-Test 1*

Maximum
Day 1: 119/1–55 odd, 56
Day 2: 120/P: 2–4, 6, 7, 9,
       10, 13–16
    R 121/*Self-Test 1*

Extra Practice Problems
    p. 516

The **degree of a polynomial** is the greatest of the degrees of its terms *after it has been simplified*. Since the polynomial $-2x^3 + 3x^2 + 5x^2 + 2x^3 - 6$, in Example 1, can be simplified to $8x^2 - 6$, the degree of the polynomial is 2, *not* 3.

To add two polynomials, you write the sum and simplify by adding similar terms.

EXAMPLE 2 Add $3x^2y - 7x^2 + y^2 + 2$ and $x^2y + 5x^2 - 9$.

SOLUTION 1 $(3x^2y - 7x^2 + y^2 + 2) + (x^2y + 5x^2 - 9) =$
$(3 + 1)x^2y + (-7 + 5)x^2 + y^2 + (2 - 9) = 4x^2y - 2x^2 + y^2 - 7$

SOLUTION 2 You may also add vertically:

$$3x^2y - 7x^2 + y^2 + 2$$
$$\underline{x^2y + 5x^2 - 9}$$
$$4x^2y - 2x^2 + y^2 - 7$$

Subtracting polynomials is very much like subtracting real numbers. To subtract a number, you add the opposite of that number. To subtract a polynomial, you add the opposite of that polynomial and simplify.

EXAMPLE 3 Subtract $-3a^2 - 2ab + b^2 - 3$ from $5a^2 - 3ab - 7b^2 + 4$.

SOLUTION 1 $(5a^2 - 3ab - 7b^2 + 4) - (-3a^2 - 2ab + b^2 - 3) =$
$5a^2 - 3ab - 7b^2 + 4 + 3a^2 + 2ab - b^2 + 3 =$
$(5 + 3)a^2 + (-3 + 2)ab + (-7 - 1)b^2 + (4 + 3) =$
$8a^2 - ab - 8b^2 + 7$

SOLUTION 2 Subtract the lower polynomial from the one above it.

$$5a^2 - 3ab - 7b^2 + 4$$
$$\underline{-3a^2 - 2ab + b^2 - 3}$$
$$8a^2 - ab - 8b^2 + 7$$

To subtract one polynomial from another, add the opposite of each term you are subtracting.

Oral Exercises

1. State the degree of the monomial $3xy^3z^2$ in each variable. x: 1; y: 3; z: 2

State the degree of each polynomial. If the polynomial is a binomial or a trinomial, state this fact. (b = binomial; t = trinomial)

2. $3 + 2x - x^2$ 2; t   **3.** $x^2 + y^2$ 2; b   **4.** $x^2y^2 - z^3$ 4; b

5. $t^3 - 3t^2 + 4t$ 3; t   **6.** $uv^3 + u^3v + u^2v + uv^2$ 4   **7.** $r^4 + 3s^4 + 2rs + r^3s^3$
6

Name the similar monomials.

8. $5a, 7ab, -2a, -4b, 8b, -9ab$ **9.** $9xy, -2x, 3y, -xy, 5yx, 11y$
5a, -2a; 7ab, -9ab; -4b, 8b   9xy, -xy, 5yx; 3y, 11y

118   CHAPTER 4

10. $4x^2$, $-8x^2y$, $-3x$, $-9x^2$, $-2xy^2$, $3x^2y$, x, $-y$ $4x^2$, $-9x^2$; $-8x^2y$, $3x^2y$; $-3x$, x

11. $13m^2n^2$, $-6m^2$, $4n^2$, $7m^2n$, $-4n^2m^2$, $-3n^2$, $8m^2n$, $9mn^2$
$13m^2n^2$, $-4n^2m^2$; $4n^2$, $-3n^2$; $7m^2n$, $8m^2n$

Add the polynomials.

12.
$5x - 5$
$\underline{2x + 7}$
$7x + 2$

13.
$7a + 5b$
$\underline{5a - b}$
$12a + 4b$

14.
$7n - 4k$
$\underline{5n + 2k}$
$12n - 2k$

15.
$3a - 2b + 1$
$\underline{4a + 9b - 7}$
$7a + 7b - 6$

16.
$4x^2 - 3x + 2$
$\underline{x^2 + 1}$
$5x^2 - 3x + 3$

17.
$9y^2 - 3y + 2$
$\underline{y^2 - 4y}$
$10y^2 - 7y + 2$

18.
$a^2 + 3ab + b^2$
$\underline{2a^2 + 5ab - b^2}$
$3a^2 + 8ab$

19.
$2x - 3y + 4z$
$\underline{-4x - 4z}$
$-2x - 3y$

20.
$1 - 6x$
$\underline{5 - 4x + 3x^2}$
$6 - 10x + 3x^2$

21–29. In Exercises 12–20, state the opposite of the lower polynomial. Then subtract by adding that opposite to the upper polynomial.

Simplify.

30. $(2x + 5) + (3x - 1)$ $5x + 4$

31. $(4y + 7) - (y - 1)$ $3y + 8$

Written Exercises

Copy each polynomial and underline similar terms in the same way. Then simplify the polynomial.

SAMPLE $\underline{4n^2t} - \underline{\underline{3nt^2}} + \underline{n^2t} - \underline{\underline{nt^2}}$; $5n^2t - 4nt^2$

A **1.** $\underline{2rt} - 6 + \underline{rt}$ $3rt - 6$

3. $\underline{2x^2} - \underline{\underline{4x}} + \underline{\underline{5x}} - \underline{3x^2}$ $-x^2 + x$

5. $-\underline{5abc} + 2bc - 3ac + \underline{abc}$ $-4abc + 2bc - 3ac$

7. $-\underline{3m^2n} - 2mn^2 + \underline{5m^2n} - 2mn$
$2m^2n - 2mn^2 - 2mn$

Add.

9.
$4x - 3$
$\underline{2x + 4}$
$6x + 1$

10.
$9a + 2b$
$\underline{4a - 3b}$
$13a - b$

11.
$3r - 2s$
$\underline{-5r + 7s}$
$-2r + 5s$

12.
$5a - 2b$
$\underline{2a + 6b}$
$7a + 4b$

13.
$3s + 7t - 1$
$\underline{5s + t - 2}$
$8s + 8t - 3$

14.
$4x - 2xy + y$
$\underline{3x - xy - y}$
$7x - 3xy$

15.
$3x^2 + 5x + 2$
$\underline{x^2 - 2x - 1}$
$4x^2 + 3x + 1$

16.
$y^2 - y - 7$
$\underline{3y^2 + y - 8}$
$4y^2 - 15$

17.
$2n^2 - 5$
$\underline{-n^2 + 4n - 2}$
$n^2 + 4n - 7$

18.
$3a - 2b + c$
$\underline{-a + 4b}$
$2a + 2b + c$

19.
$5x^2 - 3x - 4$
$2x^2 - 5$
$\underline{x^2 + 5x + 7}$
$8x^2 + 2x - 2$

20.
$6r^2 - s^2$
$s^2 - 8$
$\underline{-2r^2 + 3s^2 - 2}$
$4r^2 + 3s^2 - 10$

2. $-4a + 2b$
4. $6y^3 - 3y^2 - 5y$
2. $-4a + \underline{3b} - \underline{b}$
4. $\underline{4y^3} - 3y^2 + \underline{2y^3} - 5y$
6. $-\underline{6r^2t} - 6r^2 + \underline{rt^2} - \underline{r^2t}$
8. $\underline{3xy^2z} - \underline{\underline{2xyz^2}} + \underline{\underline{7xyz^2}} - \underline{3x^2yz}$
6. $-7r^2t - 6r^2 + rt^2$
8. $3xy^2z + 5xyz^2 - 3x^2yz$

21–30. In Exercises 9–18, subtract the lower polynomial from the one above it.

POLYNOMIALS AND PROBLEM SOLVING   **119**

Simplify. **35.** $x^3 + 2x^2 + 3x - 16$

31. $(2a + 3b - 4) + (5a - b + 7)$ $7a + 2b + 3$ **32.** $(2x^2 - 3x + 5) + (x^2 - 7x - 9)$

33. $(7a^2 - 2ab + b^2) + (-a^2 - b^2)$ $6a^2 - 2ab$ **34.** $(1 - c - c^2) + (2c - 3c^2)$

35. $(x^3 - x - 7) + (2x^2 + 4x - 9)$ **36.** $(5n^4 - 2n^3 - 1) + (2 + n^2 - n^4)$

37. $(9b - 3) - (4b + 6)$ $5b - 9$ **38.** $(4a - 7) - (5a - 9)$

39. $(2a - 3b - 5) - (6a - 7b - 2)$ $-4a + 4b - 3$ **40.** $(7c - 8d - 11) - (-c + 5d + 2)$

41. $(x^2 - 5x + 9) - (2x^2 + 3x + 1)$ $-x^2 - 8x + 8$ **42.** $(-3a^2 + 5a - 2) - (3a^2 - a + 1)$

43. $(2a^2 - b^2) - (a^2 - ab + b^2)$ $a^2 + ab - 2b^2$ **44.** $(c^2 + cd) - (-c^2 + cd + d^2)$

Solve.

B 45. $5x - (x + 3) = 5$ $\;2$ **46.** $(12n - 3) - (3n - 1) = 34$ $\;4$

47. $(2a - 5) - (3a + 2) = 5 - 3a$ $\;6$ **48.** $(5p - 3) - (p - 8) = 2p - 7$ $\;-6$

49. $(4 - 2t) - (t - 5) = 2t - 1$ $\;2$ **50.** $(4s - 7) - (2 - 3s) = -23$ $\;-2$

51. $2x^2 - 5x = (3x^2 - 7x) - (x^2 - 4)$ $\;2$ **52.** $(x^2 + 2x + 1) - (x^2 + 4x + 3) = 4$

53. $2x^2 = (3x^2 - 5x - 7) - (x^2 - x + 1)$ $\;-2$ **54.** $4 - (a^2 - 2a - 9) = 9 - (2a + a^2)$

55. The sum of $a^4 - 3a^2 + 2a - 1$ and $2a^4 - a^3 + a^2 - 2a - 2$ is subtracted from the sum of $6 + 3a^3 - a^4$ and $-6 - 2a^2 - 2a^4$. What is the difference? $-6a^4 + 4a^3 + 3$

56. By what does the sum of $3x^3 - 2x^2 + 5x$ and $x^3 + 7x^2 - 3x$ exceed the sum of $2x^3 + x^2 - 5x$ and $2x^3 - 6x + 7$? $4x^2 + 13x - 7$

Integer Problems

Solve.

A **1.** Find two consecutive integers whose sum is 33. 16, 17

2. Find three consecutive integers whose sum is -147. $-50, -49, -48$

3. Find four consecutive even integers whose sum is 116. 26, 28, 30, 32

4. Find four consecutive odd integers whose sum is 0. $-3, -1, 1, 3$

5. The sum of the least and greatest of three consecutive integers is 50. What is the middle integer? 25

6. The sum of the least and greatest of three consecutive odd integers is 110. What are the integers? 53, 55, 57

7. The greater of two consecutive integers is 10 greater than twice the lesser. Find the integers. $-9, -8$

8. The greater of two consecutive odd integers is 7 greater than twice the lesser. Find the integers. $-5, -3$

B **9.** Find three consecutive odd integers such that the sum of the greatest and twice the least is 25. 7, 9, 11

10. Find four consecutive integers such that the sum of the two greatest subtracted from twice the sum of the two least is 15. 9, 10, 11, 12

11. Find four consecutive integers such that five times the third decreased by twice the fourth is 55. 17, 18, 19, 20

12. Find four consecutive odd integers such that the third is the sum of the fourth and twice the second. -3, -1, 1, 3

13. The measures in meters of two adjacent sides of a rectangle are consecutive odd integers. The perimeter is 96 m. What are the dimensions of the rectangle? 23 m by 25 m

14. The atomic numbers of radium, thorium, and uranium are consecutive even integers in increasing order. If three times the atomic number of radium is 82 more than the sum of the atomic numbers of thorium and uranium, what are the atomic numbers of these three elements? 88, 90, 92

For Exercises 15–16 use this definition: The product of any real number and an integer is called a *multiple* of the real number.

C 15. The ages of three sisters are consecutive multiples of 4. Three years ago the sum of their ages was 39. Find their present ages. 12, 16, 20

16. Find four consecutive multiples of 3 such that twice the sum of the two greatest integers exceeds three times the least by 21. -9, -6, -3, 0

Self-Test 1

VOCABULARY   power (p. 113)
base (p. 113)
exponent (p. 113)
exponential form (p. 114)
factored form (p. 114)
monomial (p. 117)
constant (p. 117)
polynomial (p. 117)

binomial (p. 117)
trinomial (p. 117)
coefficient (p. 117)
similar terms (p. 117)
simplify a polynomial (p. 117)
degree of a monomial (p. 117)
degree of a polynomial
   (p. 118)

1. Write in exponential form: $2 \cdot a \cdot a \cdot a \cdot b \cdot c \cdot c$ Obj. 4-1, p. 113

2. Simplify $3 + (-3)^2 \times (-1)^3$.

3. Evaluate $\dfrac{(2x - y)^3}{12x^2 - (2y)^2}$ if $x = -1$ and $y = 2$.

4. Add.   5. Subtract the lower polynomial.   Obj. 4-2, p. 117

$x^2 - 3x - 5$ $4a^2 + 2ab - b^2$
$5x^2 + 3x + 1$ $2a^2 - 2ab - 7b^2$

Check your answers with those at the back of the book.

POLYNOMIALS AND PROBLEM SOLVING   **121**

Teaching Suggestions p. T74

Suggested Extensions p. T75

Chalkboard Examples

1. a. How many factors of x are there in x^5? 5
   b. How many factors of x are there in x^6? 6
   c. Simplify $x^5 \cdot x^6$.
   $x^5 \cdot x^6 = x^{5+6} = x^{11}$

Simplify.

2. $(3x^2y^4z)(10xy^2z^6)$
   $3 \cdot 10 \cdot x^{2+1} \cdot y^{4+2} \cdot z^{1+6} =$
   $30x^3y^6z^7$
3. $(3d^3)(4d^2) - (2d)(d^4)$
   $3 \cdot 4d^{3+2} - 2d^{1+4} =$
   $12d^5 - 2d^5 = 10d^5$
4. $-x^3y^8 - (2x^2y^3)(-4xy^5)$
   $-x^3y^8 - (-8x^3y^8) =$
   $-x^3y^8 + 8x^3y^8 = 7x^3y^8$
5. $(s^{n-1})(3s^{n+3}) + (-s^n)(s^n)$
   $3 \cdot s^{(n-1)+(n+3)} + (-s^{2n}) =$
   $3s^{2n+2} - s^{2n}$
6. $(-t)^2(-t)^3(-t)^4$
   $-1 \cdot t^2 \cdot t^3 \cdot t^4 =$
   $-t^{2+3+4} = -t^9$

MULTIPLICATION

4-3 *Multiplying Monomials*

OBJECTIVE To multiply monomials.

When you multiply two powers having the same base, you add the exponents as shown below.

$$x^3 \cdot x^4 = x^{3+4} = x^7$$
$$y^6 \cdot y^2 = y^{6+2} = y^8$$

You can understand why you add exponents if you remember that an exponent indicates the number of times the base is used as a factor.

$$x^3 \cdot x^4 = \underbrace{\overbrace{(x \cdot x \cdot x)}^{3 \text{ factors}} \cdot \overbrace{(x \cdot x \cdot x \cdot x)}^{4 \text{ factors}}}_{7 \text{ factors}} = x^7$$

$$a^m \cdot a^n = \underbrace{\overbrace{(a \cdot a \cdot \cdots \cdot a)}^{m \text{ factors}} \cdot \overbrace{(a \cdot a \cdot \cdots \cdot a)}^{n \text{ factors}}}_{m + n \text{ factors}} = a^{m+n}$$

The following general rule applies when two powers to be multiplied have the same base.

> RULE OF EXPONENTS FOR MULTIPLICATION
>
> For all positive integers m and n,
>
> $$\mathbf{a^m \cdot a^n = a^{m+n}}$$

When you multiply two monomials, you use the rule of exponents along with the commutative and associative axioms for multiplication.

EXAMPLE 1

$(2x^3y^4)(-3xy^5) = [2 \cdot (-3)](x^3 \cdot x)(y^4 \cdot y^5)$ Commutative and associative axioms for multiplication

$= -6x^4y^9$ Rule of exponents for multiplication

EXAMPLE 2

$(3a^5b)(-2ab^3) + (4a^3b^2)(a^3b^2) = -6a^6b^4 + 4a^6b^4$
$= -2a^6b^4$

Oral Exercises

Simplify each expression.

1. $a^4 \cdot a^6$ a^{10}
2. $a^{12} \cdot a^3$ a^{15}
3. $b^3 \cdot b^3$ b^6
4. $a^n \cdot a^n$ a^{2n}
5. $a^n \cdot a$ a^{n+1}
6. $b^{2n} \cdot b^{3n}$ b^{5n}
7. $(2x)(3x)$ $6x^2$
8. $(2x)(3x)(4x)$
9. $2p \cdot p^2$ $2p^3$
10. $\left(-\frac{1}{2}x\right)(4x^2)$ $-2x^3$
11. $(-c^4d^2)(-c^3d^3)$ c^7d^5
12. $(9x^9)(2x^2)$
13. $(2x^3y^2)(1.2xy^4)$ $2.4x^4y^6$
14. $(3rs)(-2r^4s^3)$ $-6r^5s^4$
15. $(-x)^2(-x)^3$ $-x^5$
16. $(-x)^2 \cdot x^3$

8. $24x^3$
12. $18x^{11}$
16. x^5

Written Exercises

Simplify each expression.

A
1. $a^3 \cdot a^5 \cdot a^2$ a^{10}
2. $2 \cdot b^3 \cdot b^2 \cdot b$ $2b^6$
3. $(3c^4)(5c^2)$ $15c^6$
4. $(4x^3)(2x^5)(3x)$ $24x^9$
5. $(2c^5)(3c^4)(5c)$ $30c^{10}$
6. $(-4a^3)(-3a)$ $12a^4$
7. $(xy^2)(x^3y)$ x^4y^3
8. $(ab^3)(a^2b)(b^2)$ a^3b^6
9. $(5n^2m)(6nm^2)(3m^4)$
10. $(-ab)(-ac)(-bc)$ $-a^2b^2c^2$
11. $(-x^2y^5)(-3x^4y^7)$ $3x^6y^{12}$
12. $(4c^2bd^4)(3c^5b^2)(2d^5)$
13. $\left(\frac{1}{2}n^2p\right)(2np^2)(np)$ n^4p^4
14. $\left(\frac{1}{7}a^3b\right)(7ab^4)(a^5)$ a^9b^5
15. $(-3n^2m)(-2nm^4)(n^2)$
16. $a^n \cdot a^3$ a^{n+3}
17. $b^{3n} \cdot b^{2n} \cdot b^n$ b^{6n}
18. $c^{1+n} \cdot c^n$ c^{1+2n}
19. $2^k \cdot 2^{k+1} \cdot 2^2$ 2^{2k+3}
20. $3^r \cdot 3^{r+1} \cdot 3$ 3^{2r+2}
21. $x^n \cdot x^{2n+3} \cdot x^4$ x^{3n+7}
22. $(-2)^m(-2)^{2m}(-2)^{3m}$ $(-2)^{6m}$, or 2^{6m}
23. $(-x)^2(-x)^3(-x)^5$ $(-x)^{10}$, or x^{10}
24. $(-x^2)(-x^3)(-x^5)$ $-x^{10}$

B
25. $(2a^3)(4a^2) + (3a^4)(a)$ $11a^5$
26. $(4n^3)(5n^7) - (2n^6)(4n^4)$ $12n^{10}$
27. $(3x^3)(2x^2)(5x) + (7x)(2x^5)$ $44x^6$
28. $(4r^5)(3r)\left(\frac{1}{2}r^6\right) - (3r^4)(2r^6)(-r^2)$ $12r^{12}$
29. $(8a^2b)\left(\frac{1}{4}a^4b^4\right) + (5ab^3)(2a^5b^2)$ $12a^6b^5$
30. $(7n^2)(3m^4) - (2n)(3m^4n)$ $15n^2m^4$
31. $(4a^3b^2)(2b^3) - (-3ab)(a^2b^4)$ $11a^3b^5$
32. $(4r^4s^2)(s^5) + (2s^3r^2)(s^4r^2)$ $6r^4s^7$
33. $(5ab^2c^3)(3abc) + (2ab^2c)(abc^3)$ $17a^2b^3c^4$
34. $(xy^2z^3)(3x^3yz^4) - (4xyz)(x^3y^2z^6)$ $-x^4y^3z^7$

Find in simplest form the area of each shaded region.
(Area of a rectangle = length × width)

35. $12a^2b^2$ $4ab$

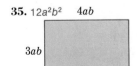

36. $12x^2$ $2x$

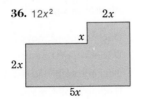

37. $19a^2$

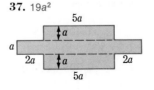

Suggested Assignments

Minimum
123/1–28, 29–35 odd

Average
123/1–37 odd
S 121/P: 13, 14

Maximum
123/1–43 odd

Additional A Exercises

Simplify each expression.

1. $(x^2)(2x)$ $2x^3$
2. $-x^3 \cdot x^2$ $-x^5$
3. $(-a^2)(4a^4)$ $-4a^6$
4. $(-a)^2(4a^4)$ $4a^6$
5. $z^2 \cdot z \cdot z^4$ z^7
6. $3 \cdot c^2 \cdot c^5$ $3c^7$

**Additional Answers
Written Exercises**

9. $90n^3m^7$
12. $24c^7b^3d^9$
15. $6n^5m^5$

Find the total surface area of each solid. (The total surface area of a solid is the sum of the areas of all its faces.)

C **38.** 22a² 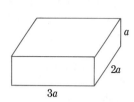 **39.** 46x² 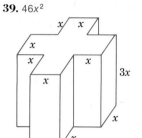 **40.** 54a²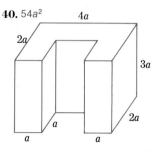

41-43. Find the volume of each solid above. (The volume can be found by multiplying the area of the bottom or top of the solid by the height of the solid.) **41.** $6a^3$ **42.** $15x^3$ **43.** $18a^3$

EXTRA

Scientific Notation

Some numbers are so large or so small that they are difficult to read and write. For example, consider the numbers

1,370,000,000,000,000 and 0.0000000165.

Scientific notation makes it easier to read such numbers and to calculate with them. Scientific notation is based on positive and negative powers of 10 as defined below.

Positive Powers of 10	Negative Powers of 10
$10^1 = 10$	$10^{-1} = 0.1$
$10^2 = 100$	$10^{-2} = 0.01$
$10^3 = 1000$	$10^{-3} = 0.001$
$10^4 = 10,000$	$10^{-4} = 0.0001$
and so on	and so on

To express a number in **scientific notation,** write it as the product of a number between 1 and 10 and an integral power of 10.

$51,400 = 5.14 \times 10^4$ Decimal point moved 4 places left
$7,080,000,000 = 7.08 \times 10^9$ Decimal point moved 9 places left
$0.009 = 9 \times 10^{-3}$ Decimal point moved 3 places right
$0.0000325 = 3.25 \times 10^{-5}$ Decimal point moved 5 places right

124 *CHAPTER 4*

Numbers written in scientific notation can be multiplied easily, using the rule of exponents for multiplication.

$$(4.1 \times 10^4)(2 \times 10^5) = (4.1 \times 2) \times (10^4 \times 10^5) = 8.2 \times 10^9$$
$$(7 \times 10^{-4})(3.1 \times 10^6) = (7 \times 3.1) \times (10^{-4} \times 10^6) = 21.7 \times 10^2 = 2.17 \times 10^3$$

Exercises

Express each of the following numbers in scientific notation.

1. 200,000 2×10^5
2. 159,000,000 1.59×10^8
3. 40,800,000,000 4.08×10^{10}
4. 0.0007 7×10^{-4}
5. 0.00000019 1.9×10^{-7}
6. 0.0000000000325 3.25×10^{-11}

Express each product in scientific notation.

7. $(3 \times 10^5)(2 \times 10^9)$
8. $(4.1 \times 10^7)(2 \times 10^{-3})$
9. $(3 \times 10^{-4})(1.2 \times 10^{-5})$
10. $(8 \times 10^7)(6 \times 10^4)$
11. $(3.1 \times 10^4)(4 \times 10^{-3})$
12. $(8 \times 10^{-5})(3 \times 10^{-2})$

13. If you have a calculator with directions for entering numbers in scientific notation, calculate $(5.2 \times 10^{13})(4.73 \times 10^{-5})$. 2.4596×10^9

14. Study the positive and negative powers of 10 defined in this section. Then guess how 10^0 is defined. $10^0 = 1$

15. The metric system is based on powers of 10. Complete each statement by writing a power of 10.

a. 1 m = __?__ cm 10^2
b. 1 km = __?__ m 10^3
c. 1 km = __?__ cm 10^5
d. 1 g = __?__ mg 10^{-3}
e. 1 kg = __?__ g 10^3
f. 1 mg = $\dfrac{?}{10^{-6}}$ kg

Calculator Key-In _____

To display very large numbers, most calculators use a form of exponential notation similar to that described in the Extra on the opposite page. Try this on a calculator:

Press the 9 key until the display is filled with 9's. Next, estimate what the answer would be if you were to multiply this large number by 2. Write your estimate on paper. Now go ahead and multiply by 2 on the calculator. Compare the displayed answer with your estimate. They should be two different forms of the same number.

Enter 9's again. Predict what the calculator will display when you multiply by 20. Try it. Were you right? What will be displayed if you multiply by 400 instead of 20?

4-4 *Powers of Monomials*

OBJECTIVE To find powers of a monomial.

To find a power of a monomial that is itself a power, you can apply the definition of a power and the rule of exponents for multiplication.

EXAMPLE 1 $(x^2)^3 = x^2 \cdot x^2 \cdot x^2 = x^{2+2+2} = x^6$

Note that $(x^2)^3 = x^6$, or $x^{2 \times 3}$. In general:

$$a^m \text{ is a factor } n \text{ times} \qquad n \text{ terms}$$

$$(a^m)^n = \overbrace{(a^m)(a^m) \cdots (a^m)} = \overbrace{a^{m+m+\cdots+m}} = a^{mn}$$

Thus, *to find a power of a power, you multiply the exponents.*

> **RULE OF EXPONENTS FOR A POWER OF A POWER**
>
> For all positive integers m and n,
>
> $$(a^m)^n = a^{mn}.$$

EXAMPLE 2 $(y^8)^7 = y^{56}$ **EXAMPLE 3** $[(-a)^5]^4 = (-a)^{20} = a^{20}$

To find a power of a product, you can apply the definition of a power and the commutative and associative axioms for multiplication.

EXAMPLE 4 $(3x)^2 = 3x \cdot 3x = 3 \cdot 3 \cdot x \cdot x = 3^2 \cdot x^2 = 9x^2$

Note that *both* the 3 and the x are squared when the product $3x$ is squared. In general:

$$ab \text{ is a factor}$$
$$m \text{ times} \qquad m \text{ factors} \qquad m \text{ factors}$$

$$(ab)^m = \overbrace{(ab)(ab) \cdots (ab)} = \overbrace{(a \cdot a \cdots a)} \overbrace{(b \cdot b \cdots \cdot b)} = a^m b^m$$

Thus, *to find a power of a product, you find the power of each factor and then multiply.*

> **RULE OF EXPONENTS FOR A POWER OF A PRODUCT**
>
> For every positive integer m,
>
> $$(ab)^m = a^m b^m.$$

EXAMPLE 5 $(3a)^4 = 3^4 \cdot a^4 = 81a^4$

EXAMPLE 6 $(-4y)^3 = (-4)^3 \cdot y^3 = -64y^3$

The rules of exponents for powers are applied in the following example.

EXAMPLE 7 $(-2x^6y^4)^3 = (-2)^3 \cdot (x^6)^3 \cdot (y^4)^3 = -8x^{18}y^{12}$

Oral Exercises

Simplify.

1. $(x^3)^2$ x^6
2. $(y^5)^3$ y^{15}
3. $(a^7)^4$ a^{28}
4. $(3^7)^2$ 3^{14}

5. $(5a)^2$ $25a^2$
6. $\left(\frac{1}{2}b\right)^2$ $\frac{1}{4}b^2$
7. $\left(\frac{1}{3}ab\right)^2$ $\frac{1}{9}a^2b^2$
8. $\left(\frac{2}{3}x\right)^3$ $\frac{8}{27}x^3$

9. $(3a^2)^2$ $9a^4$
10. $(5n^3)^3$ $125n^9$
11. $(-4x^5)^2$ $16x^{10}$
12. $(-x^2)^4$ x^8

13. $(2y^3)^4$ $16y^{12}$
14. $2(y^3)^4$ $2y^{12}$
15. $(-4a^4)^2$ $16a^8$
16. $-(4a^4)^2$ $-16a^8$

17. $(a^n)^2$ a^{2n}
18. $(a^2)^n$ a^{2n}
19. $[(-a)^n]^2$ a^{2n}
20. $(x^ny^m)^3$ $x^{3n}y^{3m}$

21. Find the values of $3a^2$ and $(3a)^2$ if $a = 4$. 48; 144
22. Find the values of $-b^4$ and $(-b)^4$ if $b = 2$. -16; 16

Written Exercises

Simplify.

A 1. $(x^4)^2$ x^8
2. $(a^8)^3$ a^{24}
3. $(2b)^3$ $8b^3$
4. $(5nm)^3$

5. $(2a^3)^4$ $16a^{12}$
6. $\left(\frac{1}{3}n^4\right)^2$ $\frac{1}{9}n^8$
7. $\left(\frac{1}{2}x^2\right)^5$ $\frac{1}{32}x^{10}$
8. $(6x^3y^2)^2$

9. $(-2b^2y^5)^3$ $-8b^6y^{15}$
10. $(-4n^2y^6)^3$ $-64n^6y^{18}$
11. $(-3t^2s^4)^4$ $81t^8s^{16}$
12. $(-x^3y)^5$

13. $(4a)(3a)^2$ $36a^3$
14. $(3n^2)(2n)^3$ $24n^5$
15. $(-5a)^2(5a^2)$ $125a^4$
16. $(-x^2y)^3(3x^4y)$

17. $(4n)^3(3n)^2$ $576n^5$
18. $(2a^2b)^3(a^2b^3)^4$ $8a^{14}b^{15}$
19. $(-3r^4s)^4\left(\frac{1}{9}rs^2\right)^2$ $r^{18}s^8$
20. $\left(\frac{1}{2}a^3\right)^4(4a^7)^3$ $4a^{33}$

Evaluate each expression if $a = 2$, $b = 3$, and $c = -4$.

21. $5b^2$ 45
22. $(5b)^2$ 225
23. $-7a^2$ -28
24. $(-7a)^2$ 196

25. $(3a + 2c)^3$ -8
26. $3a^3 + 2c^3$ -104
27. $(b + c)^2$ 1
28. $b^2 + c^2$ 25

Simplify.

B 29. $(2c)^3(3c)^2(-c)^4$ $72c^9$
30. $(5n)^3(2n^2)^2\left(\frac{1}{10}n\right)^3$ $\frac{1}{2}n^{10}$
31. $(u^2v^4)^3(4u^2v)^2$ $16u^{10}v^{14}$

32. $(2a^4b^7)^3\left(\frac{1}{2}ab^4\right)^5$ $\frac{1}{4}a^{17}b^{41}$
33. $(a^n)^3(2a^n)^4$ $16a^{7n}$
34. $(c^2)^n(c^3)^{2n}$ c^{8n}

35. $(x^2y)^n(x^2y^3)^n$ $x^{4n}y^{4n}$
36. $(a^{n+1})^3(a^n)^3$ a^{6n+3}
37. $(2a^2b^3)^4 - (3a^4b^6)^2$ $7a^8b^{12}$

38. $(5p^2q^4)^3 + (-pq^2)^6$ $126p^6q^{12}$
39. $x^3(xy^2)^2 + x(-xy)^4$ $2x^5y^4$
40. $s^2(r^2s^2)^2 + r^2(rs^3)^2$ $2r^4s^6$

POLYNOMIALS AND PROBLEM SOLVING **127**

Supplementary Material
Practice Master 18

Suggested Assignments
Minimum
127/1–20, 21–39 odd
S 123/36, 37
Average
127/1–27 odd, 29–40
S 123/32, 34
Maximum
127/1–41 odd
S 123/34, 38

Additional A Exercises

Simplify.

1. $(a^2)^2$ a^4
2. $(c^3)^5$ c^{15}
3. $(3x)^3$ $27x^3$
4. $(4y)^2$ $16y^2$
5. $(x^m)^3$ x^{3m}
6. $(z^n)^m$ z^{mn}

Additional Answers
Written Exercises

4. $125m^3n^3$
8. $36x^6y^4$
12. $-x^{15}y^5$
16. $-3x^{10}y^4$

C 41. a. Find the volumes of the two cubes shown. $8x^3$; $64x^3$

    b. How many times larger is the volume of the bigger cube than that of the smaller cube?

                             8 times

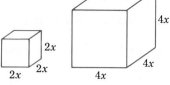

Computer Key-In

If you type the following program into a computer that accepts the language **BASIC**, the computer will then be ready to multiply any two numbers that you give it.

```
10   PRINT "TYPE IN TWO NUMBERS TO BE MULTIPLIED."
20   INPUT A
30   INPUT B
40   PRINT "PRODUCT =";A*B
50   END
```

If the absolute value of the product is greater than 999999, it will be printed in an exponential notation. For example, if you multiply 3452 by 675, the answer will be printed in this form:

$$2.33010E+06$$

The "E+06" means "times 10^6," and so

    $2.33010E+06$ means 2.33010×10^6,   or   2,330,100.

This happens to be the exact answer. However, if you multiply 67892 by 543, the answer may be printed as:

$$3.68654E+07$$

This is not an exact answer. It gives *six significant digits* of the answer 36,865,400, although the exact answer would be 36,865,356. Computers using **BASIC** commonly give such answers rounded to six significant digits.

    Verify that 999×999 is less than 999999. Then add 1 successively to one factor until the product is greater than 999999. $999 \times 1002 = 1,000,998$

    Verify that 9999×99 is less than 999999. Then keep one factor fixed and add 1 successively to the other factor until the product is greater than 999999. Do this with each factor. $9999 \times 101 = 1,009,899$; $99 \times 10,102 = 1,000,098$

    To find the product of several numbers, you can use the second program on page 46 if you change the words in lines 20 and 80 and change lines 30 and 60 as follows:

```
30   LET P=1
60   LET P=P*N
```

4-5 Multiplying a Polynomial by a Monomial

OBJECTIVE To multiply a polynomial by a monomial.

The distributive axiom and the rules of exponents enable you to multiply any polynomial by a monomial. For example:

$$3a(5a^2 - 2a + 4) = 3a(5a^2) + 3a(-2a) + 3a(4) = 15a^3 - 6a^2 + 12a$$

You may multiply either horizontally or vertically:

$$-2xy(5xy + 3x - y) = -10x^2y^2 - 6x^2y + 2xy^2$$ or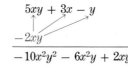

$$
\begin{array}{r}
5xy + 3x - y \\
-2xy \\
\hline
-10x^2y^2 - 6x^2y + 2xy^2
\end{array}
$$

Recall that to simplify an expression containing more than one grouping symbol, you work with the expression within the innermost grouping symbol first.

EXAMPLE Solve $20x^2 - 2[4x - 2x(1 - 5x)] = 8$

SOLUTION
$$
\begin{aligned}
20x^2 - 2[4x - 2x(1 - 5x)] &= 8 \\
20x^2 - 2[4x - 2x + 10x^2] &= 8 \\
20x^2 - 8x + 4x - 20x^2 &= 8 \\
-4x &= 8 \\
x &= -2
\end{aligned}
$$
The check is left for you.
∴ The solution is -2. **Answer**

Oral Exercises

Multiply.

1. $2(a + 5)$ **2.** $3(x - 8)$ **3.** $-7(2x + 5)$ **4.** $-\dfrac{1}{2}(2x - 2)$

5. $x(x - 6)$ **6.** $3a(2a + b)$ **7.** $5x(x + y)$ **8.** $-a(a - b)$

9. $x(x^3 + 3x^2 + 2x)$ **10.** $2c^2(3c - cd)$ **11.** $x^2y^3(x^2y + 2xy^2)$

Written Exercises

Multiply.

A **1.** $3(2x^2 + 5y + 4)$ $6x^2 + 15y + 12$ **2.** $4(3y^2 - 2y + 7)$ $12y^2 - 8y + 28$
3. $-7(2x^3 - x^2 + 5x)$ $-14x^3 + 7x^2 - 35x$ **4.** $-(2a - 3a^2 - a^3)$ $-2a + 3a^2 + a^3$
5. $3x^2(x^2 - 2xy + y^2)$ $3x^4 - 6x^3y + 3x^2y^2$ **6.** $5n^3(3n^2 + 7n - 2)$ $15n^5 + 35n^4 - 10n^3$

POLYNOMIALS AND PROBLEM SOLVING   **129**

Teaching Suggestions p. T75

Suggested Extensions p. T75

Chalkboard Examples
Multiply.
1. $-6k^2(k^2 - 4k + 12)$
$-6k^4 + 24k^3 - 72k^2$

2. $3m^2n(1 - mn + 4m^3n^2)$
$3m^2n - 3m^3n^2 + 12m^5n^3$

3. $a^3b^2 - 2a^2b^3 + 6ab^4$
$-3a^2b$
$\overline{-3a^5b^3 + 6a^4b^4 - 18a^3b^5}$

Solve.
4. $6(y - 1) - 1 = 2y + 21$
$6y - 6 - 1 = 2y + 21$
$6y - 7 = 2y + 21$
$4y = 28$
$y = 7$

5. $3x - 2[x - (1 - 2x)] =$
$2(2x + 4 - x)$
$3x - 2[x - 1 + 2x] = 2(x + 4)$
$3x - 2[3x - 1] = 2x + 8$
$3x - 6x + 2 = 2x + 8$
$-3x + 2 = 2x + 8$
$5x = -6$
$x = -\dfrac{6}{5}$

Additional Answers
Oral Exercises
1. $2a + 10$ **2.** $3x - 24$
3. $-14x - 35$ **4.** $-x + 1$
5. $x^2 - 6x$ **6.** $6a^2 + 3ab$
7. $5x^2 + 5xy$ **8.** $-a^2 + ab$
9. $x^4 + 3x^3 + 2x^2$
10. $6c^3 - 2c^3d$
11. $x^4y^4 + 2x^3y^5$

Suggested Assignments
Minimum
129/1-43 odd
S 123/30, 32, 34
Average
129/1-45 odd
S 124/39
Maximum
129/1-47 odd
S 124/40, 42

Additional A Exercises

Multiply.

1. $x(2y + z)$
$2xy + xz$

2. $5a(a - 2b)$
$5a^2 - 10ab$

3. $r^2(2r - s)$
$2r^3 - r^2s$

4. $m^3n(mn + mn^2)$
$m^4n^2 + m^4n^3$

5. $3b^2(b^3 - b)$
$3b^5 - 3b^3$

6. $-2a^4(a^2 - 2a + 3)$
$-2a^6 + 4a^5 - 6a^4$

Additional Answers
Written Exercises

7. $a^3 + 2a^2b - 4ab^2$

8. $2x^2y - 4xy^2 - y^3$

9. $16n^3m - 6n^2m^2 + 2m^3$

10. $15x^3y^2 - 6x^2y^3 + 12xy^4$

11. $-6a^3b^3 + 14a^2b^4$

12. $-3p^4q + 12p^3q^2 - 18pq^3$

33. $a - 1$ **34.** $3y - 1$

35. $-4pq - 5pqr - 6p^2q$

36. $-20k^3 - 8k^2n - 11kn^2$

37. $6a^3 - 10a^2 - 3a$

38. $6n^3$

Multiply.

7. $\frac{1}{3}a(3a^2 + 6ab - 12b^2)$

8. $\frac{1}{2}y(4x^2 - 8xy - 2y^2)$

9. $(8n^3 - 3n^2m + m^2)(2m)$

10. $(5x^2y - 2xy^2 + 4y^3)(3xy)$

11. $-2ab(3a^2b^2 - 7ab^3)$

12. $(p^3 - 4p^2q + 6q^2)(-3pq)$

13. $4n^2 + 3n + 7$
$\underline{2n}$
$8n^3 + 6n^2 + 14n$

14. $5a^3 - 3a^2 - 2$
$\underline{3a}$
$15a^4 - 9a^3 - 6a$

15. $4a^2b - 3ab^2 + b^3$
$\underline{-2a}$
$-8a^3b + 6a^2b^2 - 2ab^3$

16. $y^2z - 3yz^2 + z^3$
$\underline{-3yz}$
$-3y^3z^2 + 9y^2z^3 - 3yz^4$

Simplify.

17. $2x(3x - 5) + 4x(x + 2)$ $10x^2 - 2x$

18. $5n(2n + 4) - 3n(n - 2)$ $7n^2 + 26n$

19. $-2a(a^2 - 5) + 3a(a^2 - 6)$ $a^3 - 8a$

20. $7x(3x - 2y) - 4(5x^2 - y)$
$x^2 - 14xy + 4y$

21. $\frac{2}{3}(6x - 9) - \frac{1}{2}(8x + 6)$ -9

22. $\frac{1}{10}c(10 - 30c) - 2c(4 - c)$ $-c^2 - 7c$

23. $2a(a^2 - a + 2) - (a^3 + 5a^2 - 7a)a$
$-a^4 - 3a^3 + 5a^2 + 4a$

24. $2x^2(x + 3) - 5(x^2 - x)x$ $-3x^3 + 11x^2$

Solve.

25. $5(x - 2) - 3x = 10$ 10

26. $4(y - 3) - 12 = 8$ 8

27. $\frac{1}{3}(6 - 3n) = -12$ 14

28. $2y = -\frac{1}{2}(4y - 8)$ 1

29. $5x(x - 2) = 5x^2 + 40$ -4

30. $6a(a - 3) = 3a(2a + 12)$ 0

31. $3a\left(5 - \frac{1}{3}a\right) - (15 - a^2) = 0$ 1

32. $4(n - 7) - 2(1 - 3n)n = 6n^2$ 14

Simplify.

B **33.** $\frac{3}{5}(5a - 10b - 1) - 2\left(a - 3b + \frac{1}{5}\right)$

34. $\frac{1}{2}(4x + 3y - 1) + \frac{1}{4}(6y - 8x - 2)$

35. $2pq(1 - 4r - 3p) - 3p(2q - qr)$

36. $(4k^2 + 3kn + 2n^2)(-5k) + n(7k^2 - kn)$

37. $4a^3 - a[3 - 2a(a - 5)]$

38. $7n^2 - n[4n - 3n(2n - 1)]$

Solve.

39. $3(2y + 5) - 4(1 - 5y) = 9(3 + 2y)$ 2

40. $x - 5(x + 2) = x + 3(3 - 2x)$ 19

41. $2(5n - 4) - 3(n - 5) = 8(2n - 7)$ 7

42. $2\left(a + \frac{3}{2}\right) - 3(a - 2) = 2(a - 3)$ 5

43. $18a^2 - 2a[6a - 3(1 - a)] = -6$ -1

44. $5n - \frac{2}{3}\left[2n^2 - \frac{1}{2}n(3 + 4n)\right] = -24$ -4

Simplify. Each variable in an exponent represents a positive integer.

C **45.** $x^n(2x^n - 3x + 4)$
$2x^{2n} - 3x^{n+1} + 4x^n$

46. $a^{n+1}(a^n + a)$
$a^{2n+1} + a^{n+2}$

47. $(2b^{n+1} + 3b^2)b^{n+1}$
$2b^{2n+2} + 3b^{n+3}$

48. $(-s)^{2n}(s^{2n} - 1)$
$s^{4n} - s^{2n}$

130   *CHAPTER 4*

4-6 Multiplying Two Polynomials

OBJECTIVE   To multiply polynomials.

You have learned to use the distributive axiom to multiply a polynomial by a monomial:

$$(3x + 4)(2x) = 3x(2x) + 4(2x)$$

If you replace $2x$ in the example above by the polynomial $2x + 5$, the distributive axiom can still be applied:

$$(3x + 4)(2x + 5) = 3x(2x + 5) + 4(2x + 5)$$
$$= 6x^2 + 15x + 8x + 20$$
$$= 6x^2 + 23x + 20$$

Here is another example in which a polynomial is multiplied by a polynomial, but the work is done in vertical form.

STEP 1 Multiply by $3a$.

$$\begin{array}{r} 5a^2 - 3a - 7 \\ \underline{3a + 2} \\ 15a^3 - 9a^2 - 21a \end{array}$$

STEP 2 Multiply by 2.

$$\begin{array}{r} 5a^2 - 3a - 7 \\ \underline{3a + 2} \\ 15a^3 - 9a^2 - 21a \\ 10a^2 - 6a - 14 \end{array}$$

STEP 3   Add.

$$\begin{array}{r} 5a^2 - 3a - 7 \\ \underline{3a + 2} \\ 15a^3 - 9a^2 - 21a \\ \underline{10a^2 - 6a - 14} \\ 15a^3 + a^2 - 27a - 14 \end{array}$$

It is often helpful to rearrange the terms of a polynomial so that their degrees in a particular variable are in either decreasing or increasing order.

In order of decreasing degree in x: $3x^4 + 5x^3 - 6x + 4$

In order of increasing degree in x: $4 - 6x + 5x^3 + 3x^4$

In order of decreasing degree in a
and increasing degree in b: $-4a^3 + a^2b + 5ab^2 + 3b^3$

To see the advantage of rearranging terms, first multiply the polynomials at the left below. Then compare your work with that shown at the right, where the terms of both polynomials have been rearranged.

$$\begin{array}{l} a^3 - ab^2 + 3b^3 + 2a^2b \\ \underline{b + a} \end{array} \quad \begin{array}{l} \text{Rearrange in order} \\ \text{of decreasing degree} \\ \text{in } a. \end{array} \Big\} \begin{array}{l} a^3 + 2a^2b - ab^2 + 3b^3 \\ \underline{a + b} \\ a^4 + 2a^3b - a^2b^2 + 3ab^3 \\ \underline{ a^3b + 2a^2b^2 - ab^3 + 3b^4} \\ a^4 + 3a^3b + a^2b^2 + 2ab^3 + 3b^4 \end{array}$$

POLYNOMIALS AND PROBLEM SOLVING   **131**

Teaching Suggestions p. T76

Suggested Extensions p. T76

Chalkboard Examples

Multiply.

1. $(2x + 3)(x - 10)$
$2x^2 + 3x - 20x - 30 =$
$2x^2 - 17x - 30$

2. $(a + b)(c + d)$
$ac + bc + ad + bd$

3. $(2x^2 - x)(2 - x)$
$4x^2 - 2x - 2x^3 + x^2 =$
$-2x^3 + 5x^2 - 2x$

4. $(2y + z)(z - 4y)$
$2yz + z^2 - 8y^2 - 4yz =$
$z^2 - 8y^2 - 2yz$

5. $(3y + 4)(3y^2 + 5y - 4)$
$9y^3 + 15y^2 - 12y +$
$ 12y^2 + 20y - 16 =$
$9y^3 + 27y^2 + 8y - 16$

6. $c^2 + 2cd - d^2$
$\underline{c - 4d}$
$c^3 + 2c^2d - cd^2$
$\underline{ - 4c^2d - 8cd^2 + 4d^3}$
$c^3 - 2c^2d - 9cd^2 + 4d^3$

7. $m^2 + 3m + 9$
$\underline{m - 3}$
$m^3 + 3m^2 + 9m$
$\underline{ - 3m^2 - 9m - 27}$
$m^3 - 27$

Supplementary Materials

Practice Master 20

Progress Test 12

Suggested Assignments

Minimum
132/1–41 odd
S 130/36, 40

Average
132/1–43 odd
S 130/36, 44

Maximum
132/1–49 odd
S 130/36, 44

Additional A Exercises

Multiply.

1. $(x + 1)(x + 3)$
$x^2 + 4x + 3$

2. $(y + 4)(y + 6)$
$y^2 + 10y + 24$

3. $(a - 2)(a + 7)$
$a^2 + 5a - 14$

4. $(b - 3)(b - 4)$
$b^2 - 7b + 12$

5. $(2x + 5)(x + 1)$
$2x^2 + 7x + 5$

6. $(4a - 2)(2a + 3)$
$8a^2 + 8a - 6$

Additional Answers
Written Exercises

1. $n^2 + 7n + 12$

2. $x^2 + 7x + 10$

3. $y^2 - 4y - 21$

4. $z^2 - 25$

5. $2a^2 + 18a + 28$

6. $2b^2 + 7b - 15$

7. $2c^2 - 7c - 4$

8. $10x^2 - x - 21$

9. $3p^2 - 19p + 20$

10. $a^3 + 3a^2 + 5a + 3$

11. $x^3 - x^2 - 5x + 2$

12. $3y^3 - 2y^2 + 4y - 5$

13. $6b^3 + 11b^2 + 8b + 2$

14. $5c^3 - 36c^2 + 5c + 14$

15. $3n^4 - 17n^3 + 27n^2 - 8n$

Oral Exercises

Arrange in order of decreasing degree in the variable indicated in color.

1. $x - 3 + x^2$; x $x^2 + x - 3$

2. $3x^2 + x^3 - 5$; x $x^3 + 3x^2 - 5$

3. $4a^2b + 3b^2a - a^3$; a
$-a^3 + 4a^2b + 3b^2a$

4. $2r^4 - 3s^2r + 4sr^2 + s^3$; r
$2r^4 + 4sr^2 - 3s^2r + s^3$

Arrange in order of increasing degree in the variable indicated in color.

5. $x^2 + 2 - 3x$; x $2 - 3x + x^2$

6. $5y + 3y^3 - 7y^2$; y $5y - 7y^2 + 3y^3$

7. $c^2d^2 + cd + c^4$; c $cd + c^2d^2 + c^4$

8. $c^2d^2 + c^3d + c^4$; d $c^4 + c^3d + c^2d^2$

Complete.

9. $(2x + 5)(x + 3) = 2x(x + 3) + (?)(x + 3)$ 5

10. $(3a - 4)(a - 1) = 3a(a - 1) - (?)(a - 1)$ 4

11. $(a + 1)(a + 2) = a(a + 2) + 1(?) = a^2 + 2a + (?) + 2$ $a + 2$; a

12. $(r + 2)(r + 3) = r(?) + 2(?) = r^2 + (?)r + 2r + 6$ $r + 3$; $r + 3$; 3

13. $(t + 2)(t + 4) = t^2 + 4t + 2t + (?)$ 8

14. $(x + 2)(x - 3) = x^2 - 3x + 2x + (?)$ -6

15. $(v - 2)(v - 5) = v^2 - 5v - 2v + (?)$ 10

Written Exercises

Multiply. Use the horizontal form.

A **1.** $(n + 3)(n + 4)$ **2.** $(x + 2)(x + 5)$ **3.** $(y + 3)(y - 7)$

4. $(z + 5)(z - 5)$ **5.** $(2a + 4)(a + 7)$ **6.** $(2b - 3)(b + 5)$

7. $(c - 4)(2c + 1)$ **8.** $(5x + 7)(2x - 3)$ **9.** $(3p - 4)(p - 5)$

10. $(a + 1)(a^2 + 2a + 3)$ **11.** $(x + 2)(x^2 - 3x + 1)$ **12.** $(y - 1)(3y^2 + y + 5)$

13. $(2b + 1)(3b^2 + 4b + 2)$ **14.** $(c - 7)(5c^2 - c - 2)$ **15.** $(3n - 8)(n^3 - 3n^2 + n)$

Multiply. Use the vertical form.

16. $4n + 1$ **17.** $3a - 2$ **18.** $2n^2 + 5n + 1$ **19.** $3x^2 + x - 2$
$\underline{\quad n + 2}$ $\underline{\quad 2a - 1}$ $\underline{\quad n + 7}$ $\underline{\quad 2x + 5}$
$4n^2 + 9n + 2$ $6a^2 - 7a + 2$ $2n^3 + 19n^2 + 36n + 7$ $6x^3 + 17x^2 + x - 10$

20. $2a + b$ **21.** $3r - s$ **22.** $a^2 + ab + b^2$ **23.** $2c^2 - cd + d^2$
$\underline{\quad a + b}$ $\underline{\quad 2r + 3s}$ $\underline{\quad a + b}$ $\underline{\quad c - d}$
$2a^2 + 3ab + b^2$ $6r^2 + 7rs - 3s^2$ $a^3 + 2a^2b + 2ab^2 + b^3$ $2c^3 - 3c^2d + 2cd^2 - d^3$

Multiply using whichever form you prefer. Arrange the terms in each
factor in order of decreasing or increasing degree in some variable.

B **24.** $(3r + 2s)(5r^2 - 2rs + s^2)$ **25.** $(2n - 5)(n^2 - 3n - 7)$

26. $(a - 2)(3a^2 - 5a - 4)$ **27.** $(x - 1)(x^2 + x + 1)$

28. $(a^2 - 5)(a^2 + 5)$ **29.** $(2p - 5q)(p^3 - 3p^2q - 7pq^2)$

132

30. $(4c - 9)(c + c^2 - 7)$

31. $(5x - y)(x^2 - xy - y^2)$

32. $(3n - 7)(2 - n^2 - 4n)$

33. $(4a - b)(ab - b^2 + 3a^2)$

34. $(x + 3)(x + 3)(x + 3)$

35. $x(2x + 5)(4x + 1)$ $\quad 8x^3 + 22x^2 + 5x$

36. $(x^2 - 2x + 3)(x^2 + 2x + 1)$
$\quad\quad x^4 + 4x + 3$

37. $(3a^2 + 2ab + b^2)(a^2 - ab - b^2)$
$\quad\quad 3a^4 - a^3b - 4a^2b^2 - 3ab^3 - b^4$

Solve.

38. $(x + 2)(x + 3) - x(x + 4) = 7$ $\quad 1$

39. $(a + 7)(a + 3) - a(a + 1) = 21$ $\quad 0$

40. $(3n + 1)(4n + 5) - (2n + 3)(6n + 1) = 15$ $\quad -13$

41. $(8n + 5)(n - 1) + 12 = (4n + 3)(2n - 1)$ $\quad 2$

42. $(6x - 5)(x + 3) - (2x - 4)(3x - 1) = 35$ $\quad 2$

43. $(3y + 2)(4y - 1) - (-2y - 1)(-6y - 2) = -24$ $\quad 4$

C 44. When a certain polynomial is divided by $x - 3$, the quotient is $x^2 + x + 2$. Find the polynomial. $\quad x^3 - 2x^2 - x - 6$

45. When a certain polynomial is divided by $2x + 5$, the quotient is $2x^2 - 3x + 1$. Find the polynomial. $\quad 4x^3 + 4x^2 - 13x + 15$

Multiply.

46. $(2b^n + 1)(b^n - 2)$ $\quad 2b^{2n} - 3b^n - 2$

47. $(a^n + 1)(a^n - 1)$ $\quad a^{2n} - 1$

48. $(s^{2n} + 3)(s^{2n} - 3)$ $\quad s^{4n} - 9$

49. $(b^m + a^n)(b^m - a^n)$ $\quad b^{2m} - a^{2n}$

Self-Test 2

Simplify.

1. $x^2 \cdot x^5 \cdot x$

2. $(-3y^4)(-2y^3)$

3. $(a^3)^5$

4. $(-3x^2y^3)^2$

5. $5x(x + 4)$

6. $2a^2(a^2 - ab + b^2)$

7. $(n + 3)(n - 3)$

8. $(x - 2)(x^2 + 3x - 6)$

Obj. 4-3, p. 122
Obj. 4-4, p. 126
Obj. 4-5, p. 129
Obj. 4-6, p. 131

Check your answers with those at the back of the book.

Just for Fun

Write the number 260 using only three 4's and one other mathematical symbol. $4^4 + 4$

Write the number 24 using a digit other than 8 three times and using one other mathematical symbol. $3^3 - 3$

Chalkboard Examples

Use the given information to complete each chart.

1. Kit is three years younger than Bob.

	Age now	Age in 5 years
Bob	b	$b + 5$
Kit	$b - 3$	$(b - 3) + 5$, or $b + 2$

2. Mr. Asaka bought several boxes of raspberries at ninety cents per box and four fewer boxes of currants at sixty cents per box.

	No. of boxes	$\times$ cents per box	= Cost
Rasp-berries	r	90	$90r$
Currants	$r - 4$	60	$\uparrow$ $60(r - 4)$

3. Refer to Example 2.

a. Mr. Asaka spent a total of $6.60 on the fruit. Write an equation to express this fact.
$90r + 60(r - 4) = 660$

b. Solve the equation written in part (a) to find the number of boxes of each type of fruit that Mr. Asaka bought.
$$90r + 60r - 240 = 660$$
$$150r - 240 = 660$$
$$150r = 900$$
$$r = 6$$
Six boxes raspberries and two boxes currants

4. Solve the formula $I = Prt$ for P.
$$P = \frac{I}{rt}$$

SOLVING PROBLEMS

4-7 *Organizing Information*

OBJECTIVE   To organize facts given in a problem and write formulas in convenient form in order to solve problems.

In Chapter 1 you learned a five-step problem-solving method which included the following step:

Step 2   Choose a variable and use it with the given facts to represent the number(s) described in the problem.

Making a chart is a helpful way to carry out this step in solving certain kinds of problems. Before you can solve puzzles involving ages of people, you must learn how to use variables to represent their present ages as well as their ages in the past and in the future. For example, if you are told that Dan is two years older than Valerie, you can let x represent Valerie's age now and make the following chart.

	Age now
Valerie	x
Dan	$x + 2$

If you are then given some more information about their ages five years ago, you can enlarge the chart this way:

	Age now	Age 5 years ago
Valerie	x	$x - 5$
Dan	$x + 2$	$(x + 2) - 5$, or $x - 3$

The following example shows the solution of a word problem using this technique of organizing given facts.

EXAMPLE 1

Uncle Louis is three times as old as Michelle. In eight years their ages will total 100. How old are they now?

SOLUTION

Step 1   The problem asks for the ages of Michelle and Uncle Louis.

Step 2   Let x = Michelle's age now. Make a chart of the given facts.

134   *CHAPTER 4*

	Age now	Age in 8 years
Michelle	x	$x + 8$
Louis	$3x$	$3x + 8$

Step 3 The only fact not recorded in the chart is that in 8 years their ages will total 100. Use this fact to write an equation.

$$(x + 8) + (3x + 8) = 100$$

Step 4
$$4x + 16 = 100$$
$$4x = 84$$
$$x = 21$$

Step 5 The check is left to you.

∴ Michelle is now 21 and Uncle Louis is 63. ***Answer***

   Many problems, such as those involving area, distance, and interest, require the application of a known formula. In applying a formula, it is often useful to find an equivalent but different form in which a particular variable is expressed in terms of the other variables. For example, if you know the perimeter and the width of a rectangle, you can find a formula for the length as follows.

EXAMPLE 2 Solve $P = 2l + 2w$ for l.

SOLUTION
$$P = 2l + 2w$$
$$P - 2w = 2l$$
$$\frac{P - 2w}{2} = l \quad \textbf{\textit{Answer}}$$

Oral Exercises

Use the given information to complete each chart.

1. Karl is 4 years younger than Tom.

	Age now	Age last year
Tom	x	? $x - 1$
Karl	? $x - 4$	? $x - 5$

2. Tony is half as old as Lynn.

	Age now	Age 3 years ago
Lynn	x	? $x - 3$
Tony	? $\frac{x}{2}$	? $\frac{x}{2} - 3$

3. Kim was twice as old as Kit last year.

	Age last year	Age now
Kit	x	? $x + 1$
Kim	? $2x$	?

$2x + 1$

4. A mat is 4 cm longer than it is wide. A second mat is 1 cm wider and 2 cm longer than the first.

	length	width
First mat	? $x + 4$	x
Second mat	?	?

$x + 6$ $x + 1$

5. Solve the formula
$$A = \frac{h}{2}(a + b) \text{ for } b.$$
$$b = \frac{2A - ha}{h}$$

6. Given that $A = \frac{1}{2}bh$, complete the chart.

base (b)	height (h)	Area (A)
x	$x - 5$	a.
$2y - 6$	$y + 1$	b.
$4t$	c.	$18t^2$
$s + 2$	d.	$s^2 + 4$

a. $A = \frac{1}{2}x(x - 5)$

b. $A = \frac{1}{2}(2y - 6)(y + 1)$, or
$A = (y - 3)(y + 1)$

c. $h = 9t$

d. $h = \frac{2(s^2 + 4)}{s + 2}$

Supplementary Material

Computer Activity 12
Age Problems
  Age problems can be solved readily by students through the analysis of a computer-generated list of possible solutions.

Suggested Assignments

Minimum
Day 1: 136/1–8, 11–19 odd
  R 133/Self-Test 2
Day 2: 138/P: 1, 3, 5
  140/P: 1–3, 5, 6

Average
Day 1: 136/1–27 odd
  R 133/Self-Test 2
Day 2: 138/P: 1–9 odd
  140/P: 1, 2, 4, 5, 7

Maximum
Day 1: 136/1–27 odd
  R 133/Self-Test 2
Day 2: 138/P: 2, 4, 6, 8, 9,
  11, 12
  140/P: 1, 2, 4, 5, 8,
  10

*NOTE: Day 2 of all levels
also covers Sec. 4-8.*

Extra Practice Problems
  p. 516

Additional A Exercises

Solve for *x*.

1. $x - c = b$ $x = b + c$

2. $3x + a = m$

  $x = \dfrac{m - a}{3}$

3. $-ax - 2b = c$

  $x = -\dfrac{c + 2b}{a}$

Use the given information to
complete each chart.

4. At Burger Box the Sam-
uels ordered several burgers at 95¢ each. They also
ordered three fewer steak
sandwiches at $1.40 each.

	num-ber	× price =	Total cost
Bur-gers	x	0.95	0.95x
Steak	$(x - 3)$	1.4	

  $\overline{1.4(x - 3)}$

Solve each equation for x.

5. $x - a = b$
  $x = a + b$

6. $-x = d - 2x$
  $x = d$

7. $y = kx$
  $x = \dfrac{y}{k}$

8. $ax + b = c$
  $x = \dfrac{c - b}{a}$

Solve each formula for the variable shown in color.

9. $P = a + b + c;\ a$

  $a = P - b - c$

10. $V = Bh;\ h$

  $h = \dfrac{V}{B}$

11. $A = \dfrac{1}{2}bh;\ h$

  $h = \dfrac{2A}{b}$

12. $I = Prt;\ r$

  $r = \dfrac{I}{Pt}$

Written Exercises

A 1. a. Solve $lw = A$ for w.

  b. Copy and complete the chart.

length	width	Area	
$2x + 5$	x	?	$2x^2 + 5x$
$x + 4$	$x - 3$	?	$x^2 + x - 12$
$a + 1$	?	24	$\dfrac{24}{a + 1}$
$3n + 2$	?	15	$\dfrac{15}{3n + 2}$

2. a. Solve $rt = D$ for r.

  b. Copy and complete the chart.

rate	time	Distance	
x	2	?	$2x$
30	$n + 2$	?	$30n + 60$
?	x	20	$\dfrac{20}{x}$
?	$5 - t$	12	$\dfrac{12}{5 - t}$

Use the given information to complete each chart.

3. Sylvia has a collection of coins. She has three more quarters than
dimes and five more dimes than nickels.

	number	× value per coin	= Total value	
nickels	x	? 5	? $5x$	
dimes	? $x + 5$	? 10	?	$10x + 50$
quarters	? $x + 8$	? 25	?	$25x + 200$

4. Frank bought several boxes of strawberries costing $1 a box. He
also bought three fewer boxes of cherries costing 75 cents a box.

	number of boxes	× price per box (in cents)	= Cost	
strawberries	x	? 100	? $100x$	
cherries	? $x - 3$	? 75	?	$75x - 225$

5. The length of a rectangle is 12 cm
more than the width. A second
rectangle is 5 cm wider but 2 cm
shorter than the first rectangle.

	length	× width	= Area
first rectangle	?	x	?
second rectangle	?	?	?

6. Jo has 20 coins. She has twice as many dimes as nickels and the rest are quarters.

	number × value per coin = Total value		
nickels	x	? 5	? $5x$
dimes	? $2x$	? 10	? $20x$
quarters	?	? 25	?

$20 - 3x$ $500 - 75x$

Use the given information to complete each chart and each equation.

7. Janet is seven times as old as her dog Woofie. In two years Janet will be four times as old as Woofie.

a.

	Age now	Age in 2 years
Woofie	x	? $x + 2$
Janet	? $7x$	? $7x + 2$

b. $7x + 2 = 4(?) \quad x + 2$

8. Jean has three times as much money as her brother Jim, but when each of them earns three dollars, Jean will have twice as much as Jim.

a.

	Money now	Money after earnings
Jim	x	? $x + 3$
Jean	? $3x$	? $3x + 3$

b. $\dfrac{?}{} = 2(x + 3)$ $3x + 3$

9. Sam bought several apples at 10 cents each. He ate two and sold the rest at 15 cents each. He made a profit of 20 cents.

a.

	number × price = Cost

	number × price = Cost		
Apples bought	n	? 10	? $10n$
Apples sold	?	? 15	?

$n - 2$ $(n - 2)15$

b. $(n - 2)15 - \dfrac{?}{} = 20$ $10n$

10. Pete jogs to the gym at a rate of 15 km/h and walks back at a rate of 5 km/h. His total travel time is one hour. Pete traveled along the same route both ways.

a.

	rate × time = Distance

	rate × time = Distance		
Jogging	? 15	t	? $15t$
Walking	? 5	?	?

$1 - t$ $5 - 5t$

b. $15t = \dfrac{?}{} \quad 5 - 5t$

POLYNOMIALS AND PROBLEM SOLVING   137

---

5. $P = 2l + 2w$
(Perimeter of a rectangle)

length	width	Perimeter
a	b	$2a + 2b$
$x + 5$	$x - 1$	$2(x + 5) + 2(x - 1)$
$c + 1$	$b + 2$	$2(c + 1) + 2(b + 2)$

Additional Answers
Written Exercises
5. $x + 12$, $x^2 + 12x$
$x + 10$, $x + 5$, $x^2 + 15x + 50$

Solve for the variable shown in color.

11. $x + c = a$; x $x = a - c$ **12.** $y + 2b = b$; y $y = -b$ **13.** $2a - z = a$; z
$$z = a$$

14. $\frac{x + d}{3} = c$; x $x = 3c - d$ **15.** $a - y = 3y$; y $y = \frac{a}{4}$ **16.** $\frac{a + z - b}{2} = c$; z
$$z = 2c + b - a$$

17. $I = Prt$; t $t = \frac{I}{Pr}$ **18.** $V = \frac{1}{3}Bh$; h $h = \frac{3V}{B}$ **19.** $s = \frac{1}{2}at^2$; a
$$a = \frac{2s}{t^2}$$

B **20.** $v^2 = u^2 + 2as$; s $s = \frac{v^2 - u^2}{2a}$ **21.** $A = P + Prt$; t $t = \frac{A - P}{Pr}$ **22.** $S = (n - 2)180$; n

23. $C = 2\pi r$; r $r = \frac{C}{2\pi}$ **24.** $V = \frac{1}{3}\pi r^2 h$; h $h = \frac{3V}{\pi r^2}$ **25.** $T = 2\pi r^2 + 2\pi rh$; h

                                                       22. $n = \frac{s + 360}{180}$

26. The formula

                                                       25. $h = \frac{T - 2\pi r^2}{2\pi r}$

$$s = c + o + p$$

relates the selling price s of an item to the wholesale cost c, overhead expenses o, and profit p for the item.

a. Solve the formula for o. $o = s - c - p$

b. What is the overhead on a television set selling at \$349 if it cost the dealer \$260 and she makes a \$70 profit on the sale?   \$19

27. The formula

$$P = \frac{3}{4}R + 25$$

is used to convert a raw score R on a certain test to a percentage score P.

a. Convert the raw score 60 to a percentage score.   70
b. Solve the formula for R. $R = \frac{4P - 100}{3}$
c. What raw score corresponds to a percentage score of 82?   76

Age Problems

Solve.

A **1.** Ben is four years older than Juan. In two years, their ages will total 50. How old is each now?   Juan, 21; Ben, 25

2. Pearl is seven years younger than Dot. Five years ago their ages totaled 25. How old is each now?   Pearl, 14; Dot, 21

3. Bill is half as old as his father. Next year, their ages will total 62. How old is each now?   Bill, 20; father, 40

4. Len is ten years older than Marie. In six years, Len will be twice as old as Marie. How old is each now?   Marie, 4; Len, 14

5. Lou is 8 and his mother is 31. How long will it be before his mother is twice as old as he is?   15 years

6. Bonita is 12, exactly one third as old as her father. In how many years will she be half as old as he is?   12 years

B **7.** Jill's age next year will be twice Ann's age last year. Their present ages total 54. How old is each now? Ann, 19; Jill, 35

8. Matt is five years older than Noriko and three years younger than Cindy. Seven years ago, Cindy's age totaled the ages of Noriko and Matt. How old is each now? Noriko, 10; Matt, 15; Cindy, 18

9. George Washington was born eleven years before Thomas Jefferson. In 1770 Washington's age was three years more than seven times the age of Jefferson in 1748. How old was each man in 1750?
Jefferson, 7; Washington, 18

C **10.** Susan is six years older than Mary. She is also twice as old as Mary was when Susan was as old as Mary is now. How old is each now? Susan, 24; Mary, 18

11. In 1901 Northwestern University had been in existence five times as long as Stanford University. By 1931 Northwestern was only twice as old as Stanford. In what year was Northwestern University founded? 1851

12. For six consecutive years, a man's age was a multiple of his granddaughter's age. How old was each during the sixth year?
Granddaughter, 6; grandfather, 66

Career Note Nutritionist

Who plans your school menus and what factors contribute to the choice of foods? Nutritionists plan menus for individuals and for groups. To maintain health, the human body requires certain amounts of food energy, protein, vitamins, and minerals each day. These nutrients can be supplied by the food we eat.

It is the job of the nutritionist to plan menus which are appealing and which satisfy a significant portion of these nutritional requirements. Nutritionists also plan special menus which are salt free, low in cholesterol, high in protein, or sugar free for individuals with certain health problems. Once a menu has been planned, a nutritionist may supervise the purchasing, preparation, and serving of the food.

The minimum requirement for a career as a nutritionist is a bachelor's degree with a major in foods and nutrition. Courses should be taken in physiology, bacteriology, chemistry, food selection, meal preparation, and nutrition. Nutritionists may continue their training after graduation with an internship in a hospital.

POLYNOMIALS AND PROBLEM SOLVING **139**

4-8 *Cost, Wage, and Money Problems*

OBJECTIVE   To solve some problems involving money.

The problems in this section all involve money. Organizing the given facts in a chart will help you solve such problems.

EXAMPLE

Les spent $4.40 for several pencils costing 10 cents each and some notebooks costing 80 cents each. He bought 8 more pencils than notebooks. How many notebooks did he buy?

SOLUTION

Step 1   The problem asks for the number of notebooks Les bought.

Step 2   Let x = number of notebooks Les bought. Make a chart.

	number	×	price	=	Cost
notebooks	x		80		$80x$
pencils	$x + 8$		10		$10(x + 8)$

Step 3   The only fact not recorded in the chart is that the total cost is $4.40. Use this fact to write an equation. (Since the prices are given in terms of cents, write the total cost as 440 cents.)

$$10(x + 8) + 80x = 440$$

Step 4
$$10x + 80 + 80x = 440$$
$$90x = 360$$
$$x = 4$$

Step 5   *Check:* If the number of notebooks is 4, then the number of pencils is 4 + 8, or 12.
12 pencils at 10¢ each cost 12 × 10, or 120¢.
4 notebooks at 80¢ each cost 4 × 80, or 320¢.
120 + 320 = 440, or 440¢; that is, $4.40. √

∴ Les bought 4 notebooks. *Answer*

Problems

Copy and complete each chart and solve each problem.

A   1. At the beach refreshment stand, hot dogs cost 80 cents each and lemonade costs 50 cents. A group of students ordered twice as many hot dogs as lemonades. If their bill was $16.80, how many hot dogs were ordered?
16 hot dogs

	number	×	price	=	Cost
			0.80		0.80x
hot dogs	x		?		?
lemonade	?		?		?
	0.5x		0.50		0.25x

2. Susan makes $3 an hour working after school and $4 an hour working on Saturdays. Last week she worked a total of 12 hours and made $42.50. How many hours did she work on Saturday? 6.5 h

	hours worked $\times$ wage per hour $=$ Income		
Saturday	x	? 4	? 4x
Weekdays	? 12 − x	? 3	?

3(12 − x)

Solve.

B **3.** A student company made some school book cov- 27 covers ers at a cost of 10 cents each. They sold all but three of them at 15 cents each. Their profit was 90 cents. How many covers did they make?

4. Some Booster Club members made cupcakes at a cost of 20 cents each. They sold all but two at 30 cents each. If the club's profit was $3.00, how many cupcakes did they make? 36 cupcakes

5. Acme Appliance Company bought several Model H television sets costing $325 each. They gave away one set as a door prize and sold the rest for $399 each. If their profit was $1821, find how many sets they bought. 30 sets

6. Joyce has a collection of dimes and quarters worth $13.60. She has four more quarters than dimes. How many dimes does she have? 36 dimes

7. Hank has a pocketful of nickels, dimes, and quarters. He has 18 coins in all worth $2.00. Find how many of each coin he has, if he has twice as many dimes as nickels. 5 nickels; 10 dimes; 3 quarters

8. In a collection of coins worth $9.13, there are twice as many dimes as quarters, four more nickels than dimes, and twice as many pennies as nickels. How many of each kind of coin are in the collection? 68 pennies; 34 nickels; 30 dimes; 15 quarters

C **9.** Nadia has seven more nickels than Dora has dimes. If Dora gives Nadia four of her dimes, then Dora will have the same value of money as Nadia. How much money do they have together? $3.80

10. Ned has some nickels, Dick has some dimes, and Quincy has some quarters. Dick has five more dimes than Quincy has quarters. If Ned gives Dick a nickel, Dick gives Quincy a dime, and Quincy gives Ned a quarter, they will all have the same value of money. How many coins did each have originally? Ned, 13 nickels; Dick, 9 dimes; Quincy, 4 quarters

POLYNOMIALS AND PROBLEM SOLVING **141**

Extra Practice Problems
p. 516

Additional A Exercises

Complete each chart and solve each problem.

1. Elrod and Susan went to the record store during its annual sale. Together they spent $38.50. If each record cost $3.50 and Susan bought one more than Elrod, how many records did each purchase?

	number $\times$ price $=$ Cost		
Elrod	x	3.5	3.5x
Susan	$x + 1$	3.5	

3.5(x + 1)

Elrod, 5; Susan, 6

2. Joanne works every weekend. She receives $4 an hour on Saturdays and $6 an hour on Sundays. Last weekend she worked twice as many hours on Saturday as on Sunday and received $42. How many hours did she work each day?

	hours worked $\times$ wage per h $=$ Income		
Sat.	2x	4	8x
Sun.	x	6	6x

Saturday, 6 h; Sunday, 3 h

4-9 *Distance-Rate-Time Problems*

OBJECTIVE   To solve some problems involving uniform motion.

An object is said to be in **uniform motion** when it moves without changing its speed, or rate. The three examples which follow illustrate three types of problems involving uniform motion. Each is solved using a chart, a sketch, and the formula:

$$\text{Distance} = \text{rate} \times \text{time}$$
$$D = rt$$

In your work you will use the symbols s for seconds, min for minutes, and h for hours.

EXAMPLE 1   (Motion in opposite directions)

Bud and Ruth leave the same point driving in opposite directions. Traffic conditions enable Bud to average 10 km/h more than Ruth. After two hours they are 308 km apart. Find the rate of each.

SOLUTION

Step 1   The problem asks for Ruth's rate and Bud's rate.

Step 2   Let x = Ruth's rate. Make a chart and a sketch of the given facts.

	rate	× time	= Distance
Ruth	x	2	$2x$
Bud	$x + 10$	2	$2(x + 10)$

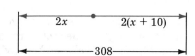

Step 3   The sketch will help you write this equation:
$$2x + 2(x + 10) = 308$$

Step 4
$$2x + 2x + 20 = 308$$
$$4x = 288$$
$$x = 72$$
$$x + 10 = 82$$

Step 5   *Check:* In two hours, Ruth traveled 2(72), or 144 km. In two hours, Bud traveled 2(72 + 10), or 164 km. 144 + 164 = 308   √

∴ Ruth's rate is 72 km/h and Bud's rate is 82 km/h.   ***Answer***

EXAMPLE 2   (Motion in the same direction)

Jay begins bicycling north at 20 km/h at noon. Alex leaves from the same place fifteen minutes later to catch him. If Alex bicycles north at 24 km/h, when will he catch Jay?

142   *CHAPTER 4*

SOLUTION

Step 1 The problem asks for the time at which Alex will catch Jay.

Step 2 Let x = Jay's time. Make a chart and a sketch of the given facts. Since the rates are given in terms of kilometers per hour, time must be expressed in hours. Fifteen minutes is a quarter of an hour.

	rate	$\times$ time	= Distance
Jay	20	x	$20x$
Alex	24	$x - \frac{1}{4}$	$24\left(x - \frac{1}{4}\right)$

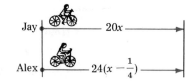

Step 3 When Alex catches Jay, the distances both have traveled will be equal. Thus, you have this equation to solve:

$$20x = 24\left(x - \frac{1}{4}\right)$$

Step 4
$$20x = 24x - 6$$
$$-4x = -6$$
$$x = 1\frac{1}{2}$$

Step 5 The check is left to you.

$\therefore$ Alex will catch Jay $1\frac{1}{2}$ hours after noon, or at 1:30 P.M. ***Answer***

EXAMPLE 3 (Round trip)

Jill walks from her home to the movies at 8 km/h and gets a ride back home at 40 km/h. If her total traveling time is half an hour, how long did it take Jill to walk to the movies and how far was it?

SOLUTION

Step 1 The problem asks for the time and the distance of Jill's walk.

Step 2 Let x = time of Jill's walk in hours. Make a chart and a sketch of the given facts.

	rate	$\times$ time	= Distance
To movies	8	x	$8x$
Return home	40	$0.5 - x$	$40(0.5 - x)$

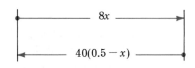

Step 3 In all round-trip problems, the distance going equals the distance returning. Thus, you have this equation to solve:

$$8x = 40(0.5 - x)$$

Steps 4 and 5 are left to you. You should find that it took Jill 25 min to walk about 3.3 km to the movies. ***Answer***

POLYNOMIALS AND PROBLEM SOLVING **143**

---

5. A sailboat leaves its mooring at 7 A.M. and sails southeast at 3 knots. At 9:30 A.M., a motorboat departs from the same mooring and travels southeast at 8 knots. At what time will the motorboat catch up with the sailboat?

slbt.'s dist. = mrbt.'s dist.
Let t = number of hours sailboat travels.

$$3t = 8\left(t - \frac{5}{2}\right)$$
$$3t = 8t - 20$$
$$5t = 20$$
$$t = 4$$

At 11 A.M.

6. On a cross-country ski trail, Jennifer and Michael average 5 km/h skiing to the end of the trail, and 3 km/h skiing back to the beginning. If the total time spent skiing was 4 h, how much time was spent on the return trip? What was the length of the round trip?

dist. out = dist. back
$$r_1 \cdot t_1 = r_2 \cdot t_2$$
$$5(4 - t_2) = 3t_2$$
$$20 - 5t_2 = 3t_2$$
$$8t_2 = 20$$
$$t_2 = 2.5$$
2.5 h for the return trip; round trip = 15 km

Suggested Assignments

Minimum
Day 1: 144/*P*: 1–4, 7
      S 141/*P*: 8
Day 2: 144/*P*: 9, 10, 13, 14
      S 132/2, 8, 38

Average
Day 1: 144/*P*: 1–5, 8
      S 141/*P*: 9
Day 2: 144/*P*: 9, 10, 12–14
      S 132/8, 10, 40

Maximum
      144/*P*: 1–9 odd, 10,
      12–14
      S 132/6, 10, 42

Extra Practice Problems
      p. 516

Additional A Exercises

Solve.

1. Tom and Larraine leave a toll booth at the same time. Larraine drives east at 90 km/h and Tom goes west at 70 km/h. After how many hours are they 480 km apart?   3 h

2. A freight train leaves a railroad station at 7:00 A.M. traveling at 80 km/h. One hour later an express train leaves the same station on a parallel track, traveling in the same direction at 120 km/h. When will the express catch the freight?   3 h or 10 A.M.

3. José bicycles to school at 20 km/h. After school he finds that his bike has a flat tire and he must walk home. If he walks at 10 km/h and his total traveling time for the round trip is one hour, how long did it take him to walk home?   40 min

Problems

Solve.

A 1. Two jets leave Washington, D.C., at the same time, one traveling north at 850 km/h and the other traveling south at 750 km/h. In how many hours will they be 4800 km apart? 3 h

2. Barry and Juan live 36 km apart. At noon each leaves his house and bicycles toward the other. Barry bicycles at 11 km/h and Juan at 13 km/h. At what time will they meet? 1:30 P.M.

3. At 7:00 A.M. a train which averages 100 km/h leaves Charleville headed for Mirabeau. At 8:00 A.M. a train which also averages 100 km/h leaves Mirabeau headed for Charleville. The distance between the two cities is 900 km. At what time will the trains pass each other? Noon

4. A car and a bike set out at 1:00 P.M. from the same point headed in the same direction. After 1 hour the car is 60 km ahead of the bike. Find how fast each travels, given that the car travels four times as fast as the bike. Bike, 20 km/h; Car, 80 km/h

5. Jeanne and Teresa leave their campsite and paddle their canoe down a river at a constant rate of 6 km/h. Four hours later, Mei Ling leaves the campsite in a motorboat and travels down the river with the camping supplies. If the motorboat travels at 18 km/h, how long does it take to overtake the canoe? 2 h

6. A mover's van left Middleton at 8:00 A.M. and drove to Bayside at an average speed of 70 km/h. At 9:00 A.M. the same day, the Rileys left Middleton following the same route as the van. If both arrived in Bayside at 4:00 P.M. what was the Rileys' average speed? 80 km/h

7. Walt rode his bike from home to the bicycle repair shop and then walked home. He averaged 18 km/h riding and 6 km/h walking. If his total travel time was one hour, how far is it to the shop from Walt's home? 4.5 km

8. Running at the average rate of 400 m/min, Pam dashed to the end of the course. She then walked back to her starting position at an average rate of 80 m/min. How long was the course if it took her 6 min to make the dash and walk back? 400 m

B 9. Using the butterfly stroke to swim the length of the pool, Rita averaged 1.5 m/s. Swimming back, she used the breast stroke and averaged 1.2 m/s. The entire swim took 1 min 15 s. How long was the pool? 50 m

144   *CHAPTER 4*

10. Helaine Fabre left on a business trip at 9:00 A.M. traveling at 30 km/h through the downtown traffic. After she left, her secretary discovered that some important papers had been left behind. The secretary set out at 9:10 A.M. to catch her. If the secretary traveled at 50 km/h, at what time did she catch up with Helaine? 9:25 A.M.

11. A ski lift carries Claude up a slope at the rate of 4 km/h, and he returns from the top to the bottom on a path parallel to the lift at 36 km/h. How long is the lift if the round trip traveling time is 20 min? 1.2 km

12. If I leave now and drive at 60 km/h, I can be in Ashton in time for my appointment. On the other hand, if I eat first and leave in half an hour, I will have to drive at 80 km/h to make my appointment. How far is it to Ashton? 120 km

13. The Walkers averaged 60 km/h driving from their house to the airport but they arrived 15 min late. If they had averaged 90 km/h they would have been on time. How far is it from their house to the airport? 45 km

14. Two cars heading for Montreal on the same route left a service area at the same time. Their average speeds differed by 16 km/h. Four hours later, the faster car reached Montreal, and the other car reached Montreal an hour after that. Find the average speed of each car. 64 km/h; 80 km/h

Biography Elijah McCoy

Elijah McCoy (1844–1929) was an American engineer and inventor. Born in Ontario, Canada, he went to Edinburgh, Scotland, in 1858 to serve as an apprentice to a mechanical engineer. Upon returning to the United States, he took a job on the Michigan Central Railroad. There he received the inspiration for his life's work— the invention and improvement of an automatic lubricator. He took out the first of over fifty patents in 1872 for a "lubricator cup," which allowed oil to drip continuously onto the moving parts of a machine while it was operating. Elijah McCoy's invention saved a great deal of time and work, because previously, machines had to be stopped regularly so that their parts could be lubricated.

The expression "the real McCoy" which is used to indicate that a thing is genuine probably came from buyers who wanted only the quality McCoy lubricator for their machines.

POLYNOMIALS AND PROBLEM SOLVING   **145**

Chalkboard Examples

1. A rectangle is 3 times as long as it is wide. If the length is increased by 4 and the width by 6, the area is increased by 90. What were the original dimensions of the rectangle?
   Step 2 Let x = the width of the rectangle. Then $3x$ = the length.
   Step 3 $(3x + 4)(x + 6) = 3x^2 + 90$
   $3x^2 + 22x + 24 = 3x^2 + 90$
   $22x + 24 = 90$
   $22x = 66$
   $x = 3$
   $\therefore$ The width was equal to 3 and the length was equal to 9.

2. Find the area of a uniform walk which surrounds a circular garden. The diameter of the garden is 10 m and the width of the walk is 2 m.

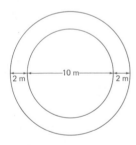

   Area of walk = area of outer circle − area of inner circle = $\pi(5 + 2)^2 - \pi(5)^2 = 24\pi$ m^2

4-10 *Area Problems*

OBJECTIVE To solve some problems involving area.

To solve some problems involving area, you will need to multiply and add or subtract polynomials. Sketches are especially helpful in solving such problems.

The units of square measure that you will use most often are square centimeters (cm^2) and square meters (m^2).

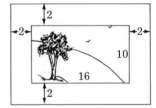

A photograph 10 cm wide and 16 cm long is surrounded by a border 2 cm wide. To find the area of the border, you subtract the areas of the two rectangles.

Area of Border = Area of outer rectangle − Area of inner rectangle
$$= (16 + 4)(10 + 4) - 16 \cdot 10$$
$$= (20)(14) - 160 = 280 - 160 = 120$$

Thus, the area of the border is 120 cm^2.

EXAMPLE

A photograph is twice as long as it is wide. It is mounted so that a border 2 cm wide completely surrounds the photograph. Find the dimensions of the photograph if the area of the border is 136 cm^2.

SOLUTION

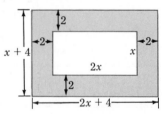

Step 1 The problem asks for the dimensions of the photograph.

Step 2 Let x = width of the photograph. Show the other dimensions in a sketch.

Step 3 Area of border = Area of photograph and border − Area of photograph
$$136 = (2x + 4)(x + 4) - (2x)(x)$$

Step 4
$$136 = 2x^2 + 12x + 16 - 2x^2$$
$$136 = 12x + 16$$
$$120 = 12x$$
$$10 = x$$

Step 5 *Check:* Area of photograph and border = $(2x + 4)(x + 4) = (24)(14) = 336$
Area of photograph = $(2x)(x) = (20)(10) = 200$
Area of Border = $336 - 200 = 136$ $\sqrt{}$

$\therefore$ The dimensions of the photograph are 20 cm and 10 cm. ***Answer***

146   *CHAPTER 4*

Problems

Solve.

A

6 cm by 12 cm

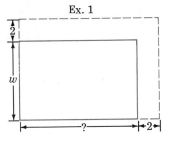

Ex. 1

1. A rectangle is twice as long as it is wide. If its length and width are both increased by 2 cm, the area of the rectangle is increased by 40 cm². Find the dimensions of the original rectangle.

2. A photo is 10 cm longer than it is wide. It is mounted in a frame 3 cm wide. The area of the frame is 156 cm². Find the dimensions of the picture. 5 cm by 15 cm

3. A rectangular pool is 8 m longer than it is wide. A walkway 1 m wide surrounds the pool. Find the dimensions of the pool if the area of the walkway is 100 m². 20 m by 28 m

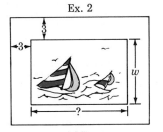

Ex. 2

4. A poster is three times as long as it is wide. It is mounted on a piece of cardboard so that there is a strip 10 cm wide all around the poster. If the area of this bordering strip is 2800 cm², find the dimensions of the poster. 30 cm by 90 cm

B

5. A page of a book is 6 cm longer than it is wide. By increasing the length by 3 cm and the width by 2 cm, the book designer can increase the area of the page by 68 cm². Find the dimensions of the page. 10 cm by 16 cm

6. An instrument is mounted on a rectangular base twice as long as it is wide. A design engineer must reduce the length of the base by 3 cm and the width by 1 cm to fit the instrument into the space available on a space vehicle. This change will reduce the area of the base by 27 cm². Find the original dimensions of the base. 6 cm by 12 cm

7. A circular pool is surrounded by a walkway 2 m wide. Find the radius of the pool if the area of the walkway is 176 m². (*Hint:* The formula for the area of a circle with radius r is $A = \pi r^2$. Use $\frac{22}{7}$ as an approximation for π.) 13 m

8. When the radius of a circular ripple in a pond increases by 4 cm, the area it encloses increases by 352 cm². Find the radius of the ripple after the increase. (See the hint for Exercise 7.) 16 cm

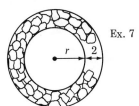

Ex. 7

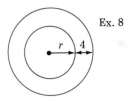

Ex. 8

POLYNOMIALS AND PROBLEM SOLVING **147**

Supplementary Materials

Practice Master 22

Progress Test 13

Suggested Assignments

Minimum
Day 1: 147/*P*: 1–4
Day 2: 147/*P*: 5, 7
   R 148/*Self-Test 3*

Average
Day 1: 147/*P*: 1–3, 5, 7
Day 2: 147/*P*: 6, 8, 9
   R 148/*Self-Test 3*

Maximum
Day 1: 147/*P*: 1–7 odd
Day 2: 147/*P*: 8–10
   R 148/*Self-Test 3*

Extra Practice Problems
   p. 517

Additional A Exercises

Solve.

1. A painting is three times as long as it is wide. It is held in a frame which has a uniform width of 5 cm. Find the dimensions of the painting if the area of the frame is 500 cm². 10 cm by 30 cm

2. A certain rectangular city block is twice as long as it is wide. The sidewalk surrounding it is 3 m wide. Find the area of the city block without the sidewalk if the area of the sidewalk is 2286 m². 31,250 m²

C **9.** Two plastic containers have square bases, but the base of one container is 10 cm longer and wider than that of the other. Both containers are filled with water to a depth of 30 cm. Find the dimensions of the base of each container if the volume of water in the larger container exceeds that in the smaller container by 15,000 cm³ (cubic centimeters). (*Hint:* Use the formula: Volume of a box = length × width × height.) 20 cm by 20 cm; 30 cm by 30 cm

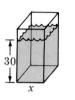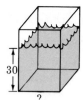

10. One planting box has a rectangular base that is 8 cm longer than it is wide. A larger planter is 2 cm wider and 4 cm longer than the first one. If each is filled to a depth of 10 cm, the larger planter has 840 cm³ more soil than the smaller. What are the dimensions of the base of the smaller planter? (See the hint for Exercise 9.) 10 cm by 18 cm

Self-Test 3

VOCABULARY   uniform motion (p. 142)

1. Copy and complete the chart. Use the fact that Ruth is three years younger than Dan.

Obj. 4-7, p. 134

	Age now	Age in 5 years
Dan	x	?
Ruth	?	?

2. Solve the formula $V = lwh$ for w.

Solve.

3. At a lunch stand, a hamburger costs 85 cents and a slice of pizza costs 65 cents. A family bought twice as many hamburgers as slices of pizza for a total cost of $4.70. How many slices of pizza did the family buy?

Obj. 4-8, p. 140

4. Two planes leave an airport at the same time, one traveling east at 750 km/h and the other traveling west at 850 km/h. In how many hours will they be 3200 km apart?

Obj. 4-9, p. 142

5. The screen of a Model A television set is a rectangle that is 10 cm wider than it is high. Model B has a screen 2 cm wider and 3 cm higher and has 241 cm² more area than the Model A screen. Find the dimensions of the Model A screen.

Obj. 4-10, p. 146

Check your answers with those at the back of the book.

148   *CHAPTER 4*

Quick Quiz

1. Copy and complete the chart. Use the fact that Nina is two years older than John.

	Age now	Age 3 yrs. ago
Nina	x	$x - 3$
John	$x - 2$	$x - 5$

2. Solve the formula $I = Prt$ for t.

$$t = \frac{I}{Pr}$$

3. A collection of coins consists of nickels and quarters only. If the value of the collection is $7.65, and if there are three more nickels than quarters, find the number of each type of coin.   28 nickels, 25 quarters

4. A rectangle is 4 cm longer than it is wide. A second rectangle has the same area, but it is 4 cm longer and 2 cm narrower than the first rectangle. Find the dimensions of each rectangle.
first rectangle, 8 cm by 12 cm; second rectangle, 6 cm by 16 cm

Chapter Summary

1. The expression b^n is an abbreviation for $\underbrace{b \cdot b \cdot b \cdot \ \cdots \ \cdot b.}_{n \text{ factors}}$

   The base is b and the exponent is n.

2. To simplify expressions that contain powers, the steps listed on page 114 are followed.

3. To add (or subtract) polynomials, you add (or subtract) their similar terms. Similar terms have the same variables to the same powers.

4. Rules of Exponents
   $$a^m \cdot a^n = a^{m+n} \qquad (a^m)^n = a^{mn} \qquad (ab)^m = a^m b^m$$

5. Polynomials can be multiplied in a vertical or horizontal form by applying the distributive property (p. 131). Before multiplying, it is wise to rearrange the terms of each polynomial in order of increasing or decreasing degree in one variable.

6. Organizing the facts of a word problem in a chart is often helpful. A three-column chart can be used to solve problems about costs, coins, distances, and areas. The formulas which head these columns are all similar:

   number $\times$ price = Cost
   number $\times$ value per coin = Total value
   rate $\times$ time = Distance
   length $\times$ width = Area

Supplementary Materials
Progress Tests 14, 15

Extra Practice pp. 497–498

Chapter Review

Give the letter of the correct answer.

1. Express the square of $(a + b)$ in exponential form. 4-1

    a. $a + b^2$ **b.** $a^2 + b$ **c.** $a^2 + b^2$ **d.** $(a + b)^2$

2. Find the value of $4xy^2 - 2y^3$ if $x = 3$ and $y = -2$.

    a. 32   **b.** 64   **c.** 112   **d.** -16

3. Simplify $(4x^2 - 2x + 5) + (2x^2 - 2x - 8)$. 4-2

    a. $2x^2 + 13$ **b.** $6x^2 - 3$

    c. $6x^2 - 4x - 3$ **d.** $6x^2 - 4x + 13$

4. Subtract $4a^2 + 7a - 5$ from $3a^2 - 2a - 4$.

    a. $-a^2 - 9a + 1$ **b.** $-a^2 - 9a - 9$

    c. $-a^2 + 5a + 1$ **d.** $7a^2 + 5a - 9$

5. Solve $5x^2 - 3x = (3x^2 - 7x) + (8x - 2 + 2x^2)$.

    a. $x = -2$ **b.** $x = 2$ **c.** $x = -\dfrac{1}{2}$ **d.** $x = \dfrac{1}{2}$

POLYNOMIALS AND PROBLEM SOLVING   149

6. Simplify $\left(-\frac{1}{2}a^3b^2\right)(4ab^4)(-ab^2)$.

a. $2a^4b^8$ b. $-2a^5b^8$ c. $2a^5b^8$ d. $2a^3b^{16}$

7. Simplify $(4x^3y^2)(2y^3) - (-3xy)(x^2y^4)$.

a. $11x^3y^5$ b. $5x^3y^5$ c. $11x^3y^6$ d. $5x^3y^6$

8. Simplify $(-2a^2b^3)^3$.

a. $-6a^6b^9$ b. $-6a^5b^6$ c. $-8a^5b^6$ d. $-8a^6b^9$

9. Simplify $(2n)^3(3n^4)^2$.

a. $72n^{11}$ b. $36n^{11}$ c. $36n^9$ d. $6n^{11}$

10. Find the solution of $21x - 6x(4x - 1) = 9 - (4x)(6x)$.

a. $\frac{1}{2}$ b. $\frac{1}{3}$ c. $\frac{3}{5}$ d. $\frac{2}{3}$

11. Multiply: $(x - 2)(x + 1)$.

a. $x^2 - 2$ b. $x^2 - 2x - 2$ c. $x^2 - x - 2$ d. $2x - 1$

12. Multiply: $(2x - 3y)(x^3 - 4x^2y - 6xy^2)$.

a. $2x^4 - 11x^3y - 18xy^3$ b. $2x^4 - 11x^3y - 24x^2y - 18xy^3$

c. $2x^4 - 11x^3y + 18xy^3$ d. $2x^4 - 11x^3y - 24x^2y + 18xy^3$

13. Kit is x years old and Judy is seven years younger. How old will Judy be in five years?

a. $x + 12$ b. 2 c. $2x - 2$ d. $x - 2$

14. Solve the formula $F = 1.8C + 32$ for C.

a. $C = \frac{F}{1.8} - 32$ b. $C = \frac{F + 32}{1.8}$ c. $C = \frac{F - 32}{1.8}$ d. $C = 1.8(F - 32)$

15. What is the value in cents of q quarters and twice as many dimes?

a. $25q + 20$ b. $27q$ c. $35q$ d. $45q$

16. The Varsity Club bought several oranges at ten cents each. They sold all but two for fifteen cents each at the track meet and made a profit of $1.10. How many oranges did the club buy?

a. 26   b. 28   c. 24   d. 20

17. Cindy bicycles to the beach at 20 km/h and returns by car at 60 km/h. If the car trip is two hours shorter than the bicycle trip, how far did she bicycle?

a. 20 km   b. 40 km   c. 60 km   d. 80 km

18. A photo is twice as long as it is wide. It is mounted in a frame 2 cm wide. If the area of the frame is 112 cm², find the area of the photo.

a. 8 cm²   b. 16 cm²   c. 128 cm²   d. 240 cm²

4-3

4-4

4-5

4-6

4-7

4-8

4-9

4-10

Chapter Test

Alternate Test and Review
pp. T15, T24–T26

1. Write $11 \cdot a \cdot a \cdot b \cdot c \cdot c \cdot c$ in exponential form. $11a^2bc^3$ 4-1

2. Evaluate $2x^3 + y^2$ if $x = -3$ and $y = 4$. -38

Simplify.

3. $(x^3 - 2x^2 + 7) + (4 + 2x - 4x^3)$ $-3x^3 - 2x^2 + 2x + 11$ 4-2

4. $(2a^2 - 3a - 4) - (7a^2 - 5a - 9)$ $-5a^2 + 2a + 5$

Simplify.

5. $(2x^3y)(-3x^2y^3)$ $-6x^5y^4$ **6.** $(4n^4)(5n^5)(6n^6)$ $120n^{15}$ 4-3

7. $(-2k^2)^3$ $-8k^6$ **8.** $(-xy^3)(3x)^2 - (xy)^3$ $-10x^3y^3$ 4-4

9. $(p^3 - 3p^2q - 2q^2)(-4pq)$ **10.** $\dfrac{2}{5}(5a - 10) - 3(4a - b + 1)$ 4-5
       $-4p^4q + 12p^3q^2 + 8pq^3$ $-10a + 3b - 7$

Multiply.

11. $2c^3 - c^2d + 3cd^2$ **12.** $(4a - 5)(7a + a^2 - 2)$ 4-6
       $\dfrac{c \;\; - 2d}{}$ $4a^3 + 23a^2 - 43a + 10$
$2c^4 - 5c^3d - 5c^2d^2 - 6cd^3$

13. Copy and complete the chart.   4-7
       Use the fact that Peg is twice as old as Jon.

	Age now	Age 2 years ago
Jon	x	? $x - 2$
Peg	? $2x$	? $2x - 2$

14. Solve the formula $A = P + Prt$ for r. $r = \dfrac{A - P}{Pt}$

Solve.

15. The cashier's drawer has four more nickels than dimes in it. The   4-8
value of the nickels and dimes together is $2.45. How many dimes
are there? 15 dimes

16. Some campers leave a campsite and paddle a canoe down a river at   4-9
a steady rate of 8 km/h. Three hours later, a motorboat leaves the
campsite and travels down the river at 20 km/h. How long does it
take the motorboat to overtake the canoe? 2 h

17. A pool in the city plaza is 7 m longer than it is wide. A border of   4-10
plants around the pool is 1 m wide. Find the dimensions of the pool
if the area of the border is 58 m². 10 m by 17 m

POLYNOMIALS AND PROBLEM SOLVING   **151**

Cumulative Review (Chapters 1-4)

Simplify each expression.

1. $-\frac{1}{3}(56 - 83)$ 9

2. $10t \div \left(-\frac{1}{2}\right) - 20t$

3. $[-6 - (-8)] \div 4$ $\frac{1}{2}$

4. $8(3 + z) + (-5z)$ 24 + 3z **5.** $-5|-6| + 7$ -23

6. $-4(2x - y + 3z)$

7. $2^3 + 9 \div 3$ 11

8. $(-2j^2k^3)(-3jk^5)$ $6j^3k^8$

9. $(m + 3n) - (5m - 3n)$

10. $(-r^2s)^3(4rs^4)^2$ $-16r^8s^{11}$

11. $(8 - 3b)(-1 + 2b)$
$-6b^2 + 19b - 8$

12. $-5x(x^2 + 7xy - 3y^2)$

Evaluate if $q = 5$, $r = -2$, $s = 1$, $t = -3$, and $u = -0.5$.

13. $u(2q + 3t)$ -0.5

14. $\frac{2t - 9s}{q + r}$ -5

15. $(r - s)^3$ -27

16. $2r^2u$
-4

Solve each equation if $x \in \{-2, -1, 0, 1, 2\}$.

17. $-8 = x - 7$ -1

18. $2(x - 1) = x$ 2

19. $x(3x - 5) = 10 + 3x^2$
-2

Solve. (The equation may be an identity or have no root.)

20. $-9 + z = -2$ 7

21. $y - 3 = |0|$ 3

22. $3 = x + 12$ -9

23. $-80w = 16$ -0.2

24. $-2 = 0.2v$ -10

25. $-52u = 0$ 0

26. $-6t + 4 = t - 3$ 1

27. $4(s + 1) = 2 + 4s$ No root

28. $3(-1 - r) = 9$ -4

29. $2q - 5 = -(5 - 2q)$
Identity

30. $-\frac{1}{4}(4p + 8) = p + 2$ -2

31. $n(7 + n) = n^2 + 7n$
Identity

32. $5(2 - 3m) = -4(4m + 9)$ -46

33. $(2k + 1)(2k - 3) = (4k - 3)(k - 1)$ 2

34. Solve for y: $ax + by = c$. $y = \frac{-a}{b}x + \frac{c}{b}$

Solve.

35. Find three consecutive even integers such that the sum of the least and the greatest is -20. -12, -10, -8

36. Clyde is one fourth as old as his grandfather. Ten years ago, their ages totaled 60. How old is each now? Clyde, 16; grandfather, 64

37. Florence and Trudy started hiking toward each other from opposite Florence, ends of a trail 13.5 km long. Florence's average rate was 4 km/h 6.0 km; and Trudy's was 5 km/h. How far had each hiked when they met? Trudy, 7.5 km

38. One side of a square is increased by 1 cm, and an adjacent side is decreased by 3 cm. The area of the resulting rectangle is 21 cm² less than that of the square. Find the dimensions of the square. 9 cm by 9 cm

Maintaining Skills

Express each fraction in simplest form.

SAMPLE 1 $\dfrac{24}{60}$ *SOLUTION* $\dfrac{24}{60} = \dfrac{2 \times 12}{5 \times 12} = \dfrac{2}{5}$

1. $\dfrac{10}{15}$ $\dfrac{2}{3}$ 2. $\dfrac{7}{56}$ $\dfrac{1}{8}$ 3. $\dfrac{18}{49}$ $\dfrac{18}{49}$ 4. $\dfrac{42}{90}$ $\dfrac{7}{15}$ 5. $\dfrac{57}{76}$ $\dfrac{3}{4}$ 6. $\dfrac{24}{54}$ $\dfrac{4}{9}$

Express each answer in simplest form.

SAMPLE 2 $\dfrac{7}{16} - \dfrac{3}{16}$ *SOLUTION* $\dfrac{7}{16} - \dfrac{3}{16} = \dfrac{7-3}{16} = \dfrac{4}{16} = \dfrac{1}{4}$

7. $\dfrac{1}{9} + \dfrac{2}{9}$ $\dfrac{1}{3}$ 8. $\dfrac{5}{18} + \dfrac{11}{18}$ $\dfrac{8}{9}$ 9. $\dfrac{11}{15} + \dfrac{2}{15}$ $\dfrac{13}{15}$ 10. $\dfrac{17}{22} + \dfrac{5}{22}$ 1

11. $\dfrac{7}{8} - \dfrac{3}{8}$ $\dfrac{1}{2}$ 12. $\dfrac{17}{20} - \dfrac{9}{20}$ $\dfrac{2}{5}$ 13. $\dfrac{22}{27} - \dfrac{7}{27}$ $\dfrac{5}{9}$ 14. $\dfrac{27}{28} - \dfrac{3}{28}$ $\dfrac{6}{7}$

SAMPLE 3 $\dfrac{7}{12} + \dfrac{9}{10}$ *SOLUTION* The least common denominator is 60.

$$\dfrac{7}{12} \times \dfrac{5}{5} + \dfrac{9}{10} \times \dfrac{6}{6} = \dfrac{35}{60} + \dfrac{54}{60} = \dfrac{89}{60}$$

15. $\dfrac{1}{4} + \dfrac{7}{12}$ $\dfrac{5}{6}$ 16. $\dfrac{3}{5} + \dfrac{2}{9}$ $\dfrac{37}{45}$ 17. $\dfrac{3}{10} + \dfrac{7}{8}$ $\dfrac{47}{40}$ 18. $\dfrac{11}{16} + \dfrac{5}{12}$ $\dfrac{53}{48}$

19. $\dfrac{20}{27} - \dfrac{3}{7}$ $\dfrac{59}{189}$ 20. $\dfrac{13}{14} - \dfrac{8}{21}$ $\dfrac{23}{42}$ 21. $\dfrac{19}{24} - \dfrac{1}{6}$ $\dfrac{5}{8}$ 22. $\dfrac{2}{3} - \dfrac{7}{15}$ $\dfrac{1}{5}$

SAMPLE 4 $\dfrac{8}{9} \times \dfrac{5}{12}$ *SOLUTION* $\dfrac{8}{9} \times \dfrac{5}{12} = \dfrac{\overset{2}{\cancel{8}} \times 5}{9 \times \underset{3}{\cancel{12}}} = \dfrac{10}{27}$

23. $\dfrac{6}{11} \times \dfrac{1}{2}$ $\dfrac{3}{11}$ 24. $\dfrac{5}{28} \times \dfrac{24}{25}$ $\dfrac{6}{35}$ 25. $\dfrac{3}{17} \times \dfrac{7}{10}$ $\dfrac{21}{170}$ 26. $9 \times \dfrac{2}{3}$ 6

27. $\dfrac{7}{12} \times \dfrac{27}{35}$ $\dfrac{9}{20}$ 28. $\dfrac{3}{26} \times \dfrac{12}{13}$ $\dfrac{18}{169}$ 29. $\dfrac{5}{21} \times 3$ $\dfrac{5}{7}$ 30. $\dfrac{2}{15} \times \dfrac{5}{18}$ $\dfrac{1}{27}$

SAMPLE 5 $\dfrac{2}{3} \div \dfrac{8}{15}$ *SOLUTION* $\dfrac{2}{3} \div \dfrac{8}{15} = \dfrac{2}{3} \times \dfrac{15}{8} = \dfrac{\overset{1}{\cancel{2}} \times \overset{5}{\cancel{15}}}{\underset{1}{\cancel{3}} \times \underset{4}{\cancel{8}}} = \dfrac{5}{4}$

31. $\dfrac{13}{16} \div \dfrac{11}{12}$ $\dfrac{39}{44}$ 32. $\dfrac{7}{8} \div \dfrac{5}{2}$ $\dfrac{7}{20}$ 33. $15 \div \dfrac{5}{21}$ 63 34. $\dfrac{5}{9} \div \dfrac{10}{3}$ $\dfrac{1}{6}$

35. $\dfrac{9}{20} \div \dfrac{3}{4}$ $\dfrac{3}{5}$ 36. $\dfrac{8}{15} \div 4$ $\dfrac{2}{15}$ 37. $\dfrac{10}{21} \div \dfrac{24}{35}$ $\dfrac{25}{36}$ 38. $\dfrac{18}{25} \div \dfrac{16}{45}$ $\dfrac{81}{40}$

About the Photo

Regardless of the twists, turns, and other gyrations of a leaping mammal, it, or more precisely its center of gravity, moves along a parabola. The center of gravity of an object is the point in the object where one may assume its entire mass is concentrated.

Your students may be interested in how long a particular dolphin remains in the air during a jump. Surprisingly, the time span depends only on the height of the jump, and not on the horizontal distance. This time can be measured using Galileo's laws governing free falling bodies.

Assume that a particular dolphin's center of gravity reaches a maximum height of 4.9 m during the jump. If it leaves the water at time $t = 0$, the equation describing the height s of the dolphin's center of gravity at time t is $s = -4.9t^2 + 9.8t$. By setting $s = 0$, the duration of the jump can be found by factoring the resulting quadratic equation and solving for t.

The height above water of each dolphin at a given time (t) *is given by an expression in the form* at² + bt + c.

154

5

FACTORING POLYNOMIALS

Teaching References

Lesson Commentary,
pp. T78–T84

Assignment Guide,
pp. T52–T54

Supplementary Materials
Practice Masters 23–33
Progress Tests 16–19
Computer Activities
13 *Factors of* N
14 *Odd Numbers and
Squares*
15 *Factoring* X² + BX + C
Extra Practice, pp. 498–500,
517
Alternate Test, p. T16

Teaching Suggestions p. T78

Suggested Extensions p. T79

QUOTIENTS AND FACTORING

5-1 *Factoring Integers*

OBJECTIVE   To factor integers.

When you write

$$48 = 6 \cdot 8 \quad \text{or} \quad 48 = (2)(24),$$

you have *factored* 48. In the first case the factors are 6 and 8; in the second case they are 2 and 24. You could also write $48 = \left(\frac{1}{2}\right)(96)$ and call $\frac{1}{2}$ and 96 factors of 48. Usually, however, you are interested only in factors drawn from a specified set. The given number is then said to be **factored** over the given set, called the **factor set.** In this text *integers will be factored over the set of integers* unless some other set is specified. Such factors are called *integral* factors.

You can find factors by dividing. If the remainder is zero, the divisor is a factor. For example, -4 is a factor of 108 because $108 \div (-4) = -27$, but 8 is not a factor of 108 because $108 \div 8 = 13$ R4.

You can find the *positive factors* of a positive integer by dividing it by the positive integers in succession until a previous factor is repeated. Thus:

$$48 = (1)(48) = (2)(24) = (3)(16) = (4)(12) = (6)(8)$$

A set of numbers useful in factoring is the set of *prime numbers* or *primes*. A **prime number,** or **prime,** is an integer greater than 1 that has no positive integral factor other than itself and 1. The first prime numbers are

$$2, 3, 5, 7, 11, 13, 17, 19, 23, 29, \ldots.$$

Chalkboard Examples

1. Name the positive factors of 36.
1, 2, 3, 4, 6, 9, 12, 18, 36

Find the prime factorization of each number.

2. 54 $2 \cdot 3^3$

3. 31   31

4. 240 $2^4 \cdot 3 \cdot 5$

Find the GCF of each pair of numbers.

5. 92, 48   4

6. 30, 75   15

7. 72, 56   8

8. 240, 539   1

155

Computer Activity 13
Factors of N

Determining the positive factors of a number can be a long and tedious process. The computer program of this activity uses the INT function to compute systematically all positive factors of any given number. Students are asked to look for generalizations about numbers and their factors based upon the computer printouts.

Suggested Assignments

Minimum
    157/1–10, 11–45 odd

Average
    157/1–45 odd

Maximum
    157/1–45 odd

Additional A Exercises

Give all the positive factors of each number.

1. 6   1, 2, 3, 6

2. 14   1, 2, 7, 14

3. 45   1, 3, 5, 9, 15, 45

Give the prime factorization of each number.

4. 35 $5 \cdot 7$

5. 120 $2^3 \cdot 3 \cdot 5$

Find the GCF of each pair of numbers.

6. 16 and 24   8

7. 11 and 22   11

A systematic way to find the prime factors of positive integers is to try the primes, in order, as divisors. You divide by each prime as many times as possible before going on to the next. This technique is illustrated at the right. The final result is

$$588 = 2 \cdot 294$$
$$= 2 \cdot 2 \cdot 147$$
$$= 2 \cdot 2 \cdot 3 \cdot 49$$
$$= 2 \cdot 2 \cdot 3 \cdot 7 \cdot 7$$
$$= 2^2 \cdot 3 \cdot 7^2$$

$$588 = 2^2 \cdot 3 \cdot 7^2.$$

The expression of a positive integer as a product of prime factors is called the **prime factorization** of the integer.

It can be proved by advanced methods that the prime factorization of an integer is *unique* (one and only one) except for the order in which the factors may be written. (If 1 were to be considered a prime factor, the factorization would not be unique because 1 could be considered to be a factor any number of times.)

A factor of two or more integers is called a *common factor* of the integers. The greatest integer which is a factor of two or more integers is called the **greatest common factor** (GCF) of the integers.

The following example shows how you can use prime factorization to find the greatest common factor of two integers.

EXAMPLE   Find the GCF of 504 and 945.

SOLUTION   First find the prime factorizations of each integer. Then form the product of the smaller powers of each common prime factor.

$$504 = 2^3 \cdot 3^2 \cdot 7 \qquad 945 = 3^3 \cdot 5 \cdot 7$$

smaller power: 3^2 smaller power: 7

The greatest common factor of 504 and 945 is $3^2 \cdot 7$, or 63.   *Answer*

Oral Exercises

Give all the positive factors of each number.

1. 12	**2.** 40	**3.** 75	**4.** 83	**5.** 51
1, 2, 3, 4, 6, 12	1, 2, 4, 5, 8, 10, 20, 40	1, 3, 5, 15, 25, 75	1, 83	1, 3, 17, 51

State whether or not each number is a prime.

6. 7 Yes	**7.** 15 No	**8.** 31 Yes	**9.** 81 No	**10.** 91 No

Give the prime factorization of each number.

11. 12 $2^2 \cdot 3$	**12.** 40 $2^3 \cdot 5$	**13.** 1000 $2^3 \cdot 5^3$	**14.** 68 $2^2 \cdot 17$	**15.** 300 $2^2 \cdot 3 \cdot 5^2$

Find the GCF of each pair of numbers.

16. 12 and 18 6	**17.** 30 and 55 5	**18.** 27 and 45 9	**19.** 3 and 13 1

156   *CHAPTER 5*

Written Exercises

List all of the positive factors of each number.

1. 18 1, 2, 3, 6, 9, 18

2. 30 1, 2, 3, 5, 6, 10, 15, 30

3. 37 1, 37

4. 63 1, 3, 7, 9, 21, 63

5. 64 1, 2, 4, 8, 16, 32, 64

6. 49 1, 7, 49

7. 101 1, 101

8. 15 1, 3, 5, 15

9. 23 1, 23

10. 65 1, 5, 13, 65

11–20. Write all the pairs of positive and negative factors of the integers in Exercises 1–10.

SAMPLE 20

SOLUTION $(1)(20), (2)(10), (4)(5), (-1)(-20), (-2)(-10), (-4)(-5)$

21–30. Write all the pairs of positive and negative factors of the opposites of the integers in Exercises 1–10.

Give the prime factorization of each number.

B **31.** 34 $2 \cdot 17$ **32.** 45 $3^2 \cdot 5$ **33.** 63 $3^2 \cdot 7$ **34.** 104 $2^3 \cdot 13$ **35.** 128 2^7

36. 250 $2 \cdot 5^3$ **37.** 476 $2^2 \cdot 7 \cdot 17$ **38.** 539 $7^2 \cdot 11$ **39.** 408 $2^3 \cdot 3 \cdot 17$ **40.** 576 $2^6 \cdot 3^2$

Give the GCF of each group of numbers.

41. 18, 24 6

42. 15, 21 3

43. 12, 24, 30 6

44. 36, 54, 81 9

45. 21, 35, 48 1

46. 144, 180 36

Calculator Key-In _____

You can use the calculator to evaluate a polynomial for a given value of the variable. One way is to evaluate the polynomial term by term using the calculator's memory to store the partial sums.

Another way is to express the polynomial in a form that suggests a sequence of steps on the calculator. For example, to evaluate $3x^2 - 4x + 5$, you could first rewrite it as follows:

$$3x^2 - 4x + 5 = (3x - 4)x + 5$$

To evaluate the polynomial for a particular value, you can just work through the rewritten expression from left to right substituting the appropriate value for x.

Evaluate the polynomial for the given value of the variable.

1. $4x^2 + 3x - 8$; 2 14

2. $6z^2 - 3z - 5$; 4 79

3. $2x^2 + 5x + 9$; -3 12

4. $y^2 - 2y - 3$; 1.5 -3.75

5. $15k^2 - 35k + 90$; 10 1240

6. $40v^2 - 20v + 80$; 17 11,300

7. $14x^2 - 15x - 5$; -8 1011

8. $4y^2 + 4y - 5$; 0.4 -2.76

9. $10z^2 - 5z + 5$; -0.5 10

FACTORING POLYNOMIALS **157**

157

5-2 *Dividing Monomials*

OBJECTIVE   **To divide and factor monomials.**

There are three basic rules that are used to simplify fractions and quotients of monomials. The property of quotients (see Exercise 45 on page 161) enables you to express a fraction as a product.

PROPERTY OF QUOTIENTS

If c, d, x, and y are any real numbers, $d \neq 0$, and $y \neq 0$, then

$$\frac{cx}{dy} = \frac{c}{d} \cdot \frac{x}{y}.$$

EXAMPLE 1 $\dfrac{35}{48} = \dfrac{5 \cdot 7}{6 \cdot 8} = \dfrac{5}{6} \cdot \dfrac{7}{8}$

If you let $d = c$ in the quotient rule, you derive the cancellation rule stated below (see Exercise 46 on page 161).

CANCELLATION RULE FOR FRACTIONS

If c, x, and y are any real numbers, $c \neq 0$, and $y \neq 0$, then

$$\frac{cx}{cy} = \frac{x}{y}.$$

The cancellation rule enables you to divide the numerator and denominator of a fraction by the same nonzero number. In the following examples, assume that no denominator equals 0.

EXAMPLE 2 $\dfrac{4ab}{12a} = \dfrac{4a \cdot b}{4a \cdot 3} = \dfrac{b}{3}$ $\left\{\begin{array}{l}\text{The red marks indicate that both the numerator} \\ \text{and denominator are divided by } 4a.\end{array}\right.$

The cancellation rule can be used to simplify a quotient of two powers of the same number.

EXAMPLE 3 $\dfrac{x^7}{x^3} = \dfrac{x^3 \cdot x^4}{x^3} = x^4$ **EXAMPLE 4** $\dfrac{y^2}{y^8} = \dfrac{y^2}{y^2 \cdot y^6} = \dfrac{1}{y^6}$

The previous examples illustrate the rule of exponents for division shown at the top of the next page.

158   *CHAPTER 5*

In short, the rule above says that when you divide powers you subtract exponents. You have already seen that when you multiply powers you add exponents.

A quotient of monomials is said to be *simplified* when each base appears only once, when there are no powers of powers, and when all fractions have been expressed in simplest form. Examples 5 and 6 show that all three rules presented in this section may be needed to simplify quotients of monomials. In them assume that no variable equals 0. Notice how each rule is used in the examples.

EXAMPLE 5 $\quad \dfrac{8a^3}{-2a^4} = \dfrac{8}{-2} \cdot \dfrac{a^3}{a^4} = -4 \cdot \dfrac{1}{a} = -\dfrac{4}{a}$

EXAMPLE 6 $\quad \dfrac{24x^9y}{16x^3y^8} = \dfrac{24}{16} \cdot \dfrac{x^9}{x^3} \cdot \dfrac{y}{y^8} = \dfrac{3}{2} \cdot x^6 \cdot \dfrac{1}{y^7} = \dfrac{3x^6}{2y^7}$

The **greatest monomial factor** of two monomials is defined to be the common factor which has the greatest coefficient and the greatest degree in each variable. Example 7 shows how to find the greatest monomial factor of two monomials.

EXAMPLE 7 Find the greatest monomial factor of $24x^5yz$ and $32x^3y^8$.

SOLUTION Form the product of the GCF of the numerical coefficients and the smaller power of each variable that appears in both monomials.

GCF of 24 and 32: 8   Smaller power of x: x^3 Smaller power of y: y

The greatest monomial factor of $24x^5yz$ and $32x^3y^8$ is $8x^3y$.   *Answer*

Oral Exercises

Simplify each expression, assuming that no denominator equals 0.

1. $\dfrac{3x}{x}$ 3

2. $\dfrac{8a^2}{2a}$ 4a

3. $\dfrac{5b}{10}$ $\dfrac{b}{2}$

4. $\dfrac{3c^2}{c}$ 3c

5. $\dfrac{-4x^2}{-8x^3}{2x}$ $\dfrac{-4x^2-8x^3}{2x}$

6. $\dfrac{3^{10}}{3^8}$ 9

7. $\dfrac{a^8}{a^3}$ a^5

8. $\dfrac{-b^7}{b^9}$ $\dfrac{-1}{b^2}$

9. $\dfrac{(st)^7}{(st)^5}$ $(st)^2$ or s^2t^2

10. $\dfrac{a^{12}b^{15}}{a^{10}b^{20}}$ $\dfrac{a^2}{b^5}$

FACTORING POLYNOMIALS   **159**

Suggested Assignments

Minimum
   160/1–43 odd
Average
   160/1–45 odd
Maximum
   160/1–45 odd

Additional A Exercises

Simplify each expression, assuming no variable equals 0.

1. $\dfrac{6x}{2x}$ 3

2. $\dfrac{y^9}{y^5}$ y^4

3. $\dfrac{2^3}{2^4}$ $\frac{1}{2}$

4. $(2a^2b)^3$ $8a^6b^3$

5. $\dfrac{(xy)^2}{3x}$ $\dfrac{xy^2}{3}$

6. $\dfrac{-4a^3}{-2a^2}$ $2a$

Simplify each expression, assuming that no denominator equals 0.

11. $(3xy^2)^2$ $9x^2y^4$ 12. $(a^2b)^4$ a^8b^4 13. $(-2a^2)^3$ $-8a^6$ 14. $(-a^2x)^4$ a^8x^4 15. $(3x^2k^4)^3$ $27x^6k^{12}$

16. $\dfrac{4.8 \times 10^5}{2.4 \times 10^2}$ 2000   17. $\dfrac{6x^{12}y^2}{2x^8y}$ $3x^4y$ 18. $\dfrac{9r^3s}{3rs^3}$ $\dfrac{3r^2}{s^2}$ 19. $\dfrac{-3uv^2}{6uv}$ $-\frac{1}{2}v$ 20. $\dfrac{-12c^{12}}{-4c^4}$ $\frac{3c^8}$

Find the greatest monomial factor of the given monomials.

21. $8x$; $2xy$ $2x$

22. $3a^2$; $6a$ $3a$

23. $5x^2y$; $10xy^2$ $5xy$

24. $12u^3v^2$; $5uv^3$ uv^2

25. $14s^5t^2$; $21s^3t^3$ $7s^3t^2$

26. $35x^2y^4$; $15x^3y^5$ $5x^2y^4$

Written Exercises

Simplify each expression, assuming that no variable equals 0.

A 1. $\dfrac{a^7}{a^2}$ a^5 2. $\dfrac{b^{12}}{b^5}$ b^7 3. $\dfrac{-c^{14}}{c^{10}}$ $-c^4$ 4. $\dfrac{d^3}{d^9}$ $\frac{1}{d^6}$

5. $\dfrac{9a^4}{3a}$ $3a^3$ 6. $\dfrac{-18r^3t}{12rt^5}$ $\frac{-3r^2}{2t^4}$ 7. $\dfrac{-8xy}{-24xy^3}$ $\frac{1}{3y^2}$ 8. $\dfrac{13a^4b^9}{26a^2b^2}$ $\dfrac{a^2b^7}{2}$

9. $\dfrac{6(xy)^5}{8(xy)^3}$ $\frac{3x^2y^2}{4}$ 10. $\dfrac{-36u^5v^4}{27uv^6}$ $\frac{-4u^4}{3v^2}$ 11. $\dfrac{-16a^5b^3}{-24a^5b^7}$ $\frac{2}{3b^4}$ 12. $\dfrac{14x^2yz^3}{35xy^3z}$ $\dfrac{2xz^2}{5y^2}$

13. $\dfrac{(x^2)^4}{(x^3)^3}$ $\frac{1}{x}$ 14. $\dfrac{(3a)^3}{3a^3}$ 9   15. $\dfrac{(3y)^2}{(3y)^3}$ $\frac{1}{3y}$ 16. $\dfrac{5k^3}{(5k)^3}$ $\frac{1}{25}$

17. $\dfrac{(2x)^4}{2x^4}$ 8   18. $\dfrac{(-x)^8}{-x^6}$ $-x^2$ 19. $\dfrac{(-2y)^3}{(y^2)^3}$ $\frac{-8}{y^3}$ 20. $\dfrac{(a^5)^3}{(a^4)^4}$ $\frac{1}{a}$

21. $\dfrac{(4ab^2)^3}{(2a^2b)^4}$ $\frac{4b^2}{a^5}$ 22. $\dfrac{(3a^5)(2a^4)}{(6a^3)^2}$ $\frac{a^3}{6}$ 23. $\dfrac{(13c^4d)^2}{(13cd^2)^3}$ $\frac{c^5}{13d^4}$ 24. $\dfrac{-(8x^2y)^4}{(8x^2y)^5}$ $\frac{-1}{8x^2y}$

Find the missing factor.

SAMPLE $36a^5b^8 = (12a^3b^2)(\underline{\ ?\ })$

SOLUTION $\dfrac{36a^5b^8}{12a^3b^2} = 3a^2b^6$ **Answer**

25. $9a^5 = (3a)(\underline{\ ?\ })$ $3a^4$

26. $12a^2b = (3a)(\underline{\ ?\ })$ $4ab$

27. $-4c^3d^3 = (2cd^2)(\underline{\ ?\ })$ $-2c^2d$

28. $35u^5v^6 = (7uv)(\underline{\ ?\ })$ $5u^4v^5$

29. $24x^6y^4 = (-3x^2y^2)(\underline{\ ?\ })$ $-8x^4y^2$

30. $-18x^3y^5 = (-9x^2y)(\underline{\ ?\ })$ $2xy^4$

31. $98a^7b^4 = (\underline{\ ?\ })(14a^7b)$ $7b^3$

32. $156k^3z^5n = (-13k^2z)(\underline{\ ?\ })$ $-12kz^3n$

B 33. $(a^2b)^6 = (a^2b)^4(\underline{\ ?\ })$ $(a^2b)^2$

34. $(3xy)^5 = (3xy)^4(\underline{\ ?\ })$ $3xy$

35. $144x^6y^3 = (-12xy)^2(\underline{\ ?\ })$ x^4y

36. $42x^4y^5 = (3x^2y)(2xy)(\underline{\ ?\ })$ $7xy^3$

37. $36a^8b^5 = (6ab^2)(3a^4b)(\underline{\ ?\ })$ $2a^3b^2$

38. $72x^5y^8 = (3xy^2)^2(2y^3)(\underline{\ ?\ })$ $4x^3y$

Find the greatest monomial factor of the given monomials.

39. $5x^3$; $15x$ $5x$

40. $18k^2n$; $27kn$ $9kn$

41. $2rs^2t^3$; $5r^3s^3t^2$ rs^2t^2

42. $24x^2y$; $36xz^3$ $12x$

43. $25ab^2$; $15ab^2$; $36a^2b^2$ ab^2

44. $21m^3n^2$; $14m^2n^3$; $35m^4n$ $7m^2n$

Give a reason for each step in the proofs of the property of quotients and the cancellation rule for fractions. Assume that $c, d, x,$ and y are real numbers, $c \neq 0, d \neq 0,$ and $y \neq 0$. Once you prove the property of quotients, you may use it in the proof of the cancellation rule.

C 45. Property of Quotients: $\dfrac{cx}{dy} = \dfrac{c}{d} \cdot \dfrac{x}{y}$ 46. Cancellation Rule for Fractions: $\dfrac{cx}{cy} = \dfrac{x}{y}$

$\dfrac{cx}{dy} = cx\left(\dfrac{1}{dy}\right)$ (1) _?_

$= cx\left(\dfrac{1}{d} \cdot \dfrac{1}{y}\right)$ (2) _?_

$= \left(c \cdot \dfrac{1}{d}\right)\left(x \cdot \dfrac{1}{y}\right)$ (3) _?_ ; _?_

$= \dfrac{c}{d} \cdot \dfrac{x}{y}$ (4) _?_

$\dfrac{cx}{cy} = \dfrac{c}{c} \cdot \dfrac{x}{y}$ (1) _?_ Prop. of quotients

$= 1 \cdot \dfrac{x}{y}$ (2) _?_ Ax. of reciprocals

$= \dfrac{x}{y}$ (3) _?_ Ident. ax. for mult.

45. (1) Rule for division
(2) Prop. of the recip. of a product
(3) Comm. ax. for mult.;
    Assoc. ax. for mult.
(4) Rule for division

Computer Key-In _____

If you have access to a computer that will accept BASIC, you can use it to test or to find factors of integers.

You need to know that INT(N) will give the greatest integer less than or equal to N. Thus:

$$\text{INT}(4) = 4, \quad \text{INT}(4.9) = 4, \quad \text{INT}(-6.3) = -7$$

This function may then be used to find factors as follows:

(a) To test whether 5 is a factor of 12, you divide:

$$12/5 = 2.4$$

Let Q = 2.4. Then INT(2.4) = 2, and so Q $\neq$ INT(Q).

(b) To test whether 6 is a factor of 12, you divide:

$$12/6 = 2$$

Here Q = 2; INT(2) = 2, and so Q is equal to INT(Q).

To print whole-number factors of a whole number, use this program:

```
10  PRINT "WHAT IS YOUR WHOLE NUMBER";
20  INPUT W
30  FOR F=1 TO W/2
40  LET Q=W/F
50  IF Q <> INT(Q) THEN 70
60  PRINT F;" AND";Q;" ARE FACTORS OF";W;"."
70  NEXT F
80  END
```

Chalkboard Examples

Divide. Assume that the divisors are not zero.

1. $\dfrac{6x^2 + 4x}{2x}$ $3x + 2$

2. $\dfrac{4y^2 - 2yz + 8}{2y}$

$2y - z + \dfrac{4}{y}$

3. $\dfrac{a^2b + ab^2 + ab}{ab}$

$a + b + 1$

Find the greatest monomial factor. Then state each expression in factored form.

4. $3x^2 + 15y^2$
   $3;\ 3(x^2 + 5y^2)$

5. $35x^2 - 30x^3 + 10x^4$
   $5x^2;\ 5x^2(7 - 6x + 2x^2)$

6. $8a^2b - 12ab^2$
   $4ab;\ 4ab(2a - 3b)$

Supplementary Material

Practice Master 24

5-3 *Monomial Factors of Polynomials*

OBJECTIVE   To divide a polynomial by a monomial and to find a monomial factor of a polynomial.

The following result was proved earlier (see page 91) when a, b, and c are real numbers and $c \neq 0$:

$$\frac{a + b}{c} = \frac{a}{c} + \frac{b}{c}$$

This result is also true when a, b, and c are monomials and $c \neq 0$. It suggests a technique for dividing a polynomial by a monomial. To divide a polynomial by a monomial, divide each term of the polynomial by the monomial, and then add the quotients.

The examples below illustrate this technique. In them assume that no variable equals 0.

EXAMPLE 1 $\dfrac{3x^4 + 6x^3y - 9x^2y^2}{3x^2}$

SOLUTION $\dfrac{3x^4 + 6x^3y - 9x^2y^2}{3x^2} = \dfrac{3x^4}{3x^2} + \dfrac{6x^3y}{3x^2} - \dfrac{9x^2y^2}{3x^2} = x^2 + 2xy - 3y^2$

EXAMPLE 2 $\dfrac{x^2y^2 + x - y}{xy}$

SOLUTION $\dfrac{x^2y^2 + x - y}{xy} = \dfrac{x^2y^2}{xy} + \dfrac{x}{xy} - \dfrac{y}{xy} = xy + \dfrac{1}{y} - \dfrac{1}{x}$

One polynomial is said to be **evenly divisible,** or simply **divisible,** by another polynomial if the quotient is also a polynomial. Example 1 shows that $3x^4 + 6x^3y - 9x^2y^2$ is evenly divisible by $3x^2$; Example 2 shows that $x^2y^2 + x - y$ is not evenly divisible by xy.

You factor a polynomial by expressing it as a product of other polynomials. Unless otherwise stated, the *factor set for a polynomial having integral coefficients is the set of all polynomials having integral coefficients.*

You can use division to test for factors of a polynomial. Example 1 shows that you can factor $3x^4 + 6x^3y - 9x^2y^2$ as $3x^2(x^2 + 2xy - 3y^2)$. Notice that 3 and x^2 are also factors of $3x^4 + 6x^3y - 9x^2y^2$. In general, you factor the greatest monomial factor from a polynomial. The **greatest monomial factor of a polynomial** is the greatest monomial factor of its terms. Notice the factoring in Examples 3 and 4.

EXAMPLE 3   Factor $4a^2b - 6ab^2$.

SOLUTION   1. The greatest monomial factor of $4a^2b - 6ab^2$ is $2ab$.
   2. Divide $4a^2b - 6ab^2$ by $2ab$ to get $2a - 3b$.
   3. $4a^2b - 6ab^2 = 2ab(2a - 3b)$ ***Answer***

162   CHAPTER 5

EXAMPLE 4   Factor $12x^3 - 18x^2 + 6x$.

SOLUTION   1. The greatest monomial factor of $12x^3 - 18x^2 + 6x$ is $6x$.
2. Divide $12x^3 - 18x^2 + 6x$ by $6x$ to get $2x^2 - 3x + 1$.
3. $12x^3 - 18x^2 + 6x = 6x(2x^2 - 3x + 1)$ **Answer**

Oral Exercises

Divide. Assume that no denominator is zero.

1. $\dfrac{6a + 12}{6}$ $a + 2$

2. $\dfrac{9x - 6y}{3}$ $3x - 2y$

3. $\dfrac{6c - 18}{6}$ $c - 3$

4. $\dfrac{33ab - 22b}{11b}$ $3a - 2$

5. $\dfrac{27a - 18b + 9c}{9}$ $3a - 2b + c$

6. $\dfrac{4a^3 - 10a^2 + 6a}{2a}$ $2a^2 - 5a + 3$

7. $\dfrac{6x^2y - 4xy^2}{2xy}$ $3x - 2y$

8. $\dfrac{9a^3b - 12ab^4}{3ab}$ $3a^2 - 4b^3$

Factor each polynomial as a product of its greatest monomial factor and another polynomial.

9. $9ab - 6$
$3(3ab - 2)$

10. $8a^2 - 4a$
$4a(2a - 1)$

11. $16xy - 12yz$
$4y(4x - 3z)$

12. $14ab - 21bc$
$7b(2a - 3c)$

Written Exercises

Divide. Assume that no denominator is zero.

A

1. $\dfrac{3a + 6}{3}$ $a + 2$

2. $\dfrac{18a - 12}{6}$ $3a - 2$

3. $\dfrac{6x - 3}{30x - 15}$ $\dfrac{1}{5}$

4. $\dfrac{9a + 6b + 3}{3}$ $3a + 2b + 1$

5. $\dfrac{4x - 8y + 12}{4}$ $x - 2y + 3$

6. $\dfrac{x^3 + 4x^2 + x}{x}$

7. $\dfrac{10xy - 15x^2}{5x}$ $2y - 3x$

8. $\dfrac{6a - 12a^2 - 18a^3}{6a}$ $1 - 2a - 3a^2$

9. $\dfrac{14y - 21y^2 - 7y^3}{7y}$

10. $\dfrac{9a^2b - 6ab^2}{3ab}$ $3a - 2b$

11. $\dfrac{24cd^3 - 18c^2d - 12c}{-6c}$ $-4d^3 + 3cd + 2$

12. $\dfrac{25x^4y^3 - 15x^2y^5}{5xy}$

13. $\dfrac{42s^4t^4 - 35st^2}{7st^2}$ $6s^3t^2 - 5$

14. $\dfrac{8yz^2 - 24y^3z - 32yz}{-8yz}$ $-z + 3y^2 + 4$

15. $\dfrac{45d^4k^2 - 75d^3k + 30d^4}{15d^2}$
$3d^2k^2 - 5dk + 2d^2$

16. $\dfrac{32k^4z^2 - 96k^2z^4 - 48k^6z^2}{16k^2z^2}$ $2k^2 - 6z^2 - 3k^4$

Evaluate by factoring.

SAMPLE $4 \times 21 + 4 \times 79 = 4(21 + 79) = 4(100) = 400$

17. $3 \times 78 + 7 \times 78$ 780

18. $28 \times 43 - 18 \times 43$ 430

19. $13 \times 19 + 4 \times 19 + 3 \times 19$ 380

20. $9 \times 11^2 - 9 \times 11$ 990

21. $81^2 + 81 \times 19$ 8100

22. $(18)^2 - 4 \times 9$ 288

23. $32 \times 17 + 17^2 + 17$ 850

24. $216 + 2 \times 36 + 5 \times 6$ 318

25. $22 \times 14 \times 25 - 11 \times 21 \times 30$ 770

FACTORING POLYNOMIALS   **163**

Suggested Assignments

Minimum
Day 1: 163/1–25 odd
  S 160/42, 44
Day 2: 164/27–43 odd,
    P: 1, 3
  S 130/10, 12

Average
Day 1: 163/1–43 odd
Day 2: 164/45, 47, 49,
    P: 1–7 odd
  S 130/10, 12

Maximum
Day 1: 163/1–49 odd
  S 160/38, 44
Day 2: 164/P: 1–8
  R 165/Self-Test 1

Additional A Exercises

Divide. Assume that no denominator is zero.

1. $\dfrac{10x + 15}{5}$ $2x + 3$

2. $\dfrac{28y - 14}{7}$ $4y - 2$

3. $\dfrac{8x^2 - 4x^3}{2x^2}$ $4 - 2x$

Factor each polynomial as a product of its greatest monomial factor and another polynomial.

4. $8y^2 - 6y$ $2y(4y - 3)$

5. $9b^3 - 6b^2 + 3b$
$3b(3b^2 - 2b + 1)$

6. $10a - 5a^2$ $5a(2 - a)$

**Additional Answers
Written Exercises**

6. $x^2 + 4x + 1$

9. $2 - 3y - y^2$

12. $5x^3y^2 - 3xy^4$

Factor each polynomial as the product of its greatest monomial factor and another polynomial.

26. $6x + 12y$ $6(x + 2y)$ **27.** $14a - 12b$ $2(7a - 6b)$

28. $3(3p - 2q + 1)$
31. $6x(x + 2)$
28. $9p - 6q + 3$

29. $4x - 8y + 16$ $4(x - 2y + 4)$ **30.** $15a^2 - 9a$ $3a(5a - 3)$ **31.** $6x^2 + 12x$

32. $4a^3 + 8a^2$ $4a^2(a + 2)$ **33.** $12x^3 - 6x^2 + 24x$

34. $10y^3 - 5y^2 + 15y$ $5y(2y^2 - y + 3)$

    $6x(2x^2 - x + 4)$

B 35. $24a^4x - 18a^3x + 12a^2x^2$ **36.** $14s^2 + 7st$ **37.** $7s^2y - 21xy^2$

38. $8a^2b - 16ab - 24a$ **39.** $25c^3d - 15c^2d^2 + 5cd^3$ **40.** $-40r^8s^6 - 16r^9s^5$

41. $21e^3k - 49e^2k^2 + 84k^3$ **42.** $\pi r^2h + 2\pi r^2$ **43.** $\dfrac{1}{2}bh - \dfrac{1}{2}ah$

Simplify.

SAMPLE $\dfrac{5x - 10}{5} - \dfrac{12x - 9}{3} = (x - 2) - (4x - 3)$

$= x - 2 - 4x + 3 = -3x + 1$

C 44. $\dfrac{3x - 6}{3} - \dfrac{4 - 8x}{2}$ $5x - 4$ **45.** $\dfrac{15a - 5}{5} - \dfrac{9a - 12}{3}$ 3

46. $\dfrac{24x - 18}{6} + \dfrac{14x + 7}{7}$ $6x - 2$ **47.** $\dfrac{12a^2b - 6ab^2}{3ab} + \dfrac{4a^2 + 10ab}{2a}$

48. $\dfrac{a^2b + 2a^2b^2}{ab} - \dfrac{2a^3 - 6a^2b}{2a}$ $a + 5ab - a^2$ **49.** $\dfrac{a^4b^3 - b^2a^3}{a^3b} + \dfrac{b^3c - ab^3c}{bc}$

47. $6a + 3b$
49. $b^2 - b$

Problems

Write an expression in factored form for the area *A* of each shaded region.

SAMPLE

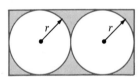

SOLUTION
A = Area of rectangle $- 2 \cdot$ area of circle
$= (4r \cdot 2r) - 2\pi r^2$
$= 2r^2(4 - \pi)$ ***Answer***

A 1.

$r^2(4 - \pi)$

2.

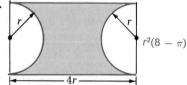

$r^2(8 - \pi)$

3.

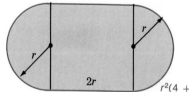

$2r$ $r^2(4 + \pi)$

4.

$4r^2(4 - \pi)$

B 5.

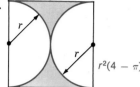

$r^2(4 - \pi)$

6.

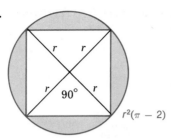

$r^2(\pi - 2)$

7.

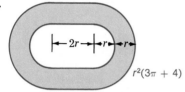

$r^2(3\pi + 4)$

8.

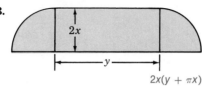

$2x(y + \pi x)$

Self-Test 1

VOCABULARY
factor (p. 155)
factor set (p. 155)
prime number (p. 155)
prime factorization (p. 156)
common factor (p. 156)
greatest common factor
(p. 156)

simplify (p. 159)
greatest monomial factor
(p. 159)
divisible (p. 162)
greatest monomial factor of
a polynomial (p. 162)

1. Find the prime factorization of 75.

2. Find all pairs of integral factors of 45.

3. Find the greatest common factor of 45 and 75.

Obj. 5-1, p. 155

Simplify, assuming no variable equals 0.

4. $-\dfrac{21x^2y^5}{7xy^6}$

5. $\dfrac{8k^2m^7}{32k^3m^3}$

Obj. 5-2, p. 158

Find the missing factor.

6. $-84 = -7(\underline{\ ?\ })$

7. $-35a^2b^5 = (7ab)(\underline{\ ?\ })$

8. Simplify $\dfrac{21t^4 + 15t^3 - 9t^2}{3t^2}$. $(t \neq 0)$

Obj. 5-3, p. 162

9. Factor $4x^4y^3 - 8x^2y^2 + 6xy^2$.

Check your answers with those at the back of the book.

FACTORING POLYNOMIALS **165**

165

Chalkboard Examples

Write each product as a trinomial.

1. $(a - b)(a - 2b)$
   $a^2 - 3ab + 2b^2$
2. $(k + 2)(k - 3)$
   $k^2 - k - 6$
3. $(y - 5)(y + 5)$ $y^2 - 25$
4. $(3m^2 - 4n)(5m^2 + 6n)$
   $15m^4 - 2m^2n - 24n^2$
5. $(4y + 5)(3y - 2)$
   $12y^2 + 7y - 10$
6. $(6x + 1)(2x + 3)$
   $12x^2 + 20x + 3$

Supplementary Material

Practice Master 25

Suggested Assignments

Minimum
Day 1: 167/1–33 odd
    R 165/Self-Test 1
Day 2: 167/18, 22, 26, 30,32,
        35, 37, 39
    S 133/40, 42, 47, 49

Average
    167/1–39 odd
    R 165/Self-Test 1
    S 133/38, 42, 46, 48

Maximum
    167/1–39 odd
    S 133/38, 40, 46, 48

PRODUCTS AND FACTORING

5-4 *Multiplying Binomials Mentally*

OBJECTIVE To find the product of two binomials.

Study the multiplication below and notice how the three terms of the product are formed. Do you see where the distributive axiom is used?

$$
\begin{array}{r}
3x + 4 \\
5x - 2 \\
\hline
15x^2 + 20x \\
- 6x - 8 \\
\hline
15x^2 + 14x - 8
\end{array}
$$

You can use the following short method to multiply binomials.

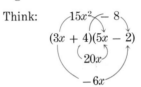

Think:

$$(3x + 4)(5x - 2)$$

Write: $15x^2 + 14x - 8$

To find the terms in the trinomial product of two binomials $(ax + b)(cx + d)$:

1. Multiply the first terms of the binomials.
2. Multiply the first term of each polynomial by the last term of the other and add these products.
3. Multiply the last terms of the binomials.

Each term of a trinomial like $15x^2 + 14x - 8$ has a standard name. A **quadratic term** is a term of degree two. A **linear term** is a term of degree one. As defined earlier, a *constant term* is a numerical term with no variable factor. The trinomial itself is called a quadratic polynomial.

$$15x^2 - 14x - 8$$

quadratic term ⏌

linear term ⏌

constant term ⏌

166   *CHAPTER 5*

Oral Exercises

State the quadratic, linear, and constant term of each product, and read the product as a polynomial.

SAMPLE $(z - 4)(z + 3)$

SOLUTION   Quadratic term, z^2; linear term, $-z$; constant term, -12;
              polynomial, $z^2 - z - 12$.

1. $(x + 2)(x + 1)$ 2. $(a + 3)(a + 4)$ 3. $(b + 4)(b + 1)$ 4. $(y + 5)(y + 6)$
5. $(x - 3)(x - 4)$ 6. $(a - 2)(a - 4)$ 7. $(b - 5)(b - 1)$ 8. $(y - 9)(y - 2)$
9. $(c - 3)(c + 4)$ 10. $(d - 2)(d + 5)$ 11. $(x - 5)(x + 3)$ 12. $(z - 1)(z + 7)$
13. $(a + 5)(2a + 1)$ 14. $(3a + 1)(a + 2)$ 15. $(y - 1)(2y - 1)$ 16. $(x - 3)(2x - 5)$

Written Exercises

Write each product as a trinomial.

A   1. $(x + 7)(x + 2)$ 2. $(y + 3)(y + 2)$ 3. $(a - 4)(a - 5)$
        4. $(b - 7)(b - 6)$ 5. $(c + 3)(c + 7)$ 6. $(k - 3)(k - 11)$
        7. $(a - 5)(a - 9)$ 8. $(1 + x)(2 + x)$ 9. $(2a + 1)(a + 5)$
        10. $(4x + 3)(x + 5)$ 11. $(2a + 9)(a - 3)$ 12. $(3a - 1)(2a - 1)$
        13. $(x - 9)(x + 7)$ 14. $(a - 5)(a + 7)$ 15. $(b - 3)(b + 8)$
        16. $(c - 7)(c + 8)$ 17. $(3k + 1)(2k + 5)$ 18. $(4a - 5)(2a - 3)$
        19. $a(7a - 5)(5a - 7)$.   20. $b(3b + 2)(7b + 8)$ 21. $2x(2x - 5)(3x + 1)$
        22. $n(4n - 7)(3n + 6)$ 23. $k(2k - 5)(7k + 4)$ 24. $3n(n - 3)(2n + 7)$

Express each product as a trinomial.

SAMPLE $(4x - 3y)(2x - 4y)$

SOLUTION $8x^2 - 22xy + 12y^2$

B   25. $(2x + 4y)(3x + 2y)$ 26. $(3x - 2y)(4x + y)$ 27. $(9a - 2b)(3a - 5b)$
        28. $(x^2 + y^2)(x^2 + 3y^2)$ 29. $(a^2 - 3)(2a^2 + 7)$ 30. $(r^2 - 2s)(3r^2 + s)$
        31. $(x^4 + 7x^2)(x^2 - 3)$ 32. $(x^3 - 2y)(3x^3 + 4y)$ 33. $(3a^4 - 5b^2)(a^4 - 2b^2)$

Solve and check:

34. $(x + 5)(x - 3) = (x - 4)(x + 9)$ 7   35. $(a - 4)(a + 4) = (a + 7)(a - 6)$ 26
36. $(6y - 5)(6y + 5) = (4y + 3)(9y - 7)$ 4   37. $(y + 1)(2y - 1) = (y - 1)^2 + (y + 1)^2$ 3
38. $(3a - 4)(4a + 5) = (6a - 2)(2a + 10)$ 0   39. $2(x + 1)(2x + 5) = (x + 3)(4x + 3)$ 1

40. Show that $(ax + by)(cx + dy) = acx^2 + (ad + bc)xy + bdy^2$.
$(ax + by)(cx + dy) = acx^2 + adxy + bcxy + bdy^2 = acx^2 + (ad + bc)xy + bdy^2$

FACTORING POLYNOMIALS   **167**

Chalkboard Examples

Express each product as a binomial.

1. $(x + 3)(x - 3)$ $x^2 - 9$

2. $(t - 5q)(t + 5q)$
$t^2 - 25q^2$

Factor.

3. $y^2 - 81$ $(y + 9)(y - 9)$

4. $4a^2 - 9b^2$
$(2a + 3b)(2a - 3b)$

5. $r^2s^2 - 16z^2$
$(rs + 4z)(rs - 4z)$

6. $25x^4 - 1$
$(5x^2 + 1)(5x^2 - 1)$

7. $-4 + a^2b^2$
$(ab - 2)(ab + 2)$

Supplementary Materials

Practice Master 26

Computer Activity 14
Odd Numbers and Squares
   Expressing any given odd number as the difference of two squares is accomplished by a short computer program. Once again, the computer's ability to make rapid calculations leaves the student free to discover general results concerning the theory of numbers.

Suggested Assignments

Minimum
Day 1: 169/1–31 odd
Day 2: 169/22–32 even,
      33–49 odd
Average
Day 1: 169/1–39 odd
Day 2: 169/26–40 even,
      41–53 odd
Maximum
Day 1: 169/1–39 odd
     S 167/30, 38, 40
Day 2: 169/26–40 even,
      41–55 odd

5-5 *Differences of Squares*

OBJECTIVE   To simplify products of the form $(a + b)(a - b)$ and to factor differences of squares.

Observe what happens when you simplify the product $(a + b)(a - b)$.

$$
\begin{array}{r}
a + b \\
a - b \\
\hline
a^2 + ab \\
- ab - b^2 \\
\hline
a^2 - b^2
\end{array}
$$

Two of the terms are opposites so the product is just a difference of two squares. This result is so useful that you should remember it in either of the following forms:

$$(a + b)(a - b) = a^2 - b^2$$

$$\begin{bmatrix}\text{Sum of two} \\ \text{numbers}\end{bmatrix} \cdot \begin{bmatrix}\text{Difference of} \\ \text{the numbers}\end{bmatrix} = [\text{First number}]^2 - [\text{Second number}]^2$$

EXAMPLE 1   Express each product as a binomial.

   a. $(x + 3)(x - 3)$ **b.** $(4y + 5)(4y - 5)$ **c.** $(6b^2 + 7c)(6b^2 - 7c)$

SOLUTION   **a.** $(x + 3)(x - 3) = x^2 - 9$
   b. $(4y + 5)(4y - 5) = 16y^2 - 25$
   c. $(6b^2 + 7c)(6b^2 - 7c) = 36b^4 - 49c^2$

   You can use the symmetric property of equality to write the statement $(a + b)(a - b) = a^2 - b^2$ in a form useful for factoring the difference of two squares.

$$a^2 - b^2 = (a + b)(a - b)$$

EXAMPLE 2   Factor. **a.** $n^2 - 16$ **b.** $4a^2 - 9b^2$

SOLUTION   **a.** $n^2 - 16 = (n + 4)(n - 4)$
   b. $4a^2 - 9b^2 = (2a)^2 - (3b)^2 = (2a + 3b)(2a - 3b)$

   In Example 2b it was important to recognize that both terms were *squares*. A monomial is a square if all powers in it are even and the numerical coefficient is the square of an integer. You can use the table at the back of the book or a calculator to determine whether or not an integer is a square. For example, the table shows that 2916 is the square of 54.

EXAMPLE 3   Factor $16x^4 - 1$.

SOLUTION $16x^4 - 1 = (4x^2 + 1)(4x^2 - 1)$ $\begin{cases}\text{Continue factoring because} \\ 4x^2 - 1 \text{ can be factored.}\end{cases}$
                $= (4x^2 + 1)(2x + 1)(2x - 1)$

168   *CHAPTER 5*

Oral Exercises

Square each monomial.

SAMPLE $-3k^2$ *SOLUTION* $(-3k^2)^2 = 9k^4$

1. $3x$ $9x^2$ **2.** $-4z$ $16z^2$ **3.** $3y^4$ $9y^8$ **4.** $-2r^2$ $4r^4$ **5.** $7x^2y$ $49x^4y^2$ **6.** $-5xy^3$ $25x^2y^6$

Express each product as a binomial.

7. $(x + 2)(x - 2)$ $x^2 - 4$ **8.** $(a + 5)(a - 5)$ $a^2 - 25$ **9.** $(s - t)(s + t)$ $s^2 - t^2$

10. $(4b + 3)(4b - 3)$ $16b^2 - 9$ **11.** $(2n - 3)(2n + 3)$ $4n^2 - 9$ **12.** $(5x - 7)(5x + 7)$ $25x^2 - 49$

Tell whether or not each binomial is the difference of two squares. If it is, factor it.

13. $x^2 - 16$ Yes; $(x + 4)(x - 4)$ **14.** $a^2 - 10$ No **15.** $k^3 - 4$ No

16. $4y^2 - 81$ Yes; $(2y + 9)(2y - 9)$ **17.** $a^4 - 1$ Yes; $(a^2 + 1)(a^2 - 1) = (a^2 + 1)(a + 1)(a - 1)$ **18.** $b^2 + 9$ No

Written Exercises

Express each product as a binomial.

A 1. $(a - 3)(a + 3)$ $a^2 - 9$ **2.** $(2 - x)(2 + x)$ $4 - x^2$ **3.** $(3b - 5)(3b + 5)$

4. $(7x - y)(7x + y)$ $49x^2 - y^2$ **5.** $(9a - 7)(9a + 7)$ $81a^2 - 49$ **6.** $(8 + 3x)(8 - 3x)$

7. $(8a - 5b)(8a + 5b)$ $64a^2 - 25b^2$ **8.** $(x^2 - 5)(x^2 + 5)$ $x^4 - 25$ **9.** $(3u^2 + v)(3u^2 - v)$

10. $(2a^2 - 5b^2)(2a^2 + 5b^2)$ $4a^4 - 25b^4$ **11.** $(rs + t^2)(rs - t^2)$ $r^2s^2 - t^4$ **12.** $(a^7 - b^4)(a^7 + b^4)$

Multiply using the form $(a + b)(a - b)$.

SAMPLE 1 $77 \times 83 = (80 - 3)(80 + 3) = 6400 - 9 = 6391$

13. 17×23 391 **14.** 28×32 896 **15.** 62×58 3596 **16.** 45×55 2475

17. 51×49 2499 **18.** 102×98 9996 **19.** 204×196 39,984 **20.** 70×130 9100

Factor. Use the table of squares.

21. $25y^2 - 9$ **22.** $49a^2 - 16$ **23.** $144 - x^2$ **24.** $169b^2 - 49c^2$

25. $9a^2 - b^2c^2$ **26.** $121 - 400r^2$ **27.** $x^6 - y^6$ **28.** $a^4 - 100$

29. $-9 + 16x^4$ **30.** $-1 + 81x^4$ **31.** $225 - a^2b^4$ **32.** $16x^4 - y^4$

B 33. $a^4b^4 - c^8$ **34.** $x^8 - 256$ **35.** $a^{16} - 1$ **36.** $81k^8 - n^8$

Factor.

SAMPLE 2 $(y + 3)^2 - y^2 = [(y + 3) - y][(y + 3) + y] = 3(2y + 3)$

37. $(x + 3)^2 - x^2$ $3(2x + 3)$ **38.** $y^2 - (y - 1)^2$ $2y - 1$

39. $(a + 1)^2 - (a - 1)^2$ $4a$ **40.** $9(x + 1)^2 - 4(x - 1)^2$ $(5x + 1)(x + 5)$

FACTORING POLYNOMIALS   **169**

169

About the Extra

This feature takes the concept of sums and differences one step further, to cubes. Just as the product $(x + y)(x - y)$ results in a middle term with a coefficient of zero, there are two pairs of opposites produced in each of the products $(x + y)(x^2 - xy + y^2)$ and $(x - y)(x^2 + xy + y^2)$. Your students should verify that these products are equal to $x^3 + y^3$ and $x^3 - y^3$ respectively.

You may wish to have your students memorize these patterns. A useful device for this purpose is to write the patterns simultaneously using colored chalk to highlight the changes in the signs. For example, $x^3 \pm y^3 =$
$$(x \pm y)(x^2 \mp xy + y^2).$$

An application of this feature is to factor integers such as 1001. This is accomplished by writing 1001 as
$10^3 + 1^3 = (10 + 1) \times (10^2 - 10 + 1) = 11 \cdot 91.$

Additional Answers
Extra

1. $(x + y)(x^2 - xy + y^2)$
$= x^3 - x^2y + xy^2 + yx^2 -$
$\qquad\qquad xy^2 + y^3$
$= x^3 + y^3$

2. $(x - y)(x^2 + xy + y^2)$
$= x^3 + x^2y + xy^2 - yx^2 -$
$\qquad\qquad xy^2 - y^3$
$= x^3 - y^3$

7. a. $z^6 - 1 = (z^2)^3 - (1)^3$
$= (z^2 - 1)(z^4 + z^2 + 1)$
$= (z - 1)(z + 1)(z^4 + z^2 + 1)$

b. $z^6 - 1 = (z^3)^2 - (1)^2$
$= (z^3 - 1)(z^3 + 1)$
$= (z - 1)(z^2 + z + 1)(z + 1) \times$
$\qquad\qquad (z^2 - z + 1)$
$= (z - 1)(z + 1)(z^2 + z + 1) \times$
$\qquad\qquad (z^2 - z + 1)$

c. $z^4 + z^2 + 1$
$= (z^4 + 2z^2 + 1) - z^2$
$= (z^2 + 1)^2 - z^2$
$= (z^2 + 1 - z)(z^2 + 1 + z)$
$= (z^2 - z + 1)(z^2 + z + 1)$

First factor out the greatest monomial factor. Then complete the factoring.

SAMPLE 3 $3x^3 - 75x = 3x(x^2 - 25) = 3x(x - 5)(x + 5)$

41. $2x^2 - 50$
$2(x + 5)(x - 5)$

42. $3y^2 - 48$
$3(y + 4)(y - 4)$

43. $45 - 5a^2$
$5(3 + a)(3 - a)$

44. $36x^2 - 81y^2$
$9(2x + 3y)(2x - 3y)$

45. $x^3 - 9x$
$x(x + 3)(x - 3)$

46. $2xy - 72x^3y$
$2xy(1 + 6x)(1 - 6x)$

47. $324 - 4k^4$
$4(9 + k^2)(3 + k)(3 - k)$

48. $\pi R^2 - \pi r^2$
$\pi(R + r)(R - r)$

Factor, assuming that n is a positive integer.

SAMPLE 4 $x^{2n} - y^2 = (x^n)^2 - y^2 = (x^n - y)(x^n + y)$

49. $x^{2n} - y^{2n}$
$(x^n + y^n)(x^n - y^n)$

50. $a^{2n} - 9$
$(a^n + 3)(a^n - 3)$

51. $b^{2n} - c^{4n}$
$(b^n + c^{2n})(b^n - c^{2n})$

52. $2x^{2n} - 98$
$2(x^n + 7)(x^n - 7)$

C 53. $a^{4n} - b^{6n}$
$(a^{2n} + b^{3n})(a^{2n} - b^{3n})$

54. $x^{2n+1} - x$
$x(x^n + 1)(x^n - 1)$

55. $y^{2n+3} - y^3$
$y^3(y^n + 1)(y^n - 1)$

56. $ab^{4n} - a$
$a(b^{2n} + 1)(b^n + 1)(b^n - 1)$

EXTRA

Sums and Differences of Cubes

The following factoring patterns indicate that both sums and differences of cubes can be factored.

$$x^3 + y^3 = (x + y)(x^2 - xy + y^2)$$

$$x^3 - y^3 = (x - y)(x^2 + xy + y^2)$$

EXAMPLE Factor $a^3 + 8$.

SOLUTION $a^3 + 8 = (a + 2)(a^2 - 2a + 4)$

1. Verify the factoring pattern for the sum of two cubes by multiplying $(x + y)(x^2 - xy + y^2)$.

2. Verify the factoring pattern for the difference of two cubes by multiplying $(x - y)(x^2 + xy + y^2)$.

Factor.

3. $n^3 + 27$
$(n + 3)(n^2 - 3n + 9)$

4. $a^3 - 8$
$(a - 2)(a^2 + 2a + 4)$

5. $x^3 + 64$
$(x + 4)(x^2 - 4x + 16)$

6. $125 - 27b^3$
$(5 - 3b)(25 + 15b + 9b^2)$

7. a. Factor $z^6 - 1$ as a difference of cubes to show that
$$z^6 - 1 = (z - 1)(z + 1)(z^4 + z^2 + 1).$$

b. Factor $z^6 - 1$ as a difference of squares to show that
$$z^6 - 1 = (z - 1)(z + 1)(z^2 + z + 1)(z^2 - z + 1).$$

c. Show that the factorizations given in parts (a) and (b) are equivalent by writing
$$z^4 + z^2 + 1 = (z^4 + 2z^2 + 1) - z^2$$
and then factoring the difference of squares on the right.

5-6 Squares of Binomials

OBJECTIVE To find squares of binomials and to factor trinomial squares.

Note what happens when you square the binomial $a + b$.

$$
\begin{array}{r}
a + b \\
a + b \\
\hline
a^2 + ab \\
ab + b^2 \\
\hline
a^2 + 2ab + b^2
\end{array}
$$

1. Square of the first term._____

2. Twice the product of the two terms._____

3. Square of the last term._____

When you square the binomial difference $a - b$, the middle term in the product will be preceded by a minus sign.

$$
\begin{array}{r}
a - b \\
a - b \\
\hline
a^2 - ab \\
- ab + b^2 \\
\hline
a^2 - 2ab + b^2
\end{array}
$$

1. Square of the first term._____

2. Twice the product of the two terms._____

3. Square of the last term._____

These results may be expressed as these two useful formulas.

$$(a + b)^2 = a^2 + 2ab + b^2$$
$$(a - b)^2 = a^2 - 2ab + b^2$$

These formulas can be used to write squares of binomials as trinomials.

EXAMPLE 1 $(x + 4)^2 = x^2 + 8x + 16$

EXAMPLE 2 $(3c + 5)^2 = 9c^2 + 30c + 25$

EXAMPLE 3 $(2s - 7t)^2 = 4s^2 - 28st + 49t^2$

EXAMPLE 4 $(6x^2 - y^3)^2 = 36x^4 - 12x^2y^3 + y^6$

The symmetric property of equality enables you to rewrite the formulas for squaring a binomial in a form useful for factoring.

$$a^2 + 2ab + b^2 = (a + b)^2$$
$$a^2 - 2ab + b^2 = (a - b)^2$$

The expressions on the left sides of the two equations above are called **trinomial squares**.

FACTORING POLYNOMIALS   **171**

To determine whether or not a trinomial is a trinomial square, ask the three questions illustrated in the next examples.

EXAMPLE 5 Is $25x^2 - 30x + 9$ a trinomial square?

SOLUTION
1. Is the first term a square?   Yes, $25x^2 = (5x)^2$
2. Is the last term a square?   Yes, $9 = 3^2$
3. Is the middle term, neglecting the   Yes, $30x = 2(5x \cdot 3)$
   sign, twice the product of $5x$ and 3?

Thus, $25x^2 - 30x + 9$ is a trinomial square, and
$25x^2 - 30x + 9 = (5x - 3)^2$. *Answer*

EXAMPLE 6 Is $16x^2 + 28xy + 49y^2$ a trinomial square?

SOLUTION
1. Is the first term a square?   Yes, $16x^2 = (4x)^2$
2. Is the last term a square?   Yes, $49y^2 = (7y)^2$
3. Is the middle term twice the product   No, $28xy \neq 2(4x \cdot 7y)$
   of $4x$ and $7y$?

Thus, $16x^2 + 28xy + 49y^2$ is not a trinomial square. *Answer*
(It would be a trinomial square if the middle term were $56xy$.)

Oral Exercises

Express each square as a trinomial.

1. $(x + 1)^2$ $x^2 + 2x + 1$ 2. $(y + 3)^2$ $y^2 + 6y + 9$ 3. $(a - 5)^2 a^2 - 10a + 25$ 4. $(x - y)^2$
   4. $x^2 - 2xy + y^2$
5. $(a + 6)^2 a^2 + 12a + 36$ 6. $(b - 8)^2 b^2 - 16b + 64$ 7. $(3x + 1)^2 9x^2 + 6x + 1$ 8. $(2k + 1)^2$
   8. $4k^2 + 4k + 1$
9. $(y^2 - 1)^2$ 10. $(a^2 + 3)^2$ 11. $(5x - 2)^2$ 12. $(2 - 5x)^2$
   $y^4 - 2y^2 + 1$ $a^4 + 6a^2 + 9$ $25x^2 - 20x + 4$ $4 - 20x + 25x^2$

Decide whether or not each polynomial is a trinomial square. If so, factor it.

13. $x^2 + 14x + 49$ Yes; $(x + 7)^2$ 14. $a^2 - 6a + 9$ Yes; $(a - 3)^2$ 15. $b^2 - 8b + 16$
    Yes; $(b - 4)^2$
16. $y^2 + 2y + 4$ No   17. $9n^2 - 12n + 4$ Yes; $(3n - 2)^2$ 18. $25x^2 - 10xy + 4y^2$
    No

19. Find the square of 31 by thinking of it as $(30 + 1)^2$.
    $(30 + 1)^2 = 900 + 60 + 1 = 961$

Written Exercises

Express each square as a trinomial.

A 1. $(x + 2)^2$ 2. $(y - 3)^2$ 3. $(a - 4)^2$ 4. $(b + 9)^2$
  5. $(2x + 3)^2$ 6. $(3y + 8)^2$ 7. $(4k - 5)^2$ 8. $(7k - 2)^2$
  9. $(4p + 3q)^2$ 10. $(8x - 5y)^2$ 11. $(3x + 7y)^2$ 12. $(2a - 9b)^2$
 13. $(ab - 5)^2$ 14. $(x^2 + 3)^2$ 15. $(y^2 - 7)^2$ 16. $(2x^2 - y^2)^2$
 17. $(-3 + 5a)^2$ 18. $(-7 - 6b)^2$ 19. $(-8x^2 + 1)^2$ 20. $(-11a^2 - b^2)^2$

172   CHAPTER 5

Suggested Assignments

Minimum
Day 1: 172/1–41 odd
Day 2: 173/43–57 odd, 59
    R 174/Self-Test 2

Average
Day 1: 172/1–41 odd
    S 170/42–54 even
Day 2: 173/47–57 odd, 59,
       60
    R 174/Self-Test 2

Maximum
Day 1: 172/1–45 odd
Day 2: 173/47–57 odd,
       59–61
    R 174/Self-Test 2

Extra Practice Problems
    p. 517

Additional A Exercises

Express each square as a tri-nomial.

1. $(x + 4)^2$ $x^2 + 8x + 16$
2. $(a + 7)^2$ $a^2 + 14a + 49$
3. $(c - 8)^2$ $c^2 - 16c + 64$
4. $(3x + 2)^2$ $9x^2 + 12x + 4$

Factor.

5. $y^2 + 10y + 25$
   $(y + 5)(y + 5)$
6. $9a^2 - 24a + 16$
   $(3a - 4)(3a - 4)$

Factor each trinomial as the square of a binomial if possible. If it is not possible, so state. (N.P. = not possible)

21. $n^2 - 2n + 1$ $(n - 1)^2$ 22. $k^2 + 6k + 9$ $(k + 3)^2$ 23. $r^2 - 4r + 4$ $(r - 2)^2$

24. $a^2 + 12a + 24$ N.P.   25. $b^2 - 18b + 81$ $(b - 9)^2$ 26. $49 - 7k + k^2$ N.P.

27. $4x^2 + 4x + 1$ $(2x + 1)^2$ 28. $9 + 12y + 4y^2$ $(3 + 2y)^2$ 29. $36 - 60a + 25a^2$

30. $25d^2 - 50d + 100$ N.P.   31. $64x^2 - 16xy + y^2$ 32. $81n^2 + nt + 9t^2$ N.P.
                                          $(8x - y)^2$ 29. $(6 - 5a)^2$

B 33. $x^4 + 2x^2 + 1$ $(x^2 + 1)^2$ 34. $y^4 + 10y^2 + 25$ $(y^2 + 5)^2$ 35. $a^2b^2 - 12ab + 36$

36. $25a^2 + 55a + 121$ N.P.   37. $a^4 - 24a^2 + 144$ 38. $(x + 1)^2 + 2(x + 1) + 1$
                                       $(a^2 - 12)^2$ 35. $(ab - 6)^2$ 38. $(x + 2)^2$

39. Express each square as a trinomial
   a. $(5x - 2)^2$ $25x^2 - 20x + 4$ **b.** $(2 - 5x)^2$ $25x^2 - 20x + 4$
   c. Notice that the answers to parts (a) and (b) are equal even though $(5x - 2)$ is not equal to $(2 - 5x)$. Explain why the squares of these binomials are equal.

40. Show that $a^4 - 8a^2 + 16$ can be factored as $(a - 2)^2(a + 2)^2$.

41. Show that $x^4 - 18x^2 + 81$ can be factored as $(x - 3)^2(x + 3)^2$.

Solve and check.

42. $x(x + 5) = (x + 2)^2$ 4   43. $(x - 4)^2 = (x - 6)(x - 1)$ 10

44. $(x - 1)(x + 1) = (x + 5)(x - 2)$ 3   45. $(x + 4)^2 = x^2 + 16$ 0

First factor out a common monomial factor. Then complete the factoring.

SAMPLE $12x^3 + 36x^2 + 27x = 3x(4x^2 + 12x + 9) = 3x(2x + 3)^2$

46. $6x^2 + 12x + 6$ $6(x + 1)^2$ 47. $3a^2 + 18a + 27$ $3(a + 3)^2$ 48. $a^3 - 10a^2 + 25a$
                                                                             $a(a - 5)^2$

49. $18x^2 - 12x + 2$ $2(3x - 1)^2$ 50. $24b - 24b^2 + 6b^3$ $6b(2 - b)^2$ 51. $20x^4 + 60x^2 + 45$

52. $2a^6 - 24a^4 + 72a^2$ 53. $16k^5 - 48k^3 + 36k$ 54. $3v^8 - 48v^5 + 192v^2$
    $2a^2(a^2 - 6)^2$ $4k(2k - 3)^2$ 51. $5(2x^2 + 3)^2$

Solve and check.   54. $3v^2(v^3 - 8)^2$ or
                                                                                  $3v^2(v - 2)^2(v^2 + 2v + 4)$

55. $(x + 3)(x + 5) = (x + 1)^2 + 13x$ 2

56. $(2x + 1)^2 - (2x - 1)^2 = (x + 6)^2 - x^2$ -9

57. $(2x - 1)^2 - (4x - 3)(x + 2) = 1 - 7x$ 3

58. $(5x + 4)^2 - (3x + 2)^2 = (4x + 4)(4x - 4)$ -1

59. The length of a rectangle is equal to four times its width. If the width of the rectangle is increased by 4 cm and its length is decreased by 4 cm, its area will be increased by 32 cm². Find the dimensions of the original rectangle. 4 cm by 16 cm

60. The sum of the squares of three consecutive integers is 22 less than three times the product of the two greater integers. Find the integers. 7, 8, 9

FACTORING POLYNOMIALS   **173**

61. The square of a two-digit number ending in 5 always ends in 25. The digits before the 25 are found by multiplying the ten's digit by one more than the ten's digit. Thus,

$$25^2 = 625 \qquad \text{and} \qquad 45^2 = 2025$$
$$(2 \times 3) \qquad\qquad (4 \times 5)$$

a. Use this rule to find the squares of 35, 55, and 85. 1225, 3025, 7225
b. Prove the rule works by letting $10t + 5$ represent a two-digit number ending in 5. Square this number and show that the result equals $t(t + 1) \times 100 + 25$.
$(10t + 5)^2 = 100t^2 + 100t + 25 = 100t(t + 1) + 25 = t(t + 1) \times 100 + 25$

Self-Test 2

VOCABULARY   linear term (p. 166)   trinomial square (p. 171)
                      quadratic term (p. 166)

Express each product as a polynomial.

1. $(3y + 5)(2y - 6)$ **2.** $2x(x - 4)(3x - 2)$ Obj. 5-4, p. 166
3. $(x - 7)(x + 7)$ **4.** $(2a + 7b)(2a - 7b)$ Obj. 5-5, p. 168

Factor.

5. $4x^2 - 49$ **6.** $36x^4 - 81$

Express each square as a trinomial.

7. $(2y + 5)^2$ **8.** $(3z - 5k)^2$ Obj. 5-6, p. 171

Factor.

9. $9a^2 + 12a + 4$ **10.** $16m^2 - 24mn + 9n^2$

Check your answers with those at the back of the book.

Biography Rosalind Franklin

Rosalind Elsie Franklin (1920–1958), a British chemist and molecular biologist, contributed significantly to the determination of the structure of deoxyribonucleic acid, or DNA. DNA appears in all cells of all living things and is responsible for determining the form and function of these cells. It is the means by which hereditary characteristics are passed on. Rosalind Franklin's X-ray studies of DNA were instrumental in the construction and verification of the DNA model.

174   *CHAPTER 5*

5-7 *Factoring Pattern for* $x^2 + bx + c$, *c positive*

OBJECTIVE To factor quadratic trinomials whose quadratic coefficient is 1 and whose constant term is positive.

In this section you will study trinomials that can be factored as a product of the form $(x + r)(x + s)$ where r and s are both positive or both negative. First look at some products of this form to see what clues they give you for factoring the trinomial.

EXAMPLE 1 $(x + 2)(x + 3) = x^2 + 5x + 6$

sum of 2 and 3   product of 2 and 3

EXAMPLE 2 $(x - 5)(x - 7) = x^2 - 12x + 35$

sum of -5 and -7 product of -5 and -7

EXAMPLE 3 $(x + r)(x + s) = x^2 + (r + s)x + rs$

Example 3 suggests the following technique for factoring polynomials with quadratic term x^2 and a positive constant term:

1. List the pairs of factors that have a product equal to the constant term.
2. Find the pair of factors in the list that have a sum equal to the coefficient of the linear term.

Examples 1 and 2 suggest that in Step 1 you can just look at the factors with the same sign as the linear term.

EXAMPLE 4 Factor $x^2 + 7x + 12$.

SOLUTION
1. List the pairs of positive factors of 12.
2. Find the factors that have a sum of 7: 3, 4.
3. $x^2 + 7x + 12 = (x + 3)(x + 4)$ **Answer**

$$
\begin{array}{c|c}
\multicolumn{2}{c}{12} \\
\hline
1 & 12 \\
2 & 6 \\
3 & 4 \ \checkmark
\end{array}
$$

Instead of writing down the factors of the constant term, it is often faster to review them mentally.

EXAMPLE 5 Factor $y^2 - 14y + 24$.

SOLUTION
1. The factoring pattern is $(y - \ )(y - \ )$.
2. Select the factors of 24 with sum -14: $-2, -12$.
3. $y^2 - 14y + 24 = (y - 2)(y - 12)$ **Answer**

FACTORING POLYNOMIALS **175**

Suggested Assignments

Minimum
176/1–37 odd

Average
176/1–45 odd

Maximum
176/1–49 odd

Additional A Exercises

Factor.

1. $x^2 + 2x + 1$
$(x + 1)(x + 1)$

2. $x^2 + 6x + 5$
$(x + 5)(x + 1)$

3. $a^2 + 8a + 12$
$(a + 6)(a + 2)$

4. $c^2 - 6c + 9$
$(c - 3)(c - 3)$

5. $y^2 - 9y + 20$
$(y - 4)(y - 5)$

6. $a^2 - 11a + 18$
$(a - 2)(a - 9)$

**Additional Answers
Written Exercises**

1. $(x + 5)(x + 1)$

2. $(x + 6)(x + 1)$

3. $(a - 3)(a - 1)$

4. $(b - 8)(b - 2)$

5. $(r + 6)(r + 3)$

6. $(v - 17)(v - 3)$

7. $(k - 7)(k - 4)$

8. $(x - 11)(x - 2)$

9. $(z - 7)(z - 6)$

10. $(y + 11)(y + 4)$

11. prime

12. $(b - 9)(b - 5)$

13. $(y + 11)(y + 5)$

14. prime

15. $(p - 9)(p - 8)$

16. $(36 - z)(2 - z)$

17. $(10 - c)(2 - c)$

18. prime

19. $(x - 5y)(x - 7y)$

20. $(a - 8b)(a - 3b)$

(continued)

176

A polynomial that cannot be rewritten as a product of polynomials of lower degree is called **irreducible**. An irreducible polynomial whose greatest monomial factor is 1 is a **prime polynomial.**

EXAMPLE 6 Factor $x^2 - x + 8$.

SOLUTION   1. List the pairs of negative factors of 8: $-1, -8; -2, -4$.

2. Neither of these pairs of factors has a sum of -1.

3. Thus, $x^2 - x + 8$ cannot be factored. It is irreducible and prime.
 Answer

Oral Exercises

For each trinomial, state the factors of the constant term whose sum is equal to the coefficient of the linear term.

SAMPLE $x^2 - 10x + 21$ **SOLUTION** $-3, -7$

1. $x^2 + 3x + 2$ 2, 1   **2.** $x^2 + 5x + 4$ 4, 1   **3.** $y^2 + 6y + 8$ 4, 2

4. $y^2 + 7y + 10$ 5, 2   **5.** $a^2 + 11a + 10$ 10, 1   **6.** $b^2 + 9b + 20$ 5, 4

7. $x^2 - 4x + 3$ $-3, -1$ **8.** $x^2 - 8x + 7$ $-7, -1$ **9.** $r^2 - 7r + 12$ $-3, -4$

10. $s^2 - 8s + 15$ $-5, -3$ **11.** $a^2 - 10a + 24$ $-6, -4$ **12.** $z^2 + 10z + 21$ 7, 3

Written Exercises

Factor. Check by multiplying the factors. If the polynomial is not factorable, write "prime."

A **1.** $x^2 + 6x + 5$ **2.** $y^2 + 7y + 6$ **3.** $a^2 - 4a + 3$

4. $b^2 - 10b + 16$ **5.** $r^2 + 9r + 18$ **6.** $v^2 - 20v + 51$

7. $k^2 - 11k + 28$ **8.** $x^2 - 13x + 22$ **9.** $z^2 - 13z + 42$

10. $y^2 + 15y + 44$ **11.** $a^2 - 17a + 50$ **12.** $b^2 - 14b + 45$

13. $y^2 + 16y + 55$ **14.** $d^2 - 14d + 32$ **15.** $p^2 - 17p + 72$

16. $72 - 38z + z^2$ **17.** $20 - 12c + c^2$ **18.** $40 - 15a + a^2$

SAMPLE 1 $a^2 - 8ab + 12b^2$

SOLUTION $a^2 - 8ab + 12b^2 = (a -)(a -)$
$= (a - 2b)(a - 6b)$ ***Answer***

19. $x^2 - 12xy + 35y^2$ **20.** $a^2 - 11ab + 24b^2$ **21.** $s^2 - 11st + 30t^2$

22. $c^2 - 19cd + 48d^2$ **23.** $b^2 + 13bc + 40c^2$ **24.** $x^2 + 15xy + 50y^2$

25. $s^2 - 13st + 42t^2$ **26.** $a^2 + 10ab + 25b^2$ **27.** $k^2 - 18ka + 36a^2$

28. $y^2 - 14yz + 49z^2$ **29.** $d^2 + 12de + 27e^2$ **30.** $y^2 - 28yz + 75z^2$

B **31.** $a^2 - 23a + 120$ **32.** $y^2 + 22y + 96$ **33.** $108 - 21a + a^2$

34. $180 - 41b + b^2$ **35.** $98n^2 - 21nx + x^2$ **36.** $112y^2 - 22yz + z^2$

Determine all integral values for k for which the trinomial can be factored.

SAMPLE 2 $x^2 + kx + 35$

SOLUTION   35 can be factored as a product of two integers in these ways:

$$1 \cdot 35 \quad 5 \cdot 7 \quad (-1)(-35) \quad (-5)(-7)$$

The corresponding values of k are 36, 12, -36, -12.

Answer

37. $x^2 + kx + 10$ 7, 11, -7, -11

38. $y^2 + ky + 4$ 4, 5, -4, -5

39. $z^2 + kz + 15$ 8, 16, -8, -16

40. $u^2 + ku + 21$ 10, 22, -10, -22

41. $r^2 + kr + 12$ 7, 8, 13, -7, -8, -13

42. $n^2 + kn + 18$ 9, 11, 19, -9, -11, -19

Factor. Check by multiplying the factors.

C 43. $(x + 2)^2 + 5(x + 2) + 4$ $(x + 3)(x + 6)$ 44. $(y - 2)^2 + 7(y - 2) + 10$ $y(y + 3)$

45. $(a + b)^2 - 6(a + b) + 8$ 46. $(a + 4)^2 - 8(a + 4) + 16$ a^2

47. $a^4 - 10a^2 + 9$ 48. $b^4 - 26b^2 + 25$ $(b + 5)(b - 5)(b + 1)(b - 1)$

49. $x^4 - 6x^2 - 27$ 50. $x^5 - 13x^3 + 36x$ $x(x + 3)(x - 3)(x + 2)(x - 2)$

45. $(a + b - 4)(a + b - 2)$

47. $(a + 3)(a - 3)(a + 1)(a - 1)$

49. $(x^2 + 3)(x + 3)(x - 3)$

ɦistorical ɳote Exponents

Down through the centuries, many forms of notation were used to represent powers of a variable before the current notation became standard. As early as 1485, Nicolas Chuquet in France used a form of exponent to describe powers, but his notation omitted the variable. He wrote

$$.2.^0, .2.^1, .2.^2, \ldots \text{ for } 2, 2x, 2x^2, \ldots.$$

To represent what you would write as

$$x^4 + 3x^2 - 7x,$$

Jobst Burgi (1522–1632), a Swiss clockmaker, used

$$\overset{iv}{1} + \overset{ii}{3} - \overset{i}{7}$$

and Simon Stevin (1548–1620), a Flemish engineer, wrote

$$\overset{4}{1} + \overset{2}{3} - \overset{1}{7}.$$

In 1637 it was René Descartes, a French mathematician, who introduced the use of small numerals with variables, and expressed powers as x, xx, x^3, x^4, ... Eventually, mathematicians used x^2 for xx.

As you can see from the dates, all this was going on while other Europeans were exploring and settling North America.

FACTORING POLYNOMIALS   177

21. $(s - 6t)(s - 5t)$

22. $(c - 16d)(c - 3d)$

23. $(b + 8c)(b + 5c)$

24. $(x + 10y)(x + 5y)$

25. $(s - 7t)(s - 6t)$

26. $(a + 5b)^2$

27. prime

28. $(y - 7z)^2$

29. $(d + 3e)(d + 9e)$

30. $(y - 25z)(y - 3z)$

31. $(a - 8)(a - 15)$

32. $(y + 16)(y + 6)$

33. $(12 - a)(9 - a)$

34. $(36 - b)(5 - b)$

35. $(14n - x)(7n - x)$

36. $(14y - z)(8y - z)$

5-8 *Factoring Pattern for* $x^2 + bx + c$, *c negative*

OBJECTIVE To factor a quadratic polynomial whose quadratic coefficient is 1 and whose constant term is negative.

The factoring which you did in the last section had this form:

$$x^2 + bx + c = (x + r)(x + s)$$

positive r and s both positive
or both negative

By contrast, the factoring which you will do in this section has the following form:

$$x^2 + bx + c = (x + r)(x + s)$$

negative r and s have
opposite signs

The procedure that you will use in this section is the same as before. You find two numbers r and s whose product is c and whose sum is b.

If a quadratic polynomial of the form $x^2 + bx + c$ (c negative) can be factored, its factors will be of the form

$$(x + r)(x + s)$$

where one of r and s, say r, is negative and s is positive.

EXAMPLE 1 Factor $a^2 + 2a - 8$.

SOLUTION
1. List the pairs of factors of -8.
2. Find the pair of factors with a sum of 2: $-2, 4$
3. $a^2 + 2a - 8 = (a + 4)(a - 2)$. **Answer**

-8	
-1	8
1	-8
-2	4 √
2	-4

It is often faster to review the factors of the constant term mentally.

EXAMPLE 2 Factor $n^2 - 6n - 27$.

SOLUTION
1. The factoring pattern is
$$(n - \ )(n + \ ).$$
2. Find the pair of factors of -27 with a sum of -6:
$-9, 3$.
3. $n^2 - 6n - 27 = (n - 9)(n + 3)$ **Answer**

178   CHAPTER 5

Oral Exercises

For each trinomial, state the factors of the constant term whose sum is equal to the coefficient of the linear term.

SAMPLE $x^2 - 7x - 8$ **SOLUTION** 1, -8

1. $a^2 + 3a - 4$ 4, -1 **2.** $x^2 + 2x - 3$ 3, -1 **3.** $t^2 + 5t - 6$ 6, -1

4. $y^2 + y - 6$ 3, -2 **5.** $y^2 - y - 6$ -3, 2   **6.** $b^2 - 8b - 9$ -9, 1

7. $b^2 + 8b - 9$ 9, -1 **8.** $u^2 - 3u - 10$ -5, 2   **9.** $r^2 + 5r - 14$ 7, -2

Written Exercises

Factor each expression. Check by multiplying the factors. If the expression is not factorable, write "prime."

A   **1.** $a^2 + 4a - 5$ **2.** $x^2 - 2x - 3$ **3.** $y^2 - 5y - 6$

    4. $b^2 + 2b - 15$ **5.** $c^2 - 11c - 10$ **6.** $r^2 + 6r - 16$

    7. $x^2 - 6x - 18$ **8.** $y^2 - 10y - 24$ **9.** $a^2 + 2a - 35$

   10. $k^2 - 2k - 20$ **11.** $z^2 + 5z - 36$ **12.** $r^2 - 3r - 40$

   13. $p^2 - 4p - 21$ **14.** $a^2 + 3a - 54$ **15.** $y^2 - 5y - 30$

   16. $z^2 - z - 72$ **17.** $a^2 - ab - 20b^2$ **18.** $y^2 - 2yz - 3z^2$

   19. $p^2 - 5pq - 50q^2$ **20.** $a^2 - 4ab - 77b^2$ **21.** $k^2 - 11kd - 60d^2$

   22. $s^2 + 14st - 72t^2$ **23.** $x^2 - 9xy - 22y^2$ **24.** $p^2 - pq - 72q^2$

B   **25.** $1 - 8ab - 20a^2b^2$ **26.** $1 - 7pq - 60p^2q^2$ **27.** $1 - ab - 56a^2b^2$

   28. $n^2 - 13nm + 48m^2$ **29.** $r^2 - 18r - 144$ **30.** $a^2 + 19a - 150$

   31. $800 - 20b - b^2$ **32.** $a^2 + 3a - 270$ **33.** $320 - 32x - x^2$

Find all the integral values of k for which the given polynomial can be factored.

34. $x^2 + kx - 12$ **35.** $y^2 + ky - 20$ **36.** $15 - kz - z^2$
     1, 4, 11, -1, -4, -11 1, 8, 19, -1, -8, -19 2, 14, -2, -14

Find two negative values for k for which the given trinomial can be factored. Answers may vary for Exs. 37–42.

C   **37.** $x^2 - 3x + k$ -4, -10 **38.** $y^2 + 2y + k$ -3, -8 **39.** $z^2 + 4z + k$ -12, -5

   40. $k - 6x - x^2$ -5, -8 **41.** $n^2 + 11n + k$ -12, -26 **42.** $k + 4m - m^2$ -3, -4

Factor.

43. $(x + 1)^2 - 2(x + 1) - 15$ **44.** $(a + b)^2 - 3(a + b) - 70$

45. $(2x - y)^2 + 16(2x - y) + 60$ **46.** $4(a^2 - 1) - x^2(a^2 - 1)$

47. $x^4 - 8x^2 - 9$ **48.** $2x^4 - 34x^2 + 32$

49. $3a^4 - 63a^2 - 300$ **50.** $(3a + b)^4 - (a + b)^4$

FACTORING POLYNOMIALS   **179**

---

2. $(x - 3)(x + 1)$

3. $(y - 6)(y + 1)$

4. $(b + 5)(b - 3)$

5. prime

6. $(r + 8)(r - 2)$

7. prime

8. $(y - 12)(y + 2)$

9. $(a + 7)(a - 5)$

10. prime

11. $(z + 9)(z - 4)$

12. $(r - 8)(r + 5)$

13. $(p - 7)(p + 3)$

14. $(a + 9)(a - 6)$

15. prime

16. $(z - 9)(z + 8)$

17. $(a - 5b)(a + 4b)$

18. $(y - 3z)(y + z)$

19. $(p - 10q)(p + 5q)$

20. $(a - 11b)(a + 7b)$

21. $(k - 15d)(k + 4d)$

22. $(s + 18t)(s - 4t)$

23. $(x - 11y)(x + 2y)$

24. $(p - 9q)(p + 8q)$

25. $(1 - 10ab)(1 + 2ab)$

26. $(1 + 5pq)(1 - 12pq)$

27. $(1 - 8ab)(1 + 7ab)$

28. prime

29. $(r - 24)(r + 6)$

30. $(a + 25)(a - 6)$

31. $(40 + b)(20 - b)$

32. $(a + 18)(a - 15)$

33. $(40 + x)(8 - x)$

43. $(x + 4)(x - 4)$

44. $(a + b - 10)(a + b + 7)$

45. $(2x - y + 10)(2x - y + 6)$

46. $(a + 1)(a - 1)(2 + x) \times$
             $(2 - x)$

47. $(x + 3)(x - 3)(x^2 + 1)$

48. $2(x - 4)(x + 4)(x - 1) \times$
             $(x + 1)$

49. $3(a - 5)(a + 5)(a^2 + 4)$

50. $8a(2a + b) \times$
            $(5a^2 + 4ab + b^2)$

5-9 Factoring Pattern for $ax^2 + bx + c$

OBJECTIVE   To factor quadratic trinomials when the coefficient of the quadratic term is a positive integer greater than 1.

If $ax^2 + bx + c$ $(a > 1)$ can be factored, the factors will have the pattern

$$(px + r)(qx + s).$$

EXAMPLE 1   Factor $5x^2 - 13x + 6$.

SOLUTION

First clue: Because the trinomial has a positive constant term and a negative linear term, both r and s will be negative.

Second clue: The product of the linear terms of the binomial factors is $5x^2$, and the product of their constant terms is 6. Thus, you can determine the possible factors as follows:

Factors of $5x^2$	Factors of 6
x and $5x$	-1 and -6
	-2 and -3

Test the possibilities to see which produces the correct linear term.

Possible Factors	Linear Term
$(x - 1)(5x - 6)$	$-6x - 5x = -11x$
$(x - 6)(5x - 1)$	$-x - 30x = -31x$
$(x - 2)(5x - 3)$	$-3x - 10x = -13x$ √
$(x - 3)(5x - 2)$	$-2x - 15x = -17x$

The third possibility produces the correct linear term.

$$5x^2 - 13x + 6 = (x - 2)(5x - 3) \quad \textbf{\textit{Answer}}$$

EXAMPLE 2   Factor $8x^2 + 26x - 7$.

SOLUTION

First clue: Because the trinomial has a negative constant term, one of r and s will be negative and the other will be positive.

Second clue: You can determine the possible factors of the quadratic and constant terms as follows:

Factors of $8x^2$	Factors of -7
x and $8x$	-1 and 7
$2x$ and $4x$	1 and -7

Test the possibilities to see which produces the correct linear term.

Possible Factors	Linear Term
$(x + 1)(8x - 7)$	x
$(x - 7)(8x + 1)$	$-55x$
$(x - 1)(8x + 7)$	$-x$
$(x + 7)(8x - 1)$	$55x$
$(2x + 1)(4x - 7)$	$-10x$
$(2x - 7)(4x + 1)$	$-26x$
$(2x - 1)(4x + 7)$	$10x$
$(2x + 7)(4x - 1)$	$26x$ ✓

The last possibility gives the correct linear term.

$$8x^2 + 26x - 7 = (2x + 7)(4x - 1) \quad \textbf{\textit{Answer}}$$

As you practice factoring, you will become able to select the correct factors without writing all the possibilities.

EXAMPLE 3 Factor $7x^2 - 16x - 15$.

SOLUTION
$$7x^2 - 16x - 15 = (7x \quad)(x \quad)$$
$$= (7x + \quad)(x - \quad)$$
$$= (7x + 5)(x - 3) \quad \textbf{\textit{Answer}}$$

Note: If you had written $(7x - \quad)(x + \quad)$ as the second step, you would have found that no such combination of factors would produce the desired linear term $-16x$.

Written Exercises

Factor. Check by multiplying the factors. If the expression is not factorable, write "prime."

A
1. $2x^2 + 5x + 3$
2. $2n^2 + 7n + 3$
3. $5a^2 + 6a + 1$
4. $8n^2 + 6n + 1$
5. $7n^2 - 8n + 1$
6. $14k^2 - 9k + 1$
7. $5y^2 - 16y + 3$
8. $7y^2 - 18y + 8$
9. $3k^2 - 5k + 1$
10. $3z^2 + z - 2$
11. $2t^2 - t - 6$
12. $3a^2 + 2a - 5$
13. $4y^2 - y - 3$
14. $9a^2 + 3a - 2$
15. $7k^2 + 19k - 6$
16. $3x^2 - 7x + 6$
17. $1 + b - 6b^2$
18. $10 + 3y - y^2$
19. $10 + y - 2y^2$
20. $6 - 23a - 4a^2$
21. $a^2 + ab - 2b^2$
22. $x^2 - xy - 56y^2$
23. $9r^2 - 25rs - 6s^2$
24. $3a^2 - 5ab - 12b^2$

B
25. $25a^2 + 10ab - 3b^2$
26. $36d^2 - 5d - 24$
27. $12x^2 + 19xy - 18y^2$
28. $20k^2 + 27k - 8$
29. $12x^2 - 4x - 21$
30. $24a^2 - 31a - 15$

FACTORING POLYNOMIALS   **181**

Suggested Assignments

Minimum
181/1–35 odd
S 179/22–32 even

Average
181/1–39 odd
S 179/44, 46

Maximum
181/1–35 odd, 37–41
S 179/44–50 even

Additional A Exercises

Factor.

1. $2x^2 + 5x + 2$
  $(2x + 1)(x + 2)$
2. $5x^2 + 8x + 3$
  $(5x + 3)(x + 1)$
3. $3x^2 + 8x + 4$
  $(3x + 2)(x + 2)$
4. $3x^2 - 4x + 1$
  $(3x - 1)(x - 1)$
5. $2x^2 - 9x + 9$
  $(2x - 3)(x - 3)$
6. $5x^2 + 9x - 2$
  $(5x - 1)(x + 2)$

**Additional Answers
Written Exercises**

1. $(2x + 3)(x + 1)$
2. $(2n + 1)(n + 3)$
3. $(5a + 1)(a + 1)$
4. $(4n + 1)(2n + 1)$
5. $(7n - 1)(n - 1)$
6. $(7k - 1)(2k - 1)$
7. $(5y - 1)(y - 3)$
8. $(7y - 4)(y - 2)$
9. prime
10. $(3z - 2)(z + 1)$
11. $(2t + 3)(t - 2)$
12. $(3a + 5)(a - 1)$
13. $(4y + 3)(y - 1)$
14. $(3a - 1)(3a + 2)$

(continued)

Factor. Check by multiplying the factors. If the expression is not factorable, write "prime."

31. $-48c^2 + 29c + 15$ $(15 - 16c)(1 + 3c)$

32. $-21b^2 + 4b + 12$ $(6 - 7b)(2 + 3b)$

33. $108x^2 + 15x - 7$ $(3x + 1)(36x - 7)$

34. $6x^2 - 17x - 45$ $(3x + 5)(2x - 9)$

35. $42y^2 + 41y + 9$ $(14y + 9)(3y + 1)$

36. $40a^2 - 7a - 21$ Prime

C **37.** $2(y + 4)^2 - (y + 4) - 3(2y + 5)(y + 5)$

38. $3(a + b)^2 - 17(a + b) - 6$ $(3a + 3b + 1)(a + b - 6)$

39. $(x^2 - 1)^2 - 14(x^2 - 1) - 15$ $x^2(x + 4)(x - 4)$

40. $(x^2 - 5x - 1)^2 - 25$ $(x - 6)(x + 1)(x - 4)(x - 1)$

41. Show that the product of $6x^2 - 13x - 5$, $15x^2 - 16x - 7$, and $10x^2 - 39x + 35$ is a *perfect square* by showing that it is the square of another polynomial.

Self-Test 3

VOCABULARY   irreducible (p. 176)
                   prime polynomial (p. 176)

Factor.

1. $y^2 + 8y + 15$ **2.** $x^2 - 10x + 16$ Obj. 5-7, p. 175

3. $n^2 - 3n - 28$ **4.** $v^2 + 9v - 36$ Obj. 5-8, p. 178

5. $6x^2 - 19x + 15$ **6.** $3x^2 + 10x - 8$ Obj. 5-9, p. 180

Check your answers with those at the back of the book.

Career Note Meteorologist

Meteorologists study the atmosphere and atmospheric phenomena. The majority of meteorologists specialize in the study of the weather. They make predictions about the weather by examining data on air pressure, temperature, humidity, wind velocity, cloud formations, air masses, and fronts. Most of this data is now collected by weather satellites and processed by computers.

Other meteorologists specialize in atmospheric pollution, weather map analysis, or meteorological instrumentation. Hydrometeorologists study the water cycle. Climatologists specialize in the study of average weather patterns.

The minimum educational requirement for a career in this field is a bachelor's degree with a major in meteorology. General background work includes courses in physics, mathematics, and chemistry.

182   *CHAPTER 5*

GENERAL FACTORING

5-10 *Factoring by Grouping*

OBJECTIVE   To factor polynomials using the distributive axiom.

One of the key tools in factoring is the distributive axiom:

$$a b + a c = a(b + c).$$

This axiom holds not only when a represents a monomial, but also when a represents any polynomial. If $a = 3 + x$,

$$(3 + x) b + (3 + x) c = (3 + x)(b + c).$$

If $a = p - 2q + r$,

$$(p - 2q + r) b + (p - 2q + r) c = (p - 2q + r)(b + c).$$

It will help you in factoring if you learn to recognize factors which are opposites of each other.

Factor	Its Opposite
$a - b$	$-(a - b)$, or $-a + b$, or $b - a$
$4z - y$	$-(4z - y)$, or $-4z + y$, or $y - 4z$
$5 - p - 2q$	$-(5 - p - 2q)$, or $-5 + p + 2q$, or $p + 2q - 5$

EXAMPLE 1   Factor $5(a - b) + 3(b - a)$.

SOLUTION   Notice that $(a - b)$ and $(b - a)$ are opposites. If you express $(b - a)$ as $-(a - b)$, you can then factor the expression using the distributive axiom.

$$5(a - b) + 3(b - a) = 5(a - b) - 3(a - b)$$
$$= 2(a - b)$$

In the following example you first group terms and then factor each group of terms.

EXAMPLE 2   Factor $rq - 2rp + 5q - 10p$.

SOLUTION $\underline{(rq - 2rp)} + \underline{(5q - 10p)} =$

$r(q - 2p) + 5(q - 2p) =$

$(r + 5)(q - 2p)$

The following example applies what you know about factoring trinomial squares and differences of squares.

EXAMPLE 3   Factor $x^2 + 6x + 9 - 9y^2$.

SOLUTION $x^2 + 6x + 9 - 9y^2 = (x + 3)^2 - (3y)^2$
$= (x + 3 - 3y)(x + 3 + 3y)$

FACTORING POLYNOMIALS   **183**

Chalkboard Examples
Factor.
1. $x^2 + 4x + 4 - 4y^2$
   $(x + 2 + 2y)(x + 2 - 2y)$
2. $a(x - y) - (y - x)$
   $(x - y)(a + 1)$
3. $xw - 3x + 2wy - 6y$
   $(x + 2y)(w - 3)$
4. $2ax + 3ay + 2bx + 3by$
   $(a + b)(2x + 3y)$
5. $t^2(t - 1) + (t - 1)$
   $(t - 1)(t^2 + 1)$
6. $x^3 + yx^2 - xy^2 - y^3$
   $(x + y)^2(x - y)$

Suggested Assignments
Minimum
Day 1: 184/1–35 odd
   R 182/*Self-Test 3*
   S 169/6, 8, 34, 38, 40
Day 2: 184/37–45 odd
   186/1–18
*Note: Day 2 finishes Sec.
   5-10 and starts Sec.
   5-11*
Average
Day 1: 184/1–35 odd
   R 182/*Self-Test 3*
   S 169/6, 8, 22, 24
Day 2: 184/37–51 odd
   S 182/36, 38, 40
Maximum
   184/1–47 odd
   R 182/*Self-Test 3*

Oral Exercises

State a pair of binomial factors whose product is equal to the given expression.

1. $3(a + b) + x(a + b)$ $(3 + x)(a + b)$

2. $x(y - 7) - 3(y - 7)$ $(x - 3)(y - 7)$

3. $r(p - 2q) - (p - 2q)$ $(r - 1)(p - 2q)$

4. $5x(x - 1) + 2(1 - x)$ $(5x - 2)(x - 1)$

5. $x(a - 5) - y(5 - a)$ $(x + y)(a - 5)$

6. $5a(2a - b) + 3b(b - 2a)$ $(5a - 3b)(2a - b)$

Written Exercises

Factor. Check by multiplying the factors.

A
1. $a(x - 5) + b(x - 5)$
2. $r(2s - 1) + k(2s - 1)$
3. $x^2(5 - r) + (5 - r)$
4. $a(y + 3) - (y + 3)$
5. $2a(4 - y) - b(4 - y)$
6. $(r - 25) + k(r - 25)$
7. $x(a + b) + y(a + b)$
8. $a(k - 3c) - (k - 3c) + b(k - 3c)$
9. $x^2(2d - e + f) + (f - e + 2d)$
10. $a(1 - x) + b(x - 1)$
11. $3a(2 - y) + 7(y - 2)$
12. $x(c - 2d) + 3(2d - c)$
13. $6c(z - 3) - (3 - z)$
14. $5a(p - 5) - 6(5 - p)$
15. $(2a - b + 3c) + x(b - 2a - 3c)$
16. $x^2 + xy + xz + yz$
17. $2p + ap + 2q + aq$
18. $y^2 - 3y + yz - 3z$
19. $pq + 2qr + 2r^2 + pr$
20. $6x - 3y + 2zx - yz$
21. $ab - 2b + ac - 2c$
22. $x^3 - 2x^2 + 3x - 6$
23. $2x^3 + x^2 + 8x + 4$
24. $2ac - 6bc - 3a + 9b$
25. $4x^2 - 8xy - 3x + 6y$
26. $3rs - s + 12r - 4$
27. $4y^2 + 8ay - y - 2a$
28. $2a^3 - a^2 - 10a + 5$
29. $4x^2 - 2xy - 7yz + 14xz$
30. $2x^3 - 6x^2 - 5x + 15$

Factor each expression as a difference of two squares.

B
31. $a^2 - (2b + 3c)^2$
32. $(p - q)^2 - r^2$
33. $36k^2 - (2a - c)^2$
34. $25 - (5x - y)^2$
35. $(x - 4y)^2 - 9$
36. $(a + b)^2 - (c + d)^2$
37. $x^2 + 6x + 9 - y^2$
38. $p^2 - 2pq + q^2 - 4$
39. $h^2 - 12h + 36 - k^2$
40. $a^2 - x^2 - 2x - 1$
41. $25 - a^2 - 4ab - 4b^2$
42. $4a - 4a^2 + 49k^2 - 1$
43. $16y^2 + 8y + 1 - 16z^2$
44. $k^2 + 2kt + t^2 - n^2 - 8n - 16$

Factor.

45. $8b - 4 + a^2 - 4b^2$
46. $x^2 - 16y^2 - 6x + 9$
47. $a^2 - b^2 - 10bc - 25c^2$
48. $8yz - 4y^2 - 4z^2 + x^2$
49. $9a^2 + 9b^2 - 9c^2 - 18ab$
50. $x^4 - 8x^2 + 16 - 16y^2$
51. $a^2 - 2ab + b^2 - 3a + 3b$
52. $x^2 - 16y^2 + 2x + 8y$

C
53. Factor $4x^4 + 1$ by writing it as $4x^4 + 4x^2 + 1 - 4x^2$, a difference of two squares. $(2x^2 - 2x + 1)(2x^2 + 2x + 1)$

54. Factor $64y^4 + 1$. $(8y^2 - 4y + 1)(8y^2 + 4y + 1)$

5-11 *Using More Than One Method of Factoring*

OBJECTIVE To factor polynomials completely.

A polynomial is said to be **factored completely** when it is expressed as the product of prime polynomials and a monomial. The following guidelines will help you factor polynomials completely.

GUIDELINES FOR FACTORING

1. Always factor out the greatest monomial factor first.
2. Look for a difference of squares.
3. Look for a trinomial square.
4. If a trinomial is not a square, look for a pair of binomial factors.
5. If a polynomial has four or more terms, look for a way to group the terms in pairs or in a group of three terms that is a trinomial square.
6. Make sure that each factor is prime. Check your work by multiplying the factors.

In each of the following examples the given polynomial is factored completely.

EXAMPLE 1 Factor $3ax^2 - 27ay^2$.

SOLUTION First factor out the greatest monomial factor. Then factor the difference of squares.

$$3ax^2 - 27ay^2 = 3a(x^2 - 9y^2)$$
$$= 3a(x + 3y)(x - 3y)$$

EXAMPLE 2 Factor $-x^2 + 8x - 16$.

SOLUTION First factor out -1. Then factor the trinomial square.

$$-x^2 + 8x - 16 = -1(x^2 - 8x + 16)$$
$$= -(x - 4)^2$$

EXAMPLE 3 Factor $12ax^2 - 14ax - 40a$.

SOLUTION First factor out the greatest monomial factor. Then find the pair of binomial factors.

$$12ax^2 - 14ax - 40a = 2a(6x^2 - 7x - 20)$$
$$= 2a(3x + 4)(2x - 5)$$

FACTORING POLYNOMIALS **185**

Chalkboard Examples

Factor completely.

1. $2a^3 - 2a$
   $2a(a + 1)(a - 1)$

2. $6x^3 + 2x^2 + 2x$
   $2x(3x^2 + x + 1)$

3. $-3k^2 + 27k - 60$
   $-3(k - 5)(k - 4)$

4. $5a^2 - 45b^2$
   $5(a + 3b)(a - 3b)$

5. $75t^4 + 60t^3 + 12t^2$
   $3t^2(5t + 2)^2$

6. $x^3 + x^2 - x - 1$
   $(x + 1)^2(x - 1)$

Supplementary Materials

Practice Master 31

Progress Test 17

Suggested Assignments

Minimum
NOTE: Day 2 of Sec. 5-10
    finishes Sec. 5-10 and
    starts Sec. 5-11
    186/19–43 odd
    S 184/47, 49, 51

Average
    186/1–43 odd
    S 184/53

Maximum
Day 1: 186/1–43 odd
    S 184/49, 51, 53
Day 2: 186/44–51
    S 184/52, 54

Additional A Exercises

Factor completely.

1. $2x^2 + 10x + 12$
$2(x + 3)(x + 2)$

2. $4x^2 + 12x - 16$
$4(x + 4)(x - 1)$

3. $3a^2 - 75$
$3(a - 5)(a + 5)$

4. $ax^2 - 16a$
$a(x - 4)(x + 4)$

5. $x^4 - 3x^3 - 10x^2$
$x^2(x - 5)(x + 2)$

6. $3x^4 - 3$
$3(x^2 + 1)(x - 1)(x + 1)$

Additional Answers
Written Exercises

1. $3a(b + 3a)(b - 3a)$
2. $a(2a + 1)(2a - 1)$
3. $2(4x^2 - 4x - 1)$
4. $2(3a - 4b)(2a + b)$
5. $4(a - 4)(a + 2)$
6. $5(3x + y)(2x - y)$
7. $(x^2 + y^2)(x + y)(x - y)$
8. $ax(a + 2x)(a - 2x)$
9. $2(x^2 + 9)(x + 3)(x - 3)$
10. $(b + 3)(a + 3)(a - 3)$
11. $(a + 2b + 1)(a - 2b - 1)$
12. $(3a + b + 2)(3a - b - 2)$
13. $(y + 2)(y - 2)(y + 1) \times (y - 1)$
14. $(x + 5)(x - 5)(x + 1) \times (x - 1)$
15. $[(b + 3)(b - 3)]^2$
16. $2(x + 2)(x - 2)(x^2 + 1)$

(continued on page 198)

Quick Quiz

Factor completely.

1. $ax + ay - x - y$
$(a - 1)(x + y)$

2. $m^2 + 2mn + n^2 - 1$
$(m + n + 1)(m + n - 1)$

3. $3xy^2 + 12xy + 12x$
$3x(y + 2)^2$

4. $2x^3 - 2x^2 - 12x$
$2x(x - 3)(x + 2)$

Oral Exercises

State the greatest monomial factor of each polynomial.

1. $3ab^2 - 27a^3$ 3a
2. $-a + 4a^3$ $-a$ or a
3. $-8x + 8x^2 - 2$ 2
4. $12a^2 - 10ab - 8b^2$ 2
5. $4(a - 1)^2 - 36$ 4
6. $30x^2 - 5xy - 5y^2$ 5

Written Exercises

A 1–6. Factor the polynomials in Oral Exercises 1-6 completely.

Factor completely.

7. $x^4 - y^4$
8. $a^3x - 4ax^3$
9. $2x^4 - 162$
10. $a^2b - 9b + 3a^2 - 27$
11. $a^2 - 1 - 4b^2 - 4b$
12. $9a^2 - b^2 - 4b - 4$
13. $y^4 - 5y^2 + 4$
14. $x^4 - 26x^2 + 25$
15. $b^4 - 18b^2 + 81$
16. $2x^4 - 6x^2 - 8$
17. $10k^3 - 25k - 15k^2$
18. $-x^2 + 6xy - 9y^2$

B 19. $2x^2 - 8y^2 + 16y - 8$
20. $x^2 - 9y^2 - 2x + 6y$
21. $4(a - 3)^2 - 4$
22. $x^8 - y^8$
23. $x^3 - x^2 - 4x + 4$
24. $a^3 + 2a^2 - 9a - 18$
25. $m^2 + m - k^2 - k$
26. $2pa + 2pr + r^2 - a^2$
27. $a^2c - 4abc - 9c^3 + 4b^2c$
28. $n(n + 1)(n + 2) - 3n(n + 1)$
29. $a(x^2 - a^2) + x(a - x)$
30. $2x^2(x + 1)(x + 3) - 6x^2$
31. $a^2(b - 3c) + 9b^2(3c - b)$
32. $(a - b)^3 + 4(b - a)$
33. $2 - 2y^2 - 8x^2 - 8xy$
34. $a^2 - 2ab + b^2 - 3a + 3b$
35. $x(x^2 - 1) - 2(x + 1)$
36. $x(x - 5)(x - 2) + 6(x - 2)$
37. $ax + 2ay - 3x^2 + 12y^2$
38. $2c^{16} - 2d^{16}$
39. $2p(p + 1)(p - 6) + 16(p + 1)$
40. $4a^2(2a - 1) - 4a(2a - 1) + (2a - 1)$
41. $p^2 - 4pq + 4q^2 - r^2 + 4sr - 4s^2$
42. $16a^2 - 16b^2 - 64bc - 64c^2$
43. $45x^2 - 177xy - 12y^2$

C 44. $(a^2 - 4)^2 - (a - 2)^2$
45. $4b^2c^2 - (b^2 + c^2 - a^2)^2$
46. $(a^2 - 9)^2 - (3 - a)^2$
47. $(a + 3b)^2 - (a^2 - 9b^2)^2$
48. $x^2(x^2 - 4) + 4x(x^2 - 4) + 4(x^2 - 4)$
49. $x^2 + 4x^2y^2 + y^2 + 2xy - x^4 - 4y^4$
50. $t^3 + t^2 - t - 1$
51. $x^3 - x^2 - 4x + 4$

Self-Test 4

VOCABULARY   factor completely (p. 185)

Factor completely.

1. $xy - 2x + 6y - 12$
2. $n^2 + 8n + 16 - 9m^2$
3. $4ax^2 - 16ax + 16a$
4. $4xy^2 - 24xy + 36x$

Obj. 5-10, p. 183
Obj. 5-11, p. 185

Check your answers with those at the back of the book.

APPLICATIONS OF FACTORING

5-12 *Solving Equations in Factored Form*

OBJECTIVE To solve equations when one side is in factored form and the other side is 0.

The **converse** of a statement in if-then form is obtained by interchanging the "if" and "then" parts of the statement. The converse of a true statement may be either true or false.

By the multiplicative property of zero you know that for any two real numbers a and b:

$$\text{If } a = 0 \text{ or } b = 0, \text{ then } ab = 0.$$

You can show (see Exercise 13 on page 188) that the converse of the statement above is also true.

$$\text{If } ab = 0, \text{ then } a = 0 \text{ or } b = 0.$$

You can use the words *if and only if* to combine a statement and its converse. The *zero-product property* below combines the multiplicative property of zero and its converse into a single statement.

ZERO-PRODUCT PROPERTY

For all real numbers a and b,

$$ab = 0 \text{ if and only if } a = 0 \text{ or } b = 0.$$

The zero-product property is useful in solving certain equations.

EXAMPLE Solve $(x + 5)(x - 4) = 0$.

SOLUTION One of the factors of the left side must be 0. Thus,

$$x + 5 = 0 \qquad \text{or} \qquad x - 4 = 0$$
$$x = -5 \qquad\qquad\qquad x = 4$$

Of course, you might have seen without writing the equations that when $x = -5$ or $x = 4$ one of the factors will be 0. Either method gives the solution set $\{-5, 4\}$. *Answer*

The zero-product property is true for any number of factors. *A product of factors is equal to zero if and only if one or more of the factors is zero.*

FACTORING POLYNOMIALS   **187**

Teaching Suggestions p. T83

Suggested Extensions p. T83

Chalkboard Examples

Solve.

1. $(a - 3)(a + 7) = 0$
   $\{3, -7\}$
2. $(x + 1)(x - 7) = 0$
   $\{-1, 7\}$
3. $23a(a - 2) = 0$ $\{0, 2\}$
4. $(4y - 1)(y - 7) = 0$
   $\left\{\dfrac{1}{4}, 7\right\}$
5. $2(3z - 2)(4z + 9) = 0$
   $\left\{\dfrac{2}{3}, \dfrac{-9}{4}\right\}$
6. $-2(x - 1)(x + 1) = 0$
   $\{1, -1\}$

Suggested Assignments

Minimum
    188/1–10
R 186/Self-Test 4
S 186/36, 38, 40

Average
    188/1–11
R 186/Self-Test 4
S 186/45, 47, 48

Maximum
    188/1–11
R 186/Self-Test 4

Additional A Exercises

Solve.

1. $5x(x - 2) = 0$ $\{0, 2\}$

2. $3y(y + 8) = 0$ $\{0, -8\}$

3. $(x + 3)(x + 2) = 0$
    $\{-3, -2\}$

4. $(x - 5)(x + 10) = 0$
    $\{5, -10\}$

5. $(y - 9)(y - 11) = 0$
    $\{9, 11\}$

6. $(y - 6)(y + 13) = 0$
    $\{6, -13\}$

Oral Exercises

State the values of the variable which make the open sentence a true statement.

1. $x(x - 9) = 0$ $0, 9$

2. $y(y + 7) = 0$ $0, -7$

3. $(z - 2)(z - 3) = 0$ $2, 3$

4. $(k + 4)(k - 5) = 0$ $-4, 5$

5. $2b(b - 6) = 0$ $0, 6$

6. $(c + 8)(c + 1) = 0$
    $-8, -1$

Written Exercises

Solve.

A   **1.** $3k(k - 7) = 0$ $\{0, 7\}$ **2.** $(x - 8)(x + 8) = 0$ $\{8, -8\}$ **3.** $(z - 7)(z - 8) = 0$ $\{7, 8\}$

   4. $(n + 17)(n + 7) = 0$
      $\{-7, -17\}$ **5.** $(y - 15)(y - 100) = 0$ **6.** $35n(n - 35) = 0$ $\{0, 35\}$
      $\{15, 100\}$

Solve.

SAMPLE $(2z - 3)(z - 5) = 0$

SOLUTION $2z - 3 = 0$ or $z - 5 = 0$

$\qquad\qquad\quad 2z = 3$ $\qquad\qquad\qquad z = 5$

$\qquad\qquad\quad z = \dfrac{3}{2}$

$\qquad\qquad \therefore$ the solution set is $\{\frac{3}{2}, 5\}$.   *Answer*

   7. $(3x - 1)(2x + 5) = 0$ **8.** $(4k + 2)(k - 3) = 0$ **9.** $(4z + 5)5z = 0$ $\{0, -\frac{5}{4}\}$
      $\{\frac{1}{3}, -\frac{5}{2}\}$ $\qquad\qquad\quad \{3, -\frac{1}{2}\}$

B **10.** $3n(n - 4)(2n + 7) = 0$ **11.** $2x(2x - 5)(5x + 2) = 0$ **12.** $m(3m - 8)(3m + 1) = 0$
      $\{0, 4, -\frac{7}{2}\}$ $\qquad\quad \{0, \frac{5}{2}, -\frac{2}{5}\}$ $\qquad\qquad \{0, \frac{8}{3}, -\frac{1}{3}\}$

C **13.** Give the missing reasons in the proof of the statement: If $ab = 0$,
      then $a = 0$ or $b = 0$.

   Case 1. If $a = 0$, then there is nothing to prove.

   Case 2. If $a \neq 0$:

$\qquad ab = 0$ $\qquad\qquad$ (1) Given

$\qquad$ There is a unique $\qquad$ (2) $\underline{\quad?\quad}$ Axiom of reciprocals
$\qquad$ real number $\frac{1}{a}$.

$\qquad \frac{1}{a}(ab) = \frac{1}{a}(0)$ $\qquad$ (3) $\underline{\quad?\quad}$ Mult. prop. of equality

$\qquad \frac{1}{a}(ab) = 0$ $\qquad\qquad$ (4) $\underline{\quad?\quad}$ Mult. prop. of zero

$\qquad \left(\frac{1}{a} \cdot a\right)b = 0$ $\qquad$ (5) $\underline{\quad?\quad}$ Assoc. ax. for mult.

$\qquad (1)b = 0$ $\qquad\qquad$ (6) $\underline{\quad?\quad}$ Axiom of reciprocals

$\qquad b = 0$ $\qquad\qquad\quad$ (7) $\underline{\quad?\quad}$ Identity axiom for mult.

188   *CHAPTER 5*

5-13 *Solving Equations by Factoring*

OBJECTIVE   To solve polynomial equations by factoring.

A **polynomial equation** is an equation whose sides are both polynomials. Polynomial equations may be named by the term of highest degree. When $a \neq 0$:

$$ax + b = 0 \quad \textbf{linear equation}$$

$$ax^2 + bx + c = 0 \quad \textbf{quadratic equation}$$

$$ax^3 + bx^2 + cx + d = 0 \quad \textbf{cubic equation}$$

Many polynomial equations can be solved by factoring and then applying the zero-product property. Often, the first step in solving such an equation is to transform it into **standard form** in which one side is 0 and the other side is a simplified polynomial arranged in descending powers of the variable.

EXAMPLE 1   Solve the quadratic equation $2x^2 = x + 1$.

SOLUTION

1. Transform into standard form.
2. Factor the left side.
3. Set each factor equal to zero and solve.
4. Check the solutions in the original equation $2x^2 = x + 1$.

$$2x^2 - x - 1 = 0$$
$$(x - 1)(2x + 1) = 0$$

$x - 1 = 0$	$2x + 1 = 0$
$x = 1$	$x = -\frac{1}{2}$

$$2(-\tfrac{1}{2})^2 \overset{?}{=} -\tfrac{1}{2} + 1 \qquad 2(1)^2 \overset{?}{=} 1 + 1$$
$$2(\tfrac{1}{4}) \overset{?}{=} \tfrac{1}{2} \qquad\qquad\qquad 2 = 2 \ \checkmark$$
$$\tfrac{1}{2} = \tfrac{1}{2} \ \checkmark$$

$\therefore$ the solution set is $\{-\tfrac{1}{2}, 1\}$.   ***Answer***

EXAMPLE 2   Solve the cubic equation $x^3 + 4x = 4x^2$

SOLUTION

1. Transform into standard form.
2. Factor completely.
3. Solve.
4. The check is left to you.

$$x^3 - 4x^2 + 4x = 0$$
$$x(x^2 - 4x + 4) = 0$$
$$x(x - 2)(x - 2) = 0$$

$x = 0$	$x = 2$	$x = 2$

$\therefore$ the solution set is $\{0, 2\}$.   ***Answer***

In the last example, 2 is called a *double root* of the equation because the factor $(x - 2)$ occurs twice in the factored form of the equation. Note, however, that 2 is listed only once in the solution set.

FACTORING POLYNOMIALS   **189**

Teaching Suggestions p. T84

Suggested Extensions p. T84

Chalkboard Examples

Solve.

1. $3x^2 - 5x = 2$
   $3x^2 - 5x - 2 = 0$
   $(3x + 1)(x - 2) = 0$
   $\left\{ -\dfrac{1}{3}, 2 \right\}$

2. $t^3 - 16t = 0$
   $t(t^2 - 16) = 0$
   $t(t - 4)(t + 4) = 0$
   $\{0, 4, -4\}$

3. $4x^2 + 112 = 44x$
   $4x^2 - 44x + 112 = 0$
   $4(x^2 - 11x + 28) = 0$
   $4(x - 4)(x - 7) = 0$
   $\{7, 4\}$

4. $d^3 - d + 2d^2 - 2 = 0$
   $d(d^2 - 1) + 2(d^2 - 1) = 0$
   $(d + 2)(d^2 - 1) = 0$
   $(d + 2)(d + 1)(d - 1) = 0$
   $\{-2, -1, 1\}$

5. $(x - 3)(x - 2) = 20$
   $x^2 - 5x + 6 = 20$
   $x^2 - 5x - 14 = 0$
   $(x - 7)(x + 2) = 0$
   $\{7, -2\}$

6. $x^2 = x$
   $x^2 - x = 0$
   $x(x - 1) = 0$
   $\{0, 1\}$

Supplementary Material

Practice Master 32

Suggested Assignments

Minimum
Day 1: 190/1–25
    S 188/11, 12
Day 2: 190/27–41 odd
Average
    190/1–43 odd
    S 188/12
Maximum
Day 1: 190/1–47 odd
    S 188/12, 13
Day 2: 190/49–55 odd
    192/P: 2, 4–6, 8–11
NOTE: *Day 2 of Sec. 5-13*
    finishes Sec. 5-13 and
    starts Sec. 5-14.

Additional A Exercises

Solve.

1. $x^2 + 2x - 3 = 0$ $\{-3, 1\}$

2. $a^2 + 5a + 6 = 0$ $\{-2, -3\}$

3. $c^2 + 4c + 4 = 0$ $\{-2\}$

4. $y^2 - 6y + 9 = 0$ $\{3\}$

5. $x^2 - 7x + 10 = 0$ $\{5, 2\}$

6. $a^2 - 8a + 12 = 0$ $\{6, 2\}$

Additional Answers
Written Exercises

1. $\{4, 9\}$ **2.** $\{7, -9\}$

3. $\{2, -4\}$ **4.** $\{2, 3\}$

5. $\{3, -2\}$ **6.** $\{5\}$

7. $\{8, -3\}$ **8.** $\{1, 9\}$

9. $\{0, 16\}$ **10.** $\{4, -4\}$

11. $\left\{\frac{3}{2}, -\frac{3}{2}\right\}$ **12.** $\{2\}$

13. $\left\{\frac{1}{3}, -1\right\}$ **14.** $\{1, 0, -1\}$

15. $\{2, 0, -2\}$ **16.** $\{6, -5\}$

17. $\left\{3, -\frac{1}{2}\right\}$ **18.** $\{0, 5\}$

19. $\{6, -6\}$ **20.** $\left\{\frac{5}{2}, -\frac{1}{2}\right\}$

21. $\left\{\frac{1}{3}, -1\right\}$ **22.** $\{3, -8\}$

23. $\{0, 2\}$ **24.** $\left\{\frac{1}{2}, -\frac{1}{3}\right\}$

25. $\left\{\frac{7}{2}, -\frac{11}{3}\right\}$ **26.** $\{3, -1\}$

27. $\left\{-\frac{3}{2}, -\frac{4}{3}\right\}$ **28.** $\left\{\frac{1}{4}, 7\right\}$

29. $\left\{5, -\frac{4}{3}\right\}$ **30.** $\left\{\frac{8}{3}, -\frac{9}{2}\right\}$

31. $\{0, 4, 8\}$ **32.** $\{0, 7\}$

33. $\{2, 3, -2, -3\}$

34. $\{2, -2, -1\}$

35. $\{1, -1\}$

36. $\{1, 3, -1, -3\}$

37. $\{1, -1\}$ **38.** $\{0, 5, 9\}$

39. $\{0, 5, -5\}$ **40.** $\{3, -4\}$

41. $\{9, -2\}$ **42.** $\{2, -2\}$

Example 2 on page 189 shows the correct way to solve an equation in which a variable or variable expression is a factor of both sides of the equation. CAUTION: Never transform an equation by dividing by an expression containing a variable. If you divide both sides of $x(x^2 - 4x + 4) = 0$ by x in Example 2, you will not be aware that 0 is a solution of the equation.

Written Exercises

Solve.

A

1. $x^2 - 13x + 36 = 0$ **2.** $y^2 + 2y - 63 = 0$ **3.** $z^2 + 2z - 8 = 0$

4. $x^2 - 5x + 6 = 0$ **5.** $x^2 - x - 6 = 0$ **6.** $x^2 + 25 = 10x$

7. $n^2 - 5n = 24$ **8.** $k^2 + 9 = 10k$ **9.** $y^2 - 16y = 0$

10. $y^2 - 16 = 0$ **11.** $4x^2 - 9 = 0$ **12.** $a^2 - 4a + 4 = 0$

13. $3x^2 + 2x - 1 = 0$ **14.** $a^3 - a = 0$ **15.** $n^3 - 4n = 0$

16. $x^2 - x - 30 = 0$ **17.** $2x^2 - 5x - 3 = 0$ **18.** $y^3 - 10y^2 + 25y = 0$

19. $n^2 = 36$ **20.** $4x^2 = 8x + 5$ **21.** $3y^2 + 2y = 1$

22. $a^2 = 24 - 5a$ **23.** $4a^2 = 8a$ **24.** $6x^2 = x + 1$

25. $6x^2 + x = 77$ **26.** $3x^2 - 6x = 9$ **27.** $6x^2 + 17x + 12 = 0$

28. $4y^2 + 7 = 29y$ **29.** $6y^2 = 22y + 40$ **30.** $6z^2 + 11z = 72$

B

31. $x^3 - 12x^2 + 32x = 0$ **32.** $y^3 + 49y = 14y^2$ **33.** $y^4 - 13y^2 + 36 = 0$

34. $t^3 + t^2 = 4t + 4$ **35.** $a^4 - 2a^2 + 1 = 0$ **36.** $2x^4 - 20x^2 + 18 = 0$

37. $9t^3 - 9t^2 - 9t + 9 = 0$ **38.** $y^3 + 45y = 14y^2$ **39.** $y^5 = 25y^3$

40. $(x - 2)(x + 3) = 6$ **41.** $(a - 5)(a - 2) = 28$ **42.** $4x^4 = 64$

C

43. $x(x - 2)^2 = 16x$ $\{6, 0, -2\}$ **44.** $2x(x - 2) = 6(x - 2)$ $\{2, 3\}$ **45.** $2(x^2 - 9) = x(3 - x)$ $\{3, -2\}$

46. $3x(x^2 - 4) = 12(x^2 - 4)$ **47.** $4(y - 1)^2 = 8(y - 1)$ **48.** $x(x + 1)(x + 2) = 5x(x + 2)$
                $\{2, 4, -2\}$ $\{1, 3\}$ $\{0, 4, -2\}$

Find an equation in standard form having the given solution set.

49. $\{1, 3\}$ $x^2 - 4x + 3 = 0$ **50.** $\{-7, 4\}$ $x^2 + 3x - 28 = 0$ **51.** $\left\{\frac{2}{3}, -\frac{1}{3}\right\}$ $9x^2 - 3x - 2 = 0$

52. $\{-3, 0, 1\}$ $x^3 + 2x^2 - 3x = 0$ **53.** $\left\{\frac{4}{5}, -\frac{4}{5}\right\}$ $25x^2 - 16 = 0$ **54.** $\{-2, -1, 0, 1, 2\}$ $x^5 - 5x^3 + 4x = 0$

55. What is wrong with the following "proof" that $2 = 1$? In Step 4, both sides of the equation are being divided by zero.

Let a and b be nonzero real numbers such that $a = b$.

$a^2 = ab$ (1) Multiply both sides by a.

$a^2 - b^2 = ab - b^2$ (2) Subtract b^2 from both sides.

$(a - b)(a + b) = b(a - b)$ (3) Factor both sides.

$(a + b) = b$ (4) Divide both sides by $a - b$.

$b + b = b$ (5) Substitute a for b (since $a = b$).

$2b = b$ (6) Combine like terms.

$2 = 1$ (7) Divide both sides by b.

5-14 *Solving Problems by Factoring*

OBJECTIVE   To solve problems involving quadratic equations.

The problems in this section all lead to polynomial equations which can be solved by factoring. Sometimes a solution of the equation may not satisfy some of the conditions of the problem. For example, a negative number could not be a length or a width. You simply discard solutions that do not make sense for the problem.

EXAMPLE 1   Jason is mowing a yard 16 m long and 12 m wide. He mows continuously around the yard working toward the center. He wonders how wide a strip must be cut before he is half done.

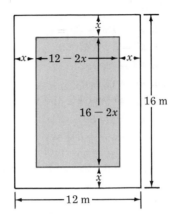

SOLUTION

Step 1   The problem asks for the width of the strip that must be cut in order for half the lawn to be mowed.

Step 2   Let x = width of the strip cut (in meters). Then the length of uncut lawn = $16 - 2x$ and the width of uncut lawn = $12 - 2x$.

Step 3   Area of uncut lawn = $\frac{1}{2}$ the area of the yard.
$$(16 - 2x)(12 - 2x) = \tfrac{1}{2}(16 \cdot 12)$$

Step 4
$$192 - 56x + 4x^2 = 96$$
$$4x^2 - 56x + 96 = 0$$
$$x^2 - 14x + 24 = 0$$
$$(x - 2)(x - 12) = 0$$

$$x - 2 = 0 \quad | \quad x - 12 = 0$$
$$x = 2 \quad | \quad x = 12$$

Step 5   *Check:* When $x = 2$, the area of the uncut lawn is $(16 - 2x) \cdot (12 - 2x) = 12 \cdot 8 = 96$, which is exactly half of $16 \cdot 12 = 192$, the area of the whole yard.

When $x = 12$, the width $12 - 2x$ is negative. Because a negative width is meaningless, we must reject $x = 12$ as an answer.

∴ the width of the strip is 2 m.   *Answer*

You may wonder how the equation in Step 3 can produce a solution, 12, which does not check. The reason is that the equation in Step 3 gives only one of the requirements of the problem. The requirements that the lawn have a positive width $(12 - 2x > 0)$ and a positive length $(16 - 2x > 0)$ were not written down. Usually, it is easier to write only the equation and then check its solutions against the other conditions stated in the problem.

FACTORING POLYNOMIALS   **191**

Teaching Suggestions p. T84

Suggested Extensions p. T84

Chalkboard Examples

Solve.

1. Find two consecutive even integers whose product is 168.
   Step 2 Let x = the first integer. Then $x + 2$ = the second integer.
   Step 3 $x(x + 2) = 168$
   Step 4 $x^2 + 2x = 168$
   $x^2 + 2x - 168 = 0$
   $(x + 14)(x - 12) = 0$
   $x = -14$ or $x = 12$
   ∴ The integers are -14 and -12, or 12 and 14.

2. The number of calories in a baked potato is 20 more than the number of calories in an apple. The product of the numbers is 6300. Find the number of calories in each.
   Step 2 Let a = number of calories in an apple. Then $a + 20$ = number of calories in baked potato.
   Step 3 $a(a + 20) = 6300$
   Step 4 $a^2 + 20a = 6300$
   $a^2 + 20a - 6300 = 0$
   $(a + 90)(a - 70) = 0$
   $a = -90$ or $a = 70$
   Reject -90
   ∴ The apple has 70 calories and the baked potato has 90 calories.

Supplementary Materials

Practice Master 33

Progress Test 18

Suggested Assignments
Minimum
Day 1: 192/P: 1, 3, 6–8
    S 190/36, 40
Day 2: 193/P: 10–12, 14, 15,
        20
Day 3: 194/P: 21–23, 26
    R 195/Self-Test 5
Average
Day 1: 192/P: 1–13 odd
    S 190/42, 44, 47
Day 2: 193/P: 16, 18, 20–23
Day 3: 194/P: 24–26
    R 195/Self-Test 5
Maximum
NOTE: Day 2 of Sec. 5-13
        finishes Sec. 5-13 and
        starts Sec. 5-14.
Day 1: 193/P: 13–20
    S 190/38–46 even
Day 2: 194/P: 23–27
    R 195/Self-Test 5

Extra Practice Problems
    p. 517

Additional A Exercises

Solve.

1. The sum of a positive
   number and its square is
   42. Find the number. 6

2. Find two consecutive positive integers whose product is 56. 7 and 8

3. The length of a rectangle
   is 5 cm more than its
   width. If the area of the
   rectangle is 84 cm², find
   its dimensions. 7 cm by
   12 cm

4. A rectangular rug is to be
   placed in a large rectangular room whose dimensions are 8 m by 6 m so
   that a strip of uniform
   width around the rug will
   be left uncovered and half
   of the area of the floor will
   be covered. Find the width
   of the strip of uncovered
   floor between the rug and
   the wall. 1 m

192

In the next example, both solutions of the equation satisfy the conditions of the problem.

You can use the formula

$$h = rt - 4.9t^2$$

to obtain a good approximation of the height h in meters that an object
will reach in t seconds when it is projected upward with an initial speed
of r meters per second (m/s).

EXAMPLE 2

A ball is thrown upward with an initial speed of
34.3 m/s. When is it directly opposite the top of a
tower 49 m high?

SOLUTION

Step 1 The problem asks for the time when the ball
        is opposite the top of the tower.

Step 2 Let $t =$ number of seconds after being
            thrown that the ball is opposite the
            top of the tower,

        and $h =$ height of ball
            $= 49$ (meters),

        and $r =$ initial speed
            $= 34.3$ (meters per second).

Step 3 $h = rt - 4.9t^2$
        $49 = 34.3t - 4.9t^2$
        $\dfrac{49}{4.9} = \dfrac{34.3t}{4.9} - \dfrac{4.9t^2}{4.9}$

Step 4 $10 = 7t - t^2$
        $t^2 - 7t + 10 = 0$
        $(t - 2)(t - 5) = 0$

Completing the solution and checking the values is left to you.

∴ the ball is opposite the top of the tower both 2 s and 5 s after being
thrown. ***Answer***

Problems

Solve.

A 1. The sum of a number and its square is 72. Find the number. 8 or −9
   2. The sum of a positive number and its square is 90. Find the number. 9
   3. A negative number is 42 less than its square. Find the number. −6

4. The square of a number is 20 more than 8 times the number. Find the number. −2 or 10

5. Find two consecutive negative integers whose product is 110. −11, −10

6. The squares of two consecutive positive even integers total 100. Find the integers. 6, 8

7. The length of a rectangle is 9 cm more than its width. Its area is 112 cm². Find the dimensions of the rectangle. 7 cm by 16 cm

8. The length of a rectangle is 4 cm more than twice its width. If the area of the rectangle is 160 cm², find its dimensions. 8 cm by 20 cm

9. A rectangle has perimeter 42 m and area 104 m². Find the dimensions of the rectangle. 8 m by 13 m

10. The dimensions of a rectangle were 5 cm by 9 cm. When both dimensions were increased by equal amounts, the area of the rectangle increased by 120 cm². Find the dimensions of the new rectangle. 11 cm by 15 cm

11. A square field has 4 m added to its length and 2 m added to its width, thereby creating a field with an area of 195 m². Find the dimensions of the original field. 11 m by 11 m

12. The sum of two numbers is 20, and the sum of their squares is 218. Find the numbers. (*Hint:* If one number is x, the other will be $20 - x$.) 7, 13

13. Find two numbers which total 13 and whose squares total 229. 15, −2

14. I am thinking of three consecutive integers. The square of the largest one equals the sum of the squares of the other two. Find the integers. 3, 4, 5 or −1, 0, 1

In Problems 15-19, use the formula stated on page 192. Notice that all numbers appearing are integral multiples of 4.9.

15. A ball is thrown upward with an initial speed of 24.5 m/s. When is it 29.4 m high? (Two answers) In 2 s and 3 s

16. A projectile is fired upward with an initial speed of 2940 m/s. After how many minutes does it hit the ground? 10 min

B 17. A cannon ball is fired upward with an initial speed of 245 m/s. A stationary balloonist at a height of 1960 m sees the ball pass on its way up. How long will it be before the ball passes the balloonist again on its way down? 30 s

18. A ball is thrown upward from the top of a 98 m tower with an initial speed of 39.2 m/s. When does it hit the ground? (*Hint:* If h is the height of the ball above the top of the tower, then $h = -98$ when the ball hits the ground.) In 10 s

19. A ball is thrown upward with an initial speed of 29.4 m/s.
   a. When is the ball 44.1 m high? In 3 s
   b. Explain why 44.1 m is the greatest height attained by the ball.

FACTORING POLYNOMIALS **193**

20. The height of a box is 8 cm, and the total surface area of the box is 114 cm². Find the length of a side of the base of the box if the base is a square.

3 cm

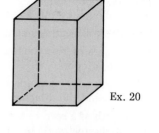

Ex. 20

21. The bottom of a box is a rectangle with dimensions in centimeters of x and $x + 2$. The height of the box is 5 cm and its total surface area is 236 cm². Find x. 6 cm

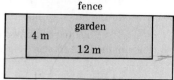

fence

22. A rug placed in a room 12 m long and 9 m wide covers half the floor area and leaves a uniform strip of bare floor around the edges. What are the dimensions of the rug? 9 m by 6 m

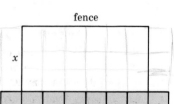

Ex. 23

23. A garden plot 4 m by 12 m has one side along a fence as shown. The area of the garden is to be doubled by digging up a border of uniform width on the other three sides. What should be the width of the border? 2 m

fence

24. The diagram shows a rectangular enclosure formed by a wall and 20 m of fencing. If the area of the enclosure is 48 m², find its dimensions.
6 m (perpendicular to wall) by 8 m (parallel to wall) or
4 m (perpendicular to wall) by 12 m (parallel to wall)

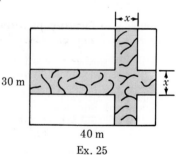

Ex. 24

25. A rectangular garden 40 m by 30 m has two paths crossing through it as shown. If the width of each path in meters is x and the area covered by the paths is 325 m², find x. $x = 5$

26. The side of one cube is 2 cm more than the side of another cube. The volumes of the cubes differ by 152 cm³. Find the lengths of the sides of each cube. 4 cm; 6 cm

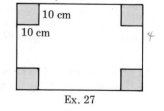

30 m

40 m

Ex. 25

C 27. A rectangular piece of cardboard is 20 cm longer than it is wide. Squares, 10 cm on a side, are cut from the corners of the cardboard, and the sides are folded up to make an open box whose volume is 8 L. Find the dimensions of the original piece of cardboard. (Remember: 1 L = 1000 cm³)
40 cm by 60 cm

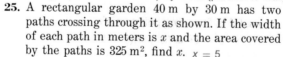

10 cm

10 cm

Ex. 27

Self-Test 5

VOCABULARY
converse of a theorem (p. 187)
polynomial equation (p. 189)
linear equation (p. 189)
quadratic equation (p. 189)
cubic equation (p. 189)
standard form (p. 189)

Solve.

1. $(x - 5)(x - 9) = 0$

2. $z(z + 5)(z - 2) = 0$

Obj. 5-12, p. 187

3. $y^2 - 7y + 10 = 0$

4. $n^2 - n - 20 = 0$

Obj. 5-13, p. 189

5. $v^2 + 8v + 16 = 0$

6. $w^3 + 3w^2 = 28w$

7. The sum of the squares of two consecutive positive integers is 145. Find the integers.

Obj. 5-14, p. 191

Check your answers with those at the back of the book.

Quick Quiz
Solve.

1. $w(w + 3)(w - 1) = 0$
    $0, -3, 1$

2. $x^2 - 12x + 36 = 0$ 6

3. $a^2 - 9a = 52$ $13, -4$

4. $4d^3 - 36d = 0$ $0, 3, -3$

5. The squares of two consecutive positive integers differ by 31. Find the integers. $15, 16$

Supplementary Material
Progress Test 19

Extra Practice pp. 498–500

Chapter Summary

1. The *greatest common factor* of two integers is the greatest integer that divides both of them evenly. The *greatest monomial factor* of two monomials is the common factor that has the greatest coefficient and the greatest degree in each variable.

2. The *cancellation rule for fractions* (page 158) and the *rule of exponents for division* (page 159) can be used to simplify quotients of monomials.

3. The following factoring patterns are useful in factoring polynomials:

   $$a^2 + 2ab + b^2 = (a + b)^2 \qquad a^2 - b^2 = (a + b)(a - b)$$
   $$a^2 - 2ab + b^2 = (a - b)^2$$

4. The guidelines for factoring on page 185 should help you *to factor polynomials completely.*

5. The *zero-product property* is useful in solving *polynomial equations.* See the examples on pages 187 and 189.

Chapter Review

Give the letter of the correct answer.

1. What is the greatest common factor of 20 and 36?

5-1

    a. 2   **(b.)** 4   **c.** 180   **d.** 720

2. Find the prime factorization of 495.

    a. $3 \cdot 5 \cdot 11$ **b.** $3 \cdot 5^2 \cdot 11$ **(c.)** $3^2 \cdot 5 \cdot 11$ **d.** $3^2 \cdot 5^2 \cdot 11$

FACTORING POLYNOMIALS   **195**

196

Additional Answers
Written Exercises
page 184

28. $(a^2 - 5)(2a - 1)$

29. $(2x + 7z)(2x - y)$

30. $(2x^2 - 5)(x - 3)$

31. $(a + 2b + 3c) \times$
$\qquad (a - 2b - 3c)$

32. $(p - q - r)(p - q + r)$

33. $(6k + 2a - c) \times$
$\qquad (6k - 2a + c)$

34. $(5 + 5x - y)$

35. $(x - 4y - 3)(x - 4y + 3)$

36. $(a + b + c + d) \times$
$\qquad (a + b - c - d)$

37. $(x + 3 - y)(x + 3 + y)$

38. $(p - q - 2)(p - q + 2)$

39. $(h - 6 + k)(h - 6 - k)$

40. $(a + x + 1)(a - x - 1)$

41. $(5 + a + 2b)(5 - a - 2b)$

42. $(7k + 2a - 1) \times$
$\qquad (7k - 2a + 1)$

43. $(4y + 1 + 4z) \times$
$\qquad (4y + 1 - 4z)$

44. $(k + t + n + 4) \times$
$\qquad (k + t - n - 4)$

45. $(a + 2b - 2)(a - 2b + 2)$

46. $(x - 3 + 4y)(x - 3 - 4y)$

47. $(a + b + 5c)(a - b - 5c)$

48. $(x + 2y - 2z) \times$
$\qquad (x - 2y + 2z)$

49. $(a - b + c)(a - b - c)$

50. $(x^2 - 4 - 4y)(x^2 - 4 + 4y)$

51. $(a - b)(a - b - 3)$

52. $(x + 4y)(x - 4y + 2)$

---

3. Simplify $\dfrac{3a^2 \cdot 2a^4}{(6a)^2}$.

    a. a^4 **(b.)** $\dfrac{a^4}{6}$ **c.** a^6 **d.** $\dfrac{a^6}{6}$

     5-2

4. What is the greatest monomial factor of $36x^2y - 24xy^2$?

    a. $3x - 2y$ **b.** $6xy$ **c.** $72xy$ **(d.)** $12xy$

5. Divide: $\dfrac{6a^2b^3 - 12a^3b^2}{3ab^2}$

     5-3

    (a.) $2ab - 4a^2$ **b.** $2ab - 12a^3b^2$ **c.** $2a^2b - 4a^2$

6. Express the product $(4x - 2)(3x + 8)$ as a polynomial.

     5-4

    (a.) $12x^2 + 26x - 16$ **b.** $12x^2 - 16x - 16$ **c.** $12x^2 - 24x - 16$

7. Express the product $(3k + 9)(3k - 9)$ as a polynomial.

     5-5

    a. $9k^2 - 27$ **b.** $9k^2 - 54k + 81$ **(c.)** $9k^2 - 81$ **d.** $9k^2 - 27$

8. Factor $9x^2 - 64$ completely.

    a. $(9x + 8)(x - 8)$ **(b.)** $(3x + 8)(3x - 8)$ **c.** $9(x^2 - 6)$

9. Express $(3a^3 - 5)^2$ as a trinomial.

     5-6

    a. $9a^6 - 25$ **b.** $9a^6 - 15a^3 + 25$ **(c.)** $9a^6 - 30a^3 + 25$

10. Factor $c^2 - 13cd + 36d^2$.

     5-7

    a. $(c - 3d)(c - 12d)$ **(b.)** $(c - 4d)(c - 9d)$ **c.** $(c - 6d)^2$

11. Factor $p^2 - 18p - 144$.

     5-8

    a. $(p - 12)^2$ **(b.)** $(p - 24)(p + 6)$ **c.** $(p + 24)(p - 6)$

12. Factor $24x^2 - 23x - 12$.

     5-9

    a. $(8x - 3)(3x + 4)$ **(b.)** $(8x + 3)(3x - 4)$ **c.** $(4x - 3)(6x + 4)$

13. Factor $4a^3 - 2a^2 - 20a + 10$ completely.

     5-10

    a. $2(2a^3 - a^2 - 10a + 5)$ **b.** $2a^2(a - 2) - 10(a - 1)$
    c. $(2a^2 - 10)(2a - 1)$ **(d.)** $2(a^2 - 5)(2a - 1)$

14. Factor $9a^2 - 9b^2 - 6b - 1$ as a difference of squares.

    a. $9(a + b)(a - b) - (6b + 1)$ **b.** $(3a + 1)(3a - 1) - 3b(3b + 2)$
    (c.) $(3a - 3b - 1)(3a + 3b + 1)$ **d.** $9a^2 - 6b - (3b + 1)(3b - 1)$

15. Factor $2n^3 + 4n^2 - 18n - 36$ completely.

     5-11

    a. $2n(n^2 - 9) + 4(n^2 - 9)$ **b.** $2n^2(n + 2) - 18(n + 2)$
    c. $(2n^2 - 18)(n + 2)$ **(d.)** $2(n + 3)(n - 3)(n + 2)$

16. Solve $3n(n - 5)(3n + 5) = 0$.

     5-12

    a. $\{3, 5, -\frac{5}{3}\}$ **b.** $\{0, 3, 5, -\frac{5}{3}\}$ **c.** $\{0, -5, \frac{5}{3}\}$ **(d.)** $\{0, 5, -\frac{5}{3}\}$

17. Solve $2x^2 + 3x - 14 = 0$.

     5-13

    a. $\{\frac{2}{7}, 2\}$ **b.** $\{-2, \frac{7}{2}\}$ **(c.)** $\{2, -\frac{7}{2}\}$ **d.** $\{7, \frac{2}{3}\}$

196   *CHAPTER 5*

18. Solve $9x^2 + 25 = 30x$.

(a.) $\left\{\frac{5}{3}\right\}$ **b.** $\left\{-\frac{5}{3}, 1\right\}$ **c.** $\left\{-\frac{5}{3}\right\}$ **d.** $\left\{\frac{5}{3}, -\frac{5}{3}\right\}$

19. The length of a rectangle is 3 cm more than its width. If the area of   5-14
the rectangle is 180 cm², find the perimeter.

a. 27 cm   (b.) 54 cm   **c.** 72 cm   **d.** 80 cm

Chapter Test ───────────────

1. Find the prime factorization of 360. $2^3 \cdot 3^2 \cdot 5$ 5-1

2. Find the greatest common factor of 54 and 96. 6

Simplify.

3. $\dfrac{-24x^5y^3}{8xy^2}$ $-3x^4y$ **4.** $\dfrac{(4a^3)^2}{(2a)(3a^2)}$ $\dfrac{8a^3}{3}$ 5-2

5. Divide: $\dfrac{3a^2b^3 - 9a^3b^2}{3ab^2}$ $ab - 3a^2$ 5-3

6. Factor $10xy^3 - 5xy^2 + 15xy$ as the product of its greatest monomial factor and another polynomial.

Express each product as a polynomial. $5xy(2y^2 - y + 3)$

7. $(3x - 1)(2x + 4)$ $6x^2 + 10x - 4$ **8.** $(2a^2 - 5)(2a^2 - 3)$ $4a^4 - 16a^2 + 15$ 5-4

9. $(3n + 2)(3n - 2)$ $9n^2 - 4$ **10.** $(4x^2 - 7y)(4x^2 + 7y)$ $16x^4 - 49y^2$ 5-5

11. $(5x + 6)^2$ $25x^2 + 60x + 36$ **12.** $(n^2 - 8)^2$ $n^4 - 16n^2 + 64$ 5-6

Factor if possible. If not possible, write "prime."

13. $9 + 12y + 4y^2$ **14.** $a^2x^2 - 12ax + 36$

15. $x^2 + 12xy + 27y^2$ **16.** $n^2 - 28n + 75$ 5-7

17. $p^2 - 9pq - 22q^2$ **18.** $x^2 - 6x - 36$ 5-8

19. $3n^2 - 5n - 12$ **20.** $25y^2 + 10y - 3$ 5-9

21. $x^2 + 4xy + 4y^2 - 4$ **22.** $4a^2 - 16ab - 3a + 12b$ 5-10

23. $3c^2 - 12d^2$ **24.** $x^4 - 16y^4$ 5-11

25. $x^4 - 10x^2 + 9$ **26.** $6ax^2 - 7ax - 20a$

27. $x^2(3 - y) + 4(y - 3)$ **28.** $-a^2 - 12a - 36$

Solve.

29. $(3x - 7)(x + 2) = 0$ $\left\{-2, \frac{7}{3}\right\}$ **30.** $2x(x + 4)(4x + 9) = 0$ $\left\{0, -4, -\frac{9}{4}\right\}$ 5-12

31. $6x^2 - 6 = 5x$ $\left\{-\frac{2}{3}, \frac{3}{2}\right\}$ **32.** $2y^4 + 72 = 26y^2$ $\{-2, 2, -3, 3\}$ 5-13

33. A border of uniform width surrounds a photograph 15 cm long and   5-14
10 cm wide. If the area of the border equals the area of the photograph, what is the width of the border? 2.5 cm

FACTORING POLYNOMIALS   **197**

Cumulative Review (Chapters 1-5)

Simplify each expression. Assume that no denominator is zero.   **3.** $2y - 28$

6. $-p^2 + 2p$

1. $0.3(-1.7) + 0.3(-0.3)$ -0.6 **2.** $-4(3n - 2 - 5n + 2)$ $8n$ **3.** $(-19 + y) - (-y + 9)$

4. $[-21d \div (-3d)] \div 14$ $\frac{1}{2}$ **5.** $2(-3)^2 \div 3 - 6$ 0 **6.** $-2p^2 + 5p - 3p + p^2$

7. $-6b\left(-b^2 + 3b - \frac{1}{2}\right)$ **8.** $\dfrac{(-3xy^2)^3}{-x^2y^4}$ $27xy^2$ **9.** $\dfrac{6a^6 - 3a^4 - 9a^3}{3a^3}$

$6b^3 - 18b^2 + 3b$

10. $z(3z - 4)(2z + 1)$ **11.** $(rs - 7t^2)(rs + 7t^2)$ $2a^3 - a - 3$

$6z^3 - 5z^2 - 4z$ $r^2s^2 - 49t^4$ **12.** $(4d + 5e)^2$

$16d^2 + 40de + 25e^2$

Evaluate if $a = -4$, $b = -1$, $c = 2$, $d = 7$, and $e = \frac{3}{2}$.

13. $(2d - c) \div ab$ 3 **14.** $e(3a + 2c)$ -12 **15.** $b^3 + 5c^2$ 19

16. Find the prime factorizations of 60 and 75 and find their GCF.

$2^2 \cdot 3 \cdot 5;\ 3 \cdot 5^2;\ 15$

Factor completely, if possible. If not possible, write "prime." ("Pr." = "prime")

17. $12r^2s^2 - 18rs^3 - 48s$ **18.** $81k^2 - z^4$ **19.** $4y^2 + 10y + 25$ Pr.

20. $p^2 - 16pq + 28q^2$ **21.** $-14x^2 + 11x + 9$ **22.** $3t^4 - 6t^3 - 24t^2$

$(p - 14q)(p - 2q)$ $(9 - 7x)(1 + 2x)$ $3t^2(t + 2)(t - 4)$

Solve each equation if $y \in \{-3, -1, 0, 1, 3\}$.

23. $5 - 2y = 5$ 0 **24.** $-y = y - 6$ -3 **25.** $-2(3y - 1) = -4$ 1

Solve. (The equation may be an identity or have no root.) ("N.R." = "no root")

26. $-\frac{1}{6}r = -\frac{1}{2}$ 3 **27.** $7 = -9 + 4t$ 4 **28.** $\dfrac{18c - 6}{3} = -2 + 2(3c)$ Identity

29. $16 = 2 - 7s$ -2 **30.** $14b = -4480$ -320 **31.** $|m| - 2 = -5$ N.R.

32. $9z - 1 = 5z + 7$ 2 **33.** $3(6y - 1) = 8y - 28$ -2.5 **34.** $(9n - 2)(5n + 4) = 0$

35. $0 = 9x^2 - 3x - 20$ **36.** $8 + 6a = 2a^2$ $\{4, -1\}$ **37.** $4d^3 - 4d^2 = -d$

$\left(\frac{5}{3}, -\frac{4}{3}\right)$

34. $\left\{\frac{2}{9}, \frac{-4}{5}\right\}$ **37.** $\left\{0, \frac{1}{2}\right\}$

38. One number is 1 more than twice another number. The sum of the numbers is 46. Find the numbers. 15, 31

39. At Crossroad Stand, an orange costs 3¢ less than an apple. Myra spent $2.34 for eight apples and six oranges. What is the cost of an orange? of an apple? 15¢;18¢

40. Find two consecutive integers such that the sum of their squares is 43 more than their product. 6 and 7 or -7 and -6

41. The dimensions of a rectangle were 5 m by 12 m. When both the length and width were increased by equal amounts, the area of the rectangle increased by 60 m². Find the dimensions of the new rectangle. 8 m by 15 m

Maintaining Skills

Express each fraction as a mixed number.

SAMPLE 1 $\frac{41}{18}$ **SOLUTION** $18\overline{)41}$; $2\frac{5}{18}$ *Answer*

$$\begin{array}{r} 2 \\ 18\overline{)41} \\ \underline{36} \\ 5 \end{array}$$

1. $\frac{59}{6}$ $9\frac{5}{6}$ 2. $\frac{113}{5}$ $22\frac{3}{5}$ 3. $\frac{74}{9}$ $8\frac{2}{9}$ 4. $\frac{64}{15}$ $4\frac{4}{15}$ 5. $\frac{163}{12}$ $13\frac{7}{12}$ 6. $\frac{397}{20}$ $19\frac{17}{20}$

Express each mixed number as a fraction.

SAMPLE 2 $3\frac{4}{5}$ **SOLUTION** $3\frac{4}{5} = 3 + \frac{4}{5} = \frac{15}{5} + \frac{4}{5} = \frac{19}{5}$

7. $2\frac{5}{8}$ $\frac{21}{8}$ 8. $7\frac{1}{6}$ $\frac{43}{6}$ 9. $8\frac{11}{14}$ $\frac{123}{14}$ 10. $15\frac{2}{3}$ $\frac{47}{3}$ 11. $1\frac{17}{24}$ $\frac{41}{24}$ 12. $45\frac{4}{5}$ $\frac{229}{5}$

Express each mixed number as a fraction before performing the indicated operation. Express answers in simplest form. (See page 153 for additional samples.)

SAMPLE 3 $3\frac{5}{12} - 1\frac{2}{3}$ **SOLUTION** $\frac{41}{12} - \frac{5}{3} = \frac{41}{12} - \frac{20}{12} = \frac{21}{12} = \frac{7}{4}$

SAMPLE 4 $2\frac{4}{9} \div 3\frac{2}{3}$ **SOLUTION** $\frac{22}{9} \div \frac{11}{3} = \frac{\overset{2}{\cancel{22}}}{\underset{3}{\cancel{9}}} \times \frac{\overset{1}{\cancel{3}}}{\underset{1}{\cancel{11}}} = \frac{2}{3}$

13. $7\frac{3}{4} + 4\frac{2}{3}$ $12\frac{5}{12}$ 14. $5\frac{8}{15} + 1\frac{4}{5}$ $7\frac{1}{3}$ 15. $2\frac{1}{8} + 2\frac{3}{20}$ $4\frac{11}{40}$ 16. $8\frac{11}{12} - 8\frac{1}{4}$ $\frac{2}{3}$

17. $6\frac{2}{7} - 5\frac{1}{2}$ $\frac{11}{14}$ 18. $9\frac{3}{8} - 4\frac{5}{6}$ $4\frac{13}{24}$ 19. $2\frac{1}{7} \times 1\frac{5}{9}$ $\frac{10}{3}$ 20. $2\frac{3}{4} \times 2\frac{2}{5}$

21. $5\frac{1}{7} \times 17\frac{1}{2}$ 90 22. $1\frac{5}{12} \div 4\frac{1}{4}$ $\frac{1}{3}$ 23. $5\frac{5}{8} \div 2\frac{7}{10}$ $\frac{25}{12}$ 24. $5\frac{3}{5} \div 2\frac{4}{5}$

20. $\frac{33}{5}$

24. 2

Simplify.

SAMPLE 5 $\left(-1\frac{1}{2} + 8 - 2\frac{1}{2}\right)\left(-\frac{1}{2}\right)^2 = (4)\left[-\frac{1}{2}\left(-\frac{1}{2}\right)\right] = 4\left(\frac{1}{4}\right) = 1$

25. $3\frac{8}{9} + \left(-\frac{1}{9}\right) + (-2) + 8\frac{2}{9}$ 10 26. $\left[-8\frac{2}{5} + \left(5 - 6\frac{1}{5}\right)\right]\left(-2\frac{1}{2}\right)$ 24

27. $\left[1\frac{7}{12} - \left(-\frac{2}{3}\right)\right]\left(-\frac{1}{3}\right)^2$ $\frac{1}{4}$ 28. $\left[2\left(-3\frac{1}{2}\right) + (-5)\left(-2\frac{1}{5}\right)\right] \div (-4)$ -1

29. $\left|-3\frac{1}{3}\right| - \left[2 + \left(-7\frac{2}{3}\right)\right]$ 9 30. $(-7.5)(0.2)(-0.5)$ 0.75

FACTORING POLYNOMIALS   **199**

27. $c(a - 2b - 3c) \times$
$(a - 2b + 3c)$
28. $n(n + 1)(n - 1)$
29. $(x - a)(a^2 + ax - x)$
30. $2x^3(x + 4)$
31. $(b - 3c)(a + 3b)(a - 3b)$
32. $(a - b)(a - b - 2) \times$
$(a - b + 2)$
33. $2(1 + 2x + y)(1 - 2x - y)$
34. $(a - b)(a - b - 3)$
35. $(x + 1)^2(x - 2)$
36. $(x - 2)^2(x - 3)$
37. $(x + 2y)(a - 3x + 6y)$
38. $2(c^8 + d^8)(c^4 + d^4) \times$
$(c^2 + d^2)(c + d)(c - d)$
39. $2(p + 1)(p - 4)(p - 2)$
40. $(2a - 1)^3$
41. $(p - 2q + r - 2s) \times$
$(p - 2q - r + 2s)$
42. $16(a + b + 2c) \times$
$(a - b - 2c)$
43. $3(15x + y)(x - 4y)$
44. $(a - 2)^2(a + 3)(a + 1)$
45. $(b + c + a)(b + c - a) \times$
$(a + b - c)(a - b + c)$
46. $(a - 3)^2(a + 2)(a + 4)$
47. $(a + 3b)^2(1 + a - 3b) \times$
$(1 - a + 3b)$
48. $(x - 2)(x + 2)^3$
49. $(x + y + x^2 - 2y^2) \times$
$(x + y - x^2 + 2y^2)$
50. $(t + 1)^2(t - 1)$
51. $(x - 1)(x - 2)(x + 2)$

Lighthouses are designed to project light over great distances. The amount of illumination (E) reaching an object from a light source depends on the power of the light source (I) and its distance (s) from the object according to the formula $E = \dfrac{I}{s^2}$.

200

6

FRACTIONS

ALGEBRAIC FRACTIONS

6-1 *Simplifying Fractions*

OBJECTIVE To simplify algebraic fractions.

The procedure for simplifying a quotient of polynomials is the same procedure you learned for simplifying a quotient of monomials. Just factor the numerator and denominator and apply the cancellation rule for fractions. When the numerator and denominator have no common factor other than 1 and -1, the quotient is said to be in *simplest form*.

EXAMPLE 1 Express $\dfrac{a^2 - 4b^2}{a^2 - 4ab + 4b^2}$ in simplest form.

SOLUTION $\dfrac{a^2 - 4b^2}{a^2 - 4ab + 4b^2} = \dfrac{(a + 2b)(a - 2b)}{(a - 2b)(a - 2b)} = \dfrac{a + 2b}{a - 2b}$ $(a \neq 2b)$

   Recall that you cannot divide by zero. Thus, you must restrict the variables in a denominator so that the denominator does not equal zero. In Example 1, a cannot equal $2b$.
   The next example shows that you must be alert to factors that are opposites of each other.

EXAMPLE 2 Express $\dfrac{2x^2 - 9x + 10}{10 + x - 2x^2}$ in simplest form.

SOLUTION $\dfrac{2x^2 - 9x + 10}{10 + x - 2x^2} = \dfrac{(2x - 5)(x - 2)}{(5 - 2x)(2 + x)}$ $(2x - 5$ and $5 - 2x$ are opposites.)

$= \dfrac{-(5 - 2x)(x - 2)}{(5 - 2x)(x + 2)}$

$= \dfrac{-(x - 2)}{x + 2} = \dfrac{2 - x}{x + 2}$ $\left(x \neq -2, x \neq \dfrac{5}{2}\right)$

201

Teaching References

Lesson Commentary,
   pp. T85–T88

Assignment Guide,
   pp. T53–T55

Supplementary Materials
   Practice Masters 34–39
   Progress Tests 20–23
   Computer Activities
   16 *Adding Powers of Fractions*
   17 *Exploring Unit Fractions*
   18 *Dividing Polynomials*

Extra Practice, pp. 500–502

Alternate Test, p. T17

Teaching Suggestions p. T85

Suggested Extensions p. T85

Chalkboard Examples

Express in simplest form, noting any restrictions on the variables.

1. $\dfrac{16x^3y^4}{56xy^5}$

   $\dfrac{2x^2}{7y}$; $x \neq 0$, $y \neq 0$

2. $\dfrac{2c^2 + 2c}{c^2 - c}$

   $\dfrac{2c(c + 1)}{c(c - 1)} = \dfrac{2(c + 1)}{c - 1}$;

   $c \neq 0$, $c \neq 1$

3. $\dfrac{6 - y - y^2}{y^2 - 4}$

   $\dfrac{(3 + y)(2 - y)}{(y + 2)(y - 2)} = -\dfrac{3 + y}{y + 2}$;

   $y \neq 2$, $y \neq -2$

4. $\dfrac{(m - n)^5}{(n - m)^6}$

   $\dfrac{(m - n)^5}{(n - m)^6} = \dfrac{1}{m - n}$;

   $m \neq n$

Suggested Assignments

Minimum
Day 1: 202/1–26
    S 160/12, 16
Day 2: 202/27–41 odd
    S 160/18, 22

Average
Day 1: 202/1–37 odd
    S 160/16, 18, 22, 24
Day 2: 203/39–45 odd
    205/1–23 odd

NOTE: Day 2 of Sec. 6-1 fin-
    ishes Sec. 6-1 and
    starts Sec. 6-2.

Maximum
Day 1: 202/1–41 odd
    S 160/22, 24, 46
Day 2: 203/43–48
    205/7–49 odd

NOTE: Day 2 of Sec. 6-1 fin-
    ishes Sec. 6-1 and
    covers Sec. 6-2.

Additional Answers
Oral Exercises

1. $x - 1$; $x \neq -1$

2. $a + 1$; $a \neq -1$

3. $\dfrac{1}{x + 5}$; $x \neq 5, -5$

4. $\dfrac{1}{2a - 9}$; $a \neq \dfrac{9}{2}$

5. $\dfrac{3}{4}$; $b \neq -2$

6. $\dfrac{x + y}{x - y}$; $x \neq y$

7. $\dfrac{x + 1}{x + 2}$; $x \neq 2, -2$

8. $\dfrac{b - 3}{b + 3}$; $b \neq 3, -3$

9. -1; $y \neq 3$

10. -2; $c \neq \dfrac{7}{2}$

11. 1; $x \neq 2$

12. $-(s - 3)$, or $3 - s$;
    $s \neq 7, -3$

Oral Exercises

Express in simplest form. State the values of the variable for which the fraction is not defined.

1. $\dfrac{x^2 - 1}{x + 1}$

2. $\dfrac{a^2 + 2a + 1}{a + 1}$

3. $\dfrac{x - 5}{x^2 - 25}$

4. $\dfrac{(2a - 9)^2}{(2a - 9)^3}$

5. $\dfrac{3b + 6}{4b + 8}$

6. $\dfrac{2x + 2y}{2x - 2y}$

7. $\dfrac{x^2 - x - 2}{x^2 - 4}$

8. $\dfrac{b^2 - 6b + 9}{b^2 - 9}$

9. $\dfrac{y - 3}{3 - y}$

10. $\dfrac{4c - 14}{7 - 2c}$

11. $\dfrac{(x - 2)^2}{(2 - x)^2}$

12. $\dfrac{(7 - s)(s^2 - 9)}{(s - 7)(s + 3)}$

Written Exercises

Express in simplest form, noting any restrictions on the variable.

A 1. $\dfrac{2x - 4}{x - 2}$

2. $\dfrac{3a + b}{9a + 3b}$

3. $\dfrac{4x - 4y}{4x + 4y}$

4. $\dfrac{y^2 + 3y}{y^2 - 6y}$

5. $\dfrac{x^2 - xy}{x^2 + xy}$

6. $\dfrac{p}{2p^2 - p}$

7. $\dfrac{2ab}{a^2b - b^2a}$

8. $\dfrac{2ab + 2ac}{4ac + 4a^2}$

9. $\dfrac{x^2 - 36}{2x - 12}$

10. $\dfrac{x^2 - 4x + 4}{x - 2}$

11. $\dfrac{4x + 20}{x^2 - 25}$

12. $\dfrac{3x + 4}{9x^2 - 16}$

13. $\dfrac{b^2 + 5b + 6}{b^2 + 6b + 8}$

14. $\dfrac{y^2 - 7y + 6}{y^2 - 1}$

15. $\dfrac{r^2 - 3r}{r^2 - 2r - 3}$

16. $\dfrac{(a - 5)(2a - 7)}{3(5 - a)(7 - 2a)}$

17. $\dfrac{3 - x}{x^2 - 9}$

18. $\dfrac{(s - 6)^2}{36 - s^2}$

19. $\dfrac{(a - b)^7}{(b - a)^8}$

20. $\dfrac{(3x - 8)^5}{(8 - 3x)^5}$

21. $\dfrac{16c^2 + 8c + 1}{1 - 16c^2}$

22. $\dfrac{b^2 + b - 12}{12 - 4b}$

23. $\dfrac{5x - x^2}{x^2 - 6x + 5}$

24. $\dfrac{6x^2 + x}{36x^2 - 1}$

B 25. The width of a rectangle is $(2x - 6)$ cm and its area is $(12x^2 - 44x + 24)$ cm^2. Find the length. $(6x - 4)$ cm $(x \neq 3)$

26. All-natural oatmeal cookies cost $(5n - 3)$ cents each. How many can you buy for $(30n^2 + 2n - 12)$ cents? $(6n + 4)$ cookies

Express in simplest form, noting any restrictions on the variable.

27. $\dfrac{2x^2 - 8}{x^2 + 4x - 12}$

28. $\dfrac{c^2 + 10cd + 25d^2}{c^2 - 25d^2}$

29. $\dfrac{16a^2 - 49b^2}{16a^2 - 56ab + 49b^2}$

30. $\dfrac{8c^2a^2 - 32}{c^3a^2 - 4ac^2 + 4c}$

31. $\dfrac{s^2 - 2s - 15}{s^2 + 10s + 21}$

32. $\dfrac{64y^2 - 4x^2}{x^2 + 3xy - 4y^2}$

33. $\dfrac{2a^2 + 2ab - 4b^2}{a^2 + 2ab - 3b^2}$

34. $\dfrac{x^2 - 9y^2}{3x^2 - 15xy + 18y^2}$

35. $\dfrac{4x^2 + 16xy + 15y^2}{2x^2 + xy - 10y^2}$

36. $\dfrac{8x^2 + 6xy - 5y^2}{16x^2 - 25y^2}$

37. $\dfrac{3x^2 - 3y^2}{3x(x - y) + 3y(x - y)}$

38. $\dfrac{x^4 - 4}{x^2(x + 2) + 2(x + 2)}$

First express the fraction in simplest form. Then evaluate it for the given values of the variables. If the original fraction has a zero denominator for these values, indicate that it cannot be evaluated for these values.

39. $\dfrac{4x^2 - y^2}{2x - y}$; $x = 4$, $y = 8$ $\quad$ $\dfrac{2x + y}{}$; cannot be eval.

40. $\dfrac{a^2 + 2ab + b^2}{2a + 2b}$; $a = -1\dfrac{1}{2}$, $b = -\dfrac{1}{2}$ $\quad$ $\dfrac{a+b}{2}$; -1

41. $\dfrac{c^2 - 4d^2}{c^2 d - 4cd^2 + 4d^3}$; $c = \dfrac{1}{2}$, $d = \dfrac{3}{4}$ $\quad$ $\dfrac{c + 2d}{d(c - 2d)}$; $-\dfrac{8}{3}$

42. $\dfrac{x^3 y - xy^3}{x^2 y + xy^2}$; $x = 6$, $y = -6$ $\quad$ $x - y$; cannot be eval.

Express in simplest form, noting any restrictions on the variable.

C 43. $\dfrac{2x^3 - 13x^2 + 15x}{15x - 7x^2 - 2x^3}$

44. $\dfrac{x^4 - 10x^2 + 9}{3 - 2x - x^2}$

45. $\dfrac{a^2 - 9b^2 - 2a + 6b}{(a + 3b)^2 - 4}$

46. $\dfrac{x^3 + 6x^2 - 4x - 24}{x^3 - 2x^2 - 36x + 72}$

47. $\dfrac{a^2 - 6ab + 9b^2 - 9}{3a - 9b - 9}$

48. $\dfrac{(a - b)^3 + 4(b - a)}{(a - b)^2 + 4(b - a) + 4}$

Biography Louise Arner Boyd

Louise Arner Boyd (1887–1972) was a geographer and polar explorer. She was born and educated in California. Her first expedition was a trip to Greenland in 1926. On succeeding expeditions she explored East Greenland, Northeast and West Greenland, and eastern arctic Canada. Her research in these areas included the collection of data for maps and studies of the geology, botany, and meteorology of the regions. While preparing for an expedition in 1928, she learned that the explorer Roald Amundsen had disappeared and she joined in the search. Though Amundsen was never found, Louise Boyd was honored by the governments of Norway and France for her efforts.

During World War II, Louise Boyd served as a consultant to the United States government. She studied radio and magnetic phenomena in the ocean surrounding Greenland and other arctic areas, and supplied maps, photographs, and firsthand geographic information about strategic areas of the arctic. In 1955 one of her childhood dreams was realized; she made a successful flight over the North Pole. Among her many honors was her election to the council of the American Geographical Society in 1960.

FRACTIONS **203**

Teaching Suggestions p. T85

Suggested Extensions p. T86

Chalkboard Examples

Express each product as a fraction in simplest form.

1. $\frac{8}{3}\cdot -\frac{42}{81}\cdot\frac{27}{28}$

$$\frac{\overset{4}{\cancel{8}}}{\cancel{3}}\cdot -\frac{\overset{14}{\cancel{42}}}{\underset{3}{\cancel{81}}}\cdot\frac{\cancel{27}}{\underset{2}{\cancel{28}}} = \frac{-4}{3}$$

2. $\frac{5k}{8k^3}\cdot\frac{24k^4}{15k^2}$

$$\frac{\cancel{5}}{\cancel{8k^2}}\cdot\frac{\cancel{24k^2}}{\underset{3}{\cancel{15}}} = 1$$

3. $\frac{x-2}{56}\cdot\frac{4}{2-x}$

$$\frac{-\cancel{(2-x)}}{14\cdot\cancel{4}}\cdot\frac{\cancel{4}}{\cancel{2-x}} = -\frac{1}{14}$$

4. $\frac{3m-m^2}{12}\cdot\frac{16}{3-7m+2m^2}$

$$\frac{m\cancel{(3-m)}}{\underset{3}{\cancel{12}}}\cdot\frac{\overset{4}{\cancel{16}}}{\cancel{(3-m)}(1-2m)}$$

$$= \frac{4m}{3(1-2m)}$$

5. $\frac{(5-y)^3}{18}\cdot\frac{8}{(y-5)^3}$

$$\frac{-\cancel{(y-5)^3}}{9\cdot\cancel{2}}\cdot\frac{4\cdot\cancel{2}}{\cancel{(y-5)^3}} = \frac{-4}{9}$$

6. $\frac{4x^2-36}{4x^2}\cdot\frac{x^4}{(3-x)^2}$

$$\frac{\cancel{4}(x+3)\cancel{(x-3)}}{\cancel{4x^2}}\cdot\frac{\overset{x^2}{\cancel{x^4}}}{\underset{x-3}{\cancel{(3-x)^2}}}$$

$$= \frac{x^2(x+3)}{x-3}$$

6-2 *Multiplying Fractions*

OBJECTIVE **To multiply algebraic fractions.**

The property of quotients states that

$$\frac{cx}{dy} = \frac{c}{d}\cdot\frac{x}{y}.$$

The symmetric property of equality makes it possible to rewrite this result as the multiplication rule for fractions, shown below. The multiplication rule for fractions enables you to express a product of two fractions as a quotient.

> MULTIPLICATION RULE FOR FRACTIONS
>
> If c, d, x, and y are any real numbers such that $d \neq 0$ and $y \neq 0$, then
>
> $$\frac{\mathbf{c}}{\mathbf{d}}\cdot\frac{\mathbf{x}}{\mathbf{y}} = \frac{\mathbf{cx}}{\mathbf{dy}}.$$

EXAMPLE 1 Multiply: $\frac{2x}{3}\cdot\frac{5}{4y}$

SOLUTION 1 $\frac{2x}{3}\cdot\frac{5}{4y} = \frac{2x\cdot 5}{3\cdot 4y}$

$$= \frac{\overset{5}{\cancel{10}}x}{\underset{6}{\cancel{12}}y} = \frac{5x}{6y} \quad (y \neq 0)$$

SOLUTION 2 $\frac{\overset{1}{\cancel{2}}x}{3}\cdot\frac{5}{\underset{2}{\cancel{4}}y} = \frac{5x}{6y}$

EXAMPLE 2 Multiply: $\frac{x^2-3x-4}{x^2-2x}\cdot\frac{x^2-4}{x-4}$

SOLUTION

$$\frac{x^2-3x-4}{x^2-2x}\cdot\frac{x^2-4}{x-4} = \frac{(x+1)(x-4)}{x(x-2)}\cdot\frac{(x-2)(x+2)}{(x-4)} \quad \text{Factor the numerators and denominators.}$$

$$= \frac{(x+1)\cancel{(x-4)}}{x\cancel{(x-2)}}\cdot\frac{\cancel{(x-2)}(x+2)}{\cancel{(x-4)}} \quad \text{Divide by common factors.}$$

$$= \frac{(x+1)(x+2)}{x} \quad (x \neq 0,\ x \neq 2,\ x \neq 4)$$ ***Answer***

Another way to write the answer to Example 2 is $\frac{x^2 + 3x + 2}{x}$. The factored form of the answer, as shown in Example 2, will be the one you should use unless otherwise directed.

If you study the denominators in the first step in Example 2, you will see that there will be a zero denominator when x equals 0, 2, or 4. Thus the answer is restricted to values of x other than 0, 2, and 4.

Hereafter, it will be assumed that the domains of the variables include no value for which any denominator is zero. Hence, it will not be necessary to show excluded values of the variables involved.

Suggested Assignments

Minimum
Day 1: 205/1–15 odd, 17–24
Day 2: 206/25, 26, 29–49 odd

Average
NOTE: Day 2 of Sec. 6-1 finishes Sec. 6-1 and starts Sec. 6-2.
206/27, 28, 29–51 odd

Maximum
NOTE: Day 2 of Sec. 6-1 finishes Sec. 6-1 and covers Sec. 6-2.

Oral Exercises

Express each product as a fraction in simplest form.

1. $\frac{2}{3} \cdot \frac{6}{5}$ $\frac{4}{5}$

2. $\frac{-3}{4} \cdot \frac{1}{9}$ $\frac{-1}{12}$

3. $\frac{-4}{7} \cdot \frac{-5}{4}$ $\frac{5}{7}$

4. $\frac{3}{8} \cdot \frac{4}{15}$ $\frac{1}{10}$

5. $\frac{1}{x} \cdot \frac{2}{y}$ $\frac{2}{xy}$

6. $\frac{x}{2} \cdot \frac{4}{y}$ $\frac{2x}{y}$

7. $\frac{a}{3} \cdot \frac{4}{a}$ $\frac{4}{3}$

8. $\frac{x}{y} \cdot \frac{y^2}{2}$ $\frac{xy}{2}$

9. $\frac{3a}{2} \cdot \frac{a}{3}$ $\frac{a^2}{2}$

10. $(3x)^2 \cdot \frac{1}{x}$ $9x$

11. $\frac{2(x-3)}{y} \cdot \frac{y^2}{x-3}$ $2y$

12. $\frac{2a-5}{b^2} \cdot \frac{b^3}{5-2a}$ $-b$

Written Exercises

Express each product as a fraction in simplest form.

A 1. $\frac{5}{2} \cdot \frac{2}{3}$ $\frac{5}{3}$

2. $\frac{3}{8} \cdot \frac{16}{9}$ $\frac{2}{3}$

3. $\frac{7}{25} \cdot \frac{5}{21}$ $\frac{1}{15}$

4. $\frac{-8}{15} \cdot \frac{3}{40}$ $\frac{-1}{25}$

5. $\frac{7}{12} \cdot \frac{4}{5} \cdot \frac{15}{14}$ $\frac{1}{2}$

6. $\frac{13}{8} \cdot \frac{15}{26} \cdot \frac{24}{25}$ $\frac{9}{10}$

7. $\frac{11}{9} \cdot \frac{81}{21} \cdot \frac{42}{33}$ 6

8. $\left(-\frac{5}{7}\right)^2 \cdot \frac{14}{25}$

9. $\frac{a}{b} \cdot \frac{b}{c}$ $\frac{a}{c}$

10. $\frac{3}{xy} \cdot \frac{2x^2}{y}$ $\frac{6x}{y^2}$

11. $\frac{4}{c^2} \cdot \frac{3c}{8}$ $\frac{3}{2c}$

12. $\frac{4}{5} \cdot \frac{15a^2}{2b}$

13. $\frac{p^2}{2q} \cdot \frac{6q^2}{p}$ $3pq$

14. $\frac{5a}{3b^2} \cdot \frac{6b^2}{a^2}$ $\frac{10}{a}$

15. $\frac{34y^4}{x^3} \cdot \frac{x}{17y}$

16. $\frac{3r^2s}{7t} \cdot \frac{14t^2}{9rs^2}$ $\frac{2rt}{3s}$

17. $\frac{a-1}{2a-3} \cdot \frac{4a-6}{1-a}$ -2

18. $\frac{x-1}{3} \cdot \frac{12}{x^2-1}$

19. $\frac{x+2}{x} \cdot \frac{x^2}{x^2-4}$ $\frac{x}{x-2}$

20. $\frac{a+b}{a-b} \cdot \frac{a^2-b^2}{4a+4b}$ $\frac{a+b}{4}$

21. $\frac{4x-xy}{8x^2y} \cdot \frac{4}{16-y^2}$

22. $\frac{y^2-5y}{5} \cdot \frac{10y}{2y-10}$ y^2

23. $\frac{(1-x)^3}{4} \cdot \frac{8}{(x-1)^2}$ $2(1-x)$

24. $\frac{a^2-c^2}{a} \cdot \frac{4}{2c-2a}$

Additional A Exercises

Express each product as a fraction in simplest form.

1. $\frac{3}{4} \cdot \frac{8}{9}$ $\frac{2}{3}$

2. $\frac{12}{13} \cdot \frac{39}{60}$ $\frac{3}{5}$

3. $\frac{x^2}{2} \cdot \frac{10}{x^3}$ $\frac{5}{x}$

4. $\frac{4a}{5} \cdot \frac{5a}{8}$ $\frac{a^2}{2}$

5. $\frac{c^2}{d} \cdot \frac{d}{c^3}$ $\frac{1}{c}$

6. $\frac{2x+1}{y^3} \cdot \frac{y}{2x+1}$ $\frac{1}{y^2}$

**Additional Answers
Written Exercises**

8. $\frac{2}{7}$

12. $\frac{6a^2}{b}$

15. $\frac{2y^3}{x^2}$

18. $\frac{4}{x+1}$

21. $\frac{1}{2xy(4+y)}$

24. $\frac{-2(a+c)}{a}$

FRACTIONS 205

Write an expression in simplest form for each of the following.

SAMPLE   The distance you go by traveling at $\frac{4v}{5}$ km/h for $\frac{3}{2}$ h.

SOLUTION $\frac{\overset{2}{4v}}{5} \cdot \frac{3}{\underset{}{2}} = \frac{6v}{5}$; $\frac{6v}{5}$ km   *Answer*

B 25. The distance you go by traveling at $\frac{3}{4}x$ km/h for $2y$ h. $\frac{3xy}{2}$ km

26. The area of a rectangle with length $\frac{5x-15}{4}$ cm and width $\frac{4x-8}{5}$ cm.
$(x-3)(x-2)$ cm²

27. The total cost of $\frac{3n}{2}$ apples that cost $\frac{8c}{3}$ cents per dozen. $\frac{nc}{3}$ cents

28. The volume of a box with length $\frac{x+3}{2y}$ cm, width $\frac{x-3}{2y}$ cm, and

height $\frac{8y}{x^2-9}$ cm. $\frac{2}{y}$ cm³

Simplify.

SAMPLE $\left(\frac{2}{3c}\right)^4 = \frac{2}{3c} \cdot \frac{2}{3c} \cdot \frac{2}{3c} \cdot \frac{2}{3c} = \frac{2^4}{(3c)^4} = \frac{16}{81c^4}$

33. $\frac{d^4}{k^2}$ **38.** $\frac{27z^6}{8x^9y^3}$

29. $\left(\frac{1}{b}\right)^3$ $\frac{1}{b^3}$ **30.** $\left(\frac{2}{3c}\right)^2$ $\frac{4}{9c^2}$ **31.** $\left(\frac{4d}{5}\right)^3$ $\frac{64d^3}{125}$ **32.** $\left(\frac{5x^2}{2}\right)^3$ $\frac{125x^6}{8}$ **33.** $\left(\frac{d^2}{k}\right)^2$

34. $\left(\frac{4ab^2}{3}\right)^3$ $\frac{64a^3b^6}{27}$ **35.** $\left(\frac{x^2}{y^3}\right)^5$ $\frac{x^{10}}{y^{15}}$ **36.** $\left(\frac{ay^3}{v^2}\right)^4$ $\frac{a^4y^{12}}{v^8}$ **37.** $\left(\frac{2an}{v^2}\right)^3$ $\frac{8a^3n^3}{v^6}$ **38.** $\left(\frac{3z^2}{2x^3y}\right)^3$

39. $\frac{x^2+y^2}{x^2+2xy+y^2} \cdot \frac{3x+3y}{6}$ $\frac{x^2+y^2}{2(x+y)}$

40. $\frac{a^2+5a+6}{4a-8} \cdot \frac{a^2-a}{a+2}$ $\frac{a(a+3)(a-1)}{4(a-2)}$

41. $\frac{4x^2-9y^2}{6x^2-9xy} \cdot \frac{6y^2}{4xy+6y^2}$ $\frac{y}{x}$

42. $\frac{b^2+b}{b^2-b} \cdot \frac{3b-21}{b^2-6b-7}$ $\frac{3}{b-1}$

43. $\frac{x^2-3x+2}{x^2+3x+2} \cdot \frac{8x+8}{4x-8}$ $\frac{2(x-1)}{x+2}$

44. $\frac{y^2+4y-21}{y^2-6y-16} \cdot \frac{y^2-8y+15}{y^2+9y+14}$

45. $\frac{4x^2-25y^2}{(5y-2x)^2} \cdot \frac{4}{4x+10y}$ $\frac{-2}{5y-2x}$

46. $\frac{3b^2-9b+6}{2b^2-10b+12} \cdot \frac{6-2b}{3-3b}$ 1

47. $\frac{2x^3-5x^2-3x}{x^2-4x} \cdot \frac{8-2x}{x^3-3x}$

48. $\frac{4b^2-2ab}{b^2-4ab+4a^2} \cdot \frac{(2a-b)^3}{2b-a}$

49. $\frac{8-2x^4}{4x^2} \cdot \frac{(4x)^2}{2+x^2}$ $8(2-x^2)$

50. $\frac{6a^2b-4ab^2}{45a^2-20b^2} \cdot \frac{30a+20b}{4a^2b^2}$ $\frac{1}{ab}$

C 51. $\frac{4z^2-4}{1+z^2} \cdot \frac{1-z}{2z} \cdot \frac{1-2z^2+z^4}{2+2z}$

52. $\frac{x^2-x-2}{x^2} \cdot \frac{x^2+x-2}{9x} \cdot \frac{54x^3}{x^4-5x^2+4}$ $\frac{6}{}$

53. $\frac{x^3+3x^2-4x-12}{2x^2-18} \cdot \frac{x^3-3x^2+3x-9}{3x^3-12x}$
$\frac{x^2+3}{6x}$

54. $\frac{a^2-(b-c)^2}{2a-2b+2c} \cdot \frac{6a-6b+6c}{b^2-(a-c)^2}$
$\frac{3(a-b+c)}{b-a+c}$

206   *CHAPTER 6*

55. If $s = \dfrac{a + b + c}{2}$, show that

$$2s(2s - 2a)(2s - 2b)(2s - 2c) = (a^2 + 2ac + c^2 - b^2)(b^2 - a^2 + 2ac - c^2).$$

55. $2s(2s - 2a)(2s - 2b) \times$
$\qquad\qquad (2s - 2c) =$
$(a + b + c)(-a + b + c) \times$
$\qquad (a - b + c)(a + b - c) =$
$(a + b + c)(a - b + c) \times$
$\qquad (-a + b + c)(a + b - c) =$
$((a + c) + b)((a + c) - b) \times$
$\qquad (b - (a - c))(b + (a - c)) =$
$((a + c)^2 - b^2)(b^2 - (a - c)^2)$
$= (a^2 + 2ac + c^2 - b^2) \times$
$\qquad (b^2 - a^2 + 2ac - c^2)$

Application Unit Pricing

The **unit price** of an item in a supermarket is its price per unit of measure. The unit price may be expressed per liter, per kilogram, or per dozen, for example.

EXAMPLE Find the unit price per kilogram for a 350 g jar of marmalade that costs $1.05.

SOLUTION Express 350 g as 0.35 kg. Then divide.

$$1.05 \div 0.35 = 3.00$$

∴ the unit price is $3.00 per kilogram.

When shopping for a particular product, you can use unit prices to compare the values of containers of different sizes. The container with the lowest unit price is the best buy. It is important to realize that the larger size of an item does not always have the lower unit price.

Although getting the best buy for your money is important, you must use common sense when shopping. It is not economical to buy a larger amount of a product, if you cannot use it up within a reasonable time. The unit price to you is the price per unit used. Another consideration is quality. Will the salad oil with the lowest price make the best salad dressing? Do the potatoes with the lowest unit price have the cooking characteristics you require?

1. What is the unit price per kilogram of a 250 g box of cereal that costs $1.15? $4.60 per kilogram

2. Which box of soap powder has a lower unit price: a 1.5 kg box for $1.85 or a 2.5 kg box for $3.15? The 1.5 kg box

3. Which bottle of wine vinegar has the lower unit price: a 700 mL bottle for 63¢ or a 1 L bottle for 88¢? The 1 L bottle

In many stores unit prices are posted on the shelves where items are kept. Watch for these unit prices as you shop and look to see how they are computed.

6-3 *Dividing Fractions*

OBJECTIVE   To divide algebraic fractions.

The rule for division of real numbers states that to divide by a real number, you multiply by its reciprocal. For example,

$$\frac{3}{5} \div \frac{2}{7} = \frac{3}{5} \cdot \frac{7}{2} = \frac{21}{10}.$$

In algebra division by fractions is defined similarly.

DIVISION RULE FOR FRACTIONS

$$\frac{a}{b} \div \frac{c}{d} = \frac{a}{b} \cdot \frac{d}{c}$$

EXAMPLE 1   Divide: $\dfrac{x^2+x-2}{x-2} \div \dfrac{5x-5}{x^2-4}$.

SOLUTION $\dfrac{x^2+x-2}{x-2} \div \dfrac{5x-5}{x^2-4} = \dfrac{x^2+x-2}{x-2} \cdot \dfrac{x^2-4}{5x-5}$ $\begin{cases}\text{Multiply by}\\\text{the reciprocal.}\end{cases}$

$\qquad\qquad = \dfrac{(x+2)(x-1)}{x-2} \cdot \dfrac{(x+2)(x-2)}{5(x-1)}$ $\begin{cases}\text{Factor.}\end{cases}$

$\qquad\qquad = \dfrac{(x+2)(x\cancel{-1})}{x\cancel{-2}} \cdot \dfrac{(x+2)(x\cancel{-2})}{5(x\cancel{-1})}$ $\begin{cases}\text{Divide by}\\\text{common factors.}\end{cases}$

$\qquad\qquad = \dfrac{(x+2)^2}{5}$

When simplifying an expression that involves both multiplication and division, do the operations in order from left to right (unless parentheses are used to indicate a different order). Remember that you can change each division sign to a multiplication sign if you also replace the fraction immediately following the division sign by its reciprocal.

EXAMPLE 2   Simplify $\dfrac{y}{y+1} \div \dfrac{y^2}{6y+18} \cdot \dfrac{y^3+y^2}{y^2-9}$.

SOLUTION $\dfrac{y}{y+1} \div \dfrac{y^2}{6y+18} \cdot \dfrac{y^3+y^2}{y^2-9} = \dfrac{y}{y+1} \cdot \dfrac{6y+18}{y^2} \cdot \dfrac{y^3+y^2}{y^2-9}$

$\qquad\qquad = \dfrac{y}{y+1} \cdot \dfrac{6(y+3)}{y^2} \cdot \dfrac{y^2(y+1)}{(y+3)(y-3)}$

$\qquad\qquad = \dfrac{y}{y\cancel{+1}} \cdot \dfrac{6(y\cancel{+3})}{\cancel{y^2}} \cdot \dfrac{\cancel{y^2}(y\cancel{+1})}{(y\cancel{+3})(y-3)}$

$\qquad\qquad = \dfrac{6y}{y-3}$

208   CHAPTER 6

Oral Exercises

Simplify.

1. $\frac{2}{3} \div \frac{1}{4}$ $\frac{8}{3}$, or $2\frac{2}{3}$ **2.** $\frac{1}{5} \div \frac{4}{7}$ $\frac{7}{20}$ **3.** $-\frac{5}{8} \div \frac{3}{4}$ $-\frac{5}{6}$ **4.** $\frac{12}{5} \div \frac{3}{10}$ 8

5. $\frac{x}{y} \div \frac{x}{2}$ $\frac{2}{y}$ **6.** $\frac{a}{b} \div \frac{b}{a}$ $\frac{a^2}{b^2}$ **7.** $3a \div \frac{a^2}{2}$ $\frac{6}{a}$ **8.** $1 \div \frac{a}{b+c}$ $\frac{b+c}{a}$

9. $\frac{x^3}{4} \div 2x^2$ $\frac{x}{8}$ **10.** $\frac{a}{b^2} \div \frac{2}{b}$ $\frac{a}{2b}$ **11.** $\frac{1}{4} \div \frac{2}{3} \cdot \frac{1}{5}$ $\frac{3}{40}$ **12.** $\frac{1}{4} \div \left(\frac{2}{3} \cdot \frac{1}{5}\right)$ $\frac{15}{8}$, or $1\frac{7}{8}$

Written Exercises

Divide. Express the answers in simplest form.

A   **1.** $\frac{3}{4} \div \frac{1}{2}$ $\frac{3}{2}$ **2.** $\frac{5}{8} \div \frac{25}{16}$ $\frac{2}{5}$ **3.** $\frac{3x}{y} \div \frac{x}{2}$ $\frac{6}{y}$ **4.** $\frac{a}{b} \div \frac{a^2}{2}$ $\frac{2}{ab}$

5. $\frac{3a^2b}{4} \div \frac{6b}{a}$ $\frac{a^3}{8}$ **6.** $\frac{4x^2}{y} \div \frac{-2x}{y^2}$ $-2xy$ **7.** $\frac{p^2}{q} \div \frac{p}{2q^2}$ $2pq$ **8.** $\frac{-3a^2}{2b} \div \frac{2a^2}{3b}$

9. $\frac{(2x)^2}{3} \div \frac{(4x)^2}{12}$ 1 **10.** $\left(\frac{3a}{2}\right)^2 \div \left(\frac{6}{a}\right)^2$ $\frac{a^4}{16}$ **11.** $\frac{9a^2}{4b} \div 6ab$ $\frac{3a}{8b^2}$ **12.** $1 \div \left(\frac{3x^2}{2}\right)^3$

13. $\frac{a+b}{5} \div \frac{a+b}{10}$ 2 **14.** $\frac{x-1}{2} \div \frac{x^2-1}{6}$ $\frac{3}{x+1}$ **15.** $\frac{y^2-4}{2y} \div (y+2)$ $\frac{y-2}{2y}$

16. $\frac{a-b}{cd^2} \div \frac{a-b}{cd^3}$ d **17.** $\frac{x-y}{x+y} \div \frac{1}{(x+y)^2}$ $(x-y)(x+y)$ **18.** $\frac{1}{10-2y} \div \frac{1}{3y-15}$ $\frac{-3}{2}$

19. $\frac{2a+2b}{a^2} \div \frac{a^2-b^2}{3a}$ **20.** $\frac{x^2+y^2}{a+b} \div \frac{7x+7y}{7a+7b}$ $\frac{x^2+y^2}{x+y}$ **21.** $1 \div \frac{x^2-y^2}{x^2-2xy+y^2}$ $\frac{x-y}{x+y}$

22. $\frac{3}{a^2-9} \div \frac{3a-6}{a-3}$ **23.** $\frac{x^2-36}{6x-36} \div \frac{x^2+12x+36}{x^3+6x^2}$ $\frac{x^2}{6}$ **24.** $\frac{3-3x}{x^2+2x-3} \div (2x-2)$

B   **25.** $\frac{6x^3}{4yz^9} \div \frac{10x^7y^4}{15z^3}$ $\frac{9}{4z^6x^4y^5}$ **26.** $\frac{21a^3b^2}{4cd^2} \div \left(\frac{5a^2b^5}{8c^3d^2} \cdot \frac{3a}{b}\right)$ $\frac{14c^2}{5b^2}$ **27.** $\frac{(4p^2)^2}{2qr^3} \div \left(\frac{8p^7}{q^4} \cdot \frac{1}{r^7}\right)$ $\frac{q^3}{p^3r^{10}}$

Simplify.

28. $\frac{6x}{6x-14} \cdot \frac{9x-21}{21} \div \frac{x^2}{35}$ $\frac{15}{x}$ **29.** $\frac{c^2}{c^2-d^2} \cdot \frac{c-d}{c+d} \div \frac{c}{(c+d)^2}$ c

30. $\frac{x^4-y^4}{2x-2y} \div \frac{x^2+y^2}{4}$ $2(x+y)$ **31.** $\frac{(2a-b)^2}{x-2y} \div \frac{4ab^2-2b^3}{4y-2x}$

32. $\frac{3a^2-9a+6}{2a^2-10a+12} \div \frac{3-3a}{6-2a}$ 1 **33.** $\frac{2a^2-13a+15}{a^2-2a} \div \frac{10-7a+a^2}{a^2-4a+4}$

34. $\frac{3n^2-14n+8}{2n^2-3n-20} \div \frac{6-25n+24n^2}{16n^2+34n-15}$ 1 **35.** $\left(\frac{2x-5}{3}\right)^4 \div \left(\frac{5-2x}{6}\right)^3$ $\frac{8(5-2x)}{3}$

36. $2x^2 \div 3x^3 \div 4x^4$ $\frac{1}{6x^5}$

Supplementary Materials

Practice Master 35

Progress Test 20

Suggested Assignments

Minimum
Day 1: 209/1–11 odd, 13–18
Day 2: 209/19–35 odd

Average
     209/1–35 odd

Maximum
     209/1–39 odd
   S 206/51, 53, 55

Additional A Exercises

Divide. Express answers in simplest form.

1. $\frac{3}{4} \div \frac{1}{8}$ 6

2. $\frac{15}{2} \div \frac{5}{4}$ 6

3. $\frac{4a}{b} \div \frac{2}{b}$ $2a$

4. $\frac{x}{12y} \div \frac{4}{3x}$ $\frac{x^2}{16y}$

5. $\frac{10c^2}{3a} \div \frac{c}{3}$ $\frac{10c}{a}$

6. $\frac{6x^3}{5a^2} \div \frac{3x^2}{a}$ $\frac{2x}{5a}$

Additional Answers Written Exercises

8. $\frac{-9}{4}$ **12.** $\frac{8}{27x^6}$

19. $\frac{6}{a(a-b)}$

22. $\frac{1}{(a+3)(a-2)}$

24. $\frac{-3}{2(x+3)(x-1)}$

31. $\frac{b-2a}{b^2}$ **33.** $\frac{2a-3}{a}$

209

Simplify.

C 37. $\dfrac{s^2 - 2s}{s^2 - 3s - 4} \cdot \dfrac{s^2 - 25}{s^2 - 4s - 5} \div \dfrac{s^2 + 5s}{5s^2 + 10s + 5}$ $\dfrac{5(s-2)}{s-4}$

38. $\dfrac{b^2 + 6b - 7}{6b^2 - 7b - 20} \cdot \dfrac{2b^2 + b - 15}{b^2 + 2b - 3} \div \dfrac{b^2 + 5b - 14}{3b^2 - 2b - 8}$ 1

39. $\dfrac{a^3 + 5a^2 - 9a - 45}{2a^2 - 9a + 9} \div \dfrac{a^2 + 10a + 25}{12 - 14a + 4a^2} \cdot \dfrac{a + 5}{a^2 - 4a + 4}$ $\dfrac{2(a+3)}{a-2}$

40. $\dfrac{x^2 - 6xy + 9y^2 - 9}{x^4 - 81y^4} \cdot \dfrac{3x - 9y}{3x - 9y + 9} \div \dfrac{x - 3y - 3}{3x^2 + 27y^2}$ $\dfrac{3}{x + 3y}$

Quick Quiz

Express in simplest form.

1. $\dfrac{x^2 - x - 2}{x^2 - 5x - 6}$ $\dfrac{x - 2}{x - 6}$

2. $\dfrac{a^2 - 49}{a^2 + 3a - 28}$ $\dfrac{a - 7}{a - 4}$

3. $\dfrac{6mn^2}{5n^2} \cdot \dfrac{3mn}{2m^4}$ $\dfrac{9}{5m^2}$

4. $\dfrac{a + 2}{2a} \div \dfrac{a^2 - 4}{(3a)^2}$ $\dfrac{9a}{2(a - 2)}$

5. $\dfrac{4x^3 - 6x^2}{3} \div 12x^2$ $\dfrac{2x - 3}{18}$

Self-Test 1

Express in simplest form.

1. $\dfrac{k^2 + 6k + 8}{k^2 - 3k - 10}$ **2.** $\dfrac{n^2 + 10n + 25}{n^2 - 25}$ Obj. 6-1, p. 201

3. $\dfrac{8a^3}{5b^6} \cdot \dfrac{9b}{10a^2}$ **4.** $\dfrac{z - 1}{9} \cdot \dfrac{12z}{z^2 - 1}$ Obj. 6-2, p. 204

5. $\dfrac{3x^3y}{8} \div \dfrac{6x}{y}$ **6.** $\dfrac{10m^2}{3n^2} \div 5\,mn$ Obj. 6-3, p. 208

Check your answers with those at the back of the book.

Just for Fun

Did you ever wonder who drew the first Hindu-Arabic numerals? One theory is that an ancient mathematician first shaped the numerals so that each would contain the corresponding number of angles. For example:

for one   for seven   for nine

The angles are counted as indicated by the dots:

Can you draw numerals for the other integers between one and nine, each with the appropriate number of angles?

210   *CHAPTER 6*

Calculator Key-In

Home Calculators and Computers

Small calculators are operated by tiny electronic circuits. The simplest calculators perform the four arithmetic operations with perhaps a square root key or a percent key also. Most calculators have capabilities far exceeding this.

Calculators designed for business applications can perform such functions as calculating the monthly payment on a mortgage and figuring compound interest. Scientific calculators can find square roots, raise numbers to powers, and calculate trigonometric functions (see Looking Ahead). In addition to their technical functions, calculators can perform social functions, such as keeping time and sounding an alarm beep at a specific time. There are also calculators with constant memories that enable them to remember a number even when the calculator is turned off.

On some calculators, each key can be used for two functions. When the key is pressed directly, it performs the function described by the label printed on it. When a "shift" key is pressed before pressing the key, it performs according to the label printed above it.

A "programmable" feature is available on some calculators. This enables the user to store sequences of operations for repeated use. This programming is done by means of special "learning" keys on the calculator and does not require the use of a special programming language.

Microcomputers for home use are also available. These can be programmed in a version of the BASIC language. They generally use a monitor like a television screen to display what is being done—the program or the results. There are some printing devices that can be added on.

When extensive data, repeated operations, or decision-making steps are involved in the solution of a problem, a computer is better suited for the job than a calculator. Speed of calculation is the major advantage of a computer.

ADDING AND SUBTRACTING FRACTIONS

6-4 *Least Common Denominators*

OBJECTIVE   To express fractions with their least common denominators.

The cancellation rule for fractions states that

$$\frac{cx}{cy} = \frac{x}{y}.$$

It enables you to express a fraction in simpler form by dividing its numerator and denominator by the same nonzero number. You can use the symmetric property of equality to rewrite the rule as

$$\frac{x}{y} = \frac{cx}{cy}.$$

In this form, it enables you to express a fraction in a different form by multiplying its numerator and denominator by the same number.

EXAMPLE 1 $\dfrac{3}{5} = \dfrac{?}{20}$ ←————————— 5 must be multiplied by 4 to get 20.

$\qquad\qquad\quad \dfrac{3}{5} = \dfrac{3 \cdot 4}{5 \cdot 4} = \dfrac{12}{20}$ ←————— Therefore, multiply 3 by 4 to get 12.

EXAMPLE 2 $\dfrac{6}{5a} = \dfrac{?}{10a^2}$ ←————————— $5a$ must be multiplied by $2a$ to get $10a^2$.

$\qquad\qquad\quad \dfrac{6}{5a} = \dfrac{12a}{10a^2}$ ←————— Therefore, multiply 6 by $2a$ to get $12a$.

EXAMPLE 3 $\dfrac{3}{x+2} = \dfrac{?}{(x+2)(x-1)}$ ←—— $(x+2)$ must be multiplied by $(x-1)$

$\qquad\qquad\quad \dfrac{3}{x+2} = \dfrac{3(x-1)}{(x+2)(x-1)}$ ←—— to get $(x+2)(x-1)$.
Therefore, multiply 3 by $(x-1)$.

The technique shown in the last three examples is used to rewrite fractions so that they have equal denominators. For example, you can express $\dfrac{3}{4}$ and $\dfrac{5}{6}$ as fractions having a common denominator of 12, 24, 36, or any other positive **multiple** of 12. (The product of a number and an integer is called a **multiple** of the number.) Usually, it is convenient to use the **least common denominator (LCD)** of two fractions. To determine the LCD of a group of fractions, find the **least common multiple** of the denominators.

212   *CHAPTER 6*

FINDING THE LEAST COMMON DENOMINATOR

1. Factor each denominator into primes
2. Form the product of the greatest powers of each prime factor occurring in the denominators.

EXAMPLE 4 What is the LCD of the fractions $\frac{2}{27}$, $\frac{1}{36}$, and $\frac{7}{30}$?

SOLUTION
1. Factor each denominator into primes.
$$27 = 3^3 \qquad 36 = 2^2 \cdot 3^2 \qquad 30 = 2 \cdot 3 \cdot 5$$

2. Greatest power of 2: 2^2
   Greatest power of 3: 3^3
   Greatest power of 5: 5^1
   $$2^2 \cdot 3^3 \cdot 5^1 = 540$$

$\therefore$ the LCD is 540. **Answer**

When the denominators of the fractions contain variables, the LCD will be the simplest of the common multiples of the denominators.

EXAMPLE 5 What is the LCD of $\frac{5}{4x - 20}$ and $\frac{7}{6x - 30}$?

SOLUTION
1. Factor each denominator completely.
$$4x - 20 = 4(x - 5) = 2^2(x - 5)$$
$$6x - 30 = 6(x - 5) = 3 \cdot 2(x - 5)$$

2. Form the product of the greatest power of each prime factor.
$$2^2 \cdot 3(x - 5) = 12(x - 5)$$

$\therefore$ the LCD is $12(x - 5)$. **Answer**

EXAMPLE 6 Express $\frac{4}{a^2 + a - 20}$ and $\frac{3}{a^2 + 10a + 25}$ with their least common denominator.

SOLUTION Find the LCD: $(a - 4)(a + 5)^2$.
$$\frac{4}{a^2 + a - 20} = \frac{4}{(a - 4)(a + 5)} = \frac{4(a + 5)}{(a - 4)(a + 5)(a + 5)} = \frac{4(a + 5)}{(a - 4)(a + 5)^2}$$

$$\frac{3}{a^2 + 10a + 25} = \frac{3}{(a + 5)^2} = \frac{3(a - 4)}{(a + 5)^2(a - 4)} = \frac{3(a - 4)}{(a - 4)(a + 5)^2}$$

FRACTIONS **213**

Supplementary Material
Computer Activity 16
Adding Powers of Fractions
  A computer program is used to generate and find the sum of a finite number of terms of a geometric sequence whose first term and common ratio are identical. Students are also asked to look for limiting values of these sums as more and more terms are added to each sequence.

Suggested Assignments
Minimum
Day 1: 214/1–23 odd
    R 210/*Self-Test 1*
Day 2: 214/25–43 odd
Average
Day 1: 214/1–31 odd
    R 210/*Self-Test 1*
Day 2: 215/33–46
    S 209/36, 37, 39
Maximum
Day 1: 214/1–43 odd
    R 210/*Self-Test 1*
Day 2: 215/45, 46, 48
    217/5–49 odd
NOTE: Day 2 of Sec. 6-4 finishes Sec. 6-4 and covers Sec. 6-5.

Oral Exercises

Find the missing numerator.

1. $\frac{3}{5} = \frac{?}{15}$ 9

2. $\frac{2}{7} = \frac{?}{28}$ 8

3. $\frac{4x}{3} = \frac{?}{6}$ 8x

4. $\frac{3}{2y} = \frac{?}{10y}$ 15

5. $\frac{1}{2} = \frac{?}{8(x + 1)}$ 4(x + 1)

6. $\frac{3}{x} = \frac{?}{2x^2}$ 6x

7. $\frac{5a}{3b} = \frac{?}{9ab}$ $15a^2$

8. $\frac{2}{(x + 1)} = \frac{?}{(x + 1)(x + 4)}$ 2(x + 4)

Find the LCD for each group of fractions.

9. $\frac{2}{9}, \frac{1}{6}$ 18

10. $\frac{8}{15}, \frac{5}{6}$ 30

11. $\frac{7}{10}, \frac{5}{12}, \frac{1}{3}$ 60

12. $\frac{4}{x}, \frac{5}{2x^2}$ $2x^2$

13. $\frac{7}{3xy}, \frac{5}{6y^2}$ $6xy^2$

14. $\frac{3}{a^2 - b^2}, \frac{1}{2(a + b)}$ 2(a − b)(a + b)

15. $\frac{9}{(x - 3)^2}, \frac{1}{(x - 3)(x - 4)}$ $(x - 3)^2(x - 4)$

16. $\frac{x}{5x - 10}, \frac{4}{3x - 6}$ 15(x − 2)

Written Exercises

Find the missing numerator.

A 1. $\frac{2}{5} = \frac{?}{15}$ 6

2. $\frac{3}{8} = \frac{?}{32}$ 12

3. $\frac{4x}{5} = \frac{?}{30}$ 24x

4. $\frac{8a}{11} = \frac{?}{33}$ 24a

5. $\frac{2a + 3}{8} = \frac{?}{24}$ 3(2a + 3)

6. $\frac{3n - 5}{2} = \frac{?}{10}$ 5(3n − 5)

7. $\frac{1 - 7x}{4} = \frac{?}{24}$ 6(1 − 7x)

8. $\frac{3d + 2c}{5} = \frac{?}{55}$

9. $\frac{x}{9} = \frac{?}{9x^2}$ x^3

10. $\frac{y}{3} = \frac{?}{6xy}$ $2xy^2$

11. $\frac{3}{5a} = \frac{?}{10a^2}$ 6a

12. $\frac{2}{3ab} = \frac{?}{6ab^2}$ 4b

13. $\frac{2}{3(x + 2)} = \frac{?}{3(x + 2)^2}$ 2(x + 2)

14. $\frac{4}{(x - 3)(x + 1)} = \frac{?}{(x - 3)^2(x + 1)}$ 4(x − 3)

15. $\frac{3}{a - 2b} = \frac{?}{2b - a}$ −3

16. $\frac{7}{5x - 3} = \frac{?}{2(3 - 5x)}$ −14

17. $\frac{1}{x - 1} = \frac{?}{x^2 - 1}$ x + 1

18. $\frac{3}{x + 1} = \frac{?}{x^2 - 1}$

19. $\frac{5}{a + 3} = \frac{?}{2a + 6}$ 10

20. $\frac{4a}{a - 2} = \frac{?}{3a - 6}$ 12a

21. $\frac{2}{x - 2} = \frac{?}{x^2 - 2x}$ 2x

22. $\frac{x}{x - 3} = \frac{?}{(x - 3)(x + 4)}$ x(x + 4)

23. $\frac{5}{2b - 3} = \frac{?}{a(3 - 2b)}$ −5a

24. $\frac{4 + x}{4 - x} = \frac{?}{16 - x^2}$

Find the LCD for each group of fractions.

25. $\frac{5}{6}, \frac{4}{9}$ 18

26. $\frac{7}{20}, \frac{11}{45}$ 180

27. $\frac{3}{2x}, \frac{1}{5y}$ 10xy

28. $\frac{1}{4a^2}, \frac{5}{6a}$ $12a^2$

29. $\frac{4}{9c}, \frac{5}{3d}, \frac{1}{d^2}$ $9cd^2$

30. $\frac{5}{16y^3}, \frac{-7}{8x}, \frac{4}{3y}$ $48xy^3$

31. $\frac{1}{2(x - 1)}, \frac{3}{x + 1}, \frac{4}{x^2 - 1}$ 2(x + 1)(x − 1)

32. $\frac{1}{2(a - b)}, \frac{-3}{4(b - a)}$ 4(a − b)

Express each group of fractions with their LCD.

B 33. $\dfrac{5}{18}, \dfrac{3}{8}$

34. $\dfrac{3}{14}, \dfrac{2}{35}, \dfrac{1}{6}$

35. $\dfrac{2x-1}{15}, \dfrac{1+x}{20}$

36. $\dfrac{5x}{12}, \dfrac{x-7}{8}, \dfrac{4x-9}{6}$

37. $\dfrac{2x-3}{6}, \dfrac{7+3y}{9}, \dfrac{x}{16}$

38. $\dfrac{5}{2y}, \dfrac{2}{3y}$

39. $\dfrac{1}{4x^2y}, \dfrac{3x}{8y^2}$

40. $\dfrac{2}{a^2b}, \dfrac{a}{2b^4}$

41. $\dfrac{4}{9-x^2}, \dfrac{3}{x+3}$

42. $\dfrac{4}{2(x-7)}, \dfrac{5}{3(x-7)}$

43. $\dfrac{1}{x^2-3x}, \dfrac{1}{x^2+2x}$

44. $\dfrac{2}{a^2-a-2}, \dfrac{1}{a^2-4}$

C 45. $\dfrac{x}{4x^2-100}, \dfrac{2}{x+5}, \dfrac{-3}{5-x}$

46. $\dfrac{2}{y^2-4}, \dfrac{3}{y^2-5y+6}, \dfrac{-1}{y^2-y-6}$

47. $\dfrac{2}{3x^2-27}, \dfrac{x}{2x+6}, \dfrac{3+x}{3-x}$

48. $\dfrac{n+3}{n^2+2n-8}, \dfrac{-4}{3n^2+21n+36}, \dfrac{n}{4n+12}$

ꜟistorical ꞁote Decimals

Computation with fractions has always presented problems. The Babyloni-ans used a place-value system partially based on 60, including fractions with denominators that were powers of 60. This system is reflected in our time measurements of minutes and seconds.

In 1579 Vieta (1540–1603) recommended using fractions with denom-inators that were powers of 10, but Simon Stevin (see page 177) is usually credited with the invention of the decimal fraction. In 1585 he published a book in which he explained how, by using decimals, all computations could be done as if with whole numbers. In his notation he indicated the decimal places by using small numerals in circles. He showed the addition of the numbers 27⓪8①4②7③, 37⓪6①7②5③, and 875⓪7①8②2③ as follows.

⓪ ① ② ③		
2 7 8 4 7		27.847
3 7 6 7 5	meaning	37.675
8 7 5 7 8 2		875.782
9 4 1 3 0 4		941.304

He wrote the sum as 941⓪3①0②4③

Following Stevin's work, the decimal point and the decimal comma, which is used in some countries today, were soon introduced. Then the small numerals in circles could be omitted.

Additional Answers Written Exercises

42. $\dfrac{12}{6(x-7)}, \dfrac{10}{6(x-7)}$

43. $\dfrac{x+2}{x(x-3)(x+2)},$
$\dfrac{x-3}{x(x-3)(x+2)}$

44. $\dfrac{2(a+2)}{(a+2)(a-2)(a+1)},$
$\dfrac{a+1}{(a+2)(a-2)(a+1)}$

45. $\dfrac{x}{4(x-5)(x+5)},$
$\dfrac{8(x-5)}{4(x-5)(x+5)},$
$\dfrac{12(x+5)}{4(x-5)(x+5)}$

46. $\dfrac{2(y-3)}{(y+2)(y-2)(y-3)},$
$\dfrac{3(y+2)}{(y+2)(y-2)(y-3)},$
$\dfrac{-(y-2)}{(y+2)(y-2)(y-3)}$

47. $\dfrac{4}{6(x+3)(x-3)},$
$\dfrac{3x(x-3)}{6(x+3)(x-3)},$
$\dfrac{-6(x+3)^2}{6(x+3)(x-3)}$

48. $\dfrac{12(n+3)^2}{12(n-2)(n+3)(n+4)},$
$\dfrac{-16(n-2)}{12(n-2)(n+3)(n+4)},$
$\dfrac{3n(n-2)(n+4)}{12(n-2)(n+3)(n+4)}$

6-5 *Adding and Subtracting Fractions*

OBJECTIVE To add and subtract algebraic fractions.

The results proved in Exercises 31 and 32 on page 91 can be used to show how to add and subtract fractions with the same denominator. Rewriting those results using the symmetric property of equality gives the following rules.

ADDITION RULE FOR FRACTIONS

$$\frac{a}{c} + \frac{b}{c} = \frac{a+b}{c}$$

SUBTRACTION RULE FOR FRACTIONS

$$\frac{a}{c} - \frac{b}{c} = \frac{a-b}{c}$$

To add fractions with the same denominator, you add their numerators. To subtract fractions with the same denominator, you subtract their numerators.

EXAMPLE 1 $\dfrac{7x}{5} + \dfrac{2x}{5} = \dfrac{7x+2x}{5} = \dfrac{9x}{5}$

EXAMPLE 2 $\dfrac{3a}{8} + \dfrac{2a-3}{8} - \dfrac{3a+5}{8} = \dfrac{(3a)+(2a-3)-(3a+5)}{8}$

$\qquad\qquad = \dfrac{3a+2a-3-3a-5}{8}$

$\qquad\qquad = \dfrac{2a-8}{8} = \dfrac{2(a-4)}{8} = \dfrac{a-4}{4}$

To add or subtract fractions with different denominators, you must first express the fractions with a common denominator. To simplify an expression involving fractions means to express it as a fraction in simplest form.

EXAMPLE 3 $\dfrac{5a}{6} + \dfrac{2a+2}{9} - \dfrac{a-4}{2} = \dfrac{15a}{18} + \dfrac{2(2a+2)}{18} - \dfrac{9(a-4)}{18}$

$\qquad\qquad = \dfrac{15a + 2(2a+2) - 9(a-4)}{18}$

$\qquad\qquad = \dfrac{15a + 4a + 4 - 9a + 36}{18}$

$\qquad\qquad = \dfrac{10a+40}{18} = \dfrac{10(a+4)}{18} = \dfrac{5(a+4)}{9}$

216 *CHAPTER 6*

EXAMPLE 4 Simplify $\dfrac{1}{x^2 + x} + \dfrac{2x}{x^2 - 1}$.

SOLUTION
$$\frac{1}{x^2 + x} + \frac{2x}{x^2 - 1} = \frac{1}{x(x + 1)} + \frac{2x}{(x + 1)(x - 1)}$$

$$= \frac{x - 1}{x(x + 1)(x - 1)} + \frac{2x^2}{x(x + 1)(x - 1)}$$

$$= \frac{x - 1 + 2x^2}{x(x + 1)(x - 1)}$$

$$= \frac{(2x - 1)(x + 1)}{x(x + 1)(x - 1)}$$

$$= \frac{2x - 1}{x(x - 1)}$$

Oral Exercises

Simplify.

1. $\dfrac{3}{10} + \dfrac{2}{10}$ $\dfrac{1}{2}$

2. $\dfrac{8}{9} - \dfrac{2}{9}$ $\dfrac{2}{3}$

3. $\dfrac{11}{12} + \dfrac{7}{12} - \dfrac{1}{12}$ $\dfrac{17}{12}$, or $1\dfrac{5}{12}$

4. $\dfrac{4}{3} - \dfrac{8}{3} - \dfrac{2}{3}$ -2

5. $\dfrac{2}{a} + \dfrac{5}{a}$ $\dfrac{7}{a}$

6. $\dfrac{8}{b} - \dfrac{9}{b}$ $\dfrac{-1}{b}$

7. $\dfrac{5}{2x} - \dfrac{3}{2x}$ $\dfrac{1}{x}$

8. $\dfrac{2a}{x + 1} + \dfrac{b}{x + 1}$ $\dfrac{2a + b}{x + 1}$

9. $\dfrac{2x}{5} + \dfrac{4x}{5}$ $\dfrac{6x}{5}$

10. $\dfrac{5n + 8}{6} - \dfrac{1}{6}$ $\dfrac{5n + 7}{6}$

11. $\dfrac{2a - 1}{3} + \dfrac{2a - 2}{3}$ $\dfrac{4a - 3}{3}$

12. $\dfrac{6n - 3}{4} + \dfrac{3 - 2n}{4}$ n

13. $\dfrac{x}{2} + \dfrac{x}{6}$ $\dfrac{2x}{3}$

14. $\dfrac{3}{a - b} + \dfrac{2}{b - a}$ $\dfrac{1}{a - b}$

15. $\dfrac{3x}{8} - \dfrac{2x + 1}{8}$ $\dfrac{x - 1}{8}$

16. $\dfrac{2a + 3}{7} - \dfrac{2a - 1}{7}$ $\dfrac{4}{7}$

Written Exercises

Simplify.

A
1. $\dfrac{5}{a} - \dfrac{3}{a} + \dfrac{9}{a}$ $\dfrac{11}{a}$

2. $\dfrac{4}{3b} + \dfrac{5}{3b} + \dfrac{2}{3b}$ $\dfrac{11}{3b}$

3. $\dfrac{7}{2c} - \dfrac{8}{2c} + \dfrac{3}{2c}$ $\dfrac{1}{c}$

4. $\dfrac{x + 2}{3} + \dfrac{2x - 4}{3}$ $\dfrac{3x - 2}{3}$

5. $\dfrac{3a + 4}{5} - \dfrac{3a - 1}{5}$ 1

6. $\dfrac{5a - 3}{8} - \dfrac{3 - 11a}{8}$ $\dfrac{8a - 3}{4}$

7. $\dfrac{y^2}{y + 2} - \dfrac{4}{y + 2}$ $y - 2$

8. $\dfrac{b^2}{b - a} - \dfrac{a^2}{b - a}$ $b + a$

9. $\dfrac{x^2}{(x + 3)^2} - \dfrac{6x - 9}{(x + 3)^2}$ $\dfrac{(x - 3)^2}{(x + 3)^2}$

10. $\dfrac{x}{2} + \dfrac{x}{4}$ $\dfrac{3x}{4}$

11. $\dfrac{a}{5} + \dfrac{2a}{15}$ $\dfrac{a}{3}$

12. $\dfrac{5r}{9} - \dfrac{r}{6}$ $\dfrac{7r}{18}$

13. $\dfrac{3}{x} + \dfrac{2}{x^2}$ $\dfrac{3x + 2}{x^2}$

14. $\dfrac{3}{5a} + \dfrac{4}{ab}$ $\dfrac{3b + 20}{5ab}$

15. $\dfrac{5}{2a} - \dfrac{3}{a^2}$ $\dfrac{5a - 6}{2a^2}$

16. $\dfrac{3x - 2}{6} + \dfrac{4x - 1}{4}$ $\dfrac{18x - 7}{12}$

17. $\dfrac{4 - 2y}{20} - \dfrac{y + 3}{25}$ $\dfrac{4 - 7y}{50}$

18. $\dfrac{2a - 2}{15} - \dfrac{3a + 2}{10}$ $\dfrac{-(a + 2)}{6}$

19. $\dfrac{2n + 4}{5} - \dfrac{n}{6} + \dfrac{3n - 2}{10}$ $\dfrac{8n + 9}{15}$

20. $\dfrac{2a - b}{3} - \dfrac{b}{6} - \dfrac{2b - 3a}{4}$ $\dfrac{17a - 12b}{12}$

21. $\dfrac{2x}{30} - \dfrac{2x - 5y}{45} - \dfrac{x - 3y}{15}$ $\dfrac{2(7y - x)}{45}$

FRACTIONS **217**

Supplementary Materials

Practice Master 36
Computer Activity 17
Exploring Unit Fractions
  Finding all ways in which a unit fraction $\dfrac{1}{n}$ can be expressed as the sum of two other unit fractions $\dfrac{1}{a}$ and $\dfrac{1}{b}$ is achieved by the computer program in this activity.

Suggested Assignments

Minimum
Day 1: 217/1–9 odd, 11–21,
  23–29 odd
Day 2: 218/31–43 odd
  R 219/Self-Test 2

Average
  217/1–47 odd

Maximum

NOTE: Day 2 of Sec. 6-4 finishes Sec. 6-4 and covers Sec. 6-5.

Additional A Exercises

Simplify.

1. $\dfrac{3}{7} + \dfrac{2}{7}$ $\dfrac{5}{7}$

2. $\dfrac{10}{17} - \dfrac{7}{17}$ $\dfrac{3}{17}$

3. $\dfrac{8}{x} + \dfrac{13}{x}$ $\dfrac{21}{x}$

4. $\dfrac{23}{y} - \dfrac{8}{y}$ $\dfrac{15}{y}$

5. $\dfrac{c}{x - 2} + \dfrac{d}{x - 2}$ $\dfrac{c + d}{x - 2}$

6. $\dfrac{3a + 5}{y + 1} - \dfrac{2a + 2}{y + 1}$ $\dfrac{a + 3}{y + 1}$

Simplify.

22. $\dfrac{1}{x-1} + \dfrac{1}{x}$ $\dfrac{2x-1}{x(x-1)}$

23. $\dfrac{3y+2}{(y+2)(y-2)}$

23. $\dfrac{2}{y-2} + \dfrac{1}{y+2}$

26. $\dfrac{5(x-1)}{(x-5)(x+5)}$

24. $\dfrac{x}{x-5} + \dfrac{4}{5-x}$ $\dfrac{x-4}{x-5}$

25. $\dfrac{7}{3a-b} + \dfrac{5}{b-3a}$ $\dfrac{2}{3a-b}$

26. $\dfrac{3}{x+5} + \dfrac{2}{x-5}$

27. $\dfrac{2}{2a-3} - \dfrac{1}{a}$ $\dfrac{3}{a(2a-3)}$

Find the perimeter and area of each figure in terms of the variable. Assume that the dimensions are given in meters.

28.

$\dfrac{x}{4}$ $\dfrac{5x}{6}$ m; $\dfrac{x^2}{24}$ m²

$\dfrac{x}{6}$

29.

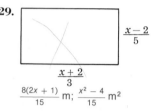

$x-2 \over 5$

$\dfrac{x+2}{3}$

$\dfrac{8(2x+1)}{15}$ m; $\dfrac{x^2-4}{15}$ m²

30.

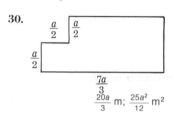

$\dfrac{a}{2}$ $\dfrac{a}{2}$

$\dfrac{a}{2}$

$\dfrac{7a}{3}$

$\dfrac{20a}{3}$ m; $\dfrac{25a^2}{12}$ m²

Simplify.

B 31. $\dfrac{x+1}{x} - \dfrac{x}{x+1}$

32. $\dfrac{n}{n-1} - \dfrac{2n}{n^2-1}$

33. $\dfrac{1}{4x-4} - \dfrac{1}{2x^2-2}$

34. $\dfrac{3a}{a-2b} + \dfrac{6b}{2b-a}$

35. $\dfrac{x}{x+y} + \dfrac{y}{x-y}$

36. $\dfrac{2}{x^2-2x} - \dfrac{3}{x^2-x-2}$

37. $\dfrac{b}{a^2-ab} - \dfrac{a}{ab-b^2}$

38. $\dfrac{1}{x-5} - \dfrac{x}{(5-x)^2}$

39. $\dfrac{a+2}{a^2+3a} - \dfrac{a-2}{a^2-3a}$

40. $\dfrac{2a}{a^3-5a^2} + \dfrac{2}{a^2+5a}$

41. $\dfrac{2}{c^2-c-2} + \dfrac{1}{c^2-4}$

42. $\dfrac{x}{(1-x)^2} + \dfrac{1}{1-x^2}$

43. $\dfrac{1}{a^2-1} + \dfrac{1}{a^2+2a+1}$

44. $\dfrac{8}{c^2-4} + \dfrac{2}{c^2-5c+6}$

45. $\dfrac{3x}{x^2+3x+2} - \dfrac{3x-6}{x^2+4x+4}$

C 46. $\dfrac{x^2+1}{x^2-1} + \dfrac{1}{x+1} + \dfrac{1}{x-1}$ $\dfrac{x+1}{x-1}$

47. $\dfrac{x}{2x-1} + \dfrac{x-1}{2x+1} - \dfrac{2x}{4x^2-1}$ $\dfrac{2x-1}{2x+1}$

48. $\dfrac{a+2}{a^2+5a+6} - \dfrac{2+a}{4-a^2} + \dfrac{2-a}{a^2+a-6}$ $\dfrac{1}{a-2}$

49. $\dfrac{x-3}{2x+6} - \dfrac{x+3}{3x-9} - \dfrac{5x^2+27}{6x^2-54}$ $\dfrac{-2x^2-15x-9}{3(x+3)(x-3)}$

50. $\dfrac{b+1}{(b-1)^2} + \dfrac{2-2b}{(b-1)^3} + \dfrac{1}{b-1}$ $\dfrac{2}{b-1}$

51. $\dfrac{1}{(a-b)(a-c)} + \dfrac{1}{(b-c)(b-a)} + \dfrac{1}{(c-a)(c-b)}$ 0

218

Self-Test 2

VOCABULARY multiple (p. 212) least common denominator
least common multiple (p. 212) (p. 212)

Express each group of fractions with their LCD.

1. $\dfrac{5}{16kz^2}, \dfrac{3k}{4}$

2. $\dfrac{1}{3(x-1)}, \dfrac{2}{x^2-1}$

Obj. 6-4, p. 212

Simplify.

3. $\dfrac{8}{3c} - \dfrac{5}{3c} + \dfrac{2}{3c}$

4. $\dfrac{n^2-9}{3} + \dfrac{4}{3}$

Obj. 6-5, p. 216

5. $\dfrac{3}{k^2-4} + \dfrac{1}{k+2}$

6. $\dfrac{7}{2a} - \dfrac{a-2}{4ab}$

Check your answers with those at the back of the book.

Just for Fun

1. a. Find each sum.

$$\frac{1}{1 \cdot 2} + \frac{1}{2 \cdot 3} = \underline{\ ?\ } \quad \tfrac{2}{3}$$

$$\frac{1}{1 \cdot 2} + \frac{1}{2 \cdot 3} + \frac{1}{3 \cdot 4} = \underline{\ ?\ } \quad \tfrac{3}{4}$$

$$\frac{1}{1 \cdot 2} + \frac{1}{2 \cdot 3} + \frac{1}{3 \cdot 4} + \frac{1}{4 \cdot 5} = \underline{\ ?\ } \quad \tfrac{4}{5}$$

b. If this addition pattern were continued for 100 fractions, what would the sum be? $\tfrac{100}{101}$

c. If this addition pattern were continued for n fractions, what would the sum be? $\tfrac{n}{n+1}$

2. a. Find each sum.

$$\frac{1}{1 \cdot 3} + \frac{1}{3 \cdot 5} = \underline{\ ?\ } \quad \tfrac{2}{5}$$

$$\frac{1}{1 \cdot 3} + \frac{1}{3 \cdot 5} + \frac{1}{5 \cdot 7} = \underline{\ ?\ } \quad \tfrac{3}{7}$$

$$\frac{1}{1 \cdot 3} + \frac{1}{3 \cdot 5} + \frac{1}{5 \cdot 7} + \frac{1}{7 \cdot 9} = \underline{\ ?\ } \quad \tfrac{4}{9}$$

b. If this addition pattern were continued for 50 fractions, what would the sum be? $\tfrac{50}{101}$

c. If this addition pattern were continued for n fractions, what would the sum be? $\tfrac{n}{2n+1}$

1. Find the LCD.

$$\frac{3}{2x}, \frac{x}{x-2}, \frac{1}{9x^3}$$

$$18x^3(x-2)$$

Simplify.

2. $\dfrac{1}{4x} - \dfrac{3}{4x} + \dfrac{7}{4x} \quad \tfrac{5}{4x}$

3. $\dfrac{x}{4x^2-1} + \dfrac{2}{2x+1} \quad \tfrac{5x-2}{4x^2-1}$

4. $\dfrac{2}{3ab} - \dfrac{b+1}{ab^2} \quad \tfrac{-b-3}{3ab^2}$

FRACTIONS **219**

POLYNOMIAL DIVISION

6-6 *Mixed Expressions*

OBJECTIVE   To write mixed expressions as fractions in simplest form.

A mixed number like $3\dfrac{1}{4}$ denotes the sum of an integer and a fraction.
Recall that it may be expressed as a fraction as follows:

$$3\frac{1}{4} = \frac{3}{1} + \frac{1}{4} = \frac{12}{4} + \frac{1}{4} = \frac{13}{4}$$

A sum or difference of a polynomial and a fraction is called **a mixed
expression.** The following example shows that a mixed expression may
be expressed as a fraction in simplest form.

EXAMPLE   Express as a fraction in simplest form.

   a. $k + \dfrac{2}{k}$ **b.** $5 - \dfrac{2x - 3}{\,\text{-}x + 1}$

SOLUTION   **a.** $k + \dfrac{2}{k} = \dfrac{k}{1} + \dfrac{2}{k} = \dfrac{k^2}{k} + \dfrac{2}{k} = \dfrac{k^2 + 2}{k}$

   b. $5 - \dfrac{2x - 3}{x + 1} = \dfrac{5}{1} - \dfrac{2x - 3}{x + 1}$

$$= \frac{5(x + 1)}{(x + 1)} - \frac{2x - 3}{x + 1}$$

$$= \frac{5x + 5 - 2x + 3}{x + 1}$$

$$= \frac{3x + 8}{x + 1}$$

Oral Exercises

State each as a fraction in simplest form.

SAMPLE $-5\dfrac{2}{3} = -\left(5 + \dfrac{2}{3}\right) = -\left(\dfrac{5}{1} + \dfrac{2}{3}\right) = -\left(\dfrac{15}{3} + \dfrac{2}{3}\right) = -\dfrac{17}{3}$

1. $3\dfrac{1}{5}$ $\dfrac{16}{5}$ **2.** $4\dfrac{2}{3}$ $\dfrac{14}{3}$ **3.** $-5\dfrac{3}{8}$ $-\dfrac{43}{8}$

5. $1 + \dfrac{1}{a}$ $\dfrac{a + 1}{a}$ **6.** $3 + \dfrac{2}{c}$ $\dfrac{3c + 2}{c}$ **7.** $x + \dfrac{5}{x}$ $\dfrac{x^2 + 5}{x}$

9. $2 + \dfrac{3}{x + 1}$ $\dfrac{2x + 5}{x + 1}$ **10.** $4 - \dfrac{1}{y + 3}$ $\dfrac{4y + 11}{y + 3}$ **11.** $\dfrac{2n}{2n + 1} - 1$ $\dfrac{-1}{2n + 1}$ **12.** $\dfrac{5a}{a - 3} + 2$

4. $-\dfrac{23}{8}$

8. $\dfrac{y^2 - 3}{y}$

4. $-2\dfrac{7}{8}$

8. $y - \dfrac{3}{y}$

$\dfrac{7a - 6}{a - 3}$

Written Exercises

Write each expression as a fraction in simplest form.

A **1.** $3\frac{1}{7}$ $\quad \frac{22}{7}$

2. $-4\frac{7}{9}$ $\quad -\frac{43}{9}$

3. $5 + \frac{2}{x}$ $\quad \frac{5x+2}{x}$

4. $7 - \frac{1}{n}$ $\quad \frac{7n-1}{n}$

5. $4 + \frac{a}{b}$ $\quad \frac{4b+a}{b}$

6. $\frac{x}{y} - 1$ $\quad \frac{x-y}{y}$

7. $\frac{3}{2n} + n$ $\quad \frac{3+2n^2}{2n}$

8. $\frac{6}{x+1} - 3$

9. $x - \frac{x-y}{3} + 2y$ $\quad \frac{2x+7y}{3}$

10. $\frac{4x-5}{2} - 2 + \frac{3x}{5}$

11. $8 - \frac{x}{2x-3}$ $\quad \frac{3(5x-8)}{2x-3}$

12. $2 + \frac{2a-3b}{a+b}$ $\quad \frac{4a-b}{a+b}$

13. $\frac{4x}{(x-2)^2} + 1$ $\quad \frac{x^2+4}{(x-2)^2}$

14. $\frac{3x}{x^2-9} - 2$ $\quad \frac{3x-2x^2+18}{(x-3)(x+3)}$

B **15.** $\frac{4}{a} + \frac{1}{b} - 2$ $\quad \frac{4b+a-2ab}{ab}$

16. $\frac{b}{a+b} + \frac{a}{b-a} + 1$

17. $\frac{x}{x+3} + \frac{x}{x-3} - 2$

18. $4 - \frac{3}{n-1} - \frac{1}{n+1}$

19. $\left(x+\frac{2}{x}\right)\left(x-\frac{3}{x}\right)$

20. $\left(4-\frac{x}{3}\right)\left(3-\frac{x}{4}\right)$ $\quad \frac{(x-12)^2}{12}$

21. $\left(\frac{x+y}{x}-1\right)\left(\frac{x}{y}+1\right)$

22. $\left(x-\frac{y^2}{x}\right) \div \left(1+\frac{y}{x}\right)$ $\quad x-y$

23. $\left(x-\frac{2}{x+1}\right)\left(1-\frac{1}{x+2}\right)$ $\quad x-1$

24. $\left(4-\frac{1}{b^2}\right) \div (2b+1)$ $\quad \frac{2b-1}{b^2}$

C **25.** $\left(1 - \frac{b^2+c^2-a^2}{2bc}\right) \div \left(1 - \frac{a^2+b^2-c^2}{2ab}\right)$ $\quad \frac{a(a+b-c)}{c(c-a+b)}$

26. $\left(2 - \frac{n}{n+1} + \frac{n}{1-n}\right) \div \left(\frac{1}{n-1} - \frac{1}{n+1}\right) - 1$

27. Find constants A and B such that $\frac{4}{x^2-4} = \frac{A}{x+2} + \frac{B}{x-2}$. $A=-1$, $B=1$

28. Find constants C and D such that $\frac{6x}{x^2-x-2} = \frac{C}{x-2} + \frac{D}{x+1}$. $C=4$, $D=2$

Just for Fun

Diophantus was a famous Greek mathematician, who lived and worked in Alexandria, Egypt, probably in the third century A.D. After he died, someone described his life in this puzzle:

> He was a boy for $\frac{1}{6}$ of his life.
> After $\frac{1}{12}$ more, he acquired a beard.
> After another $\frac{1}{7}$, he married.
> In the fifth year after his marriage his son was born.
> The son lived half as many years as his father.
> Diophantus died 4 years after his son.

How old was Diophantus when he died? Write an equation and solve it.
84 years old

Additional A Exercises

Write as a fraction in simplest form.

1. $3\frac{1}{8}$ $\quad \frac{25}{8}$

2. $4\frac{7}{12}$ $\quad \frac{55}{12}$

3. $8 + \frac{2}{x}$ $\quad \frac{8x+2}{x}$

4. $c + \frac{4}{c}$ $\quad \frac{c^2+4}{c}$

5. $a - \frac{5}{a}$ $\quad \frac{a^2-5}{a}$

6. $5 + \frac{2}{a-3}$ $\quad \frac{5a-13}{a-3}$

Additional Answers
Written Exercises

8. $\frac{3(1-x)}{x+1}$

10. $\frac{26x-45}{10}$

16. $\frac{2b^2}{(b+a)(b-a)}$

17. $\frac{18}{(x+3)(x-3)}$

18. $\frac{2(2n^2-2n-3)}{(n-1)(n+1)}$

19. $\frac{(x^2-3)(x^2+2)}{x^2}$

21. $\frac{x+y}{x}$

Teaching Suggestions p. T88

Suggested Extensions p. T88

Chalkboard Examples

Divide. Write your answer as a polynomial or mixed expression.

1. $\dfrac{6x^2 - 11x + 5}{x - 1}$

$$\begin{array}{r}
6x - 5 \\
x - 1\overline{)6x^2 - 11x + 5} \\
\underline{6x^2 - 6x} \\
-5x + 5 \\
\underline{-5x + 5} \\
0
\end{array}$$

2. $\dfrac{4w^2 + w - 2}{w + 2}$

$$\begin{array}{r}
4w - 7 + \dfrac{12}{w + 2} \\
w + 2\overline{)4w^2 + w - 2} \\
\underline{4w^2 + 8w} \\
-7w - 2 \\
\underline{-7w - 14} \\
12
\end{array}$$

3. $\dfrac{2z^3 + z + 3}{z + 1}$

$$\begin{array}{r}
2z^2 - 2z + 3 \\
z + 1\overline{)2z^3 + 0z^2 + z + 3} \\
\underline{2z^3 + 2z^2} \\
-2z^2 + z \\
\underline{-2z^2 - 2z} \\
3z + 3 \\
\underline{3z + 3} \\
0
\end{array}$$

4. $\dfrac{x^3 + 1}{x + 1}$

$$\begin{array}{r}
x^2 - x + 1 \\
x + 1\overline{)x^3 + 0x^2 + 0x + 1} \\
\underline{x^3 + x^2} \\
-x^2 + 0x \\
\underline{-x^2 - x} \\
x + 1 \\
\underline{x + 1} \\
0
\end{array}$$

6-7 *Polynomial Long Division*

OBJECTIVE To divide polynomials.

Division of one polynomial by another is very much like ordinary long division. Compare the polynomial division and the long division shown below.

Step 1
$$\begin{array}{r}
2 \\
31\overline{)658} \\
\underline{62} \\
38
\end{array}$$

Step 1
$$\begin{array}{r}
2x \\
3x + 1\overline{)6x^2 + 5x + 8} \\
\underline{6x^2 + 2x} \\
3x + 8
\end{array}$$

Step 2
$$\begin{array}{r}
21 \\
31\overline{)658} \\
\underline{62} \\
38 \\
\underline{31} \\
7
\end{array}$$

Step 2
$$\begin{array}{r}
2x + 1 \\
3x + 1\overline{)6x^2 + 5x + 8} \\
\underline{6x^2 + 2x} \\
3x + 8 \\
\underline{3x + 1} \\
7
\end{array}$$

Check: $658 \stackrel{?}{=} 21 \cdot 31 + 7$
$658 \stackrel{?}{=} 651 + 7$
$658 = 658$ ✓

$\therefore \dfrac{658}{31} = 21\dfrac{7}{31}$

Check: $6x^2 + 5x + 8 \stackrel{?}{=} (2x + 1)(3x + 1) + 7$
$6x^2 + 5x + 8 \stackrel{?}{=} (6x^2 + 5x + 1) + 7$
$6x^2 + 5x + 8 = 6x^2 + 5x + 8$ ✓

$\therefore \dfrac{6x^2 + 5x + 8}{3x + 1} = (2x + 1) + \dfrac{7}{3x + 1}$

In both divisions above, the answer was expressed in the following form:

$$\frac{\text{Dividend}}{\text{Divisor}} = \text{Quotient} + \frac{\text{Remainder}}{\text{Divisor}}$$

The following identity was used to check both divisions:

$$\text{Dividend} = \text{Quotient} \times \text{Divisor} + \text{Remainder}$$

When you divide polynomials, always make sure that the terms in each polynomial are arranged in order of decreasing degree in the variable.

EXAMPLE 1 Divide $6x^2 + 20 - 23x$ by $2x - 5$.

SOLUTION First rewrite $6x^2 + 20 - 23x$ as $6x^2 - 23x + 20$.

$$\begin{array}{r} 3x - 4 \\ 2x - 5 \overline{)6x^2 - 23x + 20} \\ \underline{6x^2 - 15x} \\ -8x + 20 \\ \underline{-8x + 20} \\ 0 \end{array}$$

Check: $(3x - 4)(2x - 5) = 6x^2 - 23x + 20$

$\therefore \dfrac{6x^2 - 23x + 20}{2x - 5} = 3x - 4$ *Answer*

Notice that in Example 1, the remainder is 0. Thus, both $(2x - 5)$ and $(3x - 4)$ are factors of $6x^2 - 23x + 20$.

EXAMPLE 2   Divide $\dfrac{2a^3 - 10}{a - 2}$. Write the answer as a mixed expression.

SOLUTION   Rewrite $2a^3 - 10$ in order of decreasing degree in a, inserting 0 coefficients as shown below.

$$\begin{array}{r} 2a^2 + 4a + 8 \\ a - 2 \overline{)2a^3 + 0a^2 + 0a - 10} \\ \underline{2a^3 - 4a^2} \\ 4a^2 + 0a \\ \underline{4a^2 - 8a} \\ 8a - 10 \\ \underline{8a - 16} \\ 6 \end{array}$$

Check: It is left to you to verify that
$(2a^2 + 4a + 8)(a - 2) + 6$ equals $2a^3 - 10$.

$\therefore \dfrac{2a^3 - 10}{a - 2} = 2a^2 + 4a + 8 + \dfrac{6}{a - 2}$ *Answer*

The division process ends when the remainder is either 0 or of lesser degree than the divisor.

Written Exercises

Divide. Write your answer as a polynomial or mixed expression. Check.

A 1. $\dfrac{x^2 + 7x + 12}{x + 3}$ $x + 4$ 2. $\dfrac{k^2 - 4k - 32}{k + 4}$ $k - 8$ 3. $\dfrac{x^2 - 5x - 36}{x - 9}$ $x + 4$ 4. $\dfrac{y^2 - 3y - 54}{y - 9}$ *4. $y + 6$*

5. $\dfrac{a^2 + 4a + 8}{a + 3}$ $a + 1 + \dfrac{5}{a + 3}$ 6. $\dfrac{y^2 + 5y + 9}{y + 2}$ $y + 3 + \dfrac{3}{y + 2}$ 7. $\dfrac{z^2 - 6z + 1}{z - 4}$ $z - 2 - \dfrac{7}{z - 4}$ 8. $\dfrac{x^2 - 1 - 4x}{x + 2}$ *8. $x - 6 + \dfrac{11}{x + 2}$*

Supplementary Materials

Practice Master 37

Progress Test 21

Computer Activity 18
Dividing Polynomials
   A computer program is used to divide a polynomial of the form $Ax^2 + Bx + C$ by a polynomial of the form $Dx + E$. The accompanying exercises emphasize the relationship between zero remainders in division and factoring.

Suggested Assignments

Minimum
Day 1: 223/1–19 odd
Day 2: 224/21–31 odd
   R 225/Self-Test 3

Average
NOTE: Day 2 of Sec. 6-6 finishes Sec. 6-6 and starts Sec. 6-7.

   224/21–35 odd
   R 225/Self-Test 3

Maximum
   223/1–37 odd
   S 221/27, 28
   R 225/Self-Test 3

Additional A Exercises

Divide. Write your answer as a polynomial or mixed expression.

1. $\dfrac{x^2 + 3x - 4}{x - 1}$ $x + 4$

2. $\dfrac{x^2 - 3x - 10}{x + 2}$ $x - 5$

3. $\dfrac{a^2 + a - 42}{a + 7}$ $a - 6$

4. $\dfrac{c^2 + 5c - 84}{c - 7}$ $c + 12$

5. $\dfrac{4x^2 + 10x - 8}{x + 4}$

   $4x - 6 + \dfrac{16}{x + 4}$

6. $\dfrac{3a^2 - 7a + 5}{a + 2}$

   $3a - 13 + \dfrac{31}{a + 2}$

Divide. Write your answer as a polynomial or mixed expression. Check.

9. $\dfrac{x^2 - 7 + 9x}{x - 3}$ **10.** $\dfrac{s - s^2 + 4}{s + 1}$ **11.** $\dfrac{x^2 + 4}{x + 1}$ **12.** $\dfrac{y^2 - 3}{y - 2}$

13. $\dfrac{2x^2 - 5x + 3}{2x - 1}$ **14.** $\dfrac{2v^2 + v - 4}{2v + 1}$ **15.** $\dfrac{5y^2 - 6y + 7}{5y - 1}$ **16.** $\dfrac{3y^2 + 8y + 5}{3y + 2}$

17. $\dfrac{6n^2 + 4n + 3}{3n - 1}$ **18.** $\dfrac{4x^2 + 1}{2x + 1}$ **19.** $\dfrac{6x^2 + xy - 2y^2}{2x + y}$ **20.** $\dfrac{6a^2 - ab + b^2}{2a + b}$

B 21. $\dfrac{x^3 + 1}{x + 1}$ $\;x^2 - x + 1$ **22.** $\dfrac{a^3 - 1}{a - 1}$ $\;a^2 + a + 1$

23. $\dfrac{x^3 - 4x^2 + x + 6}{x - 2}$ $\;x^2 - 2x - 3$ **24.** $\dfrac{6a^3 + 5a^2 - 13a + 10}{3a - 5}$

25. $\dfrac{x^3 - 2x^2 - 75}{x - 5}$ $\;x^2 + 3x + 15$ **26.** $\dfrac{2a^4 + 1 - 2a - a^3}{2a - 1}$ $\;a^3 - 1$

27. $\dfrac{a^3 + 7a^2b + 3ab^2 - 14b^3}{a + 2b}$ $\;a^2 + 5ab - 7b^2$ **28.** $\dfrac{3x^3 + 5x^2y - xy^2}{3x + 2y}$

29. $\dfrac{3a^3 - 4a^2 + 2a + 4}{a^2 - 2a + 2}$ $\;3a + 2$ **30.** $\dfrac{n^4 + 3n^3 + 3n^2 - 3n - 4}{n^2 - 1}$ $\;n^2 + 3n + 4$

31. Factor $3n^3 - 7n^2 + 4$ completely given that $3n + 2$ is one of its factors. $(3n + 2)(n - 2)(n - 1)$

32. Factor $x^3 + 4x^2 + x - 6$ given that $x - 1$ is one of its factors.

33. Factor $4x^3 - 12x^2 - 37x - 15$ given that $2x + 1$ is a factor.

34. Factor $2x^3 - 7x^2 + 4x + 4$ given that $(x - 2)^2$ is a factor. $(2x + 1)(x - 2)^2$

C 35. Show that $\dfrac{a^4 - 2a^3 + 6a - 4}{a^2 - a - 2} = a^2 - a + 1 + \dfrac{5a - 2}{a^2 - a - 2}$.

36. Divide $n^4 - n^2 - n + 7$ by $n^2 - 4$. Check by multiplying. $n^2 + 3 + \dfrac{-n + 19}{n^2 - 4}$

37. Find the value of k for which $2x + 3$ is a factor of $6x^2 + 5x + k$. -6

38. Find the value of k for which $x + 3$ is a factor of $2x^3 + 11x^2 + 13x + k$. -6

39. Find the value of k for which $y - 2$ is a factor of $y^3 - 4y^2 + ky + 6$. 1

40. When $6x^4 - 5x^3 - 37x^2 + 46x + n$ is divided by $2x - 5$, the remainder is 5. Find the value of n. -35

Just for Fun

Two bees leave two locations 180 m apart and fly, without stopping, back and forth between these two places at the rates of 4 m/s and 5 m/s, respectively. When do they meet for the first time? for the second time?

In 20 s   In 60 s

224   *CHAPTER 6*

Self-Test 3

VOCABULARY   mixed expression (p. 220)   dividend (p. 222)
                        quotient (p. 222)   divisor (p. 222)
                        remainder (p. 222)

Write each expression as a fraction in simplest form.

1. $\dfrac{7}{x + 2} - 4$

2. $3 + \dfrac{a - 4b}{a + b}$

Obj. 6-6, p. 220

Divide. Write your answer as a polynomial or a mixed expression.

3. $\dfrac{6x^2 - x - 15}{2x + 3}$

4. $\dfrac{8x^2 + 18x - 2}{4x - 1}$

Obj. 6-7, p. 222

Check your answers with those at the back of the book.

EXTRA

Complex Fractions

A complex fraction is a fraction whose numerator or denominator contains one or more fractions. A complex fraction can be expressed as a simple fraction by either of two methods.

Method 1: Simplify the numerator and denominator. Express the fraction as a quotient using the ÷ sign, and then divide.

Method 2: Multiply the numerator and denominator of the complex fraction by the LCD of all the simple fractions within them.

EXAMPLE   Simplify $\dfrac{\dfrac{a}{b} - \dfrac{b}{a}}{\dfrac{1}{2a} - \dfrac{1}{2b}}$.

SOLUTION   Method 1:

$$\frac{\dfrac{a}{b} - \dfrac{b}{a}}{\dfrac{1}{2a} - \dfrac{1}{2b}} = \frac{\dfrac{a^2 - b^2}{ab}}{\dfrac{b - a}{2ab}}$$

$$= \frac{a^2 - b^2}{ab} \div \frac{b - a}{2ab}$$

$$= \frac{(a + b)\overset{-1}{\cancel{(a - b)}}}{\cancel{ab}} \cdot \frac{2\cancel{ab}}{\cancel{b - a}}$$

$$= -2(a + b)$$

Method 2:

The LCD of all the simple fractions is $2ab$.

$$\frac{\dfrac{a}{b} - \dfrac{b}{a}}{\dfrac{1}{2a} - \dfrac{1}{2b}} = \frac{\left(\dfrac{a}{b} - \dfrac{b}{a}\right)2ab}{\left(\dfrac{1}{2a} - \dfrac{1}{2b}\right)2ab}$$

$$= \frac{2a^2 - 2b^2}{b - a}$$

$$= \frac{2(a + b)\overset{}{\cancel{(a - b)}}}{\underset{-1}{\cancel{(b - a)}}}$$

$$= -2(a + b)$$

FRACTIONS   **225**

Quick Quiz

1. Write the expression $\dfrac{6b}{a + 3b} - 2$ as a fraction in simplest form. $\dfrac{-2a}{a + 3b}$

Divide. Write your answer as a polynomial or a mixed expression.

2. $\dfrac{15x^2 + x - 2}{3x - 1}$ $5x + 2$

3. $\dfrac{16 + 4x - 6x^2}{3x + 4}$ $-2x + 4$

4. $\dfrac{2x^3 + x - 6}{x + 2}$

$2x^2 - 4x + 9 - \dfrac{24}{x + 2}$

About the Extra

This feature discusses two methods of simplifying complex fractions. The first method involves combining the numerator and the denominator of the complex fraction over their respective common denominators. The Rule for Division (To divide by b, multiply by the reciprocal of b) is then used to simplify the complex fraction.

The second method simplifies the complex fraction by multiplying its numerator and denominator by the same expression, namely the LCD of all the simple fractions. The time spent on this method will reinforce some of the major properties of fractions.

Exercises

In the following exercises you can use either Method 1 or Method 2 to simplify the fractions. Most people find Method 2 preferable, especially when simplifying more involved complex fractions.

Simplify.

A 1. $\dfrac{\frac{a}{7}}{\frac{3a}{7}}$ $\frac{1}{3}$

2. $\dfrac{\frac{3n}{2}}{\frac{9n}{4}}$ $\frac{2}{3}$

3. $\dfrac{\frac{a}{b}}{\frac{1}{b^2}}$ ab

4. $\dfrac{\frac{3k}{1}}{\frac{1}{6k}}$ $18k^2$

5. $\dfrac{\frac{1}{3} - \frac{1}{6}}{\frac{1}{3} + \frac{1}{6}}$ $\frac{1}{3}$

6. $\dfrac{\frac{1}{2} + \frac{1}{8}}{\frac{1}{4} + \frac{1}{3}}$ $\frac{15}{14}$

7. $\dfrac{\frac{3}{4} + \frac{3}{5}}{\frac{3}{4} - \frac{3}{5}}$ 9

8. $\dfrac{\frac{1}{n} - \frac{1}{2n}}{\frac{2}{n} - \frac{1}{4}}$

9. $\dfrac{\frac{x}{y^2}}{\frac{x}{y}}$ $\frac{1}{y}$

10. $\dfrac{1 - \frac{4}{x^2}}{x + 2}$ $\frac{x - 2}{x^2}$

11. $\dfrac{1 + \frac{1}{a}}{1 - \frac{1}{a^2}}$ $\frac{a}{a - 1}$

12. $\dfrac{\frac{3x}{2} + 1}{\frac{3x}{4} - \frac{1}{3x}}$ $\frac{6x}{3x - 2}$

B 13. $\dfrac{a + \frac{3a}{a - 3}}{a - \frac{3a}{a + 3}}$ $\frac{a + 3}{a - 3}$

14. $\dfrac{1 + \frac{2k}{k^2 + 1}}{1 - \frac{2k + 2}{k^2 + 1}}$ $\frac{(k + 1)^2}{k^2 - 2k - 1}$

15. $\dfrac{x - \frac{1}{2x + 1}}{1 - \frac{2}{2x + 1}}$ $x + 1$

16. $\dfrac{\frac{1}{2b - 2} - \frac{1}{b}}{\frac{2}{b} - \frac{1}{b - 1}}$ $\frac{-1}{2}$

17. $\dfrac{\frac{a}{a + b} + \frac{b}{a - b}}{\frac{a}{a - b} - \frac{b}{a + b}}$ 1

18. $\dfrac{1 - \frac{1}{2n}}{1 + 2n} \div \dfrac{1 + \frac{1}{2n}}{1 - 2n}$ $\frac{-(2n - 1)^2}{(2n + 1)^2}$

19. $\dfrac{2 + \frac{y - 2}{1 - y^2}}{2 - \frac{2}{y + 1}}$ $\frac{1 - 2y}{2(1 - y)}$

20. $\dfrac{\frac{p}{q} - \frac{p - q}{p + q}}{\frac{q}{p} + \frac{p - q}{p + q}}$ $\frac{p}{q}$

21. If $x = \dfrac{y - 1}{y + 1}$ and $y = \dfrac{1}{1 - t}$, express x in terms of t as simply as possible. $x = \frac{t}{2 - t}$

22. If $a = \dfrac{b - c}{1 + bc}$ and $b = \dfrac{1}{t - 1}$ and $c = \dfrac{1}{t + 1}$, find a in terms of t. $a = \frac{2}{t^2}$

23. A car goes d km at 40 km/h and returns the same distance at 60 km/h. Show that the average speed is 48 km/h. (*Hint:* Average speed = total distance divided by total time.)

226   CHAPTER 6

Additional Answers
Exercises

23. Average speed

$= \dfrac{\text{total distance}}{\text{total time}}$

$= \dfrac{d + d}{\frac{d}{40} + \frac{d}{60}}$

$= \dfrac{2d}{\frac{d}{40} + \frac{d}{60}} \cdot \dfrac{120}{120}$

$= \dfrac{240d}{3d + 2d} = \dfrac{240d}{5d}$

$= \dfrac{240}{5} = 48$ km/h

(continued)

226

24. A cyclist travels 10 km on a level road at x km/h and then goes 5 km on a downhill road at $2x$ km/h. Find her average speed in terms of x. (See Hint for Exercise 23.) $\frac{6x}{5}$ km/h

25. If n articles can be purchased for 4 dollars, how many of these articles can be purchased for \$4 after the price per article is increased by a half dollar? $\frac{8n}{8+n}$ articles

26. If $a = \dfrac{1-t}{1+t}$ and $t = \dfrac{1+b}{1-b}$, show that $a + b = 0$.

Simplify.

27. $\left(\dfrac{2}{x} - \dfrac{x}{2}\right) \div \left(\dfrac{x}{2} - 4 + \dfrac{6}{x}\right)$ $\frac{-2-x}{x-6}$

28. $\left(\dfrac{x}{4-x^2} + \dfrac{1}{x-2}\right) \div \left(1 - \dfrac{2}{2+x}\right)$ $\frac{-2}{x(2-x)}$

29. $\left(\dfrac{1}{a^2+a} - \dfrac{1}{a-a^2}\right) \div \left(\dfrac{1}{a^2-1} - \dfrac{1}{1+a^2}\right)$ $a^2 + 1$

30. $\left(\dfrac{1}{3} - \dfrac{2x^2}{3-3x}\right) \div \left(1 - \dfrac{x-4x^2}{x-1}\right)$ $\frac{x+1}{3(2x+1)}$

C 31. $\dfrac{a}{2}\left(\dfrac{1}{a-b} - \dfrac{1}{a+b}\right) \cdot \left(\dfrac{a^2-b^2}{a^2b+ab^2}\right) \div \dfrac{1}{a+b}$ 1

32. $\dfrac{1}{1 - \dfrac{1}{1 - \dfrac{1}{1 - \dfrac{1}{x}}}}$ $\frac{1}{x}$

26. $a + b = \dfrac{1-t}{1+t} + b$

$= \dfrac{1 - \dfrac{1+b}{1-b}}{1 + \dfrac{1+b}{1-b}} + b$

$= \dfrac{1 - \dfrac{1+b}{1-b}}{1 + \dfrac{1+b}{1-b}} \cdot \dfrac{1-b}{1-b} + b$

$= \dfrac{1-b-(1+b)}{1-b+1+b} + b$

$= \dfrac{-2b}{2} + b = -b + b = 0$

Calculator Key-In

You can use a calculator to evaluate algebraic fractions for given values of their variables. First evaluate the denominator and store its value in the calculator's memory. (You may want to review the method for evaluating a polynomial given on page 157.) Then evaluate the numerator and divide by the value of the denominator.

Evaluate each fraction for the given value of the variable.

1. $\dfrac{5}{x+3}$; $x = 6$ $0.\overline{5}$

2. $\dfrac{2y+5}{4}$; $y = 7$ 4.75

3. $\dfrac{5n-11}{2n}$; $n = 4$ 1.125

4. $\dfrac{7a+15}{3a}$; $a = 2$ 4.8$\overline{3}$

5. $\dfrac{7x^2+2x+4}{x}$; $x = 3$ 24.$\overline{3}$

6. $\dfrac{2z^2+11z-30}{2z+4}$; $z = -3$ 22.5

7. $\dfrac{a^2+5a-2}{4a}$; $a = 0.5$ 0.375

8. $\dfrac{5y^2-11y+15}{6y-5}$; $y = -2$ −3.3529412

Supplementary Materials

Practice Masters 38, 39

Progress Tests 22, 23

Extra Practice pp. 500–502

Chapter Summary

1. A fraction can be simplified by factoring its numerator and its denominator and dividing each by their common factors.

2. The following rules are used for combining fractions.

MULTIPLICATION RULE

$$\frac{c}{d} \cdot \frac{x}{y} = \frac{cx}{dy}$$

DIVISION RULE

$$\frac{a}{b} \div \frac{c}{d} = \frac{a}{b} \cdot \frac{d}{c}$$

ADDITION RULE

$$\frac{a}{c} + \frac{b}{c} = \frac{a + b}{c}$$

SUBTRACTION RULE

$$\frac{a}{c} - \frac{b}{c} = \frac{a - b}{c}$$

3. When adding or subtracting fractions with different denominators, rewrite the fractions using their *least common denominator* (*LCD*). Then apply the appropriate rule. (See the method and the examples on page 213.)

4. A sum or difference of a polynomial and a fraction is called a *mixed expression*. A mixed expression can be expressed as a fraction in simplest form.

5. When dividing polynomials, arrange the terms of the *divisor* and *dividend* in order of decreasing degree in a variable. Insert zero coefficients where the dividend is missing a power.

Chapter Review

Give the letter of the correct answer.

1. Express $\frac{3a + 6b}{3a + 3b}$ in simplest form. 6-1

   a. 3
   b. $\frac{3}{2}$
   c. $1 + 2b$
   d. $\frac{a + 2b}{a + b}$

2. Express $\frac{5x - x^2}{x^2 - 25}$ in simplest form.

   a. $\frac{x}{x - 5}$
   b. $\frac{x}{5 - x}$
   c. $\frac{-x}{x + 5}$
   d. $\frac{x}{x + 5}$

3. Express $\frac{2n^2 - 8}{n^2 + 4n - 12}$ in simplest form.

   a. $\frac{2(n + 2)}{n + 6}$
   b. $\frac{2(n - 2)}{n - 6}$
   c. $2\left(n + \frac{1}{3}\right)$
   d. $2\left(n - \frac{1}{3}\right)$

4. Multiply: $\frac{3a^2b}{8ab^3} \cdot \frac{40a^3b}{6b}$ 6-2

   a. $\frac{5a^4}{2b^2}$
   b. $\frac{120a^4}{48b^2}$
   c. $\frac{120a^5b^2}{48ab^4}$
   d. $\frac{20a^4b^2}{8}$

5. Express $\left(\dfrac{4x}{y^2}\right)^3$ in simplest form.

    a. $\dfrac{12x^3}{y^6}$ **b.** $\dfrac{64x^3}{y^6}$ **c.** $\dfrac{12x^3}{y^5}$ **d.** $\dfrac{64x^3}{y^5}$

6. Multiply: $\dfrac{x^2 - y^2}{(x + y)^2} \cdot \dfrac{x^2 + y^2}{x - y}$

    a. $x + y$ **b.** $\dfrac{x^2 + y^2}{x - y}$ **c.** $\dfrac{x^2 + y^2}{x + y}$ **d.** $\dfrac{x + y}{x - y}$

7. Divide: $\dfrac{2n^2}{5} \div \dfrac{(4n)^2}{20}$

    a. $2n$ **b.** 2 **c.** $\dfrac{1}{2n}$ **d.** $\dfrac{1}{2}$

8. Divide: $\dfrac{a^2 - 4b^2}{a^2 - ab - 2b^2} \div \dfrac{a + 2b}{2a + 2b}$

    a. 2 **b.** $\dfrac{2}{a + 2b}$ **c.** $\dfrac{a + 2b}{2}$ **d.** $\dfrac{a + 2b}{a - 2b}$

9. Simplify $\dfrac{2x}{3y} \div 4xy$.

    a. $\dfrac{8x}{3}$ **b.** $\dfrac{3}{8x^2}$ **c.** $\dfrac{1}{6y^2}$ **d.** $\dfrac{2}{3y^2}$

10. What is the LCD of $\dfrac{3}{10x}$, $\dfrac{5}{12x^2}$, and $\dfrac{1}{4y}$?   6-4

    a. $120x^3y$ **b.** $120x^2y$ **c.** $60x^3y$ **d.** $60x^2y$

11. What is the LCD of $\dfrac{2}{a^2 - 4}$ and $\dfrac{3a}{2(a - 2)}$?

    a. $2(a - 2)^2(a + 2)$ **b.** $2(a - 2)(a + 2)$
    c. $2(a - 2)(a + 2)^2$ **d.** $6a(a - 2)(a + 2)$

12. Simplify $\dfrac{2n + 3}{4} - \dfrac{n - 1}{6}$.   6-5

    a. $\dfrac{4n + 11}{12}$ **b.** $\dfrac{4n + 7}{12}$ **c.** $\dfrac{8n + 22}{24}$ **d.** $\dfrac{8n + 14}{24}$

13. Simplify $\dfrac{x}{x - 3} + \dfrac{3}{3 - x}$.

    a. $\dfrac{x - 3}{x^2 - 9}$ **b.** $\dfrac{x - 3}{3 - x}$ **c.** 1 **d.** -1

14. Simplify $\dfrac{x}{x - 1} - \dfrac{2x}{x^2 - 1}$.

    a. $\dfrac{x}{x + 1}$ **b.** $\dfrac{x^2 - x}{x^2 - 1}$ **c.** $\dfrac{x}{x - 1}$ **d.** $1 - x$

6-3

FRACTIONS   **229**

20. $-1; x \neq \dfrac{8}{3}$

21. $\dfrac{4c + 1}{1 - 4c}; c \neq \dfrac{1}{4}, \dfrac{-1}{4}$

22. $\dfrac{-(b + 4)}{4}; b \neq 3$

23. $\dfrac{-x}{x - 1}; x \neq 5, 1$

24. $\dfrac{x}{6x - 1}; x \neq \dfrac{1}{6}, -\dfrac{1}{6}$

27. $\dfrac{2(x + 2)}{x + 6}; x \neq 2, -6$

28. $\dfrac{c + 5d}{c - 5d}; c \neq 5d, -5d$

29. $\dfrac{4a + 7b}{4a - 7b}; a \neq \dfrac{7b}{4}$

30. $\dfrac{8(ca + 2)}{c(ca - 2)}; c \neq 0, \dfrac{2}{a}$

31. $\dfrac{s - 5}{s + 7}; s \neq -7, -3$

32. $\dfrac{4(4y - x)}{x - y}; x \neq y, -4y$

33. $\dfrac{2(a + 2b)}{a + 3b}; a \neq b, -3b$

34. $\dfrac{x + 3y}{3(x - 2y)}; x \neq 3y, 2y$

35. $\dfrac{2x + 3y}{x - 2y}; x \neq 2y, -\dfrac{5y}{2}$

36. $\dfrac{2x - y}{4x - 5y}; x \neq \dfrac{5y}{4}$

37. $1; x \neq y, -y$

38. $\dfrac{x^2 - 2}{x + 2}; x \neq -2$

43. $\dfrac{5 - x}{x + 5}; x \neq 0, \dfrac{3}{2}, -5$

44. $(3 - x)(x + 1); x \neq 1, -3$

45. $\dfrac{a - 3b}{a + 3b + 2}; a \neq 2 - 3b, -2 - 3b$

46. $\dfrac{x + 2}{x - 6}; x \neq 6, -6, 2$

47. $\dfrac{a - 3b + 3}{3}; a \neq 3b + 3$

48. $\dfrac{(a - b)(a - b + 2)}{a - b - 2};$ $a \neq b + 2$

15. Write $2 + \dfrac{7n}{n^2 - 9}$ as a fraction in simplest form. 6-6

   (a.) $\dfrac{2n^2 + 7n - 18}{n^2 - 9}$ **b.** $\dfrac{4 + 7n}{1}$ **c.** $\dfrac{2n + 1}{n + 3}$ **d.** $\dfrac{2n + 1}{n - 3}$

16. Simplify $z + 3 + \dfrac{1}{z - 3}$.

   (a.) $\dfrac{z^2 - 8}{z - 3}$ **b.** $\dfrac{z + 4}{z - 3}$ **c.** $\dfrac{z^2 - 8}{z^2 - 9}$ **d.** $\dfrac{z^2 - 10}{z - 3}$

17. When $x^3 - 3x^2 + 3x + 4$ is divided by $x - 2$, what is the remainder? 6-7

   a. 2   **b.** 4   (c.) 6   **d.** 8

18. When $n^3 - 8$ is divided by $n - 2$, what is the quotient?

   (a.) $n^2 + 2n + 4$ **b.** $n^2 - 2n + 4$ **c.** $n^2 + 4$ **d.** $n^2 - 4$

Alternate Test p. T17

Chapter Test

Simplify.

1. $\dfrac{5n + 25}{n^2 - 25}$ $\dfrac{5}{n - 5}$ **2.** $\dfrac{(x - 2)^2}{2 - x}$ $2 - x$ 6-1

3. $\left(\dfrac{-3}{5}\right)^2 \cdot \dfrac{50}{27}$ $\dfrac{2}{3}$ **4.** $\left(\dfrac{2x^3}{5y}\right)^2$ $\dfrac{4x^6}{25y^2}$ 6-2

5. $\dfrac{3}{a^2 - 2a - 15} \cdot \dfrac{a^2 - 9}{6a - 18}$ $\dfrac{1}{2(a - 5)}$ **6.** $\dfrac{a^2 - b^2}{a^2 + b^2} \cdot \dfrac{a + b}{a - b}$ $\dfrac{(a + b)^2}{a^2 + b^2}$

7. $\dfrac{2a}{3} \div \dfrac{9a^4}{4}$ $\dfrac{8}{27a^3}$ **8.** $\dfrac{2y^3}{9} \div \dfrac{4y}{3}$ $\dfrac{y^2}{6}$ 6-3

9. $\dfrac{1}{10x - 2x^2} \div \dfrac{x}{4x - 20}$ $\dfrac{-2}{x^2}$ **10.** $\left(\dfrac{y + 2}{y + 1}\right) \div (2y + 4) \cdot (y^2 - 2y - 3)$ $\dfrac{y - 3}{2}$

What is the LCD for each group of fractions?

11. $\dfrac{3}{4a^2}, \dfrac{5}{2ab}, \dfrac{1}{3b}$ $12a^2b$ **12.** $\dfrac{5}{x^2 - 1}, \dfrac{2x}{x^2 + 2x + 1}$ $(x - 1)(x + 1)^2$ 6-4

Simplify.

13. $\dfrac{2x - 1}{3} - \dfrac{4x - 5}{4}$ $\dfrac{-4x + 11}{12}$ **14.** $\dfrac{2y}{2y - 3} - \dfrac{3}{2y + 3}$ $\dfrac{4y^2 + 9}{(2y + 3)(2y - 3)}$ 6-5

15. $\dfrac{2}{y^2 - 2y} - \dfrac{3}{y^2 - y - 2}$ $\dfrac{-1}{y(y + 1)}$ **16.** $\dfrac{4a}{a - 2b} + \dfrac{8b}{2b - a}$ 4

17. $\dfrac{3}{4 - x} - 2$ $\dfrac{2x - 5}{4 - x}$ **18.** $\dfrac{x}{x + 2} + \dfrac{2}{x - 2} + 1$ $\dfrac{2x^2}{(x + 2)(x - 2)}$ 6-6

19. Divide $4x^3 - 2x^2 + 2$ by $2x + 1$. $2x^2 - 2x + 1 + \dfrac{1}{2x + 1}$ 6-7

20. Use long division to decide whether or not $x - 2$ is a factor of $x^3 + 6x^2 - x - 30$. It is a factor.

230   CHAPTER 6

Just for Fun

Copy the puzzle and complete it.

ACROSS

1. 7×3^2
2. $2^2 \times 3^2$
4. $3^3 - 2 \times 3$
5. $2^9 + 2^4$
7. $5^2 - 3^2$
8. $(2^3 \times 3)^2 \times 7$
11. $(6 \div 2 \times 3)^2$
13. $5 \times 2 \times 3^2$
14. $12^2 - 10^2 - 2$

DOWN

1. $5^2 \times 5^2$
3. 34×19
4. $3^3 \times 2^3 \times 13$
6. $102 \div 17 \times 2^2$
7. $2^4 \times 3^2 \div 12$
9. $186 \div 12 \times 2$
10. $99^2 - 99 \times 98$
12. $82^2 \div 82$

Puzzle grid:

1: 6	3			2: 3	3: 6
2		4: 2	1		4
5: 5	6: 2	8		7: 1	6
	8: 4	0	9: 3	2	
10: 9		11: 8	1		12: 8
13: 9	0			14: 4	2

Career Note Accountant

A company is considering building a new factory. Before making a decision, the management will discuss the financial position of the company with the chief accountant.

Accountants are responsible for recording and analyzing all financial information of a company. They prepare balance sheets, which indicate the financial position of the company, and income statements, which show profit and loss over a given period. They also prepare inventory analyses and statements for tax purposes.

Every business and government agency needs the services provided by an accountant. Accountants work for banks, department stores, sports arenas, supermarkets, large corporations, and small companies. Accountants may specialize in administrative accounting, cost accounting, managerial accounting, auditing, or budgeting.

To become a certified public accountant, or CPA, it is necessary to pass a standardized examination. Each state has its own requirements for eligibility to take this test. Most states require a bachelor's degree in accounting or a closely related field and three years of experience working for a CPA.

FRACTIONS **231**

Cumulative Review (Chapters 1-6)

Simplify each expression.

1. $2b - b^2 - 4 + b^2 + 1$ **2.** $(8c - d) - (9c - 3d)$ **3.** $(-7j^2k^3)(-3j^3k)$

4. $-3n(3 - 2n - 5n^3)$ **5.** $(8z + 9)(3z^2 - 2z)$ **6.** $(3a - 7)(2a + 1)$

7. $-(9rs^2)^2 \div (-3r^2s)^3$ **8.** $(3d^2 - 2)(3d^2 + 2)$ **9.** $(7x - 8y)^2$

Evaluate if $q = -7$, $r = -4$, $s = -0.75$, $t = 2$, and $u = 3$.

10. $2rs - qt^2$ 34   **11.** $(2q + rt + 1) \div q$ 3   **12.** $2r^2 \div 4 + 3rt$ -16

Factor completely. If the polynomial is not factorable, write "prime."

13. $100a^2 - 4b^4$ $4(5a - b^2)(5a + b^2)$ **14.** $16 - 48g + 9g^2$ Prime   **15.** $x^2 - 21xy + 54y^2$ $(x - 18y)(x - 3y)$

16. $yz + z - 2y - 2y^2$ $(y + 1)(z - 2y)$ **17.** $6k^3 + 7k^2m + 2km^2$ $k(3k + 2m)(2k + m)$ **18.** $c^2 + 5c - 126$ $(c + 14)(c - 9)$

Solve.

19. $n - 19 = |-2 - 5|$ 26   **20.** $-15 = -\dfrac{3}{7}b$ 35   **21.** $20 - 4x = -8x + 40$ 5

22. $2(k + 8) - 1 = 3$ -6 **23.** $-7y + 2 = y - 14$ 2   **24.** $24f = -16$ $-\dfrac{2}{3}$

25. $5(z + 1) - 3z = -9$ -7 **26.** $(a + 4)(a + 3) = -a$ $\{-2, -6\}$ **27.** $5m^2 + 38m = 16$ $\left\{\dfrac{2}{5}, -8\right\}$

Express in simplest form.

28. $\dfrac{2k^2 - 9k + 7}{3 - 2k - k^2}$ **29.** $\dfrac{2y^2 + 8y}{y^3 - 16y} \cdot \dfrac{4 - y}{4y^3}$ **30.** $\dfrac{3z - 2}{4} - \dfrac{6 - z}{4}$

31. $\dfrac{5r^2 + 10r}{r^2 + 4r + 4} \div \dfrac{25}{r + 2}$ **32.** $\dfrac{5}{3x} + \dfrac{1}{x^2}$ **33.** $\dfrac{4x}{x + 4} - \dfrac{3}{x + 3}$

34. $\dfrac{2n}{2n + t} + \dfrac{t}{2n - t} - 1$ **35.** $\dfrac{m^3 - 3m^2 + 20}{m + 2}$ **36.** $\dfrac{8b^2 + 14b + 6}{4b + 3}$

Solve.

37. Find three consecutive odd integers such that the difference between five times the least and twice the greatest is 61.   23, 25, 27

38. Su-Chen is 20 years younger than her mother. In 9 years she will be $\frac{3}{5}$ as old as her mother. How old is each now?   Su-Chen, 21; mother, 41

39. The length and width of a rectangle are consecutive integers. The area of the rectangle is $132\,\text{cm}^2$. Find the dimensions of the rectangle.   11 cm by 12 cm

40. While training for a bicycle race, Charles rode up a mountain road at 12 km/h and then back down at 30 km/h. If the round trip took $3\frac{1}{2}$ h, how long did the uphill trip take and how many kilometers was it?   2.5 h; 30 km

41. A power boat traveled upstream at 24 km/h and downstream at 30 km/h. How far upstream did it go if the round trip took 3 h?   40 km

Maintaining Skills

Review the five-step problem solving method described in Section 1-6.

SAMPLE The length of a rectangle is 55 cm greater than three times the width. If the perimeter is 8.7 m, find the length and the width.

SOLUTION

Step 1 Read the problem carefully. It asks for the length and the width of the rectangle.

Step 2 Choose a variable. If it is helpful, draw a diagram or make a chart of given facts.

Let w = width in centimeters.
Then $3w + 55$ = length in centimeters.

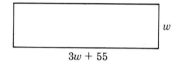

$3w + 55$

Step 3 Write an equation, using the same unit, centimeters:
$$2(3w + 55) + 2w = 870 \leftarrow 8.7 \text{ m} = 870 \text{ cm}$$

Step 4 Solve the equation. $8w + 110 = 870$
$$8w = 760$$
$$w = 95; \quad 3(95) + 55 = 340$$

Step 5 Check your results with the statement of the problem. Give the answer. The check is left to you.

$\therefore$ the length is 340 cm and the width is 95 cm. ***Answer***

Use the five-step method to solve each problem. Making charts and diagrams may help you. Remember to write each expression in terms of the same unit. Reject inappropriate roots.

1. I have $3.65 in dimes and quarters. Thirty cents more than the value of half the dimes is equal to $1. How many of each coin do I have? 14 dimes, 9 quarters

2. Trino walked for 75 min. If he had walked for 60 min at a rate 2 km/h faster, he would have gone 1 km farther. Find his average rate of walking. 4 km/h

3. The length of a rectangle is 20 mm greater than its width. The area of the rectangle is 168 cm². Find the length and width in centimeters. 12 cm by 14 cm

4. Elise is paid twice as much per hour for overtime work as for her usual work. One week she worked 44 h and earned $156. If her usual work week is 40 h, what is her usual rate? $3.25/h

The Toronto metropolitan area is approximately the same size as the Boston and Bogotá, Colombia, metropolitan areas. See the facing page for a discussion of using ratios to compare populations.

234

7

APPLYING FRACTIONS

Teaching References

Lesson Commentary,
 pp. T88–T91

Assignment Guide,
 pp. T54–T56

Supplementary Materials
 Practice Masters 40–43
 Progress Tests 24–26
 Computer Activities
 19 *Ratio Problems*
 20 *Solving Fractional
 Equations*
 21 *Repeated Discounts*

Extra Practice, pp. 502,
 517–519

Alternate Test, p. T18

RATIO AND PROPORTION

7-1 *Ratios*

OBJECTIVE   To solve problems involving ratios.

Recently, the population of the Toronto metropolitan area was 2,800,000, and the population of the Melbourne metropolitan area was 2,600,000. Although the populations of the cities differ by 200,000 people, they are approximately the same size. This relationship is indicated by the quotient, or ratio, of the populations:

$$\frac{2,800,000}{2,600,000} = \frac{14}{13}$$

The **ratio** of one number to another is the quotient of the first number divided by the second. You can express the ratio of 8 to 5 as:

1. an indicated quotient using the division sign ÷ $8 \div 5$
2. an indicated quotient using the ratio sign ∶ $8:5$
3. a fraction $\frac{8}{5}$
4. a decimal numeral 1.6

If you wish to find the ratio of the height of a 4 m tree to the height of a 50 cm sapling, you express 4 m as 400 cm and divide to find the ratio $\frac{400}{50}$ or $8:1$.

235

Chalkboard Examples

State each ratio in simplest form.

1. 12 min to 60 s   12:1

2. 6 years to 6 months   12:1

3. 5 cents to 2 dollars   1:40

4. $\dfrac{xy^2z}{wy}$ $\dfrac{xyz}{w}$, $w \neq 0$, $y \neq 0$

Figure *A* is a rectangle whose dimensions are 9 cm by 4 cm. Figure *B* is a square whose sides are 6 cm.

5. What is the ratio of the area of figure *A* to the area of figure *B*? 36:36 = 1:1

6. What is the ratio of the perimeter of figure *A* to the perimeter of figure *B*? 26:24 = 13:12

Solve, using the five-step method.

7. The ratio of boys to girls in a class of 35 students is 3:4. How many boys are there?
Step 1: Find the number of boys.
Step 2: Let $3x$ = the number of boys and $4x$ = the number of girls.
Step 3: $3x + 4x = 35$
Step 4: $7x = 35$
         $x = 5$
     Boys: $3x = 15$
     Girls: $4x = 20$
Step 5: Total is 35
∴ There are 15 boys.

Supplementary Material

Computer Activity 19
Ratio Problems
  Computer programs can be used to solve word problems involving ratios. One such program and an extension of it are presented.

236

To find the ratio of two quantities of the same kind:

1. Express the measures in the same unit.
2. Then divide them.

The ratio $\dfrac{10}{4}$ can be expressed in simplest form as $\dfrac{5}{2}$. When solving certain problems involving ratios, you need to express a ratio in a different form. If you know that two numbers are in the ratio 5:2, you can represent the numbers as $5x$ and $2x$ for some nonzero x. By the cancellation rule for fractions,

$$\frac{5x}{2x} = \frac{5}{2}.$$

EXAMPLE
Poseidon Fisheries is planning to stock the Olde Mill Pond with bass and trout in the ratio 7:8. If the pond is to be stocked with 360 fish, how many of each kind will be stocked?

SOLUTION

Step 1 The problem asks for the number of bass and the number of trout to be stocked.

Step 2 Let $7x$ = the number of bass and $8x$ = the number of trout.

Step 3 $7x + 8x = 360$ (the total number of fish)

Step 4 $15x = 360$
       $x = 24$
   Number of bass $= 7x = 7 \cdot 24 = 168$
   Number of trout $= 8x = 8 \cdot 24 = 192$

Step 5 The check is left to you.

     ∴ the pond will be stocked with 168 bass and 192 trout.   ***Answer***

  Saying that three numbers are in the ratio 4:5:8 means that the ratio of the first to the second is 4:5 and the ratio of the second to the third is 5:8.

Oral Exercises

State each ratio in simplest form.

1. 8:24 1:3   **2.** 72:12 6:1   **3.** 20:35 4:7   **4.** 8:12 2:3
5. $8a:4a$ 2:1   **6.** $32k:40k$ 4:5   **7.** $10a^3:25a$ $2a^2:5$ **8.** $rst:stu$ $r:u$

9. $\dfrac{3x^2y}{9y^2}$ $\dfrac{x^2}{3y}$ **10.** $\dfrac{(2a)^2}{4a^2}$ $\dfrac{1}{1}$ **11.** $\dfrac{(6ks)^2}{9k^2}$ $\dfrac{4s^2}{1}$ **12.** $\dfrac{pqr}{r^2sq}$ $\dfrac{p}{rs}$

Written Exercises

State each ratio in simplest form.

A **1.** 4 h to 20 min 12:1 **2.** 8 wk to 16 d 7:2 **3.** 10 cm to 1 m 1:10

4. 175 m to 14 m 25:2 **5.** 1 kg to 50 g 20:1 **6.** 80¢ to $4 1:5

7. The player-coach ratio in a league with 780 players and 30 coaches. 26:1

8. The ratio of new cars to old cars in a fleet of 1200 trolley cars that includes 640 new cars. 8:7

9. The ratio of wins to losses in 28 games with 7 losses and no ties. 3:1

10. The ratio of copper to total amount of metal in an alloy consisting of 8.4 kg of copper, 1 kg of tungsten, and 2.6 kg of tin. 7:10

11. The ratio of the number of guppies to liters of water in a 40 L tank with 24 guppies in it. 3:5

12. The ratio of the number of people to the number of apartments in a 84-unit apartment building housing 364 people. 13:3

Find the ratio of the areas of each pair of figures.

13. A rectangle with sides 6 cm and 18 cm and one with sides 4 cm and 24 cm. 9:8

14. A rectangle with sides 8 cm and 12 cm and one with sides 9 cm and 18 cm. 16:27

15. A rectangle with sides 3 m and 4 m and one with sides 75 cm and 80 cm. 20:1

16. A rectangle with sides 8 m and 12 m and a square with sides 10 m. 24:25

Find the ratio of x to y determined by each equation.

SAMPLE $5x = 8y$ *SOLUTION* $5x = 8y$

$$x = \frac{8}{5}y$$

$$\frac{x}{y} = \frac{8}{5}, \text{ or } x:y = 8:5 \quad \textit{Answer}$$

B **17.** $4x = 9y$ 9:4 **18.** $3x = 6y$ 2:1 **19.** $4y = 10x$ 2:5

20. $3x - 7y = 0$ 7:3 **21.** $9y - 12x = 0$ 3:4 **22.** $-8y + 28x = 0$ 2:7

23. $4(x + 4y) = 8(x + y)$ 2:1 **24.** $4(x - 6) = 8(y - 3)$ 2:1

C **25.** $x^2 + 2y^2 = 2xy + y^2$ 1:1 **26.** $x^2 + 5y^2 = y^2 - 4xy$ −2:1

(*Hint:* Collect terms on one side of the equation and factor the resulting polynomial.)

APPLYING FRACTIONS **237**

Suggested Assignments

Minimum
Day 1: 237/1–24
Day 2: 238/P: 1–4, 6, 7, 9

Average
Day 1: 237/1–25 odd
238/P: 1, 3, 4

Day 2: 238/P: 5, 6, 9, 12, 15
241/1–21 odd

NOTE: Day 2 of Sec. 7-1 finishes Sec. 7-1 and starts Sec. 7-2

Maximum
237/1–25
238/P: 1–15 odd

Extra Practice Problems
p. 517

Additional A Exercises

State each ratio in simplest form.

1. 7:21 1:3

2. 50:175 2:7

3. $abc:bd$ $ac:d$

4. $\dfrac{3s^2}{2s}$ $\dfrac{3s}{2}$

5. $\dfrac{a^2b^3c}{abc^2}$ $\dfrac{ab^2}{c}$

6. 3 h to 30 min 6 to 1

Problems

Solve.

A 1. Two numbers are in the ratio 5:3 and their sum is 64. Find the numbers. 24, 40

2. Two numbers are in the ratio 6:5 and their sum is 132. Find the numbers. 72, 60

3. At Garvey High School, the ratio of students taking driver education to students not taking driver education is 5:12. If there are 1530 students in the school, find the number of students taking driver education. 450 students

4. Three numbers are in the ratio 2:3:4 and their sum is 270. Find the numbers. (*Hint:* Let the numbers be $2x$, $3x$, and $4x$.) 60, 90, 120

5. A profit of $1800 is to be divided among three people in the ratio of 8:3:4. How much should each person receive? $960, $360, $480

6. The length and width of a rectangle are in a 3:2 ratio and the perimeter of the rectangle is 85 cm. Find its dimensions. 17 cm by 25.5 cm

7. In a small city, five of every eight tax dollars are spent on public education. If $3,840,000 is collected in taxes, find the amount spent on public education. $2,400,000

8. A flower wholesaler plants gladiola bulbs and expects 4 out of 5 bulbs to produce marketable flowers. Of 24,000 bulbs, how many are expected to produce marketable flowers? 19,200 bulbs

9. During a typing test Marvin typed 840 words in 21 min, and Barbara typed 750 words in 19 min. Who typed faster during the test? Marvin

B 10. Concrete can be made by mixing cement, sand, and gravel in a 1:4:5 ratio. How many cubic meters of each ingredient are needed to make 220 m³ of concrete? Cement, 22 m³; sand, 88 m³; gravel, 110 m³

11. Neighboring rectangular lots of the same depth have frontages of 40 m, 50 m, and 70 m. What assessment should be assigned to each lot if the combined lots have an assessment of $19,200? 40 m, $4800; 50 m, $6000; 70 m, $8400

12. In a group of nickels and dimes worth $6.80, the ratio of the number of nickels to the number of dimes is 3 to 7. Find the number of dimes. 56 dimes

13. In a group of dimes and quarters worth $16.10, the ratio of the number of dimes to the number of quarters is 3:8. Find the number of quarters. 56 quarters

14. A group of nickels, dimes, and quarters is worth $74. The ratio of the numbers of nickels, dimes, and quarters is 6:9:10, respectively. What number of each type of coin is there? 120 nickels, 180 dimes, 200 quarters

238   CHAPTER 7

C **15.** I am thinking of three numbers whose sum is 142. The ratio of the first number to the second is $3:8$, and the ratio of the second number to the third is $5:2$. Find the numbers. 30, 80, 32

16. Find two numbers such that their product, their sum, and their difference have the ratio $5:3:2$. 2, 10

Computer Key-In _____

If you have access to a computer that will accept BASIC, try this program for practice in adding, subtracting, and multiplying integers. Try to do the additions and subtractions mentally. This program will keep repeating the exercise until you get the right answer!

Note: Check the use of RND with your own system. INT(101*RND(1)) gives a random selection from the set $\{0, 1, 2, \ldots, 100\}$. INT(101*RND(1)−50) gives a random selection from the set $\{-50, -49, \ldots, 0, 1, 2, \ldots, 50\}$.

```
10   PRINT "HOW MANY EXERCISES WOULD YOU LIKE";
20   INPUT N
30   PRINT
40   FOR I=1 TO N
50   LET A=INT(3*RND(1)+1)
60   LET B=INT(101*RND(1)-50)
70   LET C=INT(101*RND(1)-50)
80   PRINT I;".   ";
90   GOTO A OF 100,150,200
100  PRINT "(";B;") + (";C;") =";
110  INPUT R
120  IF R=B+C THEN 250
130  PRINT "SORRY; TRY AGAIN!"
140  GOTO 100
150  PRINT "(";B;") - (";C;") =";
160  INPUT R
170  IF R=B-C THEN 250
180  PRINT "OOPS; TRY AGAIN!"
190  GOTO 150
200  PRINT "(";B;") × (";C;") = ";
210  INPUT R
220  IF R=B*C THEN 250
230  PRINT "TRY AGAIN--BE CAREFUL!"
240  GOTO 200
250  PRINT
260  NEXT I
270  END
```

7-2 *Proportion*

OBJECTIVE   To solve problems involving proportion.

An equation that states that two ratios are equal is called a **proportion.** You can write proportions in several different ways.

> $2:3 = 4:6$ read, "2 is to 3 as 4 is to 6."
>
> $\dfrac{x}{12} = \dfrac{9}{4}$ read, "x divided by 12 equals 9 divided by 4."

In the following proportion a and d are the **extremes,** and b and c are the **means.**

$$\frac{a}{b} = \frac{c}{d}$$

You can use the multiplication property of equality to show that in a proportion the product of the extremes equals the product of the means.

$$\frac{a}{b}(bd) = \frac{c}{d}(bd)$$

$$ad = bc$$

EXAMPLE 1   Solve the proportion $\dfrac{5}{x} = \dfrac{7}{3}$.

SOLUTION $5 \cdot 3 = 7x$

$15 = 7x$

$\dfrac{15}{7} = x$

$\therefore$ the solution is $\dfrac{15}{7}$.   *Answer*

EXAMPLE 2   Solve the proportion $\dfrac{7a - 5}{4} = \dfrac{a + 9}{3}$.

SOLUTION $(7a - 5)3 = 4(a + 9)$

$21a - 15 = 4a + 36$

$17a = 51$

$a = 3$

$\therefore$ the solution is 3.   *Answer*

Proportions may be used to solve word problems.

EXAMPLE 3

The Washington Farm, which has 400 ha (hectares) planted in corn, produces an annual corn harvest of 300 m³. How many additional hectares must be planted in corn to yield an annual crop of 450 m³?

240   *CHAPTER 7*

SOLUTION

Step 1 The problem asks for the number of additional hectares to be planted in corn.

Step 2 Let a = number of additional hectares to be planted in corn. Then, $400 + a$ = total number of hectares planted in corn.

Step 3 Because the yield of corn per hectare will remain the same, you can write the following proportion:

$$\frac{300}{400} = \frac{450}{400 + a}$$

Step 4 Solve.

$$\frac{3}{4} = \frac{450}{400 + a}$$

$$3(400 + a) = 4 \cdot 450$$
$$1200 + 3a = 1800$$
$$3a = 600$$
$$a = 200$$

Step 5 The check is left to you.

$\therefore$ an additional 200 ha should be planted in corn. **Answer**

Oral Exercises

State the equation that results when you equate the product of the extremes and the product of the means in each of the following proportions.

1. $\frac{2}{3} = \frac{14}{x}$ $2x = 3 \cdot 14$

2. $\frac{y}{6} = \frac{6}{4}$ $4y = 6 \cdot 6$

3. $\frac{3}{5} = \frac{6x}{10}$ $3 \cdot 10 = 30x$

4. $\frac{3k}{5} = \frac{k+5}{10}$ $30k = 5(k+5)$

5. $\frac{a-5}{8} = -\frac{3}{12}$ $12(a-5) = -3 \cdot 8$

6. $\frac{c-4}{4} = \frac{c}{6}$ $6(c-4) = 4c$

7. $\frac{3}{d-5} = \frac{4}{d}$ $3d = 4(d-5)$

8. $\frac{5}{u-2} = \frac{15}{u+4}$ $5(u+4) = 15(u-2)$

Written Exercises

Solve.

A

1. $\frac{x}{9} = \frac{7}{3}$ 21

2. $\frac{x}{5} = \frac{9}{4}$ $\frac{45}{4}$

3. $\frac{3c}{2} = \frac{2}{5}$ $\frac{4}{15}$

4. $\frac{4}{7} = \frac{2b}{3}$ $\frac{6}{7}$

5. $\frac{4}{5} = \frac{3n}{7}$ $\frac{28}{15}$

6. $\frac{3}{8c} = \frac{4}{5}$ $\frac{15}{32}$

7. $\frac{2}{9} = \frac{3}{x}$ $\frac{27}{2}$

8. $\frac{9}{4a} = \frac{3}{1}$ $\frac{3}{4}$

9. $\frac{x}{3} = \frac{2x}{5}$ 0

10. $\frac{15x}{64} = \frac{45}{32}$ 6

11. $\frac{81}{49} = \frac{27y}{14}$ $\frac{6}{7}$

12. $\frac{25}{17a} = \frac{125}{51}$ $\frac{3}{5}$

APPLYING FRACTIONS **241**

6. A student must write a 1000 word report. After writing two full pages there were 350 words. At this rate how many pages must be written to complete the assignment?

$$\frac{350}{3} = \frac{1000}{x}$$

$$350x = 2000$$

$$x = \frac{2000}{350} = \frac{40}{7} = 5\frac{5}{7}$$

$\therefore$ The student must write $5\frac{5}{7}$ pages.

Supplementary Material

Practice Master 40

Suggested Assignments

Minimum
Day 1: 241/1–31 odd
    S 101/20, 22, 24, 31, 33
Day 2: 242/P: 2, 4–6, 8, 12

Average

NOTE: Day 2 of Sec. 7-1 finishes Sec. 7-1 and starts Sec. 7-2

    242/23–31 odd,
      P: 1, 3, 5, 9, 11, 12
    S 102/36, 38

Maximum
    241/1–31 odd
    242/P: 1–11 odd
    S 238/P: 14, 16

Extra Practice Problems
p. 518

Additional A Exercises

Solve.

1. $\frac{x}{8} = \frac{7}{2}$ 28

2. $\frac{c}{10} = \frac{24}{30}$ 8

3. $\frac{20}{9} = \frac{a}{18}$ 40

4. $\frac{36}{42} = \frac{6}{y}$ 7

5. $\frac{3a}{8} = \frac{9}{2}$ 12

6. $\frac{1}{25} = \frac{3}{5a}$ 15

Solve.

SAMPLE $\quad \frac{21}{k+1} = 7 \qquad$ *SOLUTION* $\quad \frac{21}{k+1} = \frac{7}{1}; \ 21 = 7(k+1); \ 3 = k+1; \ k = 2$

13. $\frac{a-4}{6} = 5$ 34

14. $4 = \frac{c-2}{7}$ 30

15. $\frac{d+9}{2} = 5d$ 1

16. $\frac{3z}{2} = z - 4$ −8

17. $\frac{x+3}{16} = \frac{x}{10}$ 5

18. $\frac{x}{3} = \frac{2x-1}{5}$ 3

B 19. $\frac{2x+1}{18} = \frac{4x-3}{21}$ $\frac{5}{2}$

20. $\frac{6x-1}{14} = \frac{9x+2}{28}$ $\frac{4}{3}$

21. $\frac{2x-6}{2} = \frac{3x-9}{3}$ Identity

22. $\frac{4x+2}{18} = \frac{6x+3}{17}$ $-\frac{1}{2}$

23. $\frac{2a+1}{24} = \frac{a}{12}$ No root

24. $\frac{3x-5}{5} = \frac{10-6x}{-10}$ Identity

Solve for x in terms of the other variables.

25. $\frac{a}{x} = \frac{b}{c}$ $\frac{ac}{b}$

26. $\frac{l}{x} = \frac{r}{s}$ $\frac{ls}{r}$

27. $\frac{x+b}{a} = n$ $na - b$

28. $\frac{b}{q} = \frac{2}{x}$ $\frac{2q}{b}$

Find the ratio of x to y.

29. $\frac{2x+3y}{3y} = \frac{3}{4}$ $-\frac{3}{8}$

30. $\frac{5x-y}{y} = \frac{4}{3}$ $\frac{7}{15}$

31. $\frac{3x-y}{6} = \frac{8x-y}{4}$ $\frac{1}{18}$

C 32. Solve the following proportion for x if a is positive: $\frac{a}{x} = \frac{x}{1}$.
$\{\sqrt{a}, -\sqrt{a}\}$

Problems

A 1. A truck can pump 800 L of oil in 25 min. How much oil can it pump in 2 h? 3840 L

2. A recipe for two dozen bran muffins requires 750 g of bran flour. How much bran flour would be required to make three dozen muffins? 1125 g

3. The tax on a new car costing $7200 is $504. At the same tax rate, what will the tax be on a new car costing $8000? $560

4. Lonnie drove 100 km on 12 L of gasohol. How far can he travel on a full tank of 50 L? $416\frac{2}{3}$ km, or 416.67 km

5. If 2 g of hydrogen unite with 16 g of oxygen to form water, how much oxygen is required to produce 144 g of water? (Assume that no loss takes place during the reaction.) 128 g

6. The owner of a house with an assessment of $62,500 pays real estate taxes of $1250. What is the assessment on a neighboring house whose owner pays $1500 in real estate taxes? $75,000

7. If 600 shares of a certain stock earn an annual dividend of $750, how many shares are required to earn an annual dividend of $1200?
960 shares

8. In a town of 20,000 residences, a survey was taken to determine the number of residences with garbage disposals. Of the 400 residences surveyed, 352 had disposals. Assuming that the residences surveyed are a representative sample, estimate the number of households with garbage disposals. 17,600 households

9. A farm that has 100 ha planted in wheat produces 275 m³ of wheat annually. How many additional hectares should be planted in wheat so that the annual yield will be 385 m³? 40 ha

B 10. While on a business trip, Julia Wilson decided to test the accuracy of her car's odometer. For the 320 km trip from Oakdale to Alton the odometer registered 324 km. She returned by a different route and noted that the odometer registered 567 km for the round trip. How many kilometers long was the actual return trip? 240 km

11. A cubic centimeter of gold has a mass of 19.3 g, while a cubic centimeter of silver has a mass of 10.5 g. Which of the following has the greater mass: a cube of gold 1.2 cm on an edge or a cube of silver 1.4 cm on an edge? By how much? (*Hint:* Use the formula for the volume of a cube.) The cube of gold; 4.5384 g

12. If 1 cm represents 30 km on a map, and Colorado is shown by a rectangle 20 cm by 15 cm, calculate the area of Colorado in square kilometers. 270,000 km²

Self-Test 1

VOCABULARY   ratio (p. 235)   proportion (p. 240)
                  means (p. 240)   extremes (p. 240)

State each ratio in simplest form.

1. 8 m to 10 m   2. 3 h to 15 min   Obj. 7-1, p. 235

3. Two numbers are in the ratio of $3:7$ and their sum is 310. Find the numbers.

4. Solve: $\dfrac{17x}{64} = \dfrac{51}{16}$ Obj. 7-2, p. 240

5. The tax on a new car costing $7600 is $456. At the same tax rate, what will the tax be on a new car costing $8200?

Check your answers with those at the back of the book.

APPLYING FRACTIONS   **243**

FRACTIONAL EQUATIONS

7-3 *Equations with Fractional Coefficients*

OBJECTIVE To solve equations with fractional coefficients.

You can solve equations with fractional coefficients by using the least common denominator of all the fractions in the equation. Transform the equation by multiplying both sides by the least common denominator. Then solve the transformed equation.

1. $\dfrac{a}{2} + \dfrac{5a}{3} = 13$

LCD is 6

$6\left(\dfrac{a}{2}\right) + 6\left(\dfrac{5a}{3}\right) = 6(13)$

$$3a + 10a = 6(13)$$
$$13a = 6(13)$$
$$a = 6$$

2. $\dfrac{2}{3}x - \dfrac{4}{5}x = 4$

LCD is 15

$15\left(\dfrac{2}{3}x\right) - 15\left(\dfrac{4}{5}x\right) = 15(4)$

$$10x - 12x = 15(4)$$
$$-2x = 15(4)$$
$$x = -30$$

3. $\dfrac{3y-1}{4} - \dfrac{y}{3} = 1$

LCD is 12

$12\left(\dfrac{3y-1}{4}\right) - 12\left(\dfrac{y}{3}\right) = 12(1)$

$$3(3y-1) - 4(y) = 12$$
$$9y - 3 - 4y = 12$$
$$5y = 15$$
$$y = 3$$

4. $\dfrac{x-1}{2} + \dfrac{x-2}{3} = 8$

LCD is 6

$6\left(\dfrac{x-1}{2}\right) + 6\left(\dfrac{x-2}{3}\right) = 6(8)$

$$3(x-1) + 2(x-2) = 6(8)$$
$$3x - 3 + 2x - 4 = 48$$
$$5x - 7 = 48$$
$$5x = 55$$
$$x = 11$$

5. Two thirds of a number is seven more than one sixth of the number. Find the number.

(continued)

EXAMPLE Solve: $\dfrac{2x-1}{3} + \dfrac{x}{5} = 4$.

SOLUTION The LCD of the fractions is 15.

$$15\left[\left(\dfrac{2x-1}{3}\right) + \left(\dfrac{x}{5}\right)\right] = 15[4]$$
$$5(2x - 1) + 3(x) = 15[4]$$
$$10x - 5 + 3x = 60$$
$$13x - 5 = 60$$
$$13x = 65$$
$$x = 5$$

∴ the solution is 5. *Answer*

Oral Exercises

State the least common denominator of the fractions in each equation. Then tell what equation results when both sides of the equation are multiplied by the LCD.

1. $\dfrac{x}{2} + \dfrac{x}{3} = 5$ 6; $3x + 2x = 30$ **2.** $\dfrac{3y}{4} + \dfrac{y}{2} = 5$ 4; $3y + 2y = 20$ **3.** $\dfrac{k}{3} + \dfrac{2k}{5} = \dfrac{11}{15}$ 15; $5k + 6k = 11$

4. $\dfrac{a}{3} - \dfrac{a}{6} = 1$ 6; $2a - a = 6$ **5.** $\dfrac{5x}{12} - \dfrac{2x}{9} = 7$ 36; $15x - 8x = 252$ **6.** $\dfrac{2b}{5} + \dfrac{b}{3} = 0$ 15; $6b + 5b = 0$

Written Exercises

A **1–6.** Solve the equations in Oral Exercises 1–6.

1. 6 **2.** 4 **3.** 1 **4.** 6 **5.** 36 **6.** 0

Solve.

7. $\dfrac{n}{3} + \dfrac{2n}{5} = 11$ 15 **8.** $\dfrac{2a}{3} - \dfrac{a}{2} = 2$ 12 **9.** $\dfrac{3-n}{2} = \dfrac{3}{4}$ $\dfrac{3}{2}$

Solve.

10. $\frac{3}{8}k - \frac{1}{4}k = 2$ 16

11. $\frac{3}{2}x - \frac{1}{6}x + 1 = 0$ $\frac{-3}{4}$

12. $\frac{6}{7}c - \frac{1}{2}c = 5$ 14

B 13. $\frac{x-7}{5} + 2 = \frac{x+8}{10}$ 2

14. $n + \frac{n+2}{4} = 0$ $\frac{-2}{5}$

15. $\frac{x+8}{16} - \frac{x-4}{12} = 1$ $\frac{-8}{}$

16. $\frac{5x-1}{2} - \frac{3x+1}{4} = \frac{9}{2}$ 3

17. $\frac{3x-1}{4} - \frac{9-x}{6} = \frac{14}{3}$ 7

18. $\frac{x+1}{5} - \frac{3}{2} = \frac{3x-6}{10}$ -7

19. $\frac{x-5}{8} - \frac{2x+6}{9} + 1 = 0$ -3

20. $\frac{x-3}{5} - \frac{x+2}{15} + \frac{2}{3} = 0$ $\frac{1}{2}$

21. $\frac{2a-1}{6} - \frac{1-a}{4} = a$ -1

22. $\frac{4n+1}{3} - \frac{2n+1}{5} = \frac{3}{5}$ $\frac{1}{2}$

23. $\frac{x+3}{3} - \frac{x}{4} = \frac{x-2}{5}$ 12

24. $\frac{1}{2}(x-5) - (x+1) = \frac{1}{4}(x-12)$ $\frac{-2}{3}$

25. $\frac{2}{3}(x-1) - \frac{1}{5}(2x-3) = 1$ 4

26. $\frac{1}{3}(x+6) - 1 = \frac{1}{6}(9-x)$ 1

C 27. $\frac{1}{4}\left(y - \frac{1}{3}\right) - \frac{1}{6}(y-3) = \frac{2}{3}$ 3

28. $\frac{1}{2}\left(x + \frac{2}{3}\right) - \frac{1}{6}\left(7x - \frac{1}{3}\right) = \frac{1}{6}$ $\frac{1}{3}$

29. $\frac{1}{5}(2x-3) - \frac{2}{3}\left(x - \frac{1}{2}\right) = \frac{7}{15}$ $\frac{-11}{4}$

30. $\frac{3}{4}(x-2) - \frac{2}{3}\left(x - \frac{1}{2}\right) = \frac{x+1}{2}$ -4

Solve for x in terms of the other variable.

31. $\frac{x+3a}{10} - \frac{x-a}{2} = \frac{x}{5}$ $\frac{4a}{3}$

32. $\frac{x-n}{5} - \frac{7x-n}{10} = \frac{2n-x}{15}$ $\frac{-7n}{13}$

33. $\frac{1}{5}(2x-3c) - \frac{1}{3}\left(x - \frac{c}{2}\right) - \frac{x}{6} = 0$ $\frac{-13c}{3}$

Problems

A 1. One sixth of a number is 5 less than one fourth of the number. Find the number. 60

2. Two thirds of a number added to three eighths of the number is 25. Find the number. 24

3. A rectangle is 6 cm longer than it is wide. Its width is one fifth of the perimeter. Find its dimensions. 12 cm by 18 cm

4. Tom is three years older than Marcia. Three years ago Marcia's age was four fifths of Tom's. What are their present ages? Marcia, 15; Tom, 18

5. Sam is half as old as Kathy. In two years, he will be two thirds as old as Kathy. How old is each now? Sam, 2; Kathy, 4

6. David has one third more money than Carl. Together they have $42. How much does each have? Carl, $18; David, $24

APPLYING FRACTIONS **245**

LCD is 6

$$6\left(\frac{2}{3}n\right) = 6(7) + 6\left(\frac{1}{6}n\right)$$

$$4n = 42 + n$$
$$3n = 42$$
$$n = 14$$

∴ the number is 14.

6. Joe is three fourths as old as Sally. In four years he will be four fifths as old as Sally. How old is Joe now?

	Now	In 4 years
Sally	x	$x + 4$
Joe	$\frac{3}{4}x$	$\frac{4}{5}(x + 4)$

$$\frac{3}{4}x + 4 = \frac{4}{5}(x + 4)$$

LCD is 20

$$20\left(\frac{3}{4}x\right) + 20(4) =$$
$$20\left[\frac{4}{5}(x + 4)\right]$$
$$15x + 80 = 16x + 64$$
$$16 = x$$

Sally is 16 years old.

∴ Joe is $\frac{3}{4}(16)$ or 12 years old.

Suggested Assignments

Minimum
Day 1: 244/7–18, 19–25 odd
  R 243/Self-Test 1
Day 2: 245/P: 1, 3, 4, 7, 9

Average
Day 1: 244/7–31 odd
  R 243/Self-Test 1
Day 2: 245/P: 1, 3, 4, 7, 10, 12
  248/1–29 odd

NOTE: Day 2 of Sec. 7-3 finishes Sec. 7-3 and covers Sec. 7-4.

Maximum
  244/7–33 odd
  245/P: 1–11 odd
  R 243/Self-Test 1
  S 242/32

Additional A Exercises

Solve.

1. $\dfrac{a}{3} + \dfrac{a}{6} = 9$ 18

2. $\dfrac{x}{2} + \dfrac{x}{5} = 7$ 10

3. $\dfrac{c}{2} - \dfrac{c}{4} = 12$ 48

4. $\dfrac{2y}{3} + \dfrac{y}{4} = 22$ 24

5. $\dfrac{y}{5} + \dfrac{3y}{4} = 19$ 20

6. $\dfrac{3a}{5} - \dfrac{a}{2} = 8$ 80

B   7. Ann had ten dollars more than Beverly. After Ann spent half her money and Beverly spent a quarter of her money, they had equal amounts left. How much money did each have at first?   Ann, $30   Beverly, $20

8. Otis hikes up to the falls at 3 km/h and returns by the same route at 5 km/h. If the entire trip takes him 7.5 h, how far is it to the falls?   14.0625 km

9. Sally walks from her home to the recreation center at a rate of 6 km/h, and she jogs home at a rate of 12 km/h. If her jogging time is fifteen minutes less than her walking time, what is the distance to the center?   3 km

10. A group of nickels, dimes, and quarters is worth $7.60. There are two thirds as many nickels as dimes and half as many dimes as quarters. How many quarters are there?   24 quarters

11. Three fourths of the coins in a coin bank are dimes and the rest are quarters. The value of the coins is $4.95. How many dimes are there?   27 dimes

12. Ina bought a number of baseballs for her sporting goods store at $2.50 each. She sold four fifths of them at $3.50 each and gave the rest to a team she sponsored. Even so, she made a $9 profit on the baseballs. How many did she buy?   30 baseballs

ḣistorical ṅote An Ancient Equation

Equations have been used for thousands of years. Manuscripts that have been preserved since about 1900 B.C. provide some information about the equations used by the ancient Egyptians. Here is one old problem:

A quantity and its $\dfrac{1}{5}$ added together become 21.

What is the quantity?

You can write the equation $x + \dfrac{1}{5}x = 21$ and solve it by the methods you

have studied. The Egyptians used a proportion to solve it (although they did not write it the way we do). Here is their method:

Let $x = 5$.
Then $5 + 1 = 6$. But the sum is to be 21.
Therefore, the correct value of x can be found from:

$$\frac{x}{5} = \frac{21}{6}$$
$$x = \frac{5}{2} \cdot 7 = \frac{35}{2} = 17\frac{1}{2}$$

Compare this method with the one you would use.

246   *CHAPTER 7*

7-4 *Fractional Equations*

Teaching Suggestions p. T89

Suggested Extensions p. T90

OBJECTIVE To solve fractional equations.

An equation that has a variable in the denominator of one or more terms is called a **fractional equation.** You can use the multiplication property of equality to solve fractional equations.

EXAMPLE Solve: $\dfrac{x+1}{2x-2} = \dfrac{x}{6} + \dfrac{1}{x-1}$

SOLUTION 1. Factor all the denominators to determine the LCD.

$$\frac{x+1}{2(x-1)} = \frac{x}{6} + \frac{1}{x-1}$$

The LCD is $6(x-1)$; note that $x \neq 1$.

2. Multiply both sides of the equation by the LCD.

$$6(x-1)\left[\frac{x+1}{2(x-1)}\right] = 6(x-1)\left[\frac{x}{6} + \frac{1}{x-1}\right]$$

$$3(x+1) = (x-1)x + 6$$

$$3x + 3 = x^2 - x + 6$$

$$0 = x^2 - 4x + 3$$

$$0 = (x-1)(x-3)$$

$$x = 1 \text{ or } x = 3$$

3. Recall that 1 is not permissible as a solution to the original equation. Check 3 in the original equation.

$$\frac{3+1}{2 \cdot 3 - 2} \overset{?}{=} \frac{3}{6} + \frac{1}{3-1}$$

$$\frac{4}{4} \overset{?}{=} \frac{3}{6} + \frac{1}{2}$$

$$1 = 1 \ \checkmark$$

$\therefore$ the solution is 3. ***Answer***

In the preceding example you saw that 1 was not a solution of the original equation even though it satisfied the transformed equation. Notice that multiplying the equation by $6(x-1)$ led to an equation that was *not equivalent* to the given one. This new equation had the extra root 1, a number for which the multiplier $6(x-1)$ represents *zero*.

In general, multiplying both sides of an equation by a variable expression that can represent zero may produce an equation that is not equivalent to the original equation. Therefore, you must check each root of the resulting equation to see that it satisfies the original equation.

APPLYING FRACTIONS **247**

Chalkboard Examples
Solve.

1. $\dfrac{1}{3} + \dfrac{2}{x} = \dfrac{2}{3}$

Value not permitted: 0
LCD is $3x$

$$3x\left(\frac{1}{3}\right) + 3x\left(\frac{2}{x}\right) = 3x\left(\frac{2}{3}\right)$$

$$x + 6 = 2x$$
$$x = 6$$
$\therefore$ The solution is 6.

2. $\dfrac{21}{6x} - \dfrac{1}{10} = \dfrac{2}{5}$

Value not permitted: 0
LCD is $30x$

$$30x\left(\frac{21}{6x}\right) - 30x\left(\frac{1}{10}\right) = 30x\left(\frac{2}{5}\right)$$

$$105 - 3x = 12x$$
$$105 = 15x$$
$$x = 7$$
$\therefore$ The solution is 7.

3. $\dfrac{5}{y} = \dfrac{6}{y+2} + 1$

Values not permitted: 0, -2
LCD is $y(y+2)$
$5y + 10 = 6y + y(y+2)$
$0 = y^2 + 3y - 10$
$0 = (y+5)(y-2)$
$y + 5 = \ \ 0$ or $y - 2 = 0$
$\ \ y = -5$ or $y = 2$
$\therefore$ The solutions are -5 and 2.

4. $\dfrac{4}{x^2 - 4x} - \dfrac{x-3}{x-4} = \dfrac{1}{x}$

Values not permitted: 0, 4
LCD is $x(x-4)$
$4 - x(x-3) = x - 4$
$-x^2 + 2x + 8 = 0$
$(-1)(x-4)(x+2) = 0$
$x - 4 = 0$ or $x + 2 = 0$
$\ \ x = 4$ $\qquad x = -2$
4 is not permitted.
$\therefore$ The solution is -2.

(continued)

5. Maria has to walk 6 km to school every day. If she walked 3 km/h less than her usual rate, it would take her 1 h more than usual. How long does the walk usually take?

$d = r \cdot t$ or $6 = r \cdot t$
usual time $= t$

usual rate $= \dfrac{6}{t}$

slower time $= t + 1$

slower rate $= \dfrac{6}{t} - 3$

$6 = \left(\dfrac{6}{t} - 3\right)(t + 1)$

$6 = 6 - 3t + \dfrac{6}{t} - 3$

$0 = -3t + \dfrac{6}{t} - 3$

LCD $= t$
$0 = -3t^2 - 3t + 6$
$0 = t^2 + t - 2$
$0 = (t + 2)(t - 1)$
$t = -2$ or $t = 1$
reject $t = -2$
$\therefore$ It usually takes Maria 1 h to walk to school.

Supplementary Materials

Practice Master 41

Progress Test 24

Computer Activity 20
Solving Fractional Equations
Computers can reduce the amount of work needed to solve fractional equations. A program that will solve any equation of the form
$\dfrac{1}{a} + \dfrac{1}{x} = \dfrac{1}{b}$, where a and b are constants, is given.

Written Exercises

Solve. If the equation has no solution write "no solution."

A
1. $\dfrac{1}{5} + \dfrac{1}{x} = \dfrac{6}{5}$ 1

2. $\dfrac{3}{x} - \dfrac{1}{4} = \dfrac{3}{4}$ 3

3. $\dfrac{1}{x} + \dfrac{1}{3} = \dfrac{1}{2}$ 6

4. $\dfrac{1}{a} + \dfrac{1}{3} = \dfrac{8}{15}$ 5

5. $\dfrac{3}{10} = \dfrac{1}{2} - \dfrac{1}{b}$ 5

6. $\dfrac{6}{x} = \dfrac{4}{x - 1}$ 3

7. $\dfrac{1 + a}{a} = \dfrac{3}{a}$ 2

8. $\dfrac{3n + 5}{6} - \dfrac{10}{n} = \dfrac{n}{2}$ 12

9. $\dfrac{y}{y - 2} = \dfrac{4}{3}$ 8

10. $\dfrac{x}{x + 3} = \dfrac{2x}{x + 3} + 3$ $-\dfrac{9}{4}$

11. $\dfrac{a}{2a + 4} - \dfrac{1}{a + 2} = 1$ -6

12. $\dfrac{1}{x} - \dfrac{2x}{x + 1} = 0$ $\left\{\dfrac{-1}{2}, 1\right\}$

Solve.

B
13. When 100 is divided by x the quotient is 4 and the remainder is 12. Find x. 22

14. Julia Ling drove the 200 km to Richmond at a speed 10 km/h faster than usual. If she completed the trip in one hour less than usual, find her usual driving speed. 40 km/h

15. Rodney Smith can bicycle or drive the 30 km from his apartment to the river. If he drives his car, he will travel 25 km/h faster and complete the trip in fifty minutes less time. Find his speed when traveling by bike. 20 km/h

Solve. If the equation has no solution write "no solution."

16. $\dfrac{2}{x^2 - x} = \dfrac{2}{x - 1} + 1$ -2

17. $\dfrac{1}{2a - 1} - \dfrac{3}{4a^2 - 1} = 0$ 1

18. $\dfrac{y - 2}{y} - \dfrac{y - 3}{y - 6} = \dfrac{3}{y}$ $\dfrac{1}{y}$

19. $\dfrac{b + 4}{2b - 6} = \dfrac{b}{b - 3} + 2$ $\dfrac{16}{5}$

20. $\dfrac{2}{x + 1} + \dfrac{1}{x - 1} = 1$ $\{0, 3\}$

21. $\dfrac{3}{x - 1} + \dfrac{2}{x} = 4$

22. $\dfrac{1}{x - 4} = \dfrac{2}{x^2 - 16}$ -2

23. $\dfrac{a + 3}{a - 1} + \dfrac{a + 1}{a - 3} = 2$ 2

24. $\dfrac{1}{y} - \dfrac{1}{y - 2} = \dfrac{8}{4y - 3}$

25. $\dfrac{2x + 1}{3} - \dfrac{3}{2x - 1} = -2$ $\{-4, 1\}$

26. $\dfrac{4}{x^2 - 4x} + \dfrac{1}{4 - x} = 0$ No sol.

27. $\dfrac{1}{x - 4} + \dfrac{2}{x^2 - 16} = \dfrac{3}{x + 4}$ 9

28. $\dfrac{3a}{a - 1} - \dfrac{4}{a + 1} = \dfrac{4}{a^2 - 1}$

29. $\dfrac{8}{b - 1} + \dfrac{30}{1 - b^2} = \dfrac{6}{b + 1}$ 8

30. $\dfrac{1}{y} - \dfrac{2}{1 - y} = \dfrac{8}{y^2 - y}$ 3

C 31. $\dfrac{x - 2}{x^2 - x - 6} = \dfrac{1}{x^2 - 4} + \dfrac{3}{2x + 4}$ $\{1, 4\}$

32. $\dfrac{x}{x + 1} - \dfrac{x + 1}{x - 4} = \dfrac{5}{x^2 - 3x - 4}$ No sol.

33. $\dfrac{n - 4}{2n^2 + 5n - 3} + \dfrac{2n + 7}{8n^2 - 2n - 1} = \dfrac{4n - 1}{4n^2 + 13n + 3}$ $\{4, -2\}$

34. $\dfrac{2x^2}{1 - x^2} = \dfrac{x}{x - 1} - \dfrac{x}{x + 1} - \dfrac{3}{3}$

Application Optics

The curved pieces of glass or plastic in a magnifying glass or a pair of eyeglasses are examples of *lenses*. When light passes through a lens, it is bent. The most common type of lens is the *converging lens,* which is used in cameras, movie projectors, and eyeglasses. Converging lenses cause parallel rays of light to converge to a point, as shown in the photo below.

The point at which the rays converge is called the *principal focus* of the lens. The distance from the principal focus to the center of the lens is called the *focal length* of the lens.

When you look through a converging lens, the size of the image you see will be determined by the distance from the object to the lens (d_o), the distance from the image to the lens (d_i), and the focal length of the lens (f).

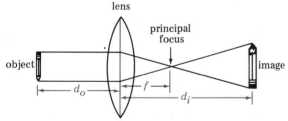

The relationship between d_o, d_i, and f is given by the following formula:

$$\frac{1}{d_o} + \frac{1}{d_i} = \frac{1}{f}$$

The apparent change in the size of an object viewed through a lens is called magnification. The magnification (M) of the image is given by the formula:

$$M = \frac{d_i}{d_o}$$

APPLYING FRACTIONS **249**

EXAMPLE

A negative is placed 75 mm from the center of the lens of a photo enlarger. If the focal length of the lens is 50 mm, find the distance from the lens to the image and the magnification of the image.

 light source

SOLUTION

1. Substitute in the formula: $\dfrac{1}{75} + \dfrac{1}{d_i} = \dfrac{1}{50}$

2. Solve for d_i.

$$150d_i\left(\frac{1}{75}\right) + 150d_i\left(\frac{1}{d_i}\right) = 150d_i\left(\frac{1}{50}\right)$$

$$2d_i + 150 = 3d_i$$

$$150 = d_i$$

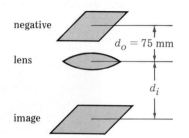

negative

$d_o = 75$ mm

lens

d_i

image

∴ the distance from the lens to the image is 150 mm.

3. Substitute in the formula for magnification.

$$M = \frac{d_i}{d_o} = \frac{150}{75} = 2$$

∴ the magnification of the image will be 2.

In each of the optical relationships described, measurements are given from the center of the converging lens. Find (a) the distance from the lens to the image; (b) the magnification of the image.

1. A slide is placed 90 mm from the converging lens in a slide viewer. The lens has a focal length of 60 mm. **a.** 180 mm **b.** 2

2. A magnifying glass with a focal length of 96 mm is positioned 120 mm above an ant. **a.** 480 mm **b.** 4

3. A slide with a sample of pond water is placed 0.5 cm from the lens of a microscope. The lens has a focal length of 0.49 cm. **a.** 24.5 cm **b.** 49

4. Opal is taking a picture of James, who is standing 550 mm from her. The lens in her camera has a focal length of 50 mm. **a.** 55 mm **b.** $\frac{1}{10}$, or 0.1

Quick Quiz

Solve.

1. $\dfrac{5}{6}x + \dfrac{1}{3}x = 14$ 12

2. $\dfrac{3y - 1}{6} - \dfrac{y}{3} = \dfrac{1}{2}$ 4

3. $\dfrac{6}{z} - \dfrac{5}{12} = \dfrac{1}{4}$ 9

4. $\dfrac{3}{x} - \dfrac{2}{x + 1} = \dfrac{2}{x}$ 1

Self-Test 2

VOCABULARY fractional equation (p. 247)

Solve.

1. $\dfrac{5}{8}n - \dfrac{1}{2}n = 6$

2. $\dfrac{2k - 3}{4} - \dfrac{k}{8} = \dfrac{1}{4}$

3. $\dfrac{2}{y} - \dfrac{1}{3} = \dfrac{1}{6}$

4. $\dfrac{1}{v} - \dfrac{2}{v - 2} = \dfrac{3}{v}$

Obj. 7-3, p. 244

Obj. 7-4, p. 247

Check your answers with those at the back of the book.

PERCENT PROBLEMS

7-5 *Percents*

OBJECTIVE   To solve problems involving percents.

The ratio of one number to another can be expressed as a percent. The word **percent** (usually denoted %) means "hundredths" or "divided by 100." For example,

$$\frac{13}{100} \text{ is called "13 percent" and written } 13\%.$$

EXAMPLE 1   Express each number as a percent.

$$\textbf{a. } \frac{4}{5} \qquad \textbf{b. } \frac{2}{3} \qquad \textbf{c. } 2.5$$

SOLUTION

a. $\dfrac{x}{100} = \dfrac{4}{5}$

$5x = 400$

$x = 80$

$\therefore \dfrac{4}{5} = 80\%$

b. $\dfrac{x}{100} = \dfrac{2}{3}$

$3x = 200$

$x = 66\dfrac{2}{3}$

$\therefore \dfrac{2}{3} = 66\dfrac{2}{3}\%$

c. $\dfrac{x}{100} = 2.5$

$x = 250$

$\therefore 2.5 = 250\%$

In problems involving percent, the word "of" indicates multiplication and the word "is" indicates equality. The next three examples illustrate this idea.

EXAMPLE 2   45% of 20 is what number?

SOLUTION $\dfrac{45}{100} \cdot 20 = x$

$9 = x$

$\therefore 45\% \text{ of } 20 \text{ is } 9.$ ***Answer***

When finding a percent of a number, it is often convenient to express the percent as a decimal and then multiply. Example 2 can be worked as follows:

$$45\% = 0.45 \qquad 45\% \text{ of } 20 = 0.45 \times 20 = 9$$

APPLYING FRACTIONS   **251**

Teaching Suggestions p. T90

Suggested Extensions p. T90

Chalkboard Examples

1. Complete the following table.

fraction	decimal	percent
$\dfrac{4}{5}$	0.8	80
$\dfrac{3}{10}$	0.3	30
$\dfrac{2}{25}$	0.08	8
$\dfrac{7}{200}$	0.035	3.5
$2\dfrac{1}{4}$	2.25	225

2. Find 25% of $18.
$P = 0.25(18) = 4.50$;
$4.50

3. What percent of 48 is 36?
$36 = P(48)$
$P = 0.75$ or 75%

4. 40 is 20% of what number?
$40 = 0.20(B)$
$B = 200$

Solve.

5. Jean deposited $236 for 3 months at $5\dfrac{3}{4}$%. Joan deposited $150 for 4 months at $6\dfrac{1}{2}$%. Who earned the greater amount of interest?

$$(236)\left(\frac{3}{12}\right)(0.0575) = 3.39$$

$$(150)\left(\frac{4}{12}\right)(0.065) = 3.25$$

Jean earned more.

(continued)

6. A company invested part of $6300 at 6% and the rest at 8%. If the annual income from each investment was the same, find the amount invested at each rate.
$(0.06)x = (0.08)(6300 - x)$
$3600 at 6% and $2700 at 8%

EXAMPLE 3   98 is 70% of what number?

SOLUTION $98 = \dfrac{70}{100} \cdot x$

$$9800 = 70x$$
$$140 = x$$

$\therefore$ 98 is 70% of 140.   *Answer*

EXAMPLE 4   What percent of 15 is 3?

SOLUTION $\dfrac{x}{100} \cdot 15 = 3$

$$15x = 300$$
$$x = 20$$

$\therefore$ 20% of 15 is 3.   *Answer*

When working investment problems, it is often convenient to express the rate of interest as a decimal. For example, you can find the interest for 1 year on $2000 invested at an $8\frac{1}{2}\%$ annual simple interest as follows:

$$8\frac{1}{2}\% = 8.5\% = 0.085 \qquad 8\frac{1}{2}\% \text{ of } \$2000 = 0.085 \times 2000 = \$170$$

Some investment problems involve an equation with coefficients expressed as decimals. Such an equation can be solved by multiplying both sides of the equation by a power of ten to get an equivalent equation with whole number coefficients.

EXAMPLE 5

Annette Lauphier invests part of $8000 at 9% annual simple interest and the rest at 11% annual simple interest. Her annual income from these investments is $850. How much is invested at each interest rate?

SOLUTION

Step 1   The problem asks for the amount of money invested at 9% and the amount invested at 11%.

Step 2   Let x = amount invested at 9%.
Then $8000 - x$ = amount invested at 11%.

Principal	$\times$ Rate	= Interest
x	0.09	$0.09x$
$8000 - x$	0.11	$0.11(8000 - x)$

Step 3 Because the total interest earned is $850, you can write the following equation:

$$0.09x + 0.11(8000 - x) = 850$$

Step 4 $100[0.09x + 0.11(8000 - x)] = 100[850] \leftarrow$ Multiply both sides by 100

$$9x + 11(8000 - x) = 85000 \qquad \text{to eliminate decimals.}$$
$$-2x + 88000 = 85000$$
$$2x = 3000$$
$$x = 1500$$

Step 5 The check is left to you.

∴ $1500 was invested at 9% and $6500 was invested at 11%. **Answer**

Oral Exercises

Express as a percent.

1. 0.72 72%   2. 0.05 5%   3. 1.25 125%   4. 0.009 0.9%   5. 0.095 9.5%

6. $\frac{1}{2}$ 50%   7. $\frac{1}{4}$ 25%   8. $\frac{3}{5}$ 60%   9. $1\frac{1}{2}$ 150%   10. $\frac{7}{50}$ 14%

Express as a fraction or mixed number in simplest form.

11. 75% $\frac{3}{4}$ 12. 20% $\frac{1}{5}$ 13. 8% $\frac{2}{25}$ 14. $\frac{1}{2}$% $\frac{1}{200}$ 15. 150% $1\frac{1}{2}$

Express as a decimal.

16. 42% 0.42   17. 3% 0.03   18. 127% 1.27   19. 0.2% 0.002   20. 4.5% 0.045

Tell whether you would multiply by 10, 100, or 1000 in order to eliminate the decimals in each equation.

21. $2.4x = 32$ 10   22. $0.5x + 0.2 = 1.4$ 10   23. $4x - 0.072 = 1.3$ 1000

Written Exercises

Solve.

A   1. 22% of 400 88   2. 3% of 72 2.16   3. $5\frac{1}{2}$% of 1000 55

4. $\frac{1}{2}$% of 36 0.18   5. 2.75% of 160 4.4   6. 120% of 45 54

7. 100% of 91 91   8. 200% of 15.3 30.6   9. $7\frac{1}{3}$% of 150 11

10. What percent of 80 is 16? 20%   11. What percent of 40 is 30? 75%
12. What percent of 300 is 240? 80%   13. What percent of 25 is 16? 64%

APPLYING FRACTIONS **253**

Suggested Assignments
Minimum
Day 1: 253/1–41 odd
  R 250/*Self-Test 2*
Day 2: 254/*P*: 1–3, 6–9
Average
Day 1: 253/1–41 odd
  R 250/*Self-Test 2*
Day 2: 254/*P*: 1, 3, 8–11
Maximum
  253/1–17 odd, 23–29
    odd, 37–41 odd
  254/*P*: 1–3, 6, 8, 9,
    11, 12
  R 250/*Self-Test 2*

Extra Practice Problems
  p. 518

Additional A Exercises
Solve.

1. 10% of 30   3
2. 25% of 80   20
3. 5% of 200   10
4. 28% of 150   42
5. 14% of 50   7
6. 2% of 350   7

14. What percent of 15 is 12? 80%   **15.** What percent of 12 is 15? 125%

16. What percent of 72 is 24? $33\frac{1}{3}$%   **17.** What percent of 180 is 45? 25%

18. What percent of 450 is 9? 2%   **19.** What percent of 20 is 2? 10%

20. What percent of 180 is 36? 20%   **21.** What percent of 36 is 54? 150%

Find the number.

22. 15 is 20% of the number. 75   **23.** 18 is 60% of the number. 30

24. 6.3 is 7% of the number. 90   **25.** 63 is 150% of the number. 42

26. 75% of the number is 270. 360   **27.** $1\frac{1}{2}$% of the number is 6. 400

28. 4% of the number is 3.4. 85   **29.** 500% of the number is 90. 18

Solve.

32. 40   **35.** 30

30. $1.2x = 36$ 30   **31.** $0.07x = 2.8$ 40   **32.** $0.2x + 0.4x = 24$

33. $0.4y - 0.7 = 2.9$ 9   **34.** $1 - 0.3x = 0.4$ 2   **35.** $0.3a + 0.03a = 9.9$

36. $0.05y = 0.06(110 - y)$ 60   **37.** $0.025k + 0.05k = 0.3$ 4   **38.** $0.16(3n - 6) = 4.8$ 12

B **39.** $0.06(1000 - x) + 0.05x = 700$ −64,000   **40.** $0.025a - 0.05(20 - 2a) = 0.2$

41. $1.2x + 3.05 = 0.95x - 0.20$ −13   **42.** $\dfrac{0.3x - 1}{5} = 0.12x + 3.2$

40. 9.6   **42.** $-56\frac{2}{3}$

Problems

Solve.

A **1.** One serving of spinach has about 2.6 mg more iron than a piece of chicken. Together they have about 5.4 mg of iron. How much iron is in a serving of spinach? 4 mg

2. Urban, 165 million; rural, 60 million

2. In a country of 225 million people, the urban population is 2.75 times the rural population. Find the urban and rural populations.

3. Find the sales tax on an $8500 automobile if the sales tax rate is 5%. $425

4. Of the 12,000 votes cast in an election, 55% were for Jefferson. How many votes were cast for the other candidates? 5400 votes

5. In an hour long television biography of a film star, 18% of the time is devoted to film clips from the star's movies. How many minutes are devoted to the film clips? 10.8 min

6. In a small village, 180 people live in wooden structures, 144 live in aluminum-clad structures, and 216 live in brick structures. What percent of the people live in each type of structure?

Wooden, $33\frac{1}{3}$%; aluminum-clad, $26\frac{2}{3}$%; brick, 40%

Solve. Assume that all interest rates indicate annual simple interest.

B 7. Ed Keely invested some money at 6% and an additional $800 at 7%. The money earned $128 interest in a year. How much was invested at 6%? $1200

8. An investment club invested part of a $10,000 amount at $7\frac{1}{2}$% and the rest at $10\frac{1}{2}$%. The interest for one year came to $930. How much money was invested at each rate? $4000 at $7\frac{1}{2}$%; $6000 at $10\frac{1}{2}$%

9. An alumni association raised $12,000 in contributions. Each year the money earns $920 interest, which is used for scholarships. Part of the $12,000 is invested at 7% and the rest at 9%. How much is invested at each rate? $8000 at 7%; $4000 at 9%

10. Nadia Goddard invested $1500 more in tax-free bonds than in stocks. The stocks paid 5% interest and the bonds paid $7\frac{1}{2}$%. If the annual income is $425, find how much she invested in all. $6500

11. Two thirds of a sum of money is invested at 5%, one-sixth at 4%, and the remainder at 6%. If the total income is $450, how much money is invested? $9000

C 12. A woman has d dollars, a part of which is invested at 5% and the rest at $6\frac{1}{2}$%. If she receives k dollars annually in interest, how much is invested at 5%? $\frac{13d - 200k}{3}$ dollars

Biography Lillian Moller Gilbreth

Lillian Moller Gilbreth (1878–1972) with her husband, Frank Gilbreth, pioneered the field of efficiency engineering. Their story and that of their twelve children was told in the novel *Cheaper by the Dozen*. Their goal was to minimize the time and human motion needed to perform tasks in the home, office, and factory.

After her husband's death in 1924, Lillian Gilbreth continued her study of "time and motion." Some of her motion saving devices are the step-on trash can, shelves in refrigerator doors, and height-adjusted kitchen counters.

Lillian Gilbreth received a master's degree in literature from the University of California and a Ph.D. in industrial psychology from Brown University in 1915. During the Depression and World War II, she served on several presidential committees. In 1936 she was voted one of the ten outstanding women of the year, and throughout her long life she received many awards and honorary degrees for her work.

APPLYING FRACTIONS **255**

Chalkboard Examples

Solve.

1. What is the percent of increase in the price of a bread which is marked up from $0.80 to $1.04?

$104 = 80 + 80R$
$24 = 80R$
$0.30 = R$
$\therefore$ The percent increase is 30%.

2. Billy was 3 kg at birth. After 6 months he showed a 100% increase. Over the second 6 month period he experienced a 75% gain. Over the third 6 month period the number of kilograms increased 25%. How many kilograms was Billy when he was 18 months old?

1st 6 mo:
$w_1 = 3 + 1.00(3)$
$w_1 = 6$
2nd 6 mo:
$w_2 = 6 + 0.75(6)$
$= 6 + 4.5$
$w_2 = 10.5$
3rd 6 mo:
$w_3 = 10.5 + 0.25(10.5)$
$= 10.5 + 2.625$
$w_3 = 13.125$
$\therefore$ Billy was 13.125 kg when he was 18 months old.

3. A dress costs $15.96 including 5% tax. What was the price of the dress without the tax?

$15.96 = B(1 + 0.05)$
$15.96 = 1.05B$
$15.20 = B$
$\therefore$ The marked price is $15.20.

4. A $50 coat is on sale at a 20% discount. How much does the coat cost, including a 6% sales tax?

$A = 50(1 - 0.20)(1 + 0.06)$
$A = 50(0.80)(1.06)$
$A = 42.40$
$\therefore$ The coat cost $42.40

7-6 *Percent Problems*

OBJECTIVE   To solve problems involving percents.

To find the percent of increase or percent of decrease in a price, measurement, or other quantity, find what percent the change is of the original quantity.

EXAMPLE 1

Arthur Singleton paid $275 per month in rent last year. This year his rent was increased to $286 per month. Find the percent of increase.

SOLUTION

Step 1   The problem asks for the percent of increase.

Step 2   Let $x\%$ = percent of increase.

Step 3   The increase is $286 - 275$, or 11.

11 is what percent of 275?

$$11 = \frac{x}{100} \cdot 275$$

Step 4
$$1100 = 275x$$
$$4 = x$$

Step 5   The check is left to you.

$\therefore$ the percent of increase is 4%.   *Answer*

A discount is an amount that is subtracted from the price of an item to create a new, lower selling price. A 20% discount on an $80 vacuum cleaner is $16; the new selling price is then $80 - 16$, or $64.

EXAMPLE 2

Betty pays $46.75 for an electronic game which is on sale at a 15% discount. What was the original price of the game?

SOLUTION

Step 1   The problem asks for the original price of the game.

Step 2   Let x = original price in dollars.

Step 3   Since the discount is 15%,
the selling price ($46.75) is 85% of the original price.

$$46.75 = \frac{85}{100} \cdot x$$

Step 4
$$4675 = 85x$$
$$55 = x$$

Step 5   The check is left to you.

$\therefore$ the original price was $55.   *Answer*

Oral Exercises

State the amount of the discount and the new selling price.

1. $40 pair of shoes at a 15% discount $6 discount; $34
2. $35 framed picture at a 20% discount $7 discount; $28
3. $150 suit at a 30% discount $45 discount; $105
4. $550 stereo at a 10% discount $55 discount; $495

Problems

Solve.

A
1. Last year 500 people attended the Senior Citizens Club picnic. This year 565 people attended the picnic. Find the percent of increase in attendance. 13%

2. In February the average price of a dozen eggs was $1.05. In May the average price was 84¢. Find the percent of decrease. 20%

3. A motel manager plans to raise by 22% the current rate of $25 for a room. What will be the new rate for a room? $30.50

4. A $180 pair of skis is on sale at a 25% discount. If there is a 5% sales tax, how much do the skis cost in all? $141.75

5. The list price of a camera is $150, but a discount of $7.50 is given if you pay cash. What is the percent of discount? 5%

6. At the close of one business day, a company's stock was trading at $24 a share. At the close of the next business day, the stock was trading at $27 a share. Find the percent of increase. 12.5%

7. In July a newspaper's circulation increased by 6% to a new high of 132,500 subscribers. What was the newspaper's circulation in June? 125,000 subscribers

8. A real estate broker receives a commission of 3% for selling a house. If the commission on a sale was $1560, what was the selling price of the house? $52,000

9. The Watanabes received $72,000 for their house after a commission of 4% of the selling price had been paid. What was the selling price? $75,000

10. When the United Fund drive in Livonia received $3800, it reached 76% of its goal. What was its goal? $5000

B 11. Shirley Jackson bought some stock valued at $62.50 a share and sold it for $67.50 a share. What was the percent of profit? 8%

12. Three quarters of one percent of the flash bulbs produced by a certain assembly line fail to flash. Of the 1.5 million bulbs produced in one month, about how many will fail to flash? 11,250 bulbs

APPLYING FRACTIONS **257**

Supplementary Material
Practice Master 42

Suggested Assignments
Minimum
  257/P: 1–13 odd
Average
  257/P: 1–13 odd
S 255/P: 12
Maximum
  257/P: 1–13 odd
S 248/31, 32, 34

Extra Practice Problems
  p. 519

Additional A Exercises
Solve.

1. An automobile with a regular price of $6000 is being sold for $5100. Find the percent of the discount. 15%

2. A $200 suit is being sold at a discount of 20%. Find the new selling price of the suit. $160

3. On a certain assembly line one out of every 50 batteries fails to work. What is the percent of failure and if 1500 batteries are produced how many will fail? 2%; 30

4. A real estate agent receives a 6% commission on the selling price of a house. If the house sells for $80,000, what is the agent's commission? $4800

Solve.

13. After two years a car purchased for $6500 has a book value of only $3900. By what percent has its value decreased? Decreased by 40%

14. Two years ago Jason Chen bought an antique dresser for $1500. It is now worth $2070. If the value of the dresser increased by 20% during the first year Jason owned it, by what percent did the value of the dresser increase during the second year? Increased by 15%

Self-Test 3

VOCABULARY   percent (p. 251)

Solve.

1. What percent of 250 is 75?   Obj. 7-5, p. 251
2. 90 is 45% of what number?
3. What is 55% of 20?
4. The price of a car was raised from $5000 to $5450. What was the   Obj. 7-6, p. 256
   percent of increase?
5. Luis bought a jacket at a sale offering 20% off the original price. If the sale price of the jacket was $60, how much was the original price?

Check your answers with those at the back of the book.

Calculator Key-In

If your calculator does not have a percent key, you can divide by 100 when entering percents. For example, you can find 7.5% of 6000 as follows:

$$7.5 \div 100 \times 6000 = 540.$$

1. Find 6.13% of 23,500. 1440.55   2. Find 6.6% of 4400. 290.4
3. Find 10.5% of 6500. 682.5   4. Find 11.84% of 7500. 888
5. Find $8\frac{1}{2}$% of 15,000. 1275   6. Find $\frac{1}{2}$% of 350. 1.75

7. Sue Lee purchased a new car at a sale offering a 15.5% discount off the original price of all new cars. If the original price of the car she bought was $6038 and the sales tax rate was 5.5%, how much did she pay in all? $5382.73

258   *CHAPTER 7*

Quick Quiz

Solve.

1. What percent of 300 is 36? 12%

2. 30 is 20% of what number? 150

3. What is 45% of 60? 27

4. The price of a guitar was raised from $300 to $321. What was the percent of the increase? 7%

5. Fred bought a pair of cross-country skis at a sale offering 15% off the original price. If the sale price of the skis was $68, how much was the original price? $80

MIXTURE AND WORK PROBLEMS

7-7 *Mixture Problems*

OBJECTIVE To solve mixture problems.

A merchant often mixes goods of two or more kinds in order to sell a blend at a given price. Similarly, a chemist often mixes solutions of different strengths of a chemical to obtain a solution of desired strength. Charts can be helpful in solving mixture problems.

EXAMPLE 1

The Green Briar Gourmet Shop sells cashews for $6.00 per kilogram and Brazil nuts for $7.50 per kilogram. The store manager wants to mix the nuts to get 15 kg of a mixture worth $6.50 per kilogram. How many kilograms of each kind of nut does the manager need?

SOLUTION

Step 1 The problem asks for the number of kilograms of cashews and the number of kilograms of Brazil nuts needed.

Step 2 Let x = number of kilograms of cashews.
Then $15 - x$ = number of kilograms of Brazil nuts.

	Number of kilograms $\times$	Price per kilogram $=$	Total cost
Cashew	x	6.00	$6x$
Brazil	$15 - x$	7.50	$7.5(15 - x)$
Mixture	15	6.50	$6.5(15)$

Step 3 Cost of cashews + Cost of Brazil nuts = Cost of mixture
$$6x + 7.5(15 - x) = 6.5(15)$$

Step 4 Multiply both sides of the equation by 10.
$$60x + 75(15 - x) = 65 \cdot 15$$
$$4x + 5(15 - x) = 65$$
$$4x + 75 - 5x = 65$$
$$-x = -10$$
$$x = 10$$

Step 5 The check is left to you.
$\therefore$ The manager needs 10 kg of cashews and 5 kg of Brazil nuts. **Answer**

Teaching Suggestions p. T91

Suggested Extensions p. T91

Chalkboard Examples

1. A certain shade of paint requires the mixer to start with white. An amount of blue which equals 25% of the amount of white must then be added. It is estimated that 10 L of the paint mixture will be needed. How much white paint and how much blue paint will be needed?
   Step 1: The amount of white and blue paint is asked for.
   Step 2: Let x = amount of white paint.

white	blue	total
x	$0.25x$	10

   Step 3: $x + 0.25x = 10$
   Step 4: $1.25x = 10$
   $x = 8$
   Step 5: $8 + (0.25)8 = 10$
   $8 + 2 = 10$
   $\therefore$ Amount of white = 8 L
   amount of blue = $0.25(8) = 2$ L

2. A certain paint mixture sells for $3.40 per liter and contains white and red paint. The white paint is valued at $3 per liter and the red at $4 per liter. If 10 L of this mixture is needed, how much white and red must be used to make it?
   Step 2: Let x = amount of red paint and $10 - x$ = amount of white paint.

   (continued)

No. L	×	$/L	=	cost
red	x	4		$4x$
white	$10 - x$	3		$30 - 3x$
mix	10	3.40		34

Step 3:
$$(4x) + (30 - 3x) = 34$$
Step 4: $x + 30 = 34$
$$x = 4 \text{ (red)}$$
$$10 - x = 6 \text{ (white)}$$
∴ 4 L of red paint and 6 L of white paint are needed.

3. How many kilograms of ore containing 5% gold must be melted down with 8 kg of 2% gold ore to produce a mixture which is 4% gold?
Step 2: Let x = no. kg 5% ore

	No. kg	×	% gold	=	amt. gold
5% ore	x		5%		$0.05x$
2% ore	8		2%		$0.02(8)$
4% ore	$x + 8$		4%		$0.04(x + 8)$

Step 3:
$$0.05x + 0.02(8) = 0.04(x + 8)$$
Step 4:
$$5x + 2(8) = 4(x + 8)$$
$$5x + 16 = 4x + 32$$
$$x = 16$$
∴ The amount needed is 16 kg.

4. How much pure alcohol should be added to 8 g of a 12% solution to produce a 20% solution?
Step 2: Let x = no. grams alcohol

(continued)

EXAMPLE 2

A chemist has 60 g of a solution that is 35% acid. How much water should be added to make a solution that is 20% acid?

SOLUTION

Step 1 The problem asks for the number of grams of water to be added.

Step 2 Let x = number of grams of water to be added.

	Total amount	× % acid =	Amount of acid
Original solution	60	35%	$0.35(60)$
New solution	$60 + x$	20%	$0.20(60 + x)$

Step 3

Acid in original solution = Acid in final solution
$$0.35(60) = 0.20(60 + x)$$

Step 4 Multiply both sides of the equation by 100.
$$35(60) = 20(60 + x)$$
$$35(3) = (60 + x)$$
$$105 = 60 + x$$
$$45 = x$$

Step 5 The check is left to you.
∴ 45 g of water should be added. **Answer**

Oral Exercises

Read each problem. Tell what goes in each blank in the chart. Do not solve the problem.

1. A grocer has two kinds of coffee; one that costs $4.00 per kilogram and another that costs $4.80 per kilogram. How many kilograms of each type of coffee should be mixed in order to have 40 kg of a blend worth $4.50 per kilogram?

	Number of kilograms	× Price per kilogram	= Total cost
Coffee A	x	4.80	? $4.80x$
Coffee B	? $40 - x$	? 4.00	? $4.00(40 - x)$
Mixture	? 40	? 4.50	? $4.50(40)$

2. How many kilograms of water must be added to 5 kg of a 20% salt solution in order to produce a 15% salt solution?

	Number of kilograms	× % salt =	Amount of salt
Original solution	5	20%	_?_ 1
Added water	x	_?_ 0%	_?_ 0x
New solution	_?_ 5 + x	_?_ 15%	_?_

.15(5 + x)

	No. g	×	% alc.	=	amt. alc.
pure	x		100%		1.00x
12% alc	8		12%		0.12(8)
20% alc	$x + 8$		20%		0.20(x + 8)

Step 3:
$x + 0.12(8) = 0.20(x + 8)$
Step 4:
$100x + 12(8) = 20(x + 8)$
$100x + 96 = 20x + 160$
$x = 0.8$
∴ The amount needed is 0.8 g.

Problems

A **1–2.** Solve the problems presented in Oral Exercises 1–2.
  1. Coffee A, 25 kg; Coffee B, 15 kg **2.** $1\frac{2}{3}$, or 1.67, kg of water
Solve.

  3. How many kilograms of pure salt must be added to 5 kg of a 20% salt solution in order to produce a 25% solution? $\frac{1}{3}$, or 0.33, kg

  4. A grocer has two varieties of tea, one that costs $3 per kilogram and another that costs $4 per kilogram. How many kilograms of each should the grocer mix in order to get 20 kg of a mixture worth $3.25 per kilogram? $3 tea, 15 kg; $4 tea, 5 kg

  5. A food processing company produces grated cheese made from two types of cheese. One type of cheese costs $2.90 per kilogram, and the other costs $3.10 per kilogram. How much of each type of cheese went into making 200 kg of cheese worth $2.95 per kilogram? $2.90 cheese, 150 kg; $3.10 cheese, 50 kg

  6. How many kilograms of water must be added to 8 kg of a 50% salt solution in order to produce a 10% salt solution? 32 kg

  7. How many grams of water must be added to 120 g of a 30% iodine solution in order to produce a 20% iodine solution? 60 g

  8. How many kilograms of water must be added to 10 kg of an 80% antifreeze solution in order to produce a 50% solution? 6 kg

  9. Suppose you have 1200 g of a 10% salt solution. How many grams of pure salt must be added to obtain a 20% salt solution? 150 g

  10. How many kilograms of pure alcohol must be added to 20 kg of 80% pure alcohol to produce an 85% pure alcohol? $6\frac{2}{3}$, or 6.67, kg

B **11.** How many kilograms of water must be *evaporated* from 9 kg of a 50% salt solution to produce a 75% salt solution? 3 kg

  12. How many kilograms of water must be evaporated from 60 kg of a 5% salt solution to produce a 25% salt solution? 48 kg

APPLYING FRACTIONS   **261**

Suggested Assignments
Minimum
Day 1: 261/P: 1–11 odd
   R 258/Self-Test 3
Day 2: 262/P: 14, 16, 17, 19
   265/P: 1–3, 5
NOTE: Day 2 of Sec. 7-7 finishes Sec. 7-7 and starts Sec. 7-8

Average
Day 1: 261/P: 1–13 odd, 14
   R 258/Self-Test 3
Day 2: 262/P: 16, 18, 20
   265/P: 1, 2, 4, 5
NOTE: Day 2 of Sec. 7-7 finishes Sec. 7-7 and starts Sec. 7-8

Maximum
   261/P: 1–19 odd, 20, 21
   R 258/Self-Test 3
   S 258/P: 14

Extra Practice Problems
p. 519

Additional A Exercises

Solve. Use a chart if necessary.

1. A hardware store sells large nails for $5.00 per kilogram and small nails for $2.00 per kilogram. The owner wants to mix the nails to get 20 kg of a mixture that would sell for $3.50 per kilogram. How many kilograms of each size nail does the owner need?

   10 kg large nails, 10 kg small nails

2. How many kilograms of antifreeze must be added to 10 kg of a 20% antifreeze solution to produce a 50% solution?   6 kg

Solve.

13. A health food store makes a blend of cereal by mixing oatmeal at $3.60 per kilogram and bran flakes at $4.80 a kilogram. How many kilograms of each should be mixed to obtain 30 kg of cereal worth $4.00 a kilogram? Oatmeal, 20 kg; bran flakes, 10 kg

14. Jack and Louis are making up a snack to take along on a hike. They mix raisins costing $5.00 per kilogram with peanuts costing $3.80 per kilogram. When they finish they will have produced 2 kg of the mixture and spent $8.10. How much of each ingredient did they use? Raisins, $\frac{5}{12}$, or 0.42, kg, peanuts, $1\frac{7}{12}$, or 1.58, kg

15. The Town Players received $1150 by selling 640 tickets to the opening night of their play. If full price tickets were $2.50 and discount tickets for students and senior citizens were $1.00, how many discount tickets were sold? 300 discount tickets

16. In a carnival shooting gallery, you pay a nickel per shot at a very tricky moving target. For every time that you hit the target you are given a dime. If Sheila took 25 shots and lost a quarter, how many times did she hit the target? 10 times

17. There are 100 pennies, nickels, dimes, and quarters mixed together in a jar. Together they are worth $8.36. There are nine more dimes than pennies and five times as many nickels as pennies. How many of each kind of coin are in the jar? 11 pennies, 55 nickels, 20 dimes, 14 quarters

18. Tyrone Smith invests $11,000 in a mixed portfolio of investments including stocks that pay 5% annually, tax-free bonds that pay $8\frac{1}{2}\%$ annually, and a savings certificate that pays 10% annually. Twice as much money is invested in bonds as in stocks, and the annual income from the portfolio is $860. How much money is invested in each type of investment? Stocks, $3000; bonds, $6000; savings, $2000

19. A metallurgist has 40 kg of an alloy that is 65% copper. How many kilograms of a second alloy that is 42% copper should be mixed with the first alloy to get a new alloy that is 50% copper? 75 kg

C 20. a. If 1 kg is simultaneously taken from each container and dumped into the other, what will the resulting alcohol percentage in each container be? I, 18%; II, 82%   **b.** I, 26%; II, 74%
   b. Answer part (a) if 2 kg is taken from each container and dumped into the other.
   c. Guess the answer to part (a) if 3 kg is taken from each container and dumped into the other.

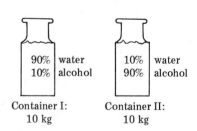

Container I: Container II:
   10 kg   10 kg

21. In one kind of concrete, the ratio of cement to sand by volume is 3:5. In another kind of concrete, the ratio of cement to sand is 4:3. Find the ratio of the volumes of the two kinds of concrete needed to form a new concrete with equal amounts of cement and sand. 4:7

7-8 Work Problems

OBJECTIVE To solve work problems.

The following formula is used to solve work problems.

$$\text{rate} \times \text{time} = \text{work done}$$
$$rt = w$$

Work rates are often expressed in terms of the job to be done. For example, if it takes you 2 days to do a job, then your rate is $\frac{1}{2}$ job per day.

Notice in the following examples that the fractional parts of a job must have a sum of 1.

EXAMPLE 1

It takes you 2 days to paint your garage and it takes your friend 3 days. How long will it take if you both work together?

SOLUTION

Step 1 The problem asks for the number of days it will take if you both work together.

Step 2 Let x = number of days required to do the job together.

	Work rate × Time = Work done		
You	$\frac{1}{2}$	x	$\frac{x}{2}$
Your friend	$\frac{1}{3}$	x	$\frac{x}{3}$

Step 3

$$\begin{array}{ccc} \text{Part of job} \\ \text{you do} \end{array} + \begin{array}{ccc} \text{Part of job} \\ \text{friend does} \end{array} = \text{Whole job}$$

$$\frac{x}{2} \quad + \quad \frac{x}{3} \quad = \quad 1$$

Step 4

$$6\left(\frac{x}{2} + \frac{x}{3}\right) = 6(1)$$
$$3x + 2x = 6$$
$$5x = 6$$
$$x = \frac{6}{5}$$

Step 5 The check is left to you.

$\therefore$ it would take $\frac{6}{5}$, or 1.2, days working together. ***Answer***

Chalkboard Examples

Solve.

1. It would take Nora 3 h to chop down the tree in front of her house. Her younger brother would need 6 h to do the same job. How much time would it take them if they worked together?

Step 2: Let x = no. of hours it took them to do the job together.

Work rate ×Time = Work done		
Nora	$\frac{1}{3}$	x	$\frac{x}{3}$
bro	$\frac{1}{6}$	x	$\frac{x}{6}$

Step 3: $\frac{x}{3} + \frac{x}{6} = 1$

Step 4: $6\left(\frac{x}{3} + \frac{x}{6}\right) = 6(1)$
$$2x + x = 6$$
$$3x = 6$$
$$x = 2$$

$\therefore$ It would take 2 h.

2. Working alone, Sean can cultivate a field in 6 h. If his brother Ian helps him, it will only take 3.5 h to cultivate the field. How long will it take Ian to do the job alone?

Step 2: Let r = no. hours for Ian

Work rate ×Time = Work done		
Sean	$\frac{1}{6}$	3.5	$\frac{1}{6}(3.5)$
Ian	$\frac{1}{r}$	3.5	$\frac{1}{r}(3.5)$

(continued)

Step 3:

$$\frac{1}{6}\left(\frac{7}{2}\right) + \frac{1}{r}\left(\frac{7}{2}\right) = 1$$

Step 4:

$$7r + 42 = 12r$$
$$42 = 5r$$
$$r = \frac{42}{5} = 8\frac{2}{5}$$
$$r = 8h \ 24 \ min$$

∴ Ian worked 8 h 24 min.

3. One pipe can fill a tank in 10 min and another can fill it in 20 min. If the first pipe is open for 5 min before the second is opened, how long will it take them to finish filling the tank?

Step 2: Let x = time to finish

	Work rate	× Time =	Work done
p_1	$\frac{1}{10}$	$x + 5$	$\frac{x+5}{10}$
p_2	$\frac{1}{20}$	x	$\frac{x}{20}$

Step 3: $\dfrac{x+5}{10} + \dfrac{x}{20} = 1$

Step 4: $2(x + 5) + x = 20$
$$3x + 10 = 20$$
$$3x = 10$$
$$x = 3\frac{1}{3}$$

∴ The solution is 3 min 20 s.

4. It would take Sam 6 h to clip the hedges by himself. Dave could do it in 4 h. If they work together for 1 h and Sam then finishes the job by himself, how long will it take to clip the hedges?

Step 2: Let x = time it took to clip the hedges.

(continued)

264

EXAMPLE 2

Working alone, Hal can mow a large lawn in 3 hours, and Kevin can mow it in $4\frac{1}{2}$ hours. Suppose that they work together for 1 hour and then Kevin leaves. How long will it take Hal to finish mowing the lawn?

SOLUTION

Step 1 The problem asks for the number of hours it will take Hal to finish mowing the lawn.

Step 2 Let x = number of hours for Hal to finish mowing the lawn. Then find Kevin's work rate and complete the chart.

Kevin's work rate: $\dfrac{1}{4\frac{1}{2}} = \dfrac{1 \cdot 2}{4\frac{1}{2} \cdot 2} = \dfrac{2}{9}$

	Work rate × Time = Work done		
Hal	$\frac{1}{3}$	$x + 1$	$\frac{1}{3}(x + 1)$
Kevin	$\frac{2}{9}$	1	$\frac{2}{9}$

Step 3

$$\underset{\text{done by Hal}}{\text{Part of job}} + \underset{\text{done by Kevin}}{\text{Part of job}} = \text{Whole job}$$

$$\frac{1}{3}(x + 1) \quad + \quad \frac{2}{9} \quad = \quad 1$$

Step 4
$$3(x + 1) + 2 = 9$$
$$3x + 5 = 9$$
$$3x = 4$$
$$x = \frac{4}{3}$$

Step 5 The check is left to you.

∴ it would take Hal $\frac{4}{3}$ hours, or 1 h 20 min, to finish the job. **Answer**

Oral Exercises

State the work rate.

SAMPLE You can do a job in 5 hours. **SOLUTION** $\frac{1}{5}$ job per hour

1. Heidi can mow the lawn in 2 hours. $\frac{1}{2}$ job per hour
2. Lionel can vacuum his room in 10 minutes. $\frac{1}{10}$ job per minute

3. Will can do the whole job in 3 days. $\frac{1}{3}$ job per day

4. A drain pipe can empty the full tank in 4 hours. $\frac{1}{4}$ job per hour

Complete the chart. Do not solve the problem.

5. Valve A can drain a swimming pool in 3 hours and Valve B can drain it in 4 hours. Find x, the amount of time it will take to drain the pool using both valves.

	Work rate	× Time =	Work done
Valve A	_?_ $\frac{1}{3}$	x	_?_ $\frac{x}{3}$
Valve B	_?_ $\frac{1}{4}$	x	_?_ $\frac{x}{4}$

6. Working alone, it will take Pete 8 hours to wallpaper his room. Working with Bernie, Pete takes only 5 hours to wallpaper the room. Find x, the time it will take Bernie working by himself.

	Work rate	× Time =	Work done
Pete	_?_ $\frac{1}{8}$	5	_?_ $\frac{5}{8}$
Bernie	$\frac{1}{x}$	5	_?_ $\frac{5}{x}$

Problems

A 1–2. Solve the problems stated in Oral Exercises 5–6.

    1. $1\frac{5}{7}$, or 1.71, h   **2.** $13\frac{1}{3}$ h, or 13 h 20 min

Solve.

3. Working alone, Valerie can paint the house in 3 days and Lina can paint it in 4 days. Suppose that Valerie works alone for two days and then is joined by Lina. Find the time it will take the two of them to finish painting the house. $\frac{4}{7}$, or 0.57, day

4. It takes Chuck 5 hours to split a cord of wood, and it takes his sister 3 hours. How long will it take them working together? $1\frac{7}{8}$, or 1.875, h

5. Paula estimates it will take her 4 hours to type a report but only 3 hours for her brother to do it. If they both type at the same time, how long will it take? $1\frac{5}{7}$, or 1.71, h

6. Ben thinks it will take him 6 hours to replant the window boxes for his apartment, and Rachel thinks it will take her 4 hours. How long will it take them working together? 2.4 h, or 2 h 24 min

	Work rate	×Time=	Work done
Sam	$\frac{1}{6}$	x	$\frac{x}{6}$
Dave	$\frac{1}{4}$	1	$\frac{1}{4}$

Step 3: $\frac{x}{6} + \frac{1}{4} = 1$

Step 4: $4x + 6 = 24$

            $4x = 18$

              $x = 4.5$

∴ It took 4.5 h to clip the hedges.

Supplementary Materials

Practice Master 43

Progress Test 25

Suggested Assignments

Minimum

NOTE: Day 2 of Sec. 7-7 finishes Sec. 7-7 and starts Sec. 7-8

  266/P: 7, 11–13
R 268/Self-Test 4
S 266/16, 17

Average

NOTE: Day 2 of Sec. 7-7 finishes Sec. 7-7 and starts Sec. 7-8

  266/P: 8, 9, 11, 12, 16, 17, 19
R 268/Self-Test 4

Maximum
  265/P: 1–19 odd
R 268/Self-Test 4

Additional A Exercises

Solve. Use a chart if necessary.

1. One pipe can fill a gasoline storage tank in 15 h, while a second pipe can fill the same tank in 10 h. How long would it take both pipes together to fill the tank? 6 h

(continued)

2. A work crew can pave a certain road in 12 d. Another crew can do the same job in 8 d. How many days will it take the two crews to pave the road if they work together? 4.8 d

Solve.

7. The main engine of a rocket fired alone can burn all the fuel in 50 seconds. The secondary engine fired alone can burn all the fuel in 80 seconds. How long can both engines be fired together before all the fuel is consumed? $30\frac{10}{13}$, or 30.77, s

8. A pump can fill a reservoir tank in 25 minutes. A second pump takes twice as long. How long will it take to fill the tank using both pumps? $16\frac{2}{3}$ min, or 16 min 40s

9. A heater takes 20 minutes to heat a room from 10° to 20°C. If a second heater is also used, it takes only 12 minutes. How long will it take the second heater working alone to produce this temperature change? 30 min

10. Nancy takes an hour and a half to rake the lawn, but it takes her only 40 minutes if her sister rakes, too. How long does it take her sister to rake the lawn alone? 1.2 h, or 1 h 12 min

11. One pipe can fill a tank in 15 minutes. If a second pipe is also used, the tank can be filled in 9 minutes. How long will it take the second pipe, by itself, to fill the tank? 22.5 min

12. A battery can operate one radio receiver for four times as long as it can operate another radio receiver. If both receivers are operated together, the battery will last 16 hours. How long will the battery operate each receiver alone? 20 h and 80 h

B 13. Lance can do a job in 30 minutes, Bob in 40 minutes, and Sid in 50 minutes. How long will it take them if they all work together? $12\frac{36}{47}$, or 12.766, min

14. Lou can plow a field in 5 hours using a tractor, and Verna can plow the field in 6 hours using a tractor. After plowing for 2 hours, Lou is joined by Verna. How long will it take them to finish plowing the field? $1\frac{7}{11}$, or 1.64, h

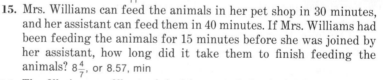

15. Mrs. Williams can feed the animals in her pet shop in 30 minutes, and her assistant can feed them in 40 minutes. If Mrs. Williams had been feeding the animals for 15 minutes before she was joined by her assistant, how long did it take them to finish feeding the animals? $8\frac{4}{7}$, or 8.57, min

16. The fill pipe can fill a tank in 3 hours and the drain pipe can drain the tank in 1 hour. If both pipes are accidentally opened, how long will it take to empty a tank filled with water? 1.5 h

17. Dan and Val addressed all the invitations to the sophomore party in 2 hours. If Dan can write three invitations in the time it takes Val to write two, how long would it have taken Val to address all the invitations by herself? 5 h

18. John can type twice as fast as Mitch. Together they can type a report in 30 minutes. How long will it take Mitch by himself? 90 min

C **19.** Ethan can do a job in 15 hours and Robin can do it in 18 hours. Ethan works for 6 hours alone and then works with Robin for three more hours before quitting. How long does it take Robin to finish the job? 4.2 h, or 4 h 12 min

20. A pump can fill an oil tank in 18 hours. Beginning with an empty tank, the pump and a second pump fill $\frac{3}{5}$ of the tank in 6 hours. If the first pump is then shut off, how long will it take the second pump to finish filling the tank? 9 h

Career Note Bilingual Math Teacher

Cuarenta y dos obreros construyen en 32 días 1320 m de un camino. ¿Qué longitud construirán 28 obreros en 17 días, trabajando en las mismas condiciones?

Algebra teachers who have Spanish-speaking students in their classes, might assign this problem as homework. Here is a translation.

Forty-two workers construct 1320 m of road in 32 days. How many meters will 28 workers construct in 17 days, working under the same conditions?

Can you follow the solution below?

Solución:	1°	42 obr.	1320 m
		1 obr.	$\frac{1320 \text{ m}}{42}$
		28 obr.	$\frac{1320 \text{ m} \times 28}{42} = 880 \text{ m}$
	2°	32 días	880 m
		1 día	$\frac{880 \text{ m}}{32}$
		17 días	$\frac{880 \text{ m} \times 17}{32} = 467,50 \text{ m}$

Bilingual mathematics teachers must be certified to teach in public schools. For certification a bachelor's degree in mathematics and courses in education are required. In addition, bilingual teachers must be fluent in two languages.

Quick Quiz

Solve.

1. An iced tea-lemonade mixture is 10% lemonade. How much iced tea must be added to 250 mL of the mixture to produce a new mixture that is 4% lemonade? 375 mL

2. It takes Jenny 30 min to trim the hedges with her electric clippers. It would take her brother 2 h to do it with the old manual clippers. How long would it take if they worked together? 24 min

3. Sam can vacuum the house in 2 h and John can do it in 4 h. One day they worked together for 1 h. John left at that point and Sam finished by himself. How long did the job take to finish? 0.5 h or 30 min

Self-Test 4

Solve.

1. How much water must be added to 20 kg of a 70% antifreeze solution to produce a 50% antifreeze solution?   Obj. 7-7, p. 259

2. A test engineer has 200 kg of gasohol that is 10% alcohol. How much alcohol must the engineer add to produce a mixture that is 20% alcohol?

3. John can wash the windows in 40 minutes. Sue can wash the windows in 1 hour. How long will it take them if they work together?   Obj. 7-8, p. 263

4. Nate can mow the lawn in 6 hours. Jane can mow the lawn in 4 hours. Jane mows the lawn for 1 hour and then is joined by Nate. How long will it take them to finish mowing the lawn?

Check your answers with those at the back of the book.

Application Gear Ratios

The *crank wheel* on a bicycle has 48 teeth. When the bicycle's *free wheel* with 24 teeth is engaged, the *gear ratio* is said to be 48:24, or 2:1. Shifting to the free wheel with 30 teeth changes the gear ratio to 48:30, or 1.6:1.

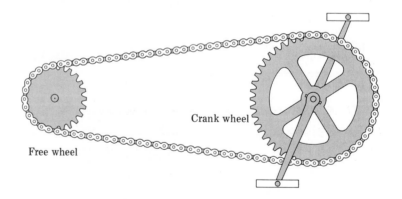

Crank wheel

Free wheel

1. Which gear ratio, 2:1 or 1.6:1, makes it easier to pedal uphill? 1.6:1

2. Find out about the gear ratios in a 10-speed bicycle and in an automobile.

268   *CHAPTER 7*

Chapter Summary ────────────────

1. A *ratio* of two numbers is their quotient. The ratio 6 to 8 can be written as $6:8$ or more simply as $3:4$ or $\frac{3}{4}$ or 0.75. If you are told that the ratio of two numbers is $5:7$, you can represent the numbers as $5x$ and $7x$.

2. A *proportion* is an equation stating that two ratios are equal. Usually the first step in solving a proportion is to equate the product of the means and the product of the extremes. Thus,

$$\text{if } \frac{a}{b} = \frac{c}{d}, \text{ then } ad = bc.$$

3. You can solve equations with fractional coefficients and *fractional equations* by multiplying each term of the equation by the LCD. This step will eliminate all fractions. Similarly, you can eliminate decimals from an equation by multiplying each term by a suitable power of 10.

4. *Percent* means hundredths. Three basic operations with percents are finding a percent of a number, finding what percent one number is of another, and finding a number when a percent of the number is known (see the examples on pages 251-252).

5. When solving word problems involving percents, it is often convenient to express the percent as a decimal. For example:

$$7\tfrac{1}{2}\% = 7.5\% = 0.075$$

6. To solve certain word problems, you need to choose the formula that applies to the problem. For example:

$$\text{Interest} = \text{Principal} \times \text{rate}$$
$$\text{Cost} = \text{Number of kilograms} \times \text{price per kilogram}$$
$$\text{Amount of Salt} = \text{Amount of mixture} \times \%\text{ salt}$$
$$\text{Amount of Work} = \text{Number of hours worked} \times \text{hourly rate}$$

Once you have chosen the appropriate formula, you can use it to make a chart that will help you solve the problem.

Chapter Review ────────────────

1. State the ratio of $4 to 75 cents in simplest form.   7-1

   a. $4:75$ **b.** $75:4$ **c.** $3:16$ **(d.)** $16:3$

2. Two numbers are in the ratio of $5:3$ and their sum is 72. Find the smaller number.

   a. 8   **b.** 9   **(c.)** 27   **d.** 45

3. A pile of nickels and quarters is worth $4.40. There are two more quarters than nickels. How many coins are there?

   a. 13   **b.** 15   **(c.)** 28   **d.** 32

APPLYING FRACTIONS   **269**

Supplementary Material

Progress Test 26

Extra Practice p. 502, 517–519

4. Solve for x: $\dfrac{35}{16} = \dfrac{21x}{32}$

7-2

(a.) $\dfrac{10}{3}$ **b.** $\dfrac{16}{3}$ **c.** $\dfrac{16}{21}$ **d.** $\dfrac{32}{21}$

5. Solve for p: $\dfrac{q}{p} = r$

a. $p = qr$ (b.) $p = \dfrac{q}{r}$ **c.** $p = \dfrac{r}{q}$ **d.** $p = \dfrac{1}{qr}$

6. If 18 grapefruit cost $6.30, how much will 24 grapefruit cost?

     a. $.35   **b.** $7.20   (c.) $8.40   **d.** $9.60

7. Solve for x: $\dfrac{3x}{4} + \dfrac{x}{6} = \dfrac{11}{3}$

7-3

(a.) 4   **b.** 2   **c.** $\dfrac{1}{4}$ **d.** $\dfrac{1}{2}$

8. Solve for n: $\dfrac{3n-1}{5} - \dfrac{2n-4}{3} = 1$

(a.) 2   **b.** -2 **c.** 38   **d.** -38

9. Three fourths of a number is 6 less than seven eighths of the number. What is the number?

     a. 8   **b.** 16   **c.** 32   (d.) 48

10. Solve for t: $\dfrac{3}{t} + \dfrac{1}{2} = \dfrac{5}{6}$

7-4

     a. 3   **b.** 6   (c.) 9   **d.** 12

11. Solve for x: $\dfrac{2}{x^2-1} = \dfrac{3}{x+1} + \dfrac{1}{x-1}$

(a.) no solutions   **b.** $\{1\}$ **c.** $\{-1\}$ **d.** $\{-1, 1\}$

12. What is 1.5% of 240?

7-5

     a. 0.036   **b.** 0.36   (c.) 3.6   **d.** 36

13. 8% of a number is 120. What is the number?

     a. 9.6   **b.** 960   **c.** 150   (d.) 1500

14. Solve for x: $1.2x - 0.072 = 0.96x$

     a. 0.03   (b.) 0.3   **c.** 3   **d.** 30

15. At a preseason sale, a $180 bicycle was sold for $150. What is the percent of discount?

7-6

     a. 15%   (b.) $16\dfrac{2}{3}\%$ **c.** 18%   **d.** 20%

16. A sporting goods store sells a pair of ice skates for 40% more than they cost the store. How much did the skates cost the store if they were sold to a customer for $70?

     a. $28   **b.** $42   (c.) $50   **d.** $56

17. How many kilograms of water should be mixed with 60 kg of a 30%   7-7
acid solution to make a 10% acid solution?

   a. 20 kg   **b.** 90 kg   (c.) 120 kg   **d.** 180 kg

18. Laura can paint her garage in 12 hours and her sister can do it in 8   7-8
hours. How long would it take them working together?

   (a.) 4 h 48 min   **b.** 5 h   **c.** 5 h 15 min   **d.** 5 h 20 min

Chapter Test ———————————————————

Alternate Test p. T18

State each ratio in simplest form.

1. 48 minutes to 2 hours 2:5   **2.** $2x^2 : 4x$ $x:2$ 7-1

3. Find the ratio of x to y if $9x - 6y = 0$. 2:3

4. The ratio of boys to girls in the sophomore class is 7:8. There are
135 sophomores in all. How many are girls? 72 girls

Solve for x.

5. $\dfrac{3}{2x} = \dfrac{7}{4}$ $\frac{6}{7}$ **6.** $\dfrac{3x-5}{4} = \dfrac{5x-11}{6}$ 7   7-2

7. $\dfrac{1}{x} = \dfrac{a}{b}$ $\frac{b}{a}$ **8.** $\dfrac{4}{3}(x-2) - \dfrac{1}{2}(2x+4) = 1$ 17

9. $\dfrac{2x}{3} - \dfrac{x}{5} = \dfrac{1}{10}$ $\frac{3}{14}$ **10.** $\dfrac{x}{2} - \dfrac{5x-3}{4} = 0$ 1   7-3

11. $\dfrac{3}{x+2} + \dfrac{2}{x} = 1$ {4, −1}   **12.** $2x - 8 = 0.04$ 4.02   7-4

13. What is 140% of 30? 42   7-5

14. What percent of 72 is 18? 25%

15. Mrs. Martindale invested part of $6000 at 8% and the rest at 10%.   7-6
Her investments earn $510 in a year. How much is invested at each
rate? $4500 at 8%; $1500 at 10%

16. A car dealer receives a 4% commission on each sale. If the commission for selling a new car was $288, how much did the car cost? $7200

17. A $120 surfboard is on sale for $96. What is the percent of the
discount? 20%

18. Ted has x nickels and $2x$ dimes worth $4.50. Find x. 18

19. How many kilograms of pure salt must be added to 8 kg of a 10%   7-7
salt solution to obtain a 20% salt solution? 1 kg

20. Joy can do a job in 2 hours and Mark can do it in 3 hours. How long   7-8
will it take them if they work together? 1.2 h, or 1 h 12 min

Cumulative Review (Chapters 1–7)

Simplify each expression.

1. $5x - 2y + 3(2y - x)$ **2.** $(-m^2n)^3(-5mn^3)^2$ **3.** $7cd(-d^3 + 2cd^2 + 3c)$

4. $(2r + 3st)^2$ **5.** $(2b^3)^4 \div (4b^2)^3$ **6.** $(6x^4 - 3x^3 + x) \div x^2$

7. $(8w^2 - z)(2w^2 + 3z)$ **8.** $(t^5 - 3m)(t^5 + 3m)$ **9.** $(9g - 5 + h)(g - 4)$

Evaluate if $p = \dfrac{1}{2}$, $q = 8$, $r = 3$, $s = -5$, and $t = -2$.

10. $2(pqs - rt) + 26$ -2 **11.** $r^2q - s \div p^2$ 92 **12.** $7st \div (qt - rs)$ -70

Factor completely if possible. If not possible, write "prime."

13. $3c^2 + 27c - 210$ **14.** $4h^2 - 20hr^2 + 25r^4$ **15.** $2d - 2 - cd^2 + cd$

16. $-81xy^2 + 121x^3$ **17.** $7j^2 + 15jm + 4m^2$ **18.** $-18 + 33v - 9v^2$

Express in simplest form.

19. $\dfrac{700x}{1.4x}$ **20.** $\dfrac{2d^2 + 8d - 10}{4d^2 + 20d}$ **21.** $\dfrac{-40r^3s^2t + 72r^2s^3t}{8r^2s^2t}$

22. $\dfrac{3e^2 - e - 2}{3e^2 + 5e + 2} \cdot \dfrac{e + 1}{2e^2}$ **23.** $\dfrac{2}{(m + 1)^2} - \dfrac{m}{m + 1}$ **24.** $\dfrac{8y^2 - 8z^2}{2y + 2z} \div \dfrac{yz - z^2}{y^2z^2}$

25. $\dfrac{8k^2 + 10k + 2}{8k + 2}$ **26.** $\dfrac{5j^2 - 17j - 40}{j - 5}$ **27.** $\dfrac{3a}{a - b} + \dfrac{2a}{a + b} + 1$

Solve. (The equation may be an identity or have no root.)

28. $-8a + 7 = 3(a - 5)$ 2 **29.** $6(5x - 2) = 12 + 30x$ No root   **30.** $2k + 5 = 0.3k + 0.41$ -2.7

31. $t(2t - 9) = -7$ $\left\{1, \frac{7}{2}\right\}$ **32.** $m^2 - 14m = 32$ $\{16, -2\}$ **33.** $\dfrac{4}{3c - 2} + \dfrac{1}{3c} = \dfrac{1}{c}$ $-\frac{2}{3}$

34. $\dfrac{1}{2} = \dfrac{6z + 2}{9z + 5}$ $\frac{1}{3}$ **35.** $\dfrac{3}{4}n - 8 = 2n - \dfrac{1}{2}$ -6 **36.** $\dfrac{3w - 2}{w - 3} + \dfrac{16}{w + 6} = 10$ $\left\{-4, \frac{30}{7}\right\}$

Solve.

37. A copying machine can duplicate a report 50 times in 55 min. An older model takes 70 min. How long would it take the machines to do the job working together? 30.8 min

38. How many liters of water must be added to 5 L of a 24% dextrose solution to produce a 16% solution? 2.5 L

39. A company invested its profits in an account paying $9\frac{1}{2}\%$. If the money had been invested at 9%, the annual interest would have been $30 less. Find the amount invested. $6000

Maintaining Skills

Simplify.

SAMPLE 1 $3(x + 5y) - 2(-x + y) = 3x + 15y + 2x - 2y = 5x + 13y$

1. $-m^2 + 3 - 5m + m^2 + m - 9$
2. $12t + 4s - 13 + 2s - 9t - 4$
3. $-5(x - 2y) + 3x - y$
4. $-(j - 2k - 3) + 4(2j + 7)$
5. $2(w + 3z) - 3(w + 2z)$
6. $-7(-3r^2 - 1) + 9(2r - 5r^2)$
7. $\frac{1}{4}(-12h^2 + 8h) - \frac{1}{2}(6h - 4)$
8. $-\frac{2}{3}(18d + 12e) - 5(2e - d)$

SAMPLE 2 $(-3b^2c^3)(2abc^2) = (-3 \cdot 2)(a)(b^2 \cdot b)(c^3 \cdot c^2) = -6ab^3c^5$

9. $(-7x^2yz^4)(-2x^3y^2z)$ $14x^5y^3z^5$
10. $(2m^2n)(-m^3p)(-3n^2p^2)$ $6m^5n^3p^3$
11. $3t^n \cdot t^2 \cdot 8t^n$ $24t^{2n+2}$
12. $(-2b)(4b^4) + (13b^3)(b^2)$ $5b^5$

SAMPLE 3 $(-5rs^3)^2 = (-5)^2(r^2)(s^3)^2 = 25r^2s^6$

13. $6c^2(-3c^4)^2$ $54c^{10}$
14. $(5t)^2(-2t^3)^3$ $-200t^{11}$
15. $(2m^2n)^2(-mn^2)^3$ $-4m^7n^8$
16. $2rs^2(-r^3s^2)^3 + (-3r^5s^4)^2$ $7r^{10}s^8$
17. $c(2cd^2)^6 - c^3d^4(-cd^2)^4$ $63c^7d^{12}$

Multiply.

SAMPLE 4 $2t^3u(u^2 + 4tu - 5t^2) = 2t^3u^3 + 8t^4u^2 - 10t^5u$

18. $2r(-9r^5 + 7r^3 + 12)$
19. $-8b^3(-3b^2 + b - 6)$
20. $-3m(m^4 - 6m^2t + 9t^2)$
21. $7pq(-2p^2q^3 + pq^4 - 5q^5)$
22. $5j^4k^3(3jk - 2j^3k^4 - 7j^5 + 10k^8)$

SAMPLE 5 $(3c - d)(2c + 7d) = 3c(2c + 7d) - d(2c + 7d)$
$= 6c^2 + 21cd - 2cd - 7d^2$
$= 6c^2 + 19cd - 7d^2$

23. $(y + 9)(y - 5)$ $y^2 + 4y - 45$
24. $(3v + 2)(v + 1)$ $3v^2 + 5v + 2$
25. $(6k - 7)(k + 4)$ $6k^2 + 17k - 28$
26. $(8b - 3)(8b + 3)$ $64b^2 - 9$
27. $(2g - 3)^2$ $4g^2 - 12g + 9$
28. $(5x + 2)(3x + 2)$ $15x^2 + 16x + 4$
29. $(r - 5)(2r^2 - r - 9)$ $2r^3 - 11r^2 - 4r + 45$
30. $(z^3 + 1)(z^3 - 1)$ $z^6 - 1$

APPLYING FRACTIONS   **273**

The speed of sea gulls relative to the ground depends on their air speed and the speed of the wind. Such relations can be described using systems of equations in more than one variable.

274

8

LINEAR EQUATIONS AND SYSTEMS

Teaching References

Lesson Commentary,
    pp. T92–T95

Assignment Guide,
    pp. T55–T58

Supplementary Materials

    Practice Masters 44–50
    Progress Tests 27–30
    Computer Activities
    22 *Equations and Ordered
        Pairs*
    23 *Solving Two Equations
        Graphically*
    24 *Systems of Linear
        Equations*

Extra Practice, pp. 503–504,
    520–521

Alternate Test and Review,
    pp. T19, T27–T29

USING TWO VARIABLES

8-1 *Coordinates in a Plane*

OBJECTIVE To graph ordered pairs of numbers in a coordinate plane.

In Section 2-1 you learned to graph a number as a point on a number line. An *ordered pair* of numbers such as $(2, -3)$ can be graphed as a point in a plane. You can construct a "number plane" as follows:

1. Draw a horizontal number line, called the **horizontal axis.**
2. Draw a second number line intersecting the first at right angles so that both number lines have the same zero point, or **origin** (O). The second number line is called the **vertical axis.**
3. Indicate the positive direction on each axis by an arrowhead. The positive direction is usually to the right on the horizontal axis and upward on the vertical axis, as shown in the first diagram.

It is convenient to draw the axes on squared paper, using the length of the side of a square as the unit of each axis. The axes separate the plane into four regions, called **quadrants,** numbered as shown.

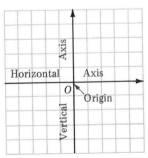
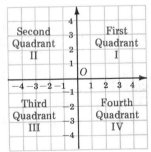

275

275

To locate the graph of the ordered pair $(2, -3)$:

1. Find the graph of 2 on the horizontal axis.
2. Find the graph of −3 on the vertical axis.
3. Think of a vertical line through the graph of 2 and a horizontal line through the graph of −3. Draw a dot at the point where these lines intersect. This point is the **graph of (2, −3).**

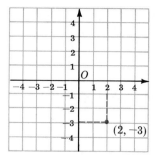

Locating a point in this way is called *plotting* the point. If you label the graph of $(2, -3)$ with the letter P, you can also refer to the point as $P(2, -3)$.

To find the ordered pair of numbers corresponding to point B shown at the right:

1. Think of a vertical line through point B. The coordinate (page 30) of the point where this line meets the horizontal axis is called the **abscissa** of B, namely −3.
2. Think of a horizontal line through B. The coordinate of the point where this line meets the vertical axis is called the **ordinate** of B, namely 4.

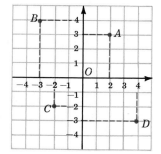

Together, the abscissa and the ordinate of B are called the **coordinates** of B. The coordinates are written as an ordered pair with the abscissa first, $(-3, 4)$. Verify the coordinates of the other points labeled in the diagram above:

$$A(2, 3) \qquad C(-2, -2) \qquad D(4, -3) \qquad O(0, 0)$$

Notice that

in the *first quadrant*, both coordinates are positive;
in the *second quadrant*, the abscissa is negative but the ordinate is positive;
in the *third quadrant*, both coordinates are negative;
in the *fourth quadrant*, the abscissa is positive but the ordinate is negative.

Points on the axes are not considered to be in any quadrant.

When a coordinate system is set up on a plane as shown in this section, the axes are called **coordinate axes** and the plane is called a **coordinate plane.** In working with a coordinate plane, you take the following facts for granted:

1. Each ordered pair of real numbers is paired with exactly one point in the coordinate plane.
2. Each point in the coordinate plane is paired with exactly one ordered pair of real numbers.

Oral Exercises

Exercises 1-44 refer to the diagram below.

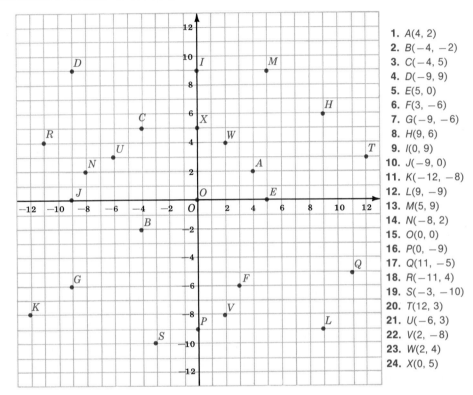

1. A(4, 2)
2. B(−4, −2)
3. C(−4, 5)
4. D(−9, 9)
5. E(5, 0)
6. F(3, −6)
7. G(−9, −6)
8. H(9, 6)
9. I(0, 9)
10. J(−9, 0)
11. K(−12, −8)
12. L(9, −9)
13. M(5, 9)
14. N(−8, 2)
15. O(0, 0)
16. P(0, −9)
17. Q(11, −5)
18. R(−11, 4)
19. S(−3, −10)
20. T(12, 3)
21. U(−6, 3)
22. V(2, −8)
23. W(2, 4)
24. X(0, 5)

1-24. State the coordinates of each point named by a letter (A-X).

Name the quadrant in which each point is located.

25. A I	**26.** F IV	**27.** N II	**28.** S III
29. D II	**30.** L IV	**31.** T I	**32.** B III

Name the point that is the graph of each ordered pair.

33. (3, −6) F	**34.** (−6, 3) U	**35.** (−9, 9) D	**36.** (9, −9) L
37. (−8, 2) N	**38.** (2, −8) V	**39.** (4, 2) A	**40.** (2, 4) W
41. (5, 0) E	**42.** (0, 5) X	**43.** (0, 9) I	**44.** (−9, 0) J

LINEAR EQUATIONS AND SYSTEMS   277

4. Draw the graph shown below on the chalkboard. Ask the class to name the coordinates of A, B, C, and D. Then have the students draw a straight line through these four points. Ask them to find the abscissa of any point that lies on the line.

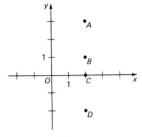

A(2, 3); B(2, 1); C(2, 0); D(2, −2); abscissa: 2

5. Repeat Exercise 4 for the graph shown below. This time, ask the students to name the ordinate of any point that lies on the line through A, B, C, and D.

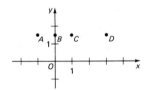

$A\left(-1, 1\frac{1}{2}\right)$, $B\left(0, 1\frac{1}{2}\right)$, $C\left(1, 1\frac{1}{2}\right)$, $D\left(3, 1\frac{1}{2}\right)$

ordinate: $1\frac{1}{2}$

6. Have students name various ordered pairs that satisfy each of the following conditions.
(Answers will vary.)
a. The ordinate is −3.
For example, (5, −3)
b. The abscissa is twice the ordinate.
For example, (8, 4)

Suggested Assignments

Minimum
  278/1–20, 21–31 odd

Average
  278/1–33 odd

Maximum
  278/1–35 odd

Additional A Exercises

Plot the graph of each ordered pair.

1. $A(2, 4)$ 　　 **2.** $B(3, 1)$
3. $C(0, 0)$ 　　 **4.** $D(0,2)$
5. $E(4, 0)$ 　　 **6.** $F(3, 3)$

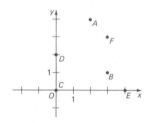

**Additional Answers
Written Exercises**

1–16.

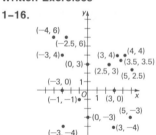

18.

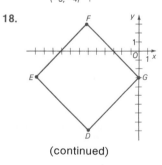

(continued)

Name the quadrants containing each point described, assuming that the points are not on the axes.

45. The abscissa is 2. I or IV 　　 **46.** The ordinate is -6. III or IV
47. The abscissa is -3. II or III 　　 **48.** The ordinate is 4.
49. The ordinate is negative. III or IV 　　 **50.** The abscissa is positive.
51. The ordinate is positive. I or II 　　 **52.** The abscissa is negative.
53. The abscissa is 0.5. I or IV 　　 **54.** The ordinate is -0.2.
55. The ordinate equals the abscissa. I or III
56. The ordinate is the opposite of the abscissa. II or IV

48. I or II
50. I or IV
52. II or III
54. III or IV

Written Exercises

Plot the graph of each ordered pair.

A　**1.** $(-3, 4)$ 　 **2.** $(3, -4)$ 　 **3.** $(-3, -4)$ 　 **4.** $(3, 4)$
　　5. $(0, -3)$ 　 **6.** $(3, 0)$ 　 **7.** $(0, 3)$ 　 **8.** $(-3, 0)$
　　9. $(-1, -1)$ 　 **10.** $(4, 4)$ 　 **11.** $(-4, 6)$ 　 **12.** $(5, -3)$
　　13. $\left(2\frac{1}{2}, 3\right)$ 　 **14.** $(5, 2.5)$ 　 **15.** $(-2.5, 6)$ 　 **16.** $(3.5, 3.5)$

In Exercises 17–20, the coordinates of the vertices of a geometric figure are given. Plot the points and name the geometric figures.

17. $A(2, 5)$ 　　 $B(8, 5)$ 　　 $C(5, -3)$ 　　 Isosceles triangle
18. $D(-6, -9)$ 　 $E(-12, -3)$ 　 $F(-6, 3)$ 　 $G(0, -3)$ Square
19. $H(4, 2)$ 　　 $I(11, 2)$ 　　 $J(11, -2)$ 　 $K(4, -2)$ Rectangle
20. $L(-5, 7)$ 　　 $M(1, 10)$ 　　 $N(1, 6)$ 　　 $P(-5, 3)$
　　　　　　　　　　　　　　　　　　　　　　　　Parallelogram

Use the diagram from the Oral Exercises on page 277 to name the point(s) described.

B　**21.** The ordinate equals the abscissa. O
　　22. The abscissa is the opposite of the ordinate. O, D, L
　　23. The abscissa is 2 more than the ordinate. A
　　24. The abscissa is 2 less than the ordinate. B, W
　　25. The abscissa is half the ordinate. O, W
　　26. The abscissa is twice the ordinate. A, B, O
　　27. The sum of the abscissa and the ordinate is 6. W, A, Q
　　28. The sum of the abscissa and the ordinate is -3. U, F
　　29. The difference between the abscissa and the ordinate is 3. G, H
　　30. The ordinate divided by the abscissa is zero. J, E

278　　*CHAPTER 8*

31. Three vertices of a square are $A(-1, -9)$, $B(3, -1)$, and $C(-5, 3)$. Plot the points. Then find the coordinates of the missing vertex D. $(-9, -5)$

32. Three vertices of a rectangle are $E(2, 8)$, $F(5, 5)$, and $G(-1, -1)$. Plot the points. Then find the coordinates of the missing vertex H. $(-4, 2)$

C 33. Three vertices of a parallelogram are $A(2, 1)$, $B(1, -2)$, and $C(4, -5)$. Plot the points. Then find the coordinates of the missing vertex D if D is in the fourth quadrant. (Two answers) $(5, -2), (3, -8)$

34. Three vertices of a parallelogram are $E(2, 4)$, $F(6, -6)$, and $G(0, -4)$. Plot the points. Then find all possible coordinates of the missing vertex H. Sketch the possible parallelograms. $(8, 2), (4, -14), (-4, 6)$

35. Plot any ten points such that the sum of the coordinates of each point is 10. What do you notice about the points? The points all lie on a line.

Career Note Drafter

In constructing a house, a jet plane, an air conditioner, or a television set, workers follow detailed engineering diagrams made by drafters. These drawings, made from several sides of the object, indicate all dimensions. The drafter prepares these drawings from sketches and specifications obtained from the architect and engineer.

Technical institutes, junior colleges, and vocational schools may offer the training required for a career as a drafter. Courses should be taken in mathematics, the physical sciences, and mechanical drawing.

LINEAR EQUATIONS AND SYSTEMS **279**

8-2 *Equations in Two Variables*

OBJECTIVE To solve equations in two variables over given domains of the variables.

Some equations have only one variable. For example:

$$2x - 7 = -1$$

Any value of x that makes the equation a true statement is a solution of the equation.

Some equations have two variables. For example:

$$2x + 3y = 8$$

Any *combination* of values of x and y that make the equation a true statement is a solution of the equation. For example, you can check that if $x = 1$ and $y = 2$, the preceding equation becomes the true statement

$$2(1) + 3(2) = 2 + 6 = 8.$$

It is customary to write a solution of an equation in the two variables x and y as an ordered pair (x, y), with the value of x written first. Thus, $(1, 2)$ is a solution of $2x + 3y = 8$. Here are a few more solutions of this equation:

$(4, 0)$ is a solution because $2(4) + 3(0) = 8 + 0 = 8.$
$(7, -2)$ is a solution because $2(7) + 3(-2) = 14 - 6 = 8.$
$(-2, 4)$ is a solution because $2(-2) + 3(4) = -4 + 12 = 8.$
$(4, -2)$ is *not* a solution because $2(4) + 3(-2) = 8 - 6 \neq 8.$

Any ordered pair of values that convert an equation in two variables into a true statement is called a **solution** of the equation. The set of all solutions is called the **solution set** of the equation. Finding the solution set is called **solving** the equation.

EXAMPLE Solve $2x + 3y = 6$ if x and y are whole numbers.

SOLUTION

1. Solve the given equation for y in terms of x.

$$2x + 3y = 6$$
$$3y = 6 - 2x$$
$$y = 2 - \tfrac{2}{3}x$$

2. Replace x with successive whole numbers and calculate the corresponding values of y.

3. If the value of y found in Step 2 is a whole number, then the pair of corresponding values is a solution of the equation.

$\therefore$ The solution set is $\{(0, 2), (3, 0)\}$. *Answer*

x	$y = 2 - \tfrac{2}{3}x$	Solution
0	$2 - \tfrac{2}{3}(0) = 2$	$(0, 2)$
1	$2 - \tfrac{2}{3}(1) = 1\tfrac{1}{3}$	No
2	$2 - \tfrac{2}{3}(2) = \tfrac{2}{3}$	No
3	$2 - \tfrac{2}{3}(3) = 0$	$(3, 0)$

Values of x greater than 3 produce negative values of y.

280   CHAPTER 8

Oral Exercises

Assume that x and y represent real numbers. State whether or not each ordered pair of numbers shown is a solution of the given equation.

1. $x + y = 6$; $(4, 3)$, $(1, 5)$ Only (1, 5)
2. $x - 2y = 10$; $(0, -5)$, $(0, 5)$ Only (0, −5)
3. $2x + y = 4$; $(1, 3)$, $(-1, 3)$ Neither
4. $3x + y = 6$; $(1, 3)$, $(2, 0)$ Both
5. $-3x + 2y = 12$; $(0, 6)$, $(-4, 0)$ Both
6. $7x - 5y = -3$; $(4, 5)$, $(-1, -2)$ Neither
7. $y = x^2$; $(2, 4)$, $(4, 2)$ Only (2, 4)
8. $y^2 = 2x$; $(2, -2)$, $(-2, 2)$ Only (2, −2)
9. $x^2 + y^2 = 25$; $(-3, -4)$, $(3, 4)$ Both
10. $x^2 - y^2 = 0$; $(1, -1)$, $(2, 2)$ Both
11. $xy = 4$; $\left(\frac{1}{8}, 2\right)$, $(-2, 2)$ Neither
12. $4x^2 + 9y^2 = 36$; $(-3, 0)$, $(4, 0)$ Only (−3, 0)

Solve each equation for y in terms of x.

13. $x + y = 4$ $y = 4 - x$
14. $x - y = 7$ $y = x - 7$
15. $y - x = -6$ $y = x - 6$
16. $3x = 5 + y$ $y = 3x - 5$
17. $2x = 8 - y$ $y = 8 - 2x$
18. $2x + 2y = 8$ $y = 4 - x$

Written Exercises

Complete each ordered pair to form a solution of the given equation. Assume that x and y represent real numbers.

A

1. $y = x - 3$; $(8, ?)$, $(5, ?)$, $(3, ?)$ 5; 2; 0
2. $y = 2x + 1$; $(2, ?)$ $(-1, ?)$ $(0, ?)$ 5; −1; 1
3. $y = \frac{1}{2}x - 2$; $(4, ?)$, $(2, ?)$, $(0, ?)$ 0; −1; −2
4. $y = 3 - 2x$; $(1, ?)$, $(-1, ?)$, $(-2, ?)$ 1; 5; 7
5. $y = \frac{3}{x + 1}$; $(2, ?)$, $(5, ?)$, $(-4, ?)$ 1; $\frac{1}{2}$; −1
6. $y = \frac{1}{1 - 2x}$; $(0, ?)$, $(-1, ?)$, $(2, ?)$ 1; $\frac{1}{3}$; $\frac{-1}{3}$
7. $x + y = 8$; $(4, ?)$, $(2, ?)$, $(-3, ?)$ 4; 6; 11
8. $2x + y = 12$; $(1, ?)$, $(-1, ?)$, $(0, ?)$ 10; 14; 12
9. $x - y = 4$; $(-1, ?)$, $(0, ?)$, $(3, ?)$ −5; −4; −1
10. $2x - y = -8$; $(0, ?)$, $(3, ?)$, $(-3, ?)$ 8; 14; 2
11. $2x + 3y = 6$; $(3, ?)$, $(-3, ?)$, $(0, ?)$ 0; 4; 2
12. $2x - 3y = 12$; $(0, ?)$, $(1, ?)$, $(-1, ?)$ −4; $\frac{-10}{3}$; $\frac{-14}{3}$

Solve each equation for y in terms of x.

13. $x + y = 6$ $y = 6 - x$
14. $2x + y = 8$ $y = 8 - 2x$
15. $x - y = 6$ $y = x - 6$
16. $y - x = -4$ $y = x - 4$
17. $2x + 3y = 12$ $y = \frac{-2}{3}x + 4$
18. $2x - 3y = 9$ $y = \frac{2}{3}x - 3$

LINEAR EQUATIONS AND SYSTEMS   **281**

Supplementary Material

Computer Activity 22
Equations and Ordered Pairs
  The solution set of an equation in two variables is a set of ordered pairs that lie on the graph of the equation. A computer can quickly determine whether a point is a solution of an equation or it can generate a number of solutions to a particular equation.

Suggested Assignments

Minimum
  281/1–31 odd
  S 278/22–30 even

Average
  281/1–37 odd
  S 278/22–34 even

Maximum
  281/9–39 odd
  S 278/30, 32, 34

Additional A Exercises

Assume x and y represent real numbers. Complete each ordered pair to form a solution of the given equation.

1. $y = x + 4$ $(2, ?)$, $(7, ?)$
   6; 11
2. $y = x - 2$ $(5, ?)$, $(2, ?)$
   3; 0
3. $y = 3x$ $(4, ?)$, $(6, ?)$
   12; 18
4. $y = -5x$ $(2, ?)$, $(4, ?)$
   −10; −20
5. $y = \frac{1}{2}x$ $(6, ?)$, $(8, ?)$

   3; 4
6. $y = \frac{1}{3}x$ $(3, ?)$, $(9, ?)$

   1; 3

Find the solution set of each equation if both x and y are members of $\{-2, -1, 0, 1, 2\}$.

19. $x + y = 1$ **20.** $x - y = 3$ **21.** $x + 2y = -1$

22. $2x + y = 4$ **23.** $3x + y = 5$ **24.** $2x - 3y = -5$

Find the solution set of each equation if both x and y are whole numbers.

B 25. $x + y = 8$ **26.** $x + 2y = 10$

27. $\frac{3}{2}x + y = 5 + x$ **28.** $x + \frac{4}{3}y = y + 10$

Find the solution set of each equation if both x and y are members of $\{0, 1, 2, 3, 4\}$.

29. $y = x^2$ **30.** $y = \frac{1}{2}x^2$ **31.** $y = x^2 - 1$ **32.** $y = x^2 + x$

33. $x^2 + y^2 = 25$ **34.** $xy = 8$ **35.** $x - xy = 4$ **36.** $x - y^2 = 0$

In each exercise, find the ordered pair that is a solution of both equations if x and y are whole numbers.

C 37. $x + y = 5;\ \ x + 2y = 9$ (1, 4)   **38.** $x + 2y = 7;\ \ 2x + y = 8$ (3, 2)

39. $x + y = 8;\ \ x + \frac{1}{2}y = 5$ (2, 6)   **40.** $x + 2y = 7;\ \ x - y = 4$ (5, 1)

ḟistorical ṅote Coordinates

Ancient Egyptians and Romans used the idea of coordinates in land surveying. The Egyptian hieroglyphic for surveyed districts was a grid.

In the seventeenth century, two mathematicians, Pierre de Fermat and René Descartes, used a version of coordinates in their work. The plane coordinate system is sometimes called a rectangular Cartesian coordinate system in honor of Descartes.

282   *CHAPTER 8*

8-3 *The Graph of a Linear Equation in Two Variables*

OBJECTIVE To graph a linear equation in two variables.

To graph the solution set of an equation in x and y, it is customary to take the horizontal axis as the **x-axis** and the vertical axis as the **y-axis.** For ordered pairs represented by (x, y), you may call the abscissa the **x-coordinate** and the ordinate the **y-coordinate.**

When x and y are whole numbers, the equation

$$x + 2y = 6$$

has the solution set $\{(0, 3), (2, 2), (4, 1), (6, 0)\}$. Do you see that the graphs of the solutions, shown at the left below, appear to lie on a straight line?

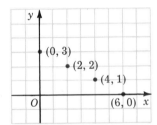
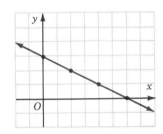

In fact, when x and y are real numbers, each solution of $x + 2y = 6$ gives the coordinates of a point on the line shown above, and the coordinates of each point on the line satisfy the equation. The line is called the **graph of the equation** in the coordinate plane, and the equation is called **an equation of the line.** The equation $x + 2y = 6$ is an example of a *linear equation.*

Any equation which can be written in the form

$$Ax + By = C$$

where A, B, and C are real numbers with A and B not both zero is called a **linear equation in two variables** x and y. If A, B, and C are integers, the equation is said to be in **standard form.**

Note that in a linear equation each term is a constant or a monomial of degree 1.

$x + 2y = 6$, $\quad 3y - \frac{1}{2}x = 3$, and $\quad x = 5$ are linear equations.

$x^2 + 2y = 6$, $\quad 3y - \frac{2}{x} = 3$, and $\quad xy = 5$ are *not* linear equations.

LINEAR EQUATIONS AND SYSTEMS **283**

Chalkboard Examples

1. Which of the following are linear equations?
   a. $4x + 3y = 12$ yes
   b. $y = -7$ yes
   c. $xy + x = 1$ no
   d. $\frac{1}{x} + \frac{2}{y} = 3$ no
   e. $3x = x + 8$ yes
   f. $y = -\frac{2}{3}x + 1$ yes
   g. $y = x(x + 2)$ no

2. Find the coordinates of the points where the graph of $x - 3y = 18$ crosses the x-axis and the y-axis.
   $(18, 0)$ and $(0, -6)$

3. Draw the graphs of:
   a. $2x - y = 2$

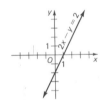

   b. $2y = 3$

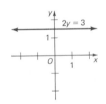

(continued)

4. Graph the following equations in the same coordinate plane.

a. $3x - 2y = 1$
b. $3x - 2y = 6$
c. $3x - 2y = 0$

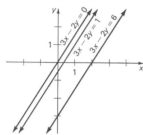

5. Write $y = \frac{1}{2}x - 1$ in standard form, then draw its graph.

$2y = x - 2$
$x - 2y = 2$

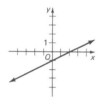

6. Graph the equations $x + 2y = -3$, $3x - y = 5$ on the same set of axes. Name the coordinates of the point where the two lines cross. $(1, -2)$

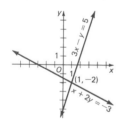

You may take the following facts for granted.

> When the variables represent real numbers:
>
> 1. The graph of every linear equation in two variables is a line in a coordinate plane.
> 2. Every line in a coordinate plane is the graph of a linear equation in two variables.

Throughout the rest of this book you may assume, unless otherwise directed, that both variables in an equation in two variables represent real numbers.

Since two points determine a line, you need to find only two solutions to graph a linear equation. As a check it is good practice to find a third solution. It is often convenient to plot the two points where the graph crosses the x-axis ($y = 0$) and the y-axis ($x = 0$).

EXAMPLE 1 Graph $2x - 3y = 6$ in a coordinate plane.

SOLUTION

Let $y = 0$: $\quad 2x - 3(0) = \quad 6$
$\qquad\qquad\qquad 2x = \quad 6$
$\qquad\qquad\qquad\quad x = \quad 3;\ Solution\ (3, 0)$

Let $x = 0$: $\quad 2(0) - 3y = \quad 6$
$\qquad\qquad\qquad -3y = \quad 6$
$\qquad\qquad\qquad\quad y = -2;\ Solution\ (0, -2)$

A third solution is $(6, 2)$.

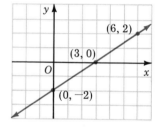

EXAMPLE 2 **a.** Graph $x = 3$ in a coordinate plane.
$\qquad\qquad\qquad$ **b.** Graph $y = -2$ in a coordinate plane.

SOLUTION

a. The equation places no restriction on y. All points with x-coordinate 3 are graphs of solutions. The graph of $x = 3$ is a vertical line.

b. The equation places no restriction on x. All points with y-coordinate -2 are graphs of solutions. The graph of $y = -2$ is a horizontal line.

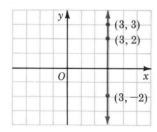

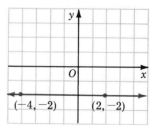

284 CHAPTER 8

Oral Exercises

State whether or not each equation is linear.

1. $x - 2y = 3$ Yes
2. $\frac{1}{3}x + \frac{1}{2}y = 6$ Yes
3. $xy = 8$ No
4. $y = x^2$ No

5. $y - 3x = 0$ Yes
6. $y - \frac{3}{x} = 2$ No
7. $y^2 - 3x = 2$ No
8. $y = 6$ Yes

9. $x = 3$ Yes
10. $\frac{1}{x} = y$ No
11. $\frac{2}{x} + \frac{2}{y} = 6$ No
12. $\frac{x}{2} + \frac{y}{2} = 6$ Yes

Classify each statement as true or false.

13. A standard form of the equation $x - \frac{1}{2}y = 3$ is $2x - y = 6$. True

14. Every equation in two variables x and y is a linear equation. False

15. A horizontal line in a coordinate plane is the graph of a linear equation. True

16. The graph of $x = 0$ is the y-axis. True

17. The graph of $y = -3$ crosses the x-axis at $(-3, 0)$. False

18. The point $(0, 0)$ is in the graph of $x - y = 6$. False

19. The x-coordinate of every solution of $x = 10$ is 10. True

20. The graph of $x + y = 3$ passes through the point $(0, 3)$ and the point $(3, 0)$. True

Written Exercises

Complete the coordinates so that each ordered pair is a solution of the given equation.

A 1. $x + 2y = 8$; $(0, ?)$, $(?, 0)$, $(2, ?)$ 4; 8; 3
2. $2x + y = 6$; $(0, ?)$, $(?, 0)$, $(?, 2)$ 6; 3; 2
3. $x - y = 7$; $(0, ?)$, $(?, 0)$, $(?, 1)$ -7; 7; 8
4. $2x + 3y = 12$; $(0, ?)$, $(?, 0)$, $(3, ?)$ 4; 6; 2

Find the coordinates of the points where the graph of each equation crosses (a) the x-axis and (b) the y-axis.

5. $3x + 4y = 12$
   a. $(4, 0)$ **b.** $(0, 3)$
6. $4x - 3y = 24$
   a. $(6, 0)$ **b.** $(0, -8)$
7. $3x + 4y = 0$
   a. $(0, 0)$ **b.** $(0, 0)$
8. $3x = 4y$
   a. $(0, 0)$ **b.** $(0, 0)$

Graph each equation in a coordinate plane.

9. $x = 5$
10. $y = -2$
11. $x + y = 5$
12. $x - y = 5$

13. $y = x + 1$
14. $y = 2x - 1$
15. $x + 2y = 6$
16. $2x - y = 12$

17. $2x - 3y = -6$
18. $3x + 2y = -6$
19. $2x + 5y = 10$
20. $2x + 5y = -10$

LINEAR EQUATIONS AND SYSTEMS **285**

Supplementary Materials

Practice Master 45

Progress Test 27

Suggested Assignments

Minimum
285/1–31 odd
S 281/14, 16, 18, 28

Average
285/1–31 odd, 35
S 281/18, 28, 34, 36, 39

Maximum
285/1–35 odd
S 282/34–40 even

Additional A Exercises

Complete the coordinates so that each ordered pair is a solution of the given equation.

1. $x + y = 7$ $(2, ?)$, $(7, ?)$
   5; 0
2. $x - y = 3$ $(8, ?)$, $(6, ?)$
   5; 3
3. $x + y = -2$ $(0, ?)$, $(-2, ?)$
   -2; 0

Find the coordinates of the points where the graph of each equation crosses (a) the x-axis and (b) the y-axis.

4. $y = x$
   $(0, 0)$; $(0, 0)$
5. $x + 2y = 2$
   $(2, 0)$; $(0, 1)$
6. $2x + 3y = 6$
   $(3, 0)$; $(0, 2)$

Write each equation in standard form. Then graph the equation.

B **21.** $3 + x = y + 5$ $x - y = 2$ **22.** $2 - y = x - 6$ $x + y = 8$ **23.** $9 - y = 8 - x$ $x - y = -1$

24. $2x - y = 3x + 6$ **25.** $2y - 3 - x = 4x$ **26.** $2y + 5x = 3x - 2$
$x + y = -6$ $5x - 2y = -3$ $x + y = -1$

Graph each pair of equations on the same set of axes. Write the coordinates of the point where the graphs cross, and show that the coordinates satisfy both equations.

27. $x + y = 7$; $x - y = 1$ (4, 3)   **28.** $2x + y = -1$; $x - 2y = -8$ (−2, 3)

29. $4x - y = 14$; $3x + 2y = 5$ (3, −2)   **30.** $2x + 3y = y - x$; $2x - 3 = 2x + y$ (0, 0)

Graph each pair of equations on the same set of axes. How are the lines related to each other?

C **31.** $x + y = 2$; $x + y = 5$ Parallel   **32.** $x - 2y = 6$; $x - 2y = 1$ Parallel

33. $x + 3y = 3$; $2x + 6y = 12$ Parallel   **34.** $x + y = 4$; $x - y = 4$ Perpendicular

35. $2x - y = 6$; $x + 2y = 6$ Perpendicular   **36.** $2x - 3y = 12$; $3x + 2y = 6$ Perpendicular

Self-Test 1

VOCABULARY   horizontal axis (p. 275)   solution of an equation in two
                    origin (p. 275)   variables (p. 280)
                    vertical axis (p. 275) x-axis (p. 283)
                    quadrant (p. 275) y-axis (p. 283)
                    graph of an ordered pair of x-coordinate (p. 283)
                       numbers (p. 276) y-coordinate (p. 283)
                    abscissa (p. 276)   graph of an equation (p. 283)
                    ordinate (p. 276)   equation of a line (p. 283)
                    coordinates (p. 276)   linear equation in two varia-
                    coordinate axes (p. 276)   bles (p. 283)
                    coordinate plane (p. 276)   standard form (p. 283)

Plot the graph of each ordered pair in a coordinate plane.

1. $(2, -2)$ **2.** $(-1, 3)$ Obj. 8-1, p. 275

3. Is $(-2, 0)$ a solution of $x - 2y = 4$ if x and y are real   Obj. 8-2, p. 280
numbers?

4. Find the solution set of $x + y = 3$ if x and y are whole
numbers.

5. Select the equations which are linear.   Obj. 8-3, p. 283
   a. $5x - y = 2$ **b.** $x = 4$ **c.** $3x^2 + y = 2$

6. Graph the equation $y = x + 3$.

Check your answers with those at the back of the book.

286   *CHAPTER 8*

Quick Quiz

1. Plot the graph of each ordered pair in a coordinate plane.
   a. $(0, -2)$ **b.** $(-1, 4)$

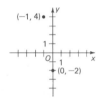

2. Which of the following equations are linear?
   a. $y = -2$ yes

   b. $\dfrac{1}{x} + \dfrac{1}{y} = 3$ no

   c. $x(2x - 1) = 0$ no

3. Determine whether or not $(1, -1)$ is a solution of $2x - 2y = 0$.
   No, $(1, -1)$ is not a solution.

4. Find the solution set of $2x + y = 4$ if x and y are whole numbers.
   $\{(0, 4), (1, 2), (2, 0)\}$

5. Draw the graph of $x - y = 2$.

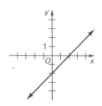

SOLVING SYSTEMS OF LINEAR EQUATIONS

8-4 *The Graphic Method*

OBJECTIVE To use graphs to solve systems of linear equations in two variables.

When two lines cross, or *intersect*, they are called **intersecting lines.** The point where they cross is called the **point of intersection.**

You have learned that the graph of a linear equation in two variables is a straight line. The graphs of the linear equations $x - y = 4$ and $2x + y = 5$ are shown. The coordinates of their point of intersection, $(3, -1)$, satisfy the equations of both lines:

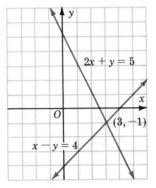

$$\begin{array}{ll} x - y = 4 & 2x + y = 5 \\ 3 - (-1) \overset{?}{=} 4 & 2(3) + (-1) \overset{?}{=} 5 \\ 3 + 1 \overset{?}{=} 4 & 6 - 1 \overset{?}{=} 5 \\ 4 = 4 \;\; \checkmark & 5 = 5 \;\; \checkmark \end{array}$$

No other ordered pair satisfies *both* equations, because no point other than the point $(3, -1)$ lies on *both* graphs.

Two equations in the same variables form a **system of equations** or a **system of simultaneous equations.** A **solution of a system** of two equations in two variables is an ordered pair of numbers that satisfy both equations. The set of all solutions is the **solution set of the system.** Finding the solution set is called *solving the system.*

Not all systems of equations have a solution, and some have more than one solution. The diagram at the right shows the graphs of the equations:

$$x + 3y = 6$$
$$x + 3y = -3$$

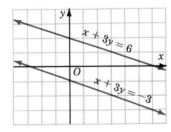

The graphs do not intersect. Lines in the same plane which do not intersect are **parallel lines.** This system has *no solution.*

The second diagram shows the graphs of:

$$x - 2y = 4$$
$$3x - 6y = 12$$

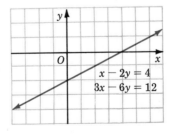

The graphs *coincide.* Every solution of either equation is a solution of the other. The equations are equivalent (divide both sides of the second equation by 3). The coordinates of every point on the line shown form a solution. This system has *an infinite set of solutions.*

LINEAR EQUATIONS AND SYSTEMS **287**

Teaching Suggestions p. T93

Suggested Extensions p. T93

Chalkboard Examples

Solve each system of equations by the graphic method.

1. $3x - y = 8$
$y = 4$
$(4, 4)$

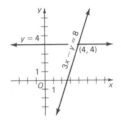

2. $x + 2y = 3$
$2x + 3y = 6$
$(3, 0)$

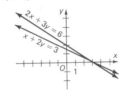

3. $3x - 5y = -6$
$x - \dfrac{5}{3}y = -2$

infinite set of solutions

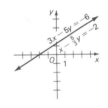

4. $3y + x = 9$
$2x + 6y = 5$
no solution

5. $y = -1$
$x = -3$
$(-3, -1)$

6. $y = \dfrac{2}{3}x + 1$

$x - y = 0$
$(3, 3)$

> ### THE GRAPHIC METHOD
>
> To solve a system of linear equations in two variables, first graph the equations in the same coordinate plane. Then consider:
>
> If the graphs are parallel, the system has no solution.
> If the graphs coincide, the system has an infinite set of solutions.
> If the graphs intersect, the coordinates of the point of intersection form the solution of the system.

Oral Exercises

State the solution of each system.

1. (1, 3)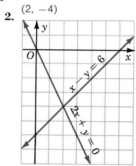

2. (2, −4)

3. (−2, 2)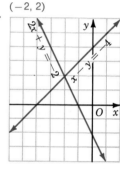

4. (−2, 0)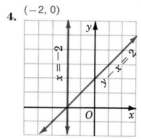

5. (0, 2)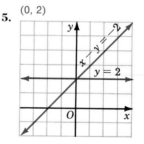

6. (−1, −3)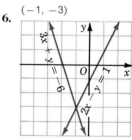

7. Suppose a system of linear equations has no solution. How are the graphs of the equations related? They are parallel lines.

8. Suppose a system of linear equations has at least two solutions. How are the graphs of the equations related? They are the same line.

9. Suppose the graphs of a pair of linear equations *appear* to intersect in the point (2, 1). How can you check whether or not (2, 1) is a solution of the system? Substitute $x = 2$ and $y = 1$ into each equation to see if both resulting statements are true.

288   *CHAPTER 8*

Written Exercises

Determine whether or not the given ordered pair is a solution of the system.

A 1. $(3, -5);$ $x - y = 8$
 $x + y = -2$ Solution

2. $(2, -1);$ $2x + y = 3$ Not a
 $x + 2y = 4$ solution

3. $(0, 0);$ $y = 3x$ Not a
 $x + y = 3$ solution

4. $(5, 2);$ $x - y = 3$
 $2x - 2y = 6$ Solution

Solve each system by the graphic method.

5. $x + y = 8$ (6, 2)
 $x - y = 4$

6. $x - 4y = 1$ (-3, -1)
 $x + y = -4$

7. $y - 2 = 0$ (-3, 2)
 $x + 3 = 0$

8. $2x - 3y = 13$ (2, -3)
 $x - 2y = 8$

9. $3x - y = -8$ (-3, -1)
 $x + 3y = -6$

10. $y = 3x$ (1, 3)
 $x + y = 4$

11. $x + 2y = 4$ (0, 2)
 $x + y = 2$

12. $y = 7 - x$ (5, 2)
 $x - y = 3$

13. $x - 2y = 3$ (-1, -2)
 $2x - 3y = 4$

14. $2x + y = 10$ (4, 2)
 $3x - 2y = 8$

15. $2x + y = 6$ No
 $y = 8 - 2x$ solution

16. $3x - y = 6$ Infinite
 $2y = 6x - 12$ set of
 solutions

Solve each system by the graphic method. Estimate each coordinate of the point of intersection to the nearest integer.

B 17. $x = y$
 $3x + 3y = 2$ (0, 0)

18. $2x - 4y = 5$
 $5x + 12y = 7$ (2, 0)

19. $2x + y = 7$
 $x - 3y = 5$ (4, 0)

20. $8x + 3y = -14$
 $7y - 12x = 21$ (-2, 0)

The solution of each system is $(-2, 3)$. Find the values of A and B.

21. $x + By = -8$
 $Ax + 4y = 6$ $A = 3; B = -2$

22. $2x + By = -16$
 $Ax + 3y = 5$ $A = 2; B = -4$

23. $Ax + 5y = 3$
 $3x + By = 12$ $A = 6; B = 6$

24. $Ax - 7y = -19$
 $3x + By = 9$ $A = -1; B = 5$

C 25. Where on the graph of $x + 3y = 20$ is the x-coordinate equal to the y-coordinate? (5, 5)

26. Where on the graph of $4x + y + 12 = 0$ is the y-coordinate twice the x-coordinate? $(-2, -4)$

27. Find the area of the triangle whose vertices are the points of intersection of the graphs of $2x + y = 5$, $y = x - 4$, and $y = 5$. 27

28. Find the area of the figure whose vertices are the points of intersection of the graphs of $x = 0$, $y = 0$, $x + 3 = 0$, and $y + 5 = 0$. 15

8-5 *The Substitution Method*

OBJECTIVE To use the substitution method to solve systems of linear equations in two variables.

When the solution of a system of equations is an ordered pair of integers, it can usually be found by the graphic method. When the coordinates are fractions, you can use the graphic method to estimate the solution or you can try another method. The following example shows you the *substitution method.*

1. In order to solve each of the following systems of equations by the substitution method, which equation would you solve and for which variable? (Do not solve the system.)

a. $2x + 5y = 7$
$2x - y = 1$
Second equation, for y

b. $3x + 3y = 1$
$3x + 1 = 7$
Second equation, for x

Solve each system by the substitution method.

2. $7x + 3y = 1$
$2x - y = -9$
$2x - y = -9$
$-2x + y = 9$
$y = 2x + 9$
$7x + 3(2x + 7) = 1$
$13x + 27 = 1$
$13x = -26$
$x = -2$
$y = 2(-2) + 9$
$y = 5$
$(-2, 5)$

3. $4y - x = 3$

$y = -\dfrac{3}{2}x$

$y = -\dfrac{3}{2}x$

$4\left(-\dfrac{3}{2}x\right) - x = 3$

$-6x - x = 3$

$-7x = 3$

$x = -\dfrac{3}{7}$

$y = -\dfrac{3}{2}\left(-\dfrac{3}{7}\right)$

$y = \dfrac{9}{14}$

$\left(-\dfrac{3}{7}, \dfrac{9}{14}\right)$

(continued)

EXAMPLE Solve: $x + 4y = 2$
$2x - 7y = -1$

SOLUTION

1. Solve for x in the first equation (since its coefficient is 1).

$x + 4y = 2$
$x = 2 - 4y$

2. Substitute this expression for x in the second equation.

$2x - 7y = -1$
$2(2 - 4y) - 7y = -1$

3. Solve for y.

$4 - 8y - 7y = -1$
$-15y = -5$

$y = \dfrac{1}{3}$

4. Find the corresponding value of x (substitute in the expression in Step 1).

$x = 2 - 4\left(\dfrac{1}{3}\right)$

$x = 2 - \dfrac{4}{3}$

$x = \dfrac{2}{3}$

Check:

$x + 4y = 2$

$\dfrac{2}{3} + 4\left(\dfrac{1}{3}\right) \overset{?}{=} 2$

$\dfrac{2}{3} + \dfrac{4}{3} \overset{?}{=} 2$

$\dfrac{6}{3} \overset{?}{=} 2$

$2 = 2$ ✓

$2x - 7y = -1$

$2\left(\dfrac{2}{3}\right) - 7\left(\dfrac{1}{3}\right) \overset{?}{=} -1$

$\dfrac{4}{3} - \dfrac{7}{3} \overset{?}{=} -1$

$-\dfrac{3}{3} \overset{?}{=} -1$

$-1 = -1$ ✓

∴ the solution is $\left(\dfrac{2}{3}, \dfrac{1}{3}\right)$. *Answer*

The systems $\begin{array}{l} x + 4y = 2 \\ 2x - 7y = -1 \end{array}$ and $\begin{array}{l} x = \dfrac{2}{3} \\ y = \dfrac{1}{3} \end{array}$ have the same solution set, $\left\{\left(\dfrac{2}{3}, \dfrac{1}{3}\right)\right\}$.

Systems of equations having the same solution set are called **equivalent systems.**

The substitution method is used to find an equivalent system whose solution can be seen at a glance. The method is most easily applied when the coefficient of one of the variables is 1 or −1.

The Substitution Method

To solve a system of linear equations in two variables:

1. Solve *one* equation for *one* of the variables.
2. Substitute the resulting expression in the *other* equation.
3. Solve the resulting equation.
4. Find the corresponding value of the first variable.

In solving equations in two variables other than x and y, it is customary to give the coordinates of a solution in alphabetical order of the variables, unless the conditions of a problem indicate otherwise. Thus, if $(2, 3)$ is a solution of an equation in the two variables r and s, then $r = 2$ and $s = 3$.

Oral Exercises

Solve for y in terms of x.

1. $x + y = 1$ $y = 1 - x$ **2.** $x - y = 1$ $y = x - 1$ **3.** $2x + y = -3$ $y = -3 - 2x$

4. $5x + y = 1$ **5.** $4x - y = 6$ **6.** $-2x - y = 8$ $y = -2x - 8$
$y = 1 - 5x$ $y = 4x - 6$

Solve for x in terms of y.

7. $x + y = 4$ $x = 4 - y$ **8.** $x - y = -2$ $x = y - 2$ **9.** $x + 3y = 7$ $x = 7 - 3y$

10. $-x + 8y = 0$ $x = 8y$ **11.** $10y - x = 1$ $x = 10y - 1$ **12.** $-x - 4y = 3$ $x = -4y - 3$

If you plan to solve the following systems by the substitution method, which equation in each pair is the better choice for Step 1?

13. $2x - 3y = 5$ **14.** $5v + u = -17$ **15.** $4a = 3b + 15$
     $x + 3y = -2$ $3u = 4v + 6$ $2b - a = 0$
     The second   The first   The second

State the solution of each system.

16. $x = 3$ (3, 1)   **17.** $y = x - 8$ **18.** $m = -2$ $(-2, -1)$
     $y = x - 2$ $y = 4$ (12, 4) $2n = m$

19. $b = \frac{1}{2}a - 2$ **20.** $y = 2x + 1$ **21.** $s = -5$ $(-17, -5)$
          $x = 3$ (3, 7) $p = 3s - 2$
     $a = 2$ $(2, -1)$

LINEAR EQUATIONS AND SYSTEMS   291

---

4. $2x - y = 5$
   $2y = 4x + 1$
     $2x - y = 5$
   $-2x + y = -5$
        $y = 2x - 5$
   $2(2x - 5) = 4x + 1$
     $4x - 10 = 4x + 1$
       $-10 = 1$
no solution, the lines are parallel

5. $y = -\dfrac{2}{3}x + 1$
   $3y + 2x = 3$
   $3\left(-\dfrac{2}{3}x + 1\right) + 2x = 3$
     $-2x + 3 + 2x = 3$
           $3 = 3$
infinite set of solutions, the lines coincide

6. $x + 2y = 4$
   $x - 3y = -1$
     $x - 3y = -1$
        $x = 3y - 1$
   $3y - 1 + 2y = 4$
     $5y - 1 = 4$
       $5y = 5$
        $y = 1$
       $x = 3 \cdot 1 - 1$
        $x = 2$
      (2, 1)

Supplementary Material

Practice Master 46

Suggested Assignments

Minimum
   292/1–6, 7–21 odd
  S 289/14, 16, 18, 22

Average
   292/1–29 odd
  S 289/16, 20, 24

Maximum
   292/7–29 odd, 30, 31

291

Additional A Exercises

Solve each system by the substitution method.

1. $y = 3$
   $x + y = 11$ (8, 3)

2. $a + b = 17$
   $b = 8$ (9, 8)

3. $r = -4$
   $r - s = -9$ (−4, 5)

4. $4x + y = 21$
   $x = 4$ (4, 5)

5. $2y + 7z = 18$
   $y = 2$ (2, 2)

6. $a = -5$
   $3a - 2b = -8$ (−5, −3)

Written Exercises

Solve each system by the substitution method.

A **1.** $y = 2$ (6, 2)
       $x = 12 - 3y$

2. $b = 3a - 2$
   $a = -3$ (−3, −11)

3. $m = 5$ (5, 1)
   $n = 6 - m$

4. $g = -2$ (−2, 10)
   $2g + h = 6$

5. $2x - y = -5$
   $x = -3$ (−3, −1)

6. $y = 4$ (2, 4)
   $3x - y = 2$

7. $y = x$ (4, 4)
   $2x + 3y = 20$

8. $3a - b = 14$
   $a = 2b - 2$ (6, 4)

9. $2m - 3n = 6$
   $m = 3 - 2n$ (3, 0)

10. $x + y = 4$ (1, 3)
   $2x + 3y = 11$

11. $2a - 3b = -11$
   $a - b = -4$ (−1, 3)

12. $m - 2n = -8$
   $n + m = 4$ (0, 4)

13. $2x + 3y = 4$ (−1, 2)
   $x - 2y = -5$

14. $3a - b = 11$
   $2a + 3b = 0$ (3, −2)

15. $x - 2y = 1$ $\left(\frac{5}{3}, \frac{1}{3}\right)$
   $x + y = 2$

16. $m - 2n = 3$ $\left(2, -\frac{1}{2}\right)$
   $5m + 4n = 8$

17. $2x + 3y = 0$ $\left(-1, \frac{2}{3}\right)$
   $x - 6y = -5$

18. $4a - b = 5$ $\left(\frac{16}{5}, \frac{39}{5}\right)$
   $3a - 2b = -6$

B **19.** $\frac{x}{2} - y = 1$ (−4, −3)
       $x + y = -7$

20. $\frac{a}{5} - b = -4$
   $a - b = 8$ (15, 7)

21. $x - y = -15$ (−10, 5)
   $\frac{1}{5}(x + y) = -1$

22. $\frac{1}{3}(x + y) = 6$
   $x - y = 4$ (11, 7)

23. $\frac{x}{3} + \frac{y}{3} = 2$ (8, −2)
   $2x + 3y = 10$

24. $\frac{x}{2} + \frac{y}{2} = 7$ (20, −6)
   $3x + 2y = 48$

In each exercise, two equivalent systems of linear equations are given. Find the values of A and B.

25. $x + y = 14$ $Ax + y = 30$
   $x - y = 2$ $2x + By = 10$
   $A = 3$; $B = -1$

26. $2x + y = 6$ $x + By = -4$
   $3x - 2y = 2$ $Ax + 3y = 10$
   $A = 2$; $B = -3$

Use the substitution method to solve each system of three equations. Express each solution as an *ordered triple* (x, y, z).

C **27.** $x = 3$
       $y = 2x - 1$ (3, 5, −8)
       $x + y + z = 0$

28. $x = 2y + 11$
   $y = -3$ (5, −3, 2)
   $x - 2y - 3z = 5$

29. $x = y + 1$
   $z = 2y$ (3, 2, 4)
   $x + y + z = 9$

30. $x = 2z - 9$
   $y = z - 1$ (−1, 3, 4)
   $2x + 3y - z = 3$

31. $x = 2z + 14$
   $y = 3z + 15$ (4, 0, −5)
   $2x - 3 = 3y - z$

32. $4y - 2z = 6x - 4y + 73$
   $y = 2 - x$ $\left(4, 6, -\frac{1}{2}\right)$
   $z = -\frac{1}{2}(x + 5)$

292   CHAPTER 8

8-6 *Solving Problems with Two Variables*

OBJECTIVE   To use systems of linear equations in two variables to solve
problems.

You have learned to solve problems using equations in one variable.
Now you can use equations in two variables.

EXAMPLE

Mike and Rose paid a total of $18 for their science
materials. Rose paid $2 more than Mike. How many
dollars did each pay for the materials?

SOLUTION

Step 1   The problem asks for the number of dollars
each paid.

Step 2   Let m = number of dollars Mike paid.
Let r = number of dollars Rose paid.

Step 3 $m + r = 18$ (Total amount paid)
$r - m = 2$ (Difference between amounts paid)

Step 4   Solve the system by the substitution method.

Solve one equation for r: $\qquad\qquad\qquad r = 18 - m$

Substitute in the other: $\qquad (18 - m) - m = 2$
Solve for m: $\qquad\qquad\qquad\quad 18 - 2m = 2$
$$-2m = -16$$
$$m = 8$$

Find the value of r: $\qquad\qquad r = 18 - m = 18 - 8$
$$r = 10$$

Step 5   Check your results in the statement of the problem, *not* in the
equations you wrote. The check is left to you.

$\therefore$ Mike paid $8 and Rose paid $10.   ***Answer***

Oral Exercises

Express each sentence as an equation in m and n.

1. The sum of two numbers m and n is 36. $m + n = 36$
2. Two numbers m and n differ by 12, and m is the greater. $m - n = 12$
3. The sum of m and twice n is 48. $m + 2n = 48$
4. Twice m exceeds n by 36. $2m - n = 36$
5. m is 1.5 greater than n. $m = n + 1.5$

LINEAR EQUATIONS AND SYSTEMS   **293**

Teaching Suggestions p. T94

Suggested Extensions p. T94

Chalkboard Examples

Solve by using a system of
two equations in two variables and the substitution
method.

1. Two numbers differ by 5.
Twice the smaller is 7
more than the larger.
What are the two num-
bers?

Let n = the larger number
m = the smaller number

$n - m = 5$
$2m = n + 7$

$n = m + 5$
$2m = n + 7$

$2m = (m + 5) + 7$
$2m = m + 12$
$m = 12$
$n = 12 + 5 = 17$

The numbers are 12 and
17.

2. A collection of 40 coins
consists of nickels and
quarters only. If the collection is worth $5.20, find
the number of nickels and
the number of quarters in
the collection.

Let n = the number of
nickels
q = the number of
quarters

$n + q = 40$
$5n + 25q = 520$

$n = 40 - q$
$n + 5q = 104$

$(40 - q) + 5q = 104$
$4q = 64$
$q = 16$

There are 16 quarters in
the collection.

(continued)

3. The perimeter of a rectangle is 9 m. Find the length and width of the rectangle if the length is twice the width.

Let l = the length of the rectangle
w = the width of the rectangle

$2l + 2w = 9$
$l = 2w$

$2(2w) + 2w = 9$
$4w + 2w = 9$
$6w = 9$

$w = \dfrac{9}{6} = \dfrac{3}{2} = 1\dfrac{1}{2}$

$l = 2w = 2\left(\dfrac{3}{2}\right) = 3$

The length of the rectangle is 3 m and the width is 1.5 m.

4. A science museum charges two dollars for admission for adults and one dollar for children. On a particular day, 295 tickets were sold and $402 was collected. How many adults and how many children were admitted that day?

Let a = the number of adults admitted
c = the number of children admitted

$a + c = 295$
$2a + c = 402$

$c = 295 - a$

$2a + (295 - a) = 402$
$a + 295 = 402$
$a = 107$

$107 + c = 295$
$c = 188$

107 adults and 188 children were admitted.

Supplementary Materials

Practice Master 47

Progress Test 28

Let s = the number of students at a concert.
Let a = the number of adults at the concert.
Express each sentence as an equation in s and a.

6. The total number of people at the concert is 480. $s + a = 480$

7. The number of students exceeds the number of adults by 320. $s - a = 320$

8. Twice the number of adults equals the number of students. $2a = s$

9. Twice the number of students is the same as four times the number of adults. $2s = 4a$

10. Half the number of students equals the number of adults. $\frac{1}{2}s = a$

Express the given facts as a system of equations in two variables.

11. The sum of two numbers is 75. Their difference is 25. $a + b = 75;\ a - b = 25$

12. One number exceeds another by 14. Their sum is 70. $a - b = 14;\ a + b = 70$

13. The difference between two numbers is 50 and one number is twice the other. $a - b = 50;\ a = 2b$

14. Together, Susan and Jill paid $24 for the radio. Susan paid twice as much as Jill. $s + j = 24;\ s = 2j$

15. George sold twice as many tickets as Michael. They sold 12 tickets in all. $g = 2m;\ g + m = 12$

16. Forty-six trees line the street. There are 14 more oaks than maples. $o + m = 46;\ o - m = 14;$

17. For the fund raising, the students washed 24 more cars than vans. They washed 72 cars and vans in all. $c + v = 72;\ c - v = 24$

18. Lake Massapoag was stocked with 10,000 fish, all bass and trout. If three times as many bass and four times as many trout are used to stock the lake next year, 36,000 fish will be needed. $b + t = 10,000;$ $3b + 4t = 36,000$

Problems

Solve by using a system of two equations in two variables and the substitution method.

A **1.** The sum of two whole numbers is 178. They differ by 6. Find the numbers. 86 and 92

2. One whole number exceeds another by 13. The sum is 109. Find the numbers. 48 and 61

3. Lake Lloyd was stocked with 12,000 perch and trout in all. Twice as many perch as trout were used to stock the lake. How many of each fish were used? 4000 trout; 8000 perch

4. The total volume of a solution in two laboratory tanks is 568 L. If there are 18 more liters in the larger tank, how many liters are in each tank? 275 L in the smaller; 293 L in the larger

294 *CHAPTER 8*

5. Exactly 639 tickets were sold for the school concert. The number of student tickets sold was twice the number of adult tickets sold. How many adult tickets were sold? student tickets? 213; 426

6. The length of a rectangle is 16 cm longer than twice the width. The perimeter is 122 cm. Find the dimensions of the rectangle. 15 cm by 46 cm

7. The prices of the tickets for the local rock concert were $6 for Friday night and $8 for Saturday night. The total attendance for the two nights was 1090. If the total receipts were $7856, how many people attended each night? Friday, 432; Saturday, 658

8. For a part-time job, Jeannie conducted a survey with two questionnaires, Type A and Type B. She chose 500 homes and mailed questionnaires at a cost of 19¢ for Type A and 23¢ for Type B. If the total cost of the mailing was $106.20, how many of each type of questionnaire did she mail? Type A, 220; Type B, 280

B 9. In this winter's bird census, the total number of blue jays and chickadees counted was 1216. Last winter 420 more jays and double the number of chickadees were counted, 2024 in all. How many of each type of bird were counted this winter? 828 blue jays; 388 chickadees

10. One number exceeds a second number by 18, and the sum of twice the greater number and three times the smaller number is 86. What are the two numbers? 10 and 28

11. Dave put up a fence around his rectangular garden. Five times the length increased by three times the width is 103 m, and three times the length decreased by 31 m is equal to the width.
   a. Find the dimensions of the garden. 11 m by 14 m
   b. Find the cost of the fence at $5.60 per meter. $280

12. At the end of the season, the coach took ten students to Burger Box. The coach and three students each ordered steak-on-a-bun while the other students ordered queen-size burgers. The total bill was $15.15. If steak-on-a-bun costs 90¢ more than a queen-size burger, find the cost of one of each. Queen-size burger, $1.05; steak-on-a-bun, $1.95

For each problem, identify the information that is not needed to solve the problem, and then solve the problem. Unneeded information underlined.

C 13. During the week a total of 486 L of gasoline was used by engines A and B of a power launch. Engine A used 74 more liters than engine B. It takes 46 L of gasoline for a round trip to the island. How many liters did each engine use during the week? A, 280 L; B, 206 L

14. The total cost of my car insurance and registration is $360. This cost is $60 more than I planned for. If the cost of the insurance is eight times the cost of registration, find the cost of each.
Registration, $40; insurance, $320

Suggested Assignments

Minimum
   294/*P*: 1–3, 5, 6
S 289/20, 23, 25
Average
   294/*P*: 1–11 odd
S 292/24, 30
Maximum
   294/*P*: 1–13 odd
S 292/32

Additional A Exercises

Solve by using a system of two equations in two variables and the substitution method.

1. The sum of two positive integers is 81. Their difference is 17. Find the integers. 49 and 32

2. A car dealer has 52 cars for sale. There are 18 more economy cars than sports cars. How many of each type of car is for sale?
35 economy cars; 17 sports cars

3. A service station sells 9600 L of gasoline every day. The station sells twice as much unleaded gas as regular gas. How much of each type of gasoline does the station sell each day?
regular: 3200 L; unleaded: 6400 L

Chalkboard Examples

Solve by the addition-or-subtraction method.

1. $x + y = 7$
$x - y = 1$

$x + y = 7$
$\underline{x - y = 1}$
$2x = 8$
$x = 4$
$4 + y = 7$
$y = 3$
$(4, 3)$

2. $3x = 2y - 2$
$y - 3x = 0$

$3x - 2y = -2$
$\underline{-3x + y = 0}$
$-y = -2$
$y = 2$
$2 - 3x = 0$

$3x = 2;\; x = \dfrac{2}{3}$

$\left(\dfrac{2}{3}, 2\right)$

3. $10y = 15x + 17$
$15x - 10y = 50$

$-15x + 10y = 17$
$\underline{15x - 10y = 50}$
$0 = 67$

no solution

4. $4x + y = 4$
$-4(x - 1) = y$

$4x + y = 4$
$\underline{-4x - y = -4}$
$0 = 0$

infinite set of solutions

8-7 *The Addition-or-Subtraction Method*

OBJECTIVE To use addition or subtraction to solve systems of linear
equations in two variables.

The *addition method* of solving a system of two linear equations in two
variables is useful when a term of one equation, other than a constant
term, is the *opposite* of a term of the other equation.

EXAMPLE 1 Solve: $2x - y = 12$
$x + y = 15$

SOLUTION   The terms in the variable y are opposites.

1. Add similar terms of the two equations to
   obtain an equation in x.

   $2x - y = 12$
   $\underline{x + y = 15}$
   $3x = 27$

2. Solve the resulting equation.

   $x = 9$

3. Substitute in either of the original equations
   to find the corresponding value of y.

   $x + y = 15$
   $9 + y = 15$
   $y = 6$

Check: $2x - y = 12$ $x + y = 15$
$2(9) - 6 \overset{?}{=} 12$ $9 + 6 \overset{?}{=} 15$
$12 = 12\;\checkmark$ $15 = 15\;\checkmark$

$\therefore$ the solution is $(9, 6)$. **Answer**

The *subtraction method* is useful when a term of one equation in a
system, other than a constant term, is *the same as* a term of the other
equation.

EXAMPLE 2 Solve: $3t - 4z = -6$
$3t - 2z = 0$

SOLUTION   The terms in the variable t are the same.

1. Subtract similar terms of the two equations
   to obtain an equation in z.

   $3t - 4z = -6$
   $\underline{3t - 2z = 0}$
   $-2z = -6$

2. Solve the resulting equation.

   $z = 3$

3. Substitute in either of the original equations
   to find the corresponding value of t.

   $3t - 4z = -6$
   $3t - 4(3) = -6$
   $3t - 12 = -6$
   $3t = 6$
   $t = 2$

Checking in both of the original equations is left to you.

$\therefore$ the solution is $(2, 3)$. **Answer**

296   *CHAPTER 8*

The *addition-or-subtraction method* is based on the addition property of equality. When a term of one equation in a system has the same absolute value as a term of the other equation, this method can be used to find an equivalent system whose solution can be seen at a glance.

ADDITION-OR-SUBTRACTION METHOD

To solve a system of linear equations in two variables:

1. Eliminate one variable by adding similar terms if two are opposites or by subtracting similar terms if two are the same.
2. Solve the resulting equation for the other variable.
3. Find the corresponding value of the first variable by substitution in either of the original equations.

Written Exercises

A Solve by the addition-or-subtraction method.

1. $x - y = 3$ (5, 2)
$x + y = 7$

2. $a - b = 2$ (2, 0)
$a + b = 2$

3. $m - 2n = 8$ (0, −4)
$m + 2n = -8$

4. $-5 = x - y$ (−3, 2)
$1 = x + 2y$

5. $a - 2b = 0$ (6, 3)
$a + 2b = 12$

6. $3x + y = 8$ (2, 2)
$3x - 2y = 2$

7. $3r - \frac{1}{2}s = 7$ (3, 4)
$2r - \frac{1}{2}s = 4$

8. $1 = -2m + n$ (−1, −1)
$1 = 2m - 3n$

9. $3k + 5m = 20$ (0, 4)
$2k - 5m = -20$

10. $2p - 3q = 5$ $(3, \frac{1}{3})$
$8 = 3p - 3q$

11. $-10 = m - 3n$ (8, 6)
$m + 2n = 20$

12. $2y + x = -7$ (−3, −2)
$3 = x - 3y$

Express each equation in standard form. Then solve by the addition-or-subtraction method.

B **13.** $2(x - y) = 14$ (4, −3)
$x + 2y = -2$

14. $p - 6q = -3$ (3, 1)
$3(p + 2q) = 15$

15. $3(r - 2s) = 6$ (2, 0)
$r + 6s = 2$

16. $3(p - 2q) = 6$ (0, −1)
$2(p + 3q) = -6$

17. $3(4a - 5b) = 27$ (1, −1)
$4(3a + 7b) = -16$

18. $2(4m - 5n) = -10$ (0, 1)
$-5(6m + 2n) = -10$

19. $\frac{1}{2}(a + b) = -1$ (1, −3)
$a - b = 4$

20. $2x + 3y = 2$ (−2, 2)
$\frac{1}{3}(2x - y) = -2$

21. $\frac{1}{3}(x + 9y) = -4$
$x - 3y = 0$ (−3, −1)

22. $a + \frac{b}{3} = -3$ (−4, 3)
$2a - b = -11$

23. $3a - b = 2a - 5$
$3b - a = 5$ (−5, 0)

24. $2(r - s) = 3 + r$
$r = 3s + 4$ (1, −1)

LINEAR EQUATIONS AND SYSTEMS   **297**

Suggested Assignments

Minimum
Day 1: 297/1–8, 9–23 odd
   S 295/P: 7, 9
Day 2: 297/18, 22
   298/P: 1–7 odd

Average
Day 1: 297/1–23 odd
   S 295/P: 12, 14
Day 2: 298/P: 1–7 odd
Maximum
   297/5–23 odd
   298/P: 1, 5, 7
   S 292/10, 12, 14

Extra Practice Problems
p. 520

Additional A Exercises

Solve by the addition-or-subtraction method.

1. $x - y = 7$
$x + y = 5$ (6, −1)

2. $m - n = 2$
$m + n = -2$ (0, −2)

3. $2a - b = 5$
$a + b = 4$ (3, 1)

4. $x - 4y = 10$
$3x + 4y = 14$ (6, −1)

5. $3c - 3d = 9$
$2c + 3d = 1$ (2, −1)

6. $4x + y = -7$
$x - y = -8$ (−3, 5)

Problems

Solve by using a system of two equations in two variables and the addition-or-subtraction method.

A **1.** The sum of two numbers is 170 and their difference is 26. Find the two numbers. 72 and 98

2. There were 200 fans at a game. If the home team's fans outnumbered the visiting team's fans by 96, how many fans were for the home team? 148 fans

3. To fill two cars at a service station required 100 L of gasoline. The second car took 16 L less than the first. How many liters of gasoline did each car take? 1st car, 58 L; 2nd car, 42 L

4. Twice the smaller of two numbers is 1 more than the greater. If they differ by 9, find the two numbers. 10 and 19

5. The Rod and Reel Club members caught 13 fish altogether. If they caught four more bass than twice the number of trout, how many of each kind of fish did they catch? 3 trout; 10 bass

6. The difference between two numbers is 20. The greater exceeds three times the smaller by 10. Find the two numbers. 25 and 5

7. To skate in the Silver Blade Hockey Club, a person must first pay a membership fee and then a fee for each session attended. After attending five sessions, Susan had paid $25 in all. After ten sessions, she has paid $40 in all. What was the membership fee and the fee for each session? Membership, $10; each session, $3

8. Large cans of frozen lemonade sell for 39¢ each and small cans for 20¢ each. Frank bought several cans and paid $2.17. He spent 17¢ less on small cans than on large cans. How many of each size did he buy? 3 large cans; 5 small cans

Application   A Computation Shortcut

Suppose that you are buying 6 articles costing $0.98 each. Can you find the total cost mentally? Use the distributive property for multiplication with respect to subtraction.

$$6(0.98) = 6(1 - 0.02)$$
$$= 6 - 0.12$$
$$= 5.88$$

∴ the items will cost $5.88.

Find each product.

1. 5(2.96) **2.** 4(3.99) **3.** 9(1.98) **4.** 10(5.94) **5.** 7(5.93) **6.** 12(3.99)
  14.8   15.96   17.82   59.40   41.51   47.88

298   *CHAPTER 8*

8-8 *Multiplication with the Addition-or-Subtraction Method*

OBJECTIVE To use multiplication with the addition-or-subtraction method to solve systems of linear equations.

To solve a system such as

$$4x - 6y = 14$$
$$5x + 2y = 8,$$

you cannot apply the addition-or-subtraction method. Neither the terms in x nor the terms in y have the same absolute value. See what happens, however, when you multiply both sides of the second equation by 3:

$$4x - 6y = 14 \longrightarrow 4x - 6y = 14$$
$$3(5x + 2y) = 3(8) \longrightarrow 15x + 6y = 24$$

You now have an equivalent system that can be solved by the addition-or-subtraction method, since the terms in y have the same absolute value.

Sometimes you may need to transform both equations by multiplication before you can apply the addition-or-subtraction method, as shown in Example 1.

EXAMPLE 1 Solve: $2r + 3t = 2$
$\qquad\qquad\qquad\quad 3r - 5t = 22$

SOLUTION

1. Transform both equations by multiplication so that the terms in r are the same.

$$3\,(2r + 3t) = 3\,(2) \longrightarrow 6r + 9t = 6$$
$$2\,(3r - 5t) = 2\,(22) \longrightarrow 6r - 10t = 44$$

2. Subtract similar terms. $\qquad\qquad\qquad\qquad 19t = -38$
3. Solve the resulting equation. $\qquad\qquad\qquad\quad t = -2$

4. Substitute in either of the *original* $\qquad 2r + 3t = 2$
   equations to find the corresponding $\qquad 2r + 3(-2) = 2$
   value of the other variable. $\qquad\qquad\quad\; 2r - 6 = 2$
   $\qquad\qquad\qquad\qquad\qquad\qquad\qquad\qquad\quad 2r = 8$
   $\qquad\qquad\qquad\qquad\qquad\qquad\qquad\qquad\quad\; r = 4$

Checking in *both* of the original equations is left to you.

∴ the solution is $(4, -2)$. ***Answer.***

To solve a system of linear equations involving fractions, it is usually convenient to clear the equations of fractions first, as shown in Example 2.

Chalkboard Examples

Solve by using multiplication with the addition-or-subtraction method.

1. $2x + 5y = 4$
$\qquad -3x + 2y = 13$

$\qquad\quad 6x + 15y = 12$
$\qquad\underline{-6x + 4y = 26}$
$\qquad\qquad\quad 19y = 38$
$\qquad\qquad\qquad y = 2$
$\qquad 2x + 5(2) = 4$
$\qquad 2x + 10 = 4$
$\qquad\qquad 2x = -6$
$\qquad\qquad\; x = -3$
$\qquad\qquad (-3, 2)$

2. $3x + 2y = 2$

$\qquad \dfrac{9}{2}x - 3y = 0$

$\qquad 9x + 6y = 6$
$\qquad\underline{9x - 6y = 0}$
$\qquad\qquad 18x = 6$

$\qquad\qquad\; x = \dfrac{1}{3}$

$\qquad 3\left(\dfrac{1}{3}\right) + 2y = 2$
$\qquad\; 1 + 2y = 2$
$\qquad\qquad\; 2y = 1$

$\qquad\qquad\; y = \dfrac{1}{2}$

$\qquad\quad \left(\dfrac{1}{3}, \dfrac{1}{2}\right)$

3. $2x - y = 1$
$\qquad 3y = 6x + 5$

$\qquad 6x - 3y = 3$
$\qquad\underline{-6x + 3y = 5}$
$\qquad\qquad\quad 0 = 8$

no solution

4. $\dfrac{x}{3} + \dfrac{y}{2} = 2$

$\qquad 4x + 6y = 24$

$\qquad 2x + 3y = 12$
$\qquad\underline{2x + 3y = 12}$
$\qquad\qquad 0 = 0$

infinite set of solutions

(continued)

5. $3x - 7y = 1$
$\ 3y - 7x = 1$

$\ \ 9x - 21y = 3$
$\underline{-49x + 21y = 7}$
$\ -40x = 10$

$$x = \frac{10}{-40} = -\frac{1}{4}$$

$$3\left(-\frac{1}{4}\right) - 7y = 1$$

$$-\frac{3}{4} - 7y = 1$$

$$-7y = \frac{7}{4};\ y = -\frac{1}{4}$$

$$\left(-\frac{1}{4},\ -\frac{1}{4}\right)$$

Supplementary Materials

Practice Master 48

Computer Activity 24
Systems of Linear Equations
  Computers can greatly reduce the work and time needed to solve systems of linear equations algebraically. The program in this activity will solve any system of two equations in two unknowns.

Suggested Assignments

Minimum
Day 1: 301/1–25 odd
  S 298/P: 8
Day 2: 302/P: 1–3, 6
  306/P: 1, 4, 5

Average
Day 1: 301/1–25 odd, 29
  S 298/P: 4, 8
Day 2: 302/P: 1–7 odd
  306/P: 2–5

Maximum
Day 1: 301/1–31 odd
  S 298/P: 6, 8
Day 2: 302/P: 1, 4, 6, 7, 10
  306/P: 4–7, 11

NOTE: Day 2 for all levels
  finishes Sec. 8-8 and
  starts Sec. 8-9.

Extra Practice Problems
  p. 520

EXAMPLE 2 Solve: $\dfrac{x}{3} - \dfrac{y}{2} = 7$

$$\frac{x}{4} + \frac{y}{3} = 1$$

SOLUTION

1. Transform each equation by multiplying by the LCD of its denominators.

$$6\left(\frac{x}{3} - \frac{y}{2}\right) = 6(7) \longrightarrow 2x - 3y = 42$$

$$12\left(\frac{x}{4} + \frac{y}{3}\right) = 12(1) \longrightarrow 3x + 4y = 12$$

2. Transform the resulting equations by multiplication so that the terms in y have the same absolute value.

$$4(2x - 3y) = 4(42) \longrightarrow 8x - 12y = 168$$
$$3(3x + 4y) = 3(12) \longrightarrow \underline{9x + 12y = 36}$$

3. Add similar terms. $17x = 204$
4. Solve the resulting equation. $x = 12$
5. Substitute in either of the original equations to find the corresponding value of y.

$$\frac{x}{3} - \frac{y}{2} = 7$$

$$\frac{12}{3} - \frac{y}{2} = 7$$

$$\frac{-y}{2} = 7 - 4 = 3$$

$$y = -6$$

The check is left to you.

$\therefore$ the solution is $(12, -6)$. *Answer*

  Instead of multiplying by the LCD in the first step of Example 2, you can multiply by 24 in the first equation and by 36 in the second equation. Thus, in one step you can clear of fractions and obtain an equivalent system whose terms in y have the same absolute value.

Oral Exercises

Explain how to use multiplication with the addition-or-subtraction method to solve each system by answering these questions:

a. Which equation(s) will you transform by multiplication?
b. By what number(s) will you multiply?
c. Will you then add or subtract similar terms?

1. $x + 2y = 11$
$\ 5x - y = 11$
Second; 2; add

2. $2a + 3b = 0$
$\ \ a + 5b = 7$
Second; 2; subtract

3. $3r - 8s = 7$
$\ \ r + 2s = -7$
Second; 4; add

300 *CHAPTER 8*

4. $3a + 2b = -12$
$5a - b = -20$
Second; 2; add

5. $2m + 3n = 4$
$3m - n = 6$
Second; 3; add

6. $5x - 3y = 29$
$x - 4y = 16$
Second; 5; subtract

7. $2p + q = -2$
$4p + 3q = -6$
First; 2; subtract

8. $3u - 4v = 1$
$2u + v = -3$
Second; 4; add

9. $x - 2y = 3$
$3x + 5y = -2$
First; 3; subtract

10. $2a + 3b = 12$
$3a + 2b = 13$

11. $3p + 2q = -4$
$2p - 3q = -7$

12. $3x + 4y = 0$
$4x + 3y = 7$

13. $2r - 5s = 15$
$3r - 2s = 6$

14. $3x + 7y = -18$
$5x - 2y = -30$

15. $5m - 2n = 7$
$2m + 7n = -5$

16. $3p + 4q = -2$
$2p - 3q = 10$

17. $4a + 3b = -24$
$5a - 2b = -7$

18. $3r - 2s = 20$
$5r - 6s = 36$

Written Exercises

A **1–18.** Solve each system of equations in the Oral Exercises by using multiplication with the addition-or-subtraction method.

Express each equation in standard form. Then solve by the addition-or-subtraction method.

19. $3a + 2b = 4$ $(2, -1)$
$\frac{1}{3}(2a + b) = 1$

20. $\frac{1}{3}(3a - 2b) = -3 (-3, 0)$
$3(a - b) = -9$

21. $\frac{x}{2} + \frac{y}{3} = -4 (-4, -6)$
$x + y = -10$

22. $4r - 5s = 26 (4, -2)$
$\frac{r}{3} + \frac{s}{5} = \frac{14}{15}$

23. $\frac{x}{6} + \frac{y}{4} = \frac{3}{2} (3, 4)$
$\frac{2x}{3} - \frac{y}{2} = 0$

24. $\frac{m}{15} + \frac{n}{5} = \frac{2}{3} (4, 2)$
$\frac{m}{2} - n = 0$

B **25.** $\frac{x-1}{2} + \frac{y-4}{4} = 2 (5, 4)$
$x + y = 9$

26. $\frac{3m-3}{2} + \frac{2n+5}{3} = 1 (1, -1)$
$2m - n = 3$

27. $\frac{a+1}{3} - \frac{b-3}{6} = 2 (2, -3)$
$3a - b = 9$

28. $\frac{2p+3}{3} - \frac{3q-2}{2} = -2 (3, 4)$
$2p - 3q = -6$

Solve each system of equations by whatever method you prefer. (*Hint:* These equations are not linear in the given variables. Let $\frac{1}{x} = a$ and $\frac{1}{y} = b$.)

C **29.** $\frac{1}{x} + \frac{1}{y} = 1 \left(\frac{1}{2}, -1\right)$
$\frac{3}{x} - \frac{2}{y} = 8$

30. $\frac{2}{x} + \frac{1}{y} = -4 \left(-\frac{1}{3}, \frac{1}{2}\right)$
$\frac{1}{x} - \frac{3}{y} = -9$

31. $\frac{3}{x} + \frac{4}{y} = 1 \left(\frac{1}{3}, -\frac{1}{2}\right)$
$\frac{2}{x} - \frac{2}{y} = 10$

LINEAR EQUATIONS AND SYSTEMS **301**

301

Problems

Solve by using a system of two equations in two variables and whatever method you prefer.

A 1. When the smaller of two numbers is subtracted from the greater, the difference is 14 less than the smaller number. The sum of the two numbers is 1 less than twice the greater number. Find the numbers. 15 and 16

2. Four times the smaller of two numbers is equal to three times the larger. When the larger is doubled, it exceeds their original sum by 5. Find the numbers. 15 and 20

3. The larger of two numbers is 16 more than the smaller. When added together, their sum is 6 less than three times the smaller. What are the numbers? 22 and 38

4. A family has $1200 more invested at 10% than at 8%. They receive $216 more per year from the money invested at the higher rate. How much has been invested at each rate? $6000 at 10%; $4800 at 8%

5. To join a nature study club, you pay a membership fee and monthly dues. At the end of six months, you will have paid $37 to the club. At the end of ten months, $45 will have been paid. What are the monthly dues and the membership fee? Membership, $25; dues, $2

6. The coach took her basketball team out at the end of the season. If five girls have superburgers and three girls have submarine sandwiches, the bill will be $10.00. If three girls have superburgers and five girls have submarines, the cost will be $10.80. Find the cost of each superburger and each submarine sandwich. Superburger, $1.10; Submarine, $1.50

B 7. My mother is four years younger than my father. When they were married, she was five sixths as old as he. How old was each when they were married? Father, 24; mother, 20

8. The Conrads bought a used car and paid $25 for a safety inspection. An engine overhaul cost three fourths of the price of the car. If the price of the car and the inspection together cost $100 more than the cost of the overhaul, find the cost of the overhaul and the price of the car. Car, $300; overhaul, $225

C 9. Creek Farm has 10 more cows than Hill Farm and 20 fewer cows than Dale Farm. If Creek Farm triples its number of cows, it will have 70 less than twice the combined total of cows on Hill and Dale farms. How many cows does Creek Farm have? 50 cows

10. The average of three numbers is 36. The second is 4 more than the first. The third is twice the first. Find the numbers. 26, 30, and 52

302   *CHAPTER 8*

302

Self-Test 2

VOCABULARY intersecting lines (p. 287)
point of intersection (p. 287)
system of simultaneous equations (p. 287)
solution of a system (p. 287)
parallel lines (p. 287)
equivalent systems (p. 291)

1. Solve by the graphic method: $y = -2x + 8$; $-2x + y = -4$ Obj. 8-4, p. 287

2. Solve by the substitution method: $d = 2c + 4$; $3c + d = 9$ Obj. 8-5, p. 290

3. Use a system of two equations in two variables and the substitution method to solve this problem: The perimeter of a rectangular garden is 60 m. The length equals twice the width. Find the length and the width. Obj. 8-6, p. 293

Solve each system by the addition-or-subtraction method.

4. $2x - 3y = -1$; $2x + 5y = 7$ Obj. 8-7, p. 296

5. $2r - 3s = -2$; $3r + 2s = 10$ Obj. 8-8, p. 299

Check your answers with those at the back of the book.

Calculator Key-In

If you used multiplication with the addition-or-subtraction method to solve the following system of linear equations

$$Ax + By = C$$
$$Dx + Ey = F,$$

you would obtain the following expressions for x and y in terms of $A, B, \ldots, F$:

$$x = \frac{CE - BF}{AE - BD} \qquad y = \frac{CD - AF}{BD - AE}$$

When the values of $A, B, \ldots, F$ in such a system are decimal fractions, it is convenient to solve the system by using a calculator to evaluate the expressions for x and y shown above. Use a calculator and this method to solve the following systems.

1. $1.2x + 4.6y = 16.2$ (2, 3)
   $3.1x + 2.1y = 12.5$

2. $2.3x + 1.6y = 14.9$ (3, 5)
   $4.1x + 3.2y = 28.3$

Quick Quiz

1. Solve by the graphic method.
   $x - 2y = 5$
   $x + 3y = 0$ (3, −1)
2. Solve by the substitution method.
   $4x - 3y = 2$
   $x = -2$ (−2, −4)
3. Solve by the addition-or-subtraction method.
   $3m - 4n = 1$
   $2m + 3n = 12$ (3, 2)
4. Solve by using a system of two equations in two variables and whatever method you prefer. The sum of two numbers is 13, and the difference between them is 2. Find the two numbers.
   $5\frac{1}{2}$ and $7\frac{1}{2}$

APPLICATIONS

8-9 *Puzzle Problems*

OBJECTIVE To use systems of equations in two variables to solve puzzle problems.

The technique of organizing given facts of a problem in a chart that you learned in Chapter 4 is also helpful when two variables are used.

EXAMPLE 1 (Age problem)

Five years ago Miguel's age was five years less than twice Rachel's age. In three years, one third of Rachel's age will be twelve years less than Miguel's age. How old are they now?

SOLUTION

Step 1 The problem asks for Miguel's age and Rachel's age now.

Step 2 Let m = Miguel's age now and r = Rachel's age now. Make a chart of the given facts.

Age	now	5 years ago	in 3 years
Miguel	m	$m - 5$	$m + 3$
Rachel	r	$r - 5$	$r + 3$

Step 3 Use the facts of the problem to write two equations.

Five years ago: $\quad m - 5 = 2(r - 5) - 5$

In three years: $\quad \frac{1}{3}(r + 3) = (m + 3) - 12$

Step 4 The equations can be simplified:

$$m - 2r = -10$$
$$3m - r = 30$$

The rest of the solution and the check are left to you. You should find that Miguel is now 14 and Rachel is 12. *Answer*

In the next example, you will use the fact that the value of a two-digit decimal numeral can be written in this general form:

$$10t + u \text{ where } \begin{cases} t \in \{1, 2, 3, 4, 5, 6, 7, 8, 9\} \\ u \in \{0, 1, 2, 3, 4, 5, 6, 7, 8, 9\} \end{cases}$$

Thus, $\quad 85 = 10 \cdot 8 + 5 \quad$ and $\quad 58 = 10 \cdot 5 + 8$

304 *CHAPTER 8*

EXAMPLE 2 (Digit problem)

The sum of the digits in a two-digit number is 12. The new number obtained when the digits are reversed is 24 less than three times the original number. Find the original two-digit number.

SOLUTION

Step 1 The problem asks for the original number.

Step 2 Let t = the tens digit of the original number.
Let u = the units digit of the original number.

	tens	units	value
original number	t	u	$10t + u$
new number	u	t	$10u + t$

Step 3 Use the facts of the problem to write two equations.

Sum of the digits of the original number: $t + u = 12$
Value of the new number: $10u + t = 3(10t + u) - 24$

Steps 4 and 5 are left to you. You should find that $t = 3$ and $u = 9$. Thus the original number is 39. *Answer*

EXAMPLE 3 (Fraction problem)

Twice the numerator of a fraction exceeds the denominator by 2. If 1 is added to both the numerator and the denominator, the resulting fraction is equal to $\frac{2}{3}$. Find the original fraction.

SOLUTION

Step 1 The problem asks for the original fraction.

Step 2 Let n = numerator of the original fraction and d = denominator of original fraction. Then $\frac{n}{d}$ = the original fraction.

Step 3 Use the facts of the problem to write two equations.

$$2n = d + 2$$
$$\frac{n + 1}{d + 1} = \frac{2}{3}$$

Step 4 The equations can be simplified:

$$\begin{array}{c} 2n = d + 2 \\ 3(n + 1) = 2(d + 1) \end{array} \quad \text{or} \quad \begin{array}{c} 2n - d = 2 \\ 3n - 2d = -1 \end{array}$$

The rest of the solution and the check are left to you. You should find that $n = 5$ and $d = 8$. Thus the original fraction is $\frac{5}{8}$. *Answer*

---

3. A two-digit number is six times the sum of its digits. If the digits are reversed, the number is decreased by 9. Find the original number.

Let t = the ten's digit of the original number.
u = the unit's digit of the original number.

$10t + u = 6(t + u)$
$10t + u = 10u + t + 9$

$4t - 5u = 0$
$t - u = 1$

$$\begin{array}{r} 4t - 5u = 0 \\ -5t + 5u = -5 \\ \hline -t = -5 \\ t = 5 \end{array}$$

$5 - u = 1$
$u = 4$

The solution is (5, 4). The number is 54.

4. The numerator of a fraction is three less than the denominator. If 4 is added to the numerator and to the denominator, the resulting fraction is equivalent to $\frac{3}{4}$. Find the original fraction.

Let n = the numerator of the original fraction
d = the denominator of the original fraction

$n = d - 3$

$\frac{n + 4}{d + 4} = \frac{3}{4}$

$n - d = -3$
$4n + 16 = 3d + 12$

$n - d = -3$
$4n - 3d = -4$

$$\begin{array}{r} -3n + 3d = -9 \\ 4n - 3d = -4 \\ \hline n = 5 \end{array}$$

$5 - d = -3$
$d = 8$

(continued)

The solution is (5, 8). The fraction is $\frac{5}{8}$.

5. The numerator of a fraction is four less than the denominator. If 1 is subtracted from the numerator and from the denominator, the resulting fraction is equivalent to $\frac{2}{3}$. Find the original fraction.

Let n = the numerator of the original fraction
d = the denominator of the original fraction

$n = d - 4$

$\dfrac{n-1}{d-1} = \dfrac{2}{3}$

$n - d = -4$
$3n - 3 = 2d - 2$

$\begin{array}{rcr} n - d &=& -4 \\ 3n - 2d &=& 1 \end{array}$

$\begin{array}{rcr} -2n + 2d &=& 8 \\ 3n - 2d &=& 1 \\ \hline n &=& 9 \end{array}$

$9 - d = -4$
$d = 13$

The solution is (9, 13). The fraction is $\frac{9}{13}$.

Suggested Assignments

NOTE: Day 2 of Sec. 8-8 for all levels finishes Sec. 8-8 and starts Sec. 8-9.

Minimum
307/P: 7–9, 13, 15, 21
R 303/Self-Test 2

Average
307/P: 7–15 odd, 19, 22
R 303/Self-Test 2
S 302/P: 9

Maximum
307/P: 13, 14, 16, 20, 21
310/P: 1. 3, 5
R 303/Self-Test 2

NOTE: Sec. 8-9 finishes Sec. 8-9 and starts Sec. 8-10.

Oral Exercises

Let n = Nan's age now and p = Peter's age now. Express the following in terms of n and p.

1. Nan's age in 3 years $n + 3$
2. Peter's age in 3 years $p + 3$
3. Nan's age 4 years ago $n - 4$
4. Peter's age 4 years ago $p - 4$
5. The sum of their ages in 3 years $n + p + 6$
6. The sum of their ages 4 years ago $n + p - 8$

A two-digit number is represented by $10t + u$, where t is the tens digit and u is the units digit. Express the following in terms of t and u.

7. The sum of the digits of the number. $t + u$
8. The new number obtained when the digits are reversed. $10u + t$
9. The new number obtained when the tens digit is increased by 1. $10(t + 1) + u$
10. The new number obtained when the units digit is decreased by 2. $10t + (u - 2)$

A fraction is represented by $\frac{n}{d}$. Express in terms of n and d the new fractions obtained by following the given directions.

11. Increase both the numerator and the denominator by 1. $\frac{n+1}{d+1}$
12. Decrease both the numerator and the denominator by 3. $\frac{n-3}{d-3}$
13. Interchange the numerator and the denominator. $\frac{d}{n}$
14. Increase the numerator by 3 and decrease the denominator by 2. $\frac{n+3}{d-2}$

Problems

Solve by using a system of two equations in two variables.

A 1. Dixie is six years older than her sister. Eight years ago she was four times as old as her sister. How old is each now? Dixie, 16; sister, 10

2. Six years ago Cindy was twice as old as Carole. In six years Carole will be as old as Cindy is now. Find their ages now. Cindy, 18; Carole, 12

3. Joe is three years older than Della. In seven years Joe will be twice as old as Della was five years ago. How old are they now? Joe, 23; Della, 20

4. Five years ago Max was one third as old as his father. In 25 years he will be three fifths as old as his father. Find their ages now. Max, 20; father, 50

5. When someone asked Mary her age and the age of her son, she said, "If you subtract 2 from my age and divide this result by 5, you will have my son's age. But in three years his age will be one fourth of mine." Find their ages now. Mary, 37; son, 7

6. In five years Art will be twice as old as Ben. Five years ago Art was three times as old as Ben. How old is each now? Art, 35; Ben, 15

Solve, assuming that each number is a two-digit number.

7. The sum of the digits of a number is 8. If the digits are reversed, the number is decreased by 54. What is the original number? 71

8. A number is 6 times the sum of its digits. The units digit is 1 less than the tens digit. Find the number. 54

9. The units digit of a number is 4 times the tens digit. If 54 is added to the number, the digits will be interchanged. Find the number. 28

10. The sum of the digits in a number is 15. If the digits are reversed, the number is increased by 27. Find the number. 69

11. The units digit of a number is 1 more than twice the tens digit. If the digits are reversed, the new number is 8 less than 3 times the original number. What is the original number? 13

12. The sum of the digits of a number is 6. The number is diminished by 36 when the digits are reversed. What is the original number? 51

Using two variables, find the original fraction in each exercise.

13. The denominator of a fraction is 7 more than the numerator. If 5 is added to each, the resulting fraction is $\frac{1}{2}$. $\frac{2}{9}$

14. The numerator of a fraction is 3 less than the denominator. If 1 is subtracted from each, the resulting fraction is $\frac{1}{2}$. $\frac{4}{7}$

15. The denominator of a fraction is 1 more than the numerator. If the numerator is decreased by 1, the resulting fraction is $\frac{3}{4}$. $\frac{7}{8}$

16. The numerator of a fraction is $\frac{1}{4}$ the sum of the denominator and 1. If 4 is added to the denominator, the resulting fraction is $\frac{1}{5}$. $\frac{3}{11}$

17. If 1 is subtracted from the numerator of a fraction, the resulting fraction is $\frac{1}{2}$. If 5 is added to the denominator of the original fraction, the resulting fraction is $\frac{1}{3}$. $\frac{3}{4}$

18. The denominator of a fraction is 1 less than twice the numerator. If 1 is subtracted from the denominator, the resulting fraction is $\frac{2}{3}$. $\frac{4}{7}$

Solve by using a system of two equations in two variables.

B 19. Grandmother is three years younger than Grandfather. On their 30th anniversary, she was $\frac{17}{18}$ as old as he. How old were they when they married? Grandmother, 21; Grandfather, 24

20. When simplified, a fraction has the value $\frac{2}{3}$. If the numerator of the original fraction is increased by 11 and the denominator decreased by 1, the new fraction is equal to the reciprocal of the original fraction. Find the original fraction. $\frac{10}{15}$

21. The sum of the digits of a three-digit number is 19. The tens digit is 3 times the hundreds digit and 2 more than the units digit. Find the number. 397

Supplementary Material
Practice Master 49

Extra Practice Problems
p. 520

Additional A Exercises

Solve by using a system of two equations in two variables.

1. Two years ago Katya's age was ten years less than her brother Bob's age. Four years from now Bob will be twice as old as Katya. How old is each now?
Bob is 16, Katya is 6

2. The sum of the digits in a two-digit number is 10. When the digits are reversed the new number obtained is 18 less than the original number. Find the original two-digit number. 64

3. Three times the numerator of a fraction exceeds the denominator by 5. If 5 is added to both the numerator and denominator, the resulting fraction equals $\frac{3}{4}$. Find the original fraction. $\frac{4}{7}$

24. Let h = the hundreds
digit of the original number, t = the tens digit of
the original number, and
u = the units digit of the
original number.
$(100h + 10t + u)$
$- (100u + 10t + h)$
$= 99h - 99u = 99(h - u)$,
which is always divisible
by 99.

25. Let t = the tens digit of
the number, and
u = the units digit of
the number.

Suppose $t + u = 9n$, where
n is a whole number.
Then $10t + u = 9t + t + u$
$= 9t + 9n = 9(t + n)$,
which is a multiple of 9.

22. A three-digit number is 297 more than the number with the digits reversed. The hundreds digit is 2 more than the tens digit, and the sum of the digits is 13. Find the original number. 643

C **23.** The numerator of a fraction is a three-digit number whose hundreds digit is 4. The denominator is the numerator with the digits reversed. If 31 is subtracted from the numerator, the value of the resulting fraction is $\frac{1}{2}$. If 167 is subtracted from the denominator, the value of the resulting fraction is $\frac{2}{3}$. Find the original fraction. $\frac{458}{854}$

24. Show that the difference between a three-digit number and the number with the order of the digits reversed is always divisible by 99.

25. Show that if the sum of the digits of a two-digit number is a multiple of 9, then the number itself is a multiple of 9.

26. Mary is twice as old as Jane was at the time when Mary was as old as Jane is now. The sum of the present ages of Mary and Jane is 28 years. How old is each person now? Mary, 16; Jane, 12

27. A man is three times as old as his son was at the time when the father was twice as old as his son will be two years from now. Find the present age of each person if the sum of their ages is 55 years. Father, 39; son, 16

Computer Key-In

You can also use a computer to solve systems of linear equations by using the formulas given in the Calculator Key-In on page 303. In writing the program in BASIC, you will need to input the six values A, B, C, D, E, F. This can be done in one step by beginning the program as follows:

```
10  PRINT "INPUT A, B, C, D, E, F"
20  INPUT A, B, C, D, E, F
```

Only one question mark will be printed. You type in all six numbers separated by commas.

To complete the program, translate the formulas into BASIC. For example,

$$\text{LET N} = \text{A*E} - \text{B*D}$$

and then write the formulas for X and Y. If N = 0, print:

$$\text{"NO UNIQUE SOLUTION"}$$

Use your program to solve the equations at the bottom of page 303.

308 *CHAPTER 8*

8-10 Uniform-Motion Problems

OBJECTIVE To use systems of equations in two variables to solve
uniform-motion problems.

Suppose that you can paddle a canoe at the rate of
7 km/h in still water. If you canoe downstream on a
river with a current of 2 km/h, your speed is increased to 7 + 2, or 9 km/h. If you paddle upstream
against the current, your speed is reduced to 7 − 2,
or 5 km/h. In general:

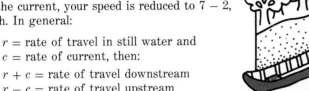

> If r = rate of travel in still water and
> c = rate of current, then:
>
> $r + c$ = rate of travel downstream
> $r - c$ = rate of travel upstream

The next example uses this principle and the basic formula for uniform-motion problems:

$$\text{Distance} = \text{rate} \times \text{time}$$
$$D = rt$$

EXAMPLE

A jet can travel the 3900 km distance from Mexico City to Caracas in
three hours with the wind. The return trip of the jet against the same
wind takes 4 h 20 min. Find the rate of the jet in still air and the rate of
the wind.

SOLUTION

Step 1 The problem asks for the rate of the jet in still air and the rate
of the wind.

Step 2 Let j = rate of jet in km/h and w = rate of wind in km/h.
(Note that 20 min is a third of an hour.)

	rate × time = Distance		
with the wind	$j + w$	3	3900
against the wind	$j - w$	$4\frac{1}{3}$	3900

Step 3 Use the given facts to write two equations.

$$3(j + w) = 3900$$
$$4\tfrac{1}{3}(j - w) = 3900$$

Steps 4 and 5 are left to you. You should find that the rate of the jet in
still air is 1100 km/h and the rate of the wind is 200 km/h. *Answer*

LINEAR EQUATIONS AND SYSTEMS **309**

Teaching Suggestions p. T95

Suggested Extensions p. T95

Chalkboard Examples

Solve by using a system of
two equations in two variables.

1. On a canoe trip, Anne and
   Chris paddled 10 km
   downstream on the Saco
   River in two hours. However, it took them five
   hours to return upstream
   to their starting point,
   paddling against the current. Find the paddling
   rate in still water and the
   rate of the current.

   Let r = the paddling rate
   in still water
   c = the rate of the
   current

   $2(r + c) = 10$
   $5(r - c) = 10$

   $\begin{aligned} r + c &= 5 \\ \underline{r - c} &= \underline{2} \\ 2r &= 7 \\ r &= 3.5 \end{aligned}$

   $3.5 + c = 5$
   $c = 1.5$

   The rate of paddling in
   still water is 3.5 km/h. The
   rate of the current is
   1.5 km/h.

2. A commuter usually travels to work on the express
   train which averages
   72 km/h. She discovers
   that if she takes the local
   train, which averages
   48 km/h, it will take her
   fifteen minutes longer to
   get to work. How far does
   she travel to work? How
   long does the trip take on
   the express train?

   Let t = time on the express train
   d = distance to work

   $72t = d$

   $48\left(t + \dfrac{1}{4}\right) = d$

   (continued)

$$72t = d$$
$$48t + 12 = d$$
$$48t + 12 = 72t$$
$$12 = 24t$$
$$t = \frac{1}{2}$$

$$d = 72\left(\frac{1}{2}\right) = 36$$

She travels 36 km to work. The trip takes her 0.5 h on the express train.

Oral Exercises

The rate of a plane is p km/h in still air. The rate of the wind is w km/h. Find the rate of the plane under the conditions described. Express your answers in terms of p and w.

1. Flying with the wind $p + w$ 2. Flying against the wind $p - w$

3. Flying against the wind if the rate of the wind increases by 15 km/h $p - (w + 15)$, or $p - w - 15$

4. Flying with the wind if the rate of the wind decreases by 20 km/h $p + (w - 20)$

The following rates are given in km/h.
c = rate of a canoe in still water
r = rate of a rowboat in still water
s = rate of a swimmer in still water
a = rate of the Androscoggin River
e = rate of the Eaton River

What rate does each expression represent?

SAMPLE $s + e$ *SOLUTION*   Rate of a swimmer swimming downstream in the Eaton River

5. $c + a$ 6. $r - e$ 7. $s + a$ 8. $c - e$
9. $r - a$ 10. $s - a$ 11. $c - a$ 12. $r + a$

Problems

Solve by using a system of two equations in two variables.

A   1. A ferry travels upstream against the current at 16 km/h but can travel with the current at 30 km/h. What is the rate of the ferry in still water? What is the rate of the current? 23 km/h; 7 km/h

2. A canoeist travels to an outpost 85 km downstream in five hours. Returning upstream, the canoeist travels 10 km in one hour. What is the rate of the canoeist in still water? What is the rate of the current? 13.5 km/h; 3.5 km/h

3. When a plane flies into the wind, it can travel 2400 km in ten hours. With the wind behind it, the plane can travel a third again as far in the same time. What is the speed of the wind and what is the speed of the plane in still air? Wind, 40 km/h; plane, 280 km/h

4. Sandy swims at 13 km/h downstream but only 3 km/h upstream. What is the rate of the current? How fast does she swim in still water? 5 km/h; 8 km/h

5. A robin flies 1500 m in 5 min with the wind. It would take 25 min to fly this distance against the wind. Find the rate of the wind and the rate of the robin in still air. Wind, 120 m/min; robin, 180 m/min

310   *CHAPTER 8*

6. The nonstop flight of 8400 km from Chicago to Rome takes seven hours with a tail wind. The return flight on the same course but against the wind takes 9 h 20 min. Find the rate of the airplane in calm conditions and find the rate of the wind. Airplane, 1050 km/h; wind, 150 km/h

7. A bush plane must return to its hangar in 3 hours for its next job. If it flies at 90 km/h and the wind speed is 20 km/h, how far can the plane fly from the hangar before it must return? $128\frac{1}{3}$, or 128.33, km

8. On a downstream trip, a boat can be rowed a distance of 66 km in three hours. Upstream, it can be rowed only 33 km in three hours. How fast is the current flowing? What is the rate of rowing in still water? 5.5 km/h; 16.5 km/h

9. A single-engine plane started out in high tail winds and made a trip of 500 km in two hours. On the return trip, the pilot was forced to land after 45 min, having traveled only 75 km. What was the rate of the plane in still air? What was the rate of the wind? 175 km/h; 75 km/h

10. A salmon swims 200 m in 12 min downstream. Swimming in the opposite direction it takes the fish 15 min to travel the same distance. Find the rate of the fish and the rate of the current. Fish, 15 m/min; current, $1\frac{2}{3}$, or 1.67, m/min

11. The 350 km trip from Paris to London takes two hours on a small aircraft flying with the wind. The return trip against the same wind takes 4 h 40 min. What is the rate of the plane without the wind? What is the rate of the wind? 125 km/h; 50 km/h

12. A power boat has a five-hour supply of gasoline. How far can this boat travel from the marina if the rate out with the current is 75 km/h and the rate in against the current is 50 km/h? 150 km

13. In three hours a glider can fly 240 km with the wind but only 210 km against the wind. Find the rate of the glider and the rate of the wind. Glider, 75 km/h; wind, 5 km/h

14. With the wind, a jet can fly a distance of 2800 km in four hours. Against the wind it can go only $\frac{6}{7}$ of the distance in the same time. Find the rate of the plane in still air and the rate of the wind. Plane, 650 km/h; wind, 50 km/h

B 15. A small craft can fly twice as far with a tail wind as it can with a head wind in the same amount of time. If the rate of the craft is s and the rate of the wind is w, find the relationship between s and w. $s = 3w$, or $w = \frac{1}{3}s$

16. An air balloon can go four times as far downwind as it can go upwind in the same amount of time. If the rate of the balloon is b and the rate of the wind is w, find the relationship between b and w. $b = \frac{5w}{3}$, or $w = \frac{3}{5}b$

17. A group of campers had to paddle downstream to get fresh supplies. On their return trip the wind had picked up so that the current was twice as strong. If it took twice as long to return to their campsite, find the relationship between their rate, s, and the rate of the current, c. $s = 5c$, or $c = \frac{1}{5}s$

LINEAR EQUATIONS AND SYSTEMS **311**

Supplementary Materials
Practice Master 50
Progress Test 29

Suggested Assignments
Minimum
Day 1: 310/*P*: 1–3, 6, 7, 9
Day 2: 311/*P*: 10, 12, 15
    R 312/*Self-Test 3*
Average
Day 1: 310/*P*: 1–11 odd
    S 308/*P*: 23
Day 2: 311/*P*: 14, 15, 17
    R 312/*Self-Test 3*
Maximum
NOTE: Sec. 8-9 finishes Sec.
    8-9 and starts Sec.
    8-10
    311/*P*: 9, 12, 15, 18
    R 312/*Self-Test 3*
    S 308/23

Extra Practice Problems
    p. 521

Additional A Exercises

Solve by using a system of two equations in two variables.

1. A boat travels upstream against the current at 10 km/h. It can travel downstream with the current at 15 km/h. What is the rate of the boat in still water and what is the rate of the current?
boat 12.5 km/h;
current 2.5 km/h

2. A plane can fly 2400 km in 4 h with the wind. It would take the plane 5 h to cover the same distance against the wind. Find the rate of the plane in still air, and the rate of the wind.
plane 540 km/h;
wind 60 km/h

18. A bird takes 45 min to make a 480 m round trip between two trees. Flying 0.25 m against the wind on the first half of the trip takes the same time as flying 0.5 m with the wind on the return flight. Find the rate of the bird in calm conditions and the rate of the wind.
Bird, 12 m/min; wind, 4 m/min

Self-Test 3

Solve by using a system of two equations in two variables.

1. Uncle Bill is twice as old as his niece Eve. Twelve years ago, he was three times as old as Eve. Find their ages now.

Obj. 8-9, p. 304

2. The sum of the digits of a two-digit number is 10. The number is 16 times the units digit. Find the number.

3. The denominator of a fraction is 9 more than the numerator. If both the numerator and the denominator are increased by 4, the value of the resulting fraction is $\frac{5}{8}$. Find the original fraction.

4. A boat can go downstream at the rate of 25 km/h. It can return against the current at only 8 km/h. Find the rate of the boat in still water and the rate of the current.

Obj. 8-10, p. 309

Check your answers with those at the back of the book.

Quick Quiz

Solve by using a system of two equations in two variables.

1. Jean is three times as old as Matthew. In 6 years, Jean will be twice as old as Matthew will be then. Find their ages now.
Matthew: 6 years;
Jean: 18 years

2. Two positive integers are in the ratio 2:5. If both numbers are decreased by 5, the new ratio will be 1:4. Find the original numbers.   10, 25

3. The sum of the digits of a two-digit number is 7. If the digits were reversed, the value of the new number would be 2 more than twice the value of the original number. Find the original number.   25

Biography   Wernher von Braun

Wernher von Braun (1912–1977) pioneered the field of rocket engineering. His work on the development of the Jupiter, Redstone, and Saturn rockets contributed in large measure to the success of the American space program in landing men on the moon.

His lifelong interest in space travel began while he was growing up in Germany and was fostered by his mother, who was an amateur astronomer. He received a doctorate in physics from the University of Berlin in 1934 and worked on the German rocket program from 1932 to 1945. After World War II, he moved to the United States and continued his work on rockets.

Wernher von Braun was not only a brilliant scientist but also a perservering leader and champion of space exploration. In 1960 he was named director of the Marshall Space Flight Center of the National Aeronautics and Space Administration at Huntsville, Alabama.

312   CHAPTER 8

Chapter Summary

1. Ordered pairs of real numbers can be graphed as points in a coordinate plane.
2. The solution set of a linear equation in two variables is a set of ordered pairs of numbers that convert the equation into a true statement. The graph of the solution set in a coordinate plane is a straight line.
3. The solutions of pairs of linear equations in two variables can be estimated by graphing, and computed by substitution or the addition-or-subtraction method.
4. Systems of linear equations in two variables may be used to solve some word problems.

Chapter Review

Supplementary Materials
Progress Tests 30, 31

Extra Practice pp. 503–504

Give the letter of the correct answer.

1. In which quadrant is the graph of $(3, -2)$?   8-1

   a. I   **b.** II   **c.** III   (**d.**) IV

2. Where is the graph of $(0, -5)$ in a coordinate plane?

   a. on the x-axis   (**b.**) on the y-axis

   c. in quadrant II   **d.** at the origin

3. Which ordered pair is a solution of $3x - 2y = -1$?   8-2

   a. $(1, 1)$ **b.** $(2, 1)$ (**c.**) $(1, 2)$ **d.** $(-1, 2)$

4. Which equation is equivalent to $-x + 3y = -3$?

   a. $y = -1 + x$ **b.** $y = \frac{1}{3}x - 3$

   (**c.**) $y = \frac{1}{3}x - 1$ **d.** $y = \frac{1}{3}x + 1$

5. Which equation is *not* linear?   8-3

   (**a.**) $4x + 5y^2 = 2$ **b.** $y = -6$

   c. $-3x + 2y = 7$ **d.** $\frac{1}{2}x = y$

6. Which is the best description of the graph of $x - y = 0$?

   a. the origin

   b. a horizontal line

   c. a vertical line

   (**d.**) a straight line passing through the points $(0, 0)$ and $(5, 5)$

7. The solution set of the system $\begin{aligned} y &= 2 \\ x + y &= 7 \end{aligned}$ is $\{(5, 2)\}$.

How are the graphs of the two equations related?

a. The graphs coincide.

b. The graphs are parallel lines.

c. The graphs are lines intersecting in the point $(5, 2)$.

d. The graphs intersect in the two points $(5, 2)$ and $(0, 2)$.

8. Which expression can be substituted for y in the second equation of the system $\begin{aligned} 2x - y &= 1 \\ 2x + 3y &= 35 \end{aligned}$ in order to solve the system by the substitution method?

a. $2x - y$ b. $1 - 2x$ c. $2x - 1$ d. $\dfrac{35}{3} - \dfrac{2}{3}x$

9. Express the given facts as a system of equations in two variables: One number is 5 less than another, and their sum is 23.

a. $\begin{aligned} x &= 5 - y \\ x + y &= 23 \end{aligned}$ b. $\begin{aligned} x &= y - 5 \\ x + (y - 5) &= 23 \end{aligned}$ c. $\begin{aligned} x - y &= 5 \\ x + y &= 23 \end{aligned}$

10. In which system of equations can you eliminate one variable by adding similar terms?

a. $\begin{aligned} x + y &= 3 \\ 2x + y &= -3 \end{aligned}$ b. $\begin{aligned} 3x - 2y &= 5 \\ 2x + 2y &= -5 \end{aligned}$ c. $\begin{aligned} 2x - 3y &= 7 \\ 5x - 3y &= 2 \end{aligned}$

11. To solve the system $\begin{aligned} 7x + 3y &= -1 \\ -9x + 4y &= 1 \end{aligned}$ you plan to transform both equations by multiplication before subtracting to eliminate one of the variables. If you multiply by 4 in the first equation, by which number should you multiply in the second equation?

a. 4   b. -4 c. 7   d. 3

12. In five years a girl will be two thirds as old as her aunt. Three years ago she was half as old as the aunt is now. How old is the girl now?

a. 11   b. 17   c. 19   d. 28

13. The units digit of a two-digit number is 4 more than the tens digit. If the digits are reversed, the new number is 10 more than twice the original number. What is the original number?

a. 26   b. 37   c. 15   d. 62

14. The denominator of a fraction exceeds the numerator by 3. If 1 is added to the denominator, a new fraction is obtained whose value is $\frac{2}{3}$. Find the original fraction.

a. $\dfrac{-4}{-7}$ b. $\dfrac{8}{11}$ c. $\dfrac{8}{12}$ d. $\dfrac{3}{6}$

314   CHAPTER 8

15. A motorboat went 18 km downstream in one hour. The return trip against the current took three hours. Find the rate of the current.

    a. 18 km/h   **b.** 12 km/h   (**c.**) 6 km/h   **d.** 3 km/h

8-10

Chapter Test

Plot the graph of each ordered pair in a coordinate plane.

1. $(-2, 4)$ **2.** $(1, -3)$ 8-1

3. Find the solution set of $2x + y = 8$ if both x and y are whole numbers. $\{(0, 8), (1, 6), (2, 4), (3, 2), (4, 0)\}$ 8-2

4. Graph $x - y = 2$ in a coordinate plane. 8-3

5. Solve by the graphic method: $\begin{aligned} x - 2y &= 2 \\ x + y &= 2 \end{aligned}$ $(2, 0)$ 8-4

6. Solve by the substitution method: $\begin{aligned} a + 2b &= 7 \\ 2a &= 3b \end{aligned}$ $(3, 2)$ 8-5

7. Use a system of two equations in two variables and the substitution method to solve this problem: Meg's bowling score was 12 more than Jan's. Their combined score was 328. Find their scores. Jan, 158; Meg, 170 8-6

Solve each system by the addition-or-subtraction method.

8. $\begin{aligned} 3x + 2y &= 13 \\ 3x - 4y &= 19 \end{aligned}$ $(5, -1)$ 8-7

9. $\begin{aligned} 3a + 4b &= -25 \\ 2a - 3b &= 6 \end{aligned}$ $(-3, -4)$ 8-8

Solve by using a system of two equations in two variables.

10. A clerk mistakenly overcharged a customer 27¢ by reversing the two digits in the price of a marking pen. If the sum of the digits was 15, what was the correct price of the pen? 69¢ 8-9

11. A salmon swims 24 km downstream from its birthplace to the ocean in three hours. The return trip upstream to spawn takes five hours. How fast does the salmon swim in still water? 6.4 km/h 8-10

Additional Answers
Chapter Test

2.

4.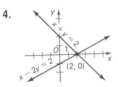

Cumulative Review   (Chapters 1–8)

Simplify each expression.

1. $-2y(y^2 - 8y - 9 + y)$ 2. $(-5a^2b^4)^3 \div (2a^7b^6)^2$ 3. $(8r^2 - 3s)(8r^2 + 3s)$

4. $(2j - k + 1)^2$ 5. $(-8 - d) - (-8d + 4)$ 6. $(8x^3 - 4x^2 + 6x) \div 2x$

Factor completely, if possible. If not possible, write "prime."

7. $1 - 18v + 81v^2$ 8. $2a^3 + 6a^2b + 4ab^2$ 9. $-m^2 - 15n + 5m + 3mn$

10. $40z^2 + z - 6$ 11. $5r^2 - r - 7$ 12. $9c^2 + 12cd + 4d^2$

Express in simplest form.

13. $\dfrac{4x^2 - 25y^2}{4x^2 - 4xy - 15y^2}$ 14. $\dfrac{1}{1 - 4c} + \dfrac{8c}{8c - 2} - 1$ 15. $\dfrac{m^2 + m - 30}{m^2 - 6m + 5} \div \dfrac{4m + 24}{m - 1}$

Divide. Express each quotient as a polynomial or a mixed expression.

16. $\dfrac{6v^2 + 7v + 5}{2v + 1}$
  $3v + 2 + \dfrac{3}{2v + 1}$

17. $\dfrac{n^3 - 5n + 2}{n - 2}$
  $n^2 + 2n - 1$

18. $\dfrac{3x^2 + 7xy + 4y^2 + 2}{3x + 4y}$
  $x + y + \dfrac{2}{3x + 4y}$

Solve. (The equation may be an identity or have no root.)

19. $5z - 1 = 2(z + 4)$ 20. $2r^2 + 26r = -72$ 21. $0.1x = 0.06x + 0.6$

22. $(5d - 1)(2d + 1) = 6$ 23. 2.8% of $k = 63$ 24. $|a| - 7 = -3$

25. $\dfrac{1}{t + 1} + \dfrac{1}{5t - 3} = \dfrac{1}{t}$ 26. $\dfrac{8s + 2}{6s - 1} = \dfrac{4s - 1}{3s - 2}$ 27. $\dfrac{2}{y - 2} = \dfrac{5}{y} + 2$

28. Solve graphically: a. $2x - y = 5$ b. $y = -4x$ No solution
                            $x + 3y = -1$ $4x + y = 6$
                            $(2, -1)$

Solve.

29. $8x - 3 = y$ $(-1, -11)$ 30. $6a - 7b = 10$ $\left(\frac{3}{2}, -\frac{1}{7}\right)$ 31. $(-2, 4)$
    $5x + 2y = -27$ $4a + 7b = 5$ $9s + 5t = 2$
                                                            $-11s + 2t = 30$

Solve.

32. The sum of two integers is -3 and their product is -40. Find the integers. -8 and 5

33. Half of a two-digit number is 6 less than the number with its digits reversed. If the sum of the digits is 12, find the number. 84

34. A plane flies 1120 km in 80 min with a tail wind. The return trip with a head wind takes 4 min more. Find the speed of the wind in kilometers per hour. 80 km/h

Maintaining Skills

Factor completely, if possible. If not possible, write "prime."

SAMPLE 1 $15y^2z - 60y = 15y(yz - 4)$

1. $2c^3 + 4c^2d$ $2c^2(c + 2d)$
2. $2\pi rh + 2\pi r^2$ $2\pi r(h + r)$
3. $9s^2 + 4st^2 - 6t^3$ Prime
4. $9p^2 + 36pq - 81q^2$ $9(p^2 + 4pq - 9q^2)$
5. $64a^3 - 40a^2 + 72a$ $8a(8a^2 - 5a + 9)$
6. $8x^3y^3 - 6x^2y^4 - 4xy^5$ $2xy^3(4x^2 - 3xy - 2y^2)$

SAMPLE 2   a. $16x^4 - 4 = 4(4x^4 - 1) = 4[(2x^2)^2 - 1^2] = 4(2x^2 + 1)(2x^2 - 1)$
         b. $49d^2 - 42d + 9 = (7d)^2 - 2(7d \cdot 3) + 3^2 = (7d - 3)^2$

7. $64a - a^3$ $a(8 - a)(8 + a)$
8. $k^2 + 8k + 2$ Prime
9. $9p^2 - 6p + 1$ $(3p - 1)^2$
10. $144q^3 - 4qr^2$
11. $100w^2 - 30w + 9$ Prime
12. $100x^2 - 16y^2$
13. $m^4 + 4m^2n + 4n^2$
14. $r^6 - 81$ $(r^3 - 9)(r^3 + 9)$
15. $3z^2 - 36zt + 108t^2$

10. $4q(6q - r)(6q + r)$
12. $4(5x - 2y)(5x + 2y)$
13. $(m^2 + 2n)^2$
15. $3(z - 6t)^2$

SAMPLE 3   a. $x^2 - 10xy + 16y^2$ b. $n^2 + 3n - 28$

SOLUTION   a. Start with $(x - \quad)(x - \quad)$; $(x - 8y)(x - 2y)$.   *Answer*
           b. Start with $(n + \quad)(n - \quad)$; $(n + 7)(n - 4)$.   *Answer*

16. $b^2 + 11b + 18$
17. $g^2 - 6g - 40$
18. $y^2 + 17yz - 38z^2$
19. $5z^2 - 50z + 120$
20. $-d^3 - 8d^2 - 7d$
21. $s^3 + s^2 - 72s$
22. $m^2 - 18m - 46$
23. $c^2 - 14cd + 33d^2$
24. $49 + 14k + k^2$

SAMPLE 4 $ac - 3bc - a + 3b = c(a - 3b) - 1(a - 3b) = (c - 1)(a - 3b)$

25. $ar - 5a - 6r + 30$
26. $s^3 - 8s^2 + 7s - 56$
27. $jx + 3x + 4j + 6$
28. $3d^4 - 6d + 2d^3 - 4$
29. $4zm - 6n + 3m - 8zn$
30. $12y - 2y^3 + 5y^2 - 30$

SAMPLE 5 $14x^2 - 25x + 6$

SOLUTION Test the possibilities for the first terms: $14x$ and x; $7x$ and $2x$.
              Test the possibilities for the second terms: 6 and 1; 2 and 3.
              $14x^2 - 25x + 6 = (7x - 2)(2x - 3)$ *Answer*

31. $12a^2 - 23a + 5$
32. $16t^2 + 18t - 9$
33. $5r^2 + 19rs + 18s^2$
34. $30y^2 - 19yz - 4z^2$
35. $-10z - 3z^2 + 27z^3$
36. $-28k^2 - 26k - 6$
37. $15b^2 + 8c^2 - 12bc$
38. $35d^2 - 2 + 9d$
39. $40x^2 + 46xv + 9v^2$

A skier's speed is determined by three factors: the steepness (or slope) of the mountain, gravity, and the friction of the snow against the skis.

Skiers on a very steep ski slope may wish to reduce the steepness by traversing the slope at an angle, instead of skiing directly down the hill. To better visualize this concept, your students may wish to consider the extreme case. If the skiers skied horizontally across the ski slope, the slope of their path would be zero, as would be their speed, unless they propelled themselves by their own physical efforts.

Expert skiers use friction to reduce their speed on steep slopes. This is accomplished by thrusting the rear edges of the skis against the snow while turning with the skis in a parallel position. Beginners accomplish the same result by keeping their skis in the shape of a V. This position is appropriately called the "snowplow." Snow conditions and ski wax are other factors which affect friction during skiing.

The steepness of the mountain is one of the factors that influence the skier's speed. Steepness is closely related to the mathematical idea of slope.

318

9

INTRODUCTION TO FUNCTIONS

Teaching References

Lesson Commentary,
    pp. T95–T100

Assignment Guide,
    pp. T57–T59

Supplementary Materials

    Practice Masters 51–58

    Progress Tests 32–35

    Computer Activities
    25 *Parallel and Perpendic-
        ular Lines*
    26 *Slope Intercept Form*
    27 *Fitting Lines to Data*

Extra Practice pp. 504–507,
    521–522

Alternate Test, p. T20

LINEAR EQUATIONS

9-1 *Slope of a Line*

OBJECTIVE To find the slope of a line.

To describe the steepness, or slope, of a hill, you may determine the vertical *rise* for every 100 m of horizontal *run* and calculate the ratio:

$$\frac{\text{rise}}{\text{run}} = \frac{75}{100} = \frac{3}{4}$$

Rise: 75 m

Run: 100 m

To describe the steepness, or slope, of a straight line, you choose any two points on the line, count the units in the rise and run, and calculate their ratio.

EXAMPLE 1

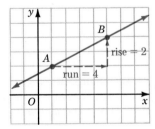

$$\text{slope} = \frac{\text{rise}}{\text{run}} = \frac{2}{4} = \frac{1}{2}$$

EXAMPLE 2

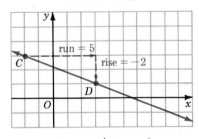

$$\text{slope} = \frac{\text{rise}}{\text{run}} = \frac{-2}{5}$$

319

Chalkboard Examples

1. Find the slope of the line passing through $(4, -2)$ and $(-2, 1)$.

$$\text{slope} = \frac{1 - (-2)}{-2 - (4)}$$

$$= \frac{3}{-6}$$

$$= -\frac{1}{2}$$

2. Find the slope of the line whose equation is $2x + 3y = 12$.

Solution 1: Graph the line.

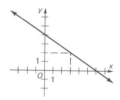

Count the number of units in the rise and the run.

$$\text{slope} = \frac{-2}{3} \quad \text{or} \quad -\frac{2}{3}.$$

Solution 2: Find two points on the line, say $(0, 4)$ and $(6, 0)$. The slope is

$$\frac{0 - 4}{6 - 0} = -\frac{2}{3}.$$

3. Find the slope of the line whose equation is $y = 2x - 6$.

Solution 1: Graph the line.

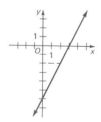

Count the number of units in the rise and run.

320

In Example 1, the line passes through the points $A(1, 2)$ and $B(5, 4)$. The rise, or *vertical change*, in moving from A to B is the difference between the y-coordinates: $4 - 2 = 2$. The run, or *horizontal change*, in moving from A to B is the difference between the x-coordinates: $5 - 1 = 4$.

Thus, the coordinates of a pair of points on a line can be used to calculate the slope of the line:

$$\textbf{slope} = \frac{\text{rise}}{\text{run}} = \frac{\text{vertical change}}{\text{horizontal change}} = \frac{\text{difference between } y\text{-coordinates}}{\text{difference between } x\text{-coordinates}}$$

If $P_1(x_1, y_1)$ and $P_2(x_2, y_2)$ are any two different points on a line,

$$\textbf{slope} = \frac{y_2 - y_1}{x_2 - x_1} \quad (x_1 \neq x_2)$$

EXAMPLE 3 Find the slope of the line whose equation is $2x - 3y = 6$.

SOLUTION Find two points on the line (page 284):

$$(0, -2) \quad \text{and} \quad (3, 0)$$

Then the slope $= \dfrac{0 - (-2)}{3 - 0} = \dfrac{2}{3}$. *Answer*

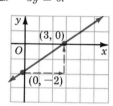

In Example 3, two convenient points were chosen, but the slope calculated using *any* two points on the line would be $\dfrac{2}{3}$.

> A basic property of a line is that its slope is constant.

EXAMPLE 4 Determine whether the points whose coordinates are given lie on the same line. If they do, find the slope of the line.

a. $\begin{array}{l} {}_1(-1, 8) \\ {}_1(\ \ 0, 6) \\ {}_1(\ \ 1, 4) \\ (\ \ 2, 2) \end{array} \begin{array}{l} {}_{-2} \\ {}_{-2} \\ {}_{-2} \end{array}$ **b.** $\begin{array}{l} {}_1(0, 0) \\ {}_1(1, 1) \\ {}_1(2, 3) \\ (3, 6) \end{array} \begin{array}{l} {}_1 \\ {}_2 \\ {}_3 \end{array}$ **c.** $\begin{array}{l} {}_2(0, 3) \\ {}_6(2, 4) \\ {}_{-4}(8, 7) \\ (4, 5) \end{array} \begin{array}{l} {}_1 \\ {}_3 \\ {}_{-2} \end{array}$

SOLUTION **a.** As you move from one point to the next, the changes in the x-coordinates and the y-coordinates are shown in color. The ratio of the vertical change to the horizontal change is constant. The points lie on a line. The slope is $\dfrac{-2}{1}$, or -2.

320   *CHAPTER 9*

b. The ratio of the vertical change to the horizontal change is *not* constant. The points do *not* lie on a line.

c. The ratio of the vertical change to the horizontal change is constant. The slope is $\frac{1}{2}$.

If you use the formula on page 320 to try to compute the "slope" of the vertical line shown at the right, you find that the denominator is zero. Since you cannot divide by zero, the formula does not apply. *Vertical lines have no slope.*

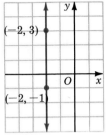

The slope of the horizontal line shown at the right is

$$\frac{-2 - (-2)}{1 - (-3)} = \frac{0}{4} = 0.$$

The slope of every horizontal line is 0.

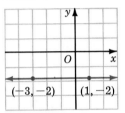

Oral Exercises

Find the slope of each line.

1. $-\frac{5}{3}$

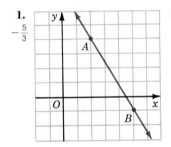

2. $\frac{1}{2}$

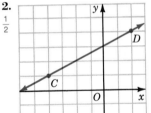

3. 0

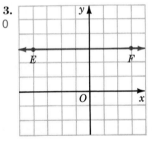

No slope

4. $\frac{5}{2}$

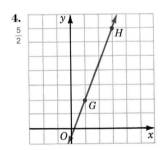

5. $\frac{2}{7}$

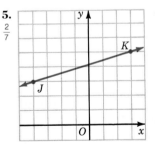

6.

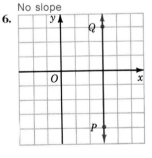

slope $= \frac{2}{1}$ or 2

Solution 2: Find two points on the line, say $(0, -6)$ and $(3, 0)$. The slope is

$$\frac{0 - (-6)}{3 - 0} = \frac{6}{3} = 2.$$

Determine whether the points in each exercise lie on the same line. If they do, find the slope of the line.

4. $\begin{array}{l} 1 \\ 1 \\ 1 \end{array}$ $\begin{array}{l} (1, 2) \\ (2, 4) \\ (3, 6) \\ (4, 8) \end{array}$ $\begin{array}{l} 2 \\ 2 \\ 2 \end{array}$

They are on the same line because the ratio of the change in *y*-coordinates to the change in *x*-coordinates is always the same.

$$\text{slope} = \frac{4 - 2}{2 - 1} = \frac{2}{1} = 2$$

5. $\begin{array}{l} 1 \\ 1 \\ 1 \end{array}$ $\begin{array}{l} (2, 3) \\ (3, 5) \\ (4, 8) \\ (5, 12) \end{array}$ $\begin{array}{l} 2 \\ 3 \\ 4 \end{array}$

They are not on the same line because the ratio of the change in *y*-coordinates to the change in *x*-coordinates varies.

6. $\begin{array}{l} -1 \\ 3 \\ -5 \end{array}$ $\begin{array}{l} (0, 3) \\ (-1, 5) \\ (2, -1) \\ (-3, 9) \end{array}$ $\begin{array}{l} 2 \\ -6 \\ 10 \end{array}$

They are on the same line because the ratio of the change in *y*-coordinates to the change in *x*-coordinates is constant.

$$\text{slope} = \frac{2}{-1} = -2$$

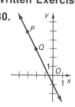
Written Exercises

In each exercise, the coordinates of two points of a line are given. Find the slope of the line.

A **1.** $(7, 3)$ $(5, 4)$ $-\frac{1}{2}$

2. $(3, -3)$ $(6, -5)$ $-\frac{2}{3}$

3. $(-6, 3)$ $(-4, 5)$ 1

4. $(3, 8)$ $(5, 4)$ -2

5. $(-4, 5)$ $(5, 4)$ $-\frac{1}{9}$

6. $(2, -5)$ $(4, 2)$ $\frac{7}{2}$

7. $(-4, -4)$ $(0, 0)$ 1

8. $(8, 3)$ $(-2, 3)$ 0

9. $(4, 6)$ $(4, -3)$

10. $(-4, -5)$ $(-2, -2)$ $\frac{3}{2}$

11. $(0, -1)$ $(3, -1)$ 0

12. $(0, 0)$ $(4, 3)$

Find the slope of each line whose equation is given.

13. $y = 4x - 3$ 4

14. $y = 4x + 5$ 4

15. $y = 2x - 3$ 2

16. $2x + y = 6$ -2

17. $x - y = 6$ 1

18. $4x - y = 16$ 4

19. $2x - 3y = 12$ $\frac{2}{3}$

20. $3x + 4y = 24$ $-\frac{3}{4}$

21. $4x - 5y = 20$ $\frac{4}{5}$

22. $5x + 4y = 20$ $-\frac{5}{4}$

23. $y = -2$ 0

24. $y - 3 = 0$ 0

Determine whether the points in each exercise lie on the same line. If they do, find the slope of the line.

25. $(0, 6)$
$(1, 4)$
$(2, 2)$
$(3, 0)$
Same line, -2

26. $(3, 5)$
$(4, 7)$
$(5, 11)$
$(6, 14)$
Not the same line

27. $(0, -1)$
$(1, -2)$
$(2, -4)$
$(3, -8)$
Not the same line

28. $(1, 1)$
$(0, 4)$
$(-1, 7)$
$(-2, 10)$
Same line, -3

Through the given point, draw a line with the given slope.

SAMPLE $A(2, 1)$; slope, -4

SOLUTION

First plot point A. Rewrite the slope as the fraction $\frac{-4}{1}$.

From point A, measure 1 unit *to the right*, and 4 units *down* to locate a second point, B. Draw the line through A and B.

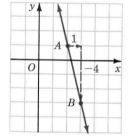

29. $A(3, 4)$; slope, 3

30. $P(-3, 5)$; slope, -2

31. $T(2, -8)$; slope, 0

32. $R(-2, 3)$; slope, $\frac{2}{3}$

33. $K(-4, 5)$; slope, $-\frac{1}{2}$

34. $N(4, -6)$; slope, $-\frac{5}{3}$

B **35.** The vertices of a triangle are $A(-5, 5)$, $B(4, 5)$, and $C(-5, -3)$. Find the slope of each side of the triangle.

36. The vertices of a rectangle are $D(-4, -2)$, $E(1, 3)$, $F(8, -4)$, and $G(3, -9)$. Find the slope of each side of the rectangle.

37. Do the points $(-2, -4)$, $(2, 8)$, and $(0, 2)$ lie on the same line? How can you use the idea of slope to show this?

38. Determine the slope of the line through the points $(2, 4)$ and $(-2, 2)$. Find the value of y if $(6, y)$ lies on this line. slope $= \frac{1}{2}$; $y = 6$

39. The slope of a line through point $(2, 4)$ is $\frac{3}{2}$. If point $(-2, y)$ lies on this line, find the value of y. $y = -2$

40. A line with slope -3 passes through the points $(-8, p)$ and $(2, 3p)$. Find the value of p. $p = -15$

C 41. The vertices of a square are $A(1, 7)$, $B(9, 5)$, $C(7, -3)$, and $D(-1, -1)$. Use the idea of slope to show that point $M(4, 2)$ lies on the diagonal joining A and C, and on the diagonal joining B and D.

42. The vertices of a right triangle are $P(-3, 4)$, $Q(-3, -4)$, and $R(7, -4)$. Use the idea of slope to show that point $S(2, 0)$ lies on the triangle.
The slopes of $\overline{PR}$ and $\overline{PS}$ are both $-\frac{4}{5}$, so S lies on $\overline{PR}$.

32.
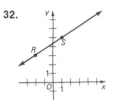

34.
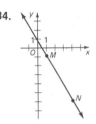

35. $\overline{AC}$, no slope; $\overline{AB}$, slope $= 0$; $\overline{BC}$, slope $= \frac{8}{9}$

36. $\overline{DE}$, slope $= 1$; $\overline{EF}$, slope $= -1$; $\overline{GF}$, slope $= 1$, $\overline{DG}$, slope $= -1$

37. Yes: If the slope of the line segment joining $(-2, -4)$ and $(2, 8)$ is the same as the slope of the line segment joining $(2, 8)$ and $(0, 2)$, then all three points lie on the same line.

41. The slopes of $\overline{AC}$ and $\overline{AM}$ are both $\frac{-5}{3}$, so M is on $\overline{AC}$. The slopes of $\overline{BM}$ and $\overline{BD}$ are both $\frac{3}{5}$, so M is on $\overline{BD}$.

Career Note   Agricultural Engineer

Population experts predict that by the year 2000 there will be six to seven billion people on this planet. All of these people must have food to eat and clothes to wear. Where will it all come from?

Finding the answer to this question is the concern of agricultural engineers. Their primary task is to develop the most efficient techniques for maximizing the amount of food and fiber that can be produced. They are involved in all phases of crop production from planting to processing. Typical tasks might include developing equipment for harvesting or designing systems for the prevention of soil erosion.

A bachelor's degree in agricultural engineering is usually the minimum requirement for a career in this field. Work for the degree includes one to two years of general course work in mathematics, chemistry, physics, basic engineering, and the social sciences.

INTRODUCTION TO FUNCTIONS   **323**

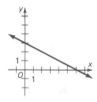
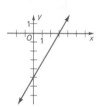
9-2 The Slope-Intercept Form of a Linear Equation

OBJECTIVE To use the slope-intercept form of a linear equation.

The table shows the coordinates of a few of the points in the graph of the linear equation $y = 2x$.

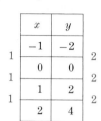

x	y
-1	-2
0	0
1	2
2	4

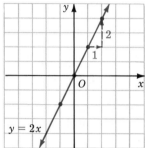

$y = 2x$

Notice that the slope of the line whose equation is $y = 2x$ is $\dfrac{2}{1}$, or 2, and that the line passes through the origin.

The graph of the equation $y = -\dfrac{1}{3}x$ is a line that has slope $-\dfrac{1}{3}$ and passes through the origin.

For every real number m, the graph in a coordinate plane of the equation

$$y = mx$$

is the line that has slope m and passes through the origin.

The graphs of the linear equations

$$y = 2x \text{ and } y = 2x + 4$$

have been drawn on the same set of axes. The lines have equal slopes, but they cross the y-axis at different points. The y-coordinate of a point where a graph intersects the y-axis is called the **y-intercept** of the graph.

To determine the y-intercept of a line, replace x with 0 in the equation of the line:

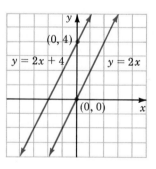

$y = 2x + 4$

$(0, 4)$

$y = 2x$

$(0, 0)$

$y = 2x$
$y = 2(0)$
$y = 0$
y-intercept: 0

$y = 2x + 4$
$y = 2(0) + 4$
$y = 4$
y-intercept: 4

324   *CHAPTER 9*

If you write $y = 2x$ as $y = 2x + 0$, you can see that the constant term in the following equations is the y-intercept of each graph:

$$y = 2x + 0 \qquad y = 2x + 4$$

For all real numbers m and b, the graph in a coordinate plane of the equation

$$y = mx + b$$

is the line whose slope is m and whose y-intercept is b. This is called the **slope-intercept form** of an equation of a line.

EXAMPLE 1 Write a linear equation in standard form whose graph has the given slope and y-intercept.

      a. $m = -3$, $b = -2$ **b.** $m = \dfrac{1}{2}$, $b = 3$

SOLUTION First write an equation of the form $y = mx + b$. Then transform it into an equivalent equation in the form $Ax + By = C$ where A, B, and C are integers.

      a. $y = -3x + (-2)$ **b.** $y = \dfrac{1}{2}x + 3$

         $3x + y = -2$ *Answer* $2y = x + 6$

                                           $-x + 2y = 6$ *Answer*

EXAMPLE 2 Use only the y-intercept and slope to graph the equation $3x - 2y = 6$.

SOLUTION Solve for y to transform the equation into the form $y = mx + b$.

$$3x - 2y = 6$$
$$-2y = -3x + 6$$
$$y = \frac{3}{2}x - 3$$

Since the y-intercept is -3, plot $(0, -3)$. Since the slope is $\dfrac{3}{2}$, measure 2 units to the right of $(0, -3)$ and 3 units up to locate a second point. Draw the line through the two points.

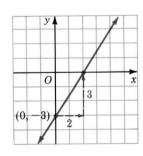

INTRODUCTION TO FUNCTIONS **325**

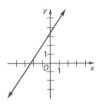

Additional A Exercises

State the slope and y-intercept of each line whose equation is given.

1. $y = 2x - 4$ $2; -4$

2. $y = \frac{1}{3}x + \frac{5}{2}$ $\frac{1}{3}; \frac{5}{2}$

3. $y = \frac{1}{5}x - \frac{7}{5}$ $\frac{1}{5}; -\frac{7}{5}$

Write an equation in standard form of the line that has the given slope and y-intercept.

4. $m = 4, b = \frac{2}{3}$

$12x - 3y = -2$

5. $m = -5, b = \frac{3}{4}$

$20x + 4y = 3$

6. $m = \frac{1}{3}, b = \frac{5}{6}$

$2x - 6y = -5$

Additional Answers
Written Exercises

6. $2x + 5y = -20$

9. $8x + 10y = 25$

13. $y = -x + 8$

14. $y = -2x - 4$

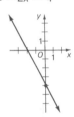

15. $y = x - 6$

16. $y = \frac{1}{2}x + 4$

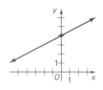

17. $y = \frac{1}{2}x - 4$

326

Oral Exercises

State the slope and y-intercept of each line whose equation is given.
In each answer, the slope is given first.

1. $y = 3x$ $3; 0$

2. $y = 3x + 4$ $3; 4$

3. $y = \frac{1}{2}x + 4$ $\frac{1}{2}; 4$

4. $y = -2x$ $-2; 0$

5. $y = -2x - \frac{1}{2}$ $-2; -\frac{1}{2}$

6. $y = \frac{3}{2}x - \frac{1}{2}$ $\frac{3}{2}; -\frac{1}{2}$

7. $y = \frac{1}{3}x$ $\frac{1}{3}; 0$

8. $y = 4x - \frac{5}{2}$ $4; -\frac{5}{2}$

State an equation of the line that has the given slope and y-intercept.

9. $m = 2, b = 3$
$y = 2x + 3$

10. $m = 2, b = 0$
$y = 2x$

11. $m = -3, b = 4$
$y = -3x + 4$

Written Exercises

Write in standard form an equation of the line that has the given slope and y-intercept.

A **1.** $m = 3, b = \frac{1}{2}$ $6x - 2y = -1$

2. $m = -2, b = \frac{2}{3}$ $6x + 3y = 2$

3. $m = \frac{1}{4}, b = 3$ $x - 4y = -12$

4. $m = -\frac{2}{3}, b = 3$ $2x + 3y = 9$

5. $m = 5, b = -\frac{2}{3}$ $15x - 3y = 2$

6. $m = -\frac{2}{5}, b = -4$

7. $m = \frac{1}{3}, b = \frac{2}{3}$ $x - 3y = -2$

8. $m = \frac{3}{2}, b = -\frac{3}{2}$ $3x - 2y = 3$

9. $m = -\frac{4}{5}, b = \frac{5}{2}$

10. $m = \frac{2}{3}, b = -\frac{3}{4}$ $8x - 12y = 9$

11. $m = 0, b = -3$ $y = -3$

12. $m = 0, b = \frac{3}{2}$ $2y = 3$

Change each equation to the slope-intercept form and draw the graph using only the y-intercept and the slope.

13. $x + y = 8$

14. $2x + y = -4$

15. $x - y = 6$

16. $-x + 2y = 8$

17. $x - 2y = 8$

18. $2y - 3x = 6$

19. $2x + 3y = 0$

20. $3x - 4y = 12$

21. $-5x + 3y = 20$

22. $3x = 2y$

23. $2x - 3y - 12 = 0$

24. $3y = 8$

B **25.** Write an equation of the line that has y-intercept -3 and that has the same slope as the graph of $y = 3x + 2$. $y = 3x - 3$

26. Write an equation of the line that has the same slope as the graph of $y - 2x = 3$ and the same y-intercept as the graph of $3y + 2x = 6$. $y = 2x + 2$

27. In the equation $3y + tx = 2$, for what value of t does the graph of the equation have slope 1? slope -1? $-3; 3$

28. In the equation $ty + 3x = 2$, for what value of t does the graph of the equation have y-intercept 1? y-intercept -1? $2; -2$

C **29.** Using the standard form of a linear equation, $Ax + By = C$, find a formula for the slope and a formula for the y-intercept in terms of the coefficients, assuming that $B \neq 0$. Slope $= -\frac{A}{B}$; y – intercept $= \frac{C}{B}$

326 CHAPTER 9

Application Line of Best Fit

Can your adult height be predicted from that of your father or mother? Will your future income be related to the number of years you attend school? When there is a clear relationship between two measurements, researchers can base predictions on data gathered about many, many people. For each person, there must be a pair of measurements.

For example, to predict a person's height at age 24 from the person's height at age 14, researchers can begin by collecting data such as that shown in the chart below for a group of adults. Each pair of heights can then be plotted as a point (x, y) on a graph.

Height at 14	Height at 24
158 cm	185 cm
150 cm	171 cm
148 cm	170 cm
154 cm	178 cm
164 cm	192 cm
152 cm	175 cm

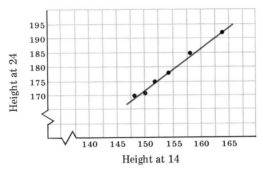

If data were plotted for many more people, the graph would contain many more points. These points would tend to cluster around a line (shown in color) called the *line of best fit*, since it fits closer to the points than all other lines. Mathematicians have derived exact formulas for determining the line of best fit, but you can fit a line quite well "by eye." From graphs based on extensive data gathered over a period of several years, predictions about an individual's growth or income can be made.

Project

a. Gather the following data from your classmates: the height of each girl and her mother; the height of each boy and his father.

b. For each girl, plot a point (x, y) on a graph such that the x-coordinate is the girl's height and the y-coordinate is her mother's height. Make a second graph in the same way using the boys' data.

c. On each graph, draw the line that seems to fit the points of the graph most closely.

d. Determine the heights of other students in the same age group as your class. Estimate the heights of their mothers or fathers from your graphs. Find out how good your estimates are. (*Note:* Your estimates may be inaccurate, but if you based your graph on more data and estimated the heights for a larger group of people, your estimates would be good in a greater percentage of cases.)

INTRODUCTION TO FUNCTIONS **327**

18. $y = \frac{3}{2}x + 3$

19. $y = -\frac{2}{3}x$

20. $y = \frac{3}{4}x - 3$

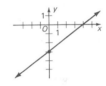

21. $y = \frac{5}{3}x + \frac{20}{3}$

22. $y = \frac{3}{2}x$

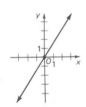

23. $y = \frac{2}{3}x - 4$

24. $y = \frac{8}{3}$

9-3 Determining an Equation of a Line

OBJECTIVE To find an equation of a line given the slope and one point on the line, or two points on the line.

The line shown below has slope $\frac{2}{3}$ and passes through the point $(-2, -1)$. The slope-intercept form of the equation of this line is

$$y = \frac{2}{3}x + b.$$

Since the point $(-2, -1)$ is on the line, its coordinates satisfy the equation. You can substitute to find the value of b:

$$-1 = \frac{2}{3}(-2) + b$$

$$-1 = -\frac{4}{3} + b$$

$$\frac{1}{3} = b$$

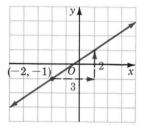

Therefore, an equation of the line with slope $\frac{2}{3}$ and passing through $(-2, -1)$ is

$$y = \frac{2}{3}x + \frac{1}{3}.$$

EXAMPLE Write an equation of the line passing through the points $(-4, 5)$ and $(2, -4)$.

SOLUTION $\text{slope} = \dfrac{\text{difference between } y\text{-coordinates}}{\text{difference between } x\text{-coordinates}}$

$$m = \frac{5 - (-4)}{-4 - 2} = \frac{9}{-6} = -\frac{3}{2}$$

Thus, the slope-intercept form of the equation is

$$y = -\frac{3}{2}x + b.$$

Choose one of the given points, say $(-4, 5)$. Since it lies on the line, its coordinates satisfy the equation. Substitute to find the value of b:

$$5 = -\frac{3}{2}(-4) + b$$

$$5 = 6 + b$$

$$-1 = b$$

$\therefore$ an equation of the line is $y = -\frac{3}{2}x - 1$. **Answer**

As shown on the opposite page, you can find an equation of a line if the slope and one point on the line are known. To determine an equation of a line when two points on the line are known, you first find the slope and then find the y-intercept as shown in the example.

Written Exercises

Each given point is on a line whose equation is $y = \frac{2}{3}x + b$. Find each value of b.

A   **1.** $(3, 4)$ 2   **2.** $(-3, 2)$ 4   **3.** $(-4, -3)$ $-\frac{1}{3}$ **4.** $(0, -2)$ -2

Write in standard form an equation of the line that has the given slope and passes through the given point.

5. $m = 2$; $(3, 1)$ $2x - y = 5$ **6.** $m = 3$; $(2, -3)$ $3x - y = 9$ **7.** $m = -4$; $(-4, -6)$ $4x + y = -22$

8. $m = -2$; $(-2, 3)$ $2x + y = -1$ **9.** $m = \frac{2}{3}$; $(3, 0)$ $2x - 3y = 6$ **10.** $m = \frac{5}{4}$; $(1, 0)$ $5x - 4y = 5$

11. $m = \frac{5}{4}$; $(-1, -5)$ $5x - 4y = 15$ **12.** $m = -\frac{2}{3}$; $(0, 0)$ $2x + 3y = 0$ **13.** $m = -\frac{1}{2}$; $(-3, -2)$ $x + 2y = -7$

14. $m = -1$; $\left(6, \frac{1}{2}\right)$ $2x + 2y = 13$ **15.** $m = 0$; $\left(\frac{3}{4}, -2\right)$ $y = -2$ **16.** $m = 0$; $\left(-2, \frac{3}{4}\right)$ $4y = 3$

Write in standard form an equation of the line passing through the given points.

17. $(0, -2)$ $(4, 5)$ $7x - 4y = 8$ **18.** $(3, 0)$ $(-2, 1)$ $x + 5y = 3$ **19.** $(3, 0)$ $(-4, 0)$ $y = 0$

20. $(-2, 1)$ $(3, 6)$ $x - y = -3$ **21.** $(2, 3)$ $(1, 5)$ $2x + y = 7$ **22.** $(6, 0)$ $(2, 1)$

23. $(2, -2)$ $(5, 6)$ **24.** $(-4, -2)$ $(0, -5)$ **25.** $(-1, -2)$ $(0, 3)$

26. $(-2, -3)$ $(-1, 2)$ $5x - y = -7$ **27.** $(-3, -1)$ $(1, -4)$ $3x + 4y = -13$ **28.** $(2, -1)$ $(-3, 4)$ $x + y = 1$

Write an equation in standard form for each line described.

B   **29.** The line that passes through the point $(-1, 4)$ and has the same slope as the graph of $2x - y = 8$. $2x - y = -6$

    30. The line that passes through the point $(-3, 0)$ and has the same slope as the graph of $x - 3y = 9$. $x - 3y = -3$

C   **31.** The line that passes through the point $(-3, -5)$ and has the same y-intercept as the graph of $x + 2y = 8$. $3x - y = -4$

    32. The line that has slope $\frac{1}{2}$ and passes through the point of intersection of the graphs of $x - 6y = 10$ and $x - y = 5$. $x - 2y = 6$

    33. The line whose x-intercept is -6 and whose y-intercept is 3. (The x-intercept of a line is the x-coordinate of the point where the line crosses the x-axis.) $x - 2y = -6$

INTRODUCTION TO FUNCTIONS   **329**

$b = -\frac{5}{2}$

$y = \frac{1}{2}x - \frac{5}{2}$

$x - 2y = 5$

Supplementary Materials

Practice Master 52
Progress Test 32

Suggested Assignments

Minimum
    329/1–4, 5–29 odd
S 326/26, 27
Average
    329/1–31 odd
S 326/24, 26
Maximum
    329/1–29 odd, 31–33
S 326/26

Additional A Exercises

Write an equation in standard form of the line that has the given slope and passes through the given point.

1. $m = 4$; $(2, 0)$
    $4x - y = 8$

2. $m = 2$; $(0, 3)$
    $2x - y = -3$

3. $m = -3$; $(1, 1)$
    $3x + y = 4$

4. $m = -6$; $(2, 4)$
    $6x + y = 16$

5. $m = \frac{1}{2}$; $(0, 4)$

    $x - 2y = -8$

6. $m = \frac{2}{3}$; $(1, 0)$

    $2x - 3y = 2$

Additional Answers Written Exercises

22. $x + 4y = 6$

23. $8x - 3y = 22$

24. $3x + 4y = -20$

25. $5x - y = -3$

Self-Test 1

VOCABULARY   slope (p. 320)   slope-intercept form of an
                   y-intercept (p. 324)   equation (p. 325)

1. Find the slope of the line that passes through the points $(1, 2)$ and $(3, 5)$.   Obj. 9-1, p. 319

2. Find the slope of the line $y = 2$.

3. Find the slope and the y-intercept of the line whose equation is $2x - 3y = 1$.   Obj. 9-2, p. 324

4. Write in standard form an equation of the line through point $(-1, 2)$ with slope 2.   Obj. 9-3, p. 328

5. Write in standard form an equation of the line through points $(-3, 0)$ and $(0, 3)$.

Check your answers with those at the back of the book.

Biography   Percy Lavon Julian

Percy Lavon Julian (1899–1975), who received a Ph.D. in organic chemistry in Vienna, is sometimes called the "soybean chemist" because of his outstanding work with this bean. Using extracts from the soybean, he was able to produce synthetic cortisone, a drug used in the treatment of arthritis; synthetic physostigmine, a drug used to treat the eye disease glaucoma; and synthetic hormones that are used in the treatment of a variety of disorders. As a result of Percy Julian's work, these drugs can be produced in large quantities, making them available to all.

Julian also used soy protein to make a foam product that was used extensively to fight gasoline and oil fires. In 1950 Percy Julian was voted Chicagoan of the Year.

FUNCTIONS

9-4 *Functions Defined by Equations*

OBJECTIVE To understand what a function is and how to find its values.

An equation such as $y = 5x + 2$ assigns to each number in the domain of the variable x another number, the value of y. For example, if the domain of x is $\{2, 4, 6\}$, the equation $y = 5x + 2$ assigns the following values to y:

$$y = 5 \cdot 2 + 2 = 12$$
$$y = 5 \cdot 4 + 2 = 22$$
$$y = 5 \cdot 6 + 2 = 32$$

Thus, the given equation pairs each member of $\{2, 4, 6\}$ with a single member of $\{12, 22, 32\}$, as shown by the diagram. This example illustrates the mathematical idea of a *function*.

A **function** consists of two sets, the **domain** and the **range**, and a *rule* which assigns to each member of the domain *exactly one* member of the range. Each member of the range must be assigned to *at least one* member of the domain.

In the preceding example, the rule that defines the function is the equation $y = 5x + 2$, the domain D is $\{2, 4, 6\}$, and the range R is $\{12, 22, 32\}$.

The rule that defines a function may also be written using an arrow notation and a single letter, such as f, g, F, or H, to name the function. The **arrow notation**

$$f: x \to 5x + 2$$

is read "the function f that assigns $5x + 2$ to x" or "the function f that pairs x with $5x + 2$." To specify a function completely, you must also describe the domain of the function. The numbers assigned by the rule then form the range.

EXAMPLE 1 List the members of the range of

$$g: x \to 6 + 3x - x^2$$

if the domain $D = \{-1, 0, 1, 2\}$.

SOLUTION In $6 + 3x - x^2$ replace x with each member of D to find the members of the range, R.

$$\therefore R = \{2, 6, 8\} \quad \textbf{\textit{Answer}}$$

x	$6 + 3x - x^2$	
-1	$6 + 3(-1) - (-1)^2 = 2$	
0	$6 + 3 \cdot 0 - 0^2$	$= 6$
1	$6 + 3 \cdot 1 - 1^2$	$= 8$
2	$6 + 3 \cdot 2 - 2^2$	$= 8$

INTRODUCTION TO FUNCTIONS **331**

Suggested Assignments

Minimum
Day 1: 333/1–31 odd
 R 330/*Self-Test 1*
Day 2: 333/33–39 odd
 336/2, 5

Average
Day 1: 333/1–35 odd
 R 330/*Self-Test 1*
Day 2: 333/37–41
 336/3, 4

Maximum
Day 1: 333/1–35 odd
 R 330/*Self-Test 1*
Day 2: 333/37–41, 43
 336/1, 3, 5, 6

*NOTE: Day 2 for all levels
finishes Sec. 9-4 and
covers Sec. 9-5.*

Notice that the function g in Example 1 assigns the number 8 to both 1 and 2. In specifying the range of g, however, you name 8 only once.

Members of the range of a function are called **values of the function.** Thus, in Example 1, the values of the function g are 2, 6, and 8. To indicate that the function g assigns to -1 the value 2, you write

$$g(-1) = 2,$$

which may be read "g of -1 equals 2" or "the value of g at -1 is 2." Notice that $g(-1)$ is not the product of g and -1. It names the number that g assigns to -1.

EXAMPLE 2   Given $F: z \to z^3 - 1$ with the set of real numbers as the domain, find   **a.** $F(1)$ **b.** $F(-1)$ **c.** $F(2)$.

SOLUTION   First write the equation: $F(z) = z^3 - 1$

Then: **a.** $F(1) = 1^3 - 1 = 0$
b. $F(-1) = (-1)^3 - 1 = -2$
c. $F(2) = 2^3 - 1 = 7$

You may use whatever variable you choose to define a function. For example, $G: t \to t^3 - 1$ with the set of real numbers as the domain is the same function as F in Example 2. Both F and G assign to each real number its cube decreased by 1.

Unless otherwise stated, you may assume in this text that each domain is the set of real numbers.

Oral Exercises

Given the function $g: x \to 3 - 2x$, find the following values of g.

1. $g(0)$ 3

2. $g(-1)$ 5

3. $g(1)$ 1

4. $g(2)$ $^{-1}$

5. $g(-2)$ 7

6. $g(5)$ -7

7. $g(8)$ -13

8. $g(-8)$ 19

State the range of each function.

9. $f: u \to u + 2, \quad D = \{0, 1, 2\}$ {2, 3, 4}

10. $g: m \to 3 - m, \quad D = \{-1, 0, 1\}$ {2, 3, 4}

11. $F: t \to t^2, \quad D = \left\{\frac{1}{2}, 0, -\frac{1}{2}\right\}$ $\left\{0, \frac{1}{4}\right\}$

12. $G: x \to x^2 + 1, \quad D = \{-1, 0, 1\}$ {1, 2}

13. $h: k \to 3k^2, \quad D = \{0, 1, 2\}$ {0, 3, 12}

14. $H: x \to x^2 + 3, \quad D = \{-1, 0, 1\}$ {3, 4}

Complete the following statements about the function $g: x \to x^2 - 1$.

15. The value of g at -2 is __?__. 3

16. The value of g at 2 is __?__. 3

17. The value of g at __?__ is -1. 0

18. The value of g at both __?__ and __?__ is 0. 1, −1

Written Exercises

Given $f: x \rightarrow 4 - 3x$, find the following values of f.

A   **1.** $f(0)$ 4   **2.** $f(-1)$ 7   **3.** $f(1)$ 1   **4.** $f(-2)$ 10

    5. $f(3)$ -5 **6.** $f(-4)$ 16   **7.** $f(\tfrac{1}{3})$ 3   **8.** $f(-\tfrac{1}{3})$ 5

Given $G(t) = t^2 + 2t$, find the following values of G.

    9. $G(0)$ 0   **10.** $G(1)$ 3   **11.** $G(2)$ 8   **12.** $G(-1)$ -1

   13. $G(-2)$ 0   **14.** $G(3)$ 15   **15.** $G(\tfrac{1}{2})$ $\tfrac{5}{4}$ **16.** $G(-\tfrac{2}{3})$ $-\tfrac{8}{9}$

Find all the values of each function.

17. $g(x) = 3x + 2,\ D = \{-1, 0, 1\}$ $\{-1, 2, 5\}$ **18.** $f(x) = 2x - 5,\ D = \{1, 2, 3\}$ $\{-3, -1, 1\}$

19. $f(x) = 3 - 4x^2,\ D = \{0, 1, 2\}$ $\{3, -1, -13\}$ **20.** $h(x) = x^2 - 3x + 1,\ D = \{-1, 0, 1\}$ $\{5, 1, -1\}$

21. $G(m) = \dfrac{6}{3m - 1},\ D = \{-1, 0, 1\}$ $\{-\tfrac{3}{2}, -6, 3\}$ **22.** $F(t) = 8 + \dfrac{1}{t + 3},\ D = \{-2, -1, 0\}$ $\{9, \tfrac{17}{2}, \tfrac{25}{3}\}$

Find the range of each function.

23. $h: t \rightarrow 3 - 2t,\ D = \{-2, 0, 2\}$ $\{7, 3, -1\}$ **24.** $g: t \rightarrow -1 - 3t,\ D = \{-3, -1, 1\}$ $\{8, 2, -4\}$

25. $r: x \rightarrow \dfrac{6}{x},\ D = \{1, 2, 3\}$ $\{6, 3, 2\}$ **26.** $k: t \rightarrow \dfrac{12}{t + 1},\ D = \{1, 2, 3\}$ $\{6, 4, 3\}$

27. $g: x \rightarrow \dfrac{x^2 + 3}{3x + 1},\ D = \{-1, 0, 1\}$ $\{-2, 3, 1\}$ **28.** $h: v \rightarrow \dfrac{v^2 + v}{v - 1},\ D = \{-3, 0, 3\}$ $\{-\tfrac{3}{2}, 0, 6\}$

B **29.** $f: t \rightarrow (3t - 1)(3t + 1),\ D = \{-1, 0, 1\}$ $\{8, -1\}$ **30.** $F: z \rightarrow (z - 2)^2,\ D = \{0, 2, 4\}$ $\{4, 0\}$

   31. $f: z \rightarrow z^2 - 3z + 2,\ D = \{1, 2, 3\}$ $\{0, 2\}$ **32.** $h: x \rightarrow x^3 - 3x^2 + 2x,\ D = \{0, 1, 2\}$ $\{0\}$

   33. $G: u \rightarrow (1 - u^2)^3,\ D = \{-2, -1, 0, 1\}$ $\{-27, 0, 1\}$

   34. $H: x \rightarrow (x^2 - 2x)^2,\ D = \{-2, 0, 1, 2\}$ $\{64, 0, 1\}$

   35. $f: z \rightarrow 3(z - 1)^2 - 8,\ D = \{-1, 0, 1, 2, 3\}$ $\{-8, -5, 4\}$

   36. $g: t \rightarrow (t - 2)(t - 1),\ D = \{\tfrac{1}{2}, 1, 1\tfrac{1}{2}, 2, 2\tfrac{1}{2}\}$ $\{-\tfrac{1}{4}, 0, \tfrac{3}{4}\}$

Given that $f(x) = 3x^2$ and $g(x) = -2x^2$, find each of the following.

37. $\tfrac{1}{2}f(4)$ 24   **38.** $2g(-2)$ -16 **39.** $f(1) + g(1)$ 1   **40.** $f(2) - g(2)$ 20

Given that $f(x) = 2x^2$ and $g(x) = 3x$, find each of the following. (*Hint:* To find $g[f(2)]$, first find $f(2)$.)

C **41.** **a.** $g(1)$ 3   **b.** $f(1)$ 2   **c.** $g[f(1)]$ 6   **d.** $f[g(1)]$ 18

   42. **a.** $g(-2)$ -6 **b.** $f(-2)$ 8   **c.** $g[f(-2)]$ 24   **d.** $f[g(-2)]$ 72

   43. **a.** Is it true that $g[f(x)] = f[g(x)]$ for all real values of x? Base your answer on your results for Exercises 41 and 42.   No

       b. Find a value of x for which $g[f(x)] = f[g(x)]$.   0

INTRODUCTION TO FUNCTIONS   **333**

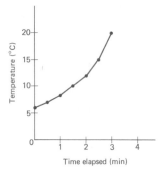
9-5 *Functions Described by Tables and Graphs*

OBJECTIVE   To define functions in other ways.

In Section 9-4 the rules for functions were given as equations or with arrow notation. There are many numerical relationships in the world around you which illustrate the idea of a function but which cannot be defined by such rules. For example, the radius of each growth ring of a tree is related to the amount of rainfall in each year of the tree's life. Also, you can relate the attendance at a movie theater to the day of the week.

Sometimes functions are defined by giving a table of corresponding values. The table below shows the attendance at the first four games the Eagles played this year. The contents of the table can also be presented as a *correspondence* and as a set of ordered pairs.

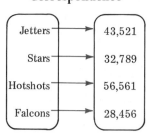

Table		**Correspondence**	**Ordered Pairs**

Table

Opponent	Attendance
Jetters	43,521
Stars	32,789
Hotshots	56,561
Falcons	28,456

Correspondence

Jetters → 43,521
Stars → 32,789
Hotshots → 56,561
Falcons → 28,456

Ordered Pairs

(Jetters,   43,521)
(Stars,   32,789)
(Hotshots, 56,561)
(Falcons, 28,456)

Corresponding to each team listed in the table there is one and only one attendance figure. Therefore, the table describes a function with domain

$$D = \{\text{Jetters, Stars, Hotshots, Falcons}\}$$

and range

$$R = \{43{,}521,\ 32{,}789,\ 56{,}561,\ 28{,}456\}.$$

It is easier to compare the attendance figures if the facts are shown in a *bar graph*. In the following graph, the members of the domain are listed down the left side. For each member of the domain a horizontal bar is drawn to represent the corresponding value in the range of the function. It is clear from the graph that the game with the greatest attendance was played against the Hotshots.

334   *CHAPTER 9*

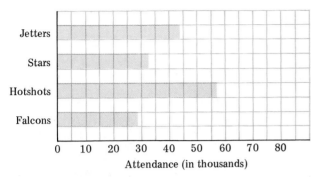

a. Why does the table describe a function?
Each member of the domain is paired with exactly one member of the range.

b. Make a bar graph for the data.

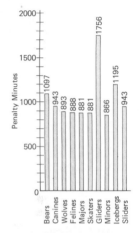

When the members of the domain of a function are in a numerical succession, you may use a *broken-line graph*. The one at the right shows the number of people immigrating to the Yukon in each year from 1972 through 1977. Note that in this graph the members of the domain are listed across the bottom.

The line segments do *not* show the number of immigrants for the months in between each year marked. They do, however, help you see the trends from year to year.

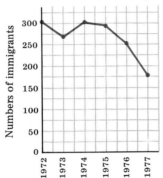

The paired numbers in the function pictured by the graph above can be displayed as the set of ordered pairs.

{(1972, 305), (1973, 268), (1974, 300), (1975, 290), (1976, 250), (1977, 174)}.

The domain of the function consists of the first coordinates of the ordered pairs, and the range consists of the second coordinates.

Oral Exercises

State the domain and range of the function shown by each table.

1.

Student	Height
Arlene	172 cm
Ben	185 cm
Carla	150 cm
Denise	163 cm
Ed	180 cm
Frank	150 cm

2.

Month	Rainfall
May	50 mm
June	92 mm
July	68 mm
August	56 mm
September	35 mm
October	19 mm

INTRODUCTION TO FUNCTIONS **335**

Supplementary Materials

Practice Master 53

Computer Activity 27
Fitting Lines to Data
In many scientific experiments one needs to find the line of best fit for the data. The program in this activity generates such a line for a given amount of data.

Suggested Assignments

NOTE: Day 2 of Sec. 9-4 for all levels finishes Sec. 9-4 and covers Sec. 9-5.

Additional Answers
Oral Exercises

1. $D = \{$Arlene, Ben, Carla, Denise, Ed, Frank$\}$;
$R = \{172, 185, 150, 163, 180\}$

2. $D = \{$May, June, July, August, September, October$\}$;
$R = \{50, 92, 68, 56, 35, 19\}$

(continued)

3. D = {Erieview Plaza, Iolani Towers, John Hancock, Main Tower, Place Victoria, Sears Tower}; R = {40, 38, 60, 26, 47, 110}

4. D = {1800, 1850, 1900, 1950, 1970, 1978, 1979}; R = {910 million, 1,130 million, 1,600 million, 2,510 million, 3,575 million, 4,219 million, 4,321 million}

5. D = {1967, 1969, 1971, 1973, 1975, 1977}; R = {49.7 million, 53.2 million, 59.8 million, 63.2 million, 54.3 million, 63.7 million}

6. D = {1950, 1954, 1958, 1962, 1966, 1970, 1974, 1978}; R = {1865, 1759, 2001, 4029, 2649, 2309, 2261, 2232}

Additional A Exercises

Team	Pts. per game
Island City	72
Edtown	81
Portown	68
Smith Port	77

1. State the domain of the function shown by the table.
{Island City, Edtown, Portown, Smith Port}

2. State the range of the function. {72, 81, 68, 77}

3. Make a bar graph for the facts shown in the table.

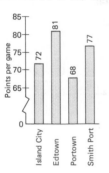

State the domain and range of the function shown by each table.

3.

Building	Stories
Erieview Plaza	40
Iolani Towers	38
John Hancock	60
Main Tower	26
Place Victoria	47
Sears Tower	110

4.

Year	World Population (millions)
1800	910
1850	1,130
1900	1,600
1950	2,510
1970	3,575
1978	4,219
1979	4,321

5.

World Cotton Production						
Year	1967	1969	1971	1973	1975	1977
Millions of bales	49.7	53.2	59.8	63.2	54.3	63.7

6.

Highest Individual NBA Scores								
Year	1950	1954	1958	1962	1966	1970	1974	1978
Points	1865	1759	2001	4029	2649	2309	2261	2232

Written Exercises

A **1–3.** Make a bar graph for the facts shown in each table in Oral Exercises 1-3.

4–6. Display the function specified by each table in Oral Exercises 4-6 as a set of ordered pairs. Then make a broken-line graph for each function.

Application   Histograms

A *histogram* is a bar graph used to summarize a large set of data. The horizontal axis of a histogram represents ranges of observed values, and the vertical axis indicates their frequencies.

EXAMPLE

The points scored in each game played by the Conestoga High School basketball team are listed on the following page.

336 *CHAPTER 9*

Draw a histogram presenting these scores in ten-point intervals.

63	67	82	87	60	53
68	79	74	79	93	71
61	59	67	48	68	73

SOLUTION

1. Use tally marks to count the number of scores within each ten-point interval. A measurement occurring on a boundary is included in the interval that will be to the measurement's left on the graph. For example, the score of 60 is counted in the interval from 50 to 60.

2. Draw the histogram.

Range	Frequency	
40–50	|	1
50–60	|||	3
60–70	卌 |	6
70–80	卌	5
80–90	||	2
90–100	|	1

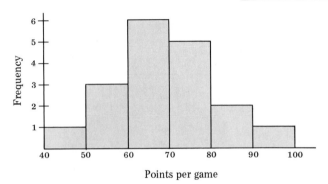

Points per game

Exercises

The following pulse rates (expressed in beats per minute) were recorded for a group of 40 people.

58	86	101	73	96	81	94	61	103	76
81	77	66	82	79	64	84	90	98	71
74	88	76	59	87	63	82	93	88	106
69	78	77	67	83	89	72	73	68	66

1. Draw a histogram for these data. Use intervals of width 10, such as 50–60 and 60–70, on the horizontal axis.

2. Which ten-unit interval represents the greatest number of people? 80–90

3. How many of the people have pulse rates between 60 and 70? 8

4. How many of the people have pulse rates greater than 80? 19

5. How many of the people have pulse rates no greater than 90? 33

INTRODUCTION TO FUNCTIONS   **337**

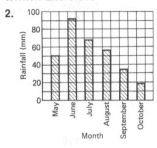
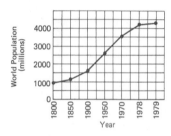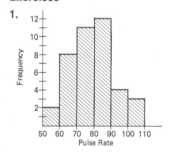

Chalkboard Examples

For the following quadratic equations, state whether each has a maximum or minimum value and find the coordinates of the vertex of the graph.

1. $y = 2x^2 + 2x$
minimum; x-coordinate of vertex:

$$-\frac{b}{2a} = -\frac{2}{2(2)} = -\frac{1}{2}$$

y-coordinate of vertex:

$$2\left(-\frac{1}{2}\right)^2 + 2\left(-\frac{1}{2}\right) = -\frac{1}{2}$$

vertex: $\left(-\frac{1}{2}, -\frac{1}{2}\right)$

2. $y = -5x^2$
maximum; x-coordinate of vertex:

$$-\frac{b}{2a} = -\frac{0}{2(-5)} = 0$$

y-coordinate of vertex:
$-5(0)^2 = 0$ vertex: $(0, 0)$

3. $y = x^2 - 3x + 2$
minimum; x-coordinate of vertex:

$$-\frac{b}{2a} = -\frac{-3}{2(1)} = \frac{3}{2}$$

y-coordinate of vertex:

$$\left(\frac{3}{2}\right)^2 - 3\left(\frac{3}{2}\right) + 2$$

$$= \frac{9}{4} - \frac{9}{2} + 2$$

$$= -\frac{1}{4}$$

vertex: $\left(\frac{3}{2}, -\frac{1}{4}\right)$

9-6 Quadratic Functions

OBJECTIVE To graph quadratic functions.

You have seen a function presented as a set of ordered pairs and shown in a bar graph or a broken-line graph. A function defined by an equation in two variables can be presented as the set of ordered pairs that is the solution set of the equation. The graph of such a function in a coordinate plane is the graph of the defining equation. For example:

> The function $f: x \rightarrow 2x - 8$ can be defined by $y = 2x - 8$.
> The graph of f is the straight line with slope 2 and y-intercept -8.

A **linear function** is a function that can be defined by a linear equation. The graph of every linear function is a straight line.

Now consider the function defined by the quadratic equation

$$y = x^2 - 2x - 3.$$

You can graph this function by first finding the coordinates of selected points, as shown in the table at the right. Then plot the points and connect them with a smooth curve.

x	$x^2 - 2x - 3 = y$
-2	$(-2)^2 - 2(-2) - 3 = 5$
-1	$(-1)^2 - 2(-1) - 3 = 0$
0	$0^2 - 2(0) - 3 = -3$
1	$1^2 - 2(1) - 3 = -4$
2	$2^2 - 2(2) - 3 = -3$
3	$3^2 - 2(3) - 3 = 0$
4	$4^2 - 2(4) - 3 = 5$

The curve shown at the right is a **parabola.** This parabola opens upward and has a **minimum point** (lowest point): $(1, -4)$. The y-coordinate of this point is the least value of the function.

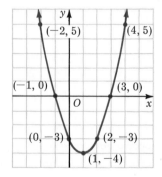

338 *CHAPTER 9*

Compare the parabola just seen with the graph of the function defined by the quadratic equation

$$y = -x^2 + 2x + 3.$$

x	$-x^2 + 2x + 3 = y$
-2	$-(-2)^2 + 2(-2) + 3 = -5$
-1	$-(-1)^2 + 2(-1) + 3 = 0$
0	$-0^2 + 2(0) + 3 = 3$
1	$-1^2 + 2(1) + 3 = 4$
2	$-2^2 + 2(2) + 3 = 3$
3	$-3^2 + 2(3) + 3 = 0$
4	$-4^2 + 2(4) + 3 = -5$

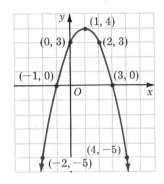

This graph is a parabola that opens downward and has a **maximum point** (highest point): $(1, 4)$. The y-coordinate of this point is the greatest value of the function.

A **quadratic function** is a function that can be defined by a quadratic equation of the form

$$y = ax^2 + bx + c \quad (a \neq 0).$$

The graph of every quadratic function is a parabola.

The minimum or maximum point of a parabola is called the **vertex**. Notice that in each example shown, the points except the vertex occur in *pairs that have the same y-coordinate*. Also, the average of the x-coordinates of any such pair is the x-coordinate of the vertex. For the parabola above:

Pairs of points		x-coordinate of vertex
$(-2, -5)$	$(4, -5)$	Average: $\dfrac{-2 + 4}{2} = 1$
$(-1, 0)$	$(3, 0)$	Average: $\dfrac{-1 + 3}{2} = 1$
$(0, 3)$	$(2, 3)$	Average: $\dfrac{0 + 2}{2} = 1$

Graph each equation. Determine the vertex by using the formula $x = -\dfrac{b}{2a}$.

4. $y = 2x^2 - 4x - 1$

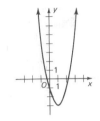

$$-\frac{b}{2a} = -\frac{-4}{2(2)}$$
$$= 1$$
$$y = 2(1)^2 - 4(1) - 1$$
$$= -3$$

Vertex is at $(1, -3)$.

5. $y = -x^2 + 4x + 1$

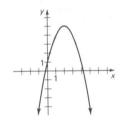

$$-\frac{b}{2a} = -\frac{4}{2(-1)}$$
$$= 2$$
$$y = -2^2 + 4(2) + 1$$
$$= 5$$

Vertex is at $(2, 5)$.

Supplementary Materials

Practice Master 54

Progress Test 33

Suggested Assignments

Minimum
341/1–25 odd

Average
341/1–25 odd, 26

Maximum
341/1–25 odd, 26

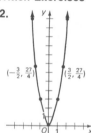
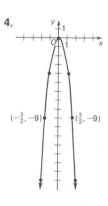
To graph an equation of the form $y = ax^2 + bx + c$ $(a \neq 0)$, it is helpful to find the x-coordinate of the vertex and then plot enough points on both sides of the vertex to enable you to draw a smooth curve.

The graphs at the right illustrate that the x-coordinate of the vertex is the same for equations that differ only in the constant term. Therefore, a formula for the x-coordinate of the vertex of $y = ax^2 + bx + c$ can be found using the two points where the graph of $y = ax^2 + bx$ crosses the x-axis:

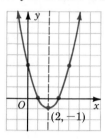

$y = x^2 - 4x + 3$

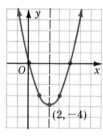

$y = x^2 - 4x$

Let $y = 0$:
$$0 = ax^2 + bx$$
$$0 = x(ax + b)$$
$$x = 0 \quad \text{or} \quad ax + b = 0$$

$$\therefore x = 0 \quad \text{or} \quad x = -\frac{b}{a}$$

The average of these x-coordinates is $\dfrac{0 + \left(-\dfrac{b}{a}\right)}{2}$, or $-\dfrac{b}{2a}$.

In general:

THE GRAPH OF $y = ax^2 + bx + c$ $(a \neq 0)$

If a is positive, the parabola opens upward.
If a is negative, the parabola opens downward.
The x-coordinate of the vertex is $-\dfrac{b}{2a}$.

Oral Exercises

State whether the graph of each quadratic equation opens upward or downward.

1. $y = x^2 - 5x - 4$ Up   **2.** $y = -2x^2 + x + 1$ Down   **3.** $y = 9 - x^2$ Down

4. $x^2 - 9 = y$ Up   **5.** $5x^2 + 5x = y$ Up   **6.** $y = -\dfrac{1}{2}x^2$ Down

340   *CHAPTER 9*

State whether the graph of each quadratic function has a minimum or a maximum point.

7. $f: x \to x^2 - 2x + 1$ Min.   8. $g: x \to -4 - 4x - x^2$ Max. 9. $h: x \to 5x^2 - 3x$ Min.

10. $T: x \to 1 - x^2$ Max.   11. $S: x \to -10x^2 + x + 5$ Max.   12. $p: x \to \frac{3}{4}x^2$ Min.

Written Exercises

Find the coordinates of the vertex of the graph of each equation. Use the vertex and six other points to graph the equation.

A 1. $y = x^2$ (0, 0)   2. $y = 3x^2$ (0, 0)   3. $y = -2x^2$ (0, 0)

4. $y = -4x^2$ (0, 0)   5. $y = \frac{1}{2}x^2$ (0, 0)   6. $y = -\frac{1}{2}x^2$ (0, 0)

7. $y = x^2 + 4x$ (−2, −4)   8. $y = -x^2 + 2x$ (1, 1)   9. $y = -x^2 - 2x + 1$
                                                                9. (−1, 2)

10. $y = x^2 - 3x - 4$ 11. $y = \frac{1}{2}x^2 - 2$ (0, −2)   12. $y = -\frac{1}{2}x^2 + 4x + 8$
    $\left(\frac{3}{2}, -\frac{25}{4}\right)$ 12. (4, 16)

Find the least value of each function.

13. $f: x \to x^2 + 3x - \frac{9}{4}$ 14. $g: x \to x^2 + 4$ 4   15. $h: x \to x^2 - x - 6$ $-\frac{25}{4}$

16. $r: x \to 4 - 6x + 3x^2$ 1   17. $F: x \to 4x^2 - 6$ −6   18. $G: x \to \frac{1}{2}x^2$ 0

Find the greatest value of each function.

19. $f: x \to -x^2 - 3x$ $\frac{9}{4}$ 20. $F: x \to -2x^2 + 4x$ 2   21. $g: x \to -x^2 - 6x - 10$ −1

22. $G: x \to 9 - 7x - 14x^2$ $\frac{79}{8}$ 23. $H: x \to -2x^2 + x$ $\frac{1}{8}$ 24. $h: x \to -\frac{1}{3}x^2$ 0

B 25. a. On the same set of axes draw the graphs of $y = x^2$, $y = x^2 + 1$, and $y = x^2 - 2$.

   b. Use your results in part (a) to describe the changes in the graph of $y = x^2 + c$ as the value of c increases; as c decreases. Graph moves up; graph moves down.

26. a. On the same set of axes draw the graphs of $y = \frac{1}{2}x^2$, $y = x^2$, and $y = 2x^2$.

   b. On the same set of axes draw the graphs of $y = -\frac{1}{2}x^2$, $y = -x^2$, and $y = -2x^2$.

   c. Use your results in parts (a) and (b) to describe the change in the graph of $y = ax^2$ as $|a|$ increases. Graph becomes steeper.

INTRODUCTION TO FUNCTIONS   **341**

6.

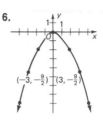

8.

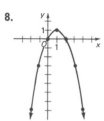

10.

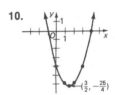

12.

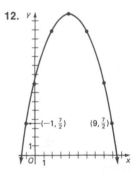

26. a.

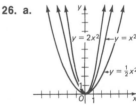

26. b.

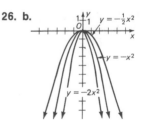

Computer Key-In

The following computer program in BASIC will compute coordinates for use in graphing quadratic functions. The program will compute the coordinates of the vertex and five points on each side of it. When you use the program, you input the values A, B, C of

$$y = Ax^2 + Bx + C.$$

```
10   PRINT "INPUT A (NOT ZERO), B, C";
20   INPUT A,B,C
30   IF A=0 THEN 10
40   LET X1=-B/(2*A)
50   LET Y1=A*X1*X1+B*X1+C
60   PRINT "VERTEX AT (";X1;",";Y1;")"
70   LET X1=INT(X1)
80   PRINT "X", "Y"
90   FOR X=X1-5 TO X1+5
100  PRINT X,A*X*X+B*X+C
110  NEXT X
120  END
```

Quick Quiz

1. If $f(x) = 3 - 2x$, find $f(-3)$.   9

2. Find the range of the given function:
$h: t \rightarrow -16t^2 + 32t$,
$D = \left\{0, \frac{1}{2}, 1, 1\frac{1}{2}, 2\right\}$

{0, 12, 16}

3. Display the function in Exercise 2 as a set of ordered pairs.

$\left\{(0, 0), \left(\frac{1}{2}, 12\right), (1, 16)\right.$

$\left(1\frac{1}{2}, 12\right), (2, 0)\right\}$

4. Find the coordinates of the vertex of the graph of $y = x^2 + 4x - 3$
$(-2, -7)$

5. Find the greatest value of the function $g(x) = 8x - x^2$.   16

Self-Test 2

VOCABULARY
function (p. 331)
domain of a function (p. 331)
range of a function (p. 331)
arrow notation (p. 331)
value of a function (p. 332)
linear function (p. 338)

parabola (p. 338)
minimum point (p. 338)
maximum point (p. 339)
quadratic function (p. 339)
vertex (p. 339)

1. Given $f(x) = 2x - 1$, find $f(3)$.

Obj. 9-4, p. 331

2. Find the range of the given function:
$g: t \rightarrow t^2 - 2t - 3$ $D = \{-1, 0, 1, 2, 3\}$

3. The table shows a function.

   a. State the domain and range of the function.

   b. Display the function as a set of ordered pairs.

Stock number	Price
N7621	$12.88
N6523	$ 9.85
V2231	$ 3.39
V2232	$ 3.39

Obj. 9-5, p. 334

4. Find the coordinates of the vertex of the graph of $y = 2x^2 + 4x - 1$.

Obj. 9-6, p. 338

5. Find the greatest value of the function
$f: x \rightarrow -\frac{1}{5}x^2.$

Check your answers with those at the back of the book.

342   *CHAPTER 9*

VARIATION

9-7 *Direct Variation*

OBJECTIVE   To use the concept of direct variation to solve problems.

The table below shows the distance, y, that a group of hikers will walk in x hours if they maintain a steady pace of 6 km/h.

Time in hours: x	Distance in kilometers: y
1	6
2	12
3	18
4	24
5	30

You can see that

$$y = 6x$$

and that this equation defines a function. Notice that if the hikers double the hiking time, the distance covered is doubled; if they triple the time, the distance is tripled. You can say that the distance *varies directly as* the time. This function is an example of a *direct variation*.

A **linear direct variation** (or simply, a **direct variation**) is a function defined by an equation of the form

$$y = kx, \text{ where } k \text{ is a nonzero constant.}$$

You can say that *y varies directly as x*, or *y varies with x*. The constant k is called the **constant of variation.**
When the domain is the set of real numbers, the graph of a direct variation is a straight line through the origin.

EXAMPLE 1   Given that d varies directly as t, and that $d = 110$ when $t = 2$, find the following:
  a. the constant of variation
  b. the value of d when $t = 3$

SOLUTION   Let $d = kt$.
  a. Substitute $d = 110$ and $t = 2$: $110 = k \cdot 2$
                                             $55 = k$ ***Answer***
  b. Substitute $k = 55$ and $t = 3$: $d = 55 \cdot 3 = 165$ ***Answer***

INTRODUCTION TO FUNCTIONS   **343**

Chalkboard Examples
Find the constant of variation.
1. a varies directly as b, and $a = 10$ when $b = 16$.

$a = kb$

$k = \dfrac{a}{b} = \dfrac{10}{16} = \dfrac{5}{8}$

2. y varies directly as x, and $x = \dfrac{2}{3}$ when $y = 14$.

$y = kx$

$k = \dfrac{y}{x} = \dfrac{14}{\frac{2}{3}} = 21$

3. If y varies directly as x, and $y = 100$ when $x = 20$, find y when $x = 3$.

Method 1
$y = kx,\ 100 = k(20)$
$k = 5$
$y = 5x,\ y = 5(3) = 15$
$\therefore\ y = 15$ when $x = 3$

Method 2

$\dfrac{y_1}{x_1} = \dfrac{y_2}{x_2},\ \dfrac{100}{20} = \dfrac{y_2}{3}$

$300 = 20\,y_2$

$y_2 = 15$

$\therefore\ y = 15$ when $x = 3$

4. Find the value of a if $(2, a)$ and $(11, 88)$ are ordered pairs of the same direct variation.

Method 1
$y = kx,\ 88 = k(11)$
$k = 8$
$y = 8x,\ a = 8(2)$
$a = 16$

Method 2

$\dfrac{y_1}{x_1} = \dfrac{y_2}{x_2},\ \dfrac{a}{2} = \dfrac{88}{11}$

$11a = 2(88)$

$a = \dfrac{2(88)}{11}$

$a = 16$

(continued)

343

5. The amount of money collected at the school musical varies directly with the number of tickets sold. The total amount collected on the first night was $412.50 for 275 admissions. How much was collected on the second night if 320 tickets were sold?

$$\frac{412.50}{375} = \frac{d_2}{320}$$

$$d_2 = 480$$

$$\$480.00$$

6. A length on a map is directly proportional to the distance it represents. A distance of 20 km is represented by 10 cm. What is the area of the actual region represented on the map as a square region 5 cm on a side?

$$10 = k(20)$$
$$0.5 = k$$
$$5 = 0.5(s)$$
$$10 = s$$

Area is 100 km²

If two ordered pairs of a direct variation defined by $y = kx$ are

$$(x_1, y_1), \quad \text{read "}x \text{ sub 1, } y \text{ sub 1," and}$$

$$(x_2, y_2), \quad \text{read "}x \text{ sub 2, } y \text{ sub 2,"}$$

and if neither pair is $(0, 0)$, then the coordinates satisfy $y = kx$:

$$y_1 = kx_1 \quad \text{and} \quad y_2 = kx_2.$$

From these equations you can write the ratios

$$\frac{y_1}{x_1} = k \quad \text{and} \quad \frac{y_2}{x_2} = k.$$

Since each ratio equals k, the ratios are equal:

$$\frac{y_1}{x_1} = \frac{y_2}{x_2}, \quad \text{read "}y_1 \text{ is to } x_1 \text{ as } y_2 \text{ is to } x_2.\text{"}$$

Since the equality of two ratios is a proportion (page 240), k is sometimes called the **constant of proportionality,** and y is said to be *directly proportional to x.*

When you use a proportion to solve a problem, you will find it helpful to recall that the product of the extremes equals the product of the means.

EXAMPLE 2

The amount of interest earned on savings is directly proportional to the amount of money saved. If $20 interest is earned on $250, how much interest will be earned on $700 in the same period of time?

SOLUTION

Step 1 The problem asks for the interest on $700.

Step 2 Let i, in dollars, be the interest on d dollars.

$$i_1 = 20 \qquad i_2 = \underline{\ ?\ }$$
$$d_1 = 250 \qquad d_2 = 700$$

Step 3 An equation can be written in the form $\frac{i_1}{d_1} = \frac{i_2}{d_2}$:

$$\frac{20}{250} = \frac{i_2}{700}$$

Step 4 $20(700) = 250i_2$
$$14,000 = 250i_2$$
$$56 = i_2$$

Step 5 The check is left to you.

$\therefore$ the interest earned on $700 is $56. *Answer*

Examples 1 and 2 illustrate two methods of solving problems involving direct variation. To solve Example 2 by the method shown in Example 1, first write the equation $i = kd$ and solve for the constant of variation, k, by using the fact that $i = 25$ when $d = 250$. Then use the resulting value of k to find the value of i when $d = 700$. Complete the problem this way for yourself. You will find the exercises and problems of this section easier if you understand *both* methods.

Oral Exercises

State whether or not the equation defines a direct variation. For each direct variation, state the constant of variation.

1. $y = 2x$ Yes; 2   **2.** $p = 6s$ Yes; 6   **3.** $xy = 8$ No   **4.** $d = 2.6t$ Yes; 2.6

5. $\frac{1}{2}x = y$ Yes; $\frac{1}{2}$ **6.** $\frac{y}{x} = 3$ Yes; 3   **7.** $p = \frac{12}{q}$ No   **8.** $C = 2\pi r$ Yes; 2π

9. $A = \pi r^2$ No   **10.** $\frac{b}{a} = 1$ Yes; 1   **11.** $y = 2x^2$ No   **12.** $\frac{x}{y} = \frac{2}{3}$ Yes; $\frac{3}{2}$

State whether or not each set of ordered pairs is a direct variation.

SAMPLE $\{(8, 6), (12, 9), (24, 18)\}$

SOLUTION $\frac{6}{8} = \frac{3}{4}, \frac{9}{12} = \frac{3}{4}, \frac{18}{24} = \frac{3}{4}$; since the ratios are equal, the function is a direct variation.

13. $\{(2, 4), (3, 6), (4, 8)\}$ Yes   **14.** $\{(1, 3), (4, 12), (-3, -9)\}$ Yes

15. $\{(0, 1), (1, 2), (2, 3)\}$ No   **16.** $\{(-1, 2), (3, -6), (5, -10)\}$ Yes

17. $\{(-1, 7), (2, -14), (-3, 21)\}$ Yes   **18.** $\{(-2, 4), (4, -8), (-6, -12)\}$
                                                                      No

Written Exercises

In Exercises 1-6, find the constant of variation.

A   **1.** y varies directly as x, and $y = 12$ when $x = 72$. $\frac{1}{6}$

     2. y varies directly as x, and $y = 2$ when $x = 6$. $\frac{1}{3}$

     3. n varies directly as m, and $n = -10$ when $m = -2$.   5

     4. t varies directly as s, and $t = 168$ when $s = 14$.   12

     5. w is directly proportional to y, and $w = 150$ when $y = 6$.   25

     6. p is directly proportional to q, and $p = 225$ when $q = 15$.   15

     7. If y varies directly as x, and $y = 300$ when $x = 3$, find y when $x = 10$.   1000

     8. If w varies directly as z, and $w = 6$ when $z = 12$, find w when $z = 15$.   7.5

INTRODUCTION TO FUNCTIONS   **345**

Suggested Assignments

Minimum
   345/1–23 odd
R 342/*Self-Test 2*

Average
   345/1–21 odd, 22
R 342/*Self-Test 2*

Maximum
   345/1–19 odd, 20–23
R 342/*Self-Test 2*

Extra Practice Problems
   p. 521

Additional A Exercises

State whether or not the equation defines a direct variation. For each direct variation, state the constant of variation.

1. $a = 4b$ direct; 4

2. $c = \frac{1}{3}d$ direct; $\frac{1}{3}$

3. $xy = 10$ not direct

4. $\frac{p}{q} = 8$ direct; 8

5. $e = \frac{2}{3}f$ direct; $\frac{2}{3}$

6. $\frac{a}{b} = \frac{3}{4}$ direct; $\frac{3}{4}$ or $\frac{4}{3}$

9. If h is directly proportional to t, and $h = 325$ when $t = 6.5$, find h when $t = 12.$ 600

10. If a is directly proportional to b, and $a = 8$ when $b = 288$, find a when $b = 20.\frac{5}{9}$

Find the missing value in each exercise if (x_1, y_1) and (x_2, y_2) are ordered pairs of the same direct variation.

11. $x_1 = 12, \ y_1 = 9$
$x_2 = 28, \ y_2 = \underline{\ ?\ } \ 21$

12. $x_1 = 25, \ y_1 = \underline{\ ?\ } \ 125$
$x_2 = 20, \ y_2 = 100$

13. $x_1 = 4.8, \quad y_1 = 2$
$\ 2.4$
$x_2 = \underline{\ ?\ }, \ y_2 = 1$

14. $x_1 = \underline{\ ?\ }_{3.75}, \ y_1 = 5$
$x_2 = 6.75, \ y_2 = 9$

15. $x_1 = \frac{1}{6}, \ y_1 = \frac{1}{8}$
$x_2 = \frac{2}{3}, \ y_2 = \underline{\ ?\ } \ \frac{1}{2}$

16. $x_1 = \frac{4}{5}, \ y_1 = \underline{\ ?\ }_{\frac{1}{\frac{1}{5}}}$
$x_2 = \frac{2}{3}, \ y_2 = \frac{1}{6}$

Translate each statement into *two* formulas expressing direct variation. Use k as the constant of variation.

SAMPLE The velocity, v, of a freely falling object varies directly as the length of time, t, that it falls.

SOLUTION $v = kt$ or $\dfrac{v_1}{t_1} = \dfrac{v_2}{t_2}$

B **17.** The weight, M, of a person on the moon is directly proportional to the person's weight, E, on earth. $M = kE$ or $\dfrac{M_1}{E_1} = \dfrac{M_2}{E_2}$

18. The perimeter, P, of a square varies directly as the length, s, of a side. $P = ks$ or $\dfrac{P_1}{s_1} = \dfrac{P_2}{s_2}$

19. The amount of money, m, earned on a job varies with the number of hours, h, of work. $m = kh$ or $\dfrac{m_1}{h_1} = \dfrac{m_2}{h_2}$

20. The amount of interest, I, paid on a bank account varies directly as the amount of money, p, in the account. $I = kp$ or $\dfrac{I_1}{P_1} = \dfrac{I_2}{P_2}$

21. The amount of pressure, P, on the inner wall of a tire is directly proportional to the temperature, T, of the air in the tire. $P = kT$ or $\dfrac{P_1}{T_1} = \dfrac{P_2}{T_2}$

22. The distance, d, traveled at a fixed rate of speed varies with the time of travel, t. $d = kt$ or $\dfrac{d_1}{t_1} = \dfrac{d_2}{t_2}$

23. The income, i, from the Varsity Club car wash is directly proportional to the number, n, of cars washed. $i = kn$ or $\dfrac{i_1}{n_1} = \dfrac{i_2}{n_2}$

Problems

Solve.

A **1.** A worker's wages are directly proportional to the number of hours worked. If $26 is earned for eight hours of work, how much is earned for forty hours of work? $130

346 *CHAPTER 9*

2. The distance traveled by a truck driver at a constant rate varies with the length of time she travels. If she travels 168 km in two hours, how far will she travel in three hours? 252 km

3. The number of words typed is directly proportional to the time spent typing. If Jim can type 225 words in five minutes, how long will it take him to type a 675-word essay? 15 min

4. An estimate of the number of hot dogs that will be sold at a baseball game varies directly as the number of people expected to attend. If it is estimated that 60,000 hot dogs will be sold when 45,000 people attend, how many hot dogs are estimated to be sold when 30,000 people attend? 40,000 hot dogs

B 5. The amount of oats required in a cookie recipe is directly proportional to the amount of flour required. If the recipe calls for three measuring cups of oats and one measuring cup of flour, how many cups of oats should be used with one and one half cups of flour? 4.5 cups

6. The amount of bend of a diving board varies directly as the mass of the diver. If a 30 kg diver causes the board to bend 1.5 cm, how much will the board bend if the diver is 65 kg? 3.25 cm

7. The amount of chlorine needed for a pool varies as the size of the pool. If 5 units of chlorine is the amount needed for 2500 L of water, how much chlorine is required for 3750 L of water? 7.5 units

8. When an electric current is 35 A (amperes), the electromotive force is 315 V (volts). Find the force when the current is 50 A if the force varies directly as the current. 450 V

9. The odometer on the Santanas' car was not measuring distance correctly. For the 220 km trip from home to the grandparents' home, the odometer registered only 216.7 km. On the return trip, the Santanas had to detour for road repairs. If the odometer registered 453.1 km for the round trip, how many actual kilometers was the detour? 20 km

10. Two thermometers are exactly the same except that thermometer F is marked off into 180 equal units and thermometer C is marked off into 100 equal units. A length equal to 66.6 units on thermometer F is equal to a length of how many units on thermometer C? 37 units

Calculator Key-In _____

The *light year* is a unit used for describing very great distances, such as the distance to a neighboring star. The distance that light travels in one year is one light year. If the speed of light is about 2.9979×10^8 m/s, about how many meters is one light year? 9.4542×10^{15} m

1. Complete this chart showing the number of items
which can be purchased
for one dollar. Graph
$np = 100$.

price (cents)	number	
1	100	
2	50	
4	?	25
5	?	20
10	?	10
20	?	5
25	?	4
50	?	2
100	?	1

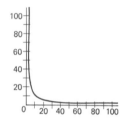

2. If a varies inversely as b
and $a = 4$ when $b = 20$,
find the constant of variation.
$ab = k$
$(4)(20) = k$
$80 = k$
$k = 80$

3. If x varies inversely as y,
$x_1 = 9$, $y_1 = 36$ and
$x_2 = 27$ then $y_2 = \underline{?}$.

$x_1 y_1 = x_2 y_2$
$9(36) = 27 y_2$
$y_2 = 12$

4. A 20 kg child sits on a
see-saw 2 m from the ful-
crum. How far from the
fulcrum should an 80 kg
adult sit in order to balance the see-saw?

(continued)

9-8 *Inverse Variation*

OBJECTIVE   To use the concept of inverse variation to solve problems.

The table shows the time, t, that it takes a car to
cover a distance of 40 km traveling at the rate of
r km/h. You can see that

$$rt = 40$$

and that this equation defines a function. Notice that
if the rate of travel is increased, the time required is
decreased so that the product is always 40. You can
say that the time *varies inversely as* the rate. This
example illustrates an *inverse variation*.

Rate in km/h: r	Time in hours: t
20	2
40	1
60	$\frac{2}{3}$
80	$\frac{1}{2}$

   An **inverse variation** is a function defined by an equation of the form

$xy = k$, when k is a nonzero constant.

$y = \dfrac{k}{x}$ for all ordered pairs other than $(0, 0)$.

You can say that y *varies inversely as* x or y *is inversely proportional to*
x. The constant k is the **constant of variation.**
   The graph of an inverse function is not a straight line since the defin-
ing equation

$$xy = k$$

is not linear; the term xy is of degree 2. The graph of $xy = 1$ is shown
below.

$xy = 1$

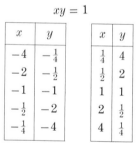

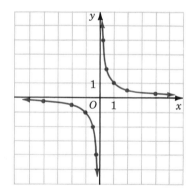

Neither x nor y can have the value 0. This graph is called a **hyperbola.**
It consists of two branches neither of which intersects an axis.
   For every nonzero value of k, the graph of $xy = k$ is a hyperbola.
When k is positive, the branches of the graph are in Quadrants I and
III. When k is negative, the graph is in Quadrants II and IV.

348   *CHAPTER 9*

In some practical problems involving inverse variation, negative answers are meaningless, and the domain and the range are limited to positive numbers. The graph of such an inverse variation has only the branch in Quadrant I.

If (x_1, y_1) and (x_2, y_2) are ordered pairs of the same inverse variation, then the coordinates satisfy the equation $xy = k$:

$$x_1y_1 = k \quad \text{and} \quad x_2y_2 = k.$$

Therefore,

$$x_1y_1 = x_2y_2.$$

Compare:

DIRECT VARIATION	INVERSE VARIATION
$y = kx$	$xy = k$
$\dfrac{y_1}{x_1} = \dfrac{y_2}{x_2}$	$x_1y_1 = x_2y_2$

These equations can be written in other equivalent forms, but the forms shown are the easiest to remember. For direct variation the quotients of coordinates are constant, and for inverse variation the products are constant.

One example of inverse variation is the law of the lever. A lever is a bar pivoted at a point called the fulcrum. If masses m_1 and m_2 are placed at distances d_1 and d_2 from the fulcrum, and the lever is at balance, then

$$m_1d_1 = m_2d_2.$$

EXAMPLE If a 10 g mass is 75 cm from the fulcrum of a lever, how far from the fulcrum is a 30 g mass which balances it?

SOLUTION Let $m_1 = 10$, $d_1 = 75$, and $m_2 = 30$. $\quad d_2 = \underline{\ ?\ }$

Use $m_1d_1 = m_2d_2$.
$$10(75) = 30d_2$$
$$25 = d_2$$

∴ the distance of the 30 g mass from the fulcrum is 25 cm. *Answer*

INTRODUCTION TO FUNCTIONS **349**

Method 1
$$m_1d_1 = m_2d_2$$
$$20 \cdot 2 = 80 \cdot d_2$$
$$\frac{40}{80} = d_2$$
$$d_2 = 0.5$$
0.5 m

Method 2
$$md = k$$
$$20 \cdot 2 = k, \ k = 40$$
$$md = 40$$
$$80 \cdot d = 40, \ d = 0.5$$
0.5 m

5. A triangle has an altitude of 2 cm and a base of 6 cm. Find the altitude of another triangle of equal area whose base is 8 cm.

$$\frac{1}{2}b_1h_1 = \frac{1}{2}b_2h_2$$

or $b_1h_1 = b_2h_2$
$$6(2) = 8h_2$$
$$h_2 = \frac{3}{2}$$

1.5 cm

6. The time it takes Margo to walk to school from her home varies inversely as her rate of walking. If she walks at a rate of 5 km/h, she will get to school in 30 min. How fast will she have to walk in order to get there in 20 min?

$$r_1t_1 = r_2t_2$$
$$5\left(\frac{1}{2}\right) = r_2\left(\frac{1}{3}\right)$$
$$\frac{5}{2} \cdot \frac{3}{1} = r_2$$
$$r_2 = 7.5$$
7.5 km/h

Supplementary Material
Practice Master 55

349

Suggested Assignments

Minimum
  350/1–13 odd
  S 346/P: 1, 3, 5

Average
  350/1–13 odd
  351/P: 1, 3, 5
  S 346/P: 1–7 odd

Maximum
  350/1–13 odd
  351/P: 1–7 odd
  S 346/P: 1–7 odd, 8, 10

Extra Practice Problems
  p. 521

Additional A Exercises

State whether each equation defines an inverse variation or a direct variation. State the constant of variation for each.

1. $y = \dfrac{7}{x}$ inverse; 7

2. $a = 5b$ direct; 5

3. $c = \dfrac{2}{d}$ inverse; 2

4. $m = \dfrac{2}{3}n$ direct; $\dfrac{2}{3}$

5. $ab = 4$ inverse; 4

6. $x = \dfrac{1}{2y}$ inverse; $\dfrac{1}{2}$

Additional Answers Written Exercises

2.

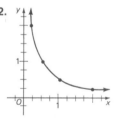

(continued)

350

Oral Exercises

State whether each equation defines an inverse variation or a direct variation. (k is a constant.)

1. $y = \dfrac{k}{x}$ Inverse

2. $\dfrac{y}{x} = k$ Direct

3. $z = \dfrac{k}{p}$ Inverse

4. $xy = 64$ Inverse

5. $d = 4.8t$ Direct

6. $s = \dfrac{1}{r}$ Inverse

7. $\dfrac{p_1}{t_1} = \dfrac{p_2}{t_2}$ Direct

8. $a_1 b_1 = a_2 b_2$ Inverse

9. $\dfrac{1}{2} = rt$ Inverse

10. $\dfrac{2}{3} = \dfrac{r}{s}$ Direct

11. $\dfrac{x}{y} = \dfrac{1}{k}$ Direct

12. $kxy = 1$ Inverse

Complete the ordered pairs so that they belong to the given function.

13. $xy = 12$: $(2, \underline{\;?\;})$ $(\underline{\;?\;}, 12)$ $(4, \underline{\;?\;})$ (2, 6); (1, 12); (4, 3)

14. $m = \dfrac{50}{n}$: $(2, \underline{\;?\;})$ $(\underline{\;?\;}, 50)$ $(25, \underline{\;?\;})$ (2, 25); (1, 50); (25, 2)

15. $200 = rt$: $(8, \underline{\;?\;})$ $(1, \underline{\;?\;})$ $(\underline{\;?\;}, 50)$ (8, 25); (1, 200); (4, 50)

16. $xy = -1$: $(-1, \underline{\;?\;})$ $\left(\dfrac{1}{2}, \underline{\;?\;}\right)$ $(\underline{\;?\;}, 4)$ $(-1, 1)$; $(\frac{1}{2}, -2)$; $(-\frac{1}{4}, 4)$

17. If $yz = k$ and y is tripled while k remains constant, how does z change? z is divided by 3.

18. If $D = rt$ and r is halved while D remains constant, how does t change? t is doubled.

Written Exercises

Graph each equation if the domain and the range are both limited to the set of positive numbers.

A **1.** $xy = 4$ **2.** $2xy = 1$ **3.** $x = \dfrac{3}{y}$ **4.** $\dfrac{x}{3} = \dfrac{4}{y}$

Find the missing value in each exercise if (x_1, y_1) and (x_2, y_2) are ordered pairs of the same inverse variation.

5. $x_1 = 5$, $y_1 = 100$, $x_2 = 4$, $y_2 = \dfrac{?}{125}$

6. $x_1 = 20$, $y_1 = 5$, $x_2 = \dfrac{?}{2}$, $y_2 = 50$

7. $x_1 = \dfrac{?}{2.1}$, $y_1 = 6.5$, $x_2 = 3.9$, $y_2 = 3.5$

8. $x_1 = 64$, $y_1 = \dfrac{?}{\frac{1}{8}}$, $x_2 = 16$, $y_2 = \dfrac{1}{2}$

Translate each statement into *two* formulas expressing inverse variation. Use k as the constant of variation.

SAMPLE   The length, l, of a rectangle of constant area varies inversely as the width, w.

SOLUTION $lw = k$ or $l_1 w_1 = l_2 w_2$

350   CHAPTER 9

B 9. The amount of information retained, i, is inversely proportional to the number of hours, h, that have passed since the information was studied. $ih = k$ or $i_1h_1 = i_2h_2$

10. The time, t, required to drive between two cities varies inversely as the rate, r, of the bus. $tr = k$ or $t_1r_1 = t_2r_2$

11. The force, f, needed to shift a heavy log varies inversely as the length, l, of the crowbar used. $fl = k$ or $f_1l_1 = f_2l_2$

12. At a fixed temperature the volume, V, of a gas varies inversely as the pressure, P. $VP = k$ or $V_1P_1 = V_2P_2$

13. The frequency, f, of a sound wave is inversely proportional to the wavelength, l. $fl = k$ or $f_1l_1 = f_2l_2$

14. The amount of current, I, flowing through a circuit is inversely proportional to the amount of resistance, R, of the circuit.
$$IR = k \text{ or } I_1R_1 = I_2R_2$$

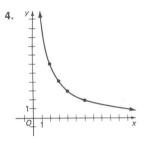

4.

Problems

Solve. In Exercises 1 and 2, apply the law of the lever.

A 1. If Susie is 30 kg and her mother is 60 kg, how far from the seesaw support must Susie sit to balance her mother who is 1 m from it? 2 m

2. Jimmy sits 1.5 m from the seesaw support to balance a friend who is 24 kg and sits 2 m from the support. How many kilograms is Jimmy? 32 kg

3. The number of days needed to finish a quilt varies inversely as the number of people working on it. It takes 14 days for two people to finish a quilt. If the job has to be finished in four days, how many people are needed? 7 people

4. Three friends on a fishing trip pay $100 each to share the rent of a cottage. The cost per person varies inversely as the number of people sharing the rent. How many people would have to share the rent of the cottage to make the cost $60 per person? 5 people

5. A jet traveling at 2400 km/h takes three hours to make a New York-to-London crossing. If another jet makes the same trip in nine hours, how fast does it fly? 800 km/h

6. A rectangle has length 36 cm and width 14 cm. Find the width of another rectangle of equal area whose length is 42 cm. 12 cm

7. The number of chairs on a ski lift varies inversely as the distance between them. When they are 10 m apart, the ski lift can accommodate 32 chairs. If 40 evenly spaced chairs are used on the lift, what space is left between them? 8 m

8. The number of plants used to fill a row of given length in a garden varies inversely as the distance between the plants. If 75 plants are used to fill the row when planted 20 cm apart, how many plants are used to fill the row when planted 15 cm apart? 100 plants

INTRODUCTION TO FUNCTIONS **351**

B **9.** The rate of travel varies inversely as the time of travel. On a holiday weekend the Lee family drove to Montreal in 7.5 h at the rate of 88 km/h. How much longer would it have taken them if they had driven at 80 km/h? 0.75 h, or 45 min

10. When the tension on a piano wire is kept constant, the number of vibrations per second varies inversely as the length of the wire. A wire 200 cm long vibrates at 320 vibrations per second. By how much should the wire be shortened to vibrate at 520 vibrations per second? Give the answer to the nearest centimeter. 77 cm

For the wave motion of sound, the following formula holds:

$$fl = v,$$

where f is the frequency (number of waves per second), l is the wavelength (in meters), and v is the speed of sound (about 335 meters per second in air). Use this information in the following problems.

C **11.** The frequency of a note an octave above a given note is twice that of the given note. How does the wavelength of the higher note compare with that of the lower note? $\frac{1}{2}$

12. If the wavelength of a note is $\frac{3}{2}$ that of a given note, how do the frequencies compare? Second frequency is $\frac{2}{3}$ of given frequency.

13. An open organ pipe produces a sound wave that has a length that is twice the length of the pipe. Find the length of an open pipe that will produce the note A with the frequency 440. Give the answer to the nearest tenth of a meter. 0.4 m

14. A stopped organ pipe produces a sound wave that has a length that is four times the length of the pipe. What is the frequency of the sound produced by a stopped organ pipe 2 meters long? 41.875

ḟistorical ṅote Function Notation

Leonhard Euler (1707–1793) was a Swiss mathematician who taught and wrote about mathematics in both St. Petersburg, Russia, and Berlin, Germany. He made contributions to many branches of mathematics and was particularly successful in devising useful notations. Among his notations was the symbol $f(x)$ to represent the value of a function. Other mathematicians before him had denoted functions with Greek letters.

9-9 *Direct and Inverse Variation Involving Squares*

OBJECTIVE   To use quadratic direct variation and variation inversely as a square in problem solving.

In the world around you, there are many examples in which a quantity varies either directly or inversely *as the square* of another quantity. For example, the area of a circle varies directly as the square of the radius: $A = \pi r^2$. This is an example of a *quadratic direct variation*.

A **quadratic direct variation** is a function defined by an equation of the form

$$y = kx^2, \text{ where } k \text{ is a nonzero constant.}$$

If (x_1, y_1) and (x_2, y_2) are ordered pairs of the same quadratic direct variation, and neither pair is $(0, 0)$, then:

$$\frac{y_1}{x_1{}^2} = \frac{y_2}{x_2{}^2}$$

You say that y *varies directly as* x^2 or y *is directly proportional to* x^2.

EXAMPLE 1   Given that z varies directly as the square of w, and $z = 4$ when $w = 2$, find the value of z when $w = 8$.

SOLUTION

Method 1

Use $z = kw^2$.
$$4 = k(2)^2$$
$$\therefore 1 = k$$
$$z = 1(8)^2$$
$$\therefore z = 64 \quad \textbf{\textit{Answer}}$$

Method 2

Use $\dfrac{z_1}{w_1{}^2} = \dfrac{z_2}{w_2{}^2}$.
$$\frac{4}{2^2} = \frac{z_2}{8^2}$$
$$1 = \frac{z_2}{64}$$
$$\therefore z_2 = 64 \quad \textbf{\textit{Answer}}$$

The intensity of sound *varies inversely as the square* of the distance of a listener from the source of sound. That is, if you halve the distance between yourself and a drummer, the intensity of the sound that reaches your ears will be quadrupled.

An **inverse variation as the square** is a function defined by an equation of the form

$$x^2 y = k, \text{ where } k \text{ is a nonzero constant.}$$

$$y = \frac{k}{x^2} \text{ for all ordered pairs other than } (0, 0).$$

You say that y *varies inversely as* x^2 or y *is inversely proportional to* x^2.

INTRODUCTION TO FUNCTIONS   353

Method 1

$y = kx^2$

$k = 6$

$y = 6x^2, y = 6 \cdot 15^2$

$y = 1350$

1350 cm²

Method 2

$\dfrac{y_1}{x_1^2} = \dfrac{y_2}{x_2^2}$

$\dfrac{600}{10^2} = \dfrac{y_2}{15^2}$

$y_2 = 1350$

1350 cm²

4. The time it takes Heather to empty a glass of lemonade varies inversely as the square of the diameter of the straw she uses. If it takes her 20 s to empty a glass with a straw 6 mm in diameter, how long would it take her to empty the glass with a straw 8 mm in diameter?

Method 1

$td^2 = k$

$k = 720$

$td^2 = 720$

$t(64) = 720, t = \dfrac{45}{4}$

11.25 s

Method 2

$t_1 d_1^2 = t_2 d_2^2$

$20 \cdot (6)^2 = t_2 \cdot (8)^2$

$t_2 = \dfrac{20 \cdot 36}{64}$

$t_2 = \dfrac{45}{4}$

11.25 s

Suggested Assignments

Minimum
354/P: 1, 2, 5–7
S 351/P: 1, 3, 5, 6

Average
354/P: 1–3, 5–7
S 351/P: 4, 6, 7, 10

Maximum
354/P: 1, 2, 5–7
S 352/10–14

354

If (x_1, y_1) and (x_2, y_2) are ordered pairs of the function defined by $x^2y = k$, then

$$x_1{}^2 y_1 = x_2{}^2 y_2.$$

EXAMPLE 2 Given that y varies inversely as the square of x, and $y = 4$ when $x = 2$, find the value of y when $x = 8$.

SOLUTION

Method 1

Use $x^2 y = k$.

$2^2(4) = k$

$\therefore 16 = k$

$8^2 y = 16$

$\therefore y = \dfrac{16}{64} = \dfrac{1}{4}$ ***Answer***

Method 2

Use $x_1{}^2 y_1 = x_2{}^2 y_2$.

$2^2(4) = 8^2(y_2)$

$16 = 64 y_2$

$\therefore y_2 = \dfrac{1}{4}$ ***Answer***

Oral Exercises

Translate each statement into a formula. Use k as a constant where needed.

1. The surface area, A, of a sphere varies directly as the square of the diameter, d, of the sphere. $A = kd^2$

2. The force of attraction, f, between two magnets is inversely proportional to the square of the distance, d, between them. $d^2 f = k$

3. The distance, d, that a ball rolls down a hill is directly proportional to the square of the time, t, that the ball rolls. $d = kt^2$

4. The time, t, required to fill a gasoline tank varies inversely as the square of the diameter, d, of the hose. $d^2 t = k$

5. The area, A, of a circular irrigation field varies directly as the square of the radius, r, of the field. $A = kr^2$

6. The intensity, i, of the sound of a parade that you hear varies inversely as the square of your distance, d, from the parade. $d^2 i = k$

Problems

Solve.

A **1.** The area of a square varies directly as the square of a side. If the area of a square 2 cm on a side is 4 cm², what is the area of a square 5 cm on a side? 25 cm²

2. The amount of material needed to cover a ball is directly proportional to the square of the radius. A ball with radius 4 cm requires 256 cm² of material to cover it. How much material is needed to cover a ball with radius 20 cm? 6400 cm²

3. The time needed to fill the gasoline tank of a car varies inversely as the square of the diameter of the hose. If a hose of diameter 2 cm takes 10 minutes to fill the tank, how long will it take to fill the same tank using a hose with diameter 5 cm? 1.6 min

4. The height of a cylinder of a given volume is inversely proportional to the square of the radius. If a cylinder of radius 2 cm has a height of 9 cm, what is the height of a cylinder of equal volume that has radius 3 cm? 4 cm

5. The distance the signal from an FM radio station travels is directly proportional to the square of the number of kilowatts (kW) it produces. A 50 kW station can broadcast a distance of 100 km. How far could the station broadcast if it produced 60 kW? 144 km

6. The distance required for a car to come to a stop varies directly as the square of the speed of the car. If the stopping distance for a car traveling 16 km/h is 7 m, what is the distance required for a car traveling 48 km/h to stop? 63 m

B 7. The exposure time required for a photograph is inversely proportional to the square of the diameter of the camera lens. If the lens diameter is 2 cm, the exposure time needed is 0.01 s. Find the diameter of the lens if an exposure time of 0.0016 s is needed. 5 cm

8. The distance an object falls varies directly as the square of the time of fall. If an object falls 78 m in 4 s, how far will it fall in 4.8 s? 112.32 m

9. The force between two magnets varies inversely as the square of the distance between them. If the magnets are initially 8 cm apart and then the distance is decreased to 0.5 cm, what is the effect on the force between them? Force is 256 times greater.

10. The brightness of the illumination of an object varies inversely as the square of the distance of the object from the source of illumination. If you move a book from a position 25 cm from a light to a position 50 cm from the light, what part of the original illumination will you get? 0.25 of the original illumination

C 11. The volume of a sphere varies directly as the cube of the radius.
   a. If the volume of a sphere of radius 5 cm is 125 times that of another sphere, what is the radius of the second sphere? 1 cm
   b. If the ratio of the radii of two spheres is 3:2, what is the ratio of the volumes of the spheres? 27:8

Extra Practice Problems
p. 522

Additional A Exercises

Solve.

1. Given that b varies directly as the square of a, and $b = 9$ when $a = 3$, find the value of b when $a = 7$. 49

2. Given that y varies directly as the square of x, and $y = 75$ when $x = 5$, find the value of y when $x = 2$. 12

3. Given that d varies inversely as the square of c, and $d = 20$ when $c = 4$, find the value of d when $c = 2$. 80

4. Given that d varies inversely as the square of a, and $d = 25$ when $a = 3$, find the value of d when $a = 5$. 9

INTRODUCTION TO FUNCTIONS 355

1. The volume of a pie varies jointly as the depth and the square of the radius of the top. A pie which is 3 cm deep and whose top has a 10 cm radius has a volume of 900 cm³. What is the volume of a similarly shaped pie that is 5 cm deep with a radius of 15 cm?

Method 1
$V = kr^2d$
$900 = k \cdot 10^2 \cdot 3$, $k = 3$
$V = 3r^2d$
$V = 3 \cdot 15^2 \cdot 5 = 3375$
3375 cm³

Method 2
$$\frac{V_1}{r_1^2 d_1} = \frac{V_2}{r_2^2 d_2}$$
$$\frac{900}{10^2 \cdot 3} = \frac{V_2}{15^2 \cdot 5}$$
$$V_2 = \frac{900 \cdot 15 \cdot 15 \cdot 5}{10 \cdot 10 \cdot 3}$$
$$= 3375$$
3375 cm³

2. The volume of a gas varies directly as the temperature and inversely as the pressure. If a certain gas has a volume of 500 cm³ at a temperature of 20°C and a pressure of 25 kg/cm², what will its volume be at 25°C with a pressure of 50 kg/cm²?

Method 1

$$V = \frac{kT}{P}$$

$$V = \frac{625T}{P} = \frac{625 \cdot 25}{50} = 312.5$$

312.5 cm³

(continued)

9-10 *Joint and Combined Variation*

OBJECTIVE To solve problems involving joint variation and combined variation.

If Susan earns $300 next summer and puts her earnings into a savings account, the amount of simple interest she receives depends on her bank's interest rate and on the length of time that she leaves the money in the account:

$$I = 300rt$$

The interest is directly proportional to the product of the rate and the time. You say that the interest *varies jointly as* the rate and the time.

In general, if a variable varies directly as the product of two or more other variables, the resulting relationship is called a **joint variation.** If z varies jointly as x and y, you can express the relationship in the following equations. For a nonzero constant k:

$$z = kxy \quad \text{and} \quad \frac{z_1}{x_1y_1} = \frac{z_2}{x_2y_2}$$

EXAMPLE 1 The volume of a cylinder, V, varies jointly as the height, h, and the square of the radius, r. If $V = 160\pi$ when $h = 10$ and $r = 4$, find V when $h = 8$ and $r = 3$.

SOLUTION Let $V_1 = 160\pi$, $h_1 = 10$, $r_1 = 4$, $h_2 = 8$, and $r_2 = 3$.
$V_2 = \underline{\ ?\ }$

$$\frac{V_1}{h_1 r_1{}^2} = \frac{V_2}{h_2 r_2{}^2}$$

$$\frac{160\pi}{10(4)^2} = \frac{V_2}{8(3)^2}$$

$$160V_2 = 72 \cdot 160\pi$$

$$V_2 = 72\pi \quad \textbf{\textit{Answer}}$$

If a variable varies *directly* as one variable and *inversely* as another, the resulting relationship is called a **combined variation.** For example, if z varies directly as x and inversely as y, you can express the relationship in the following equations. For a nonzero constant k:

$$zy = kx \left(\text{or } z = \frac{kx}{y}\right) \quad \text{and} \quad \frac{z_1y_1}{x_1} = \frac{z_2y_2}{x_2}$$

EXAMPLE 2 p varies directly as q and inversely as r^2. If $p = 1$ when $q = 6$ and $r = 2$, find p when $q = 9$ and $r = 3$.

SOLUTION Let $p_1 = 1$, $q_1 = 6$, $r_1 = 2$, $q_2 = 9$, and $r_2 = 3$. $\quad p_2 = \underline{\ ?\ }$

$$\frac{r_1{}^2 p_1}{q_1} = \frac{r_2{}^2 p_2}{q_2}$$

$$\frac{2^2 \cdot 1}{6} = \frac{3^2 \cdot p_2}{9}$$

$$54 p_2 = 36$$

$$p_2 = \frac{2}{3} \quad \textbf{\textit{Answer}}$$

Oral Exercises

Translate each statement into a formula. Use k where needed.

1. p varies jointly as q and r. $p = kqr$
2. r varies directly as d and inversely as t. $r = \frac{kd}{t}$
3. z varies directly as the square of x and inversely as y. $z = \frac{kx^2}{y}$
4. i varies directly as m and inversely as the square of d. $i = \frac{km}{d^2}$
5. u varies directly as the square of v and inversely as the square of w. $u = \frac{kv^2}{w^2}$
6. I varies jointly as P, r, and t. $I = kPrt$
7. The area, A, of a triangle varies jointly as the base, b, and the altitude, h. $A = kbh$
8. The mass, m, of a rectangular metal block varies jointly as the length, l, width, w, and thickness, t, of the block. $m = klwt$
9. The volume, V, of a gas varies directly as the temperature, T, and inversely as the pressure, P. $V = \frac{kT}{P}$
10. The power, P, of an electric circuit varies directly as the square of the voltage, V, and inversely as the resistance, R. $P = \frac{kV^2}{R}$
11. The lateral surface, S, of a cylinder varies jointly as the radius, r, and the height, h, of the cylinder. $S = krh$
12. The heat, H, generated by an electric stove element varies jointly as the resistance, R, and the square of the current, C. $H = kRC^2$

Problems

Solve.

A 1. The area of a triangle varies jointly as the base and altitude. A triangle with base 6 cm and altitude 4 cm has an area of 12 cm². What is the area if the base is 19 cm and the altitude is 6 cm? 57 cm²
2. The lateral surface area of a motor cylinder varies jointly as the radius and the height of the cylinder. For radius 5 cm and height 10 cm, the surface area is 300 cm². What is the radius if the surface area is 720 cm² and the height is 40 cm? 3 cm

Method 2

$$\frac{V_1 P_1}{T_1} = \frac{V_2 P_2}{T_2}$$

$$\frac{500 \cdot 25}{20} = \frac{V_2 \cdot 50}{25}$$

$$V_2 = 312.5$$

312.5 cm³

3. The number of hours required to address envelopes is directly proportional to the number of envelopes to be addressed and inversely proportional to the number of persons working. ($ph = ke$) If 3 typists can address 3780 envelopes in 7 h, how long will it take 5 typists to address 7200 envelopes?

Method 1

$$ph = ke$$

$$\frac{1}{180} = k$$

$$5(h) = \frac{1}{180}(7200)$$

$$h = 8$$

8 h

Method 2

$$\frac{p_1 h_1}{e_1} = \frac{p_2 h_2}{e_2}$$

$$\frac{3(7)}{3780} = \frac{5 h_2}{7200}$$

$$h_2 = 8$$

8 h

Supplementary Materials

Practice Master 56

Progress Test 34

Suggested Assignments

Minimum
Day 1: 357/*P*: 1, 4, 5, 7
     S 355/*P*: 9
Day 2: 358/*P*: 8
     R 359/*Self-Test 3*
     S 322/30, 32, 34
     S 341/10, 18, 24, 26

Average
Day 1: 357/*P*: 1–9 odd
     S 355/*P*: 10
Day 2: 358/6, 8
     R 359/*Self-Test 3*
     S 322/30, 34
     S 341/12, 16, 24

Maximum
Day 1: 357/*P*: 1, 4, 5, 7, 9
     S 355/*P*: 8, 9, 11
Day 2: 358/*P*: 10
     R 359/*Self-Test 3*
     S 341/12, 14, 22

Additional A Exercises

1. *a* varies jointly as *b* and *c*. If $a = 30$ when $b = 2$ and $c = 5$, find *a* when $b = 4$ and $c = 3$. 36

2. *x* varies jointly as *y* and the square of *z*. If $x = 90$ when $y = 5$ and $z = 3$, find *x* when $y = 4$ and $z = 5$. 200

3. *e* varies directly as *f* and inversely as *g*. If $e = 8$ when $f = 6$ and $g = 3$, find *e* when $f = 9$ and $g = 4$. 9

4. *p* varies directly as *q* and inversely as r^2. If $p = 4$ when $q = 8$ and $r = 4$, find *p* when $q = 9$ and $r = 6$. 2

Solve.

3. The volume of a motor cylinder of a truck varies jointly as the height of the cylinder and the square of the radius. A cylinder of radius 25 cm has height 8 cm and volume 15,000 cm³. What is the radius of a cylinder whose volume is 21,384 cm³ and whose height is 5.5 cm? 36 cm

4. The distance a car travels from rest varies jointly as its acceleration and the square of the time of motion. If a car travels 500 m from rest in 5 s at an acceleration of 40 m/s², how far will the car travel from rest in 10 s with an acceleration of 3 m/s²? 150 m

In Exercises 5 and 6, apply the statement: The number of persons needed to do a job varies directly as the amount of work to be done and inversely as the time in which the job must be done.

5. If 2 students in the typing pool can type 210 pages in 3 days, how many students will be needed to type 700 pages in 2 days? 10 students

6. If 2 workers can erect 400 m of fence in 10 h, how long will it take 5 workers to erect 600 m of fence? 6 h

B 7. The resistance of a wire to an electrical current varies directly as the length of the wire and inversely as the square of the diameter. 4.8 km of wire with diameter 6 mm has a resistance of 21 ohms. Find the resistance for 1.2 km of the wire with diameter 3 mm. 21 ohms

8. The area of a trapezoid varies jointly as the sum of the two parallel sides and the distance between the parallel sides. When the lengths of the parallel sides are 7 cm and 9 cm and the distance between them is 4 cm, the area is 32 cm². If the area is to remain constant and the height is reduced to 0.5 cm, what is the sum of the parallel sides? 128 cm

C 9. The heat generated by a stove element varies jointly as the resistance and the square of the current. What is the effect on the heat generated in the following cases?

   a. The current is unchanged but the resistance is doubled. Doubled

   b. The resistance is unchanged but the current is doubled. Increases 4 times

   c. The current is tripled and the resistance is doubled. Increases 18 times

10. The power in an electric circuit varies directly as the square of the voltage and inversely as the resistance. What is the effect on the power in the following cases?

   a. The resistance is constant and the voltage is doubled. Increases 4 times

   b. The voltage is constant and the resistance is doubled. Halved

   c. The voltage is doubled and the resistance is quadrupled. Unchanged

358   *CHAPTER 9*

Self-Test 3

VOCABULARY
linear direct variation (p. 343)
constant of variation (pp. 343, 348)
constant of proportionality (p. 344)
inverse variation (p. 348)
hyperbola (p. 348)

quadratic direct variation (p. 353)
inverse variation as the square (p. 353)
joint variation (p. 356)
combined variation (p. 356)

Solve.

1. Jan's earnings vary directly as the number of hours she works. If she earns $5.50 for two hours of work, how many hours does she work to earn $8.25?   Obj. 9-7, p. 343

2. The time it takes Milo to walk to school varies inversely as the rate at which he walks. If it takes him a quarter of an hour to walk to school at 6.4 km/h, how long will it take him at 4.8 km/h?   Obj. 9-8, p. 348

3. Given that y varies inversely as the square of x, and $y = 45$ when $x = 2$, find the value of y when $x = 3$.   Obj. 9-9, p. 353

4. The surface area of a sphere varies directly as the square of the radius. A tennis ball has a radius $\frac{1}{4}$ times that of a basketball. Find the surface area of the tennis ball if the surface area of the basketball is 144π cm².

5. The area of a trapezoid varies jointly as the height of the trapezoid and the sum of the bases. The area of a trapezoid is 24 cm² when the height is 4 cm and the sum of the bases is 12 cm. Find the area of another trapezoid if the height is 6 cm and the sum of the bases is 10 cm.   Obj. 9-10, p. 356

Check your answers with those at the back of the book.

Chapter Summary

1. An equation of a straight line can be found from: (a) the slope and the y-intercept; (b) the slope and any point on the line; (c) two points on the line.

2. A function can be defined by an equation, a table, a correspondence, or a set of ordered pairs.

3. The value of the function $f: x \rightarrow 5x + 2$ when $x = 6$ is denoted by $f(6)$. Thus, $f(6) = 5(6) + 2 = 32$.

4. A linear function is defined by a linear equation. Its graph is a straight line.

5. A quadratic function is defined by an equation of the form $y = ax^2 + bx + c = 0$, $a \neq 0$. Its graph is a parabola (see page 338).

INTRODUCTION TO FUNCTIONS   **359**

6. Several kinds of variation have been described (k is a nonzero constant):

    a. A linear direct variation is a linear function defined by an equation of the form $y = kx$.

    b. An inverse variation is a function defined by an equation of the form $xy = k \left(\text{or } y = \dfrac{k}{x}\right)$.

    c. A quadratic direct variation is a quadratic function defined by an equation of the form $y = kx^2$.

    d. An inverse variation as the square is a function defined by an equation of the form $x^2y = k \left(\text{or } y = \dfrac{k}{x^2}\right)$.

Supplementary Materials

Practice Masters 57, 58

Progress Test 35

Extra Practice pp. 504–507

Chapter Review

Give the letter of the correct answer.

1. Find the slope of the line that passes through the points $(-2, 4)$ and $(3, -1)$.   9-1

    a. $-\dfrac{3}{5}$ (**b.**) -1 **c.** 0   **d.** $\dfrac{1}{3}$

2. Find the slope of the line $y = -8$.

    a. -8 **b.** 1   (**c.**) 0   **d.** no slope

3. Find the slope of the line whose equation is $2x - 3y = 6$.   9-2

    a. 2   **b.** -2 **c.** $-\dfrac{2}{3}$ (**d.**) $\dfrac{2}{3}$

4. Find the y-intercept of the line whose equation is $x + 2y = 6$.

    a. 6   **b.** -6 (**c.**) 3   **d.** -3

5. Write an equation of the line through point $(2, 5)$ with slope 1.   9-3

    (**a.**) $x - y = -3$ **b.** $2x + 5y = 0$ **c.** $y = x - 3$ **d.** $x + y = 7$

6. Given $f(x) = -3x + 5$, find $f(-2)$.   9-4

    (**a.**) 11   **b.** 10   **c.** 1   **d.** 0

7. Find the range of the function $\{(F, 9), (Cl, 17), (Br, 35), (I, 53)\}$.   9-5

    a. (I, 53)   (**b.**) $\{9, 17, 35, 53\}$ **c.** $\{F, Cl, Br, I\}$ **d.** 53

8. Find the coordinates of the vertex of the graph of $y = x^2 + 6x + 5$.   9-6

    a. $(0, 5)$ **b.** $(-6, 5)$ **c.** $(3, 32)$ (**d.**) $(-3, -4)$

9. If p varies directly as q, and $p = 3$ when $q = 6$, find the value of p when $q = 18$.   9-7

    a. 36   **b.** 6   (**c.**) 9   **d.** 27

10. If y varies inversely as x, and x is doubled, then y is __?__.   9-8

    a. doubled   (**b.**) halved   **c.** quadrupled   **d.** unchanged

360   *CHAPTER 9*

11. The area, A, of a circle is directly proportional to the square of the radius, r. If $A = \pi$ when $r = 1$, find A where $r = 2$.

    a. $A = 4$ **b.** $\frac{1}{4}\pi$ **c.** 4π **d.** 2π

9-9

12. Which equation describes "y varies inversely as the square of x"?

    a. $x^2 y = k$ **b.** $y = \dfrac{k}{x}$ **c.** $y^2 = \dfrac{k}{x}$ **d.** $y = kx^2$

13. y varies jointly as w and x. If $y = 144$ when $w = 12$ and $x = 6$, find y when $w = 10$ and $x = 3$.

    a. 345.6   **b.** 240   **c.** 100   **d.** 60

9-10

Chapter Test

Alternate Test p. T20

1. Find the slope of the line through the points $(2, 1)$ and $(6, 7)$. $\frac{3}{2}$ 9-1

2. Find the slope and y-intercept of the line whose equation is $2x + 4y = 1$. Slope $= -\frac{1}{2}$; y − intercept $= \frac{1}{4}$ 9-2

3. Write an equation of the line that passes through the points $(-2, -3)$ and $(0, 0)$. $3x - 2y = 0$ 9-3

4. Given that $f(t) = t^2 - 2t + 3$, find $f(-1)$. 6   9-4

5. $\{(1, 2), (2, 4), (3, 6), (4, 8), (5, 10)\}$ expresses a function. **a.** $\{1, 2, 3, 4, 5\}$ **b.** $\{2, 4, 6, 8, 10\}$ 9-5
   a. Give the domain.   **b.** Give the range.

6. Find the coordinates of the vertex of the graph of $y = -2x^2 + 8x - 9$. $(2, -1)$ 9-6

7. The number of doughnuts a machine can make varies directly as the running time of the machine. If a machine can make 1000 doughnuts in six hours, in how many hours can it make 300 doughnuts? 1.8 h, or 1 h 48 min   9-7

8. The number of chairs in a row varies inversely as the distance between them. When they are 10 cm apart, 27 chairs fit in a row. If 45 chairs are needed in a row, how far apart should they be placed? 6 cm   9-8

9. In the design of a building, the height is directly proportional to the square of the length of the base. A building 400 m high has a base length of 100 m. If the base length is 110 m, what should the height be? 484 m   9-9

10. Translate the statement into a formula, using k as the constant of variation if needed: The force of gravity, g, between two planets is inversely proportional to the square of the distance, d, between them. $gd^2 = k$

11. The volume of a pyramid varies jointly as the altitude of the pyramid and the area of the base. A pyramid whose altitude is 6 cm and whose base area is 16 cm² has a volume of 32 cm³. Find the volume of a pyramid with altitude 8 cm and base area 9 cm². 24 cm³   9-10

INTRODUCTION TO FUNCTIONS   **361**

18. a.

b.

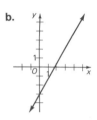

c.

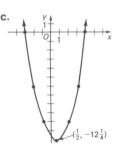

$\left(\frac{1}{2}, -12\frac{1}{4}\right)$

Cumulative Review (Chapters 1–9)

Simplify each expression.

1. $(-7 + 3x) - (9 - 2x)$ $-16 + 5x$

2. $3ab(7a^2 + 5ab - ab^3)$ $21a^3b + 15a^2b^2 - 3a^2b^4$

3. $(p + 2q)(3p - q - 1)$ $3p^2 + 5pq - p - 2q^2 - 2q$

4. $(2r^3s^2t)^3 \div (-6r^9t^2)$ $\frac{-4s^6t}{3}$

5. $(-9x^2y + 3xy^2) \div 3xy$ $-3x + y$

6. $(2cd - 3g)^2$ $4c^2d^2 - 12cdg + 9g^2$

Factor completely.

7. $25a^3 - 20a^2 - 60a$ $5a(5a + 6)(a - 2)$

8. $-36y^2 + 31yz - 3z^2$ $(-9y + z)(4y - 3z)$

9. $16t^4 - 9v^2$ $(4t^2 - 3v)(4t^2 + 3v)$

Express in simplest form.

10. $\frac{9m^2 + 30m + 25}{6m^2 + 10m}$ $\frac{3m + 5}{2m}$

11. $\frac{2b}{b^2 - 1} + \frac{b}{b + 1} + 1$ $\frac{2b - 1}{b - 1}$

12. $\frac{a^3 - 4a}{3a^2 + 9a} \cdot \frac{9 - a^2}{a^2 - a - 6}$ $-\frac{a - 2}{3}$

13. $\frac{3}{c - 2d} - \frac{2}{c + d} + \frac{1}{c}$ $\frac{2c^2 + 6cd - 2d^2}{(c - 2d)(c + d)(c)}$

14. $\frac{g^4 - 81}{g^2 + 3g} \div \frac{2g^3 + 18g}{4g^2}$ $\frac{2(g - 3)}{}$

15. $\frac{35r^3 + 55r^2 + 20r}{5r + 5}$ $r(7r + 4)$

16. Find an equation of the line: **a.** with slope -3 and passing through $(9, -8)$ $y = -3x + 19$ **b.** that contains $(2, 7)$ and $(-3, 12)$ $y = -x + 9$

17. If $f(x) = -2x^2 - x + 3$ and $D = \{-2, -1, 0, 1, 2\}$, find the range of the function. $\{-3, 2, 3, 0, -7\}$

18. Graph: **a.** $y = -4x$ **b.** $5x - 3y = 9$ **c.** $y = x^2 - x - 12$

19. Solve graphically: **a.** $x + y = 3$ $2x + y = 1$ $(-2, 5)$ **b.** $4x - y = 4$ $3x + 2y = -8$ $(0, -4)$

Solve each equation or system.

20. $-(3 - 2x) = 5(2x + 1)$ -1

21. $-3|n| = -84$ $\{28, -28\}$

22. $p\%$ of $32 = 6$ 18.75

23. $0.3v + 7 = -1.37$ -27.9

24. $8r^2 = 13r + 6$ $\left\{2, -\frac{3}{8}\right\}$

25. $(a - 1)(3a - 2) = 4$

26. $\frac{y - 9}{y + 4} = \frac{y + 3}{y + 7}$ $-\frac{25}{3}$

27. $\frac{3z}{7} + \frac{z}{2} = \frac{13}{28}$ $\frac{1}{2}$

28. $\frac{b}{b + 3} - \frac{3}{b - 1} = -\frac{1}{8}$

29. $y = 7x - 16$ $3x + 2y = 2$ $(2, -2)$

30. $4x - 5y = 0$ $8x + 5y = -60$ $(-5, -4)$

31. $6x + 2y = 3$ $-9x + 8y = 1$

25. $\left\{2, -\frac{1}{3}\right\}$

28. $\left\{5, -\frac{5}{3}\right\}$

31. $\left(\frac{1}{3}, \frac{1}{2}\right)$

32. The denominator of a fraction is 3 more than the numerator. If 25 is added to each, the resulting fraction is equivalent to 0.9. Find the original fraction. $\frac{2}{5}$

33. The volume of a sphere varies directly as the cube of the radius. If the volume of a sphere with radius 6 cm is 288π cm³, find the volume of a sphere with radius 3 cm. 36π cm³

Maintaining Skills

Simplify.

SAMPLE 1 $\dfrac{2z-8}{2z^2} \cdot \dfrac{z^3}{z^2-16} = \dfrac{2(z-4)\cdot z^3}{2z^2(z+4)(z-4)} = \dfrac{z}{z+4}$

1. $\dfrac{y-2}{21y^2} \cdot \dfrac{7y}{2-y}$ $-\dfrac{1}{3y}$

2. $\dfrac{qr^2st}{-3s^2t^2} \cdot \dfrac{2rt^3}{r^3t^2}$ $-\dfrac{2q}{3s}$

3. $\dfrac{a^2+2ab}{ab-b^2} \cdot \dfrac{5a-5b}{2b+a}$ $\dfrac{5a}{b}$

4. $\dfrac{50-2k^2}{15+3k} \cdot \dfrac{12-3k}{5k-k^2}$ $\dfrac{2(4-k)}{k}$

5. $\dfrac{8t+8}{(t-1)^2} \cdot \dfrac{7t-7}{6+6t}$ $\dfrac{28}{3(t-1)}$

6. $\dfrac{m^2+m-12}{m^2+4m} \cdot \dfrac{m^3}{m-3}$ m^2

SAMPLE 2 $\dfrac{a^2+ab-2b^2}{a^2-3ab+2b^2} \div \dfrac{a+2b}{a-2b} = \dfrac{(a+2b)(a-b)}{(a-2b)(a-b)} \cdot \dfrac{a-2b}{a+2b} = 1$

7. $-\dfrac{8t^4u}{15zt^3} \div \dfrac{2tuz^2}{3z^5}$ $-\dfrac{4z^2}{5}$

8. $2j \div \dfrac{j-5j^2}{5j-1}$ -2

9. $\dfrac{d^3-4d}{d^2-7d} \div (d-2)$ $\dfrac{d+2}{d-7}$

10. $\dfrac{3rq+3q^2}{r^2-rq} \div \dfrac{3r^2-3q^2}{r}$ $\dfrac{q}{(r-q)^2}$

11. $\dfrac{m^2-2m-8}{m^2-3m-10} \div \dfrac{m^2-3m-4}{m^2-6m+5}$ $\dfrac{m-1}{m+1}$

12. $\dfrac{9b^2+12b+4}{3b^2-b-2} \div \dfrac{9b^2-4}{3b^2-2b}$ $\dfrac{b}{b-1}$

13. $\dfrac{x^3+2x^2y}{xy+4y^2} \div \dfrac{x^2+6xy+8y^2}{x^2y-2xy^2}$ $\dfrac{x^3(x-2y)}{(x+4y)^2}$

SAMPLE 3 $\dfrac{x-1}{2x-1}+3 = \dfrac{x-1}{2x-1}+\dfrac{3(2x-1)}{2x-1} = \dfrac{x-1+6x-3}{2x-1} = \dfrac{7x-4}{2x-1}$

14. $\dfrac{z+4}{2z}+\dfrac{3z-4}{2z}$ 2

15. $\dfrac{16}{g+4}-\dfrac{g^2}{g+4}$ $4-g$

16. $\dfrac{a+3b}{a^2b^2}-\dfrac{3b+a}{a^2b^2}$ 0

17. $\dfrac{8}{3r+1}-2r$ $\dfrac{-6r^2-2r+8}{3r+1}$

18. $d-1+\dfrac{1}{d+1}$ $\dfrac{d^2}{d+1}$

19. $5-x^2+\dfrac{3}{2x}$ $\dfrac{10x-2x^3+3}{2x}$

SAMPLE 4 $\dfrac{y}{y-4}-\dfrac{y}{y+3} = \dfrac{y(y+3)-y(y-4)}{(y-4)(y+3)} = \dfrac{y^2+3y-y^2+4y}{(y-4)(y+3)} = \dfrac{7y}{(y-4)(y+3)}$

20. $\dfrac{5}{t}-\dfrac{1}{t^2}+\dfrac{3}{2t}$ $\dfrac{13t-2}{2t^2}$

21. $\dfrac{1}{6a}+\dfrac{4}{9a^2}$ $\dfrac{3a+8}{18a^2}$

22. $\dfrac{t+5}{t+2}-\dfrac{t}{t-1}$

23. $\dfrac{1-x}{x}-\dfrac{4}{x^2+4x}$ $-\dfrac{x+3}{x+4}$

24. $\dfrac{2}{x^2+x}+\dfrac{1}{x^2-x}$ $\dfrac{3x-1}{x(x+1)(x-1)}$

25. $\dfrac{p+2}{p-3}-\dfrac{p+3}{p-4}$

22. $\dfrac{2t-5}{(t-1)(t+2)}$

25. $\dfrac{-2p+1}{(p-3)(p-4)}$

These cakes are being produced by a large-scale commercial baking process. To help make production decisions, the branch of mathematics called linear programming can be used. Linear programming makes use of systems of inequalities related to quantities of materials.

364

10
INEQUALITIES

INEQUALITIES IN ONE VARIABLE

10-1 *Order of Real Numbers*

OBJECTIVE To review the concept of order of real numbers and to solve inequalities by substitution.

The horizontal number line below pictures the order (page 33) of real numbers.

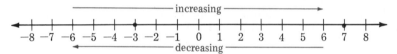

You recall that any number n is greater than every number whose graph is to the left of the graph of n, and less than every number whose graph is to the right.

Negative three is less than seven.   Seven is greater than negative three.

$$-3 < 7 \qquad\qquad\qquad 7 > -3$$

The sentence

$$-3 < x < 7$$

means "-3 is less than x and x is less than 7." Thus x represents a number *between* -3 and 7 on the number line. The sentence above may also be read as "x is greater than -3 and less than 7." (The same relationship is shown by the sentence $7 > x > -3$.)

The statement

$$-3 < 1 < 7$$

is true, but the statement

$$-3 < 8 < 7$$

is false, since 8 is not less than 7 (although -3 is less than 8).

365

Teaching References

Lesson Commentary,
   pp. T100–T103
Assignment Guide,
   pp. T57–T59

Supplementary Materials

   Practice Masters 59–62

   Progress Tests 36–38

   Computer Activities
   28 *Graphing Combined
      Inequalities*
   29 *Sign Graphs*
   30 *Integer Solutions for
      Three Inequalities*

Extra Practice, pp. 507–508,
   522

Alternate Test, p. T21

Chalkboard Examples

1. If $t \in \{1, 2, 3, 4, 5\}$, what is the solution set of $2t + 3 > 8$?
Replace t with each of its values in turn:
$2(1) + 3 > 8$ False
$2(2) + 3 > 8$ False
$2(3) + 3 > 8$ True
$2(4) + 3 > 8$ True
$2(5) + 3 > 8$ True
$\therefore$ The solution set is $\{3, 4, 5\}$.

2. Translate into symbols:
"-10 is less than x and x is less than or equal to -3."
$-10 < x \leq -3$

3. Translate into words:
$-1 \leq x < 0$
"Negative one is less than or equal to x and x is less than zero."

4. Describe in words and in symbols the set of numbers whose graph is given below.

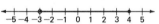

The real numbers greater than -3 and less than or equal to 4. $-3 < x \leq 4$

5. Draw the graph of $-5 < r \leq \frac{1}{2}$, given that the domain of r is the set of all real numbers.

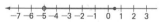

6. Classify each statement as true or false.

a. $\frac{4}{7} > \frac{7}{12}$ False

b. $|-3| + |-2| \geq |-3 - 2|$
True

c. $\frac{1}{3 + 4} < \frac{1}{3} + \frac{1}{4}$
True

For a statement like $-3 < 8 < 7$ to be true, *both* "less than" relationships must be true.

Sometimes it is convenient to indicate that one number is greater than or equal to another number. This can be written

$$x \geq 5, \text{ read "x is greater than or equal to 5."}$$

Similarly, you can write $x \leq 5$ for "x is less than or equal to 5." The statements

$$6 \geq 5 \quad \text{and} \quad 5 \geq 5$$

are both true since such statements are true *either* if the first number is greater than the second *or* if the first number equals the second.

Here are three *inequalities:*

$$-2 < 0 \qquad 4x - 3 > 2 \qquad y + 8 \leq 12$$
$$\text{the sides}$$

An **inequality** is formed by placing an inequality symbol $(>, <, \geq, \leq)$ between numerical or variable expressions, called the **sides** of the inequality.

As in the case of equations, an inequality containing a variable is called an *open sentence* (page 9). You solve such an inequality by finding the values of the variable for which the inequality is a true statement. Such values are called **solutions of the inequality;** they make up the **solution set of the inequality.**

EXAMPLE 1   If $y \in \{1, 2, 3, 4, 5, 6\}$ what is the solution set of $y + 8 \leq 12$?

SOLUTION   Replace y with each of its values in turn.

$y + 8 \leq 12$
$1 + 8 \leq 12$ True
$2 + 8 \leq 12$ True
$3 + 8 \leq 12$ True
$4 + 8 \leq 12$ True
$5 + 8 \leq 12$ False
$6 + 8 \leq 12$ False

$\therefore$ the solution set is $\{1, 2, 3, 4\}$.   *Answer*

When you show the graphs of the numbers in the solution set of an open sentence on a number line, you say that you have drawn the **graph of the open sentence.** The graph of the inequality $y + 8 \leq 12$ in Example 1 is shown below.

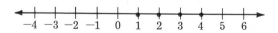

366   *CHAPTER 10*

EXAMPLE 2 Draw the graph of $-2 \le x < 3$ if the domain of x is the set of real numbers.

SOLUTION x represents a number between -2 and 3. The solution set includes -2, but not 3.

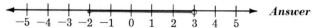 *Answer*

Notice that the graph includes all the points on the number line from the graph of -2 up to, but not including, the graph of 3. The open circle shows that 3 is not a solution.

Oral Exercises

Classify each statement as true or false.

1. $8 \ge -3$ True
2. $19 \le 21$ True
3. $-15 \le -21$ False
4. $-1 \ge -4$ True
5. $-9 < 8 < 10$ True
6. $3 > -3 > -2$ False
7. $6 > 0 > -11$ True
8. $-2.5 < 0.5 < 1.5$ True
9. $|-8| \ge 0$ True
10. $|-3| > |-10|$ False
11. $2^3 < 3^2$ True
12. $\left(\frac{1}{2}\right)^2 \ge \frac{1}{2}$ False

Describe the numbers whose graphs appear in color. There may be more than one correct description.

SAMPLE 1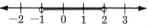

SOLUTION The real numbers between -1 and 2, or greater than -1 and less than 2

SAMPLE 2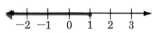

SOLUTION The real numbers less than or equal to 1

13.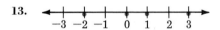
14.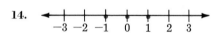
15.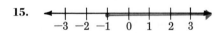
16.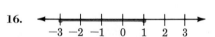
17.
18.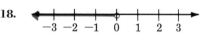
19.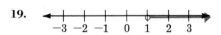
20.

Written Exercises

Translate the statements into symbols.

A
1. 5 is greater than -2. $5 > -2$
2. -7 is less than -3. $-7 < -3$
3. -15 is less than or equal to -10. $-15 \le -10$
4. 9 is greater than or equal to 6. $9 \ge 6$

INEQUALITIES **367**

Suggested Assignments
Minimum
  367/1–10, 11–31 odd
Average
  367/1–29 odd, 30–34
Maximum
  367/1–31 odd, 32–35

Additional Answers
Oral Exercises

13. The real numbers -2, 0, 1, and 3
14. The real numbers -1, 0, and 1
15. The real numbers greater than or equal to -1
16. -3, 1, and the real numbers between -3 and 1
17. 2 and the real numbers between -2 and 2
18. The negative real numbers
19. The real numbers greater than 1
20. 0 and the positive real numbers

Additional A Exercises
Translate the statements into symbols.

1. 2 is less than 13 $2 < 13$
2. -8 is greater than -15 $-8 > -15$
3. -3 is less than or equal to 0 $-3 \le 0$
4. 7 is greater than or equal to 4 $7 \ge 4$
5. 8 is greater than -1 and less than 11 $-1 < 8 < 11$
6. -4 is between -7 and 0 $-7 < -4 < 0$

367

17. $\{-4, -3, -2, -1, 0, 1, 2\}$

18. $\{3, 4\}$

19. $\{-4, -3\}$

20. $\{-4, -3, -2, -1, 0\}$

21. $\{-4, -3, -2, -1,$
      $0, 1, 2, 3, 4\}$

22. $\emptyset$

23. $\{-4, -3, -2, -1, 0, 1\}$

24. $\{-4, -3\}$

25. {the real numbers
      greater than 4}

26. {the positive numbers
      less than 5}

27. $\{-4, -3, -2, -1, 0, 1\}$

28. $\{3, 2, 1, 0, -1\}$

29. {the real numbers
      greater than or equal to
      0 and less than 5}

30. {the real numbers
      greater than -2 and less
      than 4}

31. $\{-6, -5, -4, -3, -2, -1\}$

32. $\{-6, -5, -4, -3, -2, -1\}$

Translate the statements into symbols.

5. 4 is greater than 2 and less
than 4.5. $2 < 4 < 4.5$

6. 0 is greater than -0.5 and less
than 1. $-0.5 < 0 < 1$

7. -12 is between -10 and -20. $-20 < -12 < -10$

8. 4 is between 7 and -7. $-7 < 4 < 7$

9. 8 is greater than 1 and 1 is
greater than -2. $8 > 1 > -2$

10. -2 is less than -1 and -1 is
less than $-\frac{1}{3}$. $-2 < -1 < -\frac{1}{3}$

Classify each statement as true or false.

11. $|-0.6| < -0.5$ False

12. $|-\frac{1}{2}| \geq 0$ True

13. $|-8| < |-21|$ True

14. $|3 - 2| \leq |2 - 3|$ True

15. $-5 < 2 < 8$ True

16. $7 > 0 > 2$ False

Solve each inequality if $x \in \{-4, -3, -2, -1, 0, 1, 2, 3, 4\}$.

17. $3x < 9$

18. $2x \geq 6$

19. $-4x > 8$

20. $x + 2 < 3$

21. $\frac{1}{2}x \geq -3$

22. $-12 - x > 9$

23. $1 - x \geq 0$

24. $2x + 1 \leq -4$

Solve each inequality over the given domain and draw its graph.

B 25. $28 < 7x$; {the positive numbers}

26. $3y < 15$; {the positive numbers}

27. $-4 \leq x < 2$; {the integers}

28. $3 \geq y \geq -1$; {the integers}

29. $5 > u \geq 0$; {the real numbers}

30. $-2 < m < 4$; {the real numbers}

31. $-6 \leq k < 1$; {the negative integers}

32. $4 \geq t > -7$; {the negative integers}

For each statement in Exercises 33–35: Answers may vary.

a. Find a pair of values of x and y for which the statement is true.

b. Find a pair of values of x and y for which the statement is false.

C 33. If $x \geq y$, then $|x| \geq |y|$. **a.** $x = 6$, $y = -3$ **b.** $x = 6$, $y = -7$

34. If $x \geq 0$ and $y < 0$, then $xy \geq 0$. **a.** $x = 0$, $y = -5$ **b.** $x = 3$, $y = -2$

35. If $x > y$, then $xy > y^2$. **a.** $x = 4$, $y = 1$ **b.** $x = -2$, $y = -5$

Calculator Key-In

You can compare two fractions with the aid of a calculator. First change
each fraction to a decimal by dividing numerator by denominator. Then
compare the decimals.

True or false?

1. $\frac{3}{8} > \frac{7}{20} > \frac{4}{13}$ True

2. $\frac{21}{23} < \frac{22}{24} < \frac{23}{25}$ True

3. $\frac{98}{101} > \frac{99}{102} > \frac{100}{103}$ False

368 *CHAPTER 10*

10-2 *Solving Inequalities*

OBJECTIVE To transform inequalities to find their solution sets.

Only the first of the following statements is true:

$$-5 < 2 \qquad -5 = 2 \qquad -5 > 2$$
$$\text{(true)} \qquad \text{(false)} \qquad \text{(false)}$$

In comparing real numbers, you make the following basic assumption:

> ### AXIOM OF COMPARISON
>
> For all real numbers a and b, one and only one of the following statements is true:
>
> $$a < b, \qquad a = b, \quad \text{or} \quad a > b.$$

Now suppose you know two facts about the graphs of three numbers a, b, and c.

1. The graph of a is to the left of the graph of b: $a < b$.
2. The graph of b is to the left of the graph of c: $b < c$.

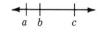

Where is the graph of a relative to the graph of c? You can see that it is to the left of c: $a < c$.

In general the following assumption is made:

> ### TRANSITIVE AXIOM OF ORDER
>
> For all real numbers a, b, and c:
>
> 1. If $a < b$ and $b < c$, then $a < c$;
> 2. If $c > b$ and $b > a$, then $c > a$.

What happens when the same number is added to each side of an inequality?

$$
\begin{array}{ccc}
3 & < & 6 \\
\downarrow & & \downarrow \\
3 + 2 & & 6 + 2 \\
\downarrow & & \downarrow \\
5 & < & 8
\end{array}
\qquad\qquad
\begin{array}{ccc}
3 & < & 6 \\
\downarrow & & \downarrow \\
3 - 2 & & 6 - 2 \\
\downarrow & & \downarrow \\
1 & < & 4
\end{array}
$$

These numerical examples suggest another axiom of order. (Recall that subtracting a number is the same as adding the opposite of that number.)

INEQUALITIES **369**

Teaching Suggestions p. T100

Suggested Extensions p. T101

Chalkboard Examples

In each exercise, assume that the domain of the variable is the set of all real numbers.

Solve and graph.

1. $2t + 3 > 15$
$\quad 2t > 12$
$\quad\quad t > 6$
$\quad$ {the real numbers greater than 6}

2. $1 - 5y > -9$
$\quad -5y > -10$
$\quad\quad y < 2$
$\quad$ {the real numbers less than 2}

3. $2(1 - k) + 3(1 + k) \leq 0$
$\quad 2 - 2k + 3 + 3k \leq 0$
$\quad\quad 5 + k \leq 0$
$\quad\quad\quad k \leq -5$
$\quad$ {the real numbers less than or equal to -5}

Solve.

4. $3(1 - x) + 4 <$
$\quad\quad\quad 7x + 1 + 2(2 - x)$
$\quad 3 - 3x + 4 <$
$\quad\quad\quad 7x + 1 + 4 - 2x$
$\quad -3x + 7 < 5x + 5$
$\quad\quad -8x < -2$
$\quad\quad\quad x > \dfrac{1}{4}$
$\quad$ {the real numbers greater than $\dfrac{1}{4}$}

5. $\dfrac{1}{2}(3w - 5) + \dfrac{1}{3}(w + 6) \geq$
$\quad\quad\quad\quad\quad\quad\quad\quad 2w$
$\quad 3(3w - 5) + 2(w + 6) \geq 12w$
$\quad 9w - 15 + 2w + 12 \geq 12w$
$\quad\quad 11w - 3 \geq 12w$
$\quad\quad\quad -w - 3 \geq 0$
$\quad\quad\quad\quad -w \geq 3$
$\quad\quad\quad\quad\quad 3 \leq -3$

(continued)

{the real numbers less than or equal to -3}

6. $\frac{2}{3}(1 - a) - 2a < -\frac{8}{5}a$

$10(1 - a) - 30a < -24a$

$10 - 10a - 30a < -24a$

$10 - 40a < -24a$

$10 < 16a$

$16a > 10$

$a > \frac{10}{16}$

$a > \frac{5}{8}$

{the real numbers greater than $\frac{5}{8}$}

Supplementary Material

Practice Master 59

Suggested Assignments

Minimum
  372/1–8, 9–35 odd
Average
  373/9–55 odd
Maximum
  373/9–63 odd

Additional Answers
Oral Exercises

1. Subtract 2 from each side.

2. Add 3 to each side.

3. Add 6 to each side.

4. Subtract 8 from each side.

5. Divide each side by 3.

6. Divide each side by 2.

7. Divide each side by -4, and reverse the direction of the inequality.

8. Multiply each side by 3.

9. Multiply each side by 5.

10. Multiply each side by -2, and reverse the direction of the inequality.

11. Divide each side by 2.

(continued)

> **ADDITION AXIOM OF ORDER**
>
> For all real numbers a, b, and c:
>
> 1. If $a < b$, then $a + c < b + c$;
> 2. If $a > b$, then $a + c > b + c$.

What happens when each side of the inequality $-3 < 2$ is multiplied by a nonzero real number?

Multiply by 5: Is it true that $5(-3) < 5(2)$?

Yes, $-15 < 10$.

Multiply by -5: Is it true that $-5(-3) < -5(2)$?

No, $15 > -10$.

This example suggests that multiplying each side of an inequality by a negative number *reverses the direction*, or order, of the inequality.

In general, the following assumption is made:

> **MULTIPLICATION AXIOM OF ORDER**
>
> For all real numbers a, b, and c such that
>
> $c > 0$:
> 1. If $a < b$, then $ac < bc$;
> 2. If $a > b$, then $ac > bc$.
>
> $c < 0$:
> 1. If $a < b$, then $ac > bc$;
> 2. If $a > b$, then $ac < bc$.

Multiplying both sides of an inequality by zero does not produce an inequality; the result is the identity $0 = 0$.

The axioms that have been stated guarantee that the following transformations of a given inequality always produce an **equivalent inequality,** that is, one with the same solution set.

> **TRANSFORMATIONS THAT PRODUCE AN EQUIVALENT INEQUALITY**
>
> 1. Substituting for either side of the inequality an expression equivalent to that side.
> 2. Adding to (or subtracting from) each side the same real number.
> 3. Multiplying (or dividing) each side by the same positive number.
> 4. Multiplying (or dividing) each side by the same negative number and reversing the direction of the inequality.

370   *CHAPTER 10*

To solve an inequality, you usually try to transform it into a simple equivalent inequality whose solution or solutions can be seen at a glance.

You may assume that the domain of all variables is the set of real numbers unless otherwise mentioned.

EXAMPLE 1   Solve $4x - 3 < 7 + 2x$ over the set of real numbers and draw its graph.

SOLUTION
$$4x - 3 < 7 + 2x$$
$$4x - 3 + 3 < 7 + 2x + 3 \qquad \text{Add 3 to each side.}$$
$$4x < 10 + 2x$$
$$4x - 2x < 10 + 2x - 2x \qquad \text{Subtract } 2x \text{ from each side.}$$
$$2x < 10$$
$$\frac{2x}{2} < \frac{10}{2} \qquad \text{Divide each side by 2.}$$
$$x < 5$$

∴ the solution set is {the real numbers less than 5}. The graph of the solution set is:

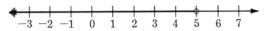

To solve an inequality, you take the same steps used to solve equations:

1. Simplify each side of the inequality.
2. Use the inverse operations to undo any indicated additions or subtractions.
3. Use the inverse operations to undo any indicated multiplications or divisions.

EXAMPLE 2   Solve and graph $2(x - 3) + 6 \geq 3(4 - x) - 2$.

SOLUTION
$$2(x - 3) + 6 \geq 3(4 - x) - 2$$
$$2x - 6 + 6 \geq 12 - 3x - 2$$
$$2x \geq 10 - 3x$$
$$5x \geq 10$$
$$x \geq 2$$

∴ the solution set is {the real numbers greater than or equal to 2}. The graph is:

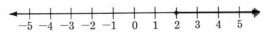

12. Multiply each side by -2, and reverse the direction of the inequality.

13. Add 3 to each side.
$y < 11$

14. Subtract 2 from each side. $4 < x$

15. Divide each side by 3.
$k > 3$

16. Divide each side by -2, and reverse the direction of the inequality. $4 > m$

17. Multiply each side by 2.
$y \geq 18$

18. Multiply each side by -2, and reverse the direction of the inequality.
$6 \geq y$

Additional A Exercises

Solve.

1. $x + 3 < 8$
{all real numbers less than 5}

2. $y - 7 > 4$
{all real numbers greater than 11}

3. $2x + 3 \leq 5$
{1, and all real numbers less than 1}

4. $-3x > 6$
{all real numbers less than -2}

5. $4x \geq -10$
{-2, and all real numbers greater than -2}

6. $2x - 6 \leq 7$
{$\frac{13}{2}$, and all real numbers less than $\frac{13}{2}$}

Additional Answers
Written Exercises

9. {the real numbers greater than 15}

10. {the real numbers less than 9}

(continued)

371

11. {the real numbers less than -24}

12. {the real numbers less than 4}

13. {the real numbers less than -48}

14. {the real numbers greater than -36}

15. {the real numbers less than or equal to -1}

16. {the real numbers greater than or equal to -3}

17. {the real numbers greater than -4}

18. {the real numbers greater than 2}

19. {the real numbers less than or equal to -20}

20. {the real numbers less than or equal to 4}

21. {the real numbers less than 6}

22. {the real numbers less than or equal to 12}

23. {the real numbers greater than -15}

24. {the real numbers less than or equal to 12}

25. {the real numbers less than 6}

26. {the real numbers greater than 8}

27. {the real numbers less than 8}

28. {the real numbers greater than 9}

29. {the real numbers greater than -4}

30. {the real numbers greater than 1}

31. {the real numbers less than or equal to 3}

32. {the real numbers less than or equal to 7}

(continued)

Oral Exercises

Tell how to transform the first inequality to obtain the second one.

1. $y + 2 < 6$
   $y < 4$

2. $m - 3 > 5$
   $m > 8$

3. $-3 < k - 6$
   $3 < k$

4. $s + 8 < 0$
   $s < -8$

5. $3k < 9$
   $k < 3$

6. $2n < -18$
   $n < -9$

7. $-4p < 16$
   $p > -4$

8. $\frac{k}{3} > 2$
   $k > 6$

9. $2 > \frac{v}{5}$
   $10 > v$

10. $\frac{x}{-2} < -4$
    $x > 8$

11. $2y < \frac{1}{3}$
    $y < \frac{1}{6}$

12. $\frac{t}{-2} > 0$
    $t < 0$

Explain how to transform each inequality in order to solve it. Then state the transformed inequality.

13. $y - 3 < 8$

14. $6 < x + 2$

15. $3k > 9$

16. $-8 < -2m$

17. $\frac{y}{2} \geq 9$

18. $-3 \leq \frac{y}{-2}$

Written Exercises

Match each inequality in Exercises 1-8 with its solution set in a-h.

A
1. $x - 3 \geq 6$ d.
2. $4 > y + 4$ h.
3. $2m \neq 8$ c.
4. $6 < 3p$ f.
5. $-16 > -4k$ b.
6. $\frac{m}{5} < -4$ g.
7. $2 - x > 0$ e.
8. $3 \leq \frac{y}{-2}$ a.

a.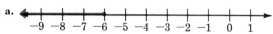

b.

c.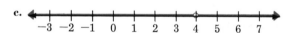

d.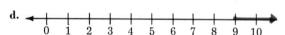

e.

f.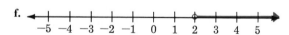

g.

h.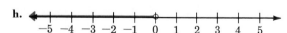

Solve each inequality and draw its graph.

9. $m - 3 > 12$

10. $y + 3 < 12$

11. $-\frac{x}{2} > 12$

12. $3p < 12$

13. $12 < \frac{x}{-4}$

14. $-12 < \frac{y}{3}$

15. $-2k \geq 2$

16. $-3p \leq 9$

17. $\frac{x}{2} - 2 > -4$

18. $3k + 1 > 7$

19. $\frac{y}{-2} \geq 10$

20. $5 \geq 2y - 3$

21. $\frac{3}{2}p - 5 < 4$

22. $-2 \leq 2 - \frac{k}{3}$

23. $-3 < 7 + \frac{2}{3}m$

24. $3 + \frac{y}{4} \leq 6$

25. $9 - \frac{3}{2}y > 0$

26. $0 > 6 - \frac{3}{4}s$

Solve each inequality.

27. $3y < 2y + 8$

28. $4m - 3 > 3m + 6$

29. $2x - 3 < 4x + 5$

30. $1 + 3r > 5 - r$

31. $6 - 2p \geq 3 - p$

32. $3(x - 5) \leq 6$

33. $8 < 4(2 - y)$

34. $2(k - 6) < 3(k - 2)$

35. $4(1 - t) \geq 2(3 - t)$

Solve each inequality and draw its graph.

B 36. $\frac{m}{3} - 2 \geq \frac{2}{3}$

37. $\frac{1}{8} < 2 - \frac{3}{4}p$

38. $3(y - 1) \geq \frac{3}{4}y$

39. $\frac{2}{3}m \leq 4(m - 5)$

40. $k + \frac{1}{2} > \frac{3}{4}(k - 2)$

41. $3p - \frac{1}{2}(p + 10) \geq 0$

42. $3(3 - m) - 5(5 + m) < 0$

43. $2(k - 3) > 3(k + 2) - 3$

44. $2(y - 2) - 4 \leq 3(y + 1) + 3$

45. $2(x - 1) - 3(x + 2) \leq 3 - 2x$

46. $3 - t + 2(t - 3) \geq 3(t + 1)$

47. $3(2x - 1) - 2(x + 1) > 3x + 8$

Given that a and b are real numbers such that $a > b$, describe the real numbers c for which each statement is true.

C 48. $ac > bc$

49. $ac < bc$

50. $ac = bc$

51. $\frac{a}{c} > \frac{b}{c}$

52. $\frac{a}{c} < \frac{b}{c}$

53. $ac^2 > bc^2$

54. $\frac{a}{c^2} < \frac{b}{c^2}$

55. $ac^2 = bc^2$

Classify each statement as true or false for all real numbers a and b such that $a > b > 0$.

56. $a > 0$ True

57. $a^2 > a$ False

58. $ab > 0$ True

59. $a + b > a$ True

60. $a^2 > b$ False

61. $a^2 > ab$ True

62. $ab > b^2$ True

63. $a^2 > b^2$ True

INEQUALITIES 373

33. {the negative real numbers}

34. {the real numbers greater than -6}

35. {the real numbers less than or equal to -1}

36. {the real numbers greater than or equal to 8}

37. {the real numbers less than $\frac{5}{2}$}

38. {the real numbers greater than or equal to $\frac{4}{3}$}

39. {the real numbers greater than or equal to 6}

40. {the real numbers greater than -8}

41. {the real numbers greater than or equal to 2}

42. {the real numbers greater than -2}

43. {the real numbers less than -9}

44. {the real numbers greater than or equal to -14}

45. {the real numbers less than or equal to 11}

46. {the real numbers less than or equal to -3}

47. {the real numbers greater than 13}

48. The positive real numbers

49. The negative real numbers

50. Zero

51. The positive real numbers

52. The negative real numbers

53. All real numbers except 0

54. No real numbers

55. Zero

Using the variable provided, translate each of the following statements into symbols.

1. The temperature (t) today is at least 28°C. $t \geq 28$

2. John's shirt (j) cost no more than $21.50.
$j \leq 21.50$

3. The air fare (a) will be between $474 and $524.
$474 < a < 524$

4. The length of the town pool (p) is no less than 25 meters. $p \geq 25$

Solve.

5. Find three consecutive positive odd integers whose sum is less than twice the largest integer.
Step 1 Find all possible sets of such integers.
Step 2 Let n = the smallest such integer.
Step 3 $n + (n + 2)$ $+ (n + 4) < 2(n + 4)$
Step 4 $3n + 6 < 2n + 8$
$n < 2$
Since n is positive,
$0 < n < 2$
so $n = 1$
Step 5 Check: $1 + 3 +$ $5 = 9$ and $2(5) = 10$ $9 < 10$ ✓
∴ The numbers are 1, 3, and 5.

6. A triangle has two equal sides each of which is 5 cm more than one third of the remaining side. If the lengths of the sides of the triangle must be integers, find the largest sides possible if the perimeter of the triangle is less than 16 cm.

(continued)

10-3 *Solving Problems Involving Inequalities*

OBJECTIVE To solve problems involving inequalities.

EXAMPLE 1

The width of a rectangle is 26 cm less than twice the length. The perimeter is less than 74 cm. Find the maximum dimensions of the rectangle if each dimension, in centimeters, is an integer.

SOLUTION

Step 1 The problem asks for the maximum length and width in centimeters. The measures must be integers. (Such measures must also be positive.)

Step 2 Let x = length in centimeters.
Then $2x - 26$ = width in centimeters.

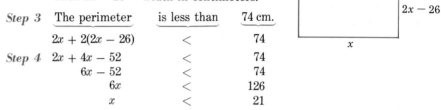

Step 3

The perimeter	is less than	74 cm.
$2x + 2(2x - 26)$	<	74

Step 4

$2x + 4x - 52$	<	74
$6x - 52$	<	74
$6x$	<	126
x	<	21

∴ the greatest length that the rectangle can have is 20 cm. The greatest width is $(2 \times 20) - 26$, or 14 cm.

Step 5 *Check:* (1) Is the width 26 cm less than twice the length?
$$14 \overset{?}{=} (2 \times 20) - 26$$
$$14 = 14 \ \checkmark$$

(2) Is the perimeter less than 74 cm?
$$(2 \times 20) + (2 \times 14) = 40 + 28 = 68; \ 68 < 74 \ \checkmark$$

(3) Are the dimensions the greatest possible? Suppose the length were the next larger integer, 21 cm. Then the width would be $(2 \times 21) - 26$, or 16 cm. The perimeter would be $(2 \times 21) + (2 \times 16)$, or 74 cm, which is *not* less than 74 cm.

∴ the dimensions are 14 cm and 20 cm. ***Answer***

EXAMPLE 2

The average of three consecutive integers is greater than 9. Find the smallest possible values for the integers.

SOLUTION

Step 1 The problem asks for the three smallest consecutive integers whose average is greater than 9.

Step 2 Let n = the least integer.
Then $n + 1$ and $n + 2$ are the next consecutive integers.

374 *CHAPTER 10*

Step 3 The average of three consecutive integers is greater than 9

$$\underbrace{\frac{n + (n + 1) + (n + 2)}{3}}_{} \qquad > \qquad 9$$

Steps 4, 5 Solving the inequality and checking that the three required consecutive integers are 9, 10, and 11 are left to you.

To translate phrases such as "is at least" and "is no less than" or "is at most" and "is no more than" into mathematical terms, you use the symbols $\geq$ or $\leq$. For example:

My grandfather's age is at least 65: $a \geq 65$

The rent is no less than \$300 per month: $r \geq 300$

The price of the paperback book is at most \$3.95: $p \leq 3.95$

Her time in the 10 km race was no more than 40 min: $t \leq 40$

Written Exercises

For each of the following:
a. Choose a variable to represent the number indicated in color.
b. Use the variable to write an inequality based on the given information. (Do not solve.)

A

1. After selling a dozen copies of the *Bulletin*, a newsdealer had fewer than 75 copies left. (The number of copies the dealer had originally) $c - 12 < 75$

2. Jim, who is over 21, is three years older than his cousin Bob. (Bob's age) $b > 18$

3. A businesswoman traveled a certain number of kilometers by automobile, and then ten times as far by airplane. Her total trip was more than 2800 km. $k + 10k > 2800$

4. The number of State College students studying mathematics is one third the number studying computer science. The total number of students enrolled in these subjects is at least 9500. $\frac{4}{3}c \geq 9500$

5. Mary's bowling score was 12 more than half Ann's score. Mary's bowling score was less than 100. $\frac{1}{2}a + 12 < 100$

6. A house and lot together cost more than \$90,000. The cost of the house was \$1000 more than seven times the cost of the lot.

7. The sum of two consecutive odd integers is less than 25 and greater than 9. (The smaller integer) $9 < n + (n + 2) < 25$

8. The product of two consecutive integers is a positive number less than 60. (The greater integer) $0 < x(x - 1) < 60$

6. $8c > 89,000$

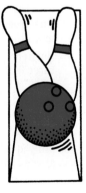

INEQUALITIES **375**

Step 2 Let $\frac{1}{3}n + 5 =$ the length of each of the two equal sides and $n =$ the length of the third side.

Step 3

$$n + 2\left(\frac{1}{3}n + 5\right) < 16$$

Step 4 $\frac{5}{3}n + 10 < 16$

$$\frac{5}{3}n < 6$$

$$n < \frac{18}{5}$$

Since n must be an integer, $n = 3$ and $\frac{1}{3}n + 5 = 6$.

$\therefore$ The lengths of the sides of the triangle are 3 cm, 6 cm, and 6 cm.

Supplementary Material
Progress Test 36

Suggested Assignments
Minimum
  375/1–11 odd
  376/*P*: 1, 3, 7
  S 373/37–43 odd

Average
  375/1–11 odd
  376/*P*: 1, 2, 5, 7, 8
  S 373/57–63 odd

Maximum
  376/9, 11, *P*: 1–19 odd
  S 373/48–62 even

Extra Practice Problems
  p. 522

Additional A Exercises

Solve.

1. The sum of three consecutive integers is less than 54. Find the greatest possible values for the integers.
16, 17, 18

2. The length of a rectangle is 5 more than twice the width. The perimeter is less than or equal to 100 cm. Find the maximum dimensions of the rectangle.
length: 35 cm
width: 15 cm

3. Two integers are in the ratio 4:9. What is the greatest possible value of each integer if their sum is less than 80?
24 and 54

For each of the following:

a. Choose a variable to represent the number indicated in color.

b. Use the variable to write an inequality based on the given information.

B **9.** The smaller of two consecutive even integers is less than or equal to 4 more than twice the larger. $x - 2 \le 2x + 4$

10. The larger of two consecutive integers is greater than 4 more than half the smaller. $x + 1 > \frac{1}{2}x + 4$

11. There are three consecutive integers such that four times the greatest diminished by twice the second is at least one more than three times the least. $4(x + 2) - 2(x + 1) \ge 3x + 1$

12. Three consecutive even integers are such that their sum is more than 24 decreased by twice the greatest of the three integers.
$3x - 6 > 24 - 2x$

Problems

Solve.

A **1.** Two integers are in the ratio 3:7. If their sum is less than 60, what is the greatest possible value of the smaller integer? 15

2. Of all pairs of consecutive even integers whose sum is less than 50, find the pair whose sum is the greatest. 22 and 24

3. The sum of two consecutive integers is less than 25. Find the pair of integers with the greatest sum. 11 and 12

4. The sum of two consecutive even integers is less than 100. Find the pair with the greatest sum. 48 and 50

5. The sum of two consecutive integers is greater than 75. Find the pair with the smallest sum. 38 and 39

6. Of all pairs of consecutive odd integers whose sum is greater than 45, find the pair whose sum is the least. 23 and 25

7. Two trucks start from the same point going in opposite directions. One truck travels at 88 km/hr, the other at 72 km/hr. How long must they travel to be at least 672 km apart? 4.2 h, or 4 h 12 min

8. Between them, Al and Ben have 48 dimes. If Al has more than three fifths as many dimes as Ben, at least how many dimes does Al have? At most how many does Ben have? Al, at least 19; Ben, at most 29

9. Marie Simone said, "Three fourths of my age two years ago is greater than or equal to two thirds of my age three years from now." At least how old is she now? 42 years

10. Milly is two thirds as old as Marcia. Four years from now she will be at most five sevenths as old as Marcia. At least how old is Milly?
16 years

376   CHAPTER 10

376

11. A purse contains 22 coins, some of which are dimes and the rest, quarters. Altogether, the coins are worth more than $3.40. At least how many of the coins are quarters? At most how many are dimes?

12. Ken has more than $10 in dimes, quarters, and half dollars. There are five times as many quarters as half dollars, and one and one half times as many dimes as quarters. At least how many of each kind of coin does Ken have? 45 dimes, 30 quarters, 6 half dollars

B 13. A pair of consecutive even integers has the property that five times the smaller is less than 4 times the greater. Find the greatest pair of integers with this property. 6 and 8

14. The average of four consecutive even integers is greater than 6. Find the smallest possible values for the integers. 4, 6, 8, and 10

15. The average of four consecutive odd integers is less than 8. Find the greatest possible values for the integers. 3, 5, 7, and 9

16. The sum of three consecutive integers decreased by 6 is greater than twice the smallest of the three. What are the three smallest possible integers? 4, 5, and 6

17. The units digit of a certain two-digit number is one more than the tens digit. Sixteen times the tens digit is greater than the number with the digits reversed. Find the least possible value of the original number. 34

18. If the digits of a certain two-digit number are reversed, the resulting number is 6 less than twice the original number. The sum of the digits is less than 8. Find the greatest possible value of the original number. 24

C 19. A family sold 2 km² more than three fifths of their farm and had more than 4 km² less than half of it left. If the farm originally contained an integral number of square kilometers, what was the greatest possible area it could have had? 19 km²

20. Two consecutive odd integers have the property that their product exceeds the square of the greater integer. Find the greatest pair of integers that have this property. −3 and −1

21. Three consecutive integers have the property that the square of the second integer decreased by the square of the smallest integer is less than the third integer. Find the integers that have this property and have a positive sum. 0, 1, and 2

22. Scott has saved quarters in a bank. On Monday he took out 2 quarters, and one sixth of what was left. On Tuesday he took out 3 quarters, and one sixth of what then remained. If he took out more on Monday than on Tuesday, what was the least possible number of quarters originally in the bank? 56 quarters

1. Translate the statement "2 is between -9 and 5" into symbols.
   $-9 < 2 < 5$

2. Solve $5x - 3 \geq 17$ if the domain of x is $\{1, 2, 3, 4, 5, 6, 7, 8\}$
   $\{4, 5, 6, 7, 8\}$

Solve and graph.

3. $y - 3 < -5$ $y < -2$

4. $2 - 4z \leq 14$ $z \geq -3$

Solve.

5. The sum of two consecutive odd integers is less than 28. Find the pair with the largest sum.   11, 13

Self-Test 1

VOCABULARY   inequality (p. 366)
solutions of an inequality (p. 366)
solution set of an inequality (p. 366)
graph of an open sentence (p. 366)
equivalent inequalities (p. 370)

1. Translate the statement "-3 is between -6 and 0" into symbols.   Obj. 10-1, p. 365

2. Solve $3x + 7 \leq 13$ if the domain of x is $\{-4, -3, -2, -1, 0, 1, 2, 3, 4\}$.   Obj. 10-2, p. 369

Solve and graph.

3. $a - 7 < -3$ 4. $5 - 2r \leq 6$

Solve.

5. The sum of two consecutive even integers is greater than 88. Find the pair with the smallest sum.   Obj. 10-3, p. 374

Check your answers with those at the back of the book.

Biography   Ada Byron Lovelace

Lady Ada Byron Lovelace (1815–1852) was the daughter of Lord Byron, the famous English poet, and Annabella Milbanke. Encouraged by her mother and friends, she studied mathematics enthusiastically. For 18 years she worked with Charles Babbage, the acknowledged father of the computer. In 1842 she began work on translating and annotating a paper detailing Babbage's Analytical Engine. Her descriptions of the way in which instructions and information were given to this precursor of the modern computer make her the first computer programmer. In recognition of her contribution to mathematics, a computer language developed in the 1970's was named after her and called ADA.

Computer Key-In

Computers and Words

Computers can handle words as well as numbers. You have already seen (page 46) that a simple PRINT statement will cause the computer to print back anything that is enclosed within quotation marks. Moreover, computers can store words in ''files'' and then later search for and find (retrieve) words and expressions that are asked for. Thus, if the texts of books and magazines have been copied into computer files, the statements about a chosen subject can be located and printed out.

Small computers can be combined with electric typewriters to make *word processors*. Generally, on one of these machines, whatever is typed is shown on a screen like a television screen and is recorded on a tape or a diskette. By using a program stored in the machine, changes can easily be made without retyping the whole page. The finished copy can then be printed out. The tapes or diskettes can be kept and changed later. Thus, a directory can be stored and updated from time to time by simply making the necessary changes. Some word processors can merge two files so that what is essentially a form letter can be addressed to individuals and contain individual details of information.

Several word processors can be connected to a central computer and storage unit. For example, in a newspaper office, one person can type in a story and store it, and then another person can call it up and edit it.

Some computers can be connected to several terminals and used on a ''time-sharing'' basis. When the terminals are at a distance, the connections are made over the telephone. Similarly, word processors can be set up to communicate with a central computer over the telephone, making an extensive word processing network.

Intersection and Union of Sets

The diagram shows the relationship among the sets:

$$A = \{1, 2, 3, 4, 5\}$$
$$B = \{2, 4, 6\}$$
$$C = \{7, 8\}$$

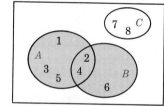

The set represented by shading consists of those members and only those members *common to both* set A and set B. You call $\{2, 4\}$ the **intersection** of $\{1, 2, 3, 4, 5\}$ and $\{2, 4, 6\}$ and write

$$\{1, 2, 3, 4, 5\} \cap \{2, 4, 6\} = \{2, 4\}$$

or

$$A \cap B = \{2, 4\}.$$

The latter is read, "The intersection of A and B is $\{2, 4\}$."

Notice in the diagram above that the regions A and C do not overlap. Two sets, such as A and C, that have no members in common are called **disjoint sets.** Their intersection is the empty set: $A \cap C = \emptyset$.

The diagram at the right again shows the sets A, B, and C. Here, the set represented by the shaded region,

$$\{1, 2, 3, 4, 5, 6\},$$

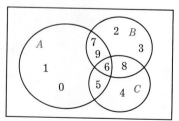

consists of the members that belong to *at least* one of the sets A and B. You call this set the **union** of A and B and write

$$\{1, 2, 3, 4, 5\} \cup \{2, 4, 6\} = \{1, 2, 3, 4, 5, 6\}$$

or

$$A \cup B = \{1, 2, 3, 4, 5, 6\}.$$

The latter is read, "The union of A and B is $\{1, 2, 3, 4, 5, 6\}$."

Exercises

Refer to the diagram and list the members of each of the following sets.

1. $A \cup B$ 2. $A \cap B$

3. $B \cap C$ 4. $B \cup C$

5. $A \cap (B \cap C)$ 6. $(A \cap B) \cup C$

7. $(A \cup B) \cap C$ 8. $(A \cup B) \cup C$

9. $(A \cap B) \cup (A \cap C)$

10. Express $\{6, 7, 8, 9\}$ in terms of A, B, and C.

Specify the union and the intersection of the given sets. If the sets are disjoint, say so.

11. {0, 1, 2, 3}, {2, 3, 4}

12. {−3, −2, −1, 0}, {−1, 0, 1}

13. {2, 4, 6}, {1, 3, 5}

14. {2, 4}, {1, 2, 3, 4, 5}

15. {2, 3, 5, 7, 11}, {1, 3, 5, 7, 9}

16. {−6, −5, −4}, {−3, −2, −1}

In Exercises 17–24, refer to the number lines shown and describe each set.

D = {the real numbers greater than −2}
E = {the real numbers between −3 and 3}
F = {the real numbers less than 1}

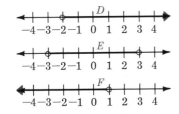

17. $D \cup F$ 18. $D \cup E$ 19. $D \cap E$ 20. $D \cap F$

21. $E \cup F$ 22. $E \cap F$ 23. $D \cap (E \cap F)$ 24. $(D \cap E) \cup F$

For each of Exercises 25 and 26, make two copies of the diagram shown at the right. On your copies shade the regions representing the sets named.

25. $A \cap (B \cup C)$; $(A \cap B) \cup (A \cap C)$

26. $A \cup (B \cap C)$; $(A \cup B) \cap (A \cup C)$

27. State a "distributive axiom" that appears to be true on the basis of Exercise 25.

28. State a "distributive axiom" that appears to be true on the basis of Exercise 26.

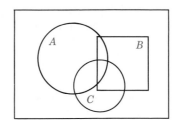

29. Copy the diagram at the right and write in the remaining members of these sets:

A = {1, 2, 3, 4, 5, 6, 7}
B = {1, 3, 5, 7, 9}
C = {3, 4, 5, 6, 7}
D = {−3, −1, 1, 3, 4}

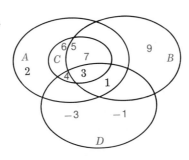

24. {the real numbers less than 3}

25.

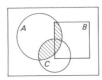

26.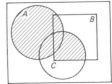

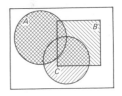

27. $A \cap (B \cup C)$
    $= (A \cap B) \cup (A \cap C)$

28. $A \cup (B \cap C)$
    $= (A \cap B) \cup (A \cup C)$

29.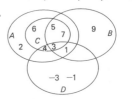

COMBINING OPEN SENTENCES

10-4 *Solving Combined Inequalities*

OBJECTIVE   To find the solution sets of combined inequalities.

In (a) and (b) below, two inequalities and their graphs are shown. In (c) the two inequalities have been joined by the word "and." A sentence formed by joining two sentences by the word *and* is called a **conjunction.** To **solve a conjunction** of open sentences, you find the values of the variable for which *both* sentences are true. Note that the conjunction in part (c) can be written in the form $-2 < x < 3$. The graph consists of the points that belong to *both* the graph of $-2 < x$ and the graph of $x < 3$.

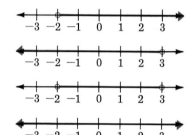

(a) $-2 < x$

(b) $x < 3$

(c) $-2 < x$ and $x < 3$

(d) $-2 < x$ or $x < 3$

In (d) above, the inequalities in (a) and (b) have been joined by the word "or." A sentence formed by joining two sentences by the word *or* is called a **disjunction.** To **solve a disjunction** of open sentences, you find the values of the variable for which *at least one* of the sentences is true (that is, one or the other or both are true). Notice that *every* real number is a solution of the disjunction in (d).

Recall that the disjunction "$y > 2$ or $y = 2$" is written $y \geq 2$. Similarly, $y \leq 2$ means "$y < 2$ or $y = 2$."

EXAMPLE 1   The solution set of "$x < 2$ and $x \geq 2$" is the empty set.

EXAMPLE 2   The solution set of "$x < 2$ or $x \geq 2$" is the set of all real numbers.

To solve conjunctions and disjunctions of inequalities, you can use the transformations listed on page 370.

EXAMPLE 3   Find the solution set of $-3 \leq x - 1 < 4$, and draw its graph.

382   *CHAPTER 10*

SOLUTION To solve the inequality $-3 \leq x - 1 < 4$, you solve the conjunction:

$$-3 \leq x - 1 \quad \text{and} \quad x - 1 < 4$$
$$-2 \leq x \quad \text{and} \quad x < 5$$
$$-2 \leq x < 5$$

∴ the solution set is $\{-2$, and the real numbers between -2 and $5\}$. The graph is:

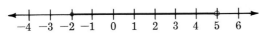

EXAMPLE 4 Solve the disjunction and draw its graph: $3y - 1 < 5$ or $3y \geq y + 6$.

SOLUTION
$$3y - 1 < 5 \quad \text{or} \quad 3y \geq y + 6$$
$$3y < 6 \quad \text{or} \quad 2y \geq 6$$
$$y < 2 \quad \text{or} \quad y \geq 3$$

∴ the solution set is $\{3$, and the real numbers greater than 3 or less than $2\}$. The graph is:

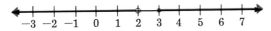

Oral Exercises

In Exercises 1–7, match each graph with one of the open sentences in a–g.

1. 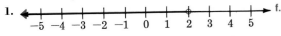 f.

2. b.

3. a.

4. g.

5. d.

6. c.

7. e.

a. $y > 2$

b. $y \geq 2$ or $y < -2$

c. $-2 < y < 2$

d. $y \leq 2$

e. $y \leq -2$ or $y > 2$

f. $y < 2$

g. $-2 \leq y \leq 2$

Supplementary Materials

Practice Master 60

Computer Activity 28
Graphing Combined Inequalities
A computer may be used to graph two inequalities on the same number line. The program in this activity prints the appropriate number line and graphs the two given inequalities. The student must then state the conjunction or disjunction from the graph.

Suggested Assignments

Minimum
    384/1–25 odd
R 378/*Self-Test 1*
S 376/*P*: 9, 13

Average
    384/1–27 odd
R 378/*Self-Test 1*
S 376/*P*: 9, 14

Maximum
    384/1–37 odd
R 378/*Self-Test 1*
S 377/*P*: 20, 22

Additional A Exercises

Solve each open sentence.

1. $1 < x - 2 < 6$
   {all real numbers between 3 and 8}

2. $3 < x + 3 < 7$
   {all real numbers between 0 and 4}

3. $-2 \leq y - 3 \leq 2$
   {1, 5, and all real numbers between 1 and 5}

4. $-4 \leq y + 2 \leq 0$
   {−6, −2 and all real numbers between −6 and −2}

5. $-3 < 2x - 1 < 5$
   {all real numbers between −1 and 3}

6. $5 < 3x - 4 < 17$
   {all real numbers between 3 and 7}

INEQUALITIES   **383**

1.

2.

3.

4.

5. {the real numbers be-
   tween -3 and 2}

6. {3, and the real numbers
   between 0 and 3}

7. {5, and the real numbers
   between 0 and 5}

8. {-3, and the real numbers between -3 and 2}

9. {-1, and the real numbers between -1 and 2}

10. {-1, 5, and the real
    numbers between -1
    and 5}

11. {-2, and the real num-
    bers between -2 and 1}

12. {3, and the real numbers
    between -1 and 3}

13. {3, and the real numbers
    less than -1 or greater
    than 3}

14. {-8, -2, and the real
    numbers less than -8 or
    greater than -2}

15. {-2, 2, and the real
    numbers less than -2 or
    greater than 2}

16. {the real numbers less
    than -3 or greater than
    2}

(continued)

In Exercises 8–12, match each open sentence with an equivalent inequality in a–e.

8. $y < 2$ and $y > -3$ e.   a. $y \geq 2$
9. $y = 2$ or $y < 2$ c.   b. $-3 \leq y \leq 2$
10. $y \leq 2$ and $y > -3$ d.   c. $y \leq 2$
11. $y = 2$ or $y > 2$ a.   d. $-3 < y \leq 2$
12. $y \leq 2$ and $y \geq -3$ b. e. $-3 < y < 2$

Written Exercises

Draw the graph of each open sentence.

A 1. $-3 < y \leq 2$ 2. $x > 2$ or $x \leq -3$
   3. $4 \leq m \leq 8$ 4. $k < -3$ or $k \geq 0$

Solve each open sentence and graph each solution set which is not empty.

5. $-2 < y + 1 < 3$ 6. $-1 < x - 1 \leq 2$
7. $-3 < -3 + y \leq 2$ 8. $-1 \leq 2 + y < 4$
9. $-1 \leq 2y + 1 < 5$ 10. $-3 \leq 2y - 1 \leq 9$
11. $-5 \leq 3x + 1 < 4$ 12. $-5 < 3x - 2 \leq 7$
13. $y - 1 < -2$ or $y - 1 \geq 2$ 14. $k + 5 \leq -3$ or $k + 5 \geq 3$
15. $3m + 1 \leq -5$ or $3m - 1 \geq 5$ 16. $1 + 2y < -5$ or $1 + 2y > 5$
17. $2y - 1 \leq -3$ or $3 \leq 2y - 1$ 18. $1 + 2k < -7$ or $7 < 1 + 2k$

B 19. $-3 < -x \leq 5$ 20. $-5 \leq -x + 1 < 3$
   21. $-6 \leq -2x \leq 4$ 22. $-5 < -2x + 1 \leq 3$
   23. $-2y < -4$ or $-2y > 4$ 24. $-2y + 1 \leq -5$ or $-2y + 1 \geq 5$
   25. $-3m < 6$ and $4 < -2m$ 26. $-8 < -4k$ or $2k - 1 > -3$
   27. $-3 \leq 2 - y < 4$ 28. $-2 < -3 - y \leq 3$
   29. $3 - m > 4$ or $m - 3 > 4$ 30. $t - 4 \geq 3$ or $4 - t \geq 3$
   31. $3 - 2p > 5$ or $3 - 2p < -7$
   32. $5 - 3k \geq 8$ or $-4 \geq 5 - 3k$
   33. $2y + 1 \geq -3$ and $2y + 1 \leq y + 3$
   34. $8 - 2y \leq 2 - y$ and $1 - 2y \geq -3$

C 35. $2 - y < 2y - 1 \leq 3 + y$
   36. $3 - t \leq 1 - 2t$ or $t + 3 > 3t - 1$
   37. $2(1 - t) \geq 4$ or $3t - 1 \leq 2t + 5$
   38. $1 - 3t \leq 3 - 4t \leq 2t - 3$

39. Find the value of a so that the solution set of

$$a - 3 \le y - 4 \le 5$$

will be the same as the solution set of

$$2y - 3 \le 6 + y \quad \text{and} \quad y - 2 \ge 4. \quad a = 5$$

40. Find an example of real values of $a, b, c,$ and d for which the following statement is *false:* If $a < b$ and $c < d$, then $ac < bd$. Answers may vary. One example is $a = -3, b = -1, c = -5, d = -2.$

ḣistorical Note   Greater Than—Less Than

The symbols $>$ and $<$ for "is greater than" and "is less than" were invented by Thomas Harriot, an English mathematician and astronomer. The symbols appeared in his algebra book, published in 1631, ten years after his death. At that time many mathematicians were using the symbols shown below.

The Frenchman Pierre Bouguer is credited with inventing the symbols $\geqq$ and $\leqq$ in 1734. The symbols $\gg$ and $\ll$, which are used for "is much greater than" and "is much less than," and the symbols $\not>$ and $\not<$ are all modern inventions.

Career Note   Darkroom Technician

Unless you use a camera which develops film instantly, taking a picture is only part of the art of photography. An equally important part is the processing of the film.

It is the task of the darkroom technician to develop and print the film for snapshots, slides, and movies, whether in black-and-white or color. Special tasks also include cropping, enlarging, and restoring photographs.

If the photographic lab is small, darkroom technicians do these jobs manually. In a large lab they operate the machinery which processes the film automatically.

Most darkroom technicians acquire their skills informally by assisting experienced people in the trade. In general, a high school diploma is required of applicants in this field. Courses in chemistry and mathematics are desirable.

INEQUALITIES   **385**

17. $\{-1, 2,$ and the real numbers less than -1 or greater than $2\}$

18. {the real numbers less than -4 or greater than $3\}$

19. $\{-5,$ and the real numbers between -5 and $3\}$

20. $\{6,$ and the real numbers between -2 and $6\}$

21. $\{-2, 3,$ and the real numbers between -2 and $3\}$

22. $\{-1,$ and the real numbers between -1 and $3\}$

23. {the real numbers less than -2 or greater than $2\}$

24. $\{3, -2,$ and the real numbers greater than 3 or less than $-2\}$

25. $\emptyset$ **26.** {the real numbers}

27 $\{5,$ and the real numbers between -2 and $5\}$

28. $\{-6,$ and the real numbers between -6 and $1\}$

29. {the real numbers less than -1 or greater than $7\}$

30. $\{1, 7,$ and the real numbers greater than 7 or less than $1\}$

31. {the real numbers less than -1 or greater than $5\}$

32. $\{-1, 3,$ and the real numbers less than -1 or greater than $3\}$

33. $\{-2, 2,$ and the real numbers between -2 and $2\}$

34. $\emptyset$

35. $\{4,$ and the real numbers between 1 and $4\}$

36. {the real numbers less than $2\}$

37. {the real numbers less than or equal to $6\}$

38. $\{1, 2,$ and the real numbers between 1 and $2\}$

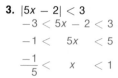

10-5 *Equations and Inequalities Involving Absolute Value*

OBJECTIVE To solve equations and inequalities involving absolute value.

You may use absolute value (page 44) to write certain open sentences in more compact form.

SENTENCE	COMPACT FORM	GRAPH

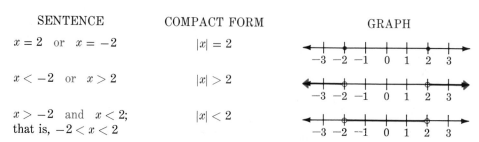

EXAMPLE 1 Solve $|3y - 2| = 4$.

SOLUTION $|3y - 2| = 4$ is a compact form of the disjunction:

$$3y - 2 = 4 \quad \text{or} \quad 3y - 2 = -4$$
$$3y = 6 \quad \text{or} \quad 3y = -2$$
$$y = 2 \quad \text{or} \quad y = -\frac{2}{3}$$

$\therefore$ the solution set is $\{-\frac{2}{3}, 2\}$.

EXAMPLE 2 Draw the graph of $|2m - 3| \geq 1$.

SOLUTION $|2m - 3| \geq 1$ is a compact form of the disjunction:

$$2m - 3 \leq -1 \quad \text{or} \quad 2m - 3 \geq 1$$
$$2m \leq 2 \quad \text{or} \quad 2m \geq 4$$
$$m \leq 1 \quad \text{or} \quad m \geq 2$$

$\therefore$ the graph is:

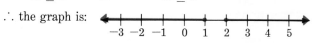

EXAMPLE 3 Solve $|3x + 1| \leq 4$.

SOLUTION $|3x + 1| \leq 4$ is a compact form of the conjunction:

$$-4 \leq 3x + 1 \leq 4$$
$$-5 \leq 3x \quad\;\; \leq 3$$
$$-\frac{5}{3} \leq x \quad\;\; \leq 1$$

$\therefore$ the solution set is $\{-\frac{5}{3}, 1$, and the real numbers between $-\frac{5}{3}$ and 1$\}$. **Answer**

Oral Exercises

State a conjunction or a disjunction that is equivalent to the given open sentence.

1. $|y| = 3$

2. $|y| > 3$

3. $|y| < 3$

4. $|y| \geq 3$

5. $|x - 1| = 2$

6. $|x - 1| > 2$

7. $|x - 1| < 2$

8. $|x - 1| \leq 2$

9. $|2m| < 4$

10. $\left|\dfrac{m}{2}\right| > 1$

11. $|3k| = 6$

12. $\left|\dfrac{k}{3}\right| \geq 2$

13. $|m - 3| < 2$

14. $|2 - y| = 3$

15. $|2k - 1| \leq 1$

16. $|8 - 2k| \geq 4$

17. $2 < |2k - 1|$

18. $5 \geq |3 - m|$

In Exercises 19–23, match each open sentence with its graph in a–e.

19. $|x| = 1$ **e.**

20. $|x| \leq 1$ **b.**

21. $|x| > 1$ **d.**

22. $|x| \geq 1$ **a.**

23. $|x| < 1$ **c.**

Written Exercises

Write an equation or an inequality involving absolute value to describe each graph. Use x as the variable.

A **1.** $|x| = 4$

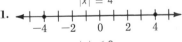

2. $|x| \leq 4$

3. $|x| < 3$

4. $|x| > 3$

5. $|x| \geq 2$

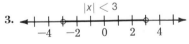

6. $|x| \leq 2$

INEQUALITIES   **387**

3. $|y| \geq 2$
{2, −2, and all real numbers greater than 2 or less than −2}

3. $|y| \geq 2$
{2, −2, and all real numbers greater than 2 or less than −2}
4. $|a - 1| = 6$ {−5, 7}
5. $|x + 2| < 4$
{all real numbers between −6 and 2}
6. $|c - 1| > 2$
{all real numbers greater than 3 or less than −1}

Additional Answers
Written Exercises

7. {3, −1}
8. {2, −4}
9. {0, 2}
10. {−1, 7}
11. {the real numbers between −2 and 2}
12. {−1, 1, and the real numbers less than −1 or greater than 1}
13. {−4, 4, and the real numbers between −4 and 4}
14. {the real numbers less than −3 or greater than 3}
15. {2, −2}
16. {6, −6}
17. {−2, 2, and the real numbers between −2 and 2}
18. {the real numbers less than −4 or greater than 4}

(continued on page 397)

Quick Quiz

Solve each open sentence and graph its solution set.

1. $3x - 2 \leq 4$ or
$\quad\quad\quad 3 - x < -2$
$x \leq 2$ or $x > 5$
2. $-7 \leq y + 2 < 0$
$-9 \leq y < -2$
3. $|z - 6| = 1$
$z = 5$ and 7
4. $|5 - x| \leq 7$
$-2 \leq x \leq 12$

388

Solve each open sentence and draw its graph.

7. $|m - 1| = 2$
8. $|k + 1| = 3$
9. $|1 - y| = 1$
10. $|3 - x| = 4$
11. $|k| < 2$
12. $|p| \geq 1$
13. $|t| \leq 4$
14. $|s| > 3$
15. $|2x| = 4$
16. $\left|\dfrac{y}{3}\right| = 2$
17. $|3k| \leq 6$
18. $\left|\dfrac{s}{4}\right| > 1$

B 19. $|y + 1| < 2$
20. $|m - 1| > 3$
21. $|t - 3| \leq 4$
22. $|6 - y| \geq 0$
23. $|2m - 1| = 5$
24. $|1 - 2a| < 3$
25. $|2p - 4| = 0$
26. $|6 - 2x| \leq 4$
27. $|p| - 2 < 5$
28. $3|y| - 4 \geq 5$
29. $|1 - 2a| - 2 > 5$
30. $|3 - 2x| - 2 < |8 - 3|$
31. $3(2|y| - 1) \geq 6$
32. $\dfrac{5 - 3|m|}{2} < 1$
33. $\left|\dfrac{y}{3} - 2\right| = 3$

C 34. $|2x - 3| = x$
35. $|2y - 1| = y + 4$
36. $|y - 2| = y - 2$
37. $|t - 2| > t - 2$
38. $|m - 2| < m - 2$
39. $|-1 - 2m| < m$

40. The solution set of $|x - a| < b$ can be interpreted geometrically as the set of real numbers whose distance from the graph of a on a number line is less than b. Using this interpretation, solve the following inequalities mentally.

a. $|x - 2| < 1$
b. $|x - 7| < 2$
c. $|x + 2| < 1$
d. $|x + 7| < 2$

Self-Test 2

VOCABULARY   conjunction (p. 382)
solve a conjunction (p. 382)
disjunction (p. 382)
solve a disjunction (p. 382)

Solve each open sentence and graph its solution set.

1. $2x - 1 > 5$ or $1 - x > 0$
2. $-3 < y - 3 \leq 4$
3. $|x - 3| = 2$
4. $|2 - t| \geq 3$

Obj. 10-4, p. 382
Obj. 10-5, p. 386

Check your answers with those at the back of the book.

388   CHAPTER 10

INEQUALITIES IN TWO VARIABLES

10-6 *Graphing Linear Inequalities*

OBJECTIVE   To graph linear inequalities in two variables.

The graph of the linear equation

$$y = x + 2$$

separates the coordinate plane into three sets of points:

>the points *on* the line,
>the points *above* the line,
>the points *below* the line.

Each of the regions above and below the line is called an **open half-plane,** and the line is the **boundary** of each half-plane.

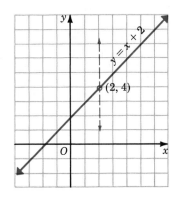

If you start at any point on the line, say $P(2, 4)$, and move upward from P, the y-coordinate increases. If you move downward from P, the y-coordinate decreases.

Thus, the upper open half-plane is the graph of

$$y > x + 2$$

and the lower open half-plane is the graph of

$$y < x + 2.$$

The graphs of

$$y > x + 2, \quad y = x + 2, \quad \text{and} \quad y < x + 2$$

completely cover the coordinate plane. The upper half-plane and the boundary line together form the graph of

$$y \geq x + 2.$$

The lower half-plane and the boundary line together form the graph of

$$y \leq x + 2.$$

The graph of an open half-plane and its boundary is called a **closed half-plane.**

Teaching Suggestions p. T102

Suggested Extensions p. T102

Chalkboard Examples

Graph each inequality.

1. $x \geq 2$

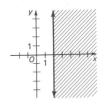

2. $y < -1$

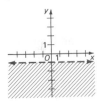

3. $y < 2x + 1$

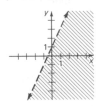

4. $2x - 5y \geq -2$

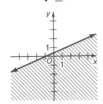

INEQUALITIES   **389**

389

The graphs of inequalities are shown by shading. If the boundary line is part of a graph, it is drawn as a solid line. If the boundary line is *not* part of the graph, it is drawn as a dashed line.

(a) $y > x + 2$ (b) $y \geq x + 2$ (c) $y < x + 2$ (d) $y \leq x + 2$

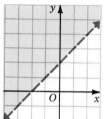 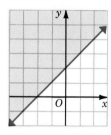 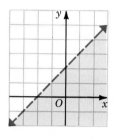 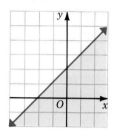

In general, to graph a linear inequality in the variables x and y, when the coefficient of y is not zero, you follow these steps:

1. Transform the given inequality into an equivalent inequality that has y alone as one side.
2. Graph the equation of the boundary. Use a solid line if the symbols $\geq$ or $\leq$ are used in the inequality; use a dashed line if $>$ or $<$ are used.
3. Shade the appropriate region.

EXAMPLE 1   Graph $2x - y \geq -4$.

SOLUTION

1. Transform the inequality:
$$2x - y \geq -4$$
$$-y \geq -4 - 2x$$
$$y \leq 4 + 2x$$

2. Draw the boundary line $y = 4 + 2x$ as a *solid* line, since the symbol $\leq$ is used in the transformed inequality.

3. Shade the region *below* the line, since $y \leq 4 + 2x$.

Check: Choose a point of the graph not on the boundary, say $(0, 0)$. See whether its coordinates satisfy the given inequality:

$$2x - y \geq -4$$
$$2(0) - 0 \overset{?}{\geq} -4$$
$$0 \geq -4 \;\checkmark$$

Thus $(0, 0)$ is in the solution set, and the correct region has been shaded.

Suggested Assignments

Minimum
391/1–29 odd
S 388/23–33 odd

Average
391/1–33 odd
S 388/29–37 odd

Maximum
391/1–33 odd, 34
R 388/*Self-Test 2*
S 388/39, 40

EXAMPLE 2   Graph $y > 2$.

SOLUTION   Graph $y = 2$ as a dashed line. Shade the region *above* the line, since $y > 2$.

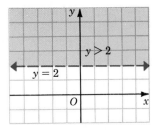

The next example shows how to graph a linear inequality in x and y when the coefficient of y is zero.

EXAMPLE 3   Graph $x > 4$.

SOLUTION

Draw the vertical line that is the graph of $x = 4$. The coordinates of any point *to the right* of that vertical line satisfy $x > 4$. Hence the graph of $x > 4$ is the open half-plane to the right of the graph of $x = 4$.

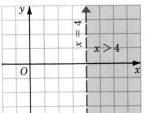

Oral Exercises

State whether or not the given points belong to the graph of the given inequality. Those underlined belong to the graph.

1. $x \geq 3$; $\underline{(3, 2)}$, $(-3, 4)$, $(0, 0)$
2. $y < -2$; $(3, -2)$, $\underline{(4, -3)}$, $(0, 0)$
3. $y < x + 2$; $\underline{(2, 3)}$, $(-2, 3)$, $\underline{(0, 0)}$
4. $y \leq 2x - 3$; $\underline{(3, 0)}$, $\underline{(2, 1)}$, $(0, 0)$
5. $x + y < 0$; $\underline{(-3, 2)}$, $(3, -2)$, $(0, 0)$
6. $x - 3y \geq -1$; $\underline{(1, -1)}$, $(-1, 1)$, $\underline{(0, 0)}$

Transform each inequality into an equivalent inequality having y alone as one side. Then state the equation of the boundary of the graph.

7. $x + y < 2$
8. $-x + y > 2$
9. $2x + y \geq 6$
10. $3x + y \leq -1$
11. $2x + 3y > 0$
12. $9x + 3y < 0$
13. $4y < x$
14. $3x > 2y$
15. $x - y \leq 1$
16. $10x - 5y \leq 0$
17. $x - 2y > 4$
18. $7 < x - y$

Written Exercises

Graph each inequality.

A   1. $y \geq 2$
   2. $y > 2$
   3. $x \leq 3$
   4. $x < 3$
   5. $x > 0$
   6. $y < 0$
   7. $y \geq -1$
   8. $x \leq -3$
   9. $y < x + 1$
   10. $y > -x + 1$
   11. $y \leq 3 - x$
   12. $y \geq 1 - 2x$

INEQUALITIES   **391**

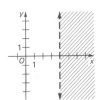
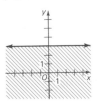

2.

4.

6.

8.

10.

12.

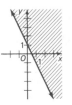

18. $y \leq 2x - 2$

21. $y \geq \frac{1}{3}x + \frac{2}{3}$

34. b.

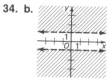

Transform each inequality into an equivalent inequality with y as one side. Then graph the inequality.

13. $x + y < 3$ $y < -x + 3$ 14. $x - y \geq 2$ $y \leq x - 2$ 15. $x - 2y \leq -5$ $y \geq \frac{1}{2}x + \frac{5}{2}$

16. $2x + y > -3$ $y > -2x - 3$ 17. $3x - y > 6$ $y < 3x - 6$ 18. $y - 2x \leq -2$

19. $3x - 2y \geq 8$ $y \leq \frac{3}{2}x - 4$ 20. $2y - 3x < 0$ $y < \frac{3}{2}x$ 21. $2x - 3y \leq x - 2$

22. $3y - 4 > 2x - 5$ $y > \frac{2}{3}x - \frac{1}{3}$ 23. $2(x - y) \geq 3x + 5$ $y \leq -\frac{1}{2}x - \frac{5}{2}$ 24. $2y - 6 < 2(x + 2y)$ $y > -x - 3$

In each of Exercises 25–33, write an inequality whose graph is shown.

B 25.

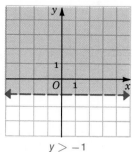

$y > -1$

26.

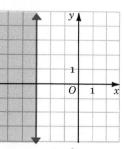

$x \leq -3$

27.

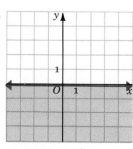

$y \leq 0$

28.

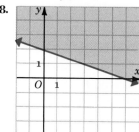

$y \geq -\frac{1}{3}x + 2$

29.

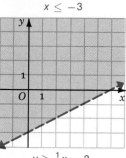

$y > \frac{1}{2}x - 3$

30.

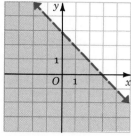

$y < -x + 3$

31.

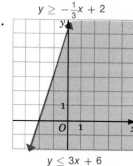

$y \leq 3x + 6$

32.

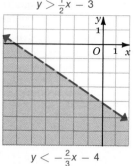

$y < -\frac{2}{3}x - 4$

33.

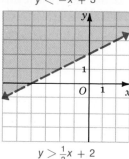

$y > \frac{1}{2}x + 2$

C 34. **a.** If $|y| > 1$ is graphed in a coordinate plane, which of the following points belong to the graph?

     $(0, 0)$ $(3, 0)$ $\left(-2, \frac{1}{2}\right)$ $(0, 1)$ $(0, -1)$ $\left(\frac{1}{2}, -2\right)$ $(-3, 2)$ $\left(\frac{1}{2}, -2\right)$ and $(-3, 2)$

     b. Graph $|y| > 1$ in a coordinate plane.

35. Graph $|x| \geq 2$ in a coordinate plane.

392   *CHAPTER 10*

10-7 *Systems of Linear Inequalities*

OBJECTIVE   To graph the solution set of a system of two linear inequalities in two variables.

You can use graphs to find the solution set of a system of linear inequalities in two variables.

EXAMPLE   Graph the solution set of the system:

$$x + y \le 4$$
$$x - 2y \le 4$$

SOLUTION   1. First transform each inequality into an equivalent one with y as one
side.

$$x + y \le 4 \rightarrow y \le -x + 4$$
$$x - 2y \le 4 \rightarrow y \ge \tfrac{1}{2}x - 2$$

2. Draw the graph of $y = -x + 4$, the boundary of the first inequality.
Use a solid line, and shade the region below this line to show the
graph of $y \le -x + 4$ (colored shading).

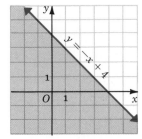

3. In the same coordinate system, draw the graph of $y = \tfrac{1}{2}x - 2$, the
boundary of the second inequality. Use a solid line, and shade
the region above this line to show the graph of $y \ge \tfrac{1}{2}x - 2$ (gray
shading).

4. The doubly shaded region resulting from Steps 2 and 3 is the graph
of the solution set of the given system.

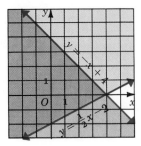

Teaching Suggestions p. T103

Suggested Extensions p. T103

Chalkboard Examples
Graph the solution of each of
the following systems of inequalities.

1. $x > -1$
   $y < 3$

2. $x < 2$
   $x > -2$

Supplementary Materials
Practice Master 62

Progress Test 37

Computer Activity 30
*Integer Solutions for Three
Inequalities*
   A computer can easily find
all nonnegative integer pairs
that satisfy each of three different inequalities. This activity presents such a program
along with a number of problems to be solved.

Suggested Assignments
Minimum
Day 1: 394/1–21 odd
   R 388/*Self-Test 2*
Day 2: 394/12–22 even
   R 396/*Self-Test 3*

Average
Day 1: 394/1–21 odd
   R 388/*Self-Test 2*
   S 392/34
Day 2: 395/23–25
   R 396/*Self-Test 3*
   S 377/P: 17, 19

Maximum
Day 1: 394/1–23 odd
   S 392/35
Day 2: 395/24–27
   R 396/*Self-Test 3*

394

Additional A Exercises

Graph each pair of inequalities and indicate the solution set of the system with cross-hatching or shading.

1. $x \leq 4$
   $y \geq -1$

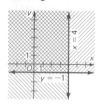

2. $x > -2$
   $y < 3$

Additional Answers
Written Exercises

2.

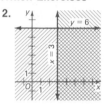

4.

6.

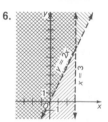

8.

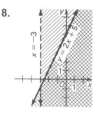

Oral Exercises

Give a system of two linear inequalities whose solution set is shown by the shaded region in each graph.

1.

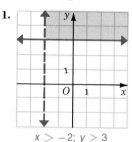

$x > -2;\ y \geq 3$

2.

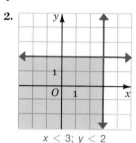

$x \leq 3;\ y \leq 2$

3.

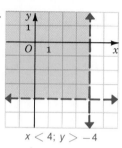

$x < 4;\ y > -4$

State whether or not each ordered pair is a solution of the system:

$$y \geq 5$$
$$x < 3$$

4. $(0, 0)$ No   **5.** $(3, 5)$ No   **6.** $(2, 5)$ Yes   **7.** $(-3, 5)$ Yes   **8.** $(-3, -5)$ No

State whether or not each point belongs to the graph of the solution set of the system:

$$y \leq 2$$
$$x - y \leq 6$$

9. $(0, -6)$ Yes   **10.** $(8, 2)$ Yes   **11.** $(9, 2)$ No   **12.** $(-10, 2)$ Yes   **13.** $(-10, 3)$ No

Written Exercises

Graph each pair of inequalities and indicate the solution set of the system with crosshatching or shading.

A **1.** $y \geq 0$ **2.** $y \leq 6$ **3.** $y > 4$ **4.** $y < -3$
        $x \geq 0$ $x \geq 3$ $x < -2$ $x > 3$

5. $y < x$ **6.** $y > 2x$ **7.** $x \leq 5$ **8.** $x > -3$
      $x > 3$ $x < 3$ $y > 6 - x$ $y \leq 2x + 5$

9. $y \leq x - 1$ **10.** $y < 3x + 3$ **11.** $y > 2x - 3$ **12.** $y < 2x + 2$
      $y \geq 1 - x$ $y > -3x + 3$ $y < 2x + 4$ $y > 2 - 2x$

B **13.** $x + y \leq 9$ **14.** $x + y \geq 3$ **15.** $3x - y > -2$
        $x - y \geq 3$ $2x - y > 9$ $x - y \leq -6$

16. $x - y < 5$ **17.** $2x - 3y < -12$ **18.** $2x - 3y > 0$
        $x - 3y > 9$ $2x + 3y > 0$ $x - 6y \leq -5$

394   *CHAPTER 10*

Write a system of linear inequalities whose solution set is shown by the shaded region in each graph.

19.

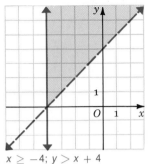

$x \geq -4;\ y > x + 4$

20.

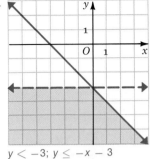

$y < -3;\ y \leq -x - 3$

21.

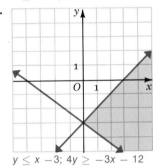

$y \leq x - 3;\ 4y \geq -3x - 12$

22.

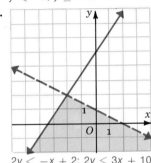

$2y < -x + 2;\ 2y \leq 3x + 10$

SAMPLE

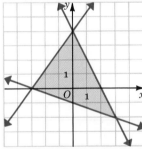

SOLUTION $y \leq \frac{4}{3}x + 4$

$$y \geq -\frac{1}{3}x - 1$$

$$y \leq -2x + 4$$

C 23.

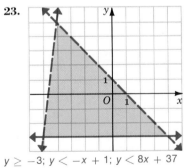

$y \geq -3;\ y < -x + 1;\ y < 8x + 37$

24.

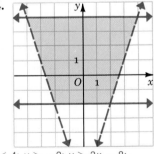

$y \leq 4;\ y \geq -2;\ y > 3x - 8;$
$y > -3x - 8$

10.

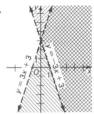

12.

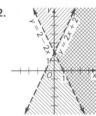

14.

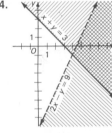

16.

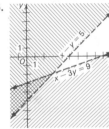

18.

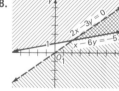

26.

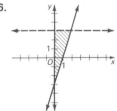

INEQUALITIES **395**

Quick Quiz

Graph each inequality in a coordinate plane.

1. $x > 2$

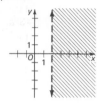

2. $3x + y \leq 1$

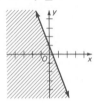

3. Graph the solution set of the system:
$x + 3y \leq 1$
$x - y < 2$

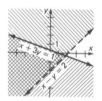

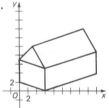
Graph each system of inequalities. Determine exactly the *corner points* of the graph of the solution set of the system, that is, the points where boundary lines intersect.

25. $y \leq -x$
$y \leq x$
$y \geq -1$
$(0, 0)$
$(-1, -1)$
$(1, -1)$

26. $3x - y \leq 3$
$x \geq 0$
$y < 3$
$(0, 3)$
$(2, 3)$
$(0, -3)$

27. $x + 2y < 6$
$y \geq 0$
$2x - y + 3 > 0$
$(0, 3)$
$(6, 0)$
$\left(-\frac{3}{2}, 0\right)$

Self-Test 3

VOCABULARY   open half-plane (p. 389)   closed half-plane (p. 389)
boundary (p. 389)

Graph each inequality in a coordinate plane.

1. $y < 1$ **2.** $2x + y \geq 4$ Obj. 10-6, p. 389

3. Graph the solution set of the system: Obj. 10-7, p. 393

$$x + y > 3$$
$$2x - y > 2$$

Check your answers with those at the back of the book.

Just for Fun

1. On the same set of axes, graph the following line segments to draw a picture.

$x = 0,\ 2 \leq y \leq 7$ $x = 6,\ 0 \leq y \leq 5$
$x = 18,\ 4 \leq y \leq 9$ $x + 3y = 6,\ 0 \leq x \leq 6$
$x + 3y = 21,\ 0 \leq x \leq 6$ $x - y = -7,\ 0 \leq x \leq 3$
$x - 3y = 6,\ 6 \leq x \leq 18$ $x - 3y = -9,\ 6 \leq x \leq 18$
$x - 3y = -27,\ 3 \leq x \leq 15$ $5x + 3y = 45,\ 3 \leq x \leq 6$
$5x + 3y = 117,\ 15 \leq x \leq 18$

2. Draw a picture on graph paper using line segments. Write a set of Answers will vary.
equations and inequalities to describe your picture as in Exercise 1.

396   *CHAPTER 10*

Application   Nutrition Labeling

Have you noticed the nutrition information that is printed on the labels of many canned foods? For example, a can of corn has:

Nutrition Information per Serving

Calories 230	Carbohydrates 50 grams
Protein 4 grams	Fat 2 grams

Percentage of U.S. Recommended Daily Allowance (U.S. RDA) per Serving

Protein	6	Riboflavin (B_2) 6	
Vitamin A	4	Niacin	8
Vitamin C	20	Calcium	Less than 2
Thiamin (B_1)	2	Iron	4

What percent of the U.S. RDA of vitamin C would be provided by a meal that included two servings of corn along with other foods that provided 15% of the U.S. RDA of vitamin C? The label indicates that one serving should provide 20% of the U.S RDA of vitamin C. Thus,

$$2 \cdot 20 + 15 = 55.$$

Therefore, the meal would provide 55% of the U.S. RDA of vitamin C.

Refer to the following table to answer the questions below.

Percentage of U.S. Recommended Daily Allowance (U.S. RDA) per Serving

	Beans	Zucchini	Vegetable Juice	Grade A Milk
Protein	4	2	2	20
Vitamin A	15	20	40	10
Vitamin C	40	4	45	4
Thiamin (B_1)	4	6	4	6
Riboflavin (B_2)	10	4	2	25
Niacin	4	4	6	0
Calcium	4	2	2	30
Iron	8	8	2	0

1. Find the percent of the U.S. RDA of vitamin C that one would get from a serving of corn, a serving of beans, and a serving of vegetable juice. 105%

2. Find the percent of the U.S. RDA of niacin that one would get from the servings described in Exercise 1. 18%

3. A serving each of corn and zucchini would provide what percent of the U.S. RDA of iron? 12%

4. A serving each of corn, beans, and milk would provide what percent of the U.S. RDA of riboflavin (B_2)? 41%

INEQUALITIES   **397**

Chapter Summary ───────

1. The symbols $>$, $<$, $\geq$, and $\leq$ are used to express inequalities. $-3 < 1 < 7$ (or $7 > 1 > -3$) means that 1 is between -3 and 7.

2. Open inequalities can be solved by transformations to obtain simple equivalent inequalities whose solution sets can be seen at a glance. The graph of the solution set of an inequality in one variable can be shown on a number line.

3. Sentences joined by "and" are conjunctions. A conjunction is true if and only if it is formed of true statements. Sentences joined by "or" are disjunctions. A disjunction of statements is true if at least one of the statements is true.

4. Open sentences involving the absolute value of a variable may be written as equivalent conjunctions or disjunctions.

5. The solution set of a linear inequality in two variables is graphed in a coordinate plane.

6. The graph of the solution set of a system of inequalities consists of the points common to the graphs of all the inequalities in the system.

Chapter Review ───────

Give the letter of the correct answer.

1. Which statement is true?
   10-1

   a. $1 < -2 < 5$ **b.** $5 > -2 > 1$ **(c.)** $-2 < 1 < 5$ **d.** $-2 > 1 < 5$

2. Find the solution set of $2x - 3 \leq 4$ if the domain of x is $\{-4, -2, 0, 2, 4\}$.

   a. $\{-4, -2, 0, 2, 4\}$ **(b.)** $\{-4, -2, 0, 2\}$ **c.** $\{-2, 0, 2\}$ **d.** $\{0\}$

3. Find an inequality equivalent to $\frac{x}{-2} < -6$.
   10-2

   (a.) $x > 12$ **b.** $x < 12$ **c.** $x > 3$ **d.** $x < 3$

4. Find an inequality equivalent to $4x - 2y \leq 3$.

   a. $2y \leq 4x - 3$ **b.** $y \geq 2x - 3$ **c.** $2y - 4x \geq 3$ **(d.)** $y \geq 2x - \frac{3}{2}$

5. Represent the statement "The sum of two consecutive even integers is at most 60" as an inequality.
   10-3

   a. $n + (n + 1) \geq 60$ **b.** $n + (n + 1) \leq 60$

   c. $n + (n + 2) \geq 60$ **(d.)** $n + (n + 2) \leq 60$

398   *CHAPTER 10*

6. Which is the graph of the solution set of the disjunction "$x < 2$ or $x > 2$"?   10-4

a.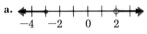

b. (number line with open circles at −2 and 2)

c. (number line)

7. Which is the graph of the conjunction "$-3 \le x$ and $x < 2$"?

a. (number line from −4 to 2)

b. (number line from −4 to 2)

c. (number line from −4 to 2)

8. Which is a compact form for the disjunction "$y < -3$ or $y > 3$"?   10-5

a. $-3 > y > 3$ **b.** $|y| > 3$ **c.** $|y| = 3$ **d.** $|y| < 3$

9. What is the equation of the boundary of the graph of the inequality $3x - 2y \le 6$?   10-6

a. $3x - 2y = 6$ **b.** $-2y = 6$ **c.** $y \le \frac{3}{2}x - 3$ **d.** $y = 0$

10. Which point belongs to the graph of the solution set of the system: 10-7

$$y \ge 3$$
$$x - y > 3?$$

a. $(0, 0)$ **b.** $(6, 3)$ **c.** $(10, 4)$ **d.** $(6, -3)$

Chapter Test

1. Classify the statement as true or false: $-4 < \frac{1}{4} < 1$ True   10-1

2. Find the solution set of $2y + 2 \le 5$ if $y \in \{-2, -1, 0, 1, 2\}$. $\{-2, -1, 0, 1\}$

3. Solve the inequality $2 - \frac{1}{2}x \ge 3$ and graph the solution set on a number line. $\{-2$ and the real numbers less than $-2\}$ 10-2

4. Of all pairs of consecutive odd integers whose sum is less than 20, find the pair whose sum is the greatest. 7 and 9   10-3

Solve each open sentence and graph its solution set.

5. $-5 < 2x - 1 < 3$ {the real numbers between -2 and 2}   10-4

6. $|y + 3| > 2$ {the real numbers greater than -1 or less than -5}   10-5

Graph each inequality in a coordinate plane.

7. $x > -3$ **8.** $3x + y \le -3$ 10-6

9. Graph the solution set of the system: $2x - y \ge 2$ 10-7
$$x - y < 2$$

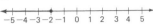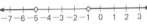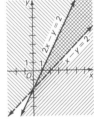

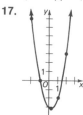
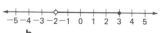

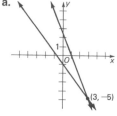
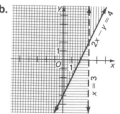
Cumulative Review (Chapters 1–10)

Factor completely.

1. $15u^2 - 44uv + 21v^2$
$(5u - 3v)(3u - 7v)$

2. $48d^2 - 144d - 4d^3$
$-4d(d - 6)^2$

3. $2g - 3gh + 3h - 2$
$(2 - 3h)(g - 1)$

Simplify. In Exercise 14, divide.

4. $-3t(rt - t^2 + 4rt^2)$

5. $6 + 5y - 3(7y + 2)$

6. $2h(h + 8)(7h - 2)$

7. $(-6m^5 + 9m^2) \div 1.5m^2$

8. $(3a^4b^2)^3 \div (-9ab^4)^2$

9. $(c + d - 1)^2$

10. $\dfrac{200j^2 - 2k^2}{k^2 + 7kj - 30j^2}$

11. $\dfrac{5x}{12} - \dfrac{x}{8} - \dfrac{14}{3x}$

12. $\dfrac{4r^2 - 6r}{r^2 - r} \div \dfrac{9 - 4r^2}{18 - 12r}$

13. $\dfrac{-28 + 7c}{(c - 4)^2} + \dfrac{c + 1}{4 - c}$
$-\dfrac{c - 6}{c - 4}$, or $\dfrac{6 - c}{c - 4}$

14. $\dfrac{8y^4 + 6y^3 - 25y^2 + 9}{-4y + 3}$
$-2y^3 - 3y^2 + 4y + 3$

15. $\dfrac{z^4 - 81}{2z - 4} \cdot \dfrac{z^2 + 2z - 8}{z^2 + z - 12}$
$\dfrac{(z^2 + 9)(z + 3)}{2}$

16. Find an equation of the line: **a.** with slope 4 and passing through $(-2, -5)$ **b.** containing $(-3, 0)$ and $(7, -6)$. $y = 4x + 3;\ y = -\dfrac{3}{5}x - \dfrac{9}{5}$

17. If $g(x) = 2x^2 - x - 3$, find $g(2)$ and $g(-4)$, and graph $g(x)$. 3; 33

18. Graph: **a.** $-3 < 2x + 1 \le 7$ **b.** $5 - y < -1$ or $5 - y > 1$

19. Solve graphically: **a.** $4x + 3y = -3$ **b.** $x < 3$
$5x + 2y = 5$ $2x - y \le 4$
$(3, -5)$

Solve each equation, inequality, or system.

20. $4(8 - 3p) = 3(p - 1)$

21. $8 - |k| = -1$

22. $1.3d = 1.9d - 0.03$

23. 1.8% of $150 = t$

24. $1 = 12g^2 - 4g$

25. $(s - 4)(s + 6) = 7s$

26. $7 - 9b < 34$

27. $3(n - 4) \ge 2(n + 1)$

28. $-88 \ne -18w + 2$

29. $\dfrac{m}{2} - \dfrac{4}{m + 2} = \dfrac{5}{2}$

30. $\dfrac{3q - 2}{5q + 6} = \dfrac{q + 1}{q}$

31. $\dfrac{g - 2}{3} + 1 \le \dfrac{g + 7}{5}$

32. $x = 3y + 4$
$3x - 7y = 6\,(-5, -3)$

33. $4x + 9y = 14$
$-7x + 9y = -8\left(2, \dfrac{2}{3}\right)$

34. $5a + 3b = 31$
$2a - 5b = 62\,(11, -8)$

Solve.

35. Bob and Jenny took as long to row 15 km downstream as they did to row 9 km upstream. If their rate in still water was 6 km/h faster than the speed of the current, find the speed of the current. 2 km/h

36. A pouch contains 19 coins, some of which are dimes and some of which are nickels. The total value of the coins is more than $1.15. At least how many of the coins are dimes and at most how many are nickels? At least 5 dimes; at most 14 nickels

Maintaining Skills

Divide. Write your answer as a polynomial or a mixed expression.

SAMPLE 1 $\dfrac{2a^2 - 3}{a + 3}$ **SOLUTION**

$$\begin{array}{r} 2a - 6 \\ a+3\overline{)2a^2 + 0a - 3} \\ \underline{2a^2 + 6a } \\ -6a - 3 \\ \underline{-6a - 18} \\ 15 \end{array}$$

$2a - 6 + \dfrac{15}{a + 3}$ **Answer**

1. $\dfrac{n^2 + 6n - 1}{n + 4}$ $\quad n + 2 - \dfrac{9}{n+4}$

2. $\dfrac{6x^2 + 7x - 5}{2x - 1}$ $\quad 3x + 5$

3. $\dfrac{r^2 + 8r + 18}{r + 5}$ $\quad r + 3 + \dfrac{3}{r+5}$

4. $\dfrac{12p^2 - p - 6}{4p - 3}$ $\quad 3p + 2$

5. $\dfrac{12s^2 - 20}{2s + 3}$ $\quad 6s - 9 + \dfrac{7}{2s+3}$

6. $\dfrac{2a^2 - 7ab + b^2}{a - 3b}$ $\quad 2a - b - \dfrac{2b^2}{a - 3b}$

7. $\dfrac{c^3 - c^2 + 1}{c + 1}$ $\quad c^2 - 2c + 2 - \dfrac{1}{c+1}$

8. $\dfrac{t^4 - 1}{t + 1}$ $\quad t^3 - t^2 + t - 1$

Solve.

SAMPLE 2 $\dfrac{2}{3}x - \dfrac{5}{12}x = -\dfrac{3}{2}$

SOLUTION $12\left(\dfrac{2}{3}x - \dfrac{5}{12}x\right) = 12\left(-\dfrac{3}{2}\right);$

$8x - 5x = -18;\ 3x = -18;\ x = -6$ **Answer**

9. $\dfrac{6r - 1}{5} = \dfrac{4r + 1}{3} - 4$ $\quad$

10. $0.15x = 0.2x - 0.9$ $\quad 18$

11. $\dfrac{20d - 8}{9} = \dfrac{2}{3}(4d + 2)$ $\quad -5$

12. $\dfrac{7m}{4} = \dfrac{m + 5}{6} + \dfrac{m}{8}$ $\quad \frac{4}{7}$

13. $\dfrac{z}{7} - 3 = \dfrac{z + 3}{16} - \dfrac{3}{2}$ $\quad 21$

14. $3t + \dfrac{6 - t}{3} = \dfrac{t}{2} + 2$

15. $\dfrac{5y}{6} = \dfrac{3y}{5} + \dfrac{7}{3}$ $\quad 10$

16. $\dfrac{3a + 5}{2} = -\dfrac{4 - 9a}{25} - \dfrac{7}{3}$

17. $\dfrac{3k}{7} - \dfrac{k - 1}{3} = \dfrac{3 - 4k}{21}$

14. 0 **17.** $-\dfrac{2}{3}$

Solve, and check each root.

SAMPLE 3 $\dfrac{2x + 3}{x} = \dfrac{1}{2}$

SOLUTION $2x\left(\dfrac{2x + 3}{x}\right) = 2x\left(\dfrac{1}{2}\right);\ 4x + 6 = x;\ 3x = -6;\ x = -2$ **Answer**

18. $\dfrac{z - 3}{z} = \dfrac{4}{z}$ $\quad 7$

19. $\dfrac{b + 2}{b + 3} - \dfrac{8}{b} = 1$ $\quad -\frac{8}{3}$

20. $\dfrac{4g - 3}{2g + 1} = \dfrac{2g - 9}{g - 2}$ $\quad -3$

21. $\dfrac{r^2}{r + 2} + \dfrac{2r}{r + 2} = -r$ $\quad 0$

22. $\dfrac{m + 2}{4m} = \dfrac{m}{m + 2}$ $\quad \left\{2, -\frac{2}{3}\right\}$

23. $\dfrac{3}{y - 1} - \dfrac{7}{2y} = \dfrac{11}{40}$

24. $\dfrac{3}{v} + \dfrac{1}{v + 1} = \dfrac{4}{v - 1}$ $\quad -\frac{3}{5}$

25. $\dfrac{3 - x}{2x - 8} + 6 = \dfrac{28x}{x - 4}$ $\quad -1$

26. $\dfrac{2}{3c + 2} - \dfrac{1}{5c - 2} = \dfrac{1}{4c}$

23. $\left\{\frac{35}{11}, -4\right\}$

26. $\left\{\frac{2}{13}, 2\right\}$

22. $\{0.05\}$

23. $\{2.7\}$

24. $\left\{\frac{1}{2}, -\frac{1}{6}\right\}$

25. $\{8, -3\}$

26. {the real numbers greater than -3}

27. {the real numbers greater than or equal to 14}

28. $w \neq 5$

29. $\{6, -3\}$

30. $\left\{-\frac{1}{2}, -6\right\}$

31. {the real numbers less than or equal to 8}

The boom of this self-propelled center-post irrigation system in Nevada sweeps out a circle. If r is the length of the boom, then πr^2 will be the area of the land that is irrigated.

11

RATIONAL AND IRRATIONAL NUMBERS

Teaching References

Lesson Commentary,
   pp. T103–T107

Assignment Guide,
   pp. T58–T60

Supplementary Materials

   Practice Masters 63–69

   Progress Tests 39–42

   Computer Activities
   31 *Fractions for Repeating Decimals*
   32 *Simplifying Radicals*
   33 *Solving Radical Equations*

Extra Practice, pp. 508–512,
   522–523

Alternate Test, p. T22

RATIONAL NUMBERS

11-1 *Properties of Rational Numbers*

OBJECTIVE   To learn and apply some properties of real numbers.

A real number that is a quotient of two integers is called a **rational number.** Thus, the following numbers are rational numbers:

$$0 = \frac{0}{1} \qquad 2 = \frac{2}{1} \qquad 5\frac{1}{2} = \frac{11}{2} \qquad 0.37 = \frac{37}{100} \qquad -\frac{2}{3} = \frac{-2}{3}$$

Using the properties of fractions, a rational number can be expressed as a quotient of integers in an unlimited number of ways:

$$1 = \frac{4}{4} = \frac{-8}{-8} = \frac{37}{37} = \cdots \qquad -2\frac{1}{2} = \frac{-5}{2} = \frac{10}{-4} = \cdots \qquad 24\% = \frac{24}{100} = \frac{12}{50} = \cdots$$

To determine the greater of two rational numbers, you can write them with the same positive denominator and compare their numerators.

EXAMPLE 1   Compare $\frac{9}{4}$ and $\frac{15}{7}$.

SOLUTION   The LCD is 28.

$$\frac{9}{4} = \frac{63}{28} \qquad \frac{15}{7} = \frac{60}{28}$$

Because $63 > 60$, $\frac{63}{28} > \frac{60}{28}$.

Thus, $\frac{9}{4} > \frac{15}{7}$.   *Answer*

403

Teaching Suggestions p. T103

Suggested Extensions p. T103

Chalkboard Examples

Replace the _?_ with <, =, or > to make a true statement.

1. $\frac{3}{4} \underline{?} \frac{2}{3}$

   Common denominator is 12.

   $\frac{3}{4} = \frac{9}{12}, \frac{2}{3} = \frac{8}{12}$

   $\frac{9}{12} > \frac{8}{12}$

   $\therefore \frac{3}{4} > \frac{2}{3}$

2. $\frac{43}{15} \underline{?} \frac{37}{12}$

   For this example it may be easier to compare the products of the means and extremes.

   $12 \times 43 = 516;$
   $15 \times 37 = 555$

   $12 \times 43 < 15 \times 37$

   $\therefore \frac{43}{15} < \frac{37}{12}$

3. $-\frac{4}{5} \underline{?} -\frac{23}{34}$

   Write with positive denominators;

   $\frac{-4}{5} \underline{?} \frac{-23}{34}$

   $-4 \times 34 = -136;$
   $5 \times (-23) = -115$

   $\therefore -\frac{4}{5} < -\frac{23}{34}$

4. Arrange in order, from least to greatest.

   $\frac{2}{3}, \frac{5}{8}, \frac{3}{4}$

   Common denominator is 24.

   $\frac{16}{24}, \frac{15}{24}, \frac{18}{24}$

   $\therefore$ The solution is $\frac{5}{8}, \frac{2}{3}, \frac{3}{4}$

(continued)

The procedure shown in Example 1 may be generalized as shown below. (See Exercise 35 on page 407 for a proof.)

> For all integers a and b and all positive integers c and d:
>
> $$\frac{a}{c} > \frac{b}{d} \text{ if and only if } ad > bc.$$
>
> Similarly, $\frac{a}{c} < \frac{b}{d}$ if and only if $ad < bc$.

Thus, $\frac{5}{7} > \frac{2}{3}$ because $5(3) > 2(7)$;

$-\frac{3}{8} > -\frac{4}{5}$ because $-3(5) > -4(8)$.

EXAMPLE 2 Compare $-\frac{5}{8}$ and $-\frac{7}{12}$.

SOLUTION Write $-\frac{5}{8}$ as $\frac{-5}{8}$ and $-\frac{7}{12}$ as $\frac{-7}{12}$. Then use the technique shown above to compare $\frac{-5}{8}$ and $\frac{-7}{12}$.

$(-5)(12) < (-7)(8)$ because $-60 < -56$.

Thus, $-\frac{5}{8} < -\frac{7}{12}$. ***Answer***

Rational numbers differ from integers in several ways: For each integer, there is a next larger integer. For example, -3 follows -4, 1 follows 0, and 8 follows 7. There is, however, no "next larger" rational number after a given rational number. One property that the set of rationals has that the set of integers does not have is the following:

> THE BETWEENNESS PROPERTY
>
> Between every pair of different rational numbers there is another rational number.

If a and b are rational numbers, and $a < b$, then:

the number halfway from a to b is $a + \frac{1}{2}(b - a)$;

the number one third of the way from a to b is $a + \frac{1}{3}(b - a)$;

and so on.

Thus, it is possible to find an endless number of rational numbers between two given rational numbers.

EXAMPLE 3 Find a rational number between $\frac{7}{5}$ and $\frac{13}{8}$.

SOLUTION The number halfway between $\frac{7}{5}$ and $\frac{13}{8}$ will be $\frac{7}{5} + \frac{1}{2}\left(\frac{13}{8} - \frac{7}{5}\right)$.

$$\frac{13}{8} - \frac{7}{5} = \frac{65}{40} - \frac{56}{40} = \frac{9}{40}$$

$$\frac{7}{5} + \frac{1}{2}\left(\frac{9}{40}\right) = \frac{7}{5} + \frac{9}{80} = \frac{112}{80} + \frac{9}{80} = \frac{121}{80}$$

Check: Is $\frac{7}{5} < \frac{121}{80} < \frac{13}{8}$?

$7(80) \overset{?}{<} 5(121)$ $8(121) \overset{?}{<} 80(13)$

$560 < 605$ ✓ $968 < 1040$ ✓

$\therefore$ a rational number between $\frac{7}{5}$ and $\frac{13}{8}$ is $\frac{121}{80}$. ***Answer.***

(In fact, $\frac{121}{80}$ is halfway between the two numbers.)

In the last example, observe that $\frac{121}{80}$ is also the average of $\frac{7}{5}$ and $\frac{13}{8}$. In general, the number halfway between two numbers is the average of the two numbers because

$$a + \frac{1}{2}(b - a) = \frac{2a}{2} + \frac{b - a}{2} = \frac{a + b}{2}.$$

Oral Exercises

Express each number as a quotient of integers.

SAMPLE 2.9   ***ONE SOLUTION*** $\frac{29}{10}$

1. 4.8 $\frac{48}{10}$, or $\frac{24}{5}$ **2.** $-\frac{1}{8}$ $\frac{-1}{8}$, or $\frac{1}{-8}$ **3.** $-2\frac{1}{5}$ $\frac{-11}{5}$, or $\frac{11}{-5}$ **4.** 31% $\frac{31}{100}$

5. -5 $\frac{-5}{1}$, or $\frac{5}{-1}$ **6.** 18 $\frac{18}{1}$ **7.** 0 $\frac{0}{1}$ $\frac{-1}{6}$, or $\frac{1}{-6}$ **8.** $\frac{4}{6} + \left(-\frac{5}{6}\right)$

Which rational number in each pair is greater?

9. $\frac{5}{9}, \frac{7}{9}$ $\frac{7}{9}$ **10.** $-3, \frac{1}{2}$ $\frac{1}{2}$ $-\frac{2}{5}$ **11.** $-\frac{2}{5}, -\frac{4}{5}$

12. 7, $\frac{46}{7}$ 7   **13.** $\frac{5}{8}, \frac{3}{4}$ $\frac{3}{4}$ $-\frac{13}{3}$ **14.** $-\frac{9}{2}, -\frac{13}{3}$

5. Find the number half way between $\frac{9}{2}$ and $\frac{14}{3}$.

Formula: $a + \frac{1}{2}(b - a)$

$$\frac{9}{2} + \frac{1}{2}\left(\frac{14}{3} - \frac{9}{2}\right)$$

$$\frac{9}{2} + \frac{1}{2}\left(\frac{1}{6}\right)$$

$$\frac{54}{12} + \frac{1}{12} = \frac{55}{12}$$

6. Find the number two-thirds of the way from $\frac{9}{2}$ to $\frac{14}{3}$.

Formula: $a + \frac{2}{3}(b - a)$

$$\frac{9}{2} + \frac{2}{3}\left(\frac{14}{3} - \frac{9}{2}\right)$$

$$\frac{9}{2} + \frac{2}{3}\left(\frac{1}{6}\right)$$

$$\frac{81}{18} + \frac{2}{18} = \frac{83}{18}$$

If $x \in \{0, 1, 2, 3\}$ state whether the value of each fraction increases or decreases as x takes on its values in increasing order.

7. $\frac{x}{2}$ Increases

8. $\frac{1}{x + 3}$ Decreases

9. $\frac{2}{5 + x}$ Decreases

Suggested Assignments

Minimum
  406/1–33 odd

Average
  406/1–33 odd

Maximum
  406/1–35 odd

Which rational number in each pair is greater?

1. $\dfrac{1}{2}, \dfrac{2}{3}$ $\dfrac{2}{3}$

2. $\dfrac{3}{4}, \dfrac{7}{8}$ $\dfrac{7}{8}$

3. $\dfrac{8}{9}, \dfrac{9}{10}$ $\dfrac{9}{10}$

Arrange each group of numbers in order from least to greatest.

4. $\dfrac{1}{5}, \dfrac{2}{3}, \dfrac{3}{4}, \dfrac{1}{2}$

$\dfrac{1}{5}, \dfrac{1}{2}, \dfrac{2}{3}, \dfrac{3}{4}$

5. $\dfrac{2}{5}, \dfrac{4}{9}, \dfrac{8}{11}, \dfrac{3}{4}$

$\dfrac{2}{5}, \dfrac{4}{9}, \dfrac{8}{11}, \dfrac{3}{4}$

6. $\dfrac{3}{8}, \dfrac{2}{9}, \dfrac{3}{5}, \dfrac{1}{2}$

$\dfrac{2}{9}, \dfrac{3}{8}, \dfrac{1}{2}, \dfrac{3}{5}$

Written Exercises

Replace the __?__ with <, =, or > to make a true statement.

A
1. $\dfrac{1}{8}$ __?__ $\dfrac{5}{32}$ <

2. $\dfrac{3}{4}$ __?__ $\dfrac{9}{13}$ >

3. $-\dfrac{11}{14}$ __?__ $-\dfrac{19}{25}$ <

4. $\dfrac{22}{27}$ __?__ $\dfrac{31}{38}$ <

5. $\dfrac{123}{47}$ __?__ $\dfrac{190}{82}$ >

6. $\dfrac{25}{95}$ __?__ $\dfrac{55}{209}$ =

7. $-12\dfrac{1}{4}$ __?__ $-\dfrac{149}{12}$ >

8. $21\dfrac{3}{5}$ __?__ $\dfrac{131}{6}$ <

9. $\dfrac{423}{8}$ __?__ $52\dfrac{5}{7}$ >

Arrange each group of numbers in order from least to greatest.

10. $\dfrac{1}{4}, -\dfrac{2}{3}, \dfrac{5}{8}$ $-\dfrac{2}{3}, \dfrac{1}{4}, \dfrac{5}{8}$

11. $-\dfrac{5}{7}, -\dfrac{3}{5}, \dfrac{2}{9}$ $-\dfrac{5}{7}, -\dfrac{3}{5}, \dfrac{2}{9}$

12. $-4.2, -\dfrac{38}{9}, -4$ $-\dfrac{38}{9}, -4.2, -4$

13. $2.3, \dfrac{57}{25}, \dfrac{91}{40}$ $\dfrac{91}{40}, \dfrac{57}{25}, 2.3$

14. $\dfrac{7}{24}, \dfrac{4}{15}, \dfrac{5}{16}, \dfrac{1}{2}$ $\dfrac{4}{15}, \dfrac{7}{24}, \dfrac{5}{16}, \dfrac{1}{2}$

15. $\dfrac{3}{7}, \dfrac{5}{6}, \dfrac{3}{5}, \dfrac{7}{9}$ $\dfrac{3}{7}, \dfrac{3}{5}, \dfrac{7}{9}, \dfrac{5}{6}$

Find the number halfway between the given numbers.

16. $\dfrac{4}{7}, \dfrac{5}{6}$ $\dfrac{59}{84}$

17. $\dfrac{2}{3}, \dfrac{5}{12}$ $\dfrac{13}{24}$

18. $-\dfrac{4}{25}, -\dfrac{9}{50}$ $-\dfrac{17}{100}$

19. $-\dfrac{7}{35}, -\dfrac{26}{140}$ $-\dfrac{27}{140}$

20. $-2\dfrac{2}{3}, -3\dfrac{3}{4}$ $-\dfrac{77}{24}$

21. $-5\dfrac{1}{5}, 6\dfrac{4}{9}$ $\dfrac{28}{45}$

If $x \in \{0, 1, 2, 3\}$ state whether each fraction increases or decreases in value as x takes on its values in increasing order.

22. $\dfrac{x}{4}$ Increases

23. $\dfrac{7}{x+1}$ Decreases

24. $\dfrac{x+1}{5}$ Increases

25. $\dfrac{7-2x}{9}$ Decreases

26. $\dfrac{7}{6-x}$ Increases

B 27. Find the number one fourth of the way from $\dfrac{5}{8}$ to $1\dfrac{1}{2}$. $\dfrac{27}{32}$

28. Find the number one third of the way from $-\dfrac{1}{5}$ to $-\dfrac{5}{6}$. $-\dfrac{37}{90}$

29. Find the number one sixth of the way from $-\dfrac{3}{4}$ to $\dfrac{1}{3}$. $-\dfrac{41}{72}$

30. Find the number three fourths of the way from $\dfrac{1}{2}$ to $\dfrac{8}{9}$. $\dfrac{19}{24}$

31. Find a rational number between $\dfrac{1}{2}$ and $\dfrac{1}{3}$. For example, $\dfrac{5}{12}$

32. Find a rational number between $-\dfrac{1}{5}$ and $-\dfrac{1}{4}$. For example, $-\dfrac{9}{40}$

33. Write an expression for the number halfway between $\dfrac{5a}{6}$ and $-\dfrac{a}{7}$. $\dfrac{29a}{84}$

406   *CHAPTER 11*

34. Write an expression for the number one third of the way from $-\dfrac{6b}{5}$ to $-\dfrac{2b}{9}$. $-\dfrac{118b}{135}$

C 35. Give the reason for each statement in the proof of the following theorem: For all integers a and b and all positive integers c and d,

$\dfrac{a}{c} > \dfrac{b}{d}$ if and only if $ad > bc$.

1. $\dfrac{a}{c} > \dfrac{b}{d}$ 1. given

2. $\dfrac{ad}{cd} > \dfrac{bc}{cd}$ 2. __?__ Cancellation rule for fractions

3. $ad > bc$ 3. __?__ Multiplication axiom of order

∴ if $\dfrac{a}{c} > \dfrac{b}{d}$, then $ad > bc$.

4. $ad > bc$ 4. given

5. $\dfrac{ad}{cd} > \dfrac{bc}{cd}$ (since $cd > 0$)   5. __?__ Multiplication axiom of order

6. $\dfrac{a}{c} > \dfrac{b}{d}$ 6. __?__ Cancellation rule for fractions

∴ if $ad > bc$, then $\dfrac{a}{c} > \dfrac{b}{d}$.

∴ $\dfrac{a}{c} > \dfrac{b}{d}$ if and only if $ad > bc$.

Biography Pierre de Fermat

Pierre de Fermat (1601–1665) was a lawyer and legislator by profession in Toulouse, France. He achieved some fame as a poet and scholar, but his primary contribution was made in the field of pure mathematics. In the theory of numbers there are two theorems which bear his name. One of these, Fermat's Last Theorem, states that if x, y, and z are integers, then the equation $x^n + y^n = z^n$ has no solution when $n > 2$ and $xyz \neq 0$. To this day the truth of this theorem remains an open question. Fermat also contributed to the foundations of differential calculus, integral calculus, and probability.

RATIONAL AND IRRATIONAL NUMBERS **407**

11-2 *Decimal Forms for Rational Numbers*

OBJECTIVE   To express rational numbers as decimals or fractions.

To change a common fraction to a decimal, you divide the numerator by the denominator. If there is a remainder of zero, the decimal is called a **terminating, ending,** or **finite decimal.** The division at the right shows that $\dfrac{5}{32}$ can be expressed as the terminating decimal 0.15625.

$$\dfrac{5}{32} = 5 \div 32 = 0.15625$$

```
        0.15625
   32)5.00000
      3 2
      1 80
      1 60
        200
        192
         80
         64
        160
        160
          0
```

If there is no zero remainder, you continue dividing until the remainders start to repeat.

$$\dfrac{11}{18} \longrightarrow$$
```
     0.611
18)11.000
   10 8
      20
      18
      20
      18
       2
```

$$\dfrac{9}{11} \longrightarrow$$
```
     0.8181
11)9.0000
   8 8
     20
     11
     90
     88
     20
     11
      9
```

$$\dfrac{7}{13} \longrightarrow$$
```
      0.5384615
13)7.0000000
   6 5
     50
     39
    110
    104
     60
     52
     80
     78
     20
     13
     70
     65
      5
```

The decimal quotients shown above are **nonterminating, unending,** or **infinite.** They are also called **repeating** or **periodic** because the same digit (or block of digits) repeats unendingly.

$$\dfrac{11}{18} = 0.611 \ldots \qquad \dfrac{9}{11} = 0.8181 \ldots \qquad \dfrac{7}{13} = 0.538461538 \ldots$$

The dots indicate that the decimals continue unendingly. A bar is used to indicate the block of digits that repeat, as shown below.

$$\dfrac{11}{18} = 0.6\overline{1} \qquad \dfrac{9}{11} = 0.\overline{81} \qquad \dfrac{7}{13} = 0.\overline{538461}$$

408   *CHAPTER 11*

When you divide a positive integer n by a positive integer d, the remainder r at each step must be zero or a positive integer less than d. If the divisor is 7, the remainders will be 0, 1, 2, 3, 4, 5, or 6, and the division will terminate or begin repeating within 6 steps after only zeros remain to be brought down. In general:

> For every integer n and every positive integer d, the decimal numeral of the rational number $\frac{n}{d}$ either terminates or eventually repeats in a block of fewer than d digits.

To express a terminating decimal as a common fraction, express the decimal as a common fraction with a power of ten as the denominator. It is usual to express the fraction in simplest form.

$$0.83 = \frac{83}{100} \qquad 0.328 = \frac{328}{1000} = \frac{41}{125}$$

To express a repeating decimal as a common fraction you may use the method shown in the following examples.

EXAMPLE 1 Express $0.2\overline{45}$ as a common fraction.

SOLUTION Let $N =$ the number. Multiply the given number N by 10^n where n is the number of digits in the block of repeating digits. Because $n = 2$ for $0.2\overline{45}$, you multiply by 10^2, or 100.

$$100N = 24.5\overline{45}$$
$$\text{Subtract} \quad \underline{N = 0.2\overline{45}}$$
$$99N = 24.300$$
$$N = \frac{24.3}{99} = \frac{243}{990} = \frac{27}{110}$$

$$\therefore 0.2\overline{45} = \frac{27}{110}. \quad \textit{Answer}$$

EXAMPLE 2 Express $0.\overline{528}$ as a common fraction.

SOLUTION Let $N =$ the number.

$$1000N = 528.\overline{528}$$
$$\text{Subtract} \quad \underline{N = 0.\overline{528}}$$
$$999N = 528$$
$$N = \frac{528}{999} = \frac{176}{333}$$

$$\therefore 0.\overline{528} = \frac{176}{333}. \quad \textit{Answer}$$

RATIONAL AND IRRATIONAL NUMBERS   **409**

Supplementary Materials

Practice Master 63

Computer Activity 31
Fractions for Repeating Decimals
   Changing repeating decimals to fractions can be a tedious procedure for some students. This activity provides a computer program to accomplish this task. An improved version of the program is also given which reduces the fraction to lowest terms.

Suggested Assignments

Minimum
    410/1–37 odd
Average
    410/1–41 odd
Maximum
    410/1–41 odd
S 406/26, 34

All terminating decimals and all repeating decimals represent rational numbers that can be written in the form $\frac{n}{d}$ where n is an integer and d is a positive integer.

It is often convenient to use an approximation of a lengthy decimal. For example, you may approximate $\frac{5}{12}$ as

$$0.41667 \quad \text{or} \quad 0.417 \quad \text{or} \quad 0.42.$$

To round a decimal:
1. If the first digit dropped is 5 or more, add 1 to the last digit retained;
2. If the first digit dropped is less than 5, leave the retained digits unchanged.

The following examples show approximations of nonterminating decimals. The symbol $\approx$ is read, "is approximately equal to."

$$\frac{13}{30} = 0.433\ldots \approx 0.43 \text{ to the nearest hundredth}$$
$$\approx 0.4 \text{ to the nearest tenth}$$

$$\frac{23}{33} = 0.\overline{69} \quad \approx 0.70 \text{ to the nearest hundredth}$$
$$\approx 0.7 \text{ to the nearest tenth}$$

$$\frac{196}{111} = 1.\overline{765} \quad \approx 1.8 \text{ to the nearest tenth}$$
$$\approx 2 \text{ to the nearest unit}$$

Oral Exercises

Round each number to the nearest tenth.

1. 4.893 4.9   **2.** -0.249 -0.2 **3.** $3.\overline{5}$ 3.6   **4.** $2.96\overline{7}$ 3.0   **5.** $0.1\overline{4}$ 0.1

6–10. Round the numbers in Exercises 1–5 to the nearest hundredth.
6. 4.89   **7.** -0.25 **8.** 3.56   **9.** 2.97   **10.** 0.14

Written Exercises

Express each rational number as a terminating or repeating decimal.

A 1. $\frac{4}{9}$ $0.\overline{4}$ **2.** $\frac{15}{4}$ 3.75   **3.** $\frac{5}{8}$ 0.625   **4.** $\frac{7}{12}$
$0.58\overline{3}$

5. $\frac{3}{5}$ 0.6 **6.** $-\frac{9}{25}$ -0.36 **7.** $\frac{69}{50}$ 1.38 **8.** $\frac{11}{9}$ $1.\overline{2}$

9. $\frac{9}{16}$ 0.5625 **10.** $-\frac{7}{18}$ $-0.3\overline{8}$ **11.** $-\frac{11}{20}$ -0.55 **12.** $\frac{5}{7}$

13. $-\frac{5}{11}$ $-0.\overline{45}$ **14.** $\frac{27}{32}$ 0.84375 **15.** $-3\frac{7}{8}$ -3.875 **16.** $2\frac{22}{99}$

12. $0.\overline{714285}$ **16.** $2.\overline{2}$

Express each rational number as a fraction in simplest form.

17. 0.33 $\frac{33}{100}$ **18.** 0.6 $\frac{3}{5}$ **19.** $0.222\ldots$ $\frac{2}{9}$ **20.** 0.58 $\frac{29}{50}$

21. $0.\overline{63}$ $\frac{7}{11}$ **22.** 0.725 $\frac{29}{40}$ **23.** $-0.41\overline{6}$ $-\frac{5}{12}$ **24.** 3.9 $\frac{39}{10}$

25. $1.4\overline{6}$ $\frac{22}{15}$ **26.** $4.\overline{18}$ $\frac{46}{11}$ **27.** $-3.0\overline{8}$ $-\frac{139}{45}$ **28.** $0.\overline{428571}$ $\frac{3}{7}$

Express both numbers as fractions and find their product.

B **29.** $\frac{1}{4}$ and 0.5 **30.** 0.375 and $\frac{4}{5}$ **31.** $0.444\ldots$ and $\frac{3}{4}$

32. $-4.333\ldots$ and $1.\overline{6}$ **33.** $0.8\overline{1}$ and $0.\overline{814}$ **34.** $0.36\overline{3}$ and -0.3

Find the difference of the given numbers. Then find a number between them.

35. $\frac{3}{4}$ and 0.758 **36.** $\frac{1}{8}$ and 0.123 **37.** 0.66 and $0.\overline{6}$

38. 0.29 and $0.\overline{29}$ **39.** $\frac{5}{44}$ and $0.11\overline{38}$ **40.** $\frac{5}{6}$ and 0.84

$\frac{1}{7} = 0.\overline{142857}$; $\frac{3}{7} = 0.\overline{428571}$

C **41. a.** Express $\frac{1}{7}$ and $\frac{3}{7}$ as repeating decimals.

b. In the decimals that you found in part (a), what is the relationship between the blocks of digits that repeat?

c. Express $\frac{2}{7}$, $\frac{4}{7}$, and $\frac{6}{7}$ as decimals. $\frac{2}{7} = 0.\overline{285714}$; $\frac{4}{7} = 0.\overline{571428}$; $\frac{6}{7} = 0.\overline{857142}$

42. a. Express $\frac{1}{9}$, $\frac{5}{9}$, and $\frac{7}{9}$ as repeating decimals. $0.\overline{1}$; $0.\overline{5}$; $0.\overline{7}$

b. Express $\frac{1}{18}$, $\frac{5}{18}$, and $\frac{7}{18}$ as repeating decimals. $0.05\overline{5}$; $0.27\overline{7}$; $0.38\overline{8}$

c. What is the relationship between the decimals in part (a) and part (b)? Each decimal in (b) is half the corresponding decimal in (a).

43. Since $\frac{1}{99} = 0.\overline{01}$, then $\frac{n}{99} = n(0.\overline{01})$ for $n < 100$.

a. Confirm the fact stated above by expressing $\frac{7}{99}$, $\frac{15}{99}$ and $\frac{86}{99}$ as decimals. $\frac{7}{99} = 0.\overline{07}$; $\frac{15}{99} = 0.\overline{15}$; $\frac{86}{99} = 0.\overline{86}$

b. Express 1 as $\frac{99}{99}$ to show that $0.\overline{9} = 1$. $1 = \frac{99}{99} = 0.\overline{99} = 0.\overline{9}$

11-3 *Rational Square Roots*

OBJECTIVE   To find the square roots of numbers and quotients that have rational square roots.

Recall that subtracting a number is the inverse of adding that number, and dividing by a (nonzero) number is the inverse of multiplying by that number. The inverse of squaring a number is finding a square root. If $a^2 = b$ then a is called a **square root** of b. Because $6^2 = 36$ and $(-6)^2 = 36$, both 6 and -6 are square roots of 36.

The symbol $\sqrt{}$ is used to denote the **principal,** or positive, square root of a positive number. Thus,

$$\sqrt{36} = 6 \quad \text{and} \quad -\sqrt{36} = -6.$$

The symbol $\sqrt{}$ is called the **radical sign,** and $\sqrt{36}$ is an example of a **radical.** An expression written beneath the radical sign, such as 36, is called the **radicand.** Often it is convenient to use *plus-or-minus* notation with radicals, for example:

$$\pm\sqrt{36}, \text{ read "positive or negative square root of 36."}$$

For all positive real numbers c, the symbol $\sqrt{c}$ denotes the principal square root of c.

It follows from the definition of square root that $(\sqrt{c})^2 = c$.

Zero has only one square root, namely zero itself: $\sqrt{0} = 0$

Because the square of every real number is either positive or zero, *negative numbers do not have square roots in the set of real numbers.*

The values of certain square roots are easy to find, for example $\sqrt{25} = 5$. To find other square roots, it is often helpful to factor the radicand.

Notice that
$$\sqrt{4 \cdot 25} = \sqrt{100} = 10$$
and
$$\sqrt{4} \cdot \sqrt{25} = 2 \cdot 5 = 10.$$

This relationship suggests the following fact about square roots.

PRODUCT PROPERTY OF SQUARE ROOTS

For any nonnegative real numbers a and b:

$$\sqrt{ab} = \sqrt{a} \cdot \sqrt{b}$$

EXAMPLE 1   Find $\sqrt{225}$.

SOLUTION $\sqrt{225} = \sqrt{9} \cdot \sqrt{25} = 3 \cdot 5 = 15$.

If you cannot see any squares that divide the radicand, you can begin by factoring the radicand. (See the material on factoring integers on page 156.)

EXAMPLE 2   Find $\sqrt{1764}$.

SOLUTION $\sqrt{1764} = \sqrt{2^2 \cdot 3^2 \cdot 7^2}$

$\qquad\qquad = \sqrt{2^2} \cdot \sqrt{3^2} \cdot \sqrt{7^2}$

$\qquad\qquad = 2 \cdot 3 \cdot 7 = 42$

The examples

$$\sqrt{\frac{36}{9}} = \sqrt{4} = 2 \quad \text{and} \quad \frac{\sqrt{36}}{\sqrt{9}} = \frac{6}{3} = 2$$

suggest another property of square roots.

QUOTIENT PROPERTY OF SQUARE ROOTS

For any nonnegative real number a and any positive real number b:

$$\sqrt{\frac{a}{b}} = \frac{\sqrt{a}}{\sqrt{b}}$$

EXAMPLE 3   Find $\sqrt{\dfrac{81}{676}}$.

SOLUTION $\sqrt{\dfrac{81}{676}} = \dfrac{\sqrt{81}}{\sqrt{676}} = \dfrac{9}{\sqrt{2^2 \cdot 13^2}} = \dfrac{9}{2 \cdot 13} = \dfrac{9}{26}$

Oral Exercises

Find the indicated square roots.

1. $\sqrt{4}$ 2
2. $\sqrt{1}$ 1
3. $\sqrt{100}$ 10
4. $\sqrt{7^2}$ 7
5. $\sqrt{33^2}$ 33

6. $(\sqrt{6})^2$ 6
7. $(\sqrt{19})^2$ 19
8. $\sqrt{\dfrac{1}{9}}$ $\tfrac{1}{3}$
9. $\sqrt{5^2 - 3^2}$ 4
10. $\sqrt{5^2} - \sqrt{3^2}$ 2

11. $\sqrt{\dfrac{1}{64}}$ $\tfrac{1}{8}$
12. $\sqrt{\dfrac{100}{9}}$ $\tfrac{10}{3}$
13. $\left(\sqrt{\dfrac{7}{12}}\right)^2$ $\tfrac{7}{12}$
14. $\sqrt{\left(\dfrac{3}{5}\right)^2}$ $\tfrac{3}{5}$
15. $\sqrt{\dfrac{81}{25}}$ $\tfrac{9}{5}$

RATIONAL AND IRRATIONAL NUMBERS   **413**

Supplementary Material
Progress Test 39

Suggested Assignments
Minimum
   414/1–39 odd
S 411/41
Average
   414/1–43 odd
S 411/42
Maximum
   414/1–43 odd
S 411/43

Find the indicated square roots.

1. $\sqrt{144}$ 12
2. $\sqrt{169}$ 13
3. $(\sqrt{21})^2$ 21
4. $\sqrt{32^2}$ 32
5. $\sqrt{\dfrac{4}{25}}$ $\dfrac{2}{5}$
6. $\sqrt{\dfrac{64}{121}}$ $\dfrac{6}{11}$

Written Exercises

Find the indicated square roots.

A 1. $\sqrt{256}$ 16   2. $\sqrt{900}$ 30   3. $\sqrt{225}$ 15   4. $\sqrt{625}$ 25   5. $\sqrt{361}$ 19

6. $-\sqrt{1849}$ -43 7. $-\sqrt{2704}$ -52 8. $\sqrt{2401}$ 49   9. $\sqrt{5184}$ 72   10. $\pm\sqrt{44100}$

11. $\sqrt{\dfrac{49}{3600}}$ $\dfrac{7}{60}$ 12. $\sqrt{\dfrac{1}{196}}$ $\dfrac{1}{14}$ 13. $\sqrt{\dfrac{169}{64}}$ $\dfrac{13}{8}$ 14. $\sqrt{\dfrac{16}{729}}$ $\dfrac{4}{27}$ 15. $\sqrt{\dfrac{121}{625}}$ $\dfrac{11}{25}$

16. $-\sqrt{\dfrac{324}{529}}$ $-\dfrac{18}{23}$ 17. $\sqrt{\dfrac{49}{1225}}$ $\dfrac{1}{5}$ 18. $\pm\sqrt{\dfrac{25}{784}}$ 19. $-\sqrt{\dfrac{484}{289}}$ 20. $\pm\sqrt{\dfrac{529}{10000}}$

$\pm\dfrac{5}{28}$ $-\dfrac{22}{17}$ 10. ±210

$SAMPLE$ $\sqrt{0.49} = \sqrt{\dfrac{49}{100}}$

$= \dfrac{\sqrt{49}}{\sqrt{100}} = \dfrac{7}{10} = 0.7$ 20. $\pm\dfrac{23}{100}$

21. $\sqrt{0.04}$ 0.2   22. $\sqrt{0.81}$ 0.9   23. $-\sqrt{1.44}$ $\overset{-1.2}{}$ 24. $\sqrt{2.56}$ 1.6   25. $\sqrt{5.29}$ 2.3

26. $-\sqrt{0.0121}$ 27. $\pm\sqrt{0.0729}$ 28. $\sqrt{0.1225}$ 29. $\pm\sqrt{0.0049}$ 30. $\sqrt{0.0324}$

-0.11 ±0.27 0.35 ±0.07 0.18

Evaluate the expression $(\sqrt{a})^2 - \sqrt{a^2 + b^2}$ for the given values of a and b.

31. $a = 3, b = 4$ -2 32. $a = 8, b = 6$ -2 33. $a = 5, b = 12$ -8 34. $a = 7, b = 24$

-18

Find the indicated square roots.

$SAMPLE$ $\sqrt{\dfrac{48}{75}} = \sqrt{\dfrac{3 \cdot 16}{3 \cdot 25}} = \sqrt{\dfrac{16}{25}} = \dfrac{4}{5}$

B 35. $\sqrt{\dfrac{12}{75}}$ $\dfrac{2}{5}$ 36. $\sqrt{\dfrac{98}{32}}$ $\dfrac{7}{4}$ 37. $-\sqrt{\dfrac{33}{132}}$ $-\dfrac{1}{2}$ 38. $\pm\sqrt{\dfrac{108}{147}}$ $\pm\dfrac{6}{7}$ 39. $\sqrt{\dfrac{243}{300}}$ $\dfrac{9}{10}$

40. $\pm\sqrt{\dfrac{400}{484}}$ 41. $\sqrt{\dfrac{18}{338}}$ $\dfrac{3}{13}$ 42. $-\sqrt{\dfrac{80}{1125}}$ 43. $\pm\sqrt{\dfrac{507}{1200}}$ 44. $\sqrt{\dfrac{1458}{20000}}$

$\pm\dfrac{10}{11}$ $-\dfrac{4}{15}$ $\pm\dfrac{13}{20}$ $\dfrac{27}{100}$

Calculator Key-In

Use a calculator to approximate each square root to the indicated decimal place.

To the nearest thousandth:

1. $\sqrt{5}$ 2.236   2. $\sqrt{2}$ 1.414   3. $\sqrt{3.15}$ 1.775   4. $\sqrt{0.625}$ 0.791   5. $\sqrt{0.453}$

0.673

To the nearest ten thousandth:

6. $\sqrt{4000}$ 7. $\sqrt{3533}$ 8. $\sqrt{2175}$ 9. $\sqrt{3750}$ 10. $\sqrt{8145}$

63.2456   59.4390   46.6369   61.2372   90.2497

Self-Test 1

VOCABULARY   rational number (p. 403)   square root (p. 412)
terminating decimal (p. 408)   principal square root (p. 412)
repeating decimal (p. 408)   radicand (p. 412)

Find a rational number halfway between the given numbers.

1. $\frac{2}{3}$ and $\frac{3}{4}$

2. $1\frac{1}{5}$ and $1\frac{1}{3}$ Obj. 11-1, p. 403

Which rational number is greater?

3. $\frac{4}{5}$ or $\frac{5}{7}$

4. $\frac{3}{4}$ or $\frac{8}{11}$

5. Express $\frac{37}{50}$ as a decimal.   Obj. 11-2, p. 408

6. Express $\frac{7}{44}$ as a decimal.

7. Express $2.\overline{13}$ as a fraction in simplest form.

Find the indicated square roots.

8. $\sqrt{729}$ **9.** $\sqrt{\dfrac{441}{1024}}$ **10.** $\sqrt{1.44}$ Obj. 11-3, p. 412

Check your answers with those at the back of the book.

Historical Note π

An English writer, William Jones, in 1706 was the first person to use the Greek letter π to stand for the ratio of the circumference of a circle to the diameter.

The value $\frac{22}{7}$, which is used today as an approximation for π, was used as early as the first century. By the sixteenth century, the value of π correct to thirty-five decimal places was known, and by the mid-nineteenth century, its value had been calculated to over seven hundred places.

It wasn't until the late nineteenth century, however, that it was first proved that π cannot be expressed as a ratio of integers and is thus *not* a rational number.

RATIONAL AND IRRATIONAL NUMBERS   **415**

IRRATIONAL NUMBERS

11-4 *Irrational Square Roots*

OBJECTIVE   To find decimal approximations to irrational square roots.

In this section you will see that those integers that are not squares of integers do not have rational square roots. The following proof shows that if an integer has a rational square root, then the integer is equal to the square of an integer.

1. Let n be a positive integer that has a rational square root.

2. Then $\sqrt{n} = \dfrac{a}{b}$, where a and b are positive integers that have no common prime factors.

3. If $\sqrt{n} = \dfrac{a}{b}$, then $n = \dfrac{a^2}{b^2}$. Since a^2 has the same prime factors as a, and b^2 has the same prime factors as b, a^2 and b^2 have no common prime factors. Thus, $\dfrac{a^2}{b^2}$ is in simplest form.

4. If a fraction in simplest form is equal to an integer, the denominator of the fraction must be 1. From Step 3 you know that $\dfrac{a^2}{b^2}$ is equal to the integer n and that $\dfrac{a^2}{b^2}$ is in simplest form. Thus, $b^2 = 1$.

5. Therefore, $n = \dfrac{a^2}{b^2} = \dfrac{a^2}{1} = a^2$. Thus, n is the square of an integer.

Since integers like 2, 5, and 6 are not squares of integers, the numbers $\sqrt{2}$, $\sqrt{5}$, and $\sqrt{6}$ are not in the set of rational numbers. These numbers are in another major subset of the real numbers called the set of *irrational numbers*.

Irrational numbers are real numbers that cannot be expressed in the form $\dfrac{a}{b}$, where a and b are integers.

Irrational square roots are not the only irrational numbers, however. For example, π is an irrational number.

The set of real numbers is made up of the rational numbers and the irrational numbers. By advanced methods, it can be shown that there are both rational and irrational numbers between any two real numbers. The set of real numbers has the *property of completeness*, which is stated at the top of the next page.

416   *CHAPTER 11*

Supplementary Material
Practice Master 64

Suggested Assignments
Minimum
  418/1–19 odd
R 415/Self-Test 1
Average
  418/1–19 odd
R 415/Self-Test 1
Maximum
  418/1–19 odd
R 415/Self-Test 1

```
┌─────────────────────────────────────────────────┐
│           PROPERTY OF COMPLETENESS               │
│ Every decimal represents a real number, and every real number │
│ can be represented as a decimal.                 │
└─────────────────────────────────────────────────┘
```

Terminating and repeating decimals represent rational numbers. Therefore, the decimals for irrational numbers neither terminate nor repeat. You can use a calculator or a table of square roots to get a decimal approximation of an irrational square root. For example, the Table of Square Roots on page 526 indicates that $\sqrt{73} \approx 8.544$. The product and quotient properties of square roots can be used with the table to approximate irrational square roots.

EXAMPLE 1 Approximate $\sqrt{1224}$ to the nearest hundredth.

SOLUTION $\sqrt{1224} = \sqrt{2^2 \cdot 3^2 \cdot 34} = \sqrt{2^2} \cdot \sqrt{3^2} \cdot \sqrt{34} = 6\sqrt{34}$
From the table: $\sqrt{34} \approx 5.831$
$6\sqrt{34} \approx 6 \cdot 5.831 = 34.986$
$\therefore \sqrt{1224} \approx 34.99$ **Answer**

EXAMPLE 2 Approximate $\sqrt{0.93}$ to the nearest ten thousandth.

SOLUTION $\sqrt{0.93} = \sqrt{\dfrac{93}{100}} = \dfrac{\sqrt{93}}{\sqrt{100}} \approx \dfrac{9.644}{10} = 0.9644$
$\therefore \sqrt{0.93} \approx 0.9644$ **Answer**

If you divide a positive number by a positive divisor which is smaller than the square root of that number, the quotient will be larger than the square root. This property forms the basis for the *divide-and-average method* of approximating a square root.

EXAMPLE 3 Approximate $\sqrt{38}$ to the nearest ten thousandth using the divide-and-average method.

SOLUTION 1. Select the integer whose square is nearest 38 as your first approximation, a. Since $6^2 = 36$, let $a = 6$.
2. Divide 38 by a, carrying out the division to two more digits than are in the divisor.
$$38 \div 6 \approx 6.33$$
3. Find the average of a and $\dfrac{38}{a}$.
$$\tfrac{1}{2}(6 + 6.33) \approx 6.17$$

(*Solution continued on page 418.*)

RATIONAL AND IRRATIONAL NUMBERS **417**

4. Use the average as the new value for a. Continue repeating steps 2 and 3 as often as necessary.

(Step 2)   (Step 3)

$$38 \div 6.17 = 6.1588 \longrightarrow \frac{1}{2}(6.17 + 6.1588) \approx 6.1644$$

$$38 \div 6.1644 = 6.164428$$

5. The approximation is accurate to at least as many digits as match in a and $38 \div a$.

$$\therefore \ \sqrt{38} \approx 6.1644 \quad \textbf{\textit{Answer}}$$

Oral Exercises

State whether the following represent rational or irrational numbers.

1. $\sqrt{11}$
Irrational

2. $\sqrt{64}$
Rational

3. $\sqrt{15}$
Irrational

4. $\sqrt{61.8}$
Irrational

5. $\sqrt{0.81}$
Rational

Express as a product of a number between 1 and 100 and a power of 100.

SAMPLE $437 = 4.37 \times 100$

6. 600
6 × 100

7. 7200
72 × 100

8. 5103
51.03 × 100

9. 80,000
8 × 100²

10. 134,000
13.4 × 100²

Express as a quotient of a number between 1 and 100 and a power of 100.

SAMPLE $0.07 = \dfrac{7}{100}$

11. 0.04 $\frac{4}{100}$

12. 0.063 $\frac{6.3}{100}$

13. 0.305 $\frac{30.5}{100}$

14. 0.0067 $\frac{67}{100^2}$

15. 0.0185 $\frac{1.85}{100}$

Written Exercises

In Exercises 1–15, use the table on page 526 as necessary. In Exercises 1–5, approximate each square root to the nearest tenth.

A   **1.** $-\sqrt{500}$
-22.4

2. $\sqrt{5300}$
72.8

3. $\sqrt{800}$
28.3

4. $-\sqrt{3700}$
-60.8

5. $\sqrt{9900}$
99.5

Approximate each square root to the nearest hundredth.

6. $\sqrt{43}$ 6.56

7. $\sqrt{89}$ 9.43

8. $\sqrt{0.26}$ 0.51

9. $\sqrt{0.58}$ 0.76

10. $\sqrt{0.07}$
0.26

Approximate each square root to the nearest unit.

11. $\sqrt{730,000}$
854

12. $\sqrt{170,000}$
412

13. $\sqrt{260,000}$
510

14. $\sqrt{390,000}$
624

15. $\sqrt{940,000}$
970

Approximate each square root to the nearest hundredth using the divide-and-average method.

16. $\sqrt{29}$ 5.39

17. $\sqrt{13}$ 3.61

18. $\sqrt{42.3}$ 6.50

19. $-\sqrt{350}$
-18.71

20. $\sqrt{23.8}$
4.88

418   *CHAPTER 11*

11-5 *Square Roots of Variable Expressions*

OBJECTIVE To find square roots of variable expressions and to use them to solve equations and problems.

Does $\sqrt{y^2} = y$? Not necessarily. Recall that the square root symbol, $\sqrt{\ }$, stands for the nonnegative square root of a number. For example, when $y = -6$:

$$\sqrt{(-6)^2} = -(-6) = 6$$

If there are variables in the radicand, you must be careful to use absolute value signs when needed, as shown below:

$$\sqrt{y^2} = |y|$$

EXAMPLE 1 Simplify: **a.** $\sqrt{64x^2}$ **b.** $\sqrt{25a^8}$ **c.** $\sqrt{x^2 + 6x + 9}$

SOLUTION
a. $\sqrt{64x^2} = 8|x|$
b. $\sqrt{25a^8} = 5a^4$ (a^4 is always nonnegative)
c. $\sqrt{x^2 + 6x + 9} = \sqrt{(x + 3)^2} = |x + 3|$

EXAMPLE 2 Solve $x^2 = 49$

SOLUTION 1

$$x^2 = 49$$
$$x^2 - 49 = 0$$
$$(x - 7)(x + 7) = 0$$
$$x = 7 \text{ or } x = -7$$

SOLUTION 2

$$x^2 = 49$$
$$x = \pm\sqrt{49} = \pm 7$$

Check: $7^2 = 49$ and $(-7)^2 = 49$ ✓

$\therefore$ the solution set is $\{7, -7\}$. ***Answer***

Solution 2 is based upon the following:

> **PROPERTY OF SQUARE ROOTS OF EQUAL NUMBERS**
>
> If r and s are any real numbers,
>
> $r^2 = s^2$ if and only if $r = s$ or $r = -s$.

Oral Exercises

Simplify.

1. $\sqrt{81x^2}$ $9|x|$
2. $\sqrt{121b^2}$ $11|b|$
3. $\sqrt{64a^4}$ $8a^2$
4. $\sqrt{100x^2y^2}$ $10|xy|$
5. $\sqrt{0.09y^8}$ 5. $0.3y^4$
6. $\sqrt{\dfrac{c^2}{25}}$ $\dfrac{|c|}{5}$
7. $\pm\sqrt{\dfrac{d^4}{49}}$ $\pm\dfrac{d^2}{7}$
8. $-\sqrt{\dfrac{x^2y^2}{9}}$ $-\dfrac{|xy|}{3}$
9. $\sqrt{\dfrac{m^3n^3}{81}}$ 9. $\dfrac{|mn|}{9}\sqrt{mn}$
10. $\sqrt{\dfrac{r^{12}}{36n^6}}$ 10. $\dfrac{r^6}{6|n^3|}$

Teaching Suggestions p. T105

Suggested Extensions p. T105

Chalkboard Examples

Simplify.

1. $\sqrt{36x^2}$

$\sqrt{6^2 \cdot x^2} = 6|x|$

2. $\sqrt{225z^8}$

$\sqrt{3^2 \cdot 5^2 \cdot (z^4)^2} =$
$15|z^4| = 15z^4$,
since z^4 is nonnegative

3. $\sqrt{25r^2 - 30rs + 9s^2}$

$\sqrt{(5r - 3s)^2} = |5r - 3s|$

Solve. Approximate irrational solutions to the nearest tenth.

4. $3x^2 - 192 = 0$

$3x^2 = 192$
$x^2 = 64$
$x = \pm 8$
$\therefore$ The solution set is $\{8, -8\}$.

5. $2k^2 = 686$

$k^2 = 343$
$k = \pm\sqrt{7^2 \cdot 7}$
$k = \pm 7\sqrt{7} \approx \pm 7(2.646)$
$\therefore$ The solution set is $\{18.5, -18.5\}$.

6. $9a^2 - 49 = 0$

$9a^2 = 49$

$a^2 = \dfrac{49}{9}$

$a = \sqrt{\dfrac{49}{9}} = \pm\dfrac{7}{3}$

$\therefore$ The solution set is $\left\{\dfrac{7}{3}, \dfrac{-7}{3}\right\}$.

Suggested Assignments

Minimum
420/1–31 odd, *P*: 1, 3

Average
420/1–35 odd, *P*: 1, 3, 5

Maximum
420/1–35 odd, *P*: 1–9 odd

Extra Practice Problems
p. 522

Written Exercises

Simplify.

A 1. $-\sqrt{0.36t^6}$ $-0.6|t^3|$
2. $-\sqrt{1.96x^2y^4}$ $-1.4|x|y^2$
3. $\sqrt{2.25a^4b^2}$ $1.5a^2|b|$
4. $\sqrt{625z^6}$ $25|z^3|$
5. $\sqrt{3.61k^6n^2}$ $1.9|k^3n|$

6. $\sqrt{\dfrac{4}{144}}$ $\dfrac{1}{6}$
7. $\sqrt{\dfrac{n^6}{169}}$ $\dfrac{|n^3|}{13}$
8. $\sqrt{\dfrac{n^{72}}{6400}}$ $\dfrac{n^{36}}{80}$
9. $\sqrt{\dfrac{8100}{k^{10}}}$ $\dfrac{90}{|k^5|}$
10. $\sqrt{\dfrac{144k^8}{25x^6}}$

11. $\sqrt{x^2 + 10x + 25}$ $|x + 5|$
12. $\sqrt{y^2 - 8y + 16}$ $|y - 4|$
13. $\sqrt{81 + 18k + k^2}$ $|k + 9|$

Solve.

14. $m^2 = 36$ $\{6, -6\}$
15. $r^2 - 81 = 0$ $\{9, -9\}$
16. $b^2 - 49 = 0$ $\{7, -7\}$
17. $25x^2 - 9 = 0$ $\{\frac{3}{5}, -\frac{3}{5}\}$
18. $16x^2 - 81 = 0$ $\{\frac{9}{4}, -\frac{9}{4}\}$
19. $6y^2 - 24 = 0$
20. $2b^2 - 50 = 0$ $\{5, -5\}$
21. $18t^2 - 2 = 0$ $\{\frac{1}{3}, -\frac{1}{3}\}$
22. $4n^2 - 36 = 0$
19. $\{2, -2\}$ 22. $\{3, -3\}$

Find both roots of each equation to the nearest tenth.

B 23. $x^2 = 748$ $\{27.3, -27.3\}$
24. $a^2 = 381$ $\{19.5, -19.5\}$
25. $m^2 = 6.8$ $\{\pm 2.6\}$
26. $y^2 - 14.2 = 0$ $\{3.8, -3.8\}$
27. $b^2 - 131 = 0$ $\{11.4, -11.4\}$
28. $c^2 - 28.4 = 0$
29. $5x^2 = 620$ $\{11.1, -11.1\}$
30. $8m^2 - 1000 = 0$ $\{11.2, -11.2\}$
31. $3s^2 - 0.66 = 0$ $\{0.5, -0.5\}$

C 32. $0.7x^2 = 5.11$ $\{2.7; -2.7\}$
33. $17x^2 = 120$ $\{2.7, -2.7\}$
34. $(y - 3)^2 + (y + 3)^2 = 152$ $\{8.2, -8.2\}$
35. $(a + 2)^2 + (a - 2)^2 = 86$ $\{6.2, -6.2\}$

Problems

Solve. Find each answer to the nearest tenth. (Use $\pi \approx 3.14$.)

A 1. Find the side of a square whose area is 300 cm². 17.3 cm
2. The area of a square is 72 cm². How long is its side? 8.5 cm
3. The length of a rectangle is 4 times its width. Find the dimensions of the rectangle if its area is 204 cm². 7.1 cm by 28.4 cm
4. The altitude of a triangle is 6 times its base. Find the altitude if the area of the triangle is 36 m². 20.8 m
5. Find the radius of a circle whose area is 66 cm². 4.6 cm
6. Find the diameter of a circle with the same area as a rectangle that is 33 cm by 40 cm. 41.0 cm

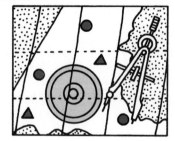

7. 42.4 cm

B 7. A water pipe is 30 cm in diameter. What is the diameter of a new pipe if the cross-sectional area of the new pipe is to be twice that of the old?
8. The search for a missing airplane covered a circular region with an area of 154 km². What was the radius of the search area? 7.0 km

9. The formula $s = 4.9t^2$ gives the approximate distance traveled in t seconds by an object falling from rest. How long does it take a rock falling from rest to travel 610 m? 11.2 s

Let a, b, and c represent the lengths of the sides of a triangle, and let $s = \frac{1}{2}(a + b + c)$. Then the area ($A$) of the triangle is given by the formula $A = \sqrt{s(s - a)(s - b)(s - c)}$. Use the formula to answer the following questions. Find each answer to the nearest tenth.

C 10. What is the area of a triangle whose sides are 5 cm, 7 cm, and 10 cm long? 16.2 cm²

11. What is the area of a triangle whose sides are 8 cm, 9 cm, and 11 cm long? 35.5 cm²

Computer Key-In _____

If you have access to a computer that will accept BASIC, you can use the program below to print successive stages of the divide-and-average method of computing the square root of a positive integer. BASIC also has a built-in square root function which will give a positive square root directly. Before running the long program, try this:

```
10  PRINT SQR(16), SQR(17), SQR(18)
20  END
```

The last line of the following program prints the positive square root as given by the built-in function for comparison.

```
10  PRINT "INPUT A POSITIVE INTEGER";
20  INPUT N
30  IF N <= 0 THEN 10
40  PRINT "WHAT FACTOR WOULD YOU LIKE TO TRY";
50  INPUT F
60  IF F <= 0 THEN 40
70  LET Q=N/F
80  PRINT F,Q
90  IF ABS(F-Q)<.00001 THEN 120
100 LET F=(F+Q)/2
110 GOTO 70
120 PRINT "CHECK:";SQR(N)
130 END
```

1. Run the program to find $\sqrt{15}$ by trying 1 as the factor. (Note: Input 15 as the positive integer.) Repeat, trying 2, 3, 4, and then 5 as factors. 3.87298

2. Compare the print-out for the five parts of Exercise 1.

Experiment with other numbers and factors.
The closer the factor tried is to the actual square root, the shorter the print-out is.

11-6 *The Pythagorean Theorem*

OBJECTIVE   To use the Pythagorean theorem and its converse to construct lengths corresponding to irrational numbers and to
solve geometric problems.

In this section you will see how the Pythagorean theorem can be used to
find lengths corresponding to irrational numbers.

THE PYTHAGOREAN THEOREM

In any right triangle, the square of the
length of the hypotenuse equals the sum
of the squares of the lengths of the other
two sides. For the triangle shown,

$$a^2 + b^2 = c^2.$$

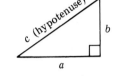

The following two diagrams suggest a proof of the theorem. Each
diagram shows a square, $(a + b)$ units on a side, divided into other figures. Each diagram suggests a different expression for the area of a
square $(a + b)$ units on a side. Equating these expressions leads to the
equation $a^2 + b^2 = c^2$.

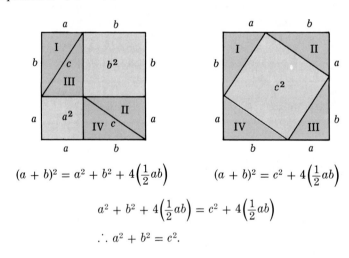

$$(a + b)^2 = a^2 + b^2 + 4\left(\frac{1}{2}ab\right) \qquad (a + b)^2 = c^2 + 4\left(\frac{1}{2}ab\right)$$

$$a^2 + b^2 + 4\left(\frac{1}{2}ab\right) = c^2 + 4\left(\frac{1}{2}ab\right)$$

$$\therefore a^2 + b^2 = c^2.$$

To draw a line segment with a length of $\sqrt{2}$ units, draw a right
triangle whose two shorter sides are 1 unit long, as shown in the diagram at the top of the next page.

422   CHAPTER 11

Then:

$$a^2 + b^2 = c^2$$
$$1^2 + 1^2 = c^2$$
$$1 + 1 = c^2$$
$$2 = c^2$$
$$\pm\sqrt{2} = c$$

∴ the length of the hypotenuse is $\sqrt{2}$ units.

The following diagrams show that a segment $\sqrt{2}$ units long can be used to construct a segment $\sqrt{3}$ units long, a segment $\sqrt{3}$ units long can be used to construct a segment $\sqrt{4}$ units long, and so on.

  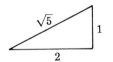 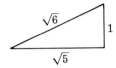

A series of such triangles can be used to locate irrational square roots such as $\sqrt{2}$, $\sqrt{3}$, and $\sqrt{5}$ on the number line. The arcs are drawn to transfer the length of the hypotenuse of each triangle to the x-axis. Note below that $-\sqrt{2}$ is located $\sqrt{2}$ units to the left of 0.

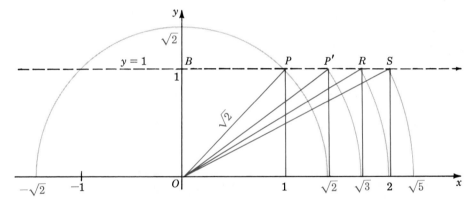

The converse of the Pythagorean theorem is also true. It can be used to test whether or not a triangle is a right triangle.

CONVERSE OF THE PYTHAGOREAN THEOREM

If the sum of the squares of the lengths of the two shorter sides of a triangle is equal to the square of the length of the longest side, then the triangle is a right triangle. The right angle will be opposite the longest side.

---

6. Find the length of a side of a square with a diagonal that is 6 cm long.

Let s = length of side

$$s^2 + s^2 = 36$$
$$2s^2 = 36$$
$$s^2 = 18$$
$$s = \sqrt{18} = 3\sqrt{2}$$
$$s \approx 3(1.414)$$
$$s \approx 4.2$$

∴ The length of a side $\approx$ 4.2 cm.

EXAMPLE Is a triangle whose sides are 5, 12, and 13 units long a right triangle?

SOLUTION
$$a^2 + b^2 = c^2$$
$$5^2 + 12^2 \overset{?}{=} 13^2$$
$$169 = 169 \quad \checkmark$$

∴ a triangle whose sides are 5, 12, and 13 units long is a right triangle. ***Answer***

Oral Exercises

State and solve an equation for the length of the unknown side.

1.

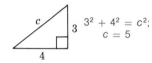

$3^2 + 4^2 = c^2$;
$c = 5$

2.

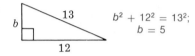

$b^2 + 12^2 = 13^2$;
$b = 5$

Written Exercises

In Exercises 1–10, refer to the right triangle drawn at the right. Find the missing length correct to the nearest hundredth.

A **1.** $a = 6$, $b = 8$, $c = $ _?_ 10.00

3. $a = 5$, $b = 9$, $c = $ _?_ 10.30

5. $a = 13$, $b = 13$, $c = $ _?_ 18.38

7. $a = $ _?_, $b = 5$, $c = 13$ 12.00

9. $a = 5$, $b = $ _?_, $c = \sqrt{30}$ 2.24

2. $a = 10$, $b = 24$, $c = $ _?_ 26.00

4. $a = 12$, $b = 7$, $c = $ _?_ 13.89

6. $a = 24$, $b = $ _?_, $c = 25$ 7.00

8. $a = 11$, $b = $ _?_, $c = 15$ 10.20

10. $a = $ _?_, $b = \sqrt{11}$, $c = \sqrt{27}$ 4.00

State whether or not the three numbers given are the lengths of the sides of a right triangle.

11. 4, 9, 12 No

12. 7, 24, 25 Yes

13. 8, 10, 13 No

14. 15, 20, 25 Yes

15. 18, 24, 28 No

16. 12, 15, 18 No

In Exercises 17–22, refer to the diagram for Exercises 1–10. Find the missing length correct to the nearest hundredth.

B **17.** $a = b = 11$, $c = $ _?_ 15.56

18. $a = 8$, $b = \frac{1}{2}a$, $c = $ _?_ 8.94

19. $a = 12$, $b = \frac{1}{4}a$, $c = $ _?_ 12.37

20. $a = 15$, $b = \frac{1}{3}a$, $c = $ _?_ 15.81

21. $a = \frac{2}{3}b$, $b = 18$, $c = $ _?_ 21.63

22. $a = \frac{4}{5}b$, $b = 20$, $c = $ _?_ 25.61

424   *CHAPTER 11*

In Exercises 23-26, refer to the diagram for Exercises 1-10 on the previous page. Find a and b correct to the nearest hundredth.

C 23. $c = 12$, $a = b$ $a = b = 8.49$

24. $c = 20$, $a = 2b$ $a = 17.89,$ $b = 8.94$

25. $c = 20$, $a = \frac{1}{2}b$ $a = 8.94,$ $b = 17.89$

26. $c = 39$, $a = \frac{2}{3}b$ $a = 21.63,$ $b = 32.45$

Problems

Make a sketch for each problem. Approximate each square root to the nearest hundredth.

A 1. Find the length of a diagonal of a rectangle whose dimensions are 5 cm by 8 cm. 9.43 cm

2. A rope 13 m long is attached to the top of a flagpole. The rope is just able to reach a point on the ground 5 m from the base of the pole. Find the height of the flagpole. 12 m

3. The diagonal of a square measures $5\sqrt{2}$ m. Find the length of a side of the square. 5 m

4. The base of an isosceles triangle is 18 cm long. The equal sides are 20 cm long. Find the altitude (a) of the triangle. 17.86 cm

B 5. A right triangle has sides whose lengths can be expressed by consecutive even integers. Determine the length of each side. 6, 8, 10

6. The dimensions of a rectangular doorway are 200 cm by 80 cm. Can a circular mirror with a diameter of 220 cm be carried through the doorway? No

C 7. What is the length of the diagonal of a cube that is 20 cm on each side? 34.64 cm

8. What is the length of the diagonal of a rectangular box with a length of 40 cm, a width of 30 cm, and a height of 80 cm? Would a meter stick fit in the box? 94.34 cm; no

9. Robin is standing on a dock 1.5 m above the water. She is drawing in a boat that is attached to the end of a 3.9 m rope. If she pulls in 1.4 m of rope, how far did she move the boat? 1.6 m

Just for Fun

An elephant ate 100 peanuts in four days, each day eating eight more than on the day before. How many peanuts did the elephant eat on the first of the four days? 13 peanuts

426

Quick Quiz

Approximate each square root to the nearest hundredth using the Table of Square Roots.

1. $\sqrt{3000}$ $10\sqrt{30} \approx 54.77$

2. $-\sqrt{0.75}$ $-\dfrac{\sqrt{75}}{10} \approx -0.87$

Simplify.

3. $\sqrt{25x^4y^8}$ $5x^2y^4$

4. $\sqrt{225a^3b^6}$ $15ab^3\sqrt{a}$

Solve.

5. $5x^2 = 45$ $\{3, -3\}$

6. $9x^2 - 49 = 0$ $\left\{\dfrac{7}{3}, -\dfrac{7}{3}\right\}$

7. Find the hypotenuse of a right triangle whose legs are 6 cm and 9 cm. State your answer correct to the nearest hundredth.
$3\sqrt{13} \approx 10.82$ cm

8. Is a triangle whose sides are 12, 16, and 20 cm long a right triangle?
Yes, since
$12^2 + 16^2 = 20^2$.

Self-Test 2

VOCABULARY   irrational numbers (p. 416)   Pythagorean theorem (p. 422)
divide-and-average method (p. 417)

Approximate each square root to the nearest hundredth using the Table of Square Roots.

1. $\sqrt{6500}$ **2.** $-\sqrt{0.83}$ Obj. 11-4, p. 416

Simplify.

3. $\sqrt{49m^2n^6}$ **4.** $\sqrt{169x^5y^4}$ Obj. 11-5, p. 419

Solve.

5. $9x^2 = 36$ **6.** $4x^2 - 49 = 0$

7. Find c correct to the nearest hundredth if $a = 5$ and $b = 9$.

8. Is a triangle with sides 10, 22, and 26 units long a right triangle?

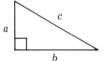

Obj. 11-6, p. 422

Check your answers with those at the back of the book.

EXTRA
The Distance Formula

The distance between two points on the x-axis or on a line parallel to that axis is the absolute value of the difference between their abscissas. Using the notation $A'B'$ to denote the distance from A' to B', you can write the following:

$$A'B' = |3 - 8| = |8 - 3| = 5$$
$$AB = |3 - 8| = |8 - 3| = 5$$

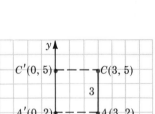

The distance between two points on the y-axis or on a line parallel to that axis is the absolute value of the difference between their ordinates:

$$A'C' = |2 - 5| = |5 - 2| = 3$$
$$AC = |2 - 5| = |5 - 2| = 3$$

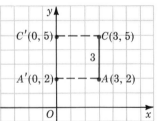

426   CHAPTER 11

To find the distance between two points not on an axis or a line parallel to an axis, use the Pythagorean theorem (page 422):

$$AD = \sqrt{(AB)^2 + (BD)^2} = \sqrt{(8-3)^2 + (5-2)^2}$$
$$= \sqrt{5^2 + 3^2} = \sqrt{25 + 9} = \sqrt{34}$$

To find the distance between any two points, use the following:

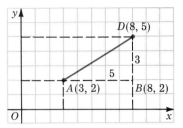

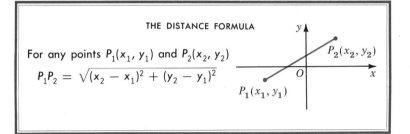

THE DISTANCE FORMULA

For any points $P_1(x_1, y_1)$ and $P_2(x_2, y_2)$

$$P_1P_2 = \sqrt{(x_2 - x_1)^2 + (y_2 - y_1)^2}$$

EXAMPLE Find the distance between points $M(-3, 8)$ and $N(5, 2)$.

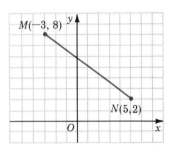

SOLUTION 1 $MN = \sqrt{(-3-5)^2 + (8-2)^2}$
$$= \sqrt{(-8)^2 + 6^2} = \sqrt{64 + 36}$$
$$= \sqrt{100} = 10$$

SOLUTION 2 $MN = \sqrt{(5-(-3))^2 + (2-8)^2}$
$$= \sqrt{8^2 + (-6)^2} = \sqrt{64 + 36}$$
$$= \sqrt{100} = 10$$

Exercises

Use the distance formula to find the distance to the nearest tenth between the points.

3. 10.0   6. 5.8

1. $(-2, 0)$, $(7, 0)$ 9.0   2. $(0, -4)$, $(0, 12)$ 16.0   3. $(1, 1)$, $(7, 9)$

4. $(-1, 2)$, $(-8, 6)$ 8.1   5. $(-1, -3)$, $(-6, -9)$ 7.8   6. $(2, -7)$, $(5, -2)$

7. $(3, 1)$, $(-3, 7)$ 8.5   8. $(-2, 1)$, $(-8, -5)$ 8.5   9. $(-7, -2)$, $(2, -2)$

10. $(4, -3)$, $(9, -8)$ 7.1   11. $(2, 3)$, $(-7, -8)$ 14.2   12. $(-8, 5)$, $(7, -2)$

9. 9.0

12. 16.6

13. Show that points $(0, 3)$, $(3, 9)$, $(6, 0)$, $(9, 6)$ are the vertices of an equal-sided quadrilateral. All the sides have length $3\sqrt{5}$.

14. Show that point $(-2, 2)$ is the midpoint of the segment joining $(-7, 0)$ and $(3, 4)$. Both shorter segments have length $\sqrt{29}$.

RATIONAL AND IRRATIONAL NUMBERS   **427**

About the Extra

The distance between any two points in a coordinate plane can be found by using the distance formula. This section develops the formula by using distances along lines parallel to the x- and y-axes and the Pythagorean theorem, thus providing an important application of the Pythagorean theorem.

One detail of the distance formula deserves some consideration. There are no absolute value signs in the formula. This is due to the fact that $|a - b|^2 = (a - b)^2$ in all cases and, therefore, the absolute value signs are unnecessary.

RADICAL EXPRESSIONS

11-7 *Multiplication, Division, and Simplification of Radicals*

OBJECTIVE   To simplify products and quotients of radicals.

You can use the product and quotient properties of square roots together with the commutative and associative axioms to multiply, divide, and simplify square-root radicals.

An expression having a square-root radical is in **simplest form** when
1. no integral radicand has a square factor other than 1,
2. no fractions are under a radical sign, and
3. no radicals are in a denominator.

EXAMPLE 1   Simplify: **a.** $\sqrt{45}$ **b.** $5\sqrt{24}$

SOLUTION   **a.** $\sqrt{45} = \sqrt{9} \cdot \sqrt{5} = 3\sqrt{5}$

b. $5\sqrt{24} = 5\sqrt{4 \cdot 6} = 5 \cdot 2\sqrt{6} = 10\sqrt{6}$

EXAMPLE 2   Simplify: **a.** $\sqrt{\dfrac{3}{7}}$ **b.** $\dfrac{4}{\sqrt{5}}$ **c.** $\dfrac{3\sqrt{13}}{4\sqrt{32}}$

SOLUTION   **a.** $\sqrt{\dfrac{3}{7}} = \dfrac{\sqrt{3}}{\sqrt{7}} = \dfrac{\sqrt{3} \cdot \sqrt{7}}{\sqrt{7} \cdot \sqrt{7}} = \dfrac{\sqrt{21}}{(\sqrt{7})^2} = \dfrac{\sqrt{21}}{7}$

b. $\dfrac{4}{\sqrt{5}} = \dfrac{4 \cdot \sqrt{5}}{\sqrt{5} \cdot \sqrt{5}} = \dfrac{4\sqrt{5}}{5}$

c. $\dfrac{3\sqrt{13}}{4\sqrt{32}} = \dfrac{3\sqrt{13} \cdot \sqrt{2}}{4\sqrt{32} \cdot \sqrt{2}} = \dfrac{3\sqrt{26}}{4\sqrt{64}} = \dfrac{3\sqrt{26}}{4 \cdot 8} = \dfrac{3\sqrt{26}}{32}$

The process of expressing a fraction with an irrational denominator such as $\dfrac{4}{\sqrt{5}}$ as a fraction with a rational denominator such as $\dfrac{4\sqrt{5}}{5}$ is called **rationalizing the denominator.**

EXAMPLE 3   Approximate $\dfrac{4}{\sqrt{5}}$ to the nearest thousandth.

SOLUTION   From Example 2(a), $\dfrac{4}{\sqrt{5}} = \dfrac{4\sqrt{5}}{5}$. From the table on page 526, $\sqrt{5} \approx 2.236$. Substitute this value for $\sqrt{5}$, as shown at the top of the next page.

$$\frac{4\sqrt{5}}{5} \approx \frac{4(2.236)}{5} = \frac{8.944}{5} = 1.7888 \qquad \therefore \frac{4}{\sqrt{5}} \approx 1.789 \quad \textit{Answer}$$

In Example 3 rationalizing the denominator made it possible to avoid dividing by a decimal. When approximating the value of a radical expression, it is not always necessary to rationalize the denominator. When using a calculator, it is better to approximate the value of the original expression directly.

Oral Exercises

Express in simplest form.

1. $\sqrt{3} \cdot \sqrt{5}$ $\sqrt{15}$ 2. $\dfrac{\sqrt{21}}{\sqrt{3}}$ $\sqrt{7}$ 3. $\dfrac{\sqrt{18}}{\sqrt{2}}$ 3   4. $\sqrt{7} \cdot 3\sqrt{2}$ $3\sqrt{14}$ 5. $\dfrac{2\sqrt{3}}{\sqrt{12}}$ 1

6. $\sqrt{18}$ $3\sqrt{2}$ 7. $\sqrt{75}$ $5\sqrt{3}$ 8. $\sqrt{48}$ $4\sqrt{3}$ 9. $\dfrac{2}{\sqrt{7}}$ $\dfrac{2\sqrt{7}}{7}$ 10. $\sqrt{\dfrac{3}{5}}$ $\dfrac{\sqrt{15}}{5}$

Written Exercises

Express in simplest form.

A   1. $\sqrt{3} \cdot 2\sqrt{3}$ 6   2. $4\sqrt{8} \cdot 3\sqrt{8}$ 96   3. $\sqrt{3} \cdot \sqrt{2} \cdot \sqrt{6}$ 6

4. $\sqrt{4} \cdot \sqrt{2} \cdot \sqrt{2}$ 4   5. $3\sqrt{3} \cdot \sqrt{2} \cdot \sqrt{7}$ $3\sqrt{42}$ 6. $3\sqrt{5} \cdot \sqrt{2} \cdot \sqrt{3}$ $3\sqrt{30}$

7. $4\sqrt{18}$ $12\sqrt{2}$ 8. $6\sqrt{50}$ $30\sqrt{2}$ 9. $4\sqrt{243}$ $36\sqrt{3}$

10. $\sqrt{\dfrac{3}{5}} \cdot \sqrt{\dfrac{5}{3}}$ 1   11. $\sqrt{\dfrac{3}{5}} \cdot \sqrt{\dfrac{10}{3}}$ $\sqrt{2}$ 12. $\sqrt{\dfrac{10}{9}} \cdot \sqrt{\dfrac{27}{5}}$ $\sqrt{6}$

13. $\sqrt{\dfrac{7}{9}} \cdot \sqrt{\dfrac{27}{21}}$ 1   14. $\sqrt{\dfrac{5}{3}} \cdot \sqrt{\dfrac{3}{20}}$ $\dfrac{1}{2}$ 15. $\sqrt{\dfrac{3}{2}} \cdot \sqrt{\dfrac{2}{27}}$ $\dfrac{1}{3}$

16. $\sqrt{3\dfrac{1}{3}} \cdot \sqrt{1\dfrac{1}{8}}$ $\dfrac{\sqrt{15}}{2}$ 17. $\dfrac{1}{4}\sqrt{\dfrac{8}{5}} \cdot \dfrac{1}{3}\sqrt{\dfrac{5}{4}}$ $\dfrac{\sqrt{2}}{12}$ 18. $\dfrac{18\sqrt{12}}{9\sqrt{3}}$ 4

19. $4\sqrt{108}$ $24\sqrt{3}$ 20. $11\sqrt{\dfrac{64}{8}}$ $22\sqrt{2}$ 21. $7\sqrt{\dfrac{32}{9}}$ $\dfrac{28\sqrt{2}}{3}$

22. $\dfrac{12\sqrt{147}}{4\sqrt{9}}$ $7\sqrt{3}$ 23. $\dfrac{5\sqrt{10}}{10\sqrt{5}}$ $\dfrac{\sqrt{2}}{2}$ 24. $\dfrac{4\sqrt{5}}{3\sqrt{72}}$ $\dfrac{\sqrt{10}}{9}$

Simplify. Assume the radicands are nonnegative real numbers.

B   25. $(-3\sqrt{a^2b})(2\sqrt{b})$ 26. $(-\sqrt{x^2y}\,\sqrt{xy^3})$ 27. $\sqrt{m}(5 + \sqrt{m})$

28. $\sqrt{c}(\sqrt{c^3} - 3)$ 29. $(4\sqrt{3})(-\sqrt{9})(\sqrt{27})$ 30. $(3\sqrt{2})(-\sqrt{6})(\sqrt{3})$

31. $(\sqrt{11x})(\sqrt{2x})(4\sqrt{x^3})$ 32. $(\sqrt{2x})(\sqrt{8x})(\sqrt{3})$ 33. $(3\sqrt{5x})^2$

34. $5y(\sqrt{3y})^2$ 35. $-6\sqrt{2\dfrac{4}{9}}$ 36. $4\sqrt{2\dfrac{1}{2}}$

C   37. $\sqrt{6m}(\sqrt{2m} - 3\sqrt{8m^2})$ 38. $2\sqrt{10x^3}(3\sqrt{2x} - 5\sqrt{8x^4})$

39. $(2\sqrt{3y^3})^3$ 40. $(\sqrt{12xy})^3(x\sqrt{5x^2y} + y\sqrt{6xy^2})$

RATIONAL AND IRRATIONAL NUMBERS   **429**

Supplementary Material
Practice Master 66

Suggested Assignments
Minimum
  429/1–33 odd
R 426/*Self-Test 2*
S 425/*P*: 3

Average
  429/1–35 odd
R 426/*Self-Test 2*
S 425/*P*: 5, 6, 8

Maximum
  429/1–35 odd
R 426/*Self-Test 2*
S 425/*P*: 6–9

Additional A Exercises
Express in simplest form.
1. $3\sqrt{5} \cdot \sqrt{5}$ 15
2. $5\sqrt{6} \cdot 2\sqrt{6}$ 60
3. $7\sqrt{2} \cdot 4\sqrt{2}$ 56
4. $3\sqrt{2} \cdot 2\sqrt{7}$ $6\sqrt{14}$
5. $4\sqrt{6} \cdot \sqrt{4}$ $8\sqrt{6}$
6. $3\sqrt{5} \cdot 4\sqrt{8}$ $24\sqrt{10}$

Additional Answers
Written Exercises
25. $-6|a|b$ 26. $-xy^2\sqrt{x}$
27. $5\sqrt{m} + m$ 28. $c^2 - 3\sqrt{c}$
29. -108 30. -18
31. $4x^2\sqrt{22x}$ 32. $4x\sqrt{3}$
33. $45x$ 34. $15y^2$
35. $-2\sqrt{22}$ 36. $2\sqrt{10}$
37. $2m\sqrt{3} - 12m\sqrt{3m}$
38. $12x^2\sqrt{5} - 40x^3\sqrt{5x}$
39. $24y^4\sqrt{3y}$
40. $24x^3y^2\sqrt{15x} + 72x^2y^3\sqrt{2y}$

430

11-8 *Addition and Subtraction of Radicals*

OBJECTIVE To simplify sums and differences of radicals.

You can use the distributive axiom to simplify the sum of $4\sqrt{5}$ and $3\sqrt{5}$ because they have $\sqrt{5}$ as a common factor.

$$4\sqrt{5} + 3\sqrt{5} = (4+3)\sqrt{5} = 7\sqrt{5}$$

On the other hand, terms that have unlike radicands cannot be combined.

$$2\sqrt{6} - 7\sqrt{13} + 3\sqrt{6} = 5\sqrt{6} - 7\sqrt{13}$$

By expressing each radical in simplest form, you can sometimes combine terms in sums and differences of radicals.

EXAMPLE   Simplify $3\sqrt{5} - 2\sqrt{3} + 3\sqrt{20} - \sqrt{12}$.

SOLUTION $3\sqrt{5} - 2\sqrt{3} + 3\sqrt{20} - \sqrt{12} = 3\sqrt{5} - 2\sqrt{3} + 3\sqrt{4\cdot 5} - \sqrt{4\cdot 3}$
$$= 3\sqrt{5} - 2\sqrt{3} + 3(2\sqrt{5}) - 2\sqrt{3}$$
$$= 3\sqrt{5} - 2\sqrt{3} + 6\sqrt{5} - 2\sqrt{3}$$
$$= 9\sqrt{5} - 4\sqrt{3} \quad \textit{Answer}$$

> To simplify sums or differences of square-root radicals:
> 1. Express each radical in simplest form.
> 2. Use the distributive axiom to add or subtract radicals with like radicands.

Oral Exercises

Indicate the terms in each expression that can be expressed with the same radicand. Then state the expression in simplest form.

1. $5\sqrt{2} + 3\sqrt{2}$ **2.** $7\sqrt{3} - 5\sqrt{3}$ **3.** $\sqrt{11} - 8\sqrt{11}$

4. $3\sqrt{5} + 5\sqrt{3} + \sqrt{5}$ **5.** $3\sqrt{11} - 2\sqrt{11} + \sqrt{6}$ **6.** $\sqrt{15} - 3\sqrt{5} + 5\sqrt{3}$

7. $7\sqrt{7} - 4\sqrt{7}$ **8.** $5\sqrt{3} - 4\sqrt{13} + 8\sqrt{13}$ **9.** $7\sqrt{15} - 4\sqrt{15} + 5\sqrt{15}$

10. $\sqrt{8} + \sqrt{2}$ **11.** $\sqrt{50} + \sqrt{2}$ **12.** $\sqrt{12} + \sqrt{3}$

Written Exercises

Simplify.

A   **1.** $5\sqrt{3} - 2\sqrt{3}$ $3\sqrt{3}$ **2.** $7\sqrt{5} + 11\sqrt{5}$ $18\sqrt{5}$ **3.** $-4\sqrt{21} - 7\sqrt{21}$ $-11\sqrt{21}$

    4. $5\sqrt{2} + \sqrt{72}$ $11\sqrt{2}$ **5.** $2\sqrt{75} - \sqrt{3}$ $9\sqrt{3}$ **6.** $-4\sqrt{5} + \sqrt{45}$ $-\sqrt{5}$

7. $3\sqrt{12} - \sqrt{50}$ $6\sqrt{3} - 5\sqrt{2}$ **8.** $\sqrt{81} - \sqrt{36}$ 3   **9.** $\sqrt{32} + 4\sqrt{8}$ $12\sqrt{2}$

10. $-2\sqrt{147} - \sqrt{27}$ $-17\sqrt{3}$ **11.** $\sqrt{125} + \sqrt{405}$ $14\sqrt{5}$ **12.** $\sqrt{144} - \sqrt{54}$ $12 - 3\sqrt{6}$

13. $5\sqrt{17} + 7\sqrt{6} - \sqrt{17}$ $4\sqrt{17} + 7\sqrt{6}$ **14.** $4\sqrt{28} + 2\sqrt{7} - \sqrt{14}$

15. $-3\sqrt{5} + 4\sqrt{180} + 2\sqrt{27}$ $21\sqrt{5} + 6\sqrt{3}$ **16.** $\sqrt{48} - \sqrt{192} + \sqrt{12}$

                                         14. $10\sqrt{7} - \sqrt{14}$ **16.** $-2\sqrt{3}$

Simplify.

SAMPLE $\sqrt{15} - \sqrt{\dfrac{3}{5}} = \sqrt{15} - \dfrac{\sqrt{3}}{\sqrt{5}} = \sqrt{15} - \dfrac{\sqrt{3}}{\sqrt{5}} \cdot \dfrac{\sqrt{5}}{\sqrt{5}}$

$$= \sqrt{15} - \dfrac{\sqrt{15}}{5}$$

$$= \dfrac{5\sqrt{15}}{5} - \dfrac{\sqrt{15}}{5} = \dfrac{4\sqrt{15}}{5}$$

17. $\sqrt{3} - \sqrt{\dfrac{1}{3}}$ $\dfrac{2\sqrt{3}}{3}$ **18.** $\sqrt{21} - \sqrt{\dfrac{5}{7}}$ $\dfrac{7\sqrt{21} - \sqrt{35}}{7}$ **19.** $4\sqrt{32} - \sqrt{\dfrac{2}{9}}$ $\dfrac{47\sqrt{2}}{3}$

20. $\sqrt{\dfrac{5}{11}} - \sqrt{\dfrac{11}{5}}$ $-\dfrac{6\sqrt{55}}{55}$ **21.** $\sqrt{\dfrac{2}{3}} - \sqrt{\dfrac{3}{8}}$ $\dfrac{\sqrt{6}}{12}$ **22.** $5\sqrt{\dfrac{16}{5}} - \sqrt{\dfrac{5}{18}}$ $\dfrac{24\sqrt{5} - \sqrt{10}}{6}$

B 23. $7\sqrt{10} - 4\sqrt{90} + 4\sqrt{\dfrac{1}{10}}$ $-\dfrac{23\sqrt{10}}{5}$ **24.** $11\sqrt{\dfrac{2}{7}} + 5\sqrt{\dfrac{7}{2}} - \sqrt{56}$ $\dfrac{29\sqrt{14}}{14}$

25. $\sqrt{\dfrac{2}{3}} + 6\sqrt{\dfrac{3}{8}} - \dfrac{1}{5}\sqrt{48}$ $\dfrac{55\sqrt{6} - 24\sqrt{3}}{30}$ **26.** $3\sqrt{\dfrac{3}{7}} + \sqrt{\dfrac{7}{3}} + \dfrac{1}{2}\sqrt{84}$ $\dfrac{37\sqrt{21}}{21}$

27. $4\sqrt{2}(\sqrt{6} + 3\sqrt{8})$ $8\sqrt{3} + 48$ **28.** $2\sqrt{3}(5\sqrt{3} - 2\sqrt{6})$ $30 - 12\sqrt{2}$

Simplify. Assume that all variables represent nonnegative real numbers.

C 29. $\sqrt{\dfrac{x^2}{64} + \dfrac{x^2}{36}}$ $\dfrac{5x}{24}$ **30.** $\sqrt{\dfrac{x^2}{9} - \dfrac{x^2}{25}}$ $\dfrac{4x}{15}$ **31.** $\sqrt{\dfrac{x^2}{a^2} + \dfrac{x^2}{b^2}}$ $\dfrac{x}{ab}\sqrt{a^2+b^2}$ **32.** $\sqrt{\dfrac{x}{a}} + \sqrt{\dfrac{a}{x}}$ $\dfrac{(x+a)\sqrt{ax}}{ax}$

Solve each equation.

33. $3x\sqrt{3} + 2\sqrt{15} = 8\sqrt{60} + x\sqrt{3}$ $7\sqrt{5}$ **34.** $a\sqrt{112} + \sqrt{63} = \sqrt{448} - a\sqrt{343}$ $\dfrac{5}{11}$

Just for Fun

An ant is at the foot of a flight of ten steps. Every day it will climb up three steps and climb back down two steps. When will it reach the top?
On the eighth day

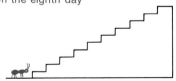

Supplementary Materials

Practice Master 67

Computer Activity 32
Simplifying Radicals
    This activity provides a program that will simplify any given radical. The student is asked to use the program on a number of radicals and is then asked to find the sum or difference of certain radical expressions.

Suggested Assignments

Minimum
    430/1–27 odd
S 425/P: 4, 6
S 429/35

Average
    430/1–29 odd, 33
S 429/37, 39

Maximum
    430/1–33 odd
S 429/37–40

Additional A Exercises

Simplify.

1. $4\sqrt{3} + 5\sqrt{3}$ $9\sqrt{3}$

2. $3\sqrt{7} + 9\sqrt{7}$ $12\sqrt{7}$

3. $11\sqrt{13} - 5\sqrt{13}$ $6\sqrt{13}$

4. $17\sqrt{5} - 14\sqrt{5}$ $3\sqrt{5}$

5. $6\sqrt{3} + 4\sqrt{3} - 2\sqrt{3}$ $8\sqrt{3}$

6. $12\sqrt{7} - 4\sqrt{7} + \sqrt{7}$ $9\sqrt{7}$

Chalkboard Examples

Simplify.

1. $(2 + \sqrt{2})(2 - \sqrt{2})$

$2^2 - (\sqrt{2})^2 = 4 - 2 = 2$

2. $(3 + 5\sqrt{3})^2$

$3^2 + 2(3)(5\sqrt{3}) + (5\sqrt{3})^2 =$

$9 + 30\sqrt{3} + 25(3) =$

$84 + 30\sqrt{3}$

3. $2\sqrt{3}(3\sqrt{3} - 2\sqrt{6})$

$2 \cdot 3(\sqrt{3})^2 - 2 \cdot 2 \cdot \sqrt{3} \cdot \sqrt{6} =$

$6 \cdot 3 - 4\sqrt{18} =$

$18 - 4\sqrt{3^2 \cdot 2} =$

$18 - 12\sqrt{2}$

4. $(7 + 6\sqrt{3})(4 - 2\sqrt{3})$

$28 + 10\sqrt{3} - 12(3) =$

$-8 + 10\sqrt{3}$

5. Rationalize the denomina-

tor of the fraction $\dfrac{3}{2 - \sqrt{3}}$.

$\dfrac{3}{2 - \sqrt{3}} \cdot \dfrac{2 + \sqrt{3}}{2 + \sqrt{3}} =$

$\dfrac{6 + 3\sqrt{3}}{4 - 3} = 6 + 3\sqrt{3}$

Supplementary Material

Practice Master 68

Suggested Assignments

Minimum
432/1–29 odd
S 431/22–28 even

Average
432/1–37 odd
S 431/30–32

Maximum
432/1–41 odd
S 431/30, 32, 34

Additional A Exercises

Express in simplest form.

1. $(6 + \sqrt{5})(6 - \sqrt{5})$ 31

2. $(5 + \sqrt{2})(5 - \sqrt{2})$ 23

(continued)

11-9 *Multiplication of Binomials Containing Radicals*

OBJECTIVE   To multiply binomials containing square-root radicals.

When working with radicals, you sometimes need to use the special methods of multiplying binomials you learned in Chapter 5.

EXAMPLE 1   Simplify $(8 + \sqrt{5})(8 - \sqrt{5})$.

SOLUTION   The pattern is $(a + b)(a - b) = a^2 - b^2$.

$$(8 + \sqrt{5})(8 - \sqrt{5}) = 8^2 - (\sqrt{5})^2$$
$$= 64 - 5 = 59$$

EXAMPLE 2   Simplify $(3 + \sqrt{5})^2$

SOLUTION   The pattern is $(a + b)^2 = a^2 + 2ab + b^2$.

$$(3 + \sqrt{5})^2 = (3)^2 + 2(3)(\sqrt{5}) + (\sqrt{5})^2$$
$$= 9 + 6\sqrt{5} + 5 = 14 + 6\sqrt{5}$$

If b and d are both nonnegative, then the binomials

$$a\sqrt{b} + c\sqrt{d} \quad \text{and} \quad a\sqrt{b} - c\sqrt{d}$$

are called **conjugates** of one another. Conjugates differ only in the sign of one term.

If a, b, c, and d are all integers, then the product

$$(a\sqrt{b} + c\sqrt{d})(a\sqrt{b} - c\sqrt{d})$$

will be an integer (see Example 1 above). Conjugates can be used to rationalize binomial denominators that contain radicals.

EXAMPLE 3   Rationalize the denominator of the fraction $\dfrac{3}{5 - 2\sqrt{7}}$.

SOLUTION $\dfrac{3}{5 - 2\sqrt{7}} = \dfrac{3}{5 - 2\sqrt{7}} \cdot \dfrac{5 + 2\sqrt{7}}{5 + 2\sqrt{7}} = \dfrac{15 + 6\sqrt{7}}{5^2 - (2\sqrt{7})^2}$

$= \dfrac{15 + 6\sqrt{7}}{25 - 28} = \dfrac{15 + 6\sqrt{7}}{-3} = -5 - 2\sqrt{7}$

Written Exercises

Express in simplest form.

A   **1.** $(4 - \sqrt{3})(4 + \sqrt{3})$ 13

3. $(7 + \sqrt{7})(7 - \sqrt{7})$ 42

2. $(\sqrt{2} + 5)(\sqrt{2} - 5)$ −23

4. $(\sqrt{13} - 7)(\sqrt{13} + 7)$ −36

5. $(\sqrt{13} - \sqrt{7})(\sqrt{13} + \sqrt{7})$ 6

7. $(4 + \sqrt{3})^2$ $19 + 8\sqrt{3}$

9. $(\sqrt{3} + 8)^2$ $67 + 16\sqrt{3}$

11. $(4\sqrt{10} + 3)^2$ $169 + 24\sqrt{10}$

13. $3\sqrt{7}(\sqrt{21} + \sqrt{7})$ $21\sqrt{3} + 21$

15. $6\sqrt{3}(5\sqrt{6} - 3\sqrt{10})$ $90\sqrt{2} - 18\sqrt{30}$

6. $(\sqrt{2} - \sqrt{6})(\sqrt{2} + \sqrt{6})$ -4

8. $(2 - \sqrt{5})^2$ $9 - 4\sqrt{5}$

10. $(3\sqrt{2} - 5)^2$ $43 - 30\sqrt{2}$

12. $(\sqrt{7} - \sqrt{3})^2$ $10 - 2\sqrt{21}$

14. $7\sqrt{5}(2\sqrt{10} - 3\sqrt{15})$ $70\sqrt{2} - 105\sqrt{3}$

16. $2\sqrt{6}(5\sqrt{2} - 4\sqrt{14})$ $20\sqrt{3} - 16\sqrt{21}$

B 17. $(4\sqrt{7} - 2)(2\sqrt{7} + 3)$

19. $(4\sqrt{11} - 3\sqrt{5})(2\sqrt{11} - 5\sqrt{5})$

21. $(9\sqrt{7} + 8\sqrt{11})(2\sqrt{7} + 7\sqrt{11})$

18. $(\sqrt{3} + 3\sqrt{5})(\sqrt{3} + 4\sqrt{5})$

20. $(6\sqrt{10} + 2\sqrt{2})(5\sqrt{10} - 5\sqrt{2})$

22. $(2\sqrt{10} - 3\sqrt{5})(3\sqrt{10} + 4\sqrt{5})$

Rationalize the denominator of each fraction.

23. $\dfrac{3}{1 + \sqrt{3}}$ $\dfrac{-3 + 3\sqrt{3}}{2}$

25. $\dfrac{5}{3 + \sqrt{5}}$ $\dfrac{15 - 5\sqrt{5}}{4}$

27. $\dfrac{2 + \sqrt{5}}{\sqrt{3} - 2}$ $-4 - 2\sqrt{3} - \sqrt{15} - 2\sqrt{5}$

29. $\dfrac{6}{3\sqrt{5} - 2}$ $\dfrac{18\sqrt{5} + 12}{41}$

24. $\dfrac{4}{\sqrt{7} - 2}$ $\dfrac{4\sqrt{7} + 8}{3}$

26. $\dfrac{1 + \sqrt{2}}{3 - \sqrt{2}}$ $\dfrac{5 + 4\sqrt{2}}{7}$

28. $\dfrac{\sqrt{3} + 5}{2 + \sqrt{7}}$ $\dfrac{\sqrt{21} + 5\sqrt{7} - 2\sqrt{3} - 10}{3}$

30. $\dfrac{4 + \sqrt{3}}{2\sqrt{2} + 1}$ $\dfrac{8\sqrt{2} - 4 + 2\sqrt{6} - \sqrt{3}}{7}$

If $f(x) = x^2 - 2x + 2$, find these function values.

31. $f(\sqrt{2})$ $4 - 2\sqrt{2}$

32. $f(\sqrt{3} + 1)$ 4

33. $f(1 - \sqrt{7})$ 8

34. $f(3 + \sqrt{5})$ $10 + 4\sqrt{5}$

35. Show that $(1 + \sqrt{2})$ and $(1 - \sqrt{2})$ are roots of the equation $x^2 - 2x - 1 = 0$.

36. Show that $(4 + \sqrt{3})$ and $(4 - \sqrt{3})$ are roots of the equation $x^2 - 8x + 13 = 0$.

37. Show that $\left(\dfrac{1}{2} + \dfrac{\sqrt{3}}{2}\right)$ and $\left(\dfrac{1}{2} - \dfrac{\sqrt{3}}{2}\right)$ are roots of the equation $2x^2 - 2x - 1 = 0$.

C 38. Write an expression in simplest form for the area of a square whose perimeter is $(9\sqrt{2} + 4)$ cm. $\dfrac{89 + 36\sqrt{2}}{8}$ cm²

Simplify each expression, assuming that the value of each variable is nonnegative.

39. $(x - \sqrt{y})(x + \sqrt{y})$ $x^2 - y$

41. $(3m\sqrt{n} - p)(4m\sqrt{n} - 5p)$
$12m^2n - 19mp\sqrt{n} + 5p^2$

40. $(x - 3\sqrt{2})^2$ $x^2 - 6\sqrt{2}x + 18$

42. $\sqrt{\dfrac{a}{b}} - 3\sqrt{\dfrac{b}{a}} + \sqrt{ab}$

3. $(2 + \sqrt{7})(2 - \sqrt{7})$ -3

4. $(3 + \sqrt{6})^2$ $15 + 6\sqrt{6}$

5. $(7 + \sqrt{7})^2$ $56 + 14\sqrt{7}$

6. $(3 + \sqrt{6})(2 + \sqrt{5})$
$6 + 3\sqrt{5} + 2\sqrt{6} + \sqrt{30}$

Additional Answers
Written Exercises

17. $50 + 8\sqrt{7}$

18. $63 + 7\sqrt{15}$

19. $163 - 26\sqrt{55}$

20. $280 - 40\sqrt{5}$

21. $742 + 79\sqrt{77}$ **22.** $-5\sqrt{2}$

42. $\dfrac{(a - 3b + ab)\sqrt{ab}}{ab}$

RATIONAL AND IRRATIONAL NUMBERS   **433**

Chalkboard Examples

Solve.

1. $\sqrt{s} = 8$
   Squaring, $\quad s = 64$
   Check: $\quad \sqrt{64} = 8 \;\checkmark$
   $\therefore$ The solution is 64.

2. $\sqrt{6x - 5} = 7$
   Squaring, $\quad 6x - 5 = 49$
   $\qquad\qquad 6x = 54$
   $\qquad\qquad\; x = 9$
   Check: $\sqrt{6 \cdot 9 - 5} = 7$
   $\qquad\qquad \sqrt{49} = 7 \;\checkmark$
   $\therefore$ The solution is 9.

3. $3\sqrt{2x} = 24$
   $\sqrt{2x} = 8$
   Squaring, $\quad 2x = 64$
   $\qquad\qquad\; x = 32$
   Check: $\;3\sqrt{2(32)} = 24$
   $\qquad\qquad 3 \cdot 8 = 24 \;\checkmark$
   $\therefore$ The solution is 32.

4. $\sqrt{2y^2 - 7} = 5$
   Squaring, $2y^2 - 7 = 25$
   $\qquad\qquad 2y^2 = 32$
   $\qquad\qquad\; y^2 = 16$
   $\qquad\qquad\;\; y = \pm 4$
   Since both roots check, the solutions are 4 and -4.

5. $\sqrt{2t^2 - 49} = t$
   Squaring $2t^2 - 49 = t^2$
   $\qquad\qquad\quad t^2 = 49$
   $\qquad\qquad\quad\; t = \pm 7$
   Since 7 checks but -7 does not, the solution is 7.

6. Three times the square root of a number is 12. Find the number.
   $3\sqrt{x} = 12$
   $\sqrt{x} = 4$
   $x = 16$
   Check: $3\sqrt{16} = 12$
   $\qquad\quad 3 \cdot 4 = 12 \;\checkmark$
   $\therefore$ The number is 16.

11-10 *Simple Radical Equations*

OBJECTIVE To solve simple radical equations.

An equation that has a variable in the radicand is called a **radical equation.** Simple radical equations are solved in Examples 1 and 2.

EXAMPLE 1 Solve $\sqrt{x} = 9$

SOLUTION $\qquad (\sqrt{x})^2 = 81 \longleftarrow$ Square both members.
$\qquad\qquad\qquad x = 81$

$\qquad$ Check: $\sqrt{81} \overset{?}{=} 9$
$\qquad\qquad\qquad\; 9 = 9 \;\checkmark$

$\qquad \therefore$ the solution is 81. ***Answer***

EXAMPLE 2 Solve $\sqrt{3x - 2} = 5$

SOLUTION $\qquad\qquad 3x - 2 = 25 \qquad$ Check: $\sqrt{3(9) - 2} \overset{?}{=} 5$
$\qquad\qquad\qquad\quad 3x = 27 \qquad\qquad\qquad \sqrt{27 - 2} \overset{?}{=} 5$
$\qquad\qquad\qquad\quad\; x = 9 \qquad\qquad\qquad\quad\; \sqrt{25} \overset{?}{=} 5$
$\qquad\qquad\qquad\qquad\qquad\qquad\qquad\qquad\qquad 5 = 5 \;\checkmark$

$\qquad \therefore$ the solution is 9. ***Answer***

When you square both members of an equation, the new equation is not necessarily equivalent to the original equation. Therefore, you must check every apparent root in the original equation to see whether it is, in fact, a root. By the multiplication property of equality, any root of the original equation is also a root of the squared equation. Thus, you are sure to find all roots of the original equation among the roots of the squared equation.

EXAMPLE 3 Solve $\sqrt{5x^2 - 36} - x = 0$

SOLUTION $\qquad \sqrt{5x^2 - 36} - x = 0$
$\qquad\qquad\quad \sqrt{5x^2 - 36} = x \longleftarrow$ Isolate the radical.
$\qquad\qquad\qquad 5x^2 - 36 = x^2$
$\qquad\qquad\qquad\qquad 4x^2 = 36$
$\qquad\qquad\qquad\qquad\; x^2 = 9$
$\qquad\qquad\qquad x = 3 \text{ or } x = -3$

$\qquad$ Check: $\quad \sqrt{5(3)^2 - 36} - 3 \overset{?}{=} 0 \qquad \sqrt{5(-3)^2 - 36} - (-3) \overset{?}{=} 0$
$\qquad\qquad\qquad\qquad \sqrt{9} - 3 \overset{?}{=} 0 \qquad\qquad\qquad \sqrt{9} + 3 \overset{?}{=} 0$
$\qquad\qquad\qquad\qquad\quad\; 0 = 0 \;\checkmark \qquad\qquad\qquad\qquad\; 6 \neq 0$

$\qquad \therefore$ the solution is 3. ***Answer***

434 *CHAPTER 11*

Oral Exercises

Solve.

1. $\sqrt{x} = 3$ 9

2. $\sqrt{y} = 7$ 49

3. $\sqrt{k} = 12$ 144

State the first step in the solution of each equation.

4. $\sqrt{2x} = 9$ $2x = 81$

5. $\sqrt{3x - 8} = 5$ $3x - 8 = 25$

6. $\sqrt{5a - 7} = a$ $5a - 7 = a^2$

Written Exercises

Solve.

A

1. $\sqrt{y} = 20$ 400

2. $\sqrt{x} = 5$ 25

3. $\sqrt{3m} = 9$ 27

4. $\sqrt{4a} = 10$ 25

5. $\sqrt{3r} = \frac{1}{4}$ $\frac{1}{48}$

6. $\sqrt{7x} = \frac{3}{5}$ $\frac{9}{175}$

7. $\sqrt{x} + 5 = 8$ 9

8. $\sqrt{z} - 4 = 7$ 121

9. $\frac{2}{3} + \sqrt{a} = 2$ $\frac{16}{9}$

10. $\sqrt{\frac{a}{3}} = 2$ 12

11. $\sqrt{\frac{x}{4}} = 5$ 100

12. $\sqrt{x + 2} = 5$ 23

13. $\sqrt{z - 7} = 8$ 71

14. $2\sqrt{3b} = 4$ $\frac{4}{3}$

15. $5\sqrt{2c} = 8$ $\frac{32}{25}$

16. $\sqrt{3s} + 4 = 7$ 3

17. $\sqrt{5x} - 3 = 12$ 45

18. $\sqrt{6a} + 9 = 11$ $\frac{2}{3}$

19. $\sqrt{3x + 2} - 1 = 3$ $\frac{14}{3}$

20. $\sqrt{8x - 1} + 2 = 9$ $\frac{25}{4}$

21. $\sqrt{5a - 3} + 8 = 11$

22. $\sqrt{\frac{5b}{4}} - 2 = 8$ 80

23. $\sqrt{\frac{9a}{7}} + 3 = 10$ $\frac{343}{9}$

24. $\sqrt{\frac{5m}{6}} - 2 = 11$

B

25. $\sqrt{\frac{3x + 1}{4}} = 5$ 33

26. $\sqrt{\frac{4t - 3}{5}} = 5$ 32

27. $\sqrt{\frac{3y - 7}{11}} = 4$ 61

28. $\sqrt{s} = 5\sqrt{3}$ 75

29. $7\sqrt{t} = 14\sqrt{5}$ 20

30. $8\sqrt{x} = 3\sqrt{6}$ $\frac{27}{32}$

31. $\sqrt{3a^2 - 4} = 11 \left\{ \pm\frac{5\sqrt{15}}{3} \right\}$

32. $4\sqrt{2r^2 - 20} = 8 \left\{ \pm 2\sqrt{3} \right\}$

33. $3\sqrt{5x^2 - 4} = 27$

34. $\sqrt{x^2 + 1} = 1 - x$ 0

35. $\sqrt{3a^2 - 32} = a$ 4

36. $\sqrt{7b^2 + 14} = 3b$

C

37. $\sqrt{a^2 + 3a} = 2$ $\{1, -4\}$

38. $\sqrt{10a^2 - 16a} = 4a$ 0

39. $\sqrt{s} + 1 = \sqrt{4s}$ 1

Problems

Solve.

A

1. Twice the square root of a number is 18. Find the number. 81

2. The square root of twice a number is 18. Find the number. 162

3. The square root of one fifth of a number is 4. Find the number. 80

4. One fifth of the square root of a number is 4. Find the number. 400

5. When 5 is subtracted from 3 times a number, the square root of the result is 8. Find the number. 23

RATIONAL AND IRRATIONAL NUMBERS **435**

Supplementary Materials

Practice Master 69

Progress Test 41

Computer Activity 33
Solving Radical Equations
The computer may be used to solve radical equations of the form $\sqrt{AX + B} = C$. A program that solves such equations is provided and the student is then asked to use it to solve a number of radical equations.

Suggested Assignments

Minimum

Day 1: 435/1–33 odd
    S 433/31, 33
Day 2: 435/34, 35, P: 1, 3,
    5, 6
    R 437/Self-Test 3

Average

Day 1: 435/1–37 odd
    S 433/39, 40
Day 2: 435/P: 1, 2, 5–7
    R 437/Self-Test 3
    S 421/P: 9

Maximum

Day 1: 435/1–37 odd
    S 433/38, 40, 42
Day 2: 435/34, 38, 39,
    P: 1–7, 9
    R 437/Self-Test 3

Extra Practice Problems
    p. 523

Additional A Exercises

Solve.

1. $\sqrt{x} = 9$ 81

2. $\sqrt{a} = 13$ 169

3. $\sqrt{2c} = 10$ 50

4. $\sqrt{5a} = 25$ 125

5. $\sqrt{y} + 3 = 11$ 64

6. $\sqrt{x} - 4 = 12$ 256

Additional Answers
Written Exercises

21. $\frac{12}{5}$

24. $\frac{1014}{5}$

33. $\{\sqrt{17}, -\sqrt{17}\}$

36. $\sqrt{7}$

6. Find the length of the hypotenuse of a right triangle whose shorter sides are $(\sqrt{6}+2)$ m and $(\sqrt{6}-2)$ m long. $2\sqrt{5}$ m

B 7. The diameter of a circle is related to the area in the formula $d = \sqrt{\dfrac{4A}{\pi}}$. Find the area of the circle whose diameter is 20 cm. Express your answer in terms of π. 100π cm²

8. The current I that flows through an electrical appliance is determined by

$$I = \sqrt{\frac{P}{R}},$$

where P is the power required and R is the resistance of the appliance. To use this formula, express the current in amperes (A), the power in watts (W), and the resistance in ohms (Ω). If an electric hair dryer has a resistance of 60 Ω and draws 4.5 A of current, how much power does it use? 1215 W

9. The geometric mean of two numbers is the positive square root of their product. Find two consecutive, positive even integers whose geometric mean is $12\sqrt{21}$. 54, 56

10. The period of a pendulum (T) is the amount of time in seconds it takes the pendulum to make a complete swing back and forth. The period is determined by the formula

$$T = 2\pi\sqrt{\frac{l}{9.8}}$$

where l is the length of the pendulum in meters. Find the length of a pendulum with a period of 5 s. Express your answer to the nearest tenth. (Use $\pi \approx 3.14$.) 6.2 m

Calculator Key-In _____

Use a calculator to approximate the value of each expression to the nearest thousandth. (Recall that it is *not* necessary to rationalize the denominator first.)

1. $\dfrac{2}{1+\sqrt{5}}$ 0.618

2. $\dfrac{5}{\sqrt{6}-1}$ 3.449

3. $\dfrac{\sqrt{7}}{\sqrt{10}+3}$ 0.429

4. $\dfrac{2+\sqrt{11}}{2\sqrt{3}}$ 1.535

5. $\dfrac{2\sqrt{10}}{\sqrt{13}}$ 1.754

6. $\dfrac{\sqrt{2}+\sqrt{13}}{\sqrt{7}+\sqrt{5}}$ 1.028

7. $\dfrac{\sqrt{7}+\sqrt{11}}{\sqrt{14}-\sqrt{6}}$ 4.614

8. $\dfrac{3\sqrt{8}+\sqrt{2}}{5\sqrt{2}-\sqrt{3}}$ 1.854

Self-Test 3

VOCABULARY   simplest form of a radical (p. 428)
conjugate (p. 432)
radical equation (p. 434)

rationalizing the denominator (p. 428)

Express in simplest form.

1. $5\sqrt{80}$

2. $\sqrt{32x^2y^4}$ Obj. 11-7, p. 428

3. $3\sqrt{5} - \sqrt{3} + 2\sqrt{5}$

4. $\sqrt{50} - 3\sqrt{2}$ Obj. 11-8, p. 430

5. $(2 + \sqrt{5})^2$

6. $(4 - \sqrt{7})(4 + \sqrt{7})$ Obj. 11-9, p. 432

Rationalize the denominator.

7. $\dfrac{3}{2 - \sqrt{3}}$

8. $\dfrac{\sqrt{5}}{4 + \sqrt{5}}$

Solve.

9. $\sqrt{x} - 2 = 3$

10. $\sqrt{\dfrac{x+1}{2}} = 5$ Obj. 11-10, p. 434

Check your answers with those at the back of the book.

Chapter Summary

1. A rational number can be expressed as a fraction in simplest form, $\dfrac{a}{b}$, where a and b are integers and $b > 0$. Rational numbers in fractional form can be expressed as either terminating or repeating decimals by dividing.

2. Irrational numbers are represented by nonterminating, nonrepeating decimals which may be rounded to a convenient number of places for use in computation. These numbers cannot be represented in fractional form.

3. Square roots may be rational or irrational. Irrational square roots may be approximated using a table of square roots or a calculator.

4. Some quadratic equations can be solved using the property of square roots of equal numbers (page 419).

5. Many problems involving right triangles can be solved using the Pythagorean theorem:
$$a^2 + b^2 = c^2$$

6. Radical expressions can be added, subtracted, multiplied, and divided. The product and quotient properties of square roots (pages 412, 413) are useful in simplifying expressions involving radicals. Divisions can often be simplified by rationalizing the denominator.

RATIONAL AND IRRATIONAL NUMBERS   **437**

Chapter Review

1. Find the rational number halfway between $\frac{5}{8}$ and $\frac{3}{4}$.   11-1

   a. $\frac{1}{2}$ (b.) $\frac{11}{16}$ c. $\frac{2}{3}$ d. $\frac{11}{8}$

2. Compare $\frac{7}{12}$ and $\frac{11}{18}$.

   a. $\frac{7}{12} > \frac{11}{18}$ (b.) $\frac{11}{18} > \frac{7}{12}$ c. $\frac{7}{12} = \frac{11}{18}$

3. Express $\frac{47}{99}$ as a decimal.   11-2

   a. 0.47 b. $0.\overline{474}$ (c.) $0.\overline{47}$ d. $0.0\overline{47}$

4. Express 0.035 as a fraction in simplest form.

   a. $\frac{7}{2000}$ b. $\frac{35}{1000}$ c. $\frac{3.5}{100}$ (d.) $\frac{7}{200}$

5. Find $\sqrt{2.89}$.   11-3

   (a.) 1.7 b. 0.17 c. 17 d. 0.017

6. Find $\sqrt{\dfrac{529}{900}}$.

   a. $\frac{29}{30}$ (b.) $\frac{23}{30}$ c. $\frac{17}{30}$ d. $\frac{7}{9}$

7. Approximate $\sqrt{3400}$ to the nearest hundredth using the Table of   11-4
   Square Roots on page 526.

   a. 538.10 b. 5.83 c. 5.831 (d.) 58.31

8. Simplify $\sqrt{121a^3b^4c^5}$.   11-5

   (a.) $11|a|b^2c^2\sqrt{ac}$ b. $11a^2b^2c^2$ c. $11|a|b^2c^2\sqrt{11ac}$

9. Solve $9x^2 = 144$.

   a. $\{4\}$ b. $\left\{\frac{1}{4}, -\frac{1}{4}\right\}$ c. $\{16\}$ (d.) $\{4, -4\}$

10. The shorter sides of a right triangle are 10 cm and 24 cm long. Find   11-6
    the length of the hypotenuse.

    a. 25 cm   (b.) 26 cm   c. 34 cm   d. 676 cm

11. Can a right triangle have sides 8 m, 15 m, and 17 m long?

    (a.) yes   b. no

12. Simplify $\sqrt{96x^4y^6}$.   11-7

    a. $16x^2|y^3|\sqrt{6}$ b. $x^2|y^3|\sqrt{96}$ (c.) $4x^2|y^3|\sqrt{6}$

13. Simplify $4\sqrt{2} + \sqrt{32} - \sqrt{16}$.   11-8

    a. $4\sqrt{2} + \sqrt{32} - 4$ (b.) $8\sqrt{2} - 4$ c. $9\sqrt{2} - 4$ d. $4\sqrt{2}$

438   *CHAPTER 11*

14. Multiply $(2 - \sqrt{5})(2 + \sqrt{5})$.   11-9

   (a.) -1 **b.** $4 - \sqrt{5}$ **c.** $4 - 4\sqrt{5}$ **d.** -21

15. Rationalize the denominator of $\dfrac{\sqrt{7}}{3 - \sqrt{3}}$.

   (a.) $\dfrac{3\sqrt{7} + \sqrt{21}}{6}$ **b.** $\dfrac{2\sqrt{21}}{3}$ **c.** $2\sqrt{7}$ **d.** $\sqrt{7} + \sqrt{21}$

16. Solve $\sqrt{\dfrac{x - 4}{9}} = 7$.   11-10

   a. 5   (b.) 445   **c.** 437   **d.** 67

Chapter Test

Alternate Test p. T22

1. Find the rational number halfway between $\dfrac{5}{6}$ and $\dfrac{7}{8}$. $\frac{41}{48}$ 11-1

2. Arrange $\dfrac{7}{12}, \dfrac{9}{24}, \dfrac{19}{48}, \dfrac{2}{3}$ in order from least to greatest. $\frac{9}{24}, \frac{19}{48}, \frac{7}{12}, \frac{2}{3}$

3. Express $\dfrac{11}{12}$ as a decimal. $0.91\overline{6}$ 11-2

4. Express $3.0\overline{4}$ as a fraction in simplest form. $\frac{137}{45}$

5. Find the indicated square roots.   11-3

   a. $\sqrt{\dfrac{729}{1764}}$ $\frac{9}{14}$ **b.** $\sqrt{0.0025}$ 0.05

6. Use the Table of Square Roots on page 526 to approximate $\sqrt{8700}$ to the nearest tenth. 93.3 11-4

7. Simplify $\sqrt{625r^4 s^3 t^2}$. $25r^2 |st| \sqrt{s}$ **8.** Solve $49x^2 = 1225$. $\{5, -5\}$ 11-5

9. In a right triangle, the hypotenuse is 17 cm long, and one of the shorter sides is 6 cm long. Find the length of the other side to the nearest hundredth. 15.91 cm   11-6

10. Is a triangle with sides 9 units, 16 units, and 25 units long a right triangle?   No

Express in simplest form.

11. $3\sqrt{180}$ $18\sqrt{5}$ **12.** $\sqrt{108x^4 y^3}$ $6x^2 |y| \sqrt{3y}$ 11-7

13. $6\sqrt{2} + \sqrt{32} - \sqrt{128}$ $2\sqrt{2}$ **14.** $\sqrt{20} - \sqrt{64} + \sqrt{125}$ $-8 + 7\sqrt{5}$ 11-8

15. $(4 + \sqrt{3})^2$ $19 + 8\sqrt{3}$ **16.** $(6 - \sqrt{7})(6 + \sqrt{7})$ 29 11-9

17. Rationalize the denominator of $\dfrac{\sqrt{6}}{3 - \sqrt{5}}$. $\frac{3\sqrt{6} + \sqrt{30}}{4}$

18. Solve $\sqrt{\dfrac{x + 12}{3}} = 5$. 63 11-10

RATIONAL AND IRRATIONAL NUMBERS   **439**

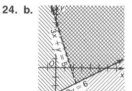
Cumulative Review (Chapters 1-11)

Factor completely.

1. $h^4 - 81r^8$

2. $80p + 110p^2 - 15p^3$

3. $12z^2 - 47z + 45$

Simplify. In Exercise 14, divide.

4. $-[1 - 2q - (-3q)]$

5. $x^2y(x^3y^2 - xy^2 + 9x)$

6. $(12a + 5b)(3a - 8b)$

7. $(5\sqrt{2} - 2\sqrt{3})^2$

8. $(1.2a^3 - 6a) \div 0.2a$

9. $(-5rt^5)^3 \div (-10r^2t)^2$

10. $\sqrt{9.61} \cdot \sqrt{576}$

11. $3(\sqrt{1210} - 3\sqrt{40})$

12. $-6\sqrt{24} \div \sqrt{15}$

13. $\dfrac{10r^2 + 48r - 72}{20r^3 - 39r^2 + 18r}$

14. $\dfrac{15x^3 - 4x^2 + 1}{3x + 1}$

15. $\dfrac{6b}{25} - \dfrac{4b}{5} + \dfrac{3b}{50}$

16. $\dfrac{3n^4 - n^3}{n^5 - 3n^4} \div \dfrac{9n^2 - 1}{3n^2 + n}$

17. $\dfrac{3}{g - 2} + \dfrac{4}{4g + 1}$

18. $\dfrac{9 - c^2}{2c + 6} \cdot \dfrac{c^2 + 6c + 8}{c^2 + c - 12}$

19. If x and y are negative integers, graph the solution set of:
   a. $3x + 2y = -17$ b. $y > -2x - 7$ c. $y - |x| = -5$

20. Find an equation of the line:
   a. with slope 0 and containing $(-8, -2)$ $y = -2$
   b. passing through $(-7, 4)$ and $(2, -5)$ $y = -x - 3$

21. If $f: x \to x^2 + 3x - 4$, find $f(-5)$ and $f(\sqrt{2} + 1)$. Graph the function f. $f(-5) = 6$, $f(\sqrt{2} + 1) = 2 + 5\sqrt{2}$

22. Graph the solution set of the disjunction "$-2x < -8$ or $x + 1 > 7$."

23. Write $-1.4\overline{3}$ as a fraction in simplest form. $-\dfrac{43}{30}$

24. Solve graphically: a. $x + y = 7$ $2x - 3y = 4$ $(5, 2)$ b. $x - 2y \le 6$ $3x + y > 5$

Solve each equation, inequality, or system.

25. $1.4(m \cdot 3) = 3m + 2\tfrac{5}{3}$

26. $-402 = |-3|t - 134$

27. 42% of $x = 10.5$ 25

28. $7k + 10 = 6k^2$ $\{2, -\tfrac{5}{6}\}$

29. $7d^2 = 756$ $\{6\sqrt{3}, -6\sqrt{3}\}$

30. $\sqrt{3 - 2x} = x$ 1

31. $-9 \le 4y + 3 < 1$

32. $(z + 5)(z + 4) = 2$

33. $7(2w - 3) \ge 11w$

34. $\dfrac{3v}{2v - 1} + \dfrac{v - 1}{3} = 3$

35. $\dfrac{b - 5}{2} < \dfrac{b - 6}{3}$

36. $\dfrac{9s^2 - 16}{3s^2 - 4s} = 5$

37. $4x + 7y = 7$ $(7, -3)$ $-x = 3y + 2$

38. $9x - 2y = 21$ $(5, 12)$ $3x + 2y = 39$

39. $5x + 4y = 1$ $4x + 6y = 5$ $(-1, \tfrac{3}{2})$

40. Evaluate $-\sqrt{179}$ to the nearest hundredth. -13.38

41. Find the length of the diagonal of a rectangle whose dimensions are 14 m by 8 m. (Approximate the square root to the nearest hundredth.) 16.12 m

Maintaining Skills

Solve each system.

SAMPLE 1 (Substitution Method)

$$5x - y = 7 \longrightarrow y = 5x - 7$$
$$7x + 2y = 3$$

$$7x + 2(5x - 7) = 3$$
$$7x + 10x - 14 = 3$$
$$17x = 17$$
$$x = 1$$

$$y = 5(1) - 7 = -2$$

$\therefore$ the solution is $(1, -2)$. ***Answer***

SAMPLE 2 (Multiplication with addition-or-subtraction method)

$$7x - 3y = -6 \longrightarrow \times 4$$
$$3x - 4y = 11 \longrightarrow \times 3$$

$$28x - 12y = -24$$
Subtract: $\underline{\quad 9x - 12y = \quad 33 \quad}$
$$19x \qquad = -57; \; x = -3$$

Substitute -3 for x in the first equation:
$$7(-3) - 3y = -6; \; -21 - 3y = -6; \; -3y = 15; \; y = -5$$

$\therefore$ the solution is $(-3, -5)$. ***Answer***

1. $-3x + 2y = 17$ $(-7, -2)$
$\quad -3x + 5y = 11$

2. $x = 4y$ $(-8, -2)$
$\quad 2x - 9y = 2$

3. $4a - b = -7$
$\quad 5a + 2b = 14$

4. $2r + 9s = 1$ $(5, -1)$
$\quad 4r + 3s = 17$

5. $8m - 5n = -14$ $(2, 6)$
$\quad 7m - 5n = -16$

6. $4 = 5x - 7y$
$\quad 21y = 15x - 12$

7. $\quad 18 = 12x - 11y$ $(-4, -6)$
$\quad -32 = 5x + 2y$

8. $3c + 2d = -6$ $(-4, 3)$
$\quad c + 3d = 5$

9. $2v - 5w = 0$
$\quad w = 2v$

10. $\quad 14x - 3y = 5$ $(1, 3)$
$\quad -14x + 15y = 31$

11. $3 = 16c + 2d$ $\left(\frac{1}{4}, -\frac{1}{2}\right)$
$\quad 2 = 14c + 3d$

12. $5j + 6k = 0$
$\quad 7j + 6k = -24$

13. $9x - 3y = 12$
$\quad 3x + 4 = y$ No root

14. $10r + 7s = 87$ $(15, -9)$
$\quad 9r + 5s = 90$

15. $-66 = 4c - 7d$
$\quad 12 = 13c + 15d$

16. $-7 = 4a - 2b$ $\left(-\frac{1}{2}, \frac{5}{2}\right)$
$\quad 1 = 3a + b$

17. $5x + 3y = -36$ $\left(-7, -\frac{1}{3}\right)$
$\quad 5x - 12y = -31$

18. $4s - 20t = 0$
$\quad 3s - 15t = 0$

19. $\frac{1}{3}(5x - y) = 16$ $(10, 2)$

$\quad 5x + 7y = 64$

20. $1 - \frac{2}{5}n = m$ $(3, -5)$

$\quad \frac{m}{6} - \frac{n}{10} = 1$

21. $\frac{3x}{4} + \frac{5y}{6} = 12$

$\quad -\frac{7x}{8} + \frac{y}{2} = -14$

About the Photo

The Verrazano-Narrows Bridge, connecting Staten Island and Brooklyn in New York City, is the longest suspension bridge in the United States. Like all bridges, it must be strong enough to support the weight of the roadway and the traffic and to endure the effects of temperature changes, snow accumulation, wind, and earthquakes.

A suspension bridge can have a longer main span (the section between the towers) than other types of bridges because the steel cables supporting the roadbed are stronger than structural steel. The 0.9 m diameter cables on the Verrazano-Narrows bridge are made from 229,300 km of 5 mm diameter wire. Here are some additional facts: The steel in the bridge has a mass of 144,000 t (metric tons). The main span is 1298 m long and the tops of the towers are 207 m above mean high water. Because of the Earth's natural curvature, the distance between the tops of the towers is 4 cm greater than the distance between their bases.

Each curved supporting cable of the Verrazano-Narrows Bridge is shaped like part of a parabola. When a cable carries no load, however, the curve it resembles is a catenary.

442

12

QUADRATIC FUNCTIONS

Teaching References

Lesson Commentary,
    pp. T107–T109

Assignment Guide,
    pp. T59–T60

Supplementary Materials
    Practice Masters 70–76

    Progress Tests 43–47

    Computer Activities
    34 *Quadratic Formula*
    35 *Partial Fractions*
    36 *Sum and Product of*
       Two Numbers

Extra Practice, pp. 512–513,
    523–524

Alternate Test and Review,
    pp. T23, T30–T31

QUADRATIC EQUATIONS

12-1 *Solving Quadratic Equations with Perfect Squares*

OBJECTIVE   To solve quadratic equations using perfect squares.

In Chapter 5 you learned how to solve certain quadratic equations by factoring. In Chapter 11 you learned how to solve quadratic equations that are in the form $x^2 = k$. In this chapter you will learn how to determine whether a quadratic equation has no roots, one root, or two roots. You will also learn how to find all the equation's roots.

    The property of square roots of equal numbers enables you to analyze equations of the form $x^2 = k$ as follows:

If $k > 0$, then $x^2 = k$ has two real-number roots: $\begin{array}{l} x = \sqrt{k} \\ x = -\sqrt{k} \end{array}$

If $k = 0$, then $x^2 = k$ has one real-number root: $x = 0$

If $k < 0$, then $x^2 = k$ has no real-number solution.

    The property of square roots of equal numbers enables you to solve other equations as well.

443

Solve.

1. $(x - 3)^2 = 121$
$x - 3 = \pm 11$
$x = 3 \pm 11$
$\{-8, 14\}$

2. $6t^2 - 100 = 0$
$6t^2 = 100$
$t^2 = \dfrac{50}{3}$
$t = \pm\dfrac{5\sqrt{2}}{\sqrt{3}}$
$\left\{\dfrac{5\sqrt{6}}{3}, -\dfrac{5\sqrt{6}}{3}\right\}$

3. $2(d + 5)^2 - 1 = 9$
$2(d + 5)^2 = 10$
$(d + 5)^2 = 5$
$d + 5 = \pm\sqrt{5}$
$d = -5 \pm \sqrt{5}$
$\{-5 + \sqrt{5}, -5 - \sqrt{5}\}$

4. $3(x + 4)^2 + 1 = 0$
$3(x + 4)^2 = -1$
$(x + 4)^2 = -\dfrac{1}{3}$
$\varnothing$

5. $x^2 - 4x + 4 = 49$
$(x - 2)^2 = 49$
$x - 2 = \pm 7$
$x = 2 \pm 7$
$\{-5, 9\}$

6. $x^2 + 16x + 64 = 200$
$(x + 8)^2 = 200$
$x + 8 = \pm 10\sqrt{2}$
$x = -8 \pm 10\sqrt{2}$
$\{-8 + 10\sqrt{2}, -8 - 10\sqrt{2}\}$

EXAMPLE 1 Solve $(x - 1)^2 = 36$.

SOLUTION

$(x - 1)^2 = 36$ 　　　 *Check:* $(-5 - 1)^2 \overset{?}{=} 36$ 　　　 $(7 - 1)^2 \overset{?}{=} 36$
$x - 1 = \pm 6$ 　　　　　　　　 $(-6)^2 \overset{?}{=} 36$ 　　　　　　　 $6^2 \overset{?}{=} 36$
$x = 1 \pm 6$ 　　　　　　　　　 $36 = 36$ ✓ 　　　　　　 $36 = 36$ ✓
$x = -5$ or $x = 7$

$\therefore$ the solution set is $\{-5, 7\}$. **Answer**

An expression such as $(x - 1)^2$, x^2, or $(4x + 1)^2$ is called a **perfect square.** Whenever an equation can be expressed in the form

$$\text{perfect square} = k \ (k \ge 0)$$

you can solve it. (You may find it helpful to reread Section 5-6 about squaring binomials.)

EXAMPLE 2 Solve: **a.** $2(x - 1)^2 = 34$ 　　　　**b.** $y^2 + 6y + 9 = 81$

SOLUTION

a. $2(x - 1)^2 = 34$ 　　　　　　**b.** $y^2 + 6y + 9 = 81$
$(x - 1)^2 = 17$ 　　　　　　　　　　$(y + 3)^2 = 81$
$x - 1 = \pm\sqrt{17}$ 　　　　　　　　$y + 3 = \pm\sqrt{81}$
$x = 1 \pm \sqrt{17}$ 　　　　　　　　　$y = -3 \pm 9$

The check is left to you. 　　　　　The check is left to you.

$\therefore$ the solution set is 　　　　　$\therefore$ the solution set is
$\{1 - \sqrt{17}, 1 + \sqrt{17}\}$. **Answer** 　　　$\{-12, 6\}$. **Answer**

The perfect squares occurring in Example 2 are $(x - 1)^2$ and $(y + 3)^2$. Note that Example 2(b) could have been solved by factoring.

An equation that has a negative number as one member and a perfect square as the other member has no real-number solutions. The reason is that the square of any real number is a nonnegative real number.

EXAMPLE 3 Solve $2(4x + 3)^2 + 9 = 1$

SOLUTION

$2(4x + 3)^2 + 9 = 1$
$2(4x + 3)^2 = -8$
$(4x + 3)^2 = -4$

$\therefore$ there is no real-number solution. **Answer**

Oral Exercises

Rewrite each trinomial as the square of a binomial.

SAMPLE $x^2 + 8x + 16 = (x + 4)^2$

1. $x^2 + 10x + 25$ $(x + 5)^2$ 　　　2. $x^2 + 6x + 9$ $(x + 3)^2$ 　　　3. $x^2 - 14x + 49$ $(x - 7)^2$

4. $x^2 + 22x + 121$ $(x + 11)^2$ 　　　5. $x^2 - 4x + 4$ $(x - 2)^2$ 　　　6. $x^2 - 18x + 81$ $(x - 9)^2$

444　　CHAPTER 12

Solve.

7. $y^2 = \frac{1}{49}$ $\left\{\frac{1}{7}, -\frac{1}{7}\right\}$

8. $4r^2 = 100$ $\{5, -5\}$

9. $4m^2 - 25 = 0$
$\left\{\frac{5}{2}, -\frac{5}{2}\right\}$

Written Exercises

Solve. Express irrational solutions in simplest radical form. If the equation has no solution, write "no solution."

A **1.** $t^2 = 100$ $\{\pm 10\}$

2. $x^2 = \frac{25}{49}$ $\left\{\pm\frac{5}{7}\right\}$

3. $y^2 = \frac{100}{121}$ $\left\{\pm\frac{10}{11}\right\}$

4. $b^2 = -1$ No sol.

5. $2x^2 = 162$ $\{\pm 9\}$

6. $4r^2 = 60$ $\{\pm\sqrt{15}\}$

7. $6x^2 = 54$ $\{\pm 3\}$

8. $x^2 - 28 = 0$ $\{\pm 2\sqrt{7}\}$

9. $x^2 + 28 = 0$ No sol.

10. $q^2 - 45 = 0$ $\{\pm 3\sqrt{5}\}$

11. $7x^2 - 14 = 0$ $\{\pm\sqrt{2}\}$

12. $6m^2 - 36 = 0$ $\{\pm\sqrt{6}\}$

13. $3y^2 - 8 = 4$ $\{\pm 2\}$

14. $2t^2 - 5 = -3$ $\{\pm 1\}$

15. $2z^2 - 15 = -1$

16. $5x^2 + 1 = 16$ $\{\pm\sqrt{3}\}$

17. $3y^2 + 7 = 1$ No sol.

18. $(x + 2)^2 = 4$

19. $(x - 1)^2 = 9$ $\{4, -2\}$

20. $(x - 3)^2 = 7$ $\{3 \pm \sqrt{7}\}$

21. $(x + 4)^2 = 6$

22. $(y - 2)^2 = 8$ $\{2 \pm 2\sqrt{2}\}$

23. $(m + 3)^2 = 27$

24. $2(m - 1)^2 = 6$

25. $3(m - 5)^2 = 15$ $\{5 \pm \sqrt{5}\}$

26. $5(r + 4)^2 = 30$

27. $4(t + 2)^2 = 40$

28. $(2z - 1)^2 = 49$ $\{4, -3\}$

29. $3(5z + 1)^2 = 48$ $\left\{\frac{3}{5}, -1\right\}$

30. $2(3z - 2)^2 = 18$

B **31.** $y^2 - 2y + 1 = 4$ $\{3, -1\}$

32. $r^2 + 10r + 25 = 81$

33. $t^2 + 12t + 36 = 49$

34. $m^2 - 16m + 64 = 36$

35. $\frac{1}{2}x^2 - \frac{2}{9} = 0$ $\left\{\pm\frac{2}{3}\right\}$

36. $\frac{1}{2}y^2 - \frac{8}{25} = 0$

37. $\frac{1}{3}t^2 - 3 = \frac{2}{3}$ $\{\pm\sqrt{11}\}$

38. $\frac{1}{5}y^2 - 2 = \frac{3}{5}$ $\{\pm\sqrt{13}\}$

39. $1.21x^2 + 3 = 3.49$

40. $0.36y^2 - 1 = 0.69$ $\left\{\pm\frac{13}{6}\right\}$

41. $0.81m^2 - 0.3 = 0.19$ $\left\{\pm\frac{7}{9}\right\}$

42. $7(y - 3)^2 = \frac{2}{7}$

43. $3(x + 4)^2 = \frac{1}{27}$ $\left\{-\frac{37}{9}, -\frac{35}{9}\right\}$

44. $\left(y - \frac{1}{3}\right)^2 = \frac{1}{3}$ $\left\{\frac{1 \pm \sqrt{3}}{3}\right\}$

45. $\left(t - \frac{3}{5}\right)^2 = \frac{2}{5}$

Solve each equation by factoring.

46. $6m^3 - 24m = 0$ $\{0, \pm 2\}$

47. $3z^3 - 27z = 0$ $\{0, \pm 3\}$

48. $\frac{1}{6}t^3 - 6t = 0$
$\{0, \pm 6\}$

49. $5y - \frac{1}{5}y^3 = 0$ $\{0, \pm 5\}$

50. $5r^3 = 125r$ $\{0, \pm 5\}$

51. $7x^3 = 343x$
$\{0, \pm 7\}$

Solve.

C **52.** $5(3x - 2)^2 = 20$ $\left\{\frac{4}{3}, 0\right\}$

53. $3(2x + 5)^2 = 27$ $\{-1, -4\}$

54. $4(7x - 4)^2 + 1 = 9$
$\left\{\frac{4 \pm \sqrt{2}}{7}\right\}$

55. $2(8x + 3)^2 + 7 = 1$ No sol.

56. $x^2 + 2x\sqrt{5} + 5 = 0$ $-\sqrt{5}$

57. $y^2 + 2y\sqrt{7} + 7 = 2$
$\{-\sqrt{7} \pm \sqrt{2}\}$

58. How many real solutions are there to the equation $a(x - b)^2 = c$ if:

    a. $a > 0$ and $c > 0$? Two

    b. $a > 0$ and $c < 0$? None

    c. $a < 0$ and $c > 0$? None

    d. $a > 0$ and $c = 0$? One

QUADRATIC FUNCTIONS **445**

Average
Day 1: 445/1–45 odd
Day 2: 445/47–57 odd
    448/1–11 odd

Maximum
Day 1: 445/1–51 odd
Day 2: 445/52–58
    448/1–17 odd

NOTE: Day 2 for both levels
finishes Sec. 12-1 and
starts Sec. 12-2.

Additional A Exercises

Solve. If the equation has no solution, write "no solution."

1. $x^2 = 81$ $\{9, -9\}$

2. $y^2 = 169$ $\{13, -13\}$

3. $a^2 = \frac{16}{49}$ $\left\{\frac{4}{7}, -\frac{4}{7}\right\}$

4. $c^2 = -64$ no solution

5. $z^2 - 36 = 0$ $\{6, -6\}$

6. $b^2 - \frac{121}{400} = 0$ $\left\{\frac{11}{20}, -\frac{11}{20}\right\}$

Additional Answers
Written Exercises

15. $\{\pm\sqrt{7}\}$ **18.** $\{0, -4\}$

21. $\{-4 \pm \sqrt{6}\}$

23. $\{-3 \pm 3\sqrt{3}\}$

24. $\{1 \pm \sqrt{3}\}$

26. $\{-4 \pm \sqrt{6}\}$

27. $\{-2 \pm \sqrt{10}\}$ **30.** $\left\{\frac{5}{3}, -\frac{1}{3}\right\}$

32. $\{4, -14\}$ **33.** $\{1, -13\}$

34. $\{2, 14\}$ **36.** $\left\{\pm\frac{4}{5}\right\}$

39. $\left\{\pm\frac{7}{11}\right\}$ **42.** $\left\{3 \pm \frac{\sqrt{2}}{7}\right\}$

45. $\left\{\frac{3 \pm \sqrt{10}}{5}\right\}$

12-2 *Completing the Square*

OBJECTIVE To "complete the square" and to use the result to solve quadratic equations.

In the previous section you learned that it is always possible to solve a quadratic equation that has the form:

$$\text{perfect square} = k \quad (k \geq 0)$$

If a quadratic equation does not have this form, it may be possible to transform it into one which does by a method called **completing the square.**

Study the perfect squares shown at the right. The main idea behind completing the square is shown.

$$(x + 3)^2 = x^2 \underline{+ 6x} + 9$$
$$\left(\dfrac{6}{2}\right)^2 = 9$$

Notice that in each case the coefficient of x^2 is one, and the constant term is the square of half the coefficient of x. This observation leads to the method described below, which you may use to solve certain quadratic equations.

$$(x - 4)^2 = x^2 \underline{- 8x} + 16$$
$$\left(-\dfrac{8}{2}\right)^2 = 16$$

$$(x + a)^2 = x^2 \underline{+ 2ax} + a^2$$
$$\left(\dfrac{2a}{2}\right)^2 = a^2$$

METHOD OF COMPLETING THE SQUARE

For $x^2 + bx + \underline{\ ?\ }$:
1. Find half the coefficient of x.
2. Square the result of Step 1.
3. Add the result of Step 2 to $x^2 + bx$.

EXAMPLE 1 Complete the square.

a. $x^2 - 12x + \underline{\ ?\ }$ **b.** $x^2 + 5x + \underline{\ ?\ }$

SOLUTION **a.** $x^2 \underline{- 12x} + 36 = (x - 6)^2$ **b.** $x^2 \underline{+ 5x} + \dfrac{25}{4} = \left(x + \dfrac{5}{2}\right)^2$
$\left(-\dfrac{12}{2}\right)^2 = 36$ $\left(\dfrac{5}{2}\right)^2 = \dfrac{25}{4}$

EXAMPLE 2 Solve $x^2 + 14x + 24 = 0$ by completing the square.

446 CHAPTER 12

SOLUTION

$$x^2 + 14x + 24 = 0$$
$$x^2 + 14x \quad = -24$$
$$x^2 + 14x + \left(\frac{14}{2}\right)^2 = -24 + \left(\frac{14}{2}\right)^2 \quad \text{Complete the square.}$$
$$x^2 + 14x + 49 = -24 + 49$$
$$(x + 7)^2 = 25$$
$$\left.\begin{array}{l} x + 7 = \pm\sqrt{25} \\ x = -7 \pm 5 \\ x = -2 \text{ or } x = -12 \end{array}\right\} \begin{array}{l} \text{Solve using the method} \\ \text{of Section 12-1.} \end{array}$$

The check is left to you.

∴ the solution set is $\{-2, -12\}$. **Answer**

EXAMPLE 3 Solve $3x^2 + 5x - 1 = 0$ by completing the square.

SOLUTION To use the method shown in Example 2, divide both sides by 3 so that the coefficient of x^2 will be 1.

$$x^2 + \frac{5}{3}x - \frac{1}{3} = 0$$
$$x^2 + \frac{5}{3}x \quad = \frac{1}{3}$$
$$x^2 + \frac{5}{3}x + \left(\frac{5}{6}\right)^2 = \frac{1}{3} + \left(\frac{5}{6}\right)^2$$
$$x^2 + \frac{5}{3}x + \frac{25}{36} = \frac{1}{3} + \frac{25}{36}$$
$$\left(x + \frac{5}{6}\right)^2 = \frac{37}{36}$$
$$x + \frac{5}{6} = \pm\frac{\sqrt{37}}{6}$$
$$x = -\frac{5}{6} \pm \frac{\sqrt{37}}{6} = \frac{-5 \pm \sqrt{37}}{6}$$

∴ the solution set is $\left\{\dfrac{-5 - \sqrt{37}}{6}, \dfrac{-5 + \sqrt{37}}{6}\right\}$. **Answer**

You can use a table of square roots or a calculator to obtain decimal approximations to irrational roots. The roots obtained in Example 3 are approximated to the nearest tenth below by using approximations from the Table of Square Roots on page 526.

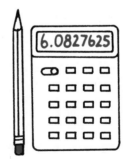

$$\frac{-5 + \sqrt{37}}{6} \approx \frac{-5 + 6.08}{6} = \frac{1.08}{6} = 0.18 \approx 0.2$$
$$\frac{-5 - \sqrt{37}}{6} \approx \frac{-5 - 6.08}{6} = -\frac{11.08}{6} \approx -1.8$$

Thus, the roots to the nearest tenth are 0.2 and -1.8.

QUADRATIC FUNCTIONS **447**

---

7. $x^2 + 2x - 360 = 0$
$$x^2 + 2x = 360$$
$$x^2 + 2x + 1 = 361$$
$$(x + 1)^2 = 361$$
$$x + 1 = \pm 19$$
$$x = -1 \pm 19$$
$$\{-20, 18\}$$

Supplementary Material

Practice Master 70

Suggested Assignments

NOTE: *Day 2 of Sec. 12-1 for both levels finishes Sec. 12-1 and starts Sec. 12-2.*

Average
  448/13–35 odd

Maximum
  448/19–35 odd, 37–39

Additional Answers
Oral Exercises

2. 25; 5   **4.** 36; 6

6. $\frac{49}{4}$; $\frac{7}{2}$ **8.** $\frac{1}{9}$; $\frac{1}{3}$

Additional A Exercises

Solve by completing the square. Give irrational roots in simplest radical form.

1. $x^2 + 2x = -1$ $\{-1\}$

2. $a^2 + 8a = -15$
$\{-3, -5\}$

3. $b^2 + 6b = 12$
$\{-3 + \sqrt{21}, -3 - \sqrt{21}\}$

4. $y^2 - 4y = 10$
$\{2 + \sqrt{14}, 2 - \sqrt{14}\}$

5. $z^2 - 10z = 21$
$\{5 + \sqrt{46}, 5 - \sqrt{46}\}$

6. $c^2 - 8c = 80$
$\{4 + 4\sqrt{6}, 4 - 4\sqrt{6}\}$

Additional Answers
Written Exercises

1. $\{2 + \sqrt{26}, 2 - \sqrt{26}\}$
or $\{7.1, -3.1\}$

2. $\{-3 + \sqrt{39}, -3 - \sqrt{39}\}$
or $\{3.2, -9.2\}$

3. $\{-4 + 2\sqrt{3}, -4 - 2\sqrt{3}\}$
or $\{-0.5, -7.5\}$

4. $\{5 + \sqrt{22}, 5 - \sqrt{22}\}$
or $\{9.7, 0.3\}$

5. $\{3 + \sqrt{6}, 3 - \sqrt{6}\}$
or $\{5.4, 0.6\}$ **6.** $\{7, 1\}$

7. $\{1 + \sqrt{6}, 1 - \sqrt{6}\}$
or $\{3.4, -1.4\}$

8. $\{12, -24\}$

9. $\{8 + 2\sqrt{137}, 8 - 2\sqrt{137}\}$
or $\{31.4, -15.4\}$

10. $\{16, -10\}$

11. $\{-1 + \sqrt{5}, -1 - \sqrt{5}\}$
or $\{1.2, -3.2\}$

12. $\left\{\dfrac{4 + \sqrt{22}}{2}, \dfrac{4 - \sqrt{22}}{2}\right\}$
or $\{4.3, -0.3\}$

Oral Exercises

Complete the square.

1. $x^2 + 4x + \underline{\ ?\ } = (x + \underline{\ ?\ })^2$ 4; 2

3. $y^2 - 6y + \underline{\ ?\ } = (y - \underline{\ ?\ })^2$ 9; 3

5. $z^2 - 5z + \underline{\ ?\ } = (z - \underline{\ ?\ })^2$ $\frac{25}{4}$; $\frac{5}{2}$

7. $t^2 + 1.8t + \underline{\ ?\ } = (t + \underline{\ ?\ })^2$ 0.81; 0.9

2. $x^2 + 10x + \underline{\ ?\ } = (x + \underline{\ ?\ })^2$

4. $y^2 - 12y + \underline{\ ?\ } = (y - \underline{\ ?\ })^2$

6. $m^2 + 7m + \underline{\ ?\ } = (m + \underline{\ ?\ })^2$

8. $r^2 - \frac{2}{3}r + \underline{\ ?\ } = (r - \underline{\ ?\ })^2$

Complete the step shown in the solution of the equation. Do not solve.

9. $x^2 + 2x - 1 = 0$

$x^2 + 2x \quad = \dfrac{?}{1}$

10. $x^2 - 8x + 3 = 1$

$x^2 - 8x \quad = \dfrac{?}{-2}$

11. $2x^2 - 12x = -4$

$x^2 - \dfrac{?}{6}x = \dfrac{?}{-2}$

Written Exercises

Solve by completing the square. Give irrational roots in simplest radical form and approximate them to the nearest tenth.

A **1.** $x^2 - 4x = 22$

2. $x^2 + 6x = 30$

3. $x^2 + 8x = -4$

4. $z^2 - 10z = -3$

5. $q^2 - 6q + 3 = 0$

6. $x^2 - 8x + 7 = 0$

7. $m^2 - 2m - 5 = 0$

8. $r^2 + 12r - 288 = 0$

9. $y^2 - 16y - 476 = 8$

10. $t^2 - 6t - 135 = 25$

11. $3a^2 + 6a = 12$

12. $2z^2 - 8z = 3$

13. $b^2 + 3b = 4$

14. $c^2 - 5c = 1$

15. $d^2 + 11d - 5 = 2$

16. $k^2 - 2k - 399 = 0$

17. $y^2 + 6y - 1591 = 0$

18. $2y^2 + 20y - 278 = 0$

Solve the equations using two methods: **(a)** completing the square and **(b)** factoring.

19. $x^2 - 13x + 40 = 0$ $\{8, 5\}$ **20.** $x^2 + 8x - 65 = 0$ $\{5, -13\}$ **21.** $y^2 - 18y - 40 = 0$

22. $2m^2 + 5m = 12$ $\left\{\frac{3}{2}, -4\right\}$ **23.** $4r^2 - 4r = 3$ $\left\{\frac{3}{2}, -\frac{1}{2}\right\}$ **24.** $3r^2 - 13r - 10 = 0$

Solve. Write irrational roots in simplest radical form.

21. $\{-2, 20\}$

24. $\left\{5, -\frac{2}{3}\right\}$

B **25.** $\frac{s^2}{2} + s = 4$ $\{2, -4\}$

26. $\frac{3x^2}{2} + x - 4 = 0$ $\left\{\frac{4}{3}, -2\right\}$ **27.** $x^2 - 2 = \frac{2x}{3}$

28. $x^2 - \frac{x}{4} = 2$

29. $\frac{3m^2}{4} - 4 = \frac{5m}{2}$

30. $\frac{x^2}{2} - \frac{x}{4} = 2$

31. $x - 2 = \frac{4 + x}{5x}$

32. $x + 2 = \frac{15 + 11x}{6x}$

33. $6x = \frac{12 + x}{x + 1}$

34. $4x = \frac{x - 6}{x + 3}$

35. $4t + \frac{t - 6}{t + 1} = 2$

36. $3m + 5 = \frac{12}{m - 2}$

Solve for x in terms of a, b, and c. State the conditions for which the equation has real roots. Explain in terms of a, b, or c.

C **37.** $x^2 + bx + 1 = 0$
$\left\{\dfrac{-b \pm \sqrt{b^2 - 4}}{2}\right\}$; $b \geq 2$ or
$b \leq -2$

38. $x^2 + bx + c = 0$
$\left\{\dfrac{-b \pm \sqrt{b^2 - 4c}}{2}\right\}$;
$b^2 - 4c \geq 0$

39. $ax^2 + bx + c = 0$
$\left\{\dfrac{-b \pm \sqrt{b^2 - 4ac}}{2a}\right\}$;
$a \neq 0$, $b^2 - 4ac \geq 0$

448   CHAPTER 12

12-3 The Quadratic Formula

OBJECTIVE To learn the quadratic formula and use it to solve equations.

Recall from Chapter 5 (page 189) that the general form of the quadratic equation is

$$ax^2 + bx + c = 0$$

where $a \neq 0$. This equation is solved below by completing the square.

$$ax^2 + bx + c = 0$$

$$x^2 + \frac{b}{a}x + \frac{c}{a} = 0 \ (a \neq 0)$$

$$x^2 + \frac{b}{a}x = -\frac{c}{a}$$

$$x^2 + \frac{b}{a}x + \left(\frac{b}{2a}\right)^2 = -\frac{c}{a} + \left(\frac{b}{2a}\right)^2 \quad \text{Complete the square.}$$

$$\left(x + \frac{b}{2a}\right)^2 = -\frac{c}{a} + \frac{b^2}{4a^2}$$

$$\left(x + \frac{b}{2a}\right)^2 = \frac{b^2 - 4ac}{4a^2}$$

$$x + \frac{b}{2a} = \pm\sqrt{\frac{b^2 - 4ac}{4a^2}} \quad \text{(If } b^2 - 4ac \geq 0)$$

$$x = -\frac{b}{2a} \pm \sqrt{\frac{b^2 - 4ac}{4a^2}}$$

$$x = -\frac{b}{2a} \pm \frac{\sqrt{b^2 - 4ac}}{2a}$$

$$x = \frac{-b \pm \sqrt{b^2 - 4ac}}{2a}$$

The last equation in the preceding proof is called the **quadratic formula.** It gives the roots of $ax^2 + bx + c = 0$ in terms of the coefficients a, b, and c. In the proof, notice the assumptions that $a \neq 0$ and that $b^2 - 4ac \geq 0$.

THE QUADRATIC FORMULA

If $\quad ax^2 + bx + c = 0, \quad a \neq 0, \quad$ and $b^2 - 4ac \geq 0,$

then $\qquad x = \dfrac{-b \pm \sqrt{b^2 - 4ac}}{2a}$

QUADRATIC FUNCTIONS   **449**

13. $\{1, -4\}$

14. $\left\{\dfrac{5 + \sqrt{29}}{2}, \dfrac{5 - \sqrt{29}}{2}\right\}$
    or $\{5.2, -0.2\}$

15. $\left\{\dfrac{-11 \pm \sqrt{149}}{2}\right\}$
    or $\{0.6, -11.6\}$

16. $\{21, -19\}$ **17.** $\{37, -43\}$

18. $\{-5 \pm 2\sqrt{41}\}$
    or $\{7.8, -17.8\}$

27. $\left\{\dfrac{1 + \sqrt{19}}{3}, \dfrac{1 - \sqrt{19}}{3}\right\}$

28. $\left\{\dfrac{1 + \sqrt{129}}{8}, \dfrac{1 - \sqrt{129}}{8}\right\}$

29. $\left\{\dfrac{5 + \sqrt{73}}{3}, \dfrac{5 - \sqrt{73}}{3}\right\}$

30. $\left\{\dfrac{1 + \sqrt{65}}{4}, \dfrac{1 - \sqrt{65}}{4}\right\}$

31. $\left\{\dfrac{11 + \sqrt{201}}{10}, \dfrac{11 - \sqrt{201}}{10}\right\}$

32. $\left\{\dfrac{3}{2}, -\dfrac{5}{3}\right\}$

33. $\left\{\dfrac{-5 \pm \sqrt{313}}{12}\right\}$

34. $\left\{-2, -\dfrac{3}{4}\right\}$

35. $\left\{\dfrac{-3 \pm \sqrt{137}}{8}\right\}$

36. $\left\{\dfrac{1 + \sqrt{265}}{6}, \dfrac{1 - \sqrt{265}}{6}\right\}$

Teaching Suggestions p. T108

Suggested Extensions p. T108

449

Solve by using the quadratic formula.

1. $x^2 + 3x - 9 = 0$

$$x = \frac{-3 \pm \sqrt{9 - 4(-9)}}{2}$$

$$x = \frac{-3 \pm \sqrt{45}}{2}$$

$$x = \frac{-3 \pm 3\sqrt{5}}{2}$$

$$\left\{\frac{-3 + 3\sqrt{5}}{2}, \frac{-3 - 3\sqrt{5}}{2}\right\}$$

2. $2x^2 - 2x = 3$

$2x^2 - 2x - 3 = 0$

$$x = \frac{2 \pm \sqrt{4 - 4(2)(-3)}}{4}$$

$$x = \frac{2 \pm \sqrt{28}}{4}$$

$$x = \frac{2 \pm 2\sqrt{7}}{4} = \frac{1 \pm \sqrt{7}}{2}$$

$$\left\{\frac{1 + \sqrt{7}}{2}, \frac{1 - \sqrt{7}}{2}\right\}$$

Supplementary Material

Practice Master 71

Suggested Assignments

Average
450/1–23 odd, 24
S 448/37, 39

Maximum
450/1–23 odd, 24
Read Extra, p. 451

Additional A Exercises

Solve by using the quadratic formula. Give irrational roots in simplest radical form.

1. $x^2 + 4x + 3 = 0$
$\{-3, -1\}$

2. $a^2 - 6a + 5 = 0$ $\{5, 1\}$

3. $c^2 + 7c + 2 = 0$

$$\left\{\frac{-7 + \sqrt{41}}{2}, \frac{-7 - \sqrt{41}}{2}\right\}$$

4. $z^2 - 2z - 3 = 0$ $\{3, -1\}$

5. $b^2 - 8b - 4 = 0$
$\{4 + 2\sqrt{5}, 4 - 2\sqrt{5}\}$

450

EXAMPLE Solve $7x^2 - 6x + 1 = 0$ using the quadratic formula.

SOLUTION $7x^2 - 6x + 1 = 0$

$$x = \frac{-b \pm \sqrt{b^2 - 4ac}}{2a} \quad \text{where } a = 7, b = -6, \text{ and } c = 1$$

$$x = \frac{-(-6) \pm \sqrt{(-6)^2 - 4(7)(1)}}{2(7)} = \frac{6 \pm \sqrt{36 - 28}}{14}$$

$$= \frac{6 \pm \sqrt{8}}{14} = \frac{6 \pm 2\sqrt{2}}{14} = \frac{3 \pm \sqrt{2}}{7}$$

The check is left to you.

$\therefore$ the solution set is $\left\{\dfrac{3 - \sqrt{2}}{7}, \dfrac{3 + \sqrt{2}}{7}\right\}$. ***Answer***

Be sure to express a quadratic equation in the form $ax^2 + bx + c = 0$ before using the quadratic formula. To solve $2x^2 = 5x - 1$, first express the equation as $2x^2 - 5x + 1 = 0$ to see the values for a, b, and c.

Oral Exercises

Answers are given in order a, b, c. Answers may vary. For example, an acceptable answer for Ex. 8 is -1, -3, 7.

State the values of a, b, and c for each equation.

1. $3x^2 + 8x + 2 = 0$ 3, 8, 2

2. $2x^2 - 9x + 6 = 0$ 2, -9, 6

3. $5x^2 + 3x - 1 = 0$ 5, 3, -1

4. $6x^2 + 11x = 3$ 6, 11, -3

5. $7y^2 - 9y = 2$ 7, -9, -2

6. $3y^2 = 7 + 2y$

7. $4r^2 = 9 + 2r$ 4, -2, -9

8. $7 - x^2 = 3x$ 1, 3, -7

9. $x^2 = 6x$

10. $y = 7y^2$ 7, -1, 0

11. $3x^2 = 4$ 3, 0, -4

12. $9t^2 = 0$

6. 3, -2, -7
9. 1, -6, 0
12. 9, 0, 0

Written Exercises

Use the quadratic formula to solve each equation. Give irrational roots in simplest radical form; also approximate them to the nearest tenth.

A
1. $x^2 + 2x - 1 = 0$

2. $x^2 + 5x + 2 = 0$

3. $x^2 + 6x + 4 = 0$

4. $2r^2 - 8r + 6 = 0$

5. $s^2 - 4s - 5 = 0$

6. $t^2 - 5t + 4 = 0$

7. $2m^2 + 5m + 2 = 0$

8. $4q^2 + 4q - 3 = 0$

9. $3a^2 - 10a - 8 = 0$

10. $3y^2 = 11y - 5$

11. $4x^2 + 5 = 9x$

12. $9x = 4 - 2x^2$

Solve.

B
13. $b^2 + 0.7b - 0.1 = 0$

14. $3z^2 - 1.2z + 0.02 = 0$

15. $4r^2 = 0.6r + 0.5$

16. $c^2 + \frac{2}{3}c - \frac{1}{2} = 0$

17. $\frac{3}{2}x^2 + \frac{1}{3}x + \frac{2}{3} = 0$

18. $\frac{1}{4}x^2 - \frac{2}{5}x = 4$

19. $\frac{3}{x} - \frac{1}{3x + 2} = \frac{1}{2}$ $\left\{\frac{7 \pm \sqrt{85}}{3}\right\}$

20. $\frac{3x}{x + 2} - \frac{x + 1}{x - 1} = 0$ $\left\{\frac{3 \pm \sqrt{13}}{2}\right\}$

21. $\dfrac{2.5}{x+2} = 4x \quad \left\{ \dfrac{-4 \pm \sqrt{26}}{4} \right\}$

22. $\dfrac{4}{x-2} - \dfrac{x-3}{x+4} = 2 \quad \left\{ \dfrac{5 \pm \sqrt{337}}{6} \right\}$

The roots of the quadratic equation $ax^2 + bx + c = 0$ are

$$\dfrac{-b \pm \sqrt{b^2 - 4ac}}{2a}.$$

C **23.** Find the sum of the roots. $\dfrac{-b}{a}$

24. Find the product of the roots. $\dfrac{c}{a}$

25. Write a quadratic equation whose roots are $2 \pm \sqrt{3}$. (*Hint:* Find the sum and product of the roots. Then use the results of Exercises 23 and 24 to find values for a, b, and c.) $x^2 - 4x + 1 = 0$

EXTRA _____

Imaginary Numbers

You know that there are no real-number solutions to the equation $x^2 = -9$. If you take another course in algebra, you will learn that equations like this have solutions that are *imaginary numbers*. Imaginary numbers involve the *imaginary unit, i*, defined to be the square root of -1. Thus:

$$x^2 = -9$$
$$x = \pm\sqrt{-9} = \pm 3\sqrt{-1} = \pm 3i$$

ꜧistorical ꞥote Variables

The history of the use of symbols to denote unknown quantities is very closely tied to the history of exponents (see page 177). One method for representing unknown quantities was the use of words such as "root," "square," and "cube." The Hindus used the names of various colors.

Gradually the words used were abbreviated. In the sixteenth and seventeenth centuries, N, Q, C, QQ, QC, . . . were used to denote quantities you would represent by x, x^2, x^3, x^4, x^5, ... Some writers even used pictorial representations of squares and cubes.

At the close of the sixteenth century, François Vieta (or Viète), a French mathematician, published a mathematics book in which he used vowels to represent unknown quantities and consonants for known quantities, giving his algebra a nearly modern appearance.

QUADRATIC FUNCTIONS **451**

Chalkboard Examples

Find the value of the discriminant of each equation. Without solving, state how many real roots each equation has.

1. $x^2 - 4x + 2 = 0$
$b^2 - 4ac = 16 - 4(1)(2)$
$= 8$; two real roots

2. $x^2 - 4x + 8 = 0$
$b^2 - 4ac = 16 - 4(1)(8)$
$= -16$; no real roots

For each of the following quadratic functions,

a. State the number of real-number roots;
b. Find the x-intercepts by the most appropriate method;
c. Graph the function.

3. $f(x) = x^2 - 4x - 1$

a. $b^2 - 4ac = 16 - 4(-1)(1)$
$= 12$; two real roots

b. $x^2 - 4x - 1 = 0$

$x^2 - 4x + 4 = 5$

$(x - 2)^2 = 5$

$x - 2 = \pm\sqrt{5}$

$x = 2 \pm \sqrt{5}$

∴ The x-intercepts are
$2 + \sqrt{5}, 2 - \sqrt{5}$.

c.

4. $y = 2x^2 - 4x + 5$
a. $b^2 - 4ac = 16 - 4(2)(5)$
$= -24$; no real roots
b. no x-intercepts

(continued)

12-4 Graphs of Quadratic Equations: The Discriminant

OBJECTIVE To use the discriminant to determine the number of roots of the equation $ax^2 + bx + c = 0$ and the number of x-intercepts of the graph of the related equation $y = ax^2 + bx + c$.

You learned in Chapter 9 (page 338) that the graph of the function defined by the quadratic equation

$$y = x^2 - 2x - 3$$

is the parabola shown at the right. The x-coordinate of a point where the curve intersects the x-axis is called an **x-intercept** of the curve. This parabola has two x-intercepts, -1 and 3, because $y = 0$ for these values of x. You can also see that the equation

$$x^2 - 2x - 3 = 0$$

has -1 and 3 as roots.

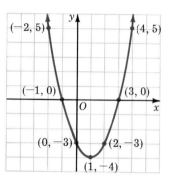

The roots of any quadratic equation of the form

$$ax^2 + bx + c = 0$$

are the x-intercepts of the graph of the related equation

$$y = ax^2 + bx + c.$$

The algebraic fact that a quadratic equation can have two, one, or no real number roots corresponds to the geometric fact that a parabola can have two, one, or no x-intercepts, as illustrated below and on the next page. In each example, the quadratic formula is used to solve the equation.

EXAMPLE 1

Equation: $x^2 - 4x + 1 = 0$

Solution: $x = \dfrac{-(-4) \pm \sqrt{(-4)^2 - 4(1)(1)}}{2(1)}$

$= \dfrac{4 \pm \sqrt{12}}{2}$

$= 2 \pm \sqrt{3}$

∴ the solution set is
$\{2 + \sqrt{3}, 2 - \sqrt{3}\}$.

Number of roots: Two real-number roots

Related equation: $y = x^2 - 4x + 1$

Graph:

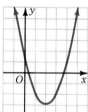

Number of x-intercepts: Two

452 CHAPTER 12

EXAMPLE 2

Equation: $x^2 - 4x + 4 = 0$

Solution: $x = \dfrac{-(-4) \pm \sqrt{(-4)^2 - 4(1)(4)}}{2(1)}$

$= \dfrac{4 \pm \sqrt{0}}{2}$

$= 2$

∴ the solution set is {2}.

Number of roots: One real-number (double) root

Related equation: $y = x^2 - 4x + 4$

Graph:

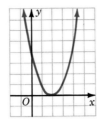

Number of x-intercepts: One

EXAMPLE 3

Equation: $x^2 - 4x + 5 = 0$

Solution: $x = \dfrac{-(-4) \pm \sqrt{(-4)^2 - 4(1)(5)}}{2(1)}$

$= \dfrac{4 \pm \sqrt{-4}}{2}$

There is no real-number root since $\sqrt{-4}$ does not exist in the set of real numbers.

Number of roots: No real-number roots

Related equation: $y = x^2 - 4x + 5$

Graph:

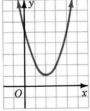

Number of x-intercepts: None

In each of Examples 1–3, the value of $b^2 - 4ac$ in the quadratic formula is shown in color. This value is the key to the number of real roots, as shown in the following chart.

	Value of $b^2 - 4ac$	Number of different real roots of $ax^2 + bx + c = 0$	Number of x-intercepts of the graph of $y = ax^2 + bx + c$
Case 1	positive	2	2
Case 2	zero	1 (a double root)	1
Case 3	negative	0	0

Note that when $b^2 - 4ac$ is negative, no real-number root of the equation exists because square roots of negative numbers do not exist in the set of real numbers.

Because the value of $b^2 - 4ac$ discriminates, or distinguishes, the three cases, it is called the **discriminant** of the quadratic equation.

QUADRATIC FUNCTIONS **453**

---

c.

5. $f\colon x \to -(x + 2)^2$

a. $-(x + 2)^2 = -x^2 - 4x - 4$

$b^2 - 4ac = 16 - 4(-1)(-4)$

$= 0$

one real-number root

b. $-(x + 2)^2 = 0$

$(x + 2)^2 = 0$

$x + 2 = 0$

$x = -2$

∴ The x-intercept is -2.

c.

Supplementary Materials

Progress Test 43

Computer Activity 34
The Quadratic Formula
   Through the use of the quadratic formula computers may be used to solve quadratic equations. This activity provides a program and asks the student to use it to solve a number of equations. The student is then asked to use these solutions to draw conclusions about the roots of quadratic equations.

Suggested Assignments

Average
  454/1–17 odd
S 282/30, 32

Maximum
  454/1–19 odd
S 282/30, 32
S 451/25

Additional A Exercises

Write the value of the discriminant of each equation.

1. $x^2 + 2x - 4 = 0$ 20

2. $x^2 - 3x + 2 = 0$ 1

3. $x^2 + 5x - 6 = 0$ 49

4. $2x^2 + 4x + 1 = 0$ 8

5. $2x^2 - 8x + 3 = 0$ 40

6. $3x^2 + 10x - 2 = 0$ 124

Oral Exercises

Classify each statement as true or false.

1. The x-coordinates of the points where the parabola $y = x^2 + 5x + 6$ crosses the x-axis are the roots of the equation $x^2 + 5x + 6 = 0$. True

2. Since the discriminant of the equation $x^2 + 5x + 6 = 0$ is 1, the equation has exactly one real-number root. False

3. The value of the discriminant of the equation $x^2 - 2x - 3 = 0$ indicates whether the roots are positive, negative, or zero. False

4. The value of $b^2 - 4ac$ in the quadratic formula is a root of the equation $ax^2 + bx + c = 0$. False

5. When the discriminant of a quadratic equation is known, the number of real roots is known. True

6. Since the discriminant of $x^2 + x + 1 = 0$ is -3, the equation has no real-number root. True

Written Exercises

Write the value of the discriminant of each equation. Then use it to decide how many different real-number roots the equation has. (Do not solve the equations.)

A **1.** $x^2 + 3x - 5 = 0$ 29; two   **2.** $x^2 - x + 3 = 0$ -11; none   **3.** $3x^2 - 5x - 1 = 0$ 37; two

4. $2x^2 - 8x + 8 = 0$ 0; one   **5.** $x^2 - 5x + 2 = 0$ 17; two   **6.** $x^2 + 4x + 9 = 0$ -20; none

7. $2x^2 - 3x - 2 = 0$ 25; two   **8.** $\frac{1}{2}x^2 - 2x + 2 = 0$ 0; one   **9.** $3y^2 - y + 1 = 0$ -11; none

10. $-4y^2 - 5y + 4 = 0$ 89; two   **11.** $2t^2 - 12t + 18 = 0$ 0; one   **12.** $\frac{1}{3}t^2 + 2t + 3 = 0$ 0; one

Without drawing the graph of the given equation, determine **(a)** how many points the parabola has in common with the x-axis, and **(b)** whether its vertex lies above, below, or on the x-axis.

SAMPLE $y = 2x - 3 - x^2$

SOLUTION   **a.** The x-intercepts of the graph are solutions of the equation
$$2x - 3 - x^2 = 0, \quad \text{or} \quad -x^2 + 2x - 3 = 0.$$
Its discriminant is $(2)^2 - 4(-1)(-3) = -8$ and therefore it has no real-number roots. The parabola has *no* points in common with the x-axis.

b. Since the parabola opens downward (see page 339), its vertex must be *below* the x-axis (otherwise the parabola would intersect the x-axis).

B **13.** $y = x^2 + 4x + 1$ Two; below   **14.** $y = x^2 - 4x + 1$ Two; below

15. $y = 3 - 2x - x^2$ Two; above   **16.** $y = 2x - 4 - x^2$ None; below

17. $y = 6 + x - 2x^2$ Two; above   **18.** $y = 4x - 4 - x^2$ One; on

454   *CHAPTER 12*

C 19. Find k so that the equation $kx^2 + 4x + 1 = 0$ has one real-number (double) root. 4

20. Find k so that the equation $x^2 - kx + 9 = 0$ has one real-number (double) root. $\{6, -6\}$

Self-Test 1

VOCABULARY   perfect square (p. 444) x-intercept (p. 452)
completing the square (p. 446)   discriminant (p. 453)
quadratic formula (p. 449)

Solve by using perfect squares.

1. $4x^2 = 64$ **2.** $(y - 5)^2 = 4$ Obj. 12-1, p. 443

Solve by completing the square.

3. $a^2 + 4a - 12 = 0$ **4.** $2x^2 - 12x + 10 = 0$ Obj. 12-2, p. 446

Solve by the quadratic formula.

5. $b^2 - 3b - 2 = 0$ **6.** $3c^2 + 7c + 1 = 0$ Obj. 12-3, p. 449

Give the number of real roots.

7. $x^2 - 10x + 24 = 0$ **8.** $2x^2 - 4x + 1 = 0$ Obj. 12-4, p. 452

Check your answers with those at the back of the book.

Just for Fun

According to the legend, the inventor of the game of chess asked to be rewarded by having one grain of wheat put on the first square of a chessboard, two grains on the second, four grains on the third, eight grains on the fourth, and so on. The total number of grains would be $2^{64} - 1$, which is several thousand times the world's annual wheat yield.

1. To find out how large 2^{64} is approximately, you could enter the number 2 on the calculator and press the squaring button a number of times. How many times? 6 times

2. Factor $2^{64} - 1$ as a difference of squares to show that it is divisible by 3, 5, and 17.

QUADRATIC FUNCTIONS   **455**

USING QUADRATIC EQUATIONS

12-5 *Methods of Solution*

OBJECTIVE To choose the best method for solving a quadratic equation.

You have learned the following four methods for solving quadratic equations.

METHODS FOR SOLVING A QUADRATIC EQUATION

1. Factoring
2. Using the property of square roots of equal numbers (p. 419)
3. Completing the square
4. Using the quadratic formula

Although the quadratic formula can be used to solve any quadratic equation in the form

$$ax^2 + bx + c = 0$$

one of the other methods may be easier. Here are some guidelines that suggest when one of the other methods may be easier:

1. If the equation is in the form $ax^2 + bx = 0$ or if the factors are easily seen, use factoring;
2. If the equation is in the form $ax^2 + c = 0$, use the property of square roots of equal numbers;
3. If the equation is in the form $x^2 + bx + c = 0$ and b is an even number, use the method of completing the square.

EXAMPLE   Solve each quadratic equation using the most convenient method.

    a. $3x^2 - 75 = 0$ **b.** $2y^2 + 7y + 4 = 0$

    c. $5z^2 - 15z = 0$ **d.** $k^2 + 10k - 5 = 0$

SOLUTION   **a.** $3x^2 - 75 = 0$ Use the property of square

                $3x^2 = 75$ roots of equal numbers.

                 $x^2 = 25$

                $x = \pm 5$

    $\therefore$ the solution set is $\{-5, 5\}$.   ***Answer***

b. $2y^2 + 7y + 4 = 0$

Since no other method suggests itself, use the quadratic formula.

$$x = \frac{-7 \pm \sqrt{(7)^2 - 4(2)(4)}}{2(2)} = \frac{-7 \pm \sqrt{17}}{4}$$

$\therefore$ the solution set is $\left\{ \dfrac{-7 - \sqrt{17}}{4}, \dfrac{-7 + \sqrt{17}}{4} \right\}$. **Answer**

c. $5z^2 - 15z = 0$ Factor.

$5z(z - 3) = 0$

$5z = 0 \quad$ or $\quad z - 3 = 0$

$\therefore$ the solution set is $\{0, 3\}$. **Answer**

d. $k^2 + 10k - 5 = 0$ Complete the square.

$k^2 + 10k = 5$

$k^2 + 10k + 25 = 30$

$(k + 5)^2 = 30$

$k + 5 = \pm\sqrt{30}$

$k = -5 \pm \sqrt{30}$

$\therefore$ the solution set is $\left\{ -5 - \sqrt{30},\, -5 + \sqrt{30} \right\}$. **Answer**

Oral Exercises

a = Use the property of square roots of equal numbers.
b = Use the quadratic formula.
c = Factor.   d = Complete the square.

For each of the following equations, state which method you would use to solve.

1. $x^2 + 3x + 2 = 0$ c

2. $5x^2 = 30$ a

3. $x^2 - 12x = 85$ c

4. $2x^2 + 7x - 8 = 0$ b

5. $6x^2 + 18x = 0$ c

6. $2x^2 + 6x + 3 = 0$

6. b

7. $10x^2 = 90$ a

8. $x^2 + 8x + 5 = 0$ b

9. $3x^2 - 10x = 4$ b

10. $9x^2 + 8x = 0$ c

11. $(x + 3)^2 = 5$ a

12. $x^2 - 6x = 60$ d

Written Exercises

A   **1–12.** Solve the quadratic equations given in Oral Exercises 1–12. Write the answers in simplest radical form.

Solve by the most efficient method. Write irrational answers in simplest radical form.

13. $3(x + 2)^2 = 12$ $\{0, -4\}$

14. $x^2 - 10x = 20$ $\{5 \pm 3\sqrt{5}\}$

15. $3x^2 + 2x - 1 = 0$ $\left\{\frac{1}{3}, -1\right\}$

16. $4x^2 + 7x - 11 = 0$ $\left\{1, -\frac{11}{4}\right\}$

17. $\frac{1}{3}x^2 + \frac{2}{5}x - 2 = 0$

18. $\frac{-1}{2x} = \frac{4x - 5}{3}$ $\left\{\frac{3}{4}, \frac{1}{2}\right\}$

19. $\frac{x + 9}{2x - 3} = \frac{x + 7}{3x + 2}$ $\{-9 \pm \sqrt{42}\}$

20. $0.3x^2 - 0.2x = 0.25$ $\left\{\frac{2 \pm \sqrt{34}}{6}\right\}$

21. $1.2x^2 - 4x - 0.6 = 0$ $\left\{\frac{10 \pm \sqrt{118}}{6}\right\}$

QUADRATIC FUNCTIONS   457

Supplementary Materials

Practice Master 72

Computer Activity 35
Partial Fractions
   It is sometimes difficult to take an algebraic fraction of the form $\dfrac{Dx + E}{x^2 + Bx + C}$ and find the two fractions that were added together to produce it. However, the task can be done easily on a computer. The student is asked to enter a program to accomplish this task and then use it to break up a number of fractions.

Suggested Assignments

Average
   457/1–27 odd
R 455/*Self-Test 1*
S 455/19

Maximum
   457/1–31 odd
R 455/*Self-Test 1*
S 455/20

Additional A Exercises

Solve by the most efficient method. Write irrational answers in simplest radical form.

1. $6x^2 = 54$ $\{3, -3\}$

2. $x^2 + 5x + 6 = 0$
   $\{-3, -2\}$

3. $x^2 - 8x + 15 = 0$ $\{3, 5\}$

4. $x^2 + 4x - 5 = 0$ $\{-5, 1\}$

5. $2x^2 - 5x + 2 = 0$ $\left\{2, \frac{1}{2}\right\}$

6. $3x^2 + 9x - 2 = 0$
   $\left\{\dfrac{-9 + \sqrt{105}}{6}, \dfrac{-9 - \sqrt{105}}{6}\right\}$

Additional Answers
Written Exercises

1. $\{-1, -2\}$ **2.** $\{\sqrt{6}, -\sqrt{6}\}$

3. $\{17, -5\}$

4. $\left\{\dfrac{-7 \pm \sqrt{113}}{4}\right\}$

5. $\{0, -3\}$

      (continued)

457

6. $\left\{\dfrac{-3 + \sqrt{3}}{2}, \dfrac{-3 - \sqrt{3}}{2}\right\}$

7. $\{3, -3\}$

8. $\{-4 + \sqrt{11}, -4 - \sqrt{11}\}$

9. $\left\{\dfrac{5 + \sqrt{37}}{3}, \dfrac{5 - \sqrt{37}}{3}\right\}$

10. $\left\{0, -\dfrac{8}{9}\right\}$

11. $\{-3 + \sqrt{5}, -3 - \sqrt{5}\}$

12. $\{3 + \sqrt{69}, 3 - \sqrt{69}\}$

17. $\left\{\dfrac{-3 \pm \sqrt{159}}{5}\right\}$

23. $\left\{\dfrac{-13 \pm \sqrt{701}}{14}\right\}$

25. $\left\{\dfrac{-29 \pm \sqrt{721}}{2}\right\}$

27. $\left\{\dfrac{5}{3}, -\dfrac{1}{7}\right\}$

Solve by the most efficient method. Write irrational answers in simplest radical form.

B **22.** $4x(x + 3) + 7(x - 2) = 1 - 6x^2 \quad \left\{\dfrac{3}{5}, -\dfrac{5}{2}\right\}$

23. $3x(x + 2) + 4(x^2 - 2) = 11 - 7x$

24. $(x + 3)^2 - 2(x + 4) = 10 \quad \{-2 \pm \sqrt{13}\}$

25. $(2x + 5)^2 - 3x(x - 3) = -5$

26. $(2x - 3)(x + 1) - 32 = x(3 - x) \quad \left\{\dfrac{2 \pm \sqrt{109}}{3}\right\}$

27. $(5x - 2)^2 = (2x + 3)^2$

Solve. Be sure that you have found all the real roots of each equation. Write irrational answers in simplest radical form. (*Hint:* Substitute y for x^2.)

C **28.** $6x^4 - 19x^2 + 10 = 0 \quad \left\{\pm\dfrac{\sqrt{10}}{2}, \pm\dfrac{\sqrt{6}}{3}\right\}$

29. $4x^4 - 25x^2 - 21 = 0 \quad \{\sqrt{7}, -\sqrt{7}\}$

30. $7x^4 + 5x^2 + 3 = 0$ No solutions

31. $3x^4 - 2x^2 = 0$
$\left\{0, \dfrac{\sqrt{6}}{3}, \dfrac{-\sqrt{6}}{3}\right\}$

Career Note Architect

Very tall skyscrapers sway slightly. They need some flexibility to withstand strong winds. Architects who design skyscrapers, office buildings, houses, schools, and shopping malls must consider more than just style. A building must be functional, structurally sound, and in compliance with local building codes and zoning laws.

Once an architect has discussed function, style, and cost of a proposed structure with a client, floor plans, elevations, and models are made. When the plans are approved by the client, the architect may work with a contractor on the construction site to make sure the plans are carried out correctly.

Architects must pass a licensing examination. The requirements for taking this test are a bachelor's degree in architecture and three years of experience in an architect's office, or a master's degree and two years of experience.

12-6 *Using Quadratic Equations to Solve Problems*

OBJECTIVE To use quadratic equations to solve problems.

EXAMPLE
A theater director needs to determine the dimensions of an area that is to be in the shape of a right triangle on the stage floor. The longest side of the triangle, which is to face the audience, is to be 8 m long. One of the shorter sides is to be 2 m longer than the other. To the nearest tenth of a meter, what are the lengths of the two shorter sides?

SOLUTION
Step 1 The problem asks for the lengths of the two shorter sides.

Step 2 Let x = the length of the shortest side. Then $(x + 2)$ = the length of the other unknown side.

Step 3 Use the Pythagorean theorem to write an equation.
$$x^2 + (x + 2)^2 = 8^2$$

Step 4
$$x^2 + x^2 + 4x + 4 = 64$$
$$2x^2 + 4x + 4 = 64$$
$$2x^2 + 4x - 60 = 0$$
$$x^2 + 2x - 30 = 0$$

Use the quadratic formula
$$x = \frac{-2 \pm \sqrt{(2)^2 - 4(1)(-30)}}{2} = \frac{-2 \pm \sqrt{124}}{2} = \frac{-2 \pm 2\sqrt{31}}{2}$$
$$x = -1 \pm \sqrt{31}$$

From the Table of Square Roots on page 526:
$$-1 + \sqrt{31} \approx -1 + 5.57 = 4.57 \approx 4.6$$
$$-1 - \sqrt{31} \approx -1 - 5.57 = -6.57 \approx -6.6$$

Step 5 Discard the negative root because a negative length has no meaning. Check 4.6.
$$(4.6)^2 + (4.6 + 2)^2 \overset{?}{=} 8^2$$
$$21.16 + 43.56 \overset{?}{=} 64$$
$$64.7 \approx 64 \quad \checkmark$$

The numbers are approximately equal so the approximate solution is correct.

∴ the shorter sides of the triangle will be 4.6 m and 6.6 m long. ***Answer***

QUADRATIC FUNCTIONS   459

Chalkboard Examples
Solve.

1. The difference between two numbers is 8 and the sum of their squares is 104. Find the numbers.
   Let n = one of the numbers.
   Then $n + 8$ = the other number.
   $$n + (n + 8)^2 = 104$$
   $$2n^2 + 16n + 64 = 104$$
   $$2n^2 + 16n - 40 = 0$$
   $$n^2 + 8n - 20 = 0$$
   $$(n + 10)(n - 2) = 0$$
   $$n = -10 \quad \text{or} \quad 2$$
   The numbers are either -10 and -2 or 2 and 10.

2. The altitude of a triangle is 1 cm less than one third of the length of the base. If the triangle has an area of 10 cm², find its altitude and its base to the nearest tenth of a centimeter.

   Let $3x$ = the base of the triangle.
   Then $x - 1$ = the altitude.
   $$\frac{1}{2} \cdot 3x \cdot (x - 1) = 10$$
   $$3x(x - 1) = 20$$
   $$3x^2 - 3x - 20 = 0$$
   $$x = \frac{3 \pm \sqrt{9 - 4(3)(-20)}}{6}$$
   $$= \frac{3 \pm \sqrt{249}}{6}$$
   $$x = \frac{3 + \sqrt{249}}{6} \approx 3.1 \quad \text{or}$$
   $$x = \frac{3 - \sqrt{249}}{6} \approx -2.1$$

   -2.1 cannot be a solution.

   ∴ The base of the triangle is 9.3 cm and the height of the triangle is 2.1 cm.

Practice Master 73

Progress Test 44

Computer Activity 36
Sum and Product of Two Numbers
 When working with quadratic equations, it is sometimes necessary to find two numbers which have a given sum and a given product. This can be done quickly on a computer. A program, as well as a number of problems, for the student is provided in this activity. The work is then extended to touch upon maximum and minimum problems.

Suggested Assignments

Average
Day 1: 460/*P*: 1, 2, 5, 7–10
  S 458/29
Day 2: 460/*P*: 6, 11–14
  R 461/Self-Test 2

Maximum
Day 1: 460/*P*: 3–5, 7–10
  S 458/24–30 even
   Read Extra, p. 462
Day 2: 460/*P*: 6, 11–14
  462/1–5
Day 3: 462/6–8
  R 461/Self-Test 2

Additional A Exercises

Solve. Give irrational roots to the nearest tenth. Use the Table of Square Roots on page 526 as necessary.

1. A rectangular parcel of land is 20 m longer than it is wide. If the area of the parcel is 1500 m², find its dimensions.
30 m by 50 m

2. Layla has a flower garden in the shape of a right triangle. The longest side is 10 m. One of the two shorter sides is twice the other. Find the lengths of the two shorter sides.
4.5 m, 9 m or 8.9 m

Problems

Solve. Give irrational roots to the nearest tenth. Use the Table of Square Roots on page 526 as necessary.

A **1.** The length of a rectangle is 3 m longer than the width. If the area of the rectangle is 40 m², find the length and width. 8 m by 5 m

2. The length of a rectangle is twice the width. The area of the rectangle is 200 cm². Find the length and width. 20 cm by 10 cm

3. The width of a rectangular playing area is 50 m shorter than its length. If the area is 8400 m², find the playing area's length and width. 120 m by 70 m

4. A rectangular bolt of cloth, purchased to make drapes, has an area of 12 m². If the piece of material is three times as long as it is wide, find its dimensions. 2 m by 6 m

5. The base of a triangle is 3 cm longer than its altitude. Find the altitude if the area of the triangle is 44 cm². (*Hint:* The area of a triangle $= \frac{1}{2} \cdot$ base $\cdot$ altitude.) 8 cm

6. The altitude of a triangle is 4 cm shorter than its base. Find the altitude if the area of the triangle is 90 cm². 11.6 cm

7. The dimensions of a framed picture are 50 cm by 30 cm. The area of the picture itself is 444 cm². Find the distance from the edge of the picture to the edge of the frame if this distance is uniform around the picture. 8.3 cm

8. Martha's garden is 5 m wide and 8 m long. Next year she plans to double the garden's area by increasing the width and length by the same number of meters. What will the new dimensions of the garden be? 10.6 m by 7.6 m

B **9.** A box without a top is to be made by cutting squares measuring 5 cm on a side from each corner of a square piece of cardboard and folding up the sides. If the box is to have a volume of 3125 cm³, what should the length of a side of the original piece of cardboard be? 35 cm

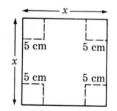

10. A mathematics class bought a $45 calculator for class use. Each student donated the same amount of money. If there had been 5 more students in the class, each would have had to pay 30¢ less. How many students were in the class? 25 students

11. Working together, Dan and Leah can mow a lawn in one hour and twelve minutes. Working alone, Leah can mow the lawn in one hour less time than it would take Dan. Find the time it takes each of them to mow the lawn working alone. Leah, 2 h; Dan, 3 h

12. A class planned a field trip at a cost of $36 to be shared equally by the students. The day before the trip 6 students found they could not go. Consequently, the other students had to pay an additional 50¢ each. How many students went on the trip? 18 students

13. One train travels at a rate 10 km/h faster than another train. If the faster train takes one hour less time than the other to travel 720 km, what is the rate of the faster train? 90 km/h

C 14. A boat can travel to a city 24 km downriver and back in five hours. If the rate of the current is 2 km/h, find the rate of the boat in still water. 10 km/h

Self-Test 2

Solve the following quadratic equations using the most convenient method.

1. $2x^2 + 3x - 7 = 0$
2. $5x^2 = 100$ Obj. 12-5, p. 456
3. $3x^2 - 9x = 0$
4. $x^2 + 4x + 2 = 0$

Solve. Give irrational roots to the nearest tenth. Use the Table of Square Roots on page 526 as necessary.

5. The areas of a square and a rectangle have a sum of 42 cm². If   Obj. 12-6, p. 459
   the rectangle is as wide as the square, but is 3 cm longer, find the length of a side of the square.

6. A soccer field is approximately 110 m by 60 m. A section of uniform width for spectators is to be placed around the field. The area of the field and the spectator section is to be 9375 m². Find the width of the spectator section.

Check your answers with those at the back of the book.

Computer Key-In

Write a program to find the solution set of any quadratic equation by using the quadratic formula. Be sure to include a special print-out if $b^2 - 4ac < 0$. Recall (page 421) that the BASIC language has a built-in square root function.

QUADRATIC FUNCTIONS   **461**

Extra Practice Problems
p. 523

Quick Quiz

Solve the following quadratic equations by the most convenient method.

1. $2x^2 - 7x - 30 = 0$
   $\left\{6, -\dfrac{5}{2}\right\}$

2. $2(x + 9)^2 = 242$
   $\{-20, 2\}$

3. $x^2 + 2x - 1368 = 0$
   $\{36, -38\}$

4. $3x^2 - 3x - 1 = 0$
   $\left\{\dfrac{3 + \sqrt{21}}{6}, \dfrac{3 - \sqrt{21}}{6}\right\}$

5. The area of a rectangular room is 65 m². Find the perimeter of the room, given that its length is 3 m more than twice its width. 36 m

EXTRA

Quadratic Inequalities

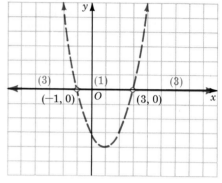

The graph of $y = x^2 - 2x - 3$ can be used to illustrate the solutions of the following:

(1) $x^2 - 2x - 3 < 0$

(2) $x^2 - 2x - 3 = 0$

(3) $x^2 - 2x - 3 > 0$

The solution set of the quadratic equation (2) is $\{-1, 3\}$. These two values of x are called the *zeros* of the quadratic function.

To solve inequality (3), reason as follows:

a. If (x, y) is on the graph, then $y = x^2 - 2x - 3$.

b. If (x, y) is *above* the x-axis, then $y > 0$.

c. Therefore, if (x, y) is on the graph *and* above the x-axis, then $y = x^2 - 2x - 3 > 0$.

d. $\therefore$ the solution set for (3) is {all real numbers less than -1 or greater than 3} because these values of x give points that are on the graph above the x-axis.

Similar reasoning shows that the solution set for (1) is {all real numbers between -1 and 3} because these values of x give points on the graph *below* the x-axis.

EXAMPLE   Solve the inequalities.

(1) $x^2 + 4x + 4 > 0$ (2) $x^2 + 4x + 4 < 0$

SOLUTION   Use the graph of $y = x^2 + 4x + 4$.

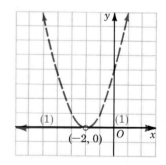

(1) Since the graph lies above the x-axis for all x except -2, $x^2 + 4x + 4 > 0$ for all $x \neq -2$.
(2) There are no values of x for which $x^2 + 4x + 4 < 0$, since the graph does not go below the x-axis.

Graph each equation and mark the sections of the x-axis which correspond to $y = 0$, $y > 0$, and $y < 0$.

1. $y = x^2 - 4$ 2. $y = 4 - x^2$ 3. $y = x^2 + 3x$

4. $y = x^2 - 6x + 8$ 5. $y = x^2 - 3x - 10$ 6. $y = 2x^2 + x - 3$

Find the values of x for which each expression represents a real number.

7. $\sqrt{x^2 + 6x}$
{all real numbers ≤ -6 or ≥ 0}

8. $\sqrt{x^2 - 5x + 6}$
{all real numbers ≤ 2 or ≥ 3}

462   *CHAPTER 12*

462

Application   Newton's Law of Motion

Newton's Law of Motion relates the force acting on an object to the object's mass and acceleration. The acceleration of an object is the rate at which the speed of the object is changing. For example, an object with a constant acceleration of 2 m/s^2 (meters per second squared) will increase its speed by 10 m/s in 5 s. The force acting on the object is expressed in newtons (N). A *newton* is the amount of force required to give a 1 kg object an acceleration of 1 m/s^2.

Before you use Newton's Law, you must know the units involved. The mass (*m*) of the object is expressed in kilograms, the object's acceleration (*a*) is expressed in meters per second squared, and the force (*F*) acting on the object is expressed in newtons. Newton's Law can then be written as follows:

$$F = ma$$

1. What force is needed to give a 9000 kg truck an acceleration of 15 m/s^2? 135,000 N
2. A baseball that has been hit with a force of 5.4 N accelerates at 36 m/s^2. What is the mass of the baseball in grams? 150 g
3. A 7.2 kg bowling ball has a force of 43.2 N applied to it. What is the bowling ball's acceleration? 6 m/s^2

Biography   Santiago Ramón y Cajal

Santiago Ramón y Cajal (1852–1934), born in Petilla de Aragon, Spain, received a degree in medicine from the University of Zaragoza in 1873. From 1892 to 1922 Cajal was a professor of histology, the study of the microscopic structure of human tissues. He made major contributions to this branch of medicine. Using stains, he was able to display nerve cells and fibers. This technique enabled him to investigate in detail the structure of the nervous system. He demonstrated that each nerve cell has its own network of fibers that do not touch the fibers of any other cell. For his work in this field he shared the Nobel prize for medicine in 1906.

QUADRATIC FUNCTIONS   **463**

Chapter Summary

1. Any quadratic equation can be solved using the quadratic formula (see item 2 below). Some quadratic equations, however, may be more easily solved by factoring, applying the property of square roots of equal numbers, or by completing the square.

2. When $ax^2 + bx + c = 0$ and $a \neq 0$, the quadratic formula is expressed as follows:

$$x = \frac{-b \pm \sqrt{b^2 - 4ac}}{2a}$$

3. The graph of a quadratic equation of the form $y = ax^2 + bx + c$ is a parabola. The x-intercepts of the parabola correspond to the roots of the related quadratic equation $ax^2 + bx + c = 0$.

4. The discriminant, $b^2 - 4ac$, is used to determine the number of roots of a quadratic equation.

  If $b^2 - 4ac > 0$, there are two real-number roots.
  If $b^2 - 4ac = 0$, there is one (double) real-number root.
  If $b^2 - 4ac < 0$, there are no real-number roots.

Chapter Review

Solve.

1. $4x^2 = 144$ 12-1
  a. $\{6\}$ **b.** $\{6, -6\}$ c. $\{36\}$ d. $\{36, -36\}$

2. $(r - 7)^2 = 9$
  a. $\{10, -10\}$ b. $\{2, -2\}$ **c.** $\{4, 10\}$ d. $\{16, -2\}$

Solve by completing the square.

3. $x^2 + 14x + 24 = 0$ 12-2
  a. $\{-12, -2\}$ b. $\{12, 2\}$ c. $\{12, -2\}$ d. $\{-12, 2\}$

4. $3x^2 + 18x - 12 = 0$
  a. $\left\{\dfrac{\sqrt{13}}{3}, \dfrac{-\sqrt{13}}{3}\right\}$ **b.** $\{-3 + \sqrt{13}, -3 - \sqrt{13}\}$
  c. $\{\sqrt{13} - 3, \sqrt{13} + 3\}$ d. $\{3 + \sqrt{13}, 3 - \sqrt{13}\}$

Solve by the quadratic formula.

5. $x^2 + 5x - 84 = 0$ 12-3
  a. $\{-12, 7\}$ b. $\{7, 12\}$ c. $\{-7, 12\}$ d. $\{-12, -7\}$

6. $2x^2 + 7x + 5 = 0$
  a. $\left\{\dfrac{5}{2}, 1\right\}$ b. $\{5, 2\}$ c. $\{-5, -2\}$ **d.** $\left\{-\dfrac{5}{2}, -1\right\}$

464   *CHAPTER 12*

7. Give the discriminant of $x^2 + 16x + 48 = 0$.   12-4

    a. 8   **b.** 12   **c.** 4   **(d.)** 64

8. How many real roots does $x^2 - 6x + 5 = 0$ have?

    a. 0   **b.** 1   **(c.)** 2   **d.** 3

9. Give the best method for solving $6x^2 - 42 = 0$.   12-5

    a. Factoring   **(b.)** Property of square roots of
                                            equal numbers

    c. Completing the square   **d.** Quadratic formula

Solve.

10. The length of a rectangle is 6 cm less than twice its width. If the   12-6
area is 108 cm² find the length and width.

    a. $l = 9$ cm   **b.** $l = 18$ cm   **c.** $l = 6$ cm   **(d.)** $l = 12$ cm
        $w = 12$ cm $w = 6$ cm $w = 18$ cm $w = 9$ cm

Chapter Test ━━━━━━━━━━━━━━

Alternate Test and Review
p. T23, T30–T31

Solve.

1. $25x^2 = 100$ $\{2, -2\}$ **2.** $9x^2 = 121$ $\left\{\frac{11}{3}, -\frac{11}{3}\right\}$ 12-1

Solve by completing the square.

3. $x^2 - 8x + 4 = 0$ $\{4 \pm 2\sqrt{3}\}$ **4.** $3x^2 + 12x - 9 = 0$ $\{-2 \pm \sqrt{7}\}$ 12-2

Solve by the quadratic formula.

5. $a^2 + 5a - 2 = 0$ $\left\{\frac{-5 \pm \sqrt{33}}{2}\right\}$ **6.** $4c^2 - 9c + 9 = 0$ No real roots   12-3

State the number of real roots.

7. $x^2 + 6x + 9 = 0$ One   **8.** $5x^2 + 10x - 3 = 0$ Two   12-4

Solve by the easiest method.

9. $5x^2 - 20x = 0$ $\{0, 4\}$ **10.** $3x^2 - 9x + 5 = 0$ $\left\{\frac{9 + \sqrt{21}}{6}, \frac{9 - \sqrt{21}}{6}\right\}$ 12-5

Solve. Approximate irrational roots to the nearest tenth.

11. A rectangle is 5 cm longer than it is wide. If the area is 84 cm², find   12-6
the length and width. Width, 7 cm; length, 12 cm

12. The side of one square is 3 times as long as the side of a second
square. If the combined area is 160 m², find the lengths of the sides
of both squares. 4 m, 12 m

QUADRATIC FUNCTIONS   **465**

Cumulative Review (Chapters 1–12)

Evaluate if $a = -8$, $b = -5$, $c = 3$, $d = 4$, and $e = \dfrac{9}{2}$.

1. $a(2b + d)$ 48   **2.** $ae \div cd + b$ -8 **3.** $ed^2 - b^3$ 197   **4.** $(3a - c) \div e$ -6

Factor completely, if possible. If not, write "prime."

5. $-21z^4 + 12z^3 - 15z^8$ **6.** $35g^2 - 2gh - 6h^2$ **7.** $100b^2 - 144y^2$

8. $6df + 7e + 2ef + 21d$ **9.** $20s^3 - 33s^2t + 10st^2$ **10.** $6r^4 + 10r^2 - 16$

Simplify. Each variable represents a positive real number.

11. $(-58 + 47) - (-58)$ **12.** $8e - 18e^2 \div 2e$ **13.** $(-4 - 9)(-2 + 5)$

14. $6a - (0.8a + 1.2b)$ **15.** $3(7c - 8) + 5 - 4c$ **16.** $(-4x^3y^2z^2)(-8xy^3z^5)$

17. $-\dfrac{2}{3}t^3v^2(-9t^2 + 3tv)$ **18.** $\dfrac{-252e^3f^2g}{-98ef^2g^3}$ **19.** $\dfrac{(6m^2n^4)^3}{(-3m^4n^3)^4}$

20. $(r^3 - r + 3)(4r - 5)$ **21.** $(9m - 2)(3m + 5)$ **22.** $(2a^2 - 7b)^2$

23. $\dfrac{49c^2 - 14cd + d^2}{49c^2 + 7cd - 2d^2}$ **24.** $\dfrac{64k^5 + 2}{2k + 1}$ **25.** $\dfrac{m^4 - 16}{2m^3 + 8m} \div \dfrac{m^3 - 2m^2}{4m^3}$

26. $\dfrac{45e^5 - 25e^3 - 27e^2}{-15e^2}$ **27.** $\dfrac{-5x^3y^2z}{-65xz^2} \cdot \dfrac{13yz^4}{x^2y^3}$ **28.** $\dfrac{s}{18} - \dfrac{s}{8} + 2$

29. $\dfrac{3n - 1}{6 - 2n} + \dfrac{4}{n - 3}$ **30.** $\dfrac{4}{w + 3} - \dfrac{3}{w - 3}$ **31.** $\dfrac{t + 1}{t + 3} - \dfrac{t}{t - 2}$

32. $-\sqrt{2.56y^8z^3}$ **33.** $3\sqrt{2}(\sqrt{45} - \sqrt{125})$ **34.** $(2\sqrt{3} - 1)^2$

35. $\sqrt{\dfrac{27a^3}{5}} \cdot \sqrt{\dfrac{160}{3a}}$ **36.** $(6 + \sqrt{6})(6 - \sqrt{10})$ **37.** $\dfrac{7 + \sqrt{5}}{1 + \sqrt{5}}$

38. Find the prime factorizations of 135 and 180, and their GCF. $135 = 5 \cdot 3^3;\ 180 = 3^2 \cdot 2^2 \cdot 5;\ \text{GCF} = 45$

39. Write $0.7\overline{81}$ as a fraction in lowest terms. $\dfrac{43}{55}$

40. If x and y are whole numbers, graph the solution set of:
  a. $5x + 3y = 28$ **b.** $2x + 3y \le 9$ **c.** $xy = 4$

41. Find an equation in standard form of the line:
  a. with slope -5 and containing $(-2, -7)$ $5x + y = -17$
  b. containing $(8, -1)$ and $(4, 5)$ $3x + 2y = 22$

42. Graph each solution set on a number line:
  a. $5(7 - 2x) + 4 = -3(8x + 1)$ **b.** $-9 \le 1 - 2x < 3$

43. If $f(x) = 2x^2 - 3x - 2$, find $f(-4)$ and $f(2\sqrt{3})$. Graph $f(x)$. 42; $22 - 6\sqrt{3}$

44. If a varies directly as b^2 and inversely as c, and $a = 75$ when $b = 5$ and $c = 2$, find a when $b = 4$ and $c = 3$. 32

Solve each equation, inequality, or system.

45. $-3(2x - 1) = 4x + 8$

46. $7w + 1 = -|-125|$

47. $18 = 6.4h + 0.72$

48. 5.4% of $y = 43.2$

49. $32 = 5b^2 + 36b$

50. $(6q + 5)(3q - 1) = 4$

51. $\frac{5}{2}t + \frac{1}{3} > 7$

52. $-\frac{44}{7} \le -\frac{3p}{5} - \frac{2}{7}$

53. $\frac{4}{3s + 2} + \frac{1}{s} = 1$

54. $2 = 14 + 3r^2$ No sol.

55. $\sqrt{1 - 5x} - 2 = 2$ -3

56. $(m + 3)^2 = 56$

57. $\frac{3j + 1}{5j - 2} = \frac{j + 1}{j + 5}$ $\left\{-\frac{1}{2}, 7\right\}$

58. $3\sqrt{2x} = 12$ 8

59. $\frac{1}{(x - 3)^2} - \frac{1}{3 - x} \ge 0$

60. $n^2 - 30n = -225$ 15

61. $d^2 = 6d + 15$ $\{3 \pm 2\sqrt{6}\}$

62. $8c^2 - 4c = 1$ $\left\{\frac{1 \pm \sqrt{3}}{4}\right\}$

63. $a - 12b = -25$
$6a + 5b = 4$ $(-1, 2)$

64. $7r + 4s = 23$
$5r - 4s = 13$ $\left(3, \frac{1}{2}\right)$

65. $5x - 8y = 7$
$4x - 7y = 11$ $(-13, -9)$

66. If y varies directly as x and $y = 3$ when $x = 54$, find y when $x = 63$. $\frac{7}{2}$

67. Two numbers differ by 6. The sum of their squares is 218. Find the numbers. 7 and 13 or -13 and -7

68. Find three consecutive odd integers whose sum is -225. $-77, -75, -73$

69. If x and $x + 7$ represent the lengths of the two shorter sides of a right triangle, and $2x + 1$ represents the length of the longest side, find the value of x. 8

70. Ed Jones invests $2800, part at $9\frac{1}{2}\%$ and the rest at 9%. If his annual interest is $258.50, how much is invested at each rate? $1300 at $9\frac{1}{2}\%$; $1500 at 9%

71. The length and the width of a rectangle are in the ratio $8:5$. If the perimeter of the rectangle is 104 cm, find the area. 640 cm²

72. How many liters of water must be evaporated from 18 L of a 24% ammonia solution to produce a 30% solution? 3.6 L

73. Marcy needs 40 min to wash and wax the family car, and Sue needs 1 h. Marcy was working for 25 min when Sue joined her. How long did it take them to finish the job? 9 min

74. A two-digit number is 7 times the sum of its digits. If the product of the digits is 18, find the number. 63

75. A plane flew 1600 km with a 20 km/h tail wind. The return trip took 10 min more. Find the speed of the plane in still air. 620 km/h

76. Two cars traveling in opposite directions left a tollbooth at 7 P.M. One car was traveling at 76 km/h and the other at 84 km/h. At what time were the cars at least 120 km apart? 7:45 P.M.

c.

42. a.

b.

43.

45. $-\frac{1}{2}$

46. -18

47. 2.7

48. 800

49. $\left\{\frac{4}{5}, -8\right\}$

50. $\left\{\frac{1}{2}, -1\right\}$

51. $\left\{\text{the real numbers greater than } \frac{8}{3}\right\}$

52. {the real numbers less than or equal to 10}

53. $\left\{-\frac{1}{3}, 2\right\}$

56. $\{-3 \pm 2\sqrt{14}\}$

59. {the real numbers greater than or equal to 2, except 3}

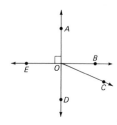
LOOKING AHEAD

GEOMETRY

Lines and Angles

OBJECTIVE To represent points, lines, planes, and angles and to measure angles.

You have been using the ideas of a *line* and a *plane* to help you visualize number relationships on a number line and in a coordinate plane. The concepts of a line and a plane as certain kinds of sets of points come from a branch of mathematics called *geometry*.

To represent a *geometric point*, you draw a dot, but a geometric point is an abstract idea, not a concrete object. The lines you draw represent the idea of a *geometric line*, which has no thickness.

A line determined by points A and B is denoted by $\overleftrightarrow{AB}$, or $\overleftrightarrow{BA}$. The arrowheads indicate that the line extends in both directions without ending.

line AB: $\overleftrightarrow{AB}$

The part of $\overleftrightarrow{AB}$ that consists of points A and B and all points of $\overleftrightarrow{AB}$ between A and B is a **line segment,** or a **segment,** denoted by $\overline{AB}$, or $\overline{BA}$. The length of $\overline{AB}$ is denoted by AB.

segment AB: $\overline{AB}$

The part of $\overleftrightarrow{AB}$ that starts at point A and extends without ending through point B is a **ray** denoted by $\overrightarrow{AB}$. A is the **endpoint** of $\overrightarrow{AB}$.

ray AB: $\overrightarrow{AB}$

An **angle** is a figure formed by two different rays that have the same endpoint. The rays are called the **sides** of the angle and the common endpoint is the **vertex** of the angle. The angle shown above is formed by $\overrightarrow{AB}$ and $\overrightarrow{AC}$. It is denoted by $\angle A$, $\angle BAC$, or $\angle CAB$.

468

To find the **degree measure** of an angle, you use a *protractor*, as shown below. Using the outer scale, you can see that the measure of $\angle POQ$ is 35° (35 *degrees*). You may write this fact as $\angle POQ = 35°$. Also, $\angle POR = 90°$ and $\angle POS = 125°$.

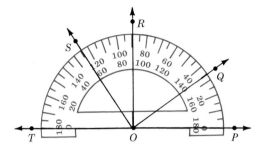

Angles are classified according to their measures.

        An **acute angle** measures between 0° and 90°.
        A **right angle** measures 90°.
        An **obtuse angle** measures between 90° and 180°.
        A **straight angle** measures 180°.

You can find $\angle QOR$ in the diagram above by subtracting 35 from 90: $\angle QOR = 55°$. Do you see that $\angle QOS$ is a right angle? that $\angle ROS = 35°$? To state that $\angle ROS$ and $\angle POQ$ have equal measures, you write $\angle ROS = \angle POQ$.

Oral Exercises

Exercises 1–8 refer to the diagram below.

Name each angle whose measure is given.

1. 110° $\angle AOE$ **2.** 60° $\angle AOC$ **3.** 25° $\angle FOH$ **4.** 90°
                                                                        $\angle AOD$ and $\angle HOD$

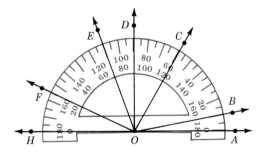

State the measure of each angle.

5. $\angle EOF$ 45°   **6.** $\angle BOE$ 100°   **7.** $\angle COF$ 95°   **8.** $\angle DOF$ 65°

LOOKING AHEAD   **469**

Identify each graph as a point, a line, a ray, or a segment.

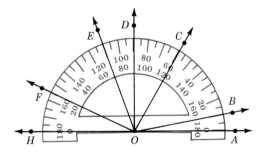

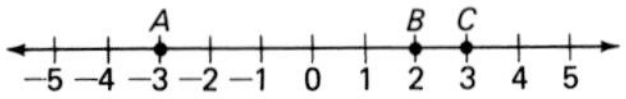

2. $x = 2$ point, B

3. $x \geq -3$ ray, $\overrightarrow{AC}$ or $\overrightarrow{AB}$

4. $-3 \leq x \leq 2$
line segment, $\overline{AB}$

5. $x > 2$ or $x < 3$
line, $\overleftrightarrow{AB}$ or $\overleftrightarrow{AC}$ or $\overleftrightarrow{BC}$

6. $x \leq 3$ and $x \geq 3$ point, C

Suggested Assignment
Maximum
   470/1–21

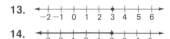
14.

15.

16.

17.

18.

19.

20.

21.

22.

Written Exercises

In Exercises 1-4, name 5 different line segments in each diagram.

A **1.** Any five of $\overline{PQ}$, $\overline{QR}$, $\overline{RS}$, $\overline{PR}$, $\overline{QS}$, $\overline{PS}$ **2.**

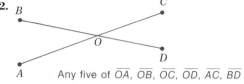

Any five of $\overline{OA}$, $\overline{OB}$, $\overline{OC}$, $\overline{OD}$, $\overline{AC}$, $\overline{BD}$

3.

4.

$\overline{XY}$, $\overline{YZ}$, $\overline{XZ}$, $\overline{WY}$, $\overline{WZ}$

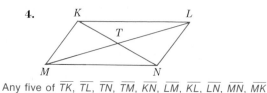

Any five of $\overline{TK}$, $\overline{TL}$, $\overline{TN}$, $\overline{TM}$, $\overline{KN}$, $\overline{LM}$, $\overline{KL}$, $\overline{LN}$, $\overline{MN}$, $\overline{MK}$

Classify each angle as acute, obtuse, or right.

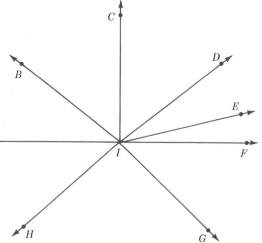

5. $\angle FIE$ Acute **6.** $\angle CIF$ Right

7. $\angle BIF$ Obtuse **8.** $\angle HIG$ Obtuse

9. $\angle HIA$ Acute **10.** $\angle CIG$ Obtuse

11. $\angle BID$ Obtuse **12.** $\angle CID$ Acute

Graph the solution set of each sentence on a number line. Identify the graph as a point, a line, a segment, or a ray.

B **13.** $x = 3$ Point **14.** $x \leq 2$ Ray **15.** $1 \leq x \leq 3$ Segment

16. $x + 5 = 1$ Point **17.** $x + 2 = 5 + x - 3$ Line **18.** $-4 \leq x - 2 \leq 4$ Segment

C **19.** $x + 5 \geq 3$ and $x - 1 \leq 3$ Segment **20.** $x + 2 \leq 7$ or $x + 3 \leq 6$ Ray

21. $2x \geq 6$ or $3x < 15$ Line **22.** $5x - 8 \leq 2$ and $3x + 5 \geq 11$ Point

Pairs of Angles

OBJECTIVE   To learn the names and properties of some special pairs of angles.

Some pairs of angles whose measures are related are given special names.

The diagram shows two lines intersecting at O and forming $\angle AOB$, $\angle BOC$, $\angle COD$, and $\angle DOA$. Two angles, such as $\angle AOB$ and $\angle COD$, whose sides are rays in the same lines but in opposite directions are called **vertical angles.** $\angle BOC$ and $\angle DOA$ are also a pair of vertical angles.

Vertical angles are equal. Use a protractor to check that $\angle AOB = \angle COD$ and $\angle BOC = \angle DOA$.

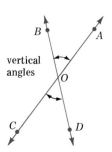

vertical angles

Two angles are **complementary angles** if the sum of their measures is 90°. Each angle is a **complement** of the other. The diagram at the left below shows a pair of complementary angles.

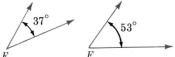

$\angle E$ and $\angle F$ are complementary.
$\angle E$ is a complement of $\angle F$.

$\angle Q$ and $\angle R$ are supplementary.
$\angle Q$ is a supplement of $\angle R$.

Two angles are **supplementary angles** if the sum of their measures is 180°. Each angle is a **supplement** of the other. The diagram at the right above shows a pair of supplementary angles.

EXAMPLE   Find the measure of an angle such that the sum of the measures of its complement and its supplement is 150°.

SOLUTION   Let n = the measure of the angle in degrees.
Then $90 - n$ = the measure of its complement,
and $180 - n$ = the measure of its supplement.

$$90 - n + 180 - n = 150$$
$$270 - 2n = 150$$
$$-2n = -120$$
$$n = 60$$

The measure of the complement is $(90 - 60)°$, or 30°.
The measure of the supplement is $(180 - 60)°$, or 120°.

Is the sum of these measures 150°? Yes, $30 + 120 = 150$.

∴ the measure of the angle is 60°. **Answer**

LOOKING AHEAD   **471**

Teaching Suggestions p. T110

Suggested Extensions p. T111

Chalkboard Examples

1. Find the measure of the complement and the supplement of each angle.
   a. **36°**   54°; 144°
   b. **3°**   87°; 177°
   c. **x°** $(90 - x)°$; $(180 - x)°$
   d. **120°**   none; 60°
   e. **$(90 - y)°$**   y°; $(90 + y)°$

2. The product of the measures of two vertical angles is 36 less than twenty times the measure of one vertical angle. Find the measure of each.
   Let n = the measure of each of the vertical angles.
   $$n^2 + 36 = 20n$$
   $$n^2 - 20n + 36 = 0$$
   $$(n - 2)(n - 18) = 0$$
   $$n = 2 \quad \text{or} \quad n = 18$$
   (both answers check)
   The vertical angles are each 2° or each 18°.

3. The measure of the supplement of an angle is 10° more than two times the measure of its complement. What is the measure of the angle?
   Let x = the measure of the angle.
   $$180 - x - 10 = 2(90 - x)$$
   $$170 - x = 180 - 2x$$
   $$x = 10$$
   The measure of the angle is 10°.

   (continued)

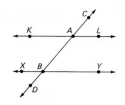

4. In the diagram above, $\overleftrightarrow{KL}$, $\overleftrightarrow{XY}$, and $\overleftrightarrow{AB}$ are all straight lines. If $\angle KAB = \angle ABY$,

a. Name all the angles that have measures equal to the measure of $\angle CAL$.
$\angle KAB$, $\angle ABY$, $\angle XBD$

b. Name all the angles that are supplementary to $\angle DBX$.
$\angle DBY$, $\angle XBA$, $\angle BAL$, $\angle KAC$

Supplementary Material

Practice Master 77

Suggested Assignment

Maximum
   472/1–11 odd
S 424/8, 10, 12

Oral Exercises

State the measure of the complement of an angle with the given measure.

1. 70° 20°   **2.** 8° 82°   **3.** 35° 55°   **4.** 13° 77°   **5.** y degrees $(90 - y)°$ **6.** $3y$ degrees $(90 - 3y)°$

State the measure of the supplement of the angle with the given measure.

7. 130° 50°   **8.** 20° 160°   **9.** 90° 90°   **10.** 46° 134°   **11.** x degrees $(180 - x)°$ **12.** $5x$ degrees $(180 - 5x)°$

Classify each statement as true or false.

13. If two angles have equal measures, then their supplements have equal measures. True

14. The measures of two complementary angles are never equal. False

15. If an angle is obtuse, its supplement is acute. True

16. If an angle is a right angle, its supplement is a right angle. True

17. If an angle is acute, its complement is obtuse. False

Written Exercises

In Exercises 1–4 use the diagram. Assume that the measures of $\angle ACB$ and $\angle EGF$ are equal.

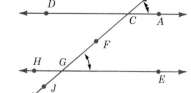

$\angle EGF$, $\angle DCF$, $\angle HGJ$

A   **1.** List all the angles with measures equal to the measure of $\angle ACB$.

2. List all the angles that are supplementary to $\angle ACB$.

3. If $\angle ACB = 40°$, then $\angle BCD = \underline{?°}$. 140°

4. If $\angle FGH = 140°$, then $\angle FGE = \underline{?°}$. 40°   **2.** $\angle BCD$, $\angle ACF$, $\angle FGH$, $\angle EGJ$

5. What are the measures of two supplementary angles, the larger of which measures 4 times the smaller? 36° and 144°

6. What are the measures of two supplementary angles, the smaller of which measures 32° less than the larger? 74° and 106°

7. Find the measure of the angle which measures 20° more than its complement. 55°

8. Find the measures of two complementary angles if the measure of the larger is twice the measure of the smaller. 30° and 60°

B   **9.** An acute angle has a measure of $(x + 2y)°$. What is the difference between the measures of the supplement and complement of this angle? 90°

472

10. The sum of the measures of two vertical angles is 10 times the measure of the supplement of one of the angles. Find the measure of one of the vertical angles. 150°

11. The sum of the measures of a complement and a supplement of an angle is 140.° Find the measure of the angle. 65°

C **12.** The ratio of the measures of the complements of two angles is 3:4, while the ratio of the measures of their supplements is 9:10. Find the measure of each angle. 45°, 30°

Just for Fun _____

Find the value of x such that the sum of the expressions is the same in each row, column, or diagonal. x = 12

x	5	$x - 2$
$x - 5$	9	11
8	$x + 1$	$x - 6$

Historical Note   Multiplication Sign

The arrows in the diagram below show the pattern for finding the product 25 × 43 as calculated at the right below.

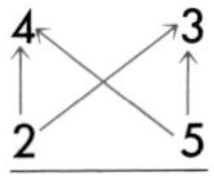

$$5 \times 3 = \quad 15$$
$$5 \times 40 = \quad 200$$
$$20 \times 3 = \quad 60$$
$$20 \times 40 = \quad \underline{800}$$
$$1075$$

This method for multiplication was used in the sixteenth century by some mathematicians.

William Oughtred, an English clergyman, used a small raised cross to indicate multiplication in a mathematics book published in 1631. This symbol was not widely used until the latter half of the nineteenth century, however.

In 1698, the dot for multiplication was introduced by Gottfried W. von Leibniz, a German mathematician. He thought the sign × could be mistaken too easily for the letter x. In the United States, the multiplication dot is raised and the decimal point is on the line of writing. In some other countries, the usage is reversed.

Chalkboard Examples

Find the value of x.

1.

$$30 + 2x + x = 180$$
$$3x = 150$$
$$x = 50$$

2.

$$x + (x + 10) + 90 = 180$$
$$2x + 100 = 180$$
$$2x = 80$$
$$x = 40$$

3.

$$x^2 + x^2 = 4^2$$
$$2x^2 = 16$$
$$x^2 = 8$$
$$x = 2\sqrt{2} \text{ cm}$$

4. The measures of two angles of a triangle are equal. The measure of the third angle is one-fifth the sum of the other two angles. Find the measure of each angle.

Let x = the measure of each of the two equal angles.

$$x + x + \frac{1}{5}(x + x) = 180$$

$$5x + 5x + x + x = 900$$
$$12x = 900$$
$$x = 75$$

The angles are 75°, 75°, and 30°.

474

Triangles

OBJECTIVE To learn some properties of triangles.

A **triangle** is the figure formed by three segments joining three points not on a line, as shown below. Each segment is a **side** of the triangle. Each of the three points is a **vertex** of the triangle.

"Triangle ABC" can be written $\triangle ABC$.

Sides of $\triangle ABC$: $\overline{AB}$, $\overline{BC}$, $\overline{CA}$

Vertices of $\triangle ABC$: A, B, C

Angles of $\triangle ABC$: $\angle A$, $\angle B$, $\angle C$

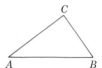

In any triangle, the sum of the measures of the angles is 180°. You can check this statement for a particular triangle by measuring its angles with a protractor and finding the sum of the measures. Also, if you tear off the corners of a paper triangle and fit them together, you will find that they form a straight angle, as shown below.

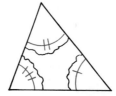

Here are some special triangles:

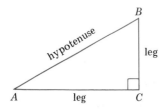
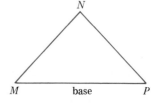
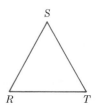

Right triangle	**Isosceles triangle**	**Equilateral triangle**
$\angle C = 90°$	$MN = NP$; $\angle M = \angle P$	$RS = ST = TR$
$AC^2 + BC^2 = AB^2$	**Base:** MP	$\angle R = \angle S = \angle T = 60°$
(Pythagorean theorem,	**Base angles:** $\angle M$ and $\angle P$	
p. 422; converse, p. 423)		

The small square in the right triangle above indicates the right angle.

Oral Exercises

Identify $\triangle ABC$ as right, isosceles, or equilateral given the information below.

1. $AC = BC$ Isosceles
2. $\angle C = 90°$ Right
3. $AB = BC = CA$ Equilateral
4. $\angle A = 30°$, $\angle C = 120°$ Isosceles
5. $\angle A = 21°$, $\angle B = 69°$ Right
6. $AC = 11$, $BC = 11$ Isosceles
7. $AC = 3$, $AB = 5$, $BC = 4$ Right
8. $\angle A = 60°$, $\angle C = 60°$ Equilateral

Written Exercises

The measures of two angles of a triangle are given. Find the measure of the third angle.

A 1. $42°$, $69°$ 69°
2. $73°$, $22°$ 85°
3. $12°$, $43°$ 125°
4. $63°$, $100°$ 17°
5. $90°$, $41°$ 49°
6. $53°$, $67°$ 60°

In Exercises 7–12, use the converse of the Pythagorean theorem to determine whether the triangle is a right triangle.

7. $\triangle ABC$: $AB = 4$, $BC = 3$, $AC = 5$ Yes
8. $\triangle DEF$: $DE = 4$, $EF = 6$, $FD = 7$ No
9. $\triangle GHI$: $GH = 12$, $HI = 5$, $IG = 13$ Yes
10. $\triangle JKL$: $JK = 6$, $KL = 8$, $LJ = 10$
11. $\triangle MNO$: $MN = 9$, $NO = 8$, $OM = 17$ No
12. $\triangle PQR$: $PQ = 24$, $QR = 7$, $RP = 25$

10. Yes
12. Yes

13. If $\triangle STU$ is a right triangle with $\angle T = 90°$, $ST = 9$, and $TU = 12$, find US. 15

14. If $\triangle XYZ$ is a right triangle with $\angle Y = 90°$, $XY = 15$, and $XZ = 17$, find YZ. 8

15. If $\triangle MNR$ is isosceles, $\angle M = 50°$, and $MN = MR$, find the measure of $\angle R$. 65°

16. If $\triangle ABC$ is a right isosceles triangle and $\angle A = 90°$ find the measures of $\angle B$ and $\angle C$. $\angle B = \angle C = 45°$

In Exercises 17-22, $\angle C = 90°$ in $\triangle ABC$. Find the length of the third side in simplest radical form given the lengths of the other two sides.

B 17. $AC = 6$, $BC = 10$ $AB = 2\sqrt{34}$
18. $AC = 9$, $BC = 6$ $AB = 3\sqrt{13}$
19. $AC = 4$, $AB = 6$ $BC = 2\sqrt{5}$
20. $AB = 15$, $AC = 6$ $BC = 3\sqrt{21}$

C 21. $AC = BC = x$ $AB = x\sqrt{2}$
22. $AC = y$, $AB = 2y$ $BC = y\sqrt{3}$

Problems

Solve.

A 1. In a right triangle the measure of one of the acute angles is 4 times the measure of the other. Find the measure of each angle. 90°, 18°, 72°

2. Find the measure of each angle of an isosceles triangle if the measure of the third angle is 7 times the measure of either of the two base angles. 20°, 20°, 140°

3. Find the measure of each angle of a triangle if the measure of the second angle is 3 times that of the first, and the measure of the third angle is 6 times that of the first. 18°, 54°, 108°

4. The measures of the angles of a triangle are in the ratio 2 to 3 to 4. Find the measure of each angle. 40°, 60°, 80°

5. The measure of the second angle of a triangle is $\frac{1}{2}$ that of the first, and the measure of the third angle is 5° more than twice that of the second. Find the measure of each angle. 70°, 35°, 75°

6. The measures of two angles of a triangle are equal. The measure of the third is $\frac{2}{7}$ of the sum of the first two. Find the measures of the angles. 70°, 70°, 40°

B 7. The measure of the second angle of a triangle is 2° more than twice the first, and the measure of the third angle is 26° less than 3 times the second. Find the measure of each angle. 22°, 46°, 112°

8. The sum of four angles about a point is 360°. The measure of the second angle is 6° more than 3 times the first, the measure of the third is 3° more than twice the first, and the measure of the fourth is 20° less than the third. What is the measure of each angle? 46°, 144°, 95°, 75°

C 9. The measure of the second angle of a triangle is 20° more than the complement of the first angle, and the third angle is 4° less than half the supplement of the first. Find the measure of each angle. 32°, 78°, 70°

Just for Fun _____

Arrange sixteen toothpicks to form the pattern shown, which has eight small equilateral triangles. Remove four toothpicks so that only four of the triangles are left.

476

Similar Triangles

OBJECTIVE To use similar triangles.

An object viewed under a magnifying lens appears larger than it is, but its shape is not changed. Two figures that have the same shape are called *similar*.

Two triangles are **similar triangles** when the measures of two angles of one triangle equal the measures of two angles of the other triangle. (Since the sum of the measures of the angles of a triangle is 180°, it follows that the remaining angles also have equal measures.) The triangles shown below are similar.

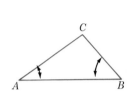 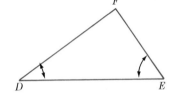

$$\angle A = \angle D, \ \angle B = \angle E, \ \angle C = \angle F$$

You can denote that triangles *ABC* and *DEF* are similar by writing

$$\triangle ABC \sim \triangle DEF.$$

Here angles with equal measures are listed in corresponding positions. They are called **corresponding angles.** The sides opposite corresponding angles are called **corresponding sides.** $\overline{AB}$ corresponds to $\overline{DE}$, and so on. *It is a geometric fact that the lengths of corresponding sides of similar triangles are proportional.* Thus,

$$\frac{AB}{DE} = \frac{BC}{EF} = \frac{CA}{FD}.$$

EXAMPLE 1 In the diagram, $\triangle ABC \sim \triangle DEF$. Find *AC* and *BC*.

SOLUTION Corresponding sides are proportional:

$$\frac{AC}{25} = \frac{18}{30} \quad \text{and} \quad \frac{BC}{20} = \frac{18}{30}$$

Solving each proportion, you will find that

$$AC = 15 \text{ and } BC = 12.$$
Answer

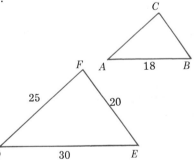

Chalkboard Examples

1.

If $\triangle MNP \sim \triangle XYZ$, find *YZ* and *ZX*.

$$\frac{YZ}{18} = \frac{4}{12}, \ YZ = 6$$

$$\frac{ZX}{21} = \frac{4}{12}, \ ZX = 7$$

2.

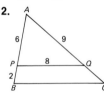

If $\triangle APQ \sim \triangle ABC$, find *QC* and *BC*.

$$\frac{AP}{AB} = \frac{AQ}{AC}, \frac{6}{8} = \frac{9}{AC},$$
$$AC = 12, \ QC = 3$$

$$\frac{AP}{PQ} = \frac{AB}{BC}, \frac{6}{8} = \frac{8}{BC},$$

$$BC = \frac{32}{3} \ \text{ or } \ 10\frac{2}{3}$$

3. Suppose that $\triangle ABC \sim \triangle DEF$. If $\angle B = 35°$ and $\angle E = (5x^2 - 18x)°$, what is the value of *x*?

$$5x^2 - 18x = 35$$

$$5x^2 - 18x - 35 = 0$$

$$(5x + 7)(x - 5) = 0$$

$$x = -\frac{7}{5} \ \text{ or } \ x = 5$$

477

4.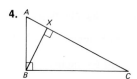

a. Name three similar triangles.

$\triangle ABC \sim \triangle AXB \sim \triangle BXC$

b. If $AX = 9$ cm and $XC = 15$ cm, find XB.

Since $\triangle AXB \sim \triangle BXC$,

$\dfrac{AX}{XB} = \dfrac{XB}{XC}$

$\dfrac{9}{XB} = \dfrac{XB}{15}$

$(XB)^2 = 9 \cdot 15$

$XB = 3\sqrt{15}$ cm

Supplementary Material

Practice Master 78

Suggested Assignment

Maximum
Day 1: 478/1–11
Day 2: 479/P: 1–6

EXAMPLE 2 In the diagram, $\triangle ABC \sim \triangle AEF$. Find EF and AF.

SOLUTION Corresponding sides are proportional:

$$\frac{5}{15} = \frac{4}{EF} \quad \text{and} \quad \frac{5}{15} = \frac{6}{AF}$$

Completing the solution is left to you.

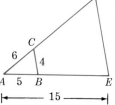

Oral Exercises

1. $\angle R$ and $\angle R$, $\angle RST$ and $\angle W$, $\angle RTS$ and $\angle Q$
2. $\overline{RS}$ and $\overline{RW}$, $\overline{RT}$ and $\overline{RQ}$, $\overline{TS}$ and $\overline{QW}$

In the diagram for Exercises 1–3, $\triangle RST \sim \triangle RWQ$.

1. Name the corresponding angles.

2. Name the corresponding sides.

3. State three equal ratios.
$\dfrac{RS}{RW} = \dfrac{RT}{RQ} = \dfrac{TS}{QW}$

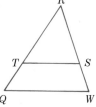

Written Exercises

1. $\angle D$ and $\angle K$, $\angle E$ and $\angle L$, $\angle F$ and $\angle J$, $\overline{DE}$ and $\overline{KL}$, $\overline{EF}$ and $\overline{LJ}$, $\overline{DF}$ and $\overline{KJ}$

A 1. In $\triangle DEF$, $\angle D = 50°$ and $\angle E = 70°$. In $\triangle JKL$, $\angle K = 50°$ and $\angle L = 70°$. Write the corresponding angles and corresponding sides.

2. In $\triangle MNP$ and $\triangle RST$, $\angle M = \angle T$ and $\angle P = \angle S$. Write three equal ratios. $\dfrac{MN}{TR} = \dfrac{NP}{RS} = \dfrac{MP}{TS}$

Classify each statement as true or false.

3. All isosceles triangles are similar. False

4. All equilateral triangles are similar. True

5. All right triangles are similar. False

6. All isosceles right triangles are similar. True

In Exercises 7–11, $\triangle ABC \sim \triangle DEF$. Find the lengths of the sides not given.

7. $AB = 5$, $BC = 3$, $AC = 4$, $ED = 10$ $EF = 6$, $DF = 8$

8. $ED = 8$, $EF = 6$, $DF = 4$, $AC = 6$ $AB = 12$, $BC = 9$

9. $AB = 6$, $BC = 9$, $AC = 12$, $EF = 3$ $DE = 2$, $DF = 4$

10. $ED = 6$, $EF = DF = 9$, $AB = 8$ $BC = AC = 12$

11. $AB = 8$, $BC = 10$, $AC = 12$, $DF = 8$ $DE = 5\frac{1}{3}$, $EF = 6\frac{2}{3}$

478

Problems

Solve.

A 1. A triangle has sides with lengths 9 cm, 15 cm, and 18 cm. If the longest side of a similar triangle is 24 cm, find its shortest side. 12 cm

2. A vertical stick 2 m long casts a shadow 1 m long at the same time a building casts a shadow 15 m long. How tall is the building? 30 m

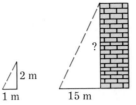

2 m
1 m   15 m

3. A person 2 m tall casts a shadow 3 m long at the same time a tree casts a shadow 15 m long. Find the height of the tree. 10 m

4. To find the length of a pond, two similar triangles were paced off. The measurements are shown on the diagram. How long is the pond? 400 m

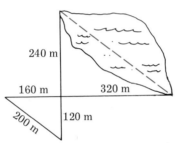

240 m

160 m   320 m

200 m   120 m

B 5. Jose rides his bike 3 m up a ramp and is 1 m above the ground. If he were to ride 6 m farther, how far above the ground would he be? 3 m

6. From a point on the ground 4 m from the base of a 5 m tree, it is possible to see the top of a 200 m building just over the top of the tree. How far is the point from the base of the building? 160 m

Just for Fun _____

A parallelogram is a figure in geometry. Geometry is a branch of mathematics. Therefore, a parallelogram is a figure in mathematics.

No canaries are in my house. My house is in the Canary Islands. Therefore, no canaries are in the Canary Islands.

Is this reasoning logical? The reasoning for the parallelogram is logical, but the reasoning for the canaries is not. There could be canaries in other parts of the Canary Islands.

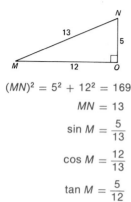

TRIGONOMETRY

Trigonometric Ratios

OBJECTIVE To find the sine, cosine, and tangent of an acute angle.

In the branch of mathematics called *trigonometry* you learn more about the measurement of triangles.

Any acute angle, such as $\angle A$ in the diagram, can be made an angle of a right triangle ABC. The legs opposite and adjacent to this angle are labeled. Ratios of the lengths of the sides of $\triangle ABC$ are called **trigonometric ratios** associated with $\angle A$. These ratios have special names and symbols.

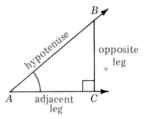

sine of $\angle A$ (symbol, $\sin A$) $= \dfrac{\text{length of leg opposite } \angle A}{\text{length of hypotenuse}} = \dfrac{BC}{AB}$

cosine of $\angle A$ (symbol, $\cos A$) $= \dfrac{\text{length of leg adjacent to } \angle A}{\text{length of hypotenuse}} = \dfrac{AC}{AB}$

tangent of $\angle A$ (symbol, $\tan A$) $= \dfrac{\text{length of leg opposite } \angle A}{\text{length of leg adjacent to } \angle A} = \dfrac{BC}{AC}$

EXAMPLE 1 Find the sine, cosine, and tangent of $\angle A$ and $\angle B$.

SOLUTION

$$\sin A = \frac{3}{5} \qquad \sin B = \frac{4}{5}$$
$$\cos A = \frac{4}{5} \qquad \cos B = \frac{3}{5}$$
$$\tan A = \frac{3}{4} \qquad \tan B = \frac{4}{3}$$

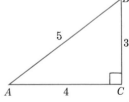

EXAMPLE 2 Find the sine, cosine, and tangent of $\angle K$.

SOLUTION First use the Pythagorean theorem to find the length of the hypotenuse.

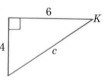

$$c^2 = 6^2 + 4^2 = 36 + 16 = 52$$
$$\therefore c = \sqrt{52} = 2\sqrt{13}$$

$$\sin K = \frac{4}{2\sqrt{13}} = \frac{2\sqrt{13}}{13} \qquad \cos K = \frac{6}{2\sqrt{13}} = \frac{3\sqrt{13}}{13} \qquad \tan K = \frac{4}{6} = \frac{2}{3}$$

480

The values of the trigonometric ratios of an angle depend only on the measure of the angle and not on the particular right triangle which contains the angle. For example, in the two right triangles below, $\angle A$ and $\angle D$ have equal measures. It can be shown that the trigonometric ratios of $\angle A$ and $\angle D$ are also equal.

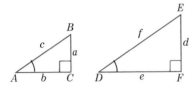

Since $\angle A = \angle D$ and $\angle C = \angle F = 90°$, the triangles are similar and their corresponding sides are proportional:

$$\frac{a}{d} = \frac{c}{f}$$

Multiplying both ratios by $\frac{d}{c}$, you obtain the equivalent proportion

$$\frac{a}{c} = \frac{d}{f}, \text{ or } \sin A = \sin D.$$

You can show similarly that $\cos A = \cos D$ and $\tan A = \tan D$.

Because the values of $\sin A$, $\cos A$, and $\tan A$ depend only on the measure of $\angle A$ and not on the triangle containing $\angle A$, you can think of these trigonometric ratios as the values of three functions each having the set of acute angles as its domain. These functions are called **trigonometric functions.**

Oral Exercises

State the value of each trigonometric ratio for the triangle shown.

1. $\sin A$ $\frac{15}{17}$
2. $\cos A$ $\frac{8}{17}$
3. $\tan A$ $\frac{15}{8}$
4. $\sin B$ $\frac{8}{17}$
5. $\cos B$ $\frac{15}{17}$
6. $\tan B$ $\frac{8}{15}$

7. $\sin X$ $\frac{35}{37}$
8. $\cos X$ $\frac{12}{37}$
9. $\tan X$ $\frac{35}{12}$
10. $\sin Y$ $\frac{12}{37}$
11. $\cos Y$ $\frac{35}{37}$
12. $\tan Y$ $\frac{12}{35}$

3.

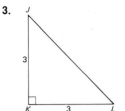

a. Find the length of the hypotenuse of the isosceles right triangle pictured.

$3^2 + 3^2 = (JL)^2$
$18 = (JL)^2$
$JL = 3\sqrt{2}$

b. Find the measure of each base angle of the isosceles right triangle pictured.

$x + x + 90 = 180$
$2x = 90$
$x = 45$
$\angle J = \angle L = 45°$

c. Using the information obtained in parts a and b, evaluate $\sin 45°$, $\cos 45°$, and $\tan 45°$.

$\sin 45° = \dfrac{3}{3\sqrt{2}} = \dfrac{\sqrt{2}}{2}$

$\cos 45° = \dfrac{3}{3\sqrt{2}} = \dfrac{\sqrt{2}}{2}$

$\tan 45° = \dfrac{3}{3} = 1$

4.

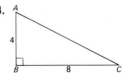

Find $\sin C$.

$b^2 = 4^2 + 8^2$
$b^2 = 16 + 64 = 80$
$b = \sqrt{80} = 4\sqrt{5}$

$\sin C = \dfrac{4}{4\sqrt{5}} = \dfrac{\sqrt{5}}{5}$

Suggested Assignment

Maximum
482/1–13

Written Exercises

For each right triangle shown, find $\cos A$, $\sin A$, $\tan A$, $\cos B$, $\sin B$, and $\tan B$. Write your answers in simplest radical form.

A 1.

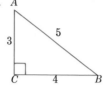

2.

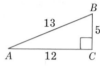

3.

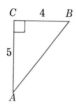

4.

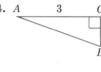

5.

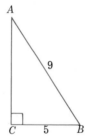

6.

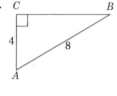

Show that for all right triangles ABC, where $\angle C$ is a right angle and $\angle A$ is an acute angle, the following statements are true.

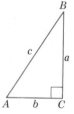

B 7. $\cos A = \sin B$ **8.** $\sin A = \cos B$

    9. $(\sin A)^2 + (\cos A)^2 = 1$ **10.** $\tan A = \dfrac{\sin A}{\cos A}$

C 11. If $\cos A = \dfrac{6}{10}$, find $\sin A$. $\dfrac{8}{10}$, or $\dfrac{4}{5}$

    12. If $\sin B = \dfrac{3}{8}$, find the sine of the complement of $\angle B$. $\dfrac{\sqrt{55}}{8}$

    13. If $\tan D = \dfrac{20}{21}$, find $\sin D$ and $\cos D$. $\sin D = \dfrac{20}{29}$, $\cos D = \dfrac{21}{29}$

482

Using Trigonometric Tables

OBJECTIVE To find values of trigonometric ratios for given angles, and measures of angles for given trigonometric ratios.

Values of the trigonometric ratios for degree measures of angles are needed to solve practical problems involving right triangles. A few values can be easily computed using the properties of special triangles and the Pythagorean theorem. For an isosceles right triangle:

$$\sin 45° = \frac{1}{\sqrt{2}} = \frac{\sqrt{2}}{2} \approx 0.707$$

$$\cos 45° = \frac{1}{\sqrt{2}} = \frac{\sqrt{2}}{2} \approx 0.707$$

$$\tan 45° = \frac{1}{1} = 1$$

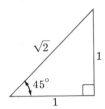

Most values of trigonometric ratios have to be computed by advanced methods. Approximate values are listed in the table of trigonometric ratios at the back of the book. You can use the table to find sin A, cos A, and tan A for any angle with whole-number measure from 1° to 89°.

To find the value of sin 63°, locate 63° in the left-hand column of the table and then read across the row to find:

$\sin 63° \approx 0.8910$

$\cos 63° \approx 0.4540$

$\tan 63° \approx 1.9626$

For ordinary computation you may write = instead of ≈ in equations such as these.

Angle	Sine	Cosine	Tangent
1°	.0175	.9998	.0175
61°	.8746	.4848	1.8040
62°	.8829	.4695	1.8807
63°	.8910	.4540	1.9626
64°	.8988	.4384	2.0503
65°	.9063	.4226	2.1445

The trigonometric table can also be used to approximate the measure of an angle if one of its trigonometric ratios is given. For example, the table indicates that an angle whose sine is approximately 0.8746 has a measure of 61°.

Suppose that cos A = 0.4273, a number not listed in the table. To find the approximate measure of $\angle A$, locate in the cosine column the entries between which 0.4273 lies:

$$\cos 64° = 0.4384 \quad \text{and} \quad \cos 65° = 0.4226.$$

Thus, $\qquad 64° < \angle A < 65°.$

Since 0.4273 is closer to 0.4226 than it is to 0.4384,

$\qquad \angle A = 65°$, to the nearest degree.

LOOKING AHEAD **483**

---

6. $\cos A = \dfrac{1}{2}$; $\sin A = \dfrac{\sqrt{3}}{2}$;

$\tan A = \sqrt{3}$;

$\cos B = \dfrac{\sqrt{3}}{2}$;

$\sin B = \dfrac{1}{2}$; $\tan B = \dfrac{\sqrt{3}}{3}$

7. $\cos A = \dfrac{b}{c} = \sin B$

8. $\sin A = \dfrac{a}{c} = \cos B$

9. $(\sin A)^2 + (\cos A)^2$

$$= \left(\frac{a}{c}\right)^2 + \left(\frac{b}{c}\right)^2 = \frac{a^2 + b^2}{c^2}$$

$$= \frac{c^2}{c^2} = 1$$

10. $\tan A = \dfrac{a}{b} = \dfrac{\frac{a}{c}}{\frac{b}{c}} = \dfrac{\sin A}{\cos A}$

Teaching Suggestions p. T112

Suggested Extensions p. T112

Chalkboard Examples

1. Use the table on page 527 to find the values of:

   a. tan 58° 1.6003

   b. sin 10° 0.1736

   c. cos 83° 0.1219

2. Use the table on page 527 to find the values of the trigonometric functions for angles of degree measure 45°, 30°, and 60°.

   tan 30° = 0.5774

   sin 30° = 0.5000

   cos 30° = 0.8660

   tan 60° = 1.7321

   sin 60° = 0.8660

   cos 60° = 0.5000

   tan 45° = 1

   sin 45° = 0.7071

   cos 45° = 0.7071

   (continued)

Oral Exercises

For Exercises 1–12, use the portion of the table of trigonometric ratios shown on the preceding page.

State the value of each trigonometric ratio.

1. sin 1°   0.0175   2. tan 1°   0.0175   3. cos 61°   0.4848
4. tan 62°   1.8807   5. sin 65°   0.9063   6. cos 64°   0.4384

Find the measure of ∠A to the nearest degree.

7. cos A = 0.9998   1°   8. tan A = 2.0503   64°   9. sin A = 0.8746   61°
10. sin A = 0.9000   64°   11. cos A = 0.4700   62°   12. tan A = 2.1337   65°

Written Exercises

Use the table at the back of the book to find sin A, cos A, and tan A for the given measure of ∠A.

A 1. 20°   2. 80°   3. 35°   4. 51°   5. 17°   6. 39°
   7. 43°   8. 26°   9. 62°   10. 18°   11. 73°   12. 84°

Find the measure of ∠A to the nearest degree.

13. sin A = 0.4695   28°   14. cos A = 0.9511   18°   15. cos A = 0.3762   68°
16. sin A = 0.9751   77°   17. tan A = 0.4245   23°   18. cos A = 0.8835   28°
19. sin A = 0.6939   44°   20. tan A = 4.0940   76°   21. tan A = 0.3788   21°
22. sin A = 0.8384   57°   23. cos A = 0.0710   86°   24. tan A = 1.2511   51°

Biography Shibasaburo Kitasato

Shibasaburo Kitasato (1852–1931) was the eldest son of the mayor of a small mountain village in Japan. He studied medicine at the University of Tokyo and graduated in 1883. After working for the Public Health Bureau, he spent six years in Germany studying under the famous bacteriologist, Robert Koch. During this time he isolated the bacterium that causes the infectious diseases symptomatic anthrax and tetanus. A paper he coauthored in 1890 marked the beginning of the science of serology, the use of immune serums or antitoxins to cure infectious diseases and prevent epidemics.

   Kitasato was elected the first president of the Japanese Medical Association in 1923 and was given the title of baron in 1924 by the emperor of Japan.

484

Numerical Trigonometry

OBJECTIVE To use trigonometric ratios to solve problems.

Using trigonometric ratios, you can solve many practical problems involving right triangles.

EXAMPLE 1 A van is moving along a straight road which makes a 7° angle with the level ground. The van passes two signposts 1500 m apart. How much higher, to the nearest meter, is the base of the second signpost above the base of the first signpost?

SOLUTION Draw a triangle showing the known values.

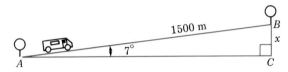

You wish to find x, the height of the base of the second signpost above the base of the first signpost. Since $\triangle ABC$ is a right triangle,

$$\sin 7° = \frac{x}{1500}, \quad \text{or} \quad x = 1500(\sin 7°).$$

From the table, $\sin 7° = 0.1219$.
Then $x = 1500(0.1219) = 182.85$

∴ to the nearest meter, the second signpost is 183 m above the first signpost. *Answer*

In surveying and navigation problems involving right triangles, the terms *angle of elevation* and *angle of depression* are used.

In the diagram below, $\angle CBA$ is an angle of elevation, since the point A is elevated with respect to the observer at B. $\angle DAB$ is an angle of depression, since the point B is depressed with respect to the observer at A.

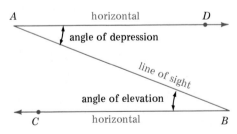

Teaching Suggestions p. T112

Suggested Extensions p. T112

Chalkboard Examples

1. Find x to the nearest centimeter.

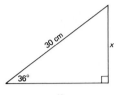

$$\sin 36° = \frac{x}{30}$$

$$0.5878 = \frac{x}{30}$$

$$x = 30(0.5878) = 17.634$$

$$\therefore x \approx 18 \text{ cm}$$

2. Find angle A to the nearest degree.

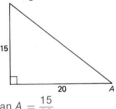

$$\tan A = \frac{15}{20}$$

$$\tan A = 0.75$$

$$\therefore \angle A \approx 37°$$

3. The angle of elevation to the top of a tree, viewed from a point 16 m from the base of the tree, is 48°. Find the height of the tree to the nearest meter.

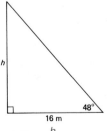

$$\tan 48° = \frac{h}{16}$$

$$1.1106 = \frac{h}{16}$$

(continued)

$h = 16(1.1106) = 17.7696$

∴ to the nearest meter, the height of the tree is 18 m.

4. A 12 m ladder rests against the side of a house. If the foot of the ladder is 5 m away from the house, find, to the nearest degree, the angle that the ladder makes with the ground.

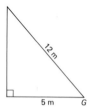

$\cos G = \dfrac{5}{12} = 0.4167$

$\angle G \approx 65°$

∴ to the nearest degree, the ladder makes an angle of 65° with the ground.

Supplementary Material

Practice Master 80

Suggested Assignment

Maximum
Day 1: 487/1–17 odd
Day 2: 487/P: 1–15 odd
Day 3: 488/P: 8, 12
 R 490/Review

EXAMPLE 2 On the top of a vertical cliff 320 m above sea level, the angle of depression of a boat out at sea is 42°. To the nearest meter, what is the distance of the boat from the base of the cliff?

SOLUTION Draw a triangle. You wish to find x, the distance of the boat from the base of the cliff. In right $\triangle ABC$ $\angle CAB = (90 - 42)° = 48°$.

$$\tan 48° = \frac{x}{320}$$

$$x = 320 \tan 48°$$

From the table, $\tan 48° = 1.1106$.
Then, $x = 320(1.1106) = 355.392$.

∴ to the nearest meter, the boat is 355 m from the base of the cliff.
Answer

Oral Exercises

State whether you would use the cosine, sine, or tangent ratio to find x for each figure.

1. sine
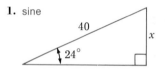

2. cosine
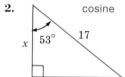

3. tangent
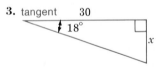

4. tangent
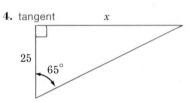

5. cosine
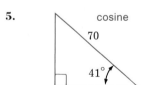

6. sine
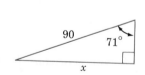

486

Written Exercises

Use the table at the back of the book as needed.

A **1–6.** In the Oral Exercises, find x for each figure. Give each length to the nearest whole number.

1. 16   **2.** 10   **3.** 10   **4.** 54   **5.** 53   **6.** 85

In right triangle ABC, with $\angle C = 90°$, find the other sides of the triangle to the nearest whole number from the following facts.

7. $\angle A = 39°$, $AB = 64$ **8.** $\angle A = 35°$, $AB = 61$

9. $\angle A = 16°$, $AC = 60$ **10.** $\angle B = 68°$, $BC = 85$
    $BC \approx 17$, $AB \approx 62$ $AC \approx 210$, $AB \approx 227$

In right $\triangle MNR$, $\angle N = 90°$. Find the measures of $\angle M$ and $\angle R$ to the nearest degree from the following facts.

                              $\angle M \approx 61°$, $\angle R \approx 29°$

B **11.** $MN = 25$, $NR = 45$ **12.** $MR = 32$, $NR = 28$

13. $RM = 40$, $MN = 38$ **14.** $MR = 45$, $NR = 27$
   $\angle M \approx 18°$; $\angle R \approx 72°$ $\angle M \approx 37°$, $\angle R \approx 53°$

In right $\triangle XYZ$, $\angle Z = 90°$. Find the measures of the other sides of the triangle to the nearest whole number from the following facts.

15. $\angle Y = 38°$, $XY = 50$ **16.** $\angle X = 72°$, $XY = 38$

17. $\angle X = 24°$, $XY = 47$ **18.** $\angle Y = 42°$, $XY = 80$
15. $YZ \approx 39$, $XZ \approx 31$ **16.** $YZ \approx 36$, $XZ \approx 12$
17. $YZ \approx 19$, $XZ \approx 43$ **18.** $YZ \approx 59$, $XZ \approx 54$

Problems

Solve each problem, drawing a sketch for each. Express distances to the nearest unit. Use the table in the back of the book as needed.

A **1.** To the nearest meter, how far is it across the swamp? 98 m   **2.** To the nearest centimeter, how high is the flagpole? 429 cm

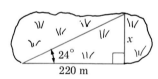

3. A 28 m long cable connects a point on the ground to the top of a pole. The cable makes a 32° angle with the ground. Find the height of the pole.
                    15 m

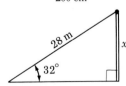

Additional Answers
Written Exercises

7. $BC \approx 40$, $AC \approx 50$
8. $BC \approx 35$, $AC \approx 50$
11. $\angle M \approx 61°$, $\angle R \approx 29°$

LOOKING AHEAD   **487**

4. A 400 cm ladder resting against a building makes a 58° angle with the ground. How far is the bottom of the ladder from the base of the building? 212 cm

5. A train increases its altitude by 11 m when traveling along 200 m of track. Find the angle of elevation of the track. 3°

Ex. 5

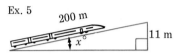

Ex. 6

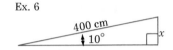

6. A ramp 400 cm long is dropped from the rear of a van to the ground. If the ramp makes a 10° angle with the ground, find how high the floor of the van is from the ground. 69 cm

7. If a rocket flies 1° off course for 5000 km, how far away from the correct path will the rocket be? 87 km

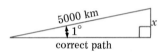

8. A surveyor is determining the direction in which tunnel AB is to be dug through a mountain. She locates point C so that $\angle C = 90°$, $AC = 1.5$ km, and $BC = 3.5$ km. Find $\angle A$ to the nearest degree. 67°

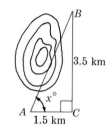

B **9.** Jon is standing 150 m from the base of a cliff. He determines that the angle of elevation to the top of the cliff is 48°. Find the height of the cliff. 167 m

10. From a helicopter the angle of depression of a stranded car is 22°. The altimeter shows that the helicopter is 1300 m above the ground. Assuming that the ground is flat in that location, determine how far the car is from a point directly below the helicopter. 3218 m

488

11. From the bow of a ship 50 m long heading directly north, a lighthouse is sighted directly west. At the same time the lighthouse is sighted at an 80° angle from the stern of the ship. Find the distance from the bow to the lighthouse. 284 m

12. A diving submarine travels through water at a steady rate of 320 m/min on a diving path that forms a 4° angle of depression with the surface of the water. After 5 min, how far is the submarine below the surface? 112 m

C 13. A trail bike driven in a straight path for 200 m makes an angle turn and travels 200 m again. At this point, the driver returns directly 240 m to the starting point. Through what angle did the driver turn? 74°

14. From a 1400 m high observation tower the angles of depression of two cars in the same direction are found to be 18° and 28°. Find the distance between the two cars. 1676 m

15. From a point in the street between two buildings, the angles of elevation of the tops of the buildings are 45° each. When the observer moves 6 m toward one of the buildings, the angles of elevation are 30° and 60°. How high is each building? 8 m and 14 m

Summary

1. Geometry deals with the properties of sets of points such as lines, rays, angles, and triangles.

2. Two angles whose sides are rays in the same lines but in opposite directions are vertical angles. Any pair of angles the sum of whose measures is 90° are complementary angles. Two angles are supplementary if the sum of their measures is 180°.

3. The sum of the measures of the angles of a triangle is 180°. Some special triangles are right triangles, isosceles triangles, and equilateral triangles.

4. Similar triangles have the same shape. Their corresponding angles have the same measure and corresponding sides are proportional.

5. Trigonometric ratios: $\cos A = \dfrac{b}{c}$, $\sin A = \dfrac{a}{c}$, $\tan A = \dfrac{a}{b}$

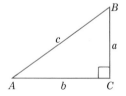

Review

Give the letter of the best answer.

1. Which symbol denotes the measure of a line segment joining points A and B?

   (a.) AB b. $\overline{AB}$ c. $\overrightarrow{AB}$ d. $\overleftrightarrow{AB}$

2. Which angle is an acute angle?

   a. $\angle A = 99°$ (b.) $\angle B = 89°$ c. $\angle C = 90°$ d. $\angle D = 100°$

3. Find the measure of the complement of an angle of 36°.

   a. 154°   b. 144°   c. 64°   (d.) 54°

4. Find the supplement of an angle with measure $x°$.

   a. $(90 - x)°$ b. $(90 + x)°$ (c.) $(180 - x)°$ d. $(180 + x)°$

5. Find the sum of the measures of the angles of an isosceles triangle.

   a. 45°   b. 90°   (c.) 180°   d. 360°

6. If $\triangle ABC \sim \triangle DEF$, $\dfrac{AB}{DE} = \dfrac{7}{2}$, and $CA = 10$, find FD.

   a. 35   (b.) $\dfrac{20}{7}$ c. $\dfrac{7}{20}$ d. 5

7. Use the diagram to find $\sin A$.

   a. $\dfrac{6}{8}$ b. $\dfrac{4}{5}$

   (c.) $\dfrac{3}{5}$ d. $\dfrac{4}{3}$

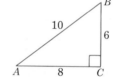

8. Use the table at the back of the book to find $\tan 72°$.

   a. 0.1228   b. 2.3090   c. 0.0777   (d.) 3.0777

9. The top of a stairway is 2 m higher than the bottom. The angle of elevation from the bottom of the stairs to the top is 25°. Find the approximate horizontal length of the stairway.

   (a.) 4.3 m   b. 1.8 m   c. 4.7 m   d. 0.9 m

490

EXTRA PRACTICE

CHAPTER 1

Simplify.

1. $4 + (3 \times 6)$ 22
2. $(4 + 3) \times 6$ 42
3. $(20 + 2) \times (7 + 3)$ 220
4. $(20 \div 2) - (7 - 3)$ 6
5. $(20 - 2) \div (7 + 2)$ 2
6. $(20 \times 2) + (7 \times 3)$ 61

Evaluate each expression if $a = 1$, $b = 2$, $c = 3$, and $d = 4$.

7. $ab + cd$ 14
8. $(b + c)(c + d)$ 35
9. $a(b + c - d)$ 1
10. $\dfrac{c + d}{a + 3b}$ 1
11. $5a - 2a$ 3
12. $5c - 2c$ 9
13. $\dfrac{ab + 2c}{a + c}$ 2
14. $2(a + bc)$ 14
15. $2a + 2bc$ 14
16. $d[a + b(c + d)]$ 60
17. $\dfrac{2c + b}{2a} - \dfrac{(a + b)(c + d)}{3b + a}$ 1

Solve each equation if $x \in \{2, 4, 6, 8, 10\}$. If there is no solution over the given domain, write "no solution."

18. $2 + x = 8$ {6}
19. $8 + x = 2$ No solution
20. $2x + 4 = x + 8$ {4}
21. $5(x - 2) = 10$ {4}
22. $x \div (4 - x) = 1$ {2}
23. $(x + 4) - (x \div 4) = 7$
24. $x(x + 1) = 27$ No solution
25. $(x - 1)(x + 1) = (x)(x) - 1$
    23. {4}
26. $x(x + 1)(x - 1) = 6$ {2}
27. $(2x)(3x)(4x) = 24x$
    No solution
    25. {2, 4, 6, 8, 10}

Represent each phrase by a variable expression. Use n to represent the number referred to.

28. Three times a number $3n$
29. Three more than a number $n + 3$, or $3 + n$
30. Three less than a number $n - 3$
31. Three divided by a number $3 \div n$, or $\frac{3}{n}$
32. Twice a number, decreased by five $2n - 5$
33. Twice a number that has been decreased by five $2(n - 5)$
34. One less than half a number $\frac{1}{2}n - 1$

Complete each statement with an expression involving the given variable.

35. Charles is x years old now. Two years from now he will be __?__ years old. $x + 2$
36. Charles is x years old now. Two years ago he was __?__ years old. $x - 2$
37. Susan can run r km/h. Francis can run twice as fast. Francis can run __?__ km/h. $2r$

Complete each statement with an expression involving the given variable.

38. Mary can do m pushups. Julia can do 3 fewer. Julia can do __?__ pushups. $m - 3$

39. A box has 22 pieces of chocolate. There are d pieces of dark chocolate and __?__ pieces of light chocolate. $22 - d$

40. Four years ago David was d years old. Now David is __?__ years old. $d + 4$

41. A record and a poster together cost m dollars. If the poster costs p dollars, then the record costs __?__ dollars. $m - p$

For each exercise, write an equation that represents the given facts in terms of the given variable.

42. The perimeter of a square is x cm and each side is 12 cm long. $x = 4 \cdot 12$, or $\frac{x}{4} = 12$

43. The side of a square is x cm long, and the perimeter is 32 cm. $4x = 32$

44. Pam can run at m km/h. In 2.5 h (hours) she can run 30 km. $2.5m = 30$

45. Scott can run at 12 km/h. In t hours he can run 8 km. $12t = 8$

46. Sarah received t on her first test and 87 on her next test. The average of her grades is 82. $(t + 87)/2 = 82$

47. The smallest of three consecutive numbers is m. The sum of the three numbers is 4224. $m + (m + 1) + (m + 2) = 4224$

48. The smallest of three consecutive numbers is m. The product of the three numbers is 716. $m(m + 1)(m + 2) = 716$

49. One number is x, and a second number is 3 times the first. The sum of the two numbers equals their product. $x + 3x = x(3x)$

50. The length of a rectangle is x cm, and the width is 6 cm less than the length. The perimeter is 24 cm. $2x + 2(x - 6) = 24$

51. Brad pays x cents for one ride on the subway. He pays \$1.75 (175 cents) for 7 rides. $7x = 175$

52. Harold is h years old now. Nine years ago he was 27 years old. $h - 9 = 27$

53. A record costs r dollars. The cost of a cassette is \$3 more than twice the cost of the record. Together, the record and tape cost \$11.40. $r + (2r + 3) = 11.4$

CHAPTER 2

Add.

1. -7
$\underline{2}$ -5

2. 6
$\underline{-7}$ -1

3. -4
$\underline{6}$ 2

4. -4
$\underline{-3}$ -7

5. -3
$\underline{-2}$ -5

6. -2
$\underline{1}$ -1

7. 1
$\underline{-1}$ 0

8. -7
$\underline{8}$ 1

9. 8
$\underline{-2}$ 6

10. -2
$\underline{-5}$ -7

11. -5
$\underline{-10}$ -15

12. -10
$\underline{5}$ -5

Simplify.

13. $(-4 + 5) + (-3)$ −2
14. $(4 + 5) + (-3)$ 6
15. $(6 + 8) + (-10)$ 4
16. $[6 + (-10)] + 12$ 8
17. $[-4 + (-5)] + 3$ −6
18. $[4 + (-5)] + (-3)$ −4
19. $[-4 + (-7)] + (-8)$ −19
20. $[12 + (-5)] + 5$ 12
21. $(6 + 7) + (-1 + 5)$ 17
22. $(-6 + 7) + (-1 + 5)$ 5
23. $[6 + (-7)] + [4 + (-6)]$ −3
24. $[8 + (-2)] + 8 + (-12)$ 2
25. $[-6 + (-7)] + (-8)$ −21
26. $(2 + 8 + 10) + (-20)$ 0
27. $-[35 + (-7)] + [-(-3 + 8)]$ −33
28. $-[8 + (-2)] + [3 + (-10)]$ −13
29. $-[35 + 5] + [-(-2 + (-8))]$ −30
30. $[-(10 + (-1)) + (-3)] + [-6 + (-4)]$ −22

Replace each _?_ with a numeral to make a true statement.

31. $8 + \text{_?_} = 10$ 2
32. $-5 + \text{_?_} = 2$ 7
33. $5 + \text{_?_} = -2$ −7
34. $-8 + \text{_?_} = -10$ −2
35. $8 + \text{_?_} = -10$ −18
36. $5 + \text{_?_} = 2$ −3
37. $-7 + \text{_?_} = -7$ 0
38. $-2 + 3 + (-5) + \dfrac{\text{_?_}}{7} = 3$

Solve each sentence if the domain of m is $\{-4, -2, 0, 2, 4\}$. If there is no solution over the given domain, write "no solution."

39. $|m + 5| = 9$ 4
40. $m + 5 < 2$ −4
41. $|m + (-3)| = 1$ $\{2, 4\}$
42. $|m + (-6)| < 3$ 4
43. $|m| + 5 = 9$ $\{-4, 4\}$
44. $|m + (-6)| < -2$ No sol.
45. $|m| + (-5) = -3$ $\{-2, 2\}$
46. $m + |m| + |m + 2| = 2$ $\{-4, 0\}$

Solve.

47. $x + 12 = -2$ −14
48. $x + 12 = 2$ −10
49. $x + 2 = 12$ 10
50. $x + (-8) = -5$ 3
51. $x + (-5) = -8$ −3
52. $x + (-12) = 2$ 14
53. $x + 8 = -88$ −96
54. $x + 51 = 50$ −1

In Exercise 55:

  a. Name a positive or a negative number to represent each measurement given in the problem.

  b. Compute the sum of the numbers.   **c.** Answer the question.

55. In a game, a playing piece is moved 3 spaces forward, 2 spaces back, 7 spaces forward, and then 2 more spaces forward. How many spaces forward from its original position is the piece now?
  a. 3, −2, 7, 2 **b.** 10 **c.** 10 spaces

In each of Exercises 56-58:

   a. Name a positive or a negative number to represent each measurement given in the problem.

   b. Compute the sum of the numbers.

   c. Answer the question.
       a. 12, -5, 21, -8, 12, -20, 2, -2 **b.** 12   **c.** 12 people

56. A bus starts with 12 people. It stops and discharges 5, and picks up 21. On the next stop it discharges 8, and picks up 12. On the next stop it discharges 20 and picks up 2. On the next stop it discharges 2. How many people are left on the bus?

57. The temperature of a liquid is 20°C at the beginning of an experiment. During the experiment, the temperature of the liquid drops 8°C, then rises 2°C, and then drops 1.5°C. What is the final temperature of the liquid? **a.** 20, -8, 2, -1.5 **b.** 12.5   **c.** 12.5°C

58. A balloon rises 1.2 km from the ground. It then rises 0.2 km, falls 0.8 km, rises 1.1 km, rises another 0.5 km, and falls 0.8 km. How high is the balloon above the ground after these changes in its position? **a.** 1.2, 0.2, -0.8, 1.1, 0.5, -0.8
        b. 1.4   **c.** 1.4 km

Simplify.

59. $10\left(\dfrac{1}{2} + \dfrac{1}{5}\right)$ 7   **60.** $13\left(1 + \dfrac{1}{13}\right)$ 14   **61.** $\dfrac{2}{3}(4) + \dfrac{2}{3}(2)$ 4

62. $3\left(\dfrac{1}{3}\right) + 8\left(\dfrac{1}{8}\right)$ 2   **63.** $21(98) + 21(2)$ 2100   **64.** $2p + 8p$ 10p

65. $6x + (-2)x$ 4x   **66.** $28w + 2w$ 30w   **67.** $-23a + 3a$ $-20a$

68. $-22x + 21x$ $-x$ **69.** $22x + (-21)x$ x   **70.** $-22x + (-21)x$
                                                        $-43x$

71. $12 + 8y + 6y$ $12 + 14y$ **72.** $-12 + 3d + (-9)d$ $-12 + (-6)d$

73. $-3h + (-3)h + (-2)h$ $-8h$ **74.** $6(x + 2y) + 3(x + 2y)$

75. $98(x + 2) + 2(x + 2)$ 100x + 200   **76.** $3(x + 1) + 2(x + 2) + (x + 3)$

77. $0.2(x + 6) + 2.2(x + 2)$ 2.4x + 5.6   **78.** $12(x + 4 + y) + 8(x + y + 4)$
                                                   74. 9x + 18y

79. $5\left(k + \dfrac{1}{5}\right) + 3(2k + m) + 2m$ **76.** 6x + 10
                          11k + 5m + 1   **78.** 20x + 20y + 80

Multiply.

80. $\begin{array}{r} -6 \\ \underline{-1} \end{array}$ 6   **81.** $\begin{array}{r} -4 \\ \underline{-2} \end{array}$ 8   **82.** $\begin{array}{r} -3 \\ \underline{2} \end{array}$ -6 6 **83.** $\begin{array}{r} -2 \\ \underline{-3} \end{array}$

84. $\begin{array}{r} -1 \\ \underline{3} \end{array}$ -3 **85.** $\begin{array}{r} 0 \\ \underline{-4} \end{array}$ 0   **86.** $\begin{array}{r} 2 \\ \underline{-5} \end{array}$ -10 -24 **87.** $\begin{array}{r} 4 \\ \underline{-6} \end{array}$

Simplify.

88. $(-1)(-2)(-3)$ -6 **89.** $(-12)(0)(12)$ 0

90. $(-2)(2) + (-1)(5)$ -9 **91.** $(-3)(98) + (-3)(2)$ -300

494   *EXTRA PRACTICE*

92. $(21)(2) + (-2)(-21)$ 84

94. $6[5 + (-2)]$ 18

96. $(-2)[-3 + (-4)]$ 14

98. $3[(-1) + (-2) + (-3) + (-4)]$ -30

100. $-2[x + y]$ $-2x + (-2)y$

102. $2(x + y + z) + (-2)(x + y + z)$ 0

104. $-10 + (-3)[2 + (-8)]$ 8

106. $\dfrac{1}{-2} \cdot \dfrac{1}{5}$ $-\frac{1}{10}$

107. $\dfrac{1}{-3} \cdot \dfrac{1}{-21}$ $\frac{1}{63}$

109. $\dfrac{1}{5}(-25)$ -5

110. $(-35)\left(-\dfrac{1}{7}\right)\left(-\dfrac{1}{5}\right)$ -1

111. $(-111)\left(\dfrac{1}{3}\right)(-10)$ 370

112. $(2ab)\left(\dfrac{1}{a}\right),\ a \neq 0$ $2b$

113. $\dfrac{1}{2}[22x + 44y]$ $11x + 22y$

114. $-\dfrac{1}{2}[44x + (-6)]$ $-22x + 3$

115. $-8\left[\dfrac{1}{4}(-x) + \dfrac{1}{2}(-y)\right]$ $2x + 4y$

116. $(-6)\left[\dfrac{1}{3}p + (-2) + \left(-\dfrac{1}{2}\right)r + \left(-\dfrac{1}{6}\right)s\right]$ $-2p + 12 + 3r + s$

93. $(1.2)(-2) + (2)(0.3)$ -1.8

95. $(6)(5) + (6)(-2)$ 18

97. $(-2)(-3) + (-2)(-4)$ 14

99. $(-3)(1) + (-3)(2) + (-3)(4)$

101. $2(x + 3) + (-4)(x + 3)$

103. $\left(-\dfrac{1}{2}\right)[32x + (-12)y]$

105. $5[5 + (-5 + 2)5] + (-5)$

108. $\dfrac{1}{r} \cdot \dfrac{1}{-5},\ r \neq 0$

CHAPTER 3

Solve each equation by transformation by addition.

1. $r + (-12) = 2$ 14

2. $y + 3 = 12$ 9

3. $m + (-12) = -3$ 9

4. $8 + t = 0$ -8

5. $8 + t = -4$ -12

6. $8 + (-t) = -4$ 12

7. $9 = 21 + (m + 2)$ -14

8. $-x + (-2) = 6$ -8

9. $612 + x = 0$ -612

10. $x + (-5) = |2 - 8|$ 11

11. $x + (-1) + 2 + (-3) = 10$ 12

Simplify.

12. $4 - 21$ -17

13. $12 - 6$ 6

14. $6 - 12$ -6

15. $27 - (-3)$ 30

16. $4 - (-5)$ 9

17. $321 - (320 + 1)$ 0

18. $(42 - 52) - 61$ -71

19. $(42 - 52) - (51 - 2)$ -59

20. $-10 - 3 - [-8 + 2]$ -7

21. $-(10 + 3) - [2 - 8]$ -7

22. $12 - 21 + 22$ 13

23. $1.23 - 2.23$ -1

24. $-3.5 - 2.5$ -6

25. $-3.5 - (-2.5)$ -1

26. $21 - [-12 - 8 - 10]$ 51

27. $12 - (-3) - [3 - (-12)]$ 0

28. $x + [x - z]$ $2x - z$

29. $x - [x - z]$ z

30. $-x - [-x - z]$ z

31. $3x + [8x - 2x]$ $9x$

32. $(3x - 5x) - (5x - 3x)$ $-4x$

33. $3m + 7 - (-7 + m)$ $2m + 14$

34. $(2t + 8) - (8t + 2) - (8 - 2t)$ $-4t - 2$

Write each phrase using symbols of algebra. Then simplify.

35. -3 decreased by 8 $-3 - 8$; -11

36. -7 decreased by -3 $-7 - (-3)$; -4

37. $(x - 5)$ less than x $x - (x - 5)$; 5

38. $(7 + y)$ less than y $y - (7 + y)$; -7

39. Subtract $3\pi + 2$ from $3\pi - 2$. $3\pi - 2 - (3\pi + 2)$; -4

40. From $5 - 6\pi$ subtract $8 - 6\pi$. $5 - 6\pi - (8 - 6\pi)$; -3

41. Decrease the sum of -8 and 17 by -6. $(-8 + 17) - (-6)$; 15

42. Decrease -18 by the sum of -34 and 12. $-18 - (-34 + 12)$; 4

Evaluate each expression if $x = 2$ and $y = -5$.

43. $x + y$ -3

44. $x - y$ 7

45. $y - x$ -7

46. $x(x - y)$ 14

47. $(x)(x) - (x)(y)$ 14

48. $2x + 3y - 3y - 2y$ 14

49. $-2(x - y)$ -14

50. $xy - 2x - 2y$ -4

51. $2xy - x - y$ -17

Solve.

52. $x + 8 = 42$ 34

53. $x + 42 = 8$ -34

54. $x - 8 = 42$ 50

55. $x - 42 = 8$ 50

56. $x - (-4) = 3$ -1

57. $x - 1 = 10$ 11

58. $2 + x = -8$ -10

59. $-2 + x = -8$ -6

60. $6 - x = -7$ 13

61. $-6 - x = -7$ 1

62. $12 = x + 10$ 2

63. $12 = x - 10$ 22

64. $8t = -24$ -3

65. $(-8)t = 32$ -4

66. $\frac{1}{2}x = -7$ -14

67. $\frac{1}{5}x = -8$ -40

68. $6m = -312$ -52

69. $\frac{2}{3}m = 10$ 15

70. $-6f = -66$ 11

71. $-5y = 210$ -42

72. $-27x = -675$ 25

Evaluate each expression if $r = -3$ and $s = -21$.

73. rs 63

74. $\frac{s}{r}$ 7

75. $\frac{-s}{r}$ -7

76. $\frac{s}{-r}$ -7

77. $-\frac{s}{r}$ -7

78. $r(r + s)$ 72

79. $\frac{rs}{-s}$ 3

80. $\frac{r}{s} + \frac{r + s}{s}$ $9\frac{}{}$ $\frac{9}{7}$

81. $\frac{2r + s}{9r}$ 1

82. $\frac{2s}{21r - s}$ 1

83. $\frac{s}{r}(2r - 8r)$ 126

Solve.

84. $2x + 8 = 12$ 2

85. $\frac{x}{3} + 5 = -2$ -21

86. $18 = 6 - 4m$ -3

87. $-12 = -3 - t$ 9

88. $5m - 2m = 0$ 0

89. $x - 4x - 8x = 22$ -2

90. $0 = 2x - 2 + 8x - 8$ 1

91. $2(x - 8) = -11$ $\frac{5}{2}$

92. $-3(x - 5) = 30$ -5

93. $2(x - 2) + 4 = 0$ 0

94. $8 - 8(x - 8) = 88$ -2

95. $2r + 3(r + 4) = 0$ $-\frac{12}{5}$

96. $12x = 4x + 16$ 2

97. $11m + 4 = 12m$ 4

98. $3x - 4x = x + 2$ -1

99. $2t = 8t - 12$ 2

100. $8t = 2t - 12$ -2

101. $12t = 12 - 8t$ $\frac{3}{5}$

102. $6x + 5 = 8x - 1$ 3

103. $8r - 3 = 3r - 8$ -1

104. $3r + 8 = 8r + 3$ 1

105. $2(x + 4) = 12x - 42$ 5

106. $8(x - 3) = 3(x - 8)$ 0

107. $4(2x - 1) = 2(1 - 4x)$ $\frac{3}{8}$

108. $3m - 3(2 - m) = -18$ -2

109. $2r = 6(3 - r) - r$ 2

110. $3(a + 7) - 7(a - 3) = 2(a - 2) - 4(a - 8)$ 7

CHAPTER 4

Simplify.

1. 5^2 25

2. $5^2 \cdot 5^2$ 625

3. 5^4 625

4. 4^3 64

5. $\left(\frac{1}{2}\right)^2$ $\frac{1}{4}$

6. $\left(\frac{3}{4}\right)^3$ $\frac{27}{64}$

7. $(5^2 - 2^5) \div (6^2 - 2^6)$ $\frac{1}{4}$

8. $6(3^2 - 2^3) + (-3)^2$ 15

9. -5^2 -25

10. $(-5)^2$ 25

11. $(-5)^3 \cdot (2)^5$ -4000

12. $(-5)^3 + (2)^5$ -93

Evaluate each expression if $a = 3$ and $x = -3$.

13. $a^2 - ax$ 18

14. $a - ax^2$ -24

15. $a - (ax)^2$ -78

16. $(a - ax)^2$ 144

17. $\frac{a + x^2}{a - x^2}$ -2

18. $\frac{x^2 + a^2}{x^2} - \frac{x^2 + a^2}{a^2}$ 0

Simplify.

19. $(2x^2 - 5x + 2) + (x^2 - 2x + 5)$

20. $(2x^2 - 5x + 2) - (x^2 - 2x + 5)$

21. $(-6x + 2y - 3) + (2x - 4y - 7)$

22. $(-6x + 2y - 3) - (2x - 4y - 7)$

23. $(a + 2b + 3c + 4d) + (4a + 3b + 2c + d)$ $5a + 5b + 5c + 5d$

24. $(a + 2b + 3c + 4d) - (4a + 3b + 2c + d)$ $-3a - b + c + 3d$

Solve.

25. $3x - (x + 2) = 8$ 5

26. $(x + 2) - 3x = 8$ -3

27. $(x + 1) - (2x + 3) = 7$ -9

28. $(2x + 1) + (7x + 2) = 21$ 2

Simplify.

29. $a^3 \cdot a^4 \cdot a^5$ a^{12}

30. $2 \cdot x^5 \cdot x^3 \cdot x$ $2x^9$

31. $3x^5 \cdot 4x^6 \cdot 5x^7$ $60x^{18}$

32. $(a^5x)(ax^5)$ a^6x^6

33. $(-4n^2m)(2n^5m^2)$ $-8n^7m^3$

34. $(-2c^2d^2)(-3c^3d^3)$ $6c^5d^5$

35. $\left(\frac{1}{3}a^3b\right)(3ab)$ a^4b^2

36. $(2^x)(2^y)$ 2^{x+y}

37. $(2x)(3y^2)$ $6xy^2$

38. $x^n \cdot x^{n+2} \cdot x^{n+3}$ x^{3n+5}

39. $(-1)^3(-1)^4(-1)^5$ 1

40. $(-a)^2(-a)^3(-a)^4(-a)^5$ a^{14}

Simplify.

$-4x^3y^2t^6$

41. $(3x^2)(4x) + (-2x)(5x^2) + (2x^3)(3)$ $8x^3$ **42.** $(2x^2yt^5)(xyt) - (3x^3yt^3)(2yt^3)$

43. $(x^3)^4$ x^{12} **44.** $(x^4)^3$ x^{12} **45.** $(2xy^2)^2$ $4x^2y^4$

46. $(-2x^2y)^3$ $-8x^6y^3$ **47.** $(-3x^2)(-3x)^2$ $-27x^4$ **48.** $(3t)^2(3t^2)^2$ $81t^6$

49. $(2a^2b^2)^2 + 6a^4b^4$ **50.** $(x^2y)^4 - (x^4y^2)^2$ 0 **51.** $(-uv)^2(2v^2)^3(u^2v)^2$ $8u^6v^{10}$
        $10a^4b^4$

Evaluate each expression if $x = -2$ and $y = 2$.

52. $(2x)^3$ -64 **53.** $8x^3$ -64 **54.** $(xy)^3$ -64

55. $x^3 + y^3$ 0 **56.** $x^2 + y^2$ 8 **57.** $(2x + y)^2$ 4

Multiply.

58. $3(x^2 + 5x + 6)$ $3x^2 + 15x + 18$ **59.** $-3x(x^2 + 5x + 6)$ $-3x^3 - 15x^2 - 18x$

60. $(-3x)^2(x^2 + 5x + 6)$ **61.** $-3x^2(x^2 + 5x + 6)$
        $9x^4 + 45x^3 + 54x^2$ $-3x^4 - 15x^3 - 18x^2$

Simplify.

62. $2x(3x + 4) + 4x(3x + 2)$ $18x^2 + 16x$ **63.** $2x(3x + 4) - 4x(3x + 2)$ $-6x^2$

64. $7t(t^2 + 4) + 8t(t^2 - 4)$ $15t^3 - 4t$ **65.** $7t(t^2 + 4) - 8t(t^2 - 4)$ $-t^3 + 60t$

66. $\frac{1}{5}(10n + 20) - \frac{3}{5}(5n - 25)$ $-n + 19$ **67.** $\frac{1}{2}(x + 2) + \frac{1}{2}(x - 2)$ x

Solve.

68. $2(x - 2) - x = 6$ 10 **69.** $6(x - 2) + 3(x - 2) = 18$ 4

70. $2x(x - 7) - 2x^2 = 14$ -1 **71.** $\frac{1}{2}x(x + 2) + 2 = \frac{1}{2}(x^2 - 2)$ -3

72. $3(x + 4) - 4(x + 3) = 4(x + 4) + 3x$ -2

73. $7x^2 - x[2x + 5(x + 1)] = 100$ -20

Multiply.

74. $(m + 3)(m - 2)$ **75.** $(m - 3)(m + 2)$ **76.** $(m + 3)(m + 2)$

77. $(m - 3)(m - 2)$ **78.** $(2x + 3)(x + 4)$ **79.** $(2x - 3)(x + 4)$

80. $(2x + 3)(x - 4)$ **81.** $(2x - 3)(x - 4)$ **82.** $(5t + 1)(5t + 1)$

83. $(3x + 2)^2$ **84.** $(x + 1)(x^2 - x + 1)$ **85.** $(2x - 1)(4x^2 + 2x + 1)$

Additional Answers

74. $m^2 + m - 6$

75. $m^2 - m - 6$

76. $m^2 + 5m + 6$

77. $m^2 - 5m + 6$

78. $2x^2 + 11x + 12$

79. $2x^2 + 5x - 12$

80. $2x^2 - 5x - 12$

81. $2x^2 - 11x + 12$

82. $25t^2 + 10t + 1$

83. $9x^2 + 12x + 4$

84. $x^3 + 1$ **85.** $8x^3 - 1$

CHAPTER 5

For each number give all the factors between 1 and 12, inclusive.

1, 3, 5

1. 132   **2.** 231 $1, 3, 7, 11$ **3.** 858 $1, 2, 3, 6, 11$ **4.** 885

5. 102 $1, 2, 3, 6$ **6.** 201 $1, 3$ **7.** 120   **8.** 210

1. 1, 2, 3, 4, 6, 11, 12   **7.** 1, 2, 3, 4, 5, 6, 8, 10, 12

498   *EXTRA PRACTICE*   **8.** 1, 2, 3, 5, 6, 7, 10

Give the prime factorization of each number.

9. 280 $2^3 \cdot 5 \cdot 7$ **10.** 600 $2^3 \cdot 3 \cdot 5^2$ **11.** 252 $2^2 \cdot 3^2 \cdot 7$ **12.** 455 $5 \cdot 7 \cdot 13$

Simplify each expression, assuming that no variable equals 0.

13. $\dfrac{(2x^3)(3x^2)}{(6x)^2}$ $\dfrac{x^3}{6}$ **14.** $\dfrac{(2x)^3(3x^2)}{6x^2}$ $4x^3$

15. $\dfrac{(2x)^3(3x)^2}{(6x)^2}$ $2x^3$ **16.** $\dfrac{(2x)^3(3x)^2}{6x^2}$ $12x^3$

Divide. Assume that no denominator equals 0.

17. $\dfrac{8r^3 - 4r}{4}$ $2r^3 - r$ **18.** $\dfrac{8r^3 - 4r}{4r}$ $2r^2 - 1$ **19.** $\dfrac{8r^3 - (4r)^2}{4r}$ $2r^2 - 4r$

20. $\dfrac{8x^2y - 12xy^2 + 2xy}{2xy}$ $4x - 6y + 1$ **21.** $\dfrac{8x^2y - 12xy^2 + 2xy}{(2xy)^2}$ $\dfrac{2}{y} - \dfrac{3}{x} + \dfrac{1}{2xy}$

Evaluate by factoring first.

22. $12 \times 48 + 12 \times 52$ 1200   **23.** $1980 \times 111 - 1980 \times 11$ 198,000

24. $\dfrac{121 \times 12 + 121 \times 3}{15 \times 9 + 15 \times 2}$ 11   **25.** $28 \times 3 - 16 \times 9 + 28 \times 9 - 16 \times 3$ 144

Factor each polynomial as a product of its greatest monomial factor and another polynomial.

26. $2x^3y^2 - 4xy$ **27.** $8x^2y - 8xy$ **28.** $2u^2 - 100u$

29. $2\pi r^2 - 2\pi r$ **30.** $lw^2 + 3lw$ **31.** $\frac{1}{3}\pi r^2 h + \pi rh$

32. $2x^3 + 8x$ **33.** $-3x^2 + 6x$ **34.** $16x^2y^2 - 8xy^2$

35. $10x^2y - 5xy^2$ **36.** $12a^2b + 6ab^2$ **37.** $10m^3r - 20mr^2 + 15mr$

Express each product as a trinomial or as a binomial.

38. $(2m + 3)(m + 1)$ **39.** $(2m - 3)(m + 1)$ **40.** $(2m - 3)(m - 1)$

41. $(2m + 3)(m - 1)$ **42.** $(4x + 5)(4x - 5)$ **43.** $(4x + 5)(4x + 5)$

44. $(2w - 1)(5w + 3)$ **45.** $(2w - 1)(5w - 3)$ **46.** $(2w + 1)(5w + 3)$

Factor. Check by multiplying the factors.

47. $4x^2 - 1$ **48.** $25 - u^6$ **49.** $b^4 - 1600c^2$

50. $4x^2 + 4x + 1$ **51.** $16a^2 + 8ab + b^2$ **52.** $144 - 24m + m^2$

53. $k^2 + 12k + 35$ **54.** $m^2 + 7m + 6$ **55.** $m^2 - 7m + 6$

56. $m^2 + 11m + 10$ **57.** $p^2 + 8p + 12$ **58.** $p^2 + 7p + 12$

59. $k^2 + 12k + 20$ **60.** $n^2 - 9n + 20$ **61.** $y^2 - 21y + 20$

62. $x^2 + 5x + 6$ **63.** $x^2 - 5x + 6$ **64.** $y^2 - 12y + 35$

65. $x^2 + 7x - 8$ **66.** $x^2 - 7x - 8$ **67.** $x^2 + 2x - 8$

68. $(x + 2)(x - 4)$
69. $(y + 10)(y - 2)$
70. $(r + 1)(r - 7)$
71. $(a + 4)(a - 3)$
72. $(a + 3)(a - 4)$
73. $(r + 11)(r - 3)$
74. $(z + 2)(z - 6)$
75. $(m + 20)(m - 1)$
76. $(x + 2)(x - 11)$
77. $(p + 1)(8p - 7)$
78. $(8k + 1)(k - 7)$
79. $(8x + 7)(x - 1)$
80. $(m + 7)(8m - 1)$
81. $(2r + 1)(4r - 7)$
82. $(4x + 1)(2x - 7)$
83. $(4y + 7)(2y - 1)$
84. $(2y + 7)(4y - 1)$
85. $(6x + 1)(x - 2)$
86. $(x - 3)(x - 1)$
87. $(2x + 1)(x - 3)$
88. $(2a + 3)(3a - 1)$
89. $(4d + 1)(3d - 2)$
90. $(3a + 5)(6a - 1)$
91. $(3x - 4)(2x - 3)$
92. $(h + 2)(2h - 3)$
93. $(x + 6)(3x - 4)$
94. $(2x + 1)(3x - 4)$
96. $(x + 1)(x - 2y)$
98. $(7x + 3)(a - b)$
100. $(x^2 - 6)(x + 1)$
102. $(3y - 2)(4y - x^2)$

107. $\left\{-\dfrac{1}{2}, -7\right\}$

109. $\{0, -1, -2\}$

111. $\{12, -2\}$ 113. $\left\{3, -\dfrac{1}{2}\right\}$

115. $\left\{5, -\dfrac{2}{3}\right\}$ 117. $\left\{-\dfrac{1}{2}, 1\right\}$

Additional Answers

6. $\dfrac{1}{2p - 1}$; $p \neq 0$ or $\dfrac{1}{2}$

7. $\dfrac{y + a}{xy + y}$; $y \neq 0$,
   $x \neq 0$ or -1

500

Factor. Check by multiplying the factors.

68. $x^2 - 2x - 8$ 69. $y^2 + 8y - 20$ 70. $r^2 - 6r - 7$

71. $a^2 + a - 12$ 72. $a^2 - a - 12$ 73. $r^2 + 8r - 33$

74. $z^2 - 4z - 12$ 75. $m^2 + 19m - 20$ 76. $x^2 - 9x - 22$

77. $8p^2 + p - 7$ 78. $8k^2 - 55k - 7$ 79. $8x^2 - x - 7$

80. $8m^2 + 55m - 7$ 81. $8r^2 - 10r - 7$ 82. $8x^2 - 26x - 7$

83. $8y^2 + 10y - 7$ 84. $8y^2 + 26y - 7$ 85. $6x^2 - 11x - 2$

86. $x^2 - 4x + 3$ 87. $2x^2 - 5x - 3$ 88. $6a^2 + 7a - 3$

89. $12d^2 - 5d - 2$ 90. $18a^2 + 27a - 5$ 91. $6x^2 - 17x + 12$

92. $2h^2 + h - 6$ 93. $3x^2 + 14x - 24$ 94. $6x^2 - 5x - 4$

Factor by grouping. Check by multiplying the factors.

95. $a(a + 3) + 3(a + 3)$ $(a + 3)^2$ 96. $x(x - 2y) - (2y - x)$

97. $x^2 + 2x + xy + 2y$ $(x + y)(x + 2)$ 98. $7ax + 3a - 7bx - 3b$

99. $x(x + 1)(x - 2) - 3x - 3$ $(x + 1)^2(x - 3)$ 100. $x^3 + x^2 - 6x - 6$

101. $64 - 64a^2 + a^4 - a^6$ $(a^4 + 64)(1 + a)(1 - a)$ 102. $12y^2 - 8y - 3yx^2 + 2x^2$

Solve and check.

103. $(x + 1)(x + 2) = x(x + 2) + 1$ $_{-1}$

104. $(2x + 1)(x + 2) = 2x^2 + 3x + 10$ $_4$

105. $x(x - 5) + (x - 2)(x - 3) = (2x - 7)(x - 3)$ $_5$

106. $(x + 4)(x - 2) = 0$ $\{2, -4\}$ 107. $(2x + 1)(x + 7) = 0$

108. $(3x - 1)(7x + 2) = 0$ $\left\{\frac{1}{3}, -\frac{2}{7}\right\}$ 109. $x(x + 1)(x + 2) = 0$

110. $(x + 200)(x - 300) = 0$ $\{300, -200\}$ 111. $2(x + 2)(x - 12) = 0$

112. $3x^2 - 2x - 1 = 0$ $\left\{1, -\frac{1}{3}\right\}$ 113. $2x^2 - 5x = 3$

114. $x^2 = 9x - 8$ $\{1, 8\}$ 115. $9x^2 - 39x - 30 = 0$

116. $3x^2 = 12x$ $\{0, 4\}$ 117. $2z^2 - 1 = z$

118. $(3x - 4)(2x + 1) = 2(2x + 1)(2x - 1)$ $\left\{-2, -\frac{1}{2}\right\}$

Find an equation in standard form having the given solution set. Let the variable be x. Answers may vary.

119. $\{-1, 2\}$
     $x^2 - x - 2 = 0$

120. $\{3, \frac{1}{3}\}$
     $3x^2 - 10x + 3 = 0$

121. $\{-7, 7\}$
     $x^2 - 49 = 0$

CHAPTER 6

Express in simplest form, noting any restrictions on the variables.

1. $\dfrac{64}{16}$ 4

2. $\dfrac{abc}{a^2b}$ $\frac{c}{a}$; $a \neq 0$, $b \neq 0$

3. $\dfrac{2(x + y)}{3(x + y)}$
   $\frac{2}{3}$; $x \neq -y$

4. $\dfrac{2x - 4y}{x - 2y}$ 2; $x \neq 2y$

5. $\dfrac{a + ab}{2a}$ $\dfrac{1 + b}{2}$; $a \neq 0$

6. $\dfrac{p}{2p^2 - p}$

7. $\dfrac{xy + ax}{x^2y + xy}$

8. $\dfrac{r^2 + 2r + 1}{2r + 2}$

9. $\dfrac{16r^2 + 8r + 1}{16r^2 - 1}$

10. $\dfrac{4a^2 - 1}{4a^2 - 4a + 1}$

11. $\dfrac{k^2 - 8k + 16}{k^2 - 9k + 20}$

12. $\dfrac{x^2 - 7x + 12}{x^2 - x - 12}$

13. $\dfrac{1 - 2x}{2x - 1}$ -1; $x \neq \dfrac{1}{2}$

14. $\dfrac{2(x - 2y)}{4(2y - x)}$ $-\dfrac{1}{2}$; $x \neq 2y$

15. $\dfrac{(2x - 5)(3x - 1)}{(5 - 2x)(3 - x)}$

16. $\dfrac{x^2 - 4x - 1}{x^2 - 2x - 1}$ $\dfrac{x^2 - 4x - 1}{x^2 - 2x - 1}$; $x^2 - 2x - 1 \neq 0$

17. $\dfrac{-4a^2}{2a^2 - 4a^3}$ $\dfrac{-2}{1 - 2a}$; $a \neq 0$ or $\dfrac{1}{2}$

18. $\dfrac{r^2 + rh - 12h^2}{r^2 - 9h^2}$ $\dfrac{r + 4h}{r + 3h}$; $r \neq 3h$ or $-3h$

Simplify.

19. $\dfrac{2}{7} \cdot 7$ 2

20. $\dfrac{2}{7} \div 7$ $\dfrac{2}{49}$

21. $2m \div \dfrac{2}{3}$ $3m$

22. $2m \cdot \dfrac{2}{3}$ $\dfrac{4m}{3}$

23. $36r^2 \div \dfrac{18r}{5}$ $10r$

24. $25a \div \dfrac{25}{a^2}$ a^3

25. $\dfrac{c - 1}{c} \cdot \dfrac{c^2}{c^2 - 1}$ $\dfrac{c}{c + 1}$

26. $\dfrac{2x - 2y}{3x + 3y} \cdot \dfrac{6x + 6y}{x^2 - y^2}$ $\dfrac{4}{x + y}$

27. $\dfrac{x^2 - 9}{x^2 + 5x + 6} \div (x + 3)$

28. $2x^2 \div (2x)^2$ $\dfrac{1}{2}$

29. $(3ab^2)^3 \div 9(ab)^3$ $3b^3$

30. $\dfrac{x}{x + 1} \cdot \dfrac{x^2 - 1}{x^2}$

31. $\dfrac{3}{a + b} + \dfrac{4}{a + b}$ $\dfrac{7}{a + b}$

32. $\dfrac{a + b}{3} + \dfrac{a + b}{4}$ $\dfrac{7(a + b)}{12}$

33. $\dfrac{2}{3x + y} - \dfrac{1}{3x + y}$

34. $\dfrac{x + y}{12} - \dfrac{2x + y}{20}$

35. $\dfrac{3x}{a + b} - \dfrac{x}{a + b}$

36. $\dfrac{3a}{a + b} + \dfrac{3b}{a + b}$

37. $\dfrac{2}{3x + 5} - \dfrac{1}{6x + 10}$

38. $\dfrac{4}{m^2 - 4} + \dfrac{2}{m + 2}$

39. $\dfrac{3}{a - 1} + \dfrac{2}{1 - a}$

40. $2 + \dfrac{1}{a + b}$

41. $m - \dfrac{mr}{m + r}$

42. $3x^2 + \dfrac{3x}{3 + x}$

43. $\dfrac{2}{2x + 1} + \dfrac{3}{3x + 1}$

44. $\dfrac{1}{2x} + \dfrac{3}{x^2 + 2x}$

45. $\dfrac{r^2}{(r + 2)^2} - \dfrac{r}{r + 2}$

46. $\dfrac{2}{x^2 - 2x} + \dfrac{1}{2 - x}$ $-\dfrac{1}{x}$

47. $\dfrac{4}{4m + 4} - \dfrac{2}{2m + 2}$ 0

48. $\dfrac{m}{n} + 3 + \dfrac{n}{m}$

49. $\dfrac{1}{x^2 - 5x + 6} - \dfrac{1}{x^2 - 3x + 2}$ $\dfrac{2}{(x - 3)(x - 2)(x - 1)}$

50. $\dfrac{1}{10x - 21} + \dfrac{x^2 + x - 6}{10x^2 + 9x - 63}$

51. $\dfrac{2}{a^2 + 4a + 4} - \dfrac{1}{a - 2} + \dfrac{6}{a + 2}$ $\dfrac{5a^2 - 2a - 32}{(a + 2)^2(a - 2)}$

52. $\dfrac{2}{1 + x} + \dfrac{3}{1 - x} + \dfrac{2x}{x^2 - 1}$

53. $1 + \dfrac{2x}{2x - 1} + \dfrac{8x^2 - 2}{1 - 4x^2}$ $\dfrac{1}{2x - 1}$

54. $\dfrac{3x + 1}{2} - \dfrac{5}{x - 4} + \dfrac{x^2}{3}$

Divide. Write your answer as a polynomial or mixed expression. Check.

55. $\dfrac{10x^2 - 7x - 12}{2x - 3}$ $5x + 4$

56. $\dfrac{6x^2 - 23x + 7}{2x - 7}$ $3x - 1$

57. $\dfrac{18a^2 + 27a + 10}{3a + 2}$ $6a + 5$

58. $\dfrac{6x^2 - 39x + 60}{2x - 5}$ $3(x - 4)$

59. $\dfrac{x^3 + x^2 + 2x - 4}{x - 1}$ $x^2 + 2x + 4$

60. $\dfrac{x^3 + 2x^2 - 16}{x - 2}$ $x^2 + 4x + 8$

EXTRA PRACTICE **501**

8. $\dfrac{r + 1}{2}$; $r \neq -1$

9. $\dfrac{4r + 1}{4r - 1}$; $r \neq \dfrac{1}{4}$ or $-\dfrac{1}{4}$

10. $\dfrac{2a + 1}{2a - 1}$; $a \neq \dfrac{1}{2}$

11. $\dfrac{k - 4}{k - 5}$; $k \neq 4$ or 5

12. $\dfrac{x - 3}{x + 3}$; $x \neq 4$ or -3

15. $-\dfrac{3x - 1}{3 - x}$ or $\dfrac{3x - 1}{x - 3}$; $x \neq \dfrac{5}{2}$ or 3

27. $\dfrac{x - 3}{(x + 3)(x + 2)}$

30. $\dfrac{x - 1}{x}$ **33.** $\dfrac{1}{3x + y}$

34. $\dfrac{-x + 2y}{60}$ **35.** $\dfrac{2x}{a + b}$

36. 3 **37.** $\dfrac{3}{2(3x + 5)}$

38. $\dfrac{2m}{(m + 2)(m - 2)}$

39. $\dfrac{1}{a - 1}$

40. $\dfrac{2a + 2b + 1}{a + b}$

41. $\dfrac{m^2}{m + r}$

42. $\dfrac{3x(x^2 + 3x + 1)}{3 + x}$

43. $\dfrac{12x + 5}{(2x + 1)(3x + 1)}$

44. $\dfrac{x + 8}{2x(x + 2)}$

45. $\dfrac{-2r}{(r + 2)^2}$

48. $\dfrac{m^2 + 3mn + n^2}{mn}$

50. $\dfrac{x - 1}{10x - 21}$

52. $\dfrac{5 - x}{(1 - x)(1 + x)}$ or $\dfrac{x - 5}{(x - 1)(x + 1)}$

54. $\dfrac{2x^3 + x^2 - 33x - 42}{6(x - 4)}$

501

Divide. Write your answer as a polynomial or mixed expression. Check.

61. $\dfrac{x^3 - 2x + 4}{x + 2}$ $x^2 - 2x + 2$ **62.** $\dfrac{2r^2 + 5r + 3}{2r + 3}$ $r + 1$ **63.** $\dfrac{7k^2 - 9k + 2}{7k - 2}$ $k - 1$

64. $\dfrac{r^3 + r^2 + r + 1}{r - 2}$ **65.** $\dfrac{p^4 + p^3 + 4p^2 + 3}{p^2 + p + 1}$ **66.** $\dfrac{6x^3 + 5x^2 + 9}{3 + 2x}$

67. $\dfrac{6m^4 + 11m^3 + m^2 - 7m - 6}{-2m - 3}$ $-3m^3 - m^2 + m + 2$ **68.** $\dfrac{6r^3 - 5r^2k + 7rk^2 - 8k^3}{r - k}$ $3x^2 - 2x + 3$

64. $r^2 + 3r + 7 + \dfrac{15}{r - 2}$ **65.** $p^2 + 3 - \dfrac{3p}{p^2 + p + 1}$ **68.** $6r^2 + rk + 8k^2$

CHAPTER 7

State each ratio in simplest form.

1. $25:40$ 5:8 **2.** $14 \text{ kg to } 140 \text{ g}$ 100:1 **3.** $28 \text{ min to } 2 \text{ h } 8 \text{ min}$ 7 to 32

4. $\dfrac{13(ab)^2}{169abc}$ $\dfrac{ab}{13c}$ **5.** $90\text{¢ to } \$60$ 3 to 200 **6.** $12x^2y : 4xy^2$ 3x:y

Solve.

7. $\dfrac{18}{81} = \dfrac{2x}{3}$ $\dfrac{1}{3}$ **8.** $\dfrac{m + 3}{7} = 8$ 53 **9.** $\dfrac{4y}{2 - y} = \dfrac{5}{3}$ $\dfrac{10}{17}$

10. $\dfrac{x - 1}{2} = \dfrac{x}{4}$ 2 **11.** $\dfrac{3}{4} = \dfrac{c - 1}{c + 5}$ 19 **12.** $\dfrac{12}{u + 1} = \dfrac{3}{u}$ $\dfrac{1}{3}$

13. $\dfrac{x + 1}{x + 2} = \dfrac{x + 5}{x + 4}$ -3 **14.** $\dfrac{x}{x - 1} = \dfrac{x + 1}{x + 2}$ $-\dfrac{1}{2}$ **15.** $\dfrac{4x}{5} + \dfrac{x}{10} = \dfrac{27}{2}$ 15

16. $\dfrac{1}{3}k + \dfrac{1}{16} = \dfrac{1}{12} + \dfrac{1}{4}k$ $\dfrac{1}{4}$ **17.** $\dfrac{4}{9}b - \dfrac{1}{5}b = 11$ 45

18. $\dfrac{3x}{7} + \dfrac{1}{2} + \dfrac{x + 4}{2} = 0$ $-\dfrac{35}{13}$ **19.** $\dfrac{3d + 1}{2} + \dfrac{2d + 1}{3} = 3d$ $+\dfrac{5}{-5}$

20. $\dfrac{1}{2} + \dfrac{1}{y} = \dfrac{1}{3} - \dfrac{1}{y}$ -12 **21.** $\dfrac{18}{x} = \dfrac{3}{x} + 3$ 5

22. $\dfrac{1}{n} + \dfrac{5}{3n} = \dfrac{3}{4}$ $\dfrac{32}{9}$ **23.** $\dfrac{a}{a + 3} - \dfrac{2}{5} = 0$ 2

24. $\dfrac{4}{5b} + \dfrac{b - 2}{b} = -\dfrac{1}{5}$ 1 **25.** $\dfrac{1}{a^2 - a} = \dfrac{3}{a} - 1$ 2

26. $1 + \dfrac{2}{y - 1} = \dfrac{2}{y^2 - y}$ -2 **27.** $\dfrac{x}{x - 2} - \dfrac{4}{x + 3} = 1$ 7

28. $\dfrac{x + 5}{6} - \dfrac{2x + 1}{12} + \dfrac{x - 10}{x - 3} = 0$ 7 **29.** $\dfrac{1}{x + 1} + \dfrac{x^2}{x^2 - 1} = 1 + \dfrac{1}{1 - x}$ $-\dfrac{1}{2}$

Replace each __?__ by a number that makes the statement true.

30. 12% of 21 is __?__. 2.52 **31.** $13\frac{1}{2}\%$ of 22 is __?__. 2.97 **32.** 12.6% of 2.4 is __?__. 0.3024

33. 10% of 3.14 is __?__. 0.314 **34.** 2% of __?__ is 122. 6100 **35.** 30% of __?__ is 24. 80

36. 250% of __?__ is 35. 14 **37.** 18% of __?__ is 39.96. 222 **38.** __?__% of 12 is 8.

39. __?__% of 42 is 24. $57\frac{1}{7}$ **40.** __?__% of 45 is 72. 160 **41.** __?__% of 158 is 52.14.

38. $66\frac{2}{3}$ **41.** 33

502 *EXTRA PRACTICE*

CHAPTER 8

Solve each equation for y in terms of x.

1. $2x + y = 8$ $y = 8 - 2x$
2. $2x - y = 8$ $y = 2x - 8$
3. $3x + 2y = 12$
4. $x + 2y = 6$ $y = 3 - \frac{1}{2}x$
5. $x - 2y = 4$ $y = \frac{1}{2}x - 2$
6. $4x - 3y = 7$
7. $8x = 4y + 20$ $y = 2x - 5$
8. $3y - 2x = 150$ $y = \frac{2}{3}x + 50$
9. $2x = 10 - 3y$

Complete each ordered pair to form a solution of the given equation. Assume that x and y represent real numbers.

10. $y = 3x + 3$; $(15, ?)$ 48
11. $y = -2x - 5$; $(-3, ?)$ 1
12. $y = 7x + 5$; $(6, ?)$ 47
13. $2x + y = 7$; $(3, ?)$ 1
14. $3x + 2y = 8$; $(2, ?)$ 1
15. $4x - 5y = 12$; $(-10, ?)$ $-\frac{52}{5}$

Find the coordinates of the points where the graph of each equation crosses (a) the x-axis and (b) the y-axis.

16. $3x = 11y$ **a.** $(0, 0)$ **b.** $(0, 0)$
17. $x - 4y = 20$ **a.** $(20, 0)$ **b.** $(0, -5)$
18. $3x + y = 12$ **a.** $(4, 0)$ **b.** $(0, 12)$
19. $2x - 10y = 20$ **a.** $(10, 0)$ **b.** $(0, -2)$
20. $4x - y = 120$ **a.** $(30, 0)$ **b.** $(0, -120)$
21. $3x + 10y = 300$ **a.** $(100, 0)$ **b.** $(0, 30)$

Graph each equation in a coordinate plane.

22. $x + y = 8$
23. $2x + y = 8$
24. $x + 2y = 8$
25. $x + 2y = 10$
26. $x + 2y = 1$
27. $5x + y = 10$
28. $x - y = 1$
29. $y = 3x - 1$
30. $3y = x + 1$

Solve each system by the graphic method.

31. $x + y = 3$
    $2x - y = 3$ $(2, 1)$
32. $3x - 2y = 4$
    $2x + y = 5$ $(2, 1)$
33. $x + y = 1$
    $3x - y = -9$ $(-2, 3)$

Solve each system by the substitution method.

34. $y = 6$
    $7x + y = 34$ $(4, 6)$
35. $x + 2y = 3$
    $2x + 3y = 9$ $(9, -3)$
36. $2x + y = 2$
    $x - 2y = 1$ $(1, 0)$

Let s = the number of students at a school association meeting. Let a = the number of adults at the meeting. Write each sentence as an equation in s and a.

37. The total number of people at the meeting is 640. $s + a = 640$
38. The number of students is one third the number of adults. $s = \frac{1}{3}a$
39. The number of adults is 160 more than twice the number of students. $a = 2s + 160$
40. Half the number of adults is 80 less than twice the number of students. $\frac{1}{2}a = 2s - 80$

3. $y = 6 - \frac{3}{2}x$

6. $y = \frac{4}{3}x - \frac{7}{3}$

9. $y = \frac{10}{3} - \frac{2}{3}x$

22.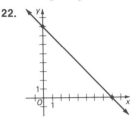

24.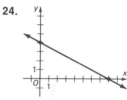

26.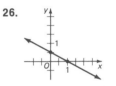

28.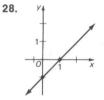

30.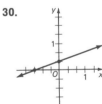

Solve each system by the addition-or-subtraction method.

41. $c + 2n = -20$
$c - 2n = 30$ $\left(5, -\frac{25}{2}\right)$

42. $25x + 16y = 91$
$16x + 16y = 64$ $(3, 1)$

43. $3x + 2y = 13$
$3x - 4y = 19$
$(5, -1)$

Solve each system by using multiplication with the addition-or-subtraction method.

44. $7m - 5n = 11$
$3m + n = -11$ $(-2, -5)$

45. $3a + 4b = -25$
$2a - 3b = 6$ $(-3, -4)$

46. $\frac{x}{3} + \frac{y}{4} = \frac{1}{12}$
$2x + 5y = 1$
$\left(\frac{1}{7}, \frac{1}{7}\right)$

Let n = Nadya's age now and d = Darrell's age now. Write the following in terms of n and d.

47. Nadya's age in 6 years $n + 6$

48. Darrell's age 2 years ago $d - 2$

49. Twice the sum of their ages $2(n + d)$

50. The sum of their ages in 1 year
$(n + 1) + (d + 1)$, or $n + d + 2$

A two-digit number is represented by $10t + u$, where t is the tens digit and u is the units digit. Write the following in terms of t and u.

51. The new number obtained when each digit is doubled. $20t + 2u$

52. The new number obtained when the units digit is halved. $10t + \frac{1}{2}u$

53. A fraction is represented by $\frac{n}{d}$. Write in terms of n and d the new fraction obtained by tripling the numerator and decreasing the denominator by 7. $\frac{3n}{d - 7}$

Let s = the rate of a swimmer in still water and r = the rate of the Raft River. Write the following in terms of s and r.

54. The rate of the swimmer swimming downstream $s + r$

55. The rate of the swimmer swimming upstream $s - r$

56. The rate of the swimmer swimming upstream in a river which flows at one quarter of the rate of the Raft River $s - \frac{1}{4}r$

CHAPTER 9

In each exercise, the coordinates of two points of a line are given. Find the slope of the line.

1. $(1, 1)$ $(8, 15)$ 2

2. $(2, 8)$ $\left(\frac{1}{3}, 3\right)$ 3

3. $(0, 3)$ $(-2, 11)$ -4

4. $(-1, 0)$ $(8, -45)$ -5

5. $(2, 4)$ $(8, 7)$ $\frac{1}{2}$

6. $(2, 5)$ $(-1, -3)$ $\frac{8}{3}$

Find the slope of each line whose equation is given.

7. $y = -2x + 6$ -2

8. $y = \frac{1}{3}x - 4$ $\frac{1}{3}$

9. $y = 2 - x$ -1

10. $3x + 2y = 48$ $-\frac{3}{2}$

11. $5x - 2y = 8$ $\frac{5}{2}$

12. $y = 14$ 0

504 *EXTRA PRACTICE*

In each exercise, determine whether the points lie on the same line. If they do, find the slope of the line.

13. $(2, 8)$
$(5, 12)$
$(8, 16)$ Yes; $\frac{4}{3}$

14. $(-3, 6)$
$(2, 7)$
$(12, 8)$ No

15. $(-2, -6)$
$(-4, -3)$
$(-8, 3)$ Yes; $-\frac{3}{2}$

16. $(0, 7)$
$(5, 9)$
$(10, 11)$
Yes; $\frac{2}{5}$

Draw the line that passes through $(6, 4)$ and has the given slope.

17. 5
18. $\frac{1}{5}$
19. -5
20. $-\frac{1}{5}$

Write in standard form an equation of the line that has the given slope and y-intercept. Answers may vary.

21. $m = 5$; $b = 10$ $5x - y = -10$

22. $m = \frac{1}{3}$; $b = -3$ $x - 3y = 9$

23. $m = -3$; $b = \frac{1}{2}$ $6x + 2y = 1$

24. $m = -\frac{2}{3}$; $b = -\frac{2}{3}$ $2x + 3y = -2$

25. The same slope as the graph of $2x - y = 2$; $b = 4$ $2x - y = -4$

26. The same slope as the graph of $y = 4x - 4$; the same y-intercept as the graph of $x + y = 2$ $4x - y = -2$

Change each equation to the slope-intercept form and draw the graph using only the y-intercept and the slope.

$y = -x - \frac{4}{5}$

27. $5x = -3y$ $y = -\frac{5}{3}x$
28. $2x - y = 5$ $y = 2x - 5$
29. $5x + 5y + 4 = 0$

30. $x - y = 5$ $y = x - 5$
31. $4x + 4y = 8$ $y = -x + 2$
32. $-3x + y = 0$ $y = 3x$

Write in standard form an equation of the line that has the given slope and passes through the given point. Answers may vary.

33. $m = 2$; $(2, 2)$ $2x - y = 2$
34. $m = -\frac{2}{3}$; $(-1, 3)$ $2x + 3y = 7$
35. $m = 4$; $(0, 0)$ $4x - y = 0$

Write in standard form an equation of the line passing through the given points. Answers may vary.

$9x + y = 44$

36. $(0, 4)$ $(2, -5)$ $9x + 2y = 8$
37. $(2, 4)$ $(5, 4)$ $y = 4$
38. $(4, 8)$ $(6, -10)$

39. If $f: x \rightarrow x + 5$, find: **a.** $f(2)$ **b.** $f(\frac{1}{2})$. **a.** 7 **b.** $5\frac{1}{2}$

40. If $g(v) = 2 - v^2$, find: **a.** $g(-2)$ **b.** $g(-3)$. **a.** -2 **b.** -7

41. If $h: u \rightarrow 2u + u^2$, find: **a.** $h(-4)$ **b.** $h(\frac{1}{4})$. **a.** 8 **b.** $\frac{9}{16}$

42. If $k(m) = m - \frac{1}{m}$, find: **a.** $k(3)$ **b.** $k(-3)$. **a.** $\frac{8}{3}$ **b.** $-\frac{8}{3}$

43. Find all the values of $F: x \rightarrow x^2 + 2$ if the domain $D = \{-1, 0, 1\}$. 2 and 3

44. Find the range of the function G if $G(x) = \frac{1}{x} + x$ and $D = \{1, 2, 3\}$. $\{2, 2\frac{1}{2}, 3\frac{1}{3}\}$

Find the coordinates of the vertex of the graph of each equation.

$(-1, 3)$

45. $y = x^2 - 4x$ $(2, -4)$
46. $y = 2x^2 - 10x + 1$
47. $y = x^2 + 2x + 4$

48. $y = -x^2 + 4x - 8$ $(2, -4)$
49. $y = -\frac{2}{3}x^2 + 6x - 12$
50. $y = -4x^2 - 4x - 8$

46. $(2\frac{1}{2}, -11\frac{1}{2})$ **49.** $(4\frac{1}{2}, 1\frac{1}{2})$
$(-\frac{1}{2}, -7)$

EXTRA PRACTICE   505

 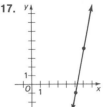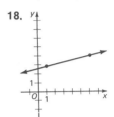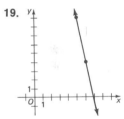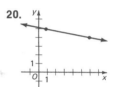
505

Find the greatest value of each function.

51. $f: x \rightarrow -x^2 - 10x$ 25

52. $g: x \rightarrow -x^2 - 10x + 4$ 29

53. $h: x \rightarrow -x^2 - 10x - 12$ 13

54. $k: x \rightarrow -2x^2 + 8$ 8

55. $F: x \rightarrow -2x^2 + 12$ 12

56. $G: x \rightarrow -2x^2 - 100$ -100

Find the least value of each function.

57. $f: x \rightarrow 2x^2 + 4x + 4$ 2

58. $g: x \rightarrow 2x^2 + 8$ 8

59. $h: x \rightarrow 2x^2 + 4x + 3$ 1

60. $k: x \rightarrow 3x^2 + 9x + 6$ $-\frac{3}{4}$

In each exercise, (a) find the constant of variation and (b) find y when $x = 4$.

61. y varies directly as x, and $y = 30$ when $x = 10$. **a.** 3   **b.** 12

62. y varies directly as x, and $y = 24$ when $x = 3$. **a.** 8   **b.** 32

63. y is directly proportional to x, and $y = 11$ when $x = 22$. **a.** $\frac{1}{2}$ **b.** 2

Translate each statement into *two* formulas expressing direct variation. Use k as the constant of variation. Answers may vary.

64. The elongation, e, of a coil spring varies directly as the mass, m, suspended from it. $e = km; \frac{e_1}{m_1} = \frac{e_2}{m_2}$

65. The circumference, C, of a circle is directly proportional to the diameter, d, of the circle. $C = kd; \frac{C_1}{d_1} = \frac{C_2}{d_2}$

66. The length, l, of a shadow of a vertical object at a given time and location varies with the height, h, of the object. $l = kh; \frac{l_1}{h_1} = \frac{l_2}{h_2}$

State whether each equation defines a direct variation or an inverse variation. Then state the constant of variation, if it can be determined.

67. $xy = 3$ Inverse; 3

68. $b = \frac{4}{c}$ Inverse; 4

69. $m = \frac{n}{3}$ Direct; $\frac{1}{3}$ or 3

70. $\frac{x}{y} = \frac{1}{3}$ Direct, $\frac{1}{3}$ or 3

71. $q = 7.5p$ Direct; 7.5

72. $5ab = 6$ Inverse; $\frac{6}{5}$

73. $x_1y_2 = x_2y_1$ Direct; cannot be determined

74. $\frac{x_1}{x_2} = \frac{y_2}{y_1}$ Inverse; cannot be determined

75. $\frac{1}{8} = uv$ Inverse; $\frac{1}{8}$

Find the missing value in each exercise if (x_1, y_1) and (x_2, y_2) are ordered pairs of the same inverse variation.

76. $x_1 = 2$, $y_1 = 3$
$x_2 = 6$, $y_2 = \underline{?}$ 1

77. $x_1 = 2$, $y_1 = 6$
$x_2 = 6$, $y_2 = \underline{?}$ 2

78. $x_1 = 1$, $y_1 = 6$
$x_2 = \underline{?}$, $y_2 = 16$ $\frac{3}{8}$

Translate each statement into *two* formulas expressing inverse variation. Use k as the constant of variation. Answers may vary.

79. The height, h, of a triangle of constant area varies inversely as the base length, b. $bh = k; b_1h_1 = b_2h_2$

80. The monthly rent, r, for each roommate in an apartment is inversely proportional to the number, n, of roommates sharing the apartment. $rn = k$; $r_1 n_1 = r_2 n_2$

Translate each statement into a formula. Use k as a constant where needed. Answers may vary.

81. Wind pressure, p, on a flat surface varies directly as the square of the wind velocity, v. $p = kv^2$

82. The height, h, of a right circular cylinder of given volume is inversely proportional to the square of the radius, r. $h = \frac{k}{r^2}$

83. The volume, V, of a rectangular container varies jointly as the length, l, the width, w, and the depth, d. $V = klwd$

84. The volume, V, of a regular square pyramid varies jointly as the height, h, and the square of the length, b, of a side of the base. $V = khb^2$

85. Centrifugal force, F, varies directly as the square of the velocity, v, of a moving body and inversely as the radius, r, of its circular path. $F = \frac{kv^2}{r}$

86. The rate of speed, r, of a moving body varies directly as the distance traveled, d, and inversely as the time traveled, t. $r = \frac{kd}{t}$

CHAPTER 10

Draw the graph of each inequality on a number line.

1. $5x < 15$ **2.** $-2x > 8$ **3.** $8 \le x < 10$

Solve each inequality.

4. $8x + 3 < 15$ **5.** $3x - 8 < 15$ **6.** $3 - x > 2$
7. $-2r + 3 < r + 1$ **8.** $0 < 6r + 4$ **9.** $0 < 4 - 6r$

Classify each statement as true or false.

10. $|2 + 8| = |2| + |8|$ True

11. $|2 - 8| = |2| - |8|$ False

12. $|(4)(-2)| = |4| \cdot |-2|$ True

13. $|2| + |-3| = |-2| + |3|$ True

Solve each open sentence.

14. $|x| = 2$ **15.** $|x| = \frac{1}{2}$ **16.** $|x + 1| = 3$
17. $|x - 8| = 1$ **18.** $|2x + 3| = 15$ **19.** $|2 - 3x| = 7$
20. $|x| < 2$ **21.** $|x| > 2$ **22.** $|x| < 20$
23. $|x + 4| < 1$ **24.** $|x - 3| > 1$ **25.** $|2x - 4| < 5$

Write an inequality based on the information given in each exercise. Answers may vary.

26. The sum of two numbers is less than 28. $x + y < 28$

27. The product of two consecutive integers is more than 152. $n(n + 1) > 152$

37. {2 and the real numbers between 0 and 2}

38. {2 and the real numbers between −3 and 2}

39. {4}

40. {the real numbers greater than 2}

41. {the real numbers between −4 and 0}

42. {3, 12, and the real numbers between 3 and 12}

43. {the real numbers}

44. $\left\{ 0 \text{ and the real numbers between 0 and } \frac{7}{2} \right\}$

45. {the real numbers greater than $\frac{1}{2}$ or less than −1}

46. {the real numbers between 0 and 5}

47. {1 and the real numbers between $\frac{2}{3}$ and 1}

48. {the real numbers greater than 9 or less than −1}

52.

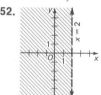

53.

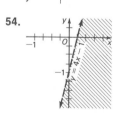

54.

(continued)

508

Write an inequality based on the information given in each exercise. Answers may vary.

28. The difference between two even integers is more than 22. $2a - 2b > 22$

29. The distance between two cities is at least 42 km. $d \geq 42$

30. The number of boxes of lunch packed is at least 28. $b \geq 28$

31. The number of peaches eaten is at most 3. $p \leq 3$

32. The number of dimes Jason has is at most $\frac{1}{2}$ as many as Dick has. $j \leq \frac{1}{2}d$

33. The number of cards Julia has is no more than 28. $c \leq 28$

34. A number is no more than $\frac{1}{2}$ and no less than $-\frac{2}{7}$. $-\frac{2}{7} \leq n \leq \frac{1}{2}$

35. Six times Clare's age is at least 4 more than Beth's age. $6c \geq b + 4$

36. The sum of two consecutive integers is no more than twice their product. $n + (n + 1) \leq 2n(n + 1)$

Solve each open sentence.

37. $x \leq 2$ and $x > 0$

38. $-3 < y \leq 2$

39. $4 \leq m$ and $m \leq 4$

40. $2 < n$ or $n \geq 4$

41. $-2 < x + 2 < 2$

42. $-1 \leq x - 4 \leq 8$

43. $x + 7 < 8$ or $x + 8 > 7$

44. $-3 \leq 2x - 3 < 4$

45. $2r + 3 < 1$ or $2r + 3 > 4$

46. $-2 < 3 - x < 3$

47. $4 < 2 + 3x \leq 5$

48. $4 - x > 5$ or $x - 4 > 5$

Determine whether or not (0, 0) belongs to the graph of each inequality.

49. $2x - y < -4$ No

50. $x + 47 \geq 0$ Yes

51. $2x - 3y < 4$ Yes

Graph each inequality in a coordinate plane.

52. $x < 2$

53. $y \geq 2x + 4$

54. $y < 4x - 1$

Graph each pair of inequalities in a coordinate plane and indicate the solution set of the system with crosshatching or shading.

55. $y \geq 3$
$\quad x \geq 2$

56. $y \leq 4$
$\quad x > 3$

57. $y > 4$
$\quad x \leq -5$

CHAPTER 11

Write each number as a quotient of integers. Answers may vary.

1. 1.3 $\frac{13}{10}$

2. $2\frac{1}{7}$ $\frac{15}{7}$

3. 12% $\frac{3}{25}$

4. $8\frac{1}{2}\%$ $\frac{17}{200}$

5. $-2\frac{5}{8}$ $-\frac{21}{8}$

6. 21.3 $\frac{213}{10}$

Replace the __?__ with <, =, or > to make a true statement.

7. -3 __?__ $-4\frac{1}{2}$ >

8. $8\frac{1}{2}$ __?__ $\frac{15}{2}$ >

9. $\frac{9}{5}$ __?__ $\frac{7}{3}$ <

10. $\frac{3}{4}$ __?__ $\frac{8}{10}$ <

11. $\frac{2}{5}$ __?__ $\frac{21}{50}$ <

12. 1.24 __?__ 1.204 >

13. $14\frac{1}{3}$ __?__ $\frac{44}{4}$ >

14. $\frac{111}{4}$ __?__ $\frac{249}{9}$ >

15. $-\frac{5}{7}$ __?__ $-\frac{12}{15}$ >

Find the number halfway between the given numbers.

16. 2 and 24 13

17. 32 and -12 10

18. $\frac{1}{2}$ and $\frac{5}{6}$ $\frac{2}{3}$

19. $\frac{4}{5}$ and $\frac{2}{15}$ $\frac{7}{15}$

20. $\frac{1}{4}$ and $\frac{7}{12}$ $\frac{5}{12}$

21. $-\frac{2}{3}$ and $-\frac{12}{13}$ $-\frac{31}{39}$

22. Find the number one third of the way from $-\frac{2}{3}$ to $\frac{1}{12}$. $-\frac{5}{12}$

23. Find the number one fifth of the way from $1\frac{1}{2}$ to $1\frac{6}{7}$. $\frac{11}{7}$

Express each rational number as a terminating or repeating decimal.

24. $\frac{3}{6}$ 0.5

25. $\frac{2}{3}$ $0.\overline{6}$

26. $\frac{10}{9}$ $1.\overline{1}$

27. $\frac{281}{10}$ 28.1

28. $\frac{2}{5}$ 0.4

29. $\frac{7}{4}$ 1.75

30. $\frac{1}{16}$ 0.0625

31. $\frac{11}{81}$ $0.\overline{135802469}$

32. $\frac{2}{7}$ $0.\overline{285714}$

33. $\frac{9}{5}$ 1.8

34. $\frac{5}{9}$ $0.\overline{5}$

35. $\frac{81}{11}$ $7.\overline{36}$

Express each rational number as a fraction in simplest form.

36. 0.22 $\frac{11}{50}$

37. 0.14 $\frac{7}{50}$

38. $0.444\ldots$ $\frac{4}{9}$

39. 2.8 $\frac{14}{5}$

40. 0.625 $\frac{5}{8}$

41. $0.\overline{62}$ $\frac{62}{99}$

42. $1.\overline{23}$ $\frac{122}{99}$

43. $1.2\overline{3}$ $\frac{37}{30}$

44. 28.82 $\frac{1441}{50}$

Find the difference of the given numbers. Then find the number halfway between them.

45. $\frac{1}{2}$ and 1.25 0.75; 0.875

46. $\frac{2}{3}$ and $0.\overline{8}$ $\frac{2}{9}$; $\frac{7}{9}$

47. 0.22 and 0.11 0.11; 0.165

48. 0.22 and $0.1\overline{5}$ $\frac{29}{450}$; $\frac{169}{900}$

49. -2.12 and $-2\frac{1}{2}$ 0.38; -2.31

50. 0.17 and $0.1\overline{7}$ $\frac{17}{9900}$; $\frac{3383}{19,800}$

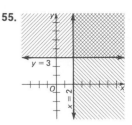

55.

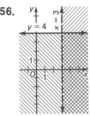

56.

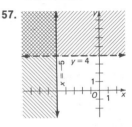

57.

Find the indicated square roots.

51. $\sqrt{961}$ 31

52. $\sqrt{196}$ 14

53. $\sqrt{1764}$ 42

54. $\sqrt{(36)(81)}$ 54

55. $\sqrt{(144)(441)}$ 252

56. $\sqrt{(2116)(900)}$

56. 1380

57. $\sqrt{\dfrac{16}{625}}$ $\dfrac{4}{25}$

58. $\sqrt{\dfrac{128}{162}}$ $\dfrac{8}{9}$

59. $\sqrt{\dfrac{450}{1250}}$ $\dfrac{3}{5}$

60. $\sqrt{0.16}$ 0.4

61. $\sqrt{0.81}$ 0.9

62. $\sqrt{0.1024}$ 0.32

Use the Table of Square Roots to approximate each square root to the nearest hundredth.

63. $\sqrt{40}$ 6.32

64. $\sqrt{83}$ 9.11

65. $\sqrt{8300}$ 91.10

66. $\sqrt{0.12}$ 0.35

67. $\sqrt{0.02}$ 0.14

68. $\sqrt{0.0062}$ 0.08

Approximate each square root to the nearest hundredth using the divide-and-average method.

69. $\sqrt{38}$ 6.16

70. $\sqrt{50}$ 7.07

71. $\sqrt{25.8}$ 5.08

Additional Answers

74. $0.2|y|$ **77.** $m^{50}n^{100}$

80. 864

Simplify.

72. $\sqrt{4t^2}$ $2|t|$

73. $\sqrt{81m^4}$ $9m^2$

74. $\sqrt{0.04y^2}$

75. $\sqrt{a^2 + 2a + 1}$ $|a + 1|$

76. $\sqrt{576a^2b^4}$ $24|a|b^2$

77. $\sqrt{m^{100}n^{200}}$

78. $\sqrt{\dfrac{27}{3}}$ 3

79. $\sqrt{16a^2 - 8a + 1}$ $|4a - 1|$

80. $\sqrt{2^{10} \cdot 3^6}$

Solve. Find both roots of each equation to the nearest tenth if the roots are irrational.

81. $m^2 = 1444$ $\{38, -38\}$

82. $x^2 - 82 = 0$ $\{9.1, -9.1\}$

83. $36t^2 - 1 = 0$ $\left\{\pm\dfrac{1}{6}\right\}$

84. $3x^2 = 243$ $\{9, -9\}$

85. $5x^2 - 4205 = 0$ $\{29, -29\}$

86. $2t^2 = 100$

87. $8r^2 - 88 = 0$ $\{3.3, -3.3\}$

88. $3a^2 - 12 = 0$ $\{2, -2\}$

89. $b^2 - 7.5 = 0$

86. $\{\pm 7.1\}$

89. $\{\pm 2.7\}$

Refer to a right triangle with hypotenuse of length c and shorter sides of lengths a and b. Find the missing length correct to the nearest hundredth.

90. $a = 4$, $b = 5$, $c = \underline{\ ?\ }$ 6.40

91. $a = 8$, $b = 6$, $c = \underline{\ ?\ }$ 10

92. $a = 20$, $b = \underline{\ ?\ }$, $c = 21$ 6.40

93. $a = \sqrt{2}$, $b = \underline{\ ?\ }$, $c = \sqrt{12}$ 3.16

94. $a = \underline{\ ?\ }$, $b = 17$, $c = 19$ 8.49

95. $a = 7$, $b = 24$, $c = \underline{\ ?\ }$ 25

96. $a = \underline{\ ?\ }$, $b = 1.2$, $c = 5.8$ 5.67

97. $a = 2\dfrac{1}{2}$, $b = 3\dfrac{1}{3}$, $c = \underline{\ ?\ }$ $4\dfrac{1}{6}$

Express in simplest form. Assume the radicands are nonnegative real numbers.

98. $\sqrt{5} \cdot \sqrt{5}$ 5

99. $2\sqrt{3} \cdot 3\sqrt{7}$ $6\sqrt{21}$

100. $\sqrt{24}$ $2\sqrt{6}$

101. $\sqrt{200}$ $10\sqrt{2}$

102. $\dfrac{3}{\sqrt{7}}$ $\dfrac{3\sqrt{7}}{7}$

103. $\sqrt{\dfrac{2}{13}}$ $\dfrac{\sqrt{26}}{13}$

104. $\sqrt{2} \cdot \sqrt{6} \cdot \sqrt{8}$ $4\sqrt{6}$ **105.** $\sqrt{\dfrac{2}{9}}$ $\dfrac{\sqrt{2}}{3}$ **106.** $\sqrt{125}$ $5\sqrt{5}$

107. $\sqrt{180}$ $6\sqrt{5}$ **108.** $2\sqrt{60} \cdot 6\sqrt{15}$ 360   **109.** $8\sqrt{x} \cdot 4\sqrt{x}$ 32x

110. $\sqrt{m}(\sqrt{m} + m)$ **111.** $\sqrt{3x} \cdot \sqrt{27x}$ 9x   **112.** $\sqrt{111x} \cdot \sqrt{3x} \cdot \sqrt{37}$ 111x

113. $\sqrt{\dfrac{1}{2}} \cdot \sqrt{\dfrac{2}{9}}$ $\dfrac{1}{3}$ **114.** $\sqrt{\dfrac{10}{3}} \cdot \sqrt{\dfrac{15}{2}}$ 5   **115.** $\sqrt{\dfrac{3}{2}} \cdot \sqrt{\dfrac{2}{5}} \cdot \sqrt{\dfrac{5}{7}} \cdot \sqrt{21}$ 3

116. $\dfrac{3}{\sqrt{3}}$ $\sqrt{3}$ **117.** $\dfrac{8}{\sqrt{8}}$ $2\sqrt{2}$ **118.** $\sqrt{1\dfrac{1}{2}} \cdot \sqrt{1\dfrac{1}{3}} \cdot \sqrt{1\dfrac{1}{4}}$ $\dfrac{\sqrt{10}}{2}$

110. $m + m\sqrt{m}$

Simplify.

119. $5\sqrt{7} + 8\sqrt{7}$ $13\sqrt{7}$ **120.** $6\sqrt{2} - 4\sqrt{2}$ $2\sqrt{2}$ **121.** $\sqrt{32} + \sqrt{\dfrac{1}{2}}$ $\dfrac{9}{2}\sqrt{2}$

122. $\sqrt{27} - \sqrt{3}$ $2\sqrt{3}$ **123.** $2\sqrt{\dfrac{5}{3}} - \sqrt{60}$ $-\dfrac{4}{3}\sqrt{15}$ **124.** $\sqrt{\dfrac{5}{6}} + \sqrt{\dfrac{6}{5}}$ $\dfrac{11}{30}\sqrt{30}$

125. $\dfrac{2}{\sqrt{2}} - 2\sqrt{\dfrac{1}{2}}$ 0   **126.** $\sqrt{2} + 2\sqrt{3} + 3\sqrt{4}$ **127.** $\sqrt{162} + 16\sqrt{2}$ $25\sqrt{2}$

128. $20\sqrt{4\dfrac{1}{2}} - 16\sqrt{2}$ $14\sqrt{2}$ **129.** $10\sqrt{\dfrac{3}{5}} - 30\sqrt{\dfrac{5}{3}}$ $-8\sqrt{15}$ **130.** $3\sqrt{18} - 5\sqrt{\dfrac{1}{2}} - 4\sqrt{\dfrac{1}{4}}$ $\dfrac{13}{2}\sqrt{2} - 2$

126. $\sqrt{2} + 2\sqrt{3} + 6$

Express in simplest form.

131. $(5 - \sqrt{2})(5 + \sqrt{2})$ 23   **132.** $(\sqrt{6} + 3)(\sqrt{6} - 3)$ -3

133. $(7 + \sqrt{12})(7 - \sqrt{12})$ 37   **134.** $(2\sqrt{6} + 1)(2\sqrt{6} - 1)$ 23

135. $(\sqrt{12} - \sqrt{5})(\sqrt{12} + \sqrt{5})$ 7   **136.** $(2 + \sqrt{5})^2$ $9 + 4\sqrt{5}$

137. $(5 - \sqrt{7})^2$ $32 - 10\sqrt{7}$ **138.** $(2 + \sqrt{8})^2$ $12 + 8\sqrt{2}$

139. $(\sqrt{7} + \sqrt{2})^2$ $9 + 2\sqrt{14}$ **140.** $(\sqrt{10} + \sqrt{5})^2$ $15 + 10\sqrt{2}$

141. $\sqrt{3}(2 + \sqrt{3})$ $2\sqrt{3} + 3$ **142.** $2\sqrt{7}(\sqrt{7} + \sqrt{2})$ $14 + 2\sqrt{14}$

143. $\left(-\dfrac{5}{2} - \dfrac{5}{2}\sqrt{3}\right)^2$ $25 + \dfrac{25}{2}\sqrt{3}$ **144.** $\sqrt{3}(\sqrt{3} - 3)$ $3 - 3\sqrt{3}$

145. $(7\sqrt{7} + \sqrt{3})(2\sqrt{7} - \sqrt{3})$ $95 - 5\sqrt{21}$ **146.** $(2\sqrt{3} + 3\sqrt{2})^2$

147. $(\sqrt{3} - \sqrt{2})^3$ $9\sqrt{3} - 11\sqrt{2}$ **148.** $\sqrt{6}(\sqrt{2} - \sqrt{3})$

146. $30 + 12\sqrt{6}$
148. $2\sqrt{3} - 3\sqrt{2}$

Rationalize the denominator.

149. $\dfrac{2}{2\sqrt{7} - 5}$ $\dfrac{4\sqrt{7} + 10}{3}$ **150.** $\dfrac{3}{3 - \sqrt{6}}$ $3 + \sqrt{6}$ **151.** $\dfrac{2 + 2\sqrt{3}}{1 + \sqrt{3}}$ 2

152. $\dfrac{6}{\sqrt{3} + \sqrt{2}}$ $6\sqrt{3} - 6\sqrt{2}$ **153.** $\dfrac{4\sqrt{7}}{\sqrt{7} - \sqrt{5}}$ $14 + 2\sqrt{35}$ **154.** $\dfrac{\sqrt{5} + \sqrt{2}}{\sqrt{5} - \sqrt{2}}$ $\dfrac{7 + 2\sqrt{10}}{3}$

Solve and check.

155. $\sqrt{x + 5} = 1$ -4 **156.** $\sqrt{4x - 11} = 1$ 3

157. $\sqrt{x - 5} = 5$ 30   **158.** $\sqrt{3r - 2} - 8 = -6$ 2

Solve and check.

159. $\sqrt{\dfrac{2x+1}{2}} = 3\ \frac{17}{2}$

160. $2\sqrt{3x} - 5 = 0\quad \overset{\frac{25}{12}}{}$

161. $\sqrt{2m-1} = m - 2\ 5$

162. $\sqrt{x+8} = \sqrt{x}$
No solution

CHAPTER 12

Rewrite each trinomial as the square of a binomial.

1. $x^2 + 6x + 9\ (x+3)^2$

2. $4x^2 + 4x + 1\ (2x+1)^2$

3. $x^2 - 22x + 121\ (x-11)^2$

4. $36x^2 + 12x + 1\ (6x+1)^2$

Solve. Express irrational solutions in simplest radical form. If the equation has no real-number solution, write "no solution."

5. $m^2 = \dfrac{1}{25}\ \left\{\frac{1}{5}, -\frac{1}{5}\right\}$

6. $2x^2 = 200\ \{10, -10\}$

7. $(x+8)^2 = 81\ \{1, -17\}$

8. $(x-4)^2 = 4\ \{6, 2\}$

9. $6m^2 + 1 = 8\ \left\{\frac{\sqrt{42}}{6}, -\frac{\sqrt{42}}{6}\right\}$

10. $7r^2 + 4 = 2$ No solution

11. $2(m-3)^2 = 14\ \{3+\sqrt{7}, 3-\sqrt{7}\}$

12. $r^2 - 10r + 25 = 144$
$\{17, -7\}$

13. $\left(x - \dfrac{2}{3}\right)^2 = \dfrac{1}{9}\ \left\{1, \frac{1}{3}\right\}$

14. $\left(t + \dfrac{8}{5}\right)^2 = \dfrac{2}{5}$
$\left\{\dfrac{-8+\sqrt{10}}{5}, \dfrac{-8-\sqrt{10}}{5}\right\}$

Complete the square.

15. $x^2 + 12x + \underline{\ ?\ } = (x + \underline{\ ?\ })^2\ 36; 6$

16. $x^2 - 8x + \underline{\ ?\ } = (x - \underline{\ ?\ })^2$

17. $x^2 - 7x + \underline{\ ?\ } = (x - \underline{\ ?\ })^2\ \frac{49}{4}; \frac{7}{2}$

18. $x^2 + 14x + \underline{\ ?\ } = (x + \underline{\ ?\ })^2$
16. 16; 4   **18.** 49; 7

Solve by completing the square. Express irrational roots in simplest radical form.

19. $x^2 + 6x = 16\ \{2, -8\}$

20. $x^2 - 20x = 21\ \{21, -1\}$

21. $2m^2 - 24m = 20\ \{6+\sqrt{46}, 6-\sqrt{46}\}$

22. $d^2 - 22d = 1\ \{11 \pm \sqrt{122}\}$

23. $y^2 - 8y = 1361\ \{4+9\sqrt{17}, 4-9\sqrt{17}\}$

24. $m^2 - 8m - 3410 = 0$

25. $t^2 - 18t - 1600 = 0\ \{50, -32\}$

26. $p^2 = 4p + 4\ \{2 \pm 2\sqrt{2}\}$

27. $x(x+1) = 1\ \left\{\dfrac{-1+\sqrt{5}}{2}, \dfrac{-1-\sqrt{5}}{2}\right\}$

28. $3x(x+5) = 3x + 4$

29. $\dfrac{4x-2}{x+4} = 4x - 2\ \left\{\frac{1}{2}, -3\right\}$

30. $\dfrac{x+1}{x+2} = x\ \left\{\dfrac{-1 \pm \sqrt{5}}{2}\right\}$

Use the quadratic formula to solve each equation. Write irrational answers in simplest radical form.

31. $x^2 + 2x - 2 = 0\ \{-1+\sqrt{3}, -1-\sqrt{3}\}$

32. $x^2 + 3x + 2 = 0\ \overset{\{-1, -2\}}{}$

33. $x^2 - 8x + 1 = 0\ \{4+\sqrt{15}, 4-\sqrt{15}\}$

34. $x^2 - 7x + 8 = 0$
$\left\{\dfrac{7+\sqrt{17}}{2}, \dfrac{7-\sqrt{17}}{2}\right\}$

512   *EXTRA PRACTICE*

35. $x^2 - 10x + 10 = 0$ $\{5 + \sqrt{15}, 5 - \sqrt{15}\}$

36. $x^2 = x + 12$ $\{4, -3\}$

37. $2x^2 - 7x + 6 = 0$ $\left\{2, \frac{3}{2}\right\}$

38. $5x^2 = 5x + 1$ $\left\{\frac{5 \pm 3\sqrt{5}}{10}\right\}$

39. $\frac{1}{2}c^2 = \frac{1}{3}c + \frac{1}{4}$ $\left\{\frac{2 + \sqrt{22}}{6}, \frac{2 - \sqrt{22}}{6}\right\}$

40. $\frac{x + 2}{x - 2} = \frac{x - 5}{6}$ $\left\{\frac{13 \pm \sqrt{177}}{2}\right\}$

Write the value of the discriminant of each equation. Then use it to decide how many different real roots the equation has. (Do not solve the equations.)

41. $x^2 + x - 3 = 0$ 13; two

42. $3x^2 + x - 1 = 0$ 13; two

43. $x^2 + 2x + 10 = 0$ −36; none

44. $10x^2 + 2x + 1 = 0$ −36; none

45. $x^2 - 4x + 3 = 0$ 4; two

46. $2x^2 + 5x - 1 = 0$ 33; two

47. $2x^2 + 8x + 21 = 0$ −104; none

48. $\frac{1}{3}k^2 + 2k + 3 = 0$ 0; one

Solve by the most efficient method. Write irrational answers in simplest radical form.

49. $3x^2 - 4x - 5 = 0$ $\left\{\frac{2 + \sqrt{19}}{3}, \frac{2 - \sqrt{19}}{3}\right\}$

$\{4 + 2\sqrt{19}, 4 - 2\sqrt{19}\}$

50. $x^2 - 8x = 60$

51. $5x^2 + 10x = 0$ $\{0, -2\}$

52. $8t^2 - 9 = 0$

53. $x(x - 5) = x + 10$ $\{-3 + \sqrt{19}, -3 - \sqrt{19}\}$

54. $13x - x^2 = 0$ $\{0, 13\}$

55. $x^2 + (x + 1)^2 = (x + 3)^2$ $\{2 + 2\sqrt{3}, 2 - 2\sqrt{3}\}$

56. $(2x + 1)^2 = x^2 + x + 7$

52. $\left\{\frac{3}{4}\sqrt{2}, -\frac{3}{4}\sqrt{2}\right\}$

56. $\{-2, 1\}$

The problems on the following pages provide extra practice in problem solving for Chapters 3-12.

PROBLEMS

Chapter 3

Solve each problem by using an equation.

1. Twelve more than a number is -122. Find the number. -134
2. The sum of a number and -21 is 2. Find the number. 23
3. A number increased by 21 is -2. Find the number. -23
4. A town's population increased by 2000. If the new population is 19,500, what was the previous population? $17,500$
5. A bird is 320 cm above the surface of a pond. How many centimeters does the bird have to dive down to catch a fish that is 25 cm below the surface of the pond? 345 cm
6. Liz sold 12 dozen eggs on a day she collected 9 dozen from her hens. If she had 20 dozen eggs at the end of the day, how many eggs did she have at the beginning of the day? 23 dozen

Express the answer to each question as the difference between two real numbers. Compute the difference. Answer the question.

7. One evening the temperature in Portland, Maine, was $-6°C$ and the temperature in Portland, Oregon, was $12°C$. How much warmer was it in Portland, Oregon, than in Portland, Maine? $12 - (-6) = 18$; $18°C$
8. Over a summer a bird loses 1.35 g and a mouse loses 0.12 g. How much more does the bird lose? $1.35 - 0.12 = 1.23$; 1.23 g
9. In a certain game David's score went from 1230 to -22. How many points did he lose? $1230 - (-22) = 1252$; 1252 points
10. A typical daytime temperature on the surface of Mars is about $-30°C$. On Earth it is about $20°C$. About how much warmer is Earth than Mars? $20 - (-30) = 50$; about $50°C$
11. Mercury freezes at $-38.87°C$, and carbon dioxide freezes at $-78°C$. What is the difference between their freezing points? $-38.87 - (-78) = 39.13$;
12. The warmest shade temperature on Earth was recorded by the National Geographic Society at El Azizia, Libya (September 13, 1922). It was $58°C$. The coldest reading was obtained at Vostok, Antarctica (August 24, 1960). It was $-88.3°C$. What is the difference between the record temperatures? $58 - (-88.3) = 146.3$; $146.3°C$

$39.13°C$

Solve each problem by using an equation.

13. A number is 3 less than 21. Find the number. 18
14. A number decreased by 12 is 32. Find the number. 44
15. Eight less than a number is 10. Find the number. 18
16. Six less than a number is -13. Find the number. -7

514 *EXTRA PRACTICE*

17. Ilona received a grade of 82 on her chemistry exam. This grade was 12 points less than her previous grade. What was her previous grade? 94

18. Jim ran the 1000 m race and cut 2.5 s off his time for last week's run. His run this week was timed at 2 min 28 s. What was his time for last week's run? 2 min 30.5 s

19. Sean must trim down from 72 kg to 68 kg in order to be on the wrestling team. How much does he have to lose? 4 kg

20. Today Soomi did 40 sit-ups in one minute, which is 6 more sit-ups in one minute than she did yesterday. How many sit-ups in one minute did she do yesterday? 34 sit-ups

21. One sixth of a fruit pie is sold for 75¢. How much will be received when all the pieces of the pie have been sold at this price? $4.50   3-4

22. A car traveled for 3 h at the rate of 50 km/h. How far did it travel? 150 km

23. The area of a rectangular piece of property bought by a city for a park is 24 km². Its length is 6 km. What is its width? 4 km

24. Twelve-year-old Angela is one fourth as old as her father. How old is her father? 48

25. Eight times a number is −256. Find the number. −32   3-6

26. A package of 6 pencils costs 96¢. How much does each pencil cost? 16¢

27. A 12-ride commuter ticket costs $25.92. How much is that for each ride? $2.16

28. A box of 15 note cards costs $2.50. About how much does one card cost? About 17¢

29. Three times a number, increased by 7, is 40. Find the number. 11   3-7

30. Forty, decreased by twice a number, is 6. Find the number. 17

31. Together, a salad and a cup of soup cost $2.55. Find the price of each if the salad costs twice as much as the soup. Soup, 85¢; salad, $1.70

32. Together, shipping and handling a package cost $2.30. The cost of shipping is 20¢ more than the cost of handling. Find the shipping cost. $1.25

33. Rene's bicycle costs $50 more than Pat's. Together, the value of the bicycles is $334. Find the cost of Rene's bicycle. $192

34. Find a number that is 12 less than twice itself. 12   3-8

35. The sum of a number and twice its opposite is the same as 8 more than the number. Find the number. −4

36. Twice a number, decreased by 12, is the same as the number increased by 12. Find the number. 24

37. Twelve, decreased by twice a number, is the same as the number increased by 6. Find the number. 2

38. Alice Ames is twice as old as Guy Gifford. Ten years from now, Alice will be 22 years older than Guy. How old is Alice Ames now? 44

EXTRA PRACTICE **515**

Chapter 4

Solve.

1. Find three consecutive integers whose sum is 96. 31, 32, 33   4-2
2. Find four consecutive integers whose sum is 94. 22, 23, 24, 25
3. Find three consecutive integers whose sum is −57. −20, −19, −18
4. Find two consecutive integers whose sum is 89. 44, 45
5. Find two consecutive odd integers whose sum is 88. 43, 45
6. Find two consecutive even integers whose sum is 86. 42, 44
7. Find three consecutive integers such that the sum of the greatest and the least is the same as the sum of the middle integer and 5. 4, 5, 6

8. Anne is 2 years older than Mary. Last year Anne was 3 times as old as Mary. How old is Anne now? 4   4-7
9. Twelve-year-old Joe's grandfather is 66. How many years ago was his grandfather 10 times older than Joe? 6
10. Melissa's cat is 5 years younger than she is. In 2 years, Melissa will be twice as old as her cat. How old is each now? Melissa, 8; cat, 3

11. Student tickets to a play cost $2.00 each and adult tickets cost $3.00 each. On Monday 26 tickets were sold and $64.00 was collected. How many student tickets were sold on Monday? 14 student tickets   4-8
12. A collection of 23 coins is worth $4.35 and contains only nickels and quarters. How many of each kind of coin are in the collection? 7 nickels 16 quarters
13. Lee Clayton makes $8 per hour doing tutoring in mathematics and $15 per hour giving music lessons. Over the weekend he worked a total of 10 hours and made $108. How many hours did he work in each subject? Mathematics, 6 h; music, 4 h

14. Marcia rode out of town on her bicycle at a rate of 24 km/h. When her bicycle broke down, she walked it back to town at a rate of 6 km/h. If she was gone a total of 5 hours, how far from town did her bicycle break down and how long did it take her to walk back? 24 km; 4 h   4-9
15. Kate and Terry started hiking up a hill at 8:00 A.M. at a rate of 4 km/h. At 11:00 A.M. their mother discovered that they had forgotten their lunches and started after them in her car at 64 km/h. When did she overtake them? 11:12 A.M.
16. Two bicyclists started at the same time from towns 84 km apart and rode toward each other. One rode twice as fast as the other. If they met after two hours, find the speed of each bicyclist.
Slower, 14 km/h; faster, 28 km/h

17. A rectangular swimming pool is 7 m longer than it is wide. It is surrounded by a concrete walk 1.5 m wide that has an area of 120 m². Find the dimensions of the pool. 22 m by 15 m   4-10

18. A rectangular picture is 3 times as long as it is wide. When it is in a frame 10 cm wide, the total area is 3600 cm² more than that of the picture alone. Find the dimensions of the picture alone. 120 cm by 40 cm

19. A square corner lot lost 94 m² of area when the two adjacent streets were widened, one by 2 m and the other by 3 m. Find the original dimensions of the lot. 20 m by 20 m

Chapter 5

Solve.

1. A rectangle is twice as long as it is wide. If the length is increased by 3 cm and the width by 5 cm, the new area will be 28 cm² more than the old area. Find the dimensions of the original rectangle. 2 cm by 1 cm   5-6

2. Find two consecutive positive integers whose product is 72. 8, 9   5-14

3. The sum of the squares of two consecutive negative odd integers is 202. Find the integers. −11, −9

4. The sum of the squares of three consecutive positive even integers is 2360. Find the integers. 26, 28, 30

5. The length of a rectangle is 5 cm greater than twice its width, and its area is 33 m². Find its dimensions. 11 m by 3 m

6. The perimeter of a rectangular wildlife preserve is 8 km, and its area is 3 km². Find its dimensions. 3 km by 1 km

7. A corner lot had dimensions 20 m by 40 m before it lost two strips of equal width when the adjacent streets were widened. Find the new dimensions of the lot if its area is now 525 m². 35 m by 15 m

8. A room can be covered with 1440 square tiles. If each tile were 2 cm longer and wider, then the room could be covered with 1210 tiles. Find the original dimensions of a tile. 22 cm by 22 cm

Chapter 7

Solve.
                  15 cm, 36 cm, 39 cm

1. The lengths of the sides of a triangle are in the ratio 5:12:13. The perimeter of the triangle is 90 cm. Find the length of each side.   7-1

2. Two numbers are in the ratio 4:5 and their sum is 45. Find the numbers. 20, 25

3. A mutual fund invests $30,000 in bonds and stocks in the ratio 3:5. How much is invested in bonds? $11,250

Solve.

4. If the Dorsey Corporation paid an annual dividend of $25 on 350 shares of stock, how much of an annual dividend did it pay on 1050 shares? $75

7-2

5. A certain car consumes 60 L of gasoline in 3 hours. Assuming that the rate of gasoline consumption remains constant, how much gasoline will the car use on a 35-hour trip? 700 L

6. An automatic doughnut machine can produce 1000 doughnuts in 6 hours. How long would it take the machine to produce 300 doughnuts? 1.8 h

7. In a survey of 40 of the 300 residences in a certain neighborhood, it was found that 16 residences were occupied by families with children. Assuming that the residences surveyed are a representative sample, estimate the number of families with children in the neighborhood. 120 families

8. One ninth of a number is 2 less than one third of the number. Find the number. 9

7-3

9. Two sides of a triangle are *each* 3 cm longer than the third side. The length of the third side is one sixth of the perimeter. Find the length of each side of the triangle. 5 cm, 5 cm, 2 cm

10. The sum of two numbers is 80. If the greater number is divided by the smaller, the quotient is 3 and the remainder is 8. Find the numbers. 18, 62

7-4

11. What number must be subtracted from the numerator and denominator of $\frac{7}{9}$ to make the resulting fraction equal to $\frac{2}{3}$? 3

12. Find two consecutive integers such that the sum of their reciprocals is $\frac{5}{6}$. 2, 3

13. The sum of two integers is 7. The difference of their reciprocals is $\frac{3}{10}$. Find the integers. 2, 5

14. The population of sheep in a farming community is 2500. What percent of the community's sheep is owned by the Skethley family if that family owns 800 sheep? 32%

7-5

15. Out of 1360 persons surveyed, 35% felt that the most serious problem facing the world today is environmental pollution. How many people gave this reply? 476

16. Pat invested a total of $14,000 in a term savings account at 12% simple interest and in a regular savings account at $5\frac{1}{2}$% simple interest. The total interest for the first year came to $1127.50. How much money did she invest at each rate? $5500 at 12%; $8500 at $5\frac{1}{2}$%

17. One year Alfredo put a sum of money into a savings account that yielded 5% simple interest and $754.00 into bonds that yielded 8% simple interest. The money he invested earned a total of $86.92 in interest that year. How much did he invest in the savings account? $532

7-6

18. The price of one share of Alcron Trucking Company stock rose from $55.20 to $57.96. Find the percent of increase. 5%

19. The list price of a typewriter is $140. If a discount of $10.50 is given for cash payment, what is the percent of discount? $7\frac{1}{2}$%

20. Six years ago the KwiKalc calculator sold for $58.00. This year it is selling for $20.30. Find the percent of decrease. 65%

21. An article with a list price of $36.00 is on sale at a 15% discount. If sales tax is 5%, how much would it cost to purchase the article on sale? $32.13

7-7

22. How many kilograms of water must be added to 160 kg of a 5% salt solution in order to produce a 4% solution? 40 kg

23. How many kilograms of pure acid must be added to 60 kg of a 70% acid solution in order to produce an 80% acid solution? 30 kg

24. A building supplies company has two kinds of sand, a white sand that sells for 12¢ per kilogram and a red-and-gray sand mix that sells for 7¢ per kilogram. How much of each type of sand should go into making 800 kg of a multicolored sand mix that sells for 9¢ per kilogram? White sand, 320 kg; red-and-gray sand, 480 kg

25. The owner of a delicatessen has pickled hot peppers that sell for $4.60 per kilogram and pickled pearl onions that sell for $5.80 per kilogram. How much of each should the deli owner mix in order to get 15 kg of a mixture that sells for $5.00 per kilogram? Peppers, 10 kg; onions, 5 kg

7-8

26. One bulldozer can complete a job in 3 days and a second, smaller bulldozer can complete the job in 5 days. How many days are required for the job if both bulldozers are used? 1.875 d

27. Pearson College owns a tabulator that can process registration data in 6 hours. Wanting to speed up the processing, the school authorized the purchase of a second tabulator that can do the job in 8 hours. How many hours will it take the two tabulators working together to process all the data? About 3.4 h

28. With drain pipes A and B open, a swimming pool can be emptied in 1.5 h. If drain pipe A can empty the pool in 3 h, how long would it take drain pipe B to empty the pool? 3 h

29. John and Mary can spade a garden in 4 days, but John can do it alone in 6 days. How long will it take Mary alone to finish the job after John works on it for 4 days by himself? 4 d

EXTRA PRACTICE **519**

Solve by using a system of equations in two variables and the substitution method.

Ninth-grade, 45 bags; tenth-grade, 20 bags

1. In a school ecology project, the ninth-grade class collected 25 more bags of aluminum cans than the tenth-grade class. The two classes collected a total of 65 bags. How many bags did each class collect?

8-6

2. The perimeter of a rectangle is 54 cm. Two times the width is 3 cm more than the length. Find the dimensions of the rectangle. Width, 10 cm; length, 17 cm

3. In one week, an engineer worked for 6 days and an assistant worked for 7 days investigating the effects of manufacturing processes which lead to air pollution. Together, they received a salary of $900. The following week, the engineer worked 5 days and the assistant worked 3 days for a combined salary of $580. Find the daily wages of each. Engineer, $80; assistant, $60

4. The *average* of two numbers is one half the sum of the numbers. Find two numbers whose average is 44 and whose difference is 44. 66, 22

5. Ten more than the first of two numbers is 3 times the second of the two numbers. Ten less than the second number is −3 times the first number. Find the two numbers. First number, 2; second number, 4

Solve by using a system of equations in two variables and whatever method you prefer.

6. The sum of two numbers is 56. The larger exceeds twice the smaller by 2. Find the numbers. 38, 18

8-7

7. A store received $823 one month from the sale of 5 tape players and 7 radios. The receipts from the tape players exceeded the receipts from the radios by $137. Find the price of each.
Tape player, $96; radio, $49

8. A rectangular rug is 1 m longer than it is wide. It is in a room with a perimeter of 18 m, and the perimeter of the rug is 4 m less than the perimeter of the room. Find the dimensions of the rug. 4 m by 3 m

8-8

9. Two boxes of apples and 3 boxes of apricots cost $24.00. Four boxes of apples and 5 boxes of apricots cost $44.00. Find the prices of a box of apples and a box of apricots. Apples, $6; apricots, $4

10. In 4 years Marcie will be as old as Lynn is now. Eight years ago the sum of their ages was 16. Find their ages. Marcie, 14; Lynn, 18

8-9

11. A father, being asked his age and that of his son, said, "If you add 4 to my age and divide the sum by 4, you will have my son's age. But 6 years ago I was $7\frac{1}{2}$ times as old as my son." Find their ages.
Father, 36; son, 10

Solve, assuming that each number is a two-digit number.

12. The sum of the digits of a number is 9. If the digits are reversed, the number is increased by 45. Find the original number. 27

13. The sum of the digits of a number is 13. If the digits are reversed, the new number is 27 less than the original number. Find the original number. 85

Using two variables, find the original fraction.

14. The denominator exceeds the numerator by 3. If 1 is added to the denominator, a fraction is obtained whose value is $\frac{2}{3}$. $\frac{8}{11}$

15. When simplified, a fraction has the value $\frac{4}{5}$. When its numerator is increased by 9, the resulting fraction is equal to the reciprocal of the value of the original fraction. $\frac{16}{20}$

Solve by using a system of equations in two variables.

16. A boat can go 72 km downstream in 2 h. In the same time it can go 48 km upstream. Find the rate of the boat in still water and the rate of the current. Boat, 30 km/h; current, 6 km/h
   8-10

17. An airplane flew 1800 km in 5 hours with the wind. The return trip against the wind took twice as long. Find the rate of the plane in still air and the rate of the wind. Plane, 270 km/h; wind, 90 km/h

Chapter 9

Solve.

1. A certain brand of salad dressing contains 7 parts oil to 3 parts vinegar. How much oil must be blended with 51 L of vinegar to make the dressing? 119 L
   9-7

2. Twelve grams of calcium chloride can absorb 5 cm^3 of water. How much calcium chloride is needed to absorb 138 cm^3 of water? 331.2 g

3. What is the mass of a 500 m reel of cable if a 1 m section has a mass of 0.87 kg? 435 kg

4. What sum at 4% simple interest yields the same yearly income as $800 at 5% simple interest? $1000
   9-8

5. A gear with 28 teeth makes 45 revolutions per minute (r.p.m.) and meshes with a gear having 20 teeth. What is the rate of the second gear if the number of r.p.m. varies inversely as the number of teeth? 63 r.p.m.

6. The length of a rectangle of a given area varies inversely as the width. If a certain rectangle has a length of 42 cm and a width of 12 cm, find the length of another rectangle of equal area whose width is 14 cm. 36 cm

Solve.

7. A diamond's price varies directly as the square of its number of carats. If a diamond that is $\frac{3}{8}$ of a carat is worth $900, find the cost of a similar diamond that is $\frac{7}{8}$ of a carat. $4900

8. The distance which a freely falling body falls varies directly as the square of the time it falls. If it falls 44.1 m in 3 s, how far will it fall in 8 s? 313.6 m

9. The height of a cone of a given volume varies inversely as the square of the radius of the base. If a cone with a radius of 6 cm has a height of 15 cm, what is the height of a cone of equal volume with a radius of 4 cm? 33.75 cm

Chapter 10

Solve.

1. Four times the smaller of two consecutive even integers is less than 3 times the larger. What are the largest possible values for the integers? 4, 6

2. Bill has at least $12.45 in dimes and quarters. He has 12 more quarters than dimes. At least how many of each coin does Bill have? 27 dimes, 39 quarters

3. Two ships are no more than 240 km apart and are sailing toward one another. The rate of one ship is 4 km/h greater than the rate of the other ship. If they meet in 3 h, find the greatest possible rate of each ship. 38 km/h, 42 km/h

Chapter 11

Solve. Find each answer to the nearest tenth. Use the approximation $\pi \approx 3.14$ when needed. Use the Table of Square Roots on page 526 as necessary.

1. The length of a rectangle is 3 times the width. Find the dimensions of the rectangle if its area is 123 cm². 19.2 cm by 6.4 cm

2. Find the diameter of a circular plot that has the same area as a rectangular one that is 22 m wide and 35 m long. 31.3 m

3. The length of the base of a triangle is 8 times the length of the altitude. Find the length of the base if the area of the triangle is 300 cm². 69.3 cm

9-9

10-3

11-5

522 *EXTRA PRACTICE*

522

Solve. Make a sketch for each problem. Approximate each square root to the nearest hundredth.

4. Find the length of a diagonal of a rectangle whose dimensions are 30 cm by 50 cm. 58.31 cm

11-6

5. The bottom of a 6 m ramp is 5 m from a loading platform. How high is the platform? 3.32 m

6. The lengths of the two shorter sides of a right triangle are two consecutive positive integers. The length of the hypotenuse is 29 cm. Find the lengths of the two shorter sides. 20 cm, 21 cm

Solve.

7. One fifth of the square root of a number is 2. Find the number. 100

11-10

8. When 7 is added to 3 times a number, the square root of the result is 5. Find the number. 6

9. The formula for finding the altitude length h of an equilateral triangle with side length s is $h = \dfrac{\sqrt{3}}{2} s$. Find the length of a side of an equilateral triangle with altitude of length $5\sqrt{3}$. 10

Chapter 12

Solve. Give irrational roots to the nearest tenth. Use the Table of Square Roots on page 526 as necessary.

1. The dimensions of a cube are such that the number of cubic centimeters in the volume is 3 times the number of centimeters in the sum of the lengths of the 12 edges. Find the length of an edge of the cube. 6 cm

12-6

2. The length of a rectangular framework is 3 times the width. If the length were shortened by 30 cm and the width were lengthened by 40 cm, the new area would be one half of the original area. Find the original width of the framework. 11.2 cm

3. One number is 2 less than another number. The sum of their squares is 3700. Find the two numbers. 42, 44 or −42, −44

4. A mat is to be made for a picture whose dimensions are 10 cm by 12.5 cm. The width of the mat is to be 0.8 times the length of the mat, so that the mat will have the same proportions as the picture. The area of the mat is to be twice the area of the picture. Find the dimensions of the mat. 17.7 cm by 14.1 cm

EXTRA PRACTICE **523**

Solve. Give irrational roots to the nearest tenth. Use the Table of Square Roots on page 526 as necessary.

5. The length of an edge of one cube is 2 cm longer than the length of an edge of a smaller cube. If the volumes differ by 488 cm³, find the edge length of each cube. 8 cm, 10 cm

6. A rug is 6 m long and 3 m wide. It has a rectangular design in the middle that takes up one half of its area. The border surrounding the design is of uniform width. Find the width of the border. 0.6 m

7. A rectangular box without a top has a total surface area of 700 cm². The length of the box is $\frac{3}{2}$ times the width. The height of the box is 1 cm greater than the width. Draw a sketch and find the dimensions of the box. 15 cm long, 10 cm wide, 11 cm high

Table of Squares of Integers from 1 to 100

Number	Square	Number	Square	Number	Square	Number	Square
1	1	26	676	51	2601	76	5776
2	4	27	729	52	2704	77	5929
3	9	28	784	53	2809	78	6084
4	16	29	841	54	2916	79	6241
5	25	30	900	55	3025	80	6400
6	36	31	961	56	3136	81	6561
7	49	32	1024	57	3249	82	6724
8	64	33	1089	58	3364	83	6889
9	81	34	1156	59	3481	84	7056
10	100	35	1225	60	3600	85	7225
11	121	36	1296	61	3721	86	7396
12	144	37	1369	62	3844	87	7569
13	169	38	1444	63	3969	88	7744
14	196	39	1521	64	4096	89	7921
15	225	40	1600	65	4225	90	8100
16	256	41	1681	66	4356	91	8281
17	289	42	1764	67	4489	92	8464
18	324	43	1849	68	4624	93	8649
19	361	44	1936	69	4761	94	8836
20	400	45	2025	70	4900	95	9025
21	441	46	2116	71	5041	96	9216
22	484	47	2209	72	5184	97	9409
23	529	48	2304	73	5329	98	9604
24	576	49	2401	74	5476	99	9801
25	625	50	2500	75	5625	100	10,000

Table of Square Roots of Integers from 1 to 100

Exact square roots are shown in red. For the others, rational approximations are given correct to three decimal places.

Number	Positive Square Root	Number	Positive Square Root	Number	Positive Square Root	Number	Positive Square Root
N	$\sqrt{N}$	N	$\sqrt{N}$	N	$\sqrt{N}$	N	$\sqrt{N}$
1	1	26	5.099	51	7.141	76	8.718
2	1.414	27	5.196	52	7.211	77	8.775
3	1.732	28	5.292	53	7.280	78	8.832
4	2	29	5.385	54	7.348	79	8.888
5	2.236	30	5.477	55	7.416	80	8.944
6	2.449	31	5.568	56	7.483	81	9
7	2.646	32	5.657	57	7.550	82	9.055
8	2.828	33	5.745	58	7.616	83	9.110
9	3	34	5.831	59	7.681	84	9.165
10	3.162	35	5.916	60	7.746	85	9.220
11	3.317	36	6	61	7.810	86	9.274
12	3.464	37	6.083	62	7.874	87	9.327
13	3.606	38	6.164	63	7.937	88	9.381
14	3.742	39	6.245	64	8	89	9.434
15	3.873	40	6.325	65	8.062	90	9.487
16	4	41	6.403	66	8.124	91	9.539
17	4.123	42	6.481	67	8.185	92	9.592
18	4.243	43	6.557	68	8.246	93	9.644
19	4.359	44	6.633	69	8.307	94	9.695
20	4.472	45	6.708	70	8.367	95	9.747
21	4.583	46	6.782	71	8.426	96	9.798
22	4.690	47	6.856	72	8.485	97	9.849
23	4.796	48	6.928	73	8.544	98	9.899
24	4.899	49	7	74	8.602	99	9.950
25	5	50	7.071	75	8.660	100	10

TABLE OF TRIGONOMETRIC RATIOS

Angle	Sine	Cosine	Tangent	Angle	Sine	Cosine	Tangent
1°	.0175	.9998	.0175	46°	.7193	.6947	1.0355
2°	.0349	.9994	.0349	47°	.7314	.6820	1.0724
3°	.0523	.9986	.0524	48°	.7431	.6691	1.1106
4°	.0698	.9976	.0699	49°	.7547	.6561	1.1504
5°	.0872	.9962	.0875	50°	.7660	.6428	1.1918
6°	.1045	.9945	.1051	51°	.7771	.6293	1.2349
7°	.1219	.9925	.1228	52°	.7880	.6157	1.2799
8°	.1392	.9903	.1405	53°	.7986	.6018	1.3270
9°	.1564	.9877	.1584	54°	.8090	.5878	1.3764
10°	.1736	.9848	.1763	55°	.8192	.5736	1.4281
11°	.1908	.9816	.1944	56°	.8290	.5592	1.4826
12°	.2079	.9781	.2126	57°	.8387	.5446	1.5399
13°	.2250	.9744	.2309	58°	.8480	.5299	1.6003
14°	.2419	.9703	.2493	59°	.8572	.5150	1.6643
15°	.2588	.9659	.2679	60°	.8660	.5000	1.7321
16°	.2756	.9613	.2867	61°	.8746	.4848	1.8040
17°	.2924	.9563	.3057	62°	.8829	.4695	1.8807
18°	.3090	.9511	.3249	63°	.8910	.4540	1.9626
19°	.3256	.9455	.3443	64°	.8988	.4384	2.0503
20°	.3420	.9397	.3640	65°	.9063	.4226	2.1445
21°	.3584	.9336	.3839	66°	.9135	.4067	2.2460
22°	.3746	.9272	.4040	67°	.9205	.3907	2.3559
23°	.3907	.9205	.4245	68°	.9272	.3746	2.4751
24°	.4067	.9135	.4452	69°	.9336	.3584	2.6051
25°	.4226	.9063	.4663	70°	.9397	.3420	2.7475
26°	.4384	.8988	.4877	71°	.9455	.3256	2.9042
27°	.4540	.8910	.5095	72°	.9511	.3090	3.0777
28°	.4695	.8829	.5317	73°	.9563	.2924	3.2709
29°	.4848	.8746	.5543	74°	.9613	.2756	3.4874
30°	.5000	.8660	.5774	75°	.9659	.2588	3.7321
31°	.5150	.8572	.6009	76°	.9703	.2419	4.0108
32°	.5299	.8480	.6249	77°	.9744	.2250	4.3315
33°	.5446	.8387	.6494	78°	.9781	.2079	4.7046
34°	.5592	.8290	.6745	79°	.9816	.1908	5.1446
35°	.5736	.8192	.7002	80°	.9848	.1736	5.6713
36°	.5878	.8090	.7265	81°	.9877	.1564	6.3138
37°	.6018	.7986	.7536	82°	.9903	.1392	7.1154
38°	.6157	.7880	.7813	83°	.9925	.1219	8.1443
39°	.6293	.7771	.8098	84°	.9945	.1045	9.5144
40°	.6428	.7660	.8391	85°	.9962	.0872	11.4301
41°	.6561	.7547	.8693	86°	.9976	.0698	14.3007
42°	.6691	.7431	.9004	87°	.9986	.0523	19.0811
43°	.6820	.7314	.9325	88°	.9994	.0349	28.6363
44°	.6947	.7193	.9657	89°	.9998	.0175	57.2900
45°	.7071	.7071	1.0000				

ANSWERS TO SELF-TESTS

Chapter 1, Self-Test 1, page 11
1. 17 **2.** 10 **3.** 2 **4.** 3 **5.** 2 **6.** 4

Chapter 1, Self-Test 2, page 25
1. $n + 3 = 5$ **2.** $2t - 1 = 11$ **3. a.** $a - 5$
b. $a - 5 = 9$ **4.** 5

Chapter 2, Self-Test 1, page 39
1.

2. $^{-}3$ is less than 2 **3.** $^{-}6, ^{-}1, 0, 5$ **4.** 8900
5. $2x + 11$

Chapter 2, Self-Test 2, page 52
1. $^{-}5$ **2.** 6 **3.** 13 **4.** -4 **5.** -12
6. -20

Chapter 2, Self-Test 3, page 64
1. $5x + 5$ **2.** $3y - 5$ **3.** -42 **4.** $-a + 6$
5. x **6.** $-6a + b$

Chapter 3, Self-Test 1, page 83
1. 8 **2.** 22 **3.** -11 **4.** -21 **5.** 20
6. -6 **7.** 41 **8.** 26 **9.** 7

Chapter 3, Self-Test 2, page 94
1. 64 **2.** -20 **3.** -6 **4.** -6 **5.** 2
6. $-4x$ **7.** -9 **8.** 7 **9.** 24

Chapter 3, Self-Test 3, page 107
1. 6 **2.** 2 **3.** 6 **4.** 5 **5.** 6 years old
6. (1) Associative axiom for addition;
(2) Axiom of opposites; (3) Identity axiom
for addition

Chapter 4, Self-Test 1, page 121
1. $2a^3bc^2$ **2.** -6 **3.** 16 **4.** $6x^2 - 4$
5. $2a^2 + 4ab + 6b^2$

Chapter 4, Self-Test 2, page 133
1. x^8 **2.** $12y^7$ **3.** a^{15} **4.** $9x^4y^6$
5. $5x^2 + 20x$ **6.** $2a^4 - 2a^3b + 2a^2b^2$
7. $n^2 - 9$ **8.** $x^3 + x^2 - 12x + 12$

Chapter 4, Self-Test 3, page 148

1.

	Age now	Age in 5 years
Dan	x	$x + 5$
Ruth	$x - 3$	$x + 2$

2. $w = \dfrac{V}{lh}$ **3.** 2 **4.** $2h$ **5.** 41 cm by 51 cm

Chapter 5, Self-Test 1, page 165
1. $3 \cdot 5^2$ **2.** $(1)(45), (3)(15), (5)(9),$
$(-1)(-45), (-3)(-15), (-5)(-9)$ **3.** 15
4. $-\dfrac{3x}{y}$ **5.** $\dfrac{m^4}{4k}$ **6.** 12 **7.** $-5ab^4$
8. $7t^2 + 5t - 3$ **9.** $2xy^2(2x^3y - 4x + 3)$

Chapter 5, Self-Test 2, page 174
1. $6y^2 - 8y - 30$ **2.** $6x^3 - 28x^2 + 16x$
3. $x^2 - 49$ **4.** $4a^2 - 49b^2$
5. $(2x + 7)(2x - 7)$ **6.** $9(2x^2 + 3)(2x^2 - 3)$
7. $4y^2 + 20y + 25$ **8.** $9z^2 - 30zk + 25k^2$
9. $(3a + 2)^2$ **10.** $(4m - 3n)^2$

Chapter 5, Self-Test 3, page 182
1. $(y + 3)(y + 5)$ **2.** $(x - 8)(x - 2)$
3. $(n - 7)(n + 4)$ **4.** $(v + 12)(v - 3)$
5. $(3x - 5)(2x - 3)$ **6.** $(3x - 2)(x + 4)$

Chapter 5, Self-Test 4, page 186
1. $(y - 2)(x + 6)$
2. $(n + 4 - 3m)(n + 4 + 3m)$
3. $4a(x - 2)^2$ **4.** $4x(y - 3)^2$

Chapter 5, Self-Test 5, page 195
1. $\{5, 9\}$ **2.** $\{0, 2, -5\}$ **3.** $\{2, 5\}$
4. $\{5, -4\}$ **5.** $\{-4\}$ **6.** $\{0, 4, -7\}$ **7.** $8, 9$

Chapter 6, Self-Test 1, page 210
1. $\dfrac{k + 4}{k - 5}$ **2.** $\dfrac{n + 5}{n - 5}$ **3.** $\dfrac{36a}{25b^5}$ **4.** $\dfrac{4z}{3(z + 1)}$
5. $\dfrac{x^2y^2}{16}$ **6.** $\dfrac{2m}{3n^3}$

Chapter 6, Self-Test 2, page 219

1. $\dfrac{5}{16kz^2}$, $\dfrac{12k^2z^2}{16kz^2}$

2. $\dfrac{x+1}{3(x-1)(x+1)}$, $\dfrac{6}{3(x'-1)(x+1)}$ 3. $\dfrac{5}{3c}$

4. $\dfrac{n^2-5}{3}$ 5. $\dfrac{k+1}{(k+2)(k-2)}$

6. $\dfrac{14b-a+2}{4ab}$

Chapter 6, Self-Test 3, page 225

1. $\dfrac{-4x-1}{x+2}$ 2. $\dfrac{4a-b}{a+b}$ 3. $3x-5$

4. $2x+5+\dfrac{3}{4x-1}$

Chapter 7, Self-Test 1, page 243
1. 4:5 2. 12:1 3. 93, 217 4. 12 5. $492

Chapter 7, Self-Test 2, page 250
1. 48 2. $\frac{8}{3}$ 3. 4 4. 1

Chapter 7, Self-Test 3, page 258
1. 30% 2. 200 3. 11 4. 9% 5. $75

Chapter 7, Self-Test 4, page 268
1. 8 kg 2. 25 kg 3. 24 min 4. 1.8 h

Chapter 8, Self-Test 1, page 286

1, 2.

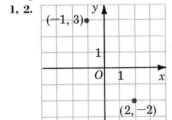

3. no 4. $\{(3,0),(2,1),(1,2),(0,3)\}$ 5. a, b

6.

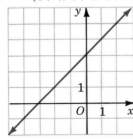

Chapter 8, Self-Test 2, page 303

1.

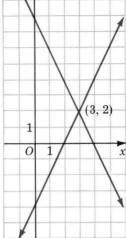

2. $(1,6)$ 3. width = 10 m; length = 20 m
4. $(1,1)$ 5. $(2,2)$

Chapter 8, Self-Test 3, page 312
1. Eve is 24 years old; Uncle Bill is 48.
2. 64 3. $\frac{11}{20}$ 4. rate of boat = 16.5 km/h,
rate of current = 8.5 km/h

Chapter 9, Self-Test 1, page 330
1. $\frac{3}{2}$ 2. 0 3. Slope is $\frac{2}{3}$; y-intercept is $-\frac{1}{3}$.
4. $2x-y=-4$ 5. $x-y=-3$

Chapter 9, Self-Test 2, page 342
1. 5 2. $\{0,-3,-4\}$
3. a. $D=\{\text{N7621, N6523, V2231, V2232}\}$,
$R=\{\$12.88, \$9.85, \$3.39\}$
b. $\{(\text{N7621}, \$12.88), (\text{N6523}, \$9.85),$
$(\text{V2231}, \$3.39), (\text{V2232}, \$3.39)\}$ 4. $(-1,-3)$
5. 0

Chapter 9, Self-Test 3, page 359
1. 3 h 2. 20 min 3. 20 4. 9π cm^2
5. 30 cm^2

Chapter 10, Self-Test 1, page 378
1. $-6<-3<0$, or $0>-3>-6$
2. $\{-4,-3,-2,-1,0,1,2\}$
3. {the real numbers less than 4}

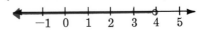

4. {the real numbers greater than or equal to $-\frac{1}{2}$}

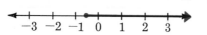

5. 44, 46

Chapter 10, Self-Test 2, page 388
1. {the real numbers less than 1 or greater than 3}

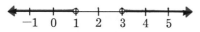

2. {7, and the real numbers between 0 and 7}

3. {1, 5}

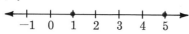

4. {-1, 5, and the real numbers less than -1 or greater than 5}

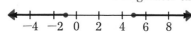

Chapter 10, Self-Test 3, page 396
1.

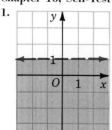

2.

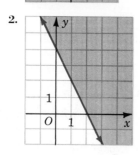

3.

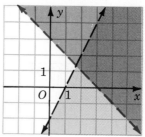

Chapter 11, Self-Test 1, page 415
1. $\frac{17}{24}$ **2.** $1\frac{4}{15}$ **3.** $\frac{4}{5}$ **4.** $\frac{3}{4}$ **5.** 0.74 **6.** $0.15\overline{90}$

7. $\frac{211}{99}$ **8.** 27 **9.** $\frac{21}{32}$ **10.** 1.2

Chapter 11, Self-Test 2, page 426
1. 80.62 **2.** -0.91 **3.** $7|mn^3|$
4. $13x^2y^2\sqrt{x}$ **5.** $\{2, -2\}$ **6.** $\{\frac{7}{2}, -\frac{7}{2}\}$
7. 10.30 **8.** no

Chapter 11, Self-Test 3, page 437
1. $20\sqrt{5}$ **2.** $4|x|y^2\sqrt{2}$ **3.** $5\sqrt{5} - \sqrt{3}$
4. $2\sqrt{2}$ **5.** $9 + 4\sqrt{5}$ **6.** 9 **7.** $6 + 3\sqrt{3}$
8. $\dfrac{4\sqrt{5} - 5}{11}$ **9.** 25 **10.** 49

Chapter 12, Self-Test 1, page 455
1. $\{4, -4\}$ **2.** $\{3, 7\}$ **3.** $\{-6, 2\}$ **4.** $\{1, 5\}$
5. $\left\{\dfrac{3 + \sqrt{17}}{2}, \dfrac{3 - \sqrt{17}}{2}\right\}$
6. $\left\{\dfrac{-7 + \sqrt{37}}{6}, \dfrac{-7 - \sqrt{37}}{6}\right\}$ **7.** two **8.** two

Chapter 12, Self-Test 2, page 461
1. $\left\{\dfrac{-3 + \sqrt{65}}{4}, \dfrac{-3 - \sqrt{65}}{4}\right\}$
2. $\{2\sqrt{5}, -2\sqrt{5}\}$ **3.** $\{0, 3\}$
4. $\{-2 + \sqrt{2}, -2 - \sqrt{2}\}$
5. 3.9 cm **6.** 7.5 m

APPENDIX

ZERO AND NEGATIVE EXPONENTS

OBJECTIVE To simplify expressions with zero and negative exponents.

In the first two parts of the Rule of Exponents for Division on page 159, $m \neq n$. However, if you were to apply these two rules to evaluate $\dfrac{a^m}{a^m}$, you would obtain the following two expressions:

$$\frac{a^m}{a^m} = a^{m-m} = a^0 \qquad \frac{a^m}{a^m} = \frac{1}{a^{m-m}} = \frac{1}{a^0}$$

Since $\dfrac{a^m}{a^m} = a^0$, and also $\dfrac{a^m}{a^m} = 1$, we state the following rule for a^0:

RULE FOR A ZERO EXPONENT

$a^0 = 1$, where a is a real number not equal to zero.

We shall not use the expression 0^0.

To apply the rule $\dfrac{a^m}{a^n} = a^{m-n}$ when $m < n$, that is, when $m - n$ is a negative number, we must give meaning to raising to a power when the exponent is negative. We apply this rule as follows:

$$\frac{a^5}{a^2} = a^{5-2} = a^3 \qquad \frac{a^2}{a^5} = a^{2-5} = a^{-3}$$

Since $\dfrac{a^5}{a^2}$ *and* $\dfrac{a^2}{a^5}$ are reciprocals, a^3 and a^{-3} must be reciprocals: that is, $a^3 = \dfrac{1}{a^{-3}}$ and $a^{-3} = \dfrac{1}{a^3}$.

The previous examples illustrate the following rules for raising to a power with negative exponents:

RULES FOR NEGATIVE EXPONENTS

$a^n = \dfrac{1}{a^{-n}}$ and $a^{-n} = \dfrac{1}{a^n}$, where a is a real number not equal to zero.

Notice how these rules are used in the examples.

EXAMPLE 1 $\quad a^3 \cdot a^{-2} = a^{3+(-2)} = a^1 = a$

EXAMPLE 2 $\quad \dfrac{12 \times 10^8}{3 \times 10^{11}} = 4 \times 10^{-3} = 0.004$

EXAMPLE 3 $\quad a^3 \cdot b^{-2} = a^3 \cdot \dfrac{1}{b^2} = \dfrac{a^3}{b^2}$

EXAMPLE 4 $\quad \dfrac{x^5}{y^{-3}} = x^5 \cdot \dfrac{1}{y^{-3}} = x^5 y^3$

EXAMPLE 5 $\quad \dfrac{x^0 y^{-2}}{z^2} = x^0 \cdot y^{-2} \cdot \dfrac{1}{z^2} = 1 \cdot \dfrac{1}{y^2} \cdot \dfrac{1}{z^2} = \dfrac{1}{y^2 z^2}$

Oral Exercises

Give an equivalent expression that does not have a zero or negative exponent. Assume that 0 is not a member of the domain of any variable.

1. 7^0 1

2. $(-2)^0$ 1

3. 5^{-2} $\frac{1}{25}$

4. 2^{-3} $\frac{1}{8}$

5. $(4)^{-2}$ $\frac{1}{16}$

6. -3^{-3} $-\frac{1}{27}$

7. 1^{-7} 1

8. $(-1)^{-4}$ 1

9. $\left(\dfrac{1}{5}\right)^{-1}$ 5

10. $\left(\dfrac{2}{3}\right)^{-1}$ $\frac{3}{2}$

11. $\dfrac{4^{-1}}{3^{-2}}$ $\frac{9}{4}$

12. $\dfrac{c^{-2}}{d^{-2}}$ $\frac{d^2}{c^2}$

13. $(2^{-1})^{-5}$ 32

14. $(3+4)^{-1}$ $\frac{1}{7}$

15. $\dfrac{48 \times 10^{-3}}{16 \times 10^{-7}}$ 30,000

16. $\dfrac{54 \times 10^{-4}}{18 \times 10^{-2}}$ 0.03

17. xy^{-2} $\frac{x}{y^2}$

18. $m^{-1}n$ $\frac{n}{m}$

19. $7y^{-3}$ $\frac{7}{y^3}$

20. $-2w^{-8}$ $-\frac{2}{w^8}$

21. $\dfrac{3a^2}{b^{-4}}$ $3a^2 b^4$

22. $\dfrac{4p^{-3}}{q}$ $\frac{4}{p^3 q}$

23. $5x^0 y^{-1}$ $\frac{5}{y}$

24. $(5x)^0 y^{-1}$ $\frac{1}{y}$

25. $\dfrac{r^0 s^{-2}}{t^{-1}}$ $\frac{t}{s^2}$

26. $\dfrac{(-1)^0 w^{-5}}{z^{-1}}$ $\frac{z}{w^5}$

27. $(a^{-2}b)^{-3}$ $\frac{a^6}{b^3}$

28. $(m^3 n^{-2})^{-1}$ $\frac{n^2}{m}$

Written Exercises

Write an equivalent expression using only positive exponents. Assume that 0 is not a member of the domain of any variable.

A 1. $\dfrac{5}{3^{-2}}$ 45

2. $\dfrac{2^{-4}}{5^{-3}}$ $\frac{125}{16}$

3. -1^0 -1

4. -1^{-3} -1

5. $\left(\dfrac{1}{2}\right)^{-2} + \left(\dfrac{2}{5}\right)^{-1}$

6. $\left(\dfrac{3}{4}\right)^{-2} - \left(\dfrac{4}{3}\right)^2$

7. $\dfrac{7 \times 10^{-13}}{1.4 \times 10^{-15}}$

8. $\dfrac{9.6 \times 10^{-10}}{1.6 \times 10^{-6}}$

5. $6\frac{1}{2}$

6. 0

7. 500

8. 0.0006

9. uv^{-4} $\frac{u}{v^4}$

10. $s^{-3}t$ $\frac{t}{s^3}$

11. $\dfrac{p^{-1}}{q^{-2}}$ $\frac{q^2}{p}$

12. $\dfrac{-a}{b^{-5}}$ $-ab^5$

13. $\dfrac{(-4)^0 m^{-2}}{n^{-3}}$ $\dfrac{n^3}{m^2}$ **14.** $\dfrac{-2^2 w^{-1}}{z^{-3}}$ $\dfrac{4z^3}{w}$ **15.** $(-3t^{-2})^0$ 1 **16.** $(c^2 d^{-4})^0$ 1

17. $(4x^{-2}y^4)^{-1}$ $\dfrac{x^2}{4y^4}$ **18.** $(2a^3 b^{-1})^{-2}$ $\dfrac{b^2}{4a^6}$ **19.** $\left(\dfrac{3}{a^2}\right)^{-1}$ $\dfrac{a^2}{3}$ **20.** $\left(\dfrac{2m^3}{n^{-2}}\right)^{-1}$ $\dfrac{1}{2m^3 n^2}$

Express each fraction as a product of powers.

SAMPLE $\dfrac{a^{-4}}{b}$ *SOLUTION* $\dfrac{a^{-4}}{b} = a^{-4} \cdot \dfrac{1}{b} = a^{-4} b^{-1}$

21. $\dfrac{x}{y^3}$ xy^{-3} **22.** $\dfrac{r^2}{s^4}$ $r^2 s^{-4}$ **23.** $\dfrac{m^{-2}}{n^{-5}}$ $m^{-2} n^5$

24. $\dfrac{p^3}{q^{-4}}$ $p^3 q^4$ **25.** $\dfrac{x^{-1}y^3}{wz^{-2}}$ $x^{-1}y^3 w^{-1}z^2$ **26.** $\dfrac{ab^{-2}}{c^{-1}d}$ $ab^{-2} cd^{-1}$

State a polynomial in simple form equivalent to each expression.

SAMPLE $\dfrac{2a^2}{a^{-3}} + (-6)^0 a^5$

SOLUTION $\dfrac{2a^2}{a^{-3}} + (-6)^0 a^5 = 2a^2 \cdot a^3 + 1 \cdot a^5$

$\qquad\qquad\qquad\quad = 2a^5 + a^5 = 3a^5$

27. $4x^2 + \dfrac{3}{x^{-2}}$ $7x^2$ **28.** $w^5 + \dfrac{(-2w)^3}{w^{-2}}$ $-7w^5$

29. $2cd^0 - \dfrac{c^{-2}}{c^{-3}}$ c **30.** $\dfrac{t^{-1}}{(2t)^{-3}} + \dfrac{6t}{2t^{-1}}$ $11t^2$

B 31. $\dfrac{1}{(rs)^{-4}} + \dfrac{3s^2 r^{-3}}{s^{-2}r^{-3}}$ $r^4 s^4 + 3s^4$ **32.** $\dfrac{16}{(-2a^{-1})^4} + \dfrac{(-2a^4)^0}{a^{-3}}$ $a^4 + a^3$

33. $\dfrac{5uv^2}{v^{-2}} - \left(\dfrac{u^{-2}v^{-1}}{5}\right)^{-2}$ $5uv^4 - 25u^4 v^2$ **34.** $\dfrac{-2y^{-3}z^2}{(y^2 z^{-1})^{-2}} + \dfrac{3yz^{-2}}{(y^{-1})^0 z^{-5}}$
$\qquad\qquad\qquad\qquad\qquad\quad -2y + 3yz^3$

35. $(c - 2d^{-2})^0 - \dfrac{1}{(3c - d)^{-1}}$ $1 - 3c + d$ **36.** $(x - 1)^2 + \dfrac{3}{(x - 1)^{-1}}$
$\qquad\qquad\qquad\qquad\qquad\quad x^2 + x - 2$

SYSTEMS OF LINEAR INEQUALITIES: APPLICATIONS

OBJECTIVE To apply systems of linear inequalities using linear programming techniques.

Problems often arise in business, industry, and other areas in which a plan of action must be determined in order to maximize or minimize a particular quantity, such as profit or cost, subject to certain conditions, or *constraints*. When the quantity can be represented by a linear equation and the constraints can be represented by a system of linear inequalities, the techniques of a branch of mathematics called *linear programming* can be used to solve the problem.

EXAMPLE

A hospital nutritionist needs to plan a dinner menu that includes the food items X and Y. Suppose that each ounce of X costs 14 cents and each ounce of Y costs 10 cents. The two foods contain the following amounts of vitamins and minerals per ounce:

Food	X	Y
Vitamin C	4 mg	5 mg
Iron	2 mg	1 mg
Magnesium	30 mg	30 mg

If the meal must contain at least 60 mg of vitamin C, 18 mg of iron, and 270 mg of magnesium, how many ounces of each food item should the nutritionist serve to *minimize the cost* of the food?

SOLUTION

Let x = number of ounces of food X
  y = number of ounces of food Y
  C = total cost for the food
Thus, $C = 0.14x + 0.10y$
We want to find the values of x and y that make C as small as possible subject to the following constraints:

$4x + 5y \geq 60$ Total amount of vitamin C must be at least 60 mg.
$2x + y \geq 18$ Total amount of iron must be at least 18 mg.
$30x + 30y \geq 270$ Total amount of magnesium must be at least 270 mg.

$\left. \begin{matrix} x \geq 0 \\ y \geq 0 \end{matrix} \right\}$ Nutritionist cannot serve a negative amount of food.

Step 1 Graph the solution set of this system of inequalities. The shaded region (solution set) is called the *feasible region* since each point in this region is a possible solution.

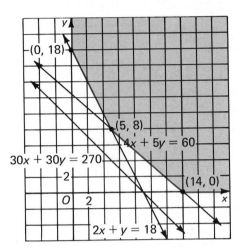

Step 2 Find the points of the feasible region where the boundary lines intersect. These points are called *corner points*. The corner points are $(0, 18)$, $(5, 8)$, and $(14, 0)$.

It can be proved in more advanced mathematics courses that if a maximum or minimum value of a *linear expression ax + by* exists, it must occur at a corner point of the feasible region.

Step 3 Evaluate the cost expression, $0.14x + 0.10y$, at each corner point.

$(0, 18)$: $C = 0.14(0) + 0.10(18) = 1.80$
$(5, 8)$: $C = 0.14(5) + 0.10(8) = 1.50$
$(14, 0)$: $C = 0.14(14) + 0.10(0) = 1.96$

The minimum value of C, which is $1.50, occurs at $(5, 8)$. Therefore, the most economical choice for the nutritionist is 5 ounces of X and 8 ounces of Y.

Written Exercises

A 1. Express each condition as an inequality:

a. It takes a carpenter 18 hours to build each oak table and 3 hours to stain each table. The carpenter has planned to work on tables *at least* 25 hours per week. $18x + 3y \geq 25$

b. A secretary pays $2 for each box of typewriter paper and $1.50 for each box of carbon paper. The company gives the secretary *at most* $15 per month to buy these supplies. $2x + 1.5y \leq 15$

2. A gardener wants to prepare a liquid fertilizer by combining two
   mixtures, A and B. Each gallon of A contains 6 parts nitrogen, 3
   parts potash, and 1 part sulphate. Each gallon of B contains 8 parts
   nitrogen, 2 parts potash, and 2 parts sulphate. Every batch of the
   final mixture must contain at least 24 parts nitrogen, 16 parts potash, and 12 parts sulphate. Choose variables for the number of gallons of A and B. Write five inequalities that express the conditions
   of the problem.

   $6x + 8y \geq 24$
   $3x + 2y \geq 16$
   $x + 2y \geq 12$
   $x \geq 0$
   $y \geq 0$

3. Graph the solution set of the system of inequalities described in
   Exercise 2. State the coordinates of the corner points for this feasible region. (0, 8), (2 ,5), (12 ,0)

4. Suppose that each gallon of A costs $7.50 and each gallon of B costs
   $6.00. How many gallons of each should be mixed if the gardener
   wants to minimize the costs per batch? 2 gal. of A, 5 gal. of B

5. Suppose that, due to a special sale, each gallon of A cost $3, but each
   gallon of B now costs $8. How many gallons of each should be mixed
   to minimize the costs? 12 gal. of A, no gal. of B

B 6. A farmer plants two crops, corn and soybeans. The expenses are $6
   for each acre of corn planted and $12 for each acre of soybeans
   planted. Each acre of corn requires 12 bushels of storage, and each
   acre of soybeans requires 16 bushels of storage. The farmer has at
   most 3600 bushels of storage available and $2400 to spend on these
   expenses. Choose variables for the number of acres of corn and soybeans planted. Write four inequalities that express the conditions of
   the problem. $6x + 12y \leq 2400$; $12x + 6y \leq 3600$; $x \geq 0$; $y \geq 0$

7. Graph the solution set of the system of inequalities described in
   Exercise 6. State the coordinates of the corner points for this feasible region. (0, 0), (0, 200), (100, 150), (300, 0)

8. Suppose that the farmer earns a profit of $24 for each acre of corn
   and $48 for each acre of soybeans. Find two ways the farmer can
   satisfy the conditions while maximizing the profits. (Notice that a
   linear programming problem can have more than one solution.)

   100 acres of corn and 150 acres of soybeans;
   no acres of corn and 200 acres of soybeans

GLOSSARY

abscissa (p. 276). The first coordinate in an ordered pair of numbers that is associated with a point in the coordinate plane.

absolute value (p. 44). The positive number of any pair of opposite real numbers is called the absolute value of each of the numbers. The absolute value of 0 is 0.

acute angle (p. 469). An angle measuring between 0° and 90°.

addition axiom of order (p. 370). For all real numbers a, b, and c:

1. If $a < b$, then $a + c < b + c$;
2. If $a > b$, then $a + c > b + c$.

addition property of equality (p. 71). For all real numbers a, b, and c, if $a = b$ then $a + c = b + c$ and $c + a = c + b$.

additive inverse (p. 43). The additive inverse of the real number a is the real number $-a$ such that $a + (-a) = 0$ and $-a + a = 0$. Also called *opposite of a*.

angle (p. 468). A figure formed by two rays starting from the same point. The point is called the *vertex* of the angle, and the rays are called the *sides*.

angles of a triangle (p. 474). *See under* triangle.

area. The area of a region is the number of unit squares it contains.

associative axioms (p. 37). For all real numbers a, b, c:

Addition: $(a + b) + c = a + (b + c)$

Multiplication: $(ab)c = a(bc)$.

average (p. 90). The average of n numbers is the sum of the numbers divided by n.

axes (p. 276). *See under* coordinate axes.

axiom (p. 36). A statement that is assumed to be true.

axiom of comparison (p. 369). For all real numbers a and b, one and only one of the following statements is true: $a < b$, $a = b$, $b < a$.

axiom of opposites (p. 43). For every real number a, there is a real number $-a$ such that $a + (-a) = 0$ and $(-a) + a = 0$.

axiom of reciprocals (p. 61). For every nonzero real number a, there is a real number $\frac{1}{a}$ such that

$$a \cdot \frac{1}{a} = 1 \text{ and } \frac{1}{a} \cdot a = 1.$$

axioms of closure (p. 36). For all real numbers a and b:

Addition: $a + b$ is a real number.

Multiplication: ab is a real number.

base (in a power) (p. 113). One of the equal factors.

base angles of an isosceles triangle (p. 474). *See under* isosceles triangle.

base of an isosceles triangle (p. 474). *See under* isosceles triangle.

between (p. 365). b is between a and c if $a < b < c$ or $c > b > a$.

binomial (p. 117). A polynomial of two terms.

boundary line (p. 389). A line which separates the plane into two half-planes.

circumference. The perimeter of a circle.

closed half-plane (p. 389). The union of an open half-plane and its boundary.

combined variation (p. 356). A function defined by an equation of the form $z = \dfrac{kx}{y}$, k a nonzero constant.

commutative axioms (p. 36). For all real numbers a and b:

Addition: $a + b = b + a$

Multiplication: $ab = ba$

complementary angles (p. 471). A pair of angles the sum of whose measures is 90°.

completing the square (p. 446). Adding a term to an expression in the form "$x^2 + bx$" to produce a trinomial square.

complex fraction (p. 225). A fraction whose numerator or denominator contains one or more fractions.

conjugates (p. 432). Two binomials of the form $x + \sqrt{y}$ and $x - \sqrt{y}$.

conjunction (p. 382). A sentence formed by joining two sentences by the word *and*.

consecutive even numbers (p. 13). Obtained by counting by twos from any even integer.

consecutive numbers (p. 12). Obtained by counting by ones from any given integer.

consecutive odd numbers (p. 13). Obtained by counting by twos from any odd integer.

constant monomial (p. 117). A numerical term with no variable expression.

constant of variation (p. 343). In a direct variation expressed by $y = kx$, k is the constant of variation. Also called *constant of proportionality.*

converse (p. 187). The converse of a theorem is obtained by interchanging the "if" and "then" portions.

coordinate (p. 30). The number assigned to a point on the number line.

coordinate axes (p. 276). The axes (horizontal and vertical) of a coordinate system set up in a plane.

coordinate plane (p. 276). A plane in which a coordinate system has been set up.

coordinate system (pp. 275–277). A system of graphing ordered pairs of numbers in relation to two *axes* (*horizontal* and *vertical*) which intersect at right angles at their zero point (the *origin*).

coordinates of a point (p. 276). The abscissa and ordinate of the point, written as an ordered pair of numbers.

correspondence (p. 334). A matching between the members of two sets.

corresponding angles (p. 477). *See under* similar triangles.

corresponding sides (p. 477). *See under* similar triangles.

cosine (p. 480). The cosine of $\angle A$ of a right triangle $=$
$$\frac{\text{length of leg adjacent to } \angle A}{\text{length of hypotenuse}}.$$

cubic equation (p. 189). A polynomial equation of degree three.

degree (measure of an angle) (p. 469). $\frac{1}{180}$ of the rotation of a ray from one direction to its opposite.

degree of a monomial (p. 117). The number of times that a variable occurs as a factor in a monomial is the degree of the monomial in that variable. The sum of the degrees in each of the variables is the degree of the monomial. A nonzero constant has degree 0. 0 has no degree.

degree of a polynomial (p. 118). The greatest of the degrees of its terms after it has been simplified.

denominator (p. 158). In the fraction $\dfrac{a}{b}$, b is the denominator.

difference (p. 76). For any two real numbers a and b, the difference $a - b$ is the number whose sum with b is a.

directly proportional (p. 344). y is directly proportional to x if (x_1, y_1) and (x_2, y_2) are ordered pairs of a function, neither of which is $(0, 0)$, and this statement is true: $\frac{y_1}{x_1} = \frac{y_2}{x_2}$.

direct variation (p. 343). A function defined by an equation of the form $y = kx$, where k is a nonzero constant.

discriminant (p. 453). The value of $b^2 - 4ac$ is called the discriminant of the quadratic equation $ax^2 + bx + c = 0$.

disjoint sets (p. 380). Sets that have no members in common.

disjunction (p. 382). A sentence formed by joining two sentences by the word *or*.

distance formula (p. 426). For any points $P_1(x_1, y_1)$ and $P_2(x_2, y_2)$:
$$P_1 P_2 = \sqrt{(x_2 - x_1)^2 + (y_2 - y_1)^2}.$$

distributive axiom of multiplication with respect to addition (p. 53). For all real numbers a, b, and c:
$$a(b + c) = ab + ac$$
$$(b + c)a = ba + ca.$$

divide-and-average method (p. 417). A way to find closer and closer approximations to the square root of a number that is not a perfect square by continuing to average pairs of factors.

domain of a function (p. 331). *See under* function.

domain of a variable (p. 9). The set of numbers that the variable may represent. Also called *replacement set*.

empty set (p. 100). The set with no members.

equal expressions (p. 2). Expressions that name the same number.

equation (p. 9). A statement formed by placing an equality symbol between two numerical or variable expressions.

equilateral triangle (p. 474). A triangle with all sides of equal length.

equivalent equations (inequalities) (pp. 72, 370). Equations (inequalities) having the same solution set over a given domain.

equivalent expressions (p. 54). Expressions which represent the same number for all values of the variables that they contain.

equivalent systems (p. 291). Systems of equations having the same solution set.

evaluate an expression (p. 2). Replace each variable in the expression by a given value of the variable, and simplify the result.

exponent (p. 113). In a power, the number of times the base occurs as a factor.

exponential form (p. 114). The expression "x^3" is the exponential form of the third power of x.

expressing in simplest form (p. 201). Dividing the numerator and the denominator of a fraction by their greatest common factor.

extremes (p. 240). In the proportion $\frac{a}{b} = \frac{c}{d}$, a and d are the extremes.

factor (p. 37). When two or more numbers are multiplied, each of the numbers is a factor of the product.

factored form (p. 114). The expression "$x \cdot x \cdot x$" is the factored form of the third power of x, that is, x^3.

factoring (pp. 155, 162). Finding the factors of a number or an expression over a specified factor set.

factor set (p. 155). The set from which factors of a number may be selected.

formula (p. 17). An expression of numerical relationships between quantities such as physical or other measurements.

fraction (p. 201). An expression in the form $\frac{a}{b}$, $b \neq 0$.

fractional equation (p. 247). An equation which has a variable in the denominator of one or more terms.

function (p. 331). A function consists of two sets, the domain and the range, together with a rule which assigns to each member of the domain exactly one member of the range. Each member of the range must be assigned to at least one member of the domain.

graph of an equation (p. 283). All points, and only those points, whose coordinates satisfy the equation.

graph of a function (p. 338). The graphs in the coordinate plane of all the ordered pairs that form the function.

graph of a number (p. 30). The point on the number line paired with the number.

graph of an ordered pair of numbers (p. 276). The point in the plane paired with an ordered pair of real numbers.

greatest common factor (p. 156). The greatest integer which is a factor of each of two or more integers.

greatest monomial factor (p. 159). The common monomial factor of two or more monomials that has the greatest coefficient and the greatest degree in each variable.

greatest monomial factor of a polynomial (p. 162). The greatest monomial factor of the terms of the polynomial.

grouping symbol (p. 5). A device used to enclose a numerical expression. Examples include parentheses, brackets, and fraction bars.

half-plane (p. 389). *See under* closed half-plane *and* open half-plane.

histogram (p. 336). A bar graph used to summarize a large set of data.

horizontal axis (p. 275). Horizontal number line in a plane.

hyperbola (p. 348). The graph of an equation of the form
$$xy = k, \ k \neq 0 \ (x \neq 0, y \neq 0).$$

hypotenuse (p. 422). The side of a right triangle opposite the right angle.

identity (p. 101). An equation which is true for every value of the variable(s).

identity axioms (pp. 41, 57). For any real number a:

Addition: $a + 0 = 0 + a = a$

Multiplication: $a \cdot 1 = 1 \cdot a = a$.

identity elements (pp. 41, 57). 0 is the identity element for addition. 1 is the identity element for multiplication.

inequality (p. 33). A statement formed by placing an inequality symbol between two numerical or variable expressions.

integers (p. 30). The numbers in the set $\{\ldots, -3, -2, -1, 0, 1, 2, 3, \ldots\}$.

integral factors (p. 155). Factors taken from the set of integers.

intersection of sets (p. 380). For any two sets A and B, the set consisting of all members belonging to both A and B is the intersection of A and B.

inverse operations (p. 96). Operations that "undo" each other; for example, addition and subtraction.

inverse variation (p. 348). A function defined by an equation of the form $xy = k$, where k is a nonzero constant.

inverse variation as the square (p. 353). A function defined by an equation of the form $x^2y = k$, where k is a nonzero constant.

irrational number (p. 416). A real number which cannot be expressed in the form $\dfrac{r}{s}$, where r and s are integers, $s \neq 0$.

irreducible polynomial (p. 176). A polynomial which is not the product of polynomials of lower positive degree belonging to a specified set.

isosceles triangle (p. 474). A triangle with two sides of equal length. If $MN = NP$ in $\triangle MNP$, MP is the *base* of the triangle and $\angle M$ and $\angle P$ are the *base angles*.

joint variation (p. 356). A function defined by the equation $z = kxy$, where k is a nonzero constant.

least common denominator (L.C.D.) (p. 212). The least positive common multiple of the denominators of two or more fractions.

leg of a right triangle (p. 474). One of the two sides which form the right angle.

linear direct variation (p. 343). *See under* direct variation.

linear equation in one variable (p. 189). A polynomial equation of degree one.

linear equation in two variables (p. 283). Any equation equivalent to one of the form $Ax + By = C$, where A, B, and C are real numbers with A and B not both zero.

linear function (p. 338). A function whose ordered pairs satisfy a linear equation.

linear term (p. 166). A term of degree one in the variable.

line segment (p. 468). A subset of a line consisting of two points and the part of the line between them.

maximum point of a quadratic function (p. 339). The point whose y-coordinate is the greatest value the function can have.

means (p. 240). In the proportion $\dfrac{a}{b} = \dfrac{c}{d}$, b and c are the means.

member of a set (p. 10). Any object in the set.

minimum point of a quadratic function (p. 338). A point whose y-coordinate is the least value the function can have.

mixed expression (p. 220). The sum or difference of a polynomial and a fraction.

mixed numeral (p. 220). A numeral, like $3\frac{2}{5}$, which denotes the sum of an integer and a fraction.

monomial (p. 117). A term which is either a numeral, a variable, or a product of a numeral and one or more variables.

monomial factor (p. 159). A monomial which is a factor of each of the terms of a polynomial.

multiple (p. 121). The product of any real number and an integer is a multiple of the real number.

multiplication axiom of order (p. 370). For all real numbers a, b, and c:

1. If $a < b$ and $c > 0$, then $ac < bc$; if $a > b$ and $c > 0$, then $ac > bc$.

2. If $a < b$ and $c < 0$, then $ac > bc$; if $a > b$ and $c < 0$, then $ac < bc$.

multiplication property of equality (p. 84). If $a = b$, then $ac = bc$ and $ca = cb$.

multiplicative inverse (p. 61). For a nonzero real number b, the real number $\frac{1}{b}$, for which $b \cdot \frac{1}{b} = 1$ and $\frac{1}{b} \cdot b = 1$. Also called *reciprocal*.

multiplicative property of -1 (p. 57). For all real numbers a, $a(-1) = -a$ and $(-1)a = -a$.

multiplicative property of zero (p. 57). $a \cdot 0 = 0$ and $0 \cdot a = 0$.

negative number (p. 30). A number paired with a point on the negative side of a number line.

nonterminating decimal (p. 408). A decimal for which the division process is unending.

numeral (p. 2). A name for a number. Also called *numerical expression*.

numerator (p. 158). In the fraction $\frac{a}{b}$, a is the numerator.

numerical coefficient (p. 117). In a term, the factor which is not a variable; for example, 5 in $5xy$.

obtuse angle (p. 469). An angle measuring between $90°$ and $180°$.

open expression (p. 2). *See under* variable expression.

open half-plane (p. 389). One of the two regions into which a line separates the plane. The boundary line is not a member of either open half-plane.

open sentence (p. 9). An equation or inequality which contains a variable.

open sentence in two variables (p. 280). An equation or inequality which contains two variables.

opposite of a number (p. 43). *See under* additive inverse.

ordered pair (p. 275). A pair of elements in which the order is specified.

ordinate (p. 276). The second coordinate in an ordered pair of numbers that is associated with a point in a coordinate plane.

origin (pp. 29, 275). The starting point, labeled "0", on a number line; the zero point of both of two number lines that intersect at right angles.

parabola (p. 338). The graph of a quadratic function.

parallel lines (p. 287). Lines that lie in the same plane but have no point in common.

percent (p. 251). A notation for a ratio with the denominator 100; $\frac{3}{100} = 3\%$.

perimeter. The perimeter of a geometric figure is the distance around it.

plotting a point (p. 276). Locating the graph of an ordered pair of real numbers on the coordinate plane.

polynomial (p. 117). A sum of monomials.

polynomial equation (p. 189). An equation in which both members are polynomials in one variable.

positive number (p. 30). A number paired with a point on the positive side of a number line.

power (p. 113). A product in which all the factors, except 1, are the same. For example, the fourth power of 5 is defined by $5^4 = 5 \cdot 5 \cdot 5 \cdot 5$.

prime factorization (p. 156). The expression of a positive integer as a product of prime factors is the prime factorization of the integer.

prime factors (p. 156). Factors which are prime numbers or prime polynomials.

prime number (p. 155). An integer, greater than one, which has no positive integral factor other than itself and one.

prime polynomial (p. 176). An irreducible polynomial whose greatest monomial factor is 1.

principal square root (p. 412). The positive square root, denoted by $\sqrt{}$.

proof (p. 104). Logical reasoning from known facts and axioms to a theorem.

property of betweenness (p. 404). Between every pair of different rational numbers there is another rational number.

property of completeness (p. 417). Every decimal represents a real number, and every real number has a decimal representation.

property of the opposite of a sum (p. 47). $-(a + b) = (-a) + (-b)$.

property of square roots of equal numbers (p. 419). If r and s are any real numbers, then $r^2 = s^2$ if and only if $r = s$ or $r = -s$.

proportion (p. 240). An equation made up of two equal ratios.

protractor (p. 469). An instrument used to find the degree measure of an angle.

Pythagorean theorem (p. 422). In any right triangle, the square of the length of the hypotenuse equals the sum of the squares of the lengths of the other two sides.

quadrant (p. 275). One of the four regions into which the coordinate axes separate the plane.

quadratic direct variation (p. 353). A function defined by an equation of the form $y = kx^2$, where k is a nonzero constant.

quadratic equation (p. 189). A polynomial equation of degree two.

quadratic formula (p. 449). If $ax^2 + bx + c = 0$, $a \neq 0$, and $b^2 - 4ac \geq 0$, then

$$x = \frac{-b \pm \sqrt{b^2 - 4ac}}{2a}.$$

quadratic function (p. 338). A function defined by an equation of the form $y = ax^2 + bx + c$, $a \neq 0$.

quadratic polynomial (p. 166). A polynomial of degree two that contains a single variable.

quadratic term (p. 166). A term of degree two in the variable.

quotient (p. 88). The quotient $a \div b$, $b \neq 0$, is the number whose product with b is a.

radical (p. 412). An expression of the form $\sqrt{a}$.

radical equation (p. 434). An equation having a variable in a radicand.

radical sign (p. 412). The symbol $\sqrt{}$.

radicand (p. 412). An expression beneath a radical sign.

range of a function (p. 331). *See under* function.

ratio (p. 235). The ratio of one number to another (not zero) is the quotient of the first number divided by the second.

rational expression (pp. 201, 403). A fraction; an expression for a rational number.

rational number (p. 403). A real number that can be expressed as a ratio of two integers (the second integer not zero).

rationalizing a denominator (p. 428). The process of changing the form of a fraction with an irrational denominator to an equal fraction with a rational denominator.

ray (p. 468). A part of a line that consists of a point A and all points on the line on one side of A.

real number (p. 30). Any number paired with a point on the number line.

reciprocal (p. 61). *See under* multiplicative inverse.

reflexive property of equality (p. 38). $a = a$.

repeating decimal (p. 408). A nonterminating decimal in which the same digit or block of digits repeats unendingly. Also called *periodic decimal*.

replacement set (p. 9). *See under* domain of a variable.

right angle (p. 469). An angle measuring $90°$.

right triangle (p. 474). A triangle with a right angle.

root of an open sentence (p. 9). A solution of the sentence.

rounding a decimal (p. 410). Breaking off a decimal to achieve an approximation, by adding 1 to the value of the last digit kept if the first digit dropped is 5 or more, or, otherwise, by leaving unchanged the digits that are kept.

satisfy (p. 9). Each member of the solution set of an open sentence satisfies that sentence.

set (p. 9). Collection of objects.

sides of an angle (p. 468). *See under* angle.

sides of an equation (p. 9). The expressions joined by the symbol of equality.

sides of an inequality (p. 366). The expressions joined by an inequality symbol.

sides of a triangle (p. 474). *See under* triangle.

significant digits (p. 128). The following numbers are expressed with 6 significant digits: 123,475; 2.00027; 235.650; 0.0123456; 243,724,000 or 2.43724×10^8.

similar terms (p. 117). Terms that are exactly alike or that differ only in their numerical coefficients.

similar triangles (p. 477). $\triangle ABC$ and $\triangle DEF$ are similar triangles if $\angle A = \angle D$, $\angle B = \angle E$, and $\angle C = \angle F$. $\angle A$ and $\angle D$ are corresponding angles (as are $\angle B$ and $\angle E$, $\angle C$ and $\angle F$). The sides opposite corresponding angles are corresponding sides.

simple form of a polynomial (p. 117). A polynomial is in simple form if no two of its terms are similar.

simple interest (p. 4). Simple interest I on an investment of P dollars at the interest rate R for T years is given by the formula $I = PRT$.

simplest form of a fraction (p. 201). The fraction $\frac{a}{b}$ is in simplest form when a and b have no common factor other than 1 and -1.

simplest form of a radical (p. 428). A radical expression in which no integral radicand has a square factor other than 1, no fractions are under a radical sign, and no radicals are in a denominator.

simplify (p. 2). Replace a numerical expression by the simplest, or most common, name of its value.

simultaneous equations (p. 287). *See under* system of simultaneous equations.

sine (p. 480). The sine of $\angle A$ of a right triangle $=$

$$\frac{\text{length of leg opposite } \angle A}{\text{length of hypotenuse}}.$$

slope of a line (p. 320). The steepness of a nonvertical line as defined by the quotient

$$\frac{\text{difference of } y\text{-coordinates}}{\text{difference of } x\text{-coordinates}}.$$

A horizontal line has slope 0; a vertical line has no slope.

slope-intercept form of a linear equation (p. 325). $y = mx + b$, where m is the slope of the line represented by the equation and b is its y-intercept.

solution (p. 9). A value of a variable that converts an open sentence into a true statement.

solution of an open sentence in two variables (p. 280). An ordered pair of values for which the sentence becomes a true sentence.

solution of a system of two equations in two variables (p. 287). An ordered pair of numbers that satisfies both equations.

solution set of an open sentence (p. 9). The set that consists of the members of the domain of the variable for which the sentence is true is called the solution set of the sentence over that domain.

solve (p. 9). Find the solution set of an open sentence over a given domain.

square root (p. 412). The number a is a square root of the number b if $a^2 = b$.

straight angle (p. 469). An angle measuring $180°$.

substitution method (p. 291). A method for finding the solution of a pair of linear equations in two variables by: (1) solving one equation for one of the variables, (2) substituting the resulting expression in the other equation, (3) solving this derived equation, (4) finding the corresponding value of the other variable.

substitution principle (p. 2). Changing the numeral by which a number is named in an expression does not change the value of the expression.

supplementary angles (p. 471). Two angles the sum of whose measures is $180°$.

symmetric property of equality (p. 38). If $a = b$, then $b = a$.

system of simultaneous equations (p. 287). A set of equations in the same variables.

tangent (p. 480). The tangent of $\angle A$ of a right triangle $=$

$$\frac{\text{length of leg opposite } \angle A}{\text{length of leg adjacent to } \angle A}.$$

term (p. 37). A mathematical expression using numerals or variables or both to indicate a product or a quotient.

terminating decimal (p. 408). A decimal for which the division process stops because a remainder of 0 is reached.

theorem (p. 104). A statement that is shown to be true using axioms, definitions, and other theorems in a logical development.

transformation. Each of the following always produces an equation equivalent to the original equation:

by addition (p. 72). Adding the same number to each member.

by division (p. 92). Dividing each member by the same nonzero number.

by multiplication (p. 84). Multiplying each member by the same nonzero number.

by substitution (p. 72). Replacing either member by an expression equivalent to it.

by subtraction (p. 81). Subtracting the same number from each member.

transitive axiom of order (p. 369). For all real numbers a, b, and c:

1. If $a < b$ and $b < c$, then $a < c$.
2. If $c > b$ and $b > a$, then $c > a$.

transitive property of equality (p. 38). If $a = b$ and $b = c$, then $a = c$.

triangle (p. 474). A figure formed by connecting three points not on a line by segments. In $\triangle ABC$: $\overline{AB}$, $\overline{BC}$, and $\overline{CA}$ are the *sides* of the triangle; A, B, and C are the *vertices* of the triangle; and $\angle BAC$, $\angle ACB$, and $\angle CBA$ are the *angles* of the triangle.

trigonometric functions (p. 481). Functions having the values $\cos A$, $\sin A$, and $\tan A$, where A is a member of the set of acute angles.

trigonometric ratios (p. 480). In a right triangle, the ratios (sine, cosine, tangent) of the sides associated with an acute angle of the triangle.

trinomial (p. 117). A polynomial of three terms.

trinomial square (p. 171). A trinomial obtained by squaring a binomial. The pattern of the terms is

$$a^2 + 2ab + b^2 \text{ or } a^2 - 2ab + b^2.$$

uniform motion (p. 142). An object which moves without changing its speed, or rate, is said to be in uniform motion.

union of sets (p. 380). For any two sets A and B, the set consisting of all members belonging to at least one of the sets A and B is the union of A and B.

unit distance (p. 29). The distance between 0 and 1 on a number line.

values of a function (p. 332). Members of the range of the function.

values of a variable (p. 1). Numbers in the domain of the variable.

variable (p. 1). A symbol used to represent one or more numbers.

variable expression (p. 2). An expression containing a variable. Also called *open expression*.

vertex of an angle (p. 468). *See under* angle.

vertex of a parabola (p. 339). The maximum or minimum point of the graph of

$$y = ax^2 + bx + c, \, a \neq 0.$$

vertical angles (p. 471). Two angles whose sides are rays in the same line but in opposite directions.

vertical axis (p. 275). A vertical number line at right angles to a horizontal number line such that both lines have the same zero point.

vertices of a triangle (p. 474). *See under* triangle.

volume. The volume of a solid is the number of unit cubes it contains.

whole numbers (p. 12). The numbers in the set $\{0, 1, 2, 3, \ldots\}$.

x-coordinate (p. 283). *See under* abscissa.

x-intercept (p. 452). The x-coordinate of a point where a graph intersects the x-axis.

y-coordinate (p. 283). *See under* ordinate.

y-intercept (p. 324). The y-coordinate of a point where a graph intersects the y-axis.

zero of a function (p. 462). A zero of a function f is a solution of the equation $f(x) = 0$.

zero-product property (p. 187). For all real numbers a and b, $ab = 0$ if and only if $a = 0$ or $b = 0$.

INDEX

Abscissa, 276
Absolute value, 44
  in open sentences, 386
Acute angle, 469
Addition
  axioms for, *see under* Axioms
  of fractions, 216-217
  identity element for, 41
  and the number line, 40
  of polynomials, 117-118
  of radical expressions, 430
  of real numbers, 40-41, 43-44, 47-48
  rules for, 48
Addition-or-subtraction method, 296-297,
    299-300
Addition property of equality, 71
Additive inverse, 43
algebra, 11
Angle(s), 468-469
  of depression, 485
  of elevation, 485
  of a triangle, 474
Application
  balancing a checkbook, 65
  computation shortcut, 298
  electrical power and energy, 94
  gear ratios, 268
  histograms, 336
  line of best fit, 327
  Newton's law of motion, 463
  nutrition labeling, 397
  optics, 249
  unit pricing, 207
  See also Problems
Area, 4, 7, 17
Arrow notation, 331
Associative axiom(s), 37
Associative operations, 77, 89
Average, 90
Axes, coordinate, 276
Axiom(s), 36, 104
  addition, of order, 370
  additive, of zero; *see* identity axiom for
    addition
  associative, 37
  of closure, 36

commutative, 36
  of comparison, 369
  distributive, 53
  identity, for addition, 41
  identity, for multiplication, 57
  multiplication, of order, 370
  multiplicative, of one; *see* identity axiom
    for multiplication
  of opposites, 43
  of reciprocals, 61
  transitive, of order, 369
  See also Property
Axis
  horizontal, 275
  vertical, 275

Bar graph, 334
Base of an isosceles triangle, 474
Base of a power, 113
between, 365
Betweenness, property of, 404
Binomial(s), 117
  containing square-root radicals, 432
  factoring products of, 168
  multiplying, mentally, 166
  product of, 131, 166, 168
  squaring, 171
Biography
  Boyd, Louise Arner, 203
  Braun, Wernher von, 312
  Cannon, Annie Jump, 16
  del Rio, Andres Manuel, 80
  Fermat, Pierre de, 407
  Franklin, Rosalind Elsie, 174
  Gilbreth, Lillian Moller, 255
  Julian, Percy Lavon, 330
  Kitasato, Shibasaburo, 484
  Lovelace, Ada Byron, 378
  McCoy, Elijah, 145
  McLennan, John Cunningham, 56
  Ramon y Cajal, Santiago, 463
Boundary line of a half-plane, 389

ACKNOWLEDGMENTS

Illustrations by ANCO/Boston and Dan Collins

Photographs provided by the following sources: opposite p. 1, United States Parachute Association; p. 11, Historical Pictures Service, Inc.; p. 16, Harvard College Observatory; p. 20, Photo Researchers/Jan Lukas; p. 21, The Foxboro Company; p. 28, Woods Hole Oceanographic Institution/Dr. John Edmond; p. 35 (left), Leo DeWys, Inc./Arthur Lavine, (right), Black Star/Gil Kerry; p. 56, University of Toronto Archives; p. 70, Leo DeWys, Inc./Rocky Weldon; p. 80, From *Discovery of the Elements*, p. 370, published by the Journal of Chemical Education; p. 112, Editorial Photocolor Archives/Beckerman; p. 139, Daniel Bernstein for New England Medical Center Hospital; p. 145, Burton Historical Collection of the Detroit Public Library; p. 154, Photo Researchers (Rapho)/Paolo Koch; p. 174, Birkbeck College of the University of London; p. 182, Photo Researchers/Harmit Singh; p. 200, Stock, Boston/ Milton Feinberg; p. 203, The American Geographical Society; p. 211, Radio Shack, a Division of Tandy Corporation; p. 231, Eric A. Roth; p. 234, NFB Phototheque/George Hunter; p. 249, Bausch & Lomb; p. 255, Historical Pictures Service, Inc.; p. 267, City of Boston Public Schools; p. 274, Stock, Boston/Barbara Alper; p. 279, North American Rockwell Microelectronics Company; p. 282, The Bettmann Archive, Inc.; p. 312, NASA; p. 318, Stock, Boston/George Bellerose; p. 323, USDA/Soil Conservation Service; p. 330, Diamond Shamrock Corporation; p. 352, The Bettmann Archive, Inc.; p. 364, Sara Lee; p. 378, British Crown copyright, reproduced with permission of the Controller of Her Britannic Majesty's Stationery Office; p. 379, Digital Equipment Corporation; p. 385, Photo Researchers/Alice Kandell; p. 402, Photo Researchers/Joe Munroe; p. 407, The Bettmann Archive, Inc.; p. 415, The Bettmann Archive, Inc.; p. 442, Monkmeyer Press Photo Service/White; p. 451, The Bettmann Archive, Inc.; p. 458, Photo Researchers (Rapho)/Ray Ellis; p. 463, Historical Pictures Service, Inc.; p. 484, National Library of Medicine

ANSWERS TO ODD-NUMBERED EXERCISES

CHAPTER 1 INTRODUCTION TO ALGEBRA

Written Exercises, pages 3–4 **1.** 10 **3.** 60
5. 9 **7.** 6 **9.** 180 **11.** 2 **13.** 10 **15.** 6
17. 21 **19.** 31 **21.** 36 **23.** 2 **25.** 0
27. 1 **29.** equal **31.** not equal **33.** 336
35. 40 **37.** $720

Written Exercises, pages 6–8 **1.** 1 **3.** 3
5. 39 **7.** 26 **9.** 7 **11.** 2 **13.** 5 **15.** 9
17. 12 **19.** 61.4 **21.** 937.5 **23.** 11.14
25. not equal **27.** equal **29.** not equal
31. equal **33.** equal **35.** not equal

Calculator Key-In, page 8 **1.** 0 **3.** 0.1
5. 333,333

Written Exercises, page 10 **1.** {5} **3.** {5}
5. {1} **7.** {5} **9.** {3} **11.** {2} **13.** {6}
15. {0, 1, 2, 3, 4, 5, 6} **17.** {4} **19.** {2}
21. {6} **23.** {4} **25.** {0, 3} **27.** {0, 9}
Answers may vary for Exs. 29 and 31.
29. $x + 3 = 5$ **31.** $2x = x + x$

Written Exercises, pages 14–15 **1.** g **3.** f
5. a **7.** $8t$ **9.** $\frac{1}{2}n$ **11.** $a + 7$ **13.** $b - 2$
15. $2q + 1$ **17.** $t - 1; t - 2$ **19.** $15 - y$
21. $x - 6$ **23.** odd; $2n + 6; 2n + 7$
25. $\frac{1}{2}r = 34$ **27.** $15 = 2z + 3$
29. $\frac{1}{3}x + 5 = 9$ **31.** $3(4 + t) = 42$
33. $2x = x + 8$
35. $x + (x + 1) + (x + 2) = 153$
37. $d + (d + 2) = (d + 4) + 9$

Just for Fun, page 15

1.

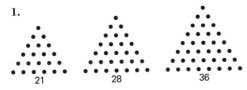

21   28   36

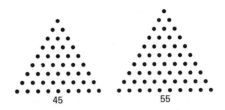

45   55

Calculator Key-In, page 16 **1. a.** 1 **b.** 2
c. 3 **d.** 4

Written Exercises, pages 18–20 **1.** $y + 3$
3. $6x$ **5.** $7x$ **7.** $15t$ **9.** $2w - 18; 6w - 36$
11. $4s = 28$ **13.** $4x = 120$ **15.** $x - 4 = 11$
17. $x - 1 = 1.50$
19. $2w + 2(w + 37) = 348$
21. $w + (w + 5) = 23$ **23.** $c + 7c = 1200$
25. $80\left(\frac{1}{2}t\right) + 100\left(\frac{1}{2}t\right) = 600$

Problems, pages 23–24 **1.** 5 touchdowns
3. $400 **5.** $3.50 **7.** 1650 students
9. a. 36 **b.** 9 **11.** 3 m **13.** $40 **15.** $200

Chapter Review, page 26 **1.** b **3.** b **5.** a
7. d

Maintaining Skills, page 27 **1.** 10,518
3. 6999 **5.** 13,268 **7.** 8392 **9.** 18,606
11. 71,288 **13.** 2,840,376 **15.** 36,279,972
17. 85 R9 **19.** 96 **21. a.** 70,570 **b.** 71,000
23. a. 87,920 **b.** 88,000 **25.** 1500
27. 1600 **29.** 15,300

CHAPTER 2 WORKING WITH REAL NUMBERS

Written Exercises, pages 31–32 **1.** 2; ⁻2;
two floors down **3.** 250; ⁻250; 250 m below
sea level **5.** 6; ⁻6; a loss of 6 points **7.** 8;
⁻8; 8 km west **9.** 1; ⁻1; one second before
liftoff **11.** 28.09; ⁻28.09; payments of
$28.09 **13.** ⁻1, 0, 1 **15.** ⁻1, 2, 5 **17.** ⁻5, ⁻3,
⁻1, 0 **19.** $\frac{⁻1}{2}, \frac{1}{2}$ **21.** E, N **23.** I, A

25. *B, Q* **27.** *F, H*

29.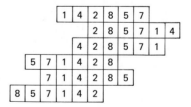
(number line from -4 to 4, dots at -4, -2, 0, 2, 4)

31. (number line from -2 to 2, dots at -1, 1)

33. (number line from -2 to 2, dots at -2, -1, 1)

35. (number line from -3 to 1, dots at -2, 0, 1)

37. 5 **39.** $^-1$ **41.** 0 **43.** 4

Written Exercises, pages 34–35 **1.** $5 > {^-2}$
3. $^-10 > {^-15}$ **5.** $4 < 4.5$ **7.** $^-12 < 0$
9. $<$ **11.** $<$ **13.** $>$ **15.** $>$ **17.** $<$
19. $>$ **21.** $^-6, {^-4}, 0, 7$ **23.** $^-5, {^-1}, 2, 3$
25. $\dfrac{^-1}{2}, \dfrac{^-1}{3}, \dfrac{^-1}{4}, \dfrac{^-1}{5}$ **27.** $^-1.4, {^-0.6}, 0.8, 1.5$

29. $3.14, 3.1416, 3.142$ **31.** $^-2\dfrac{1}{2}, {^-2}\dfrac{1}{4}, {^-2}\dfrac{1}{6}$

33. false **35.** true **37.** false **39.** true

Written Exercises, page 39 **1.** 450 **3.** 990
5. 5700 **7.** 15 **9.** 10.0
11. $x + y + z + 15$ **13.** $30kpq$
15. $4500abc$ **17. a.** 6 **b.** yes **c.** yes
19. a. 10 **b.** yes **c.** no

Written Exercises, page 42 **1.** 0 **3.** $^-1$
5. $^-64$ **7.** $^-68$ **9.** $^-18$ **11.** $^-0.4$ **13.** $^-3\dfrac{2}{3}$

15. 2.25 **17.** $y = {^-1}$ **19.** $z = {^-12}$
21. $k = 4$ **23.** $d = {^-24}$ **25.** $n = {^-0.5}$
27. $q = 0$ **29.** $r = 4$ **31.** $a = 0$ **33.** $y = 5$

Written Exercises, pages 45–46 **1.** 18
3. -4 **5.** -17 **7.** 20 **9.** -5 **11.** 6
13. 15 **15.** 17 **17.** 7 **19.** -8 **21.** 7
23. -18 **25.** $\{-2\}$ **27.** $\{2\}$ **29.** $\{2\}$
31. $\{-1, 1\}$ **33.** $\{-2, 2\}$ **35.** $\{-2\}$
37. always **39.** sometimes

Just for Fun, page 46

3	-4	1	0
-2	0	2	0
-1	4	-3	0
0	0	0	0

Written Exercises, pages 49–50 **1.** 15
3. 62 **5.** 41 **7.** 18 **9.** -12 **11.** -33
13. 158 **15.** -40 **17.** 10 **19.** -11
21. -1.4

Problems, pages 50–51 **1.** 7 yards
3. \$272 **5.** 7650 m **7.** 5 m below sea level
9. a net gain of \$31,770 **11.** 126 km/h
13. 9 over par **15.** 68 beats per minute

Calculator Key-In, page 52 **1.** \$26.67
3. 0.0909

Written Exercises, pages 55–56 **1.** 36
3. 4 **5.** 370 **7.** $15x$ **9.** $30z$ **11.** $15t$
13. $5x + 8$ **15.** $2a + 7$ **17.** $3c + 16$
19. $13a + 4$ **21.** $7x + 2$ **23.** $11x$ **25.** $2b$
27. $2m + 17k$ **29.** $8x + 10y + 3$
31. $20n + 20r$ **33.** $18x + 60$
35. $11z + 10x + 44$ **37.** $12x + 10y$
39. $6x + 6y + 3$ **41.** $182x + 172$
43. $622p + 258q + 340$

Written Exercises, pages 59–60 **1.** 120
3. 480 **5.** -105 **7.** 0 **9.** -400 **11.** 240
13. 18 **15.** -90 **17.** -60 **19.** $-6r + 42t$
21. $3a + 15b$ **23.** $2m - 1$ **25.** $8q + (-12p)$
27. $0.6a + (-2.0b)$ **29.** $-\dfrac{1}{4}x + 3y$
31. $-7a + 3b$ **33.** $t + (-9s)$ **35.** $d + 7e$
37. $-7m + (-26n)$ **39.** -4
41. (1) Identity axiom for multiplication
(2) Distributive axiom (3) Axiom of
opposites (4) Multiplicative property of
zero

Calculator Key-In, page 60 **1.** -1156
3. 11,115,556 **5.** -888 **7.** 9876 **9.** 987,654

Just for Fun, page 60

1	4	2	8	5	7			
	2	8	5	7	1	4		
		4	2	8	5	7	1	
	5	7	1	4	2	8		
		7	1	4	2	8	5	
8	5	7	1	4	2			

Written Exercises, page 63 **1.** -4
3. -10 **5.** 1 **7.** -4 **9.** $-xy$ **11.** $7y$
13. $-5x + 3$ **15.** $3c + (-2d)$
17. $-2a + 3b$ **19.** $2x + 7y$

21. $11a + (-3b)$ **23.** $-24r$ **25.** w
27. -3 **29.** π **31.** 3

Calculator Key-In, page 64 **1.** 8 **3.** -16
5. the original number

Application, page 65 To make the
checkbook register balance with the bank
statement, correct the error in subtracting
Check 320 from the balance in the
checkbook register.

Chapter Review, pages 67–68 **1.** c **3.** c
5. d **7.** b **9.** a **11.** a **13.** b **15.** a

Maintaining Skills, page 69 **1.** 47.106
3. 255.101 **5.** 22.56 **7.** 133.068 **9.** 62.909
11. 35.062 **13.** 21.827 **15.** 64.008
17. 4.3505 **19.** 0.245 **21.** 10,240
23. 0.1078 **25.** 45.756 **27.** 35.75 **29.** 6.788

CHAPTER 3 SOLVING EQUATIONS

Written Exercises, pages 73–74 **1.** 25
3. 19 **5.** 30 **7.** -16 **9.** -36 **11.** -28
13. -27 **15.** -27 **17.** 48 **19.** -4 **21.** 8
23. 0 **25.** 2 **27.** -6 **29.** 3 **31.** -4
33. -9 **35.** 9 **37.** 6, -6 **39.** 5, -5

Problems, pages 74–75 **1.** 29 **3.** -7
5. 9 touchdowns **7.** 97°C **9.** 7:30 A.M.
11. 418 employees

Written Exercises, pages 78–79 **1.** -170
3. 51 **5.** -14 **7.** -68 **9.** 176 **11.** 285
13. 117 **15.** 355 **17.** 0 **19.** -8
21. -2202 **23.** 9 **25.** 22 **27.** $-33x$
29. $x + 3$ **31.** y **33.** $h + 16$ **35.** -18
37. 4 **39.** -7 **41.** -12
43. (1) Rule for subtraction
(2) Distributive axiom of multiplication
with respect to addition   (3) Property of
opposites in products   (4) Rule for
subtraction

Problems, pages 79–80 **1.** 5°C **3.** 75
5. 73° **7.** 5730 m **9.** 146.3°C

Calculator Key-In, page 80 **1.** 963
3. -693 **5.** -2695 **7.** 0

Written Exercises, page 82 **1.** 26 **3.** -52
5. 0 **7.** 17 **9.** 21 **11.** 19 **13.** 24
15. -7 **17.** 9 **19.** 16 **21.** -13 **23.** 7
25. 6, -6

Problems, pages 82–83 **1.** 34 **3.** 44
5. 29 students **7.** 94 **9.** $10.99
11. 18.5 km

Written Exercises, page 86 **1.** 168
3. -144 **5.** 7 **7.** -170 **9.** 512 **11.** -7
13. 5 **15.** -3 **17.** 6 **19.** $-\dfrac{2}{5}$ **21.** $\dfrac{4}{11}$
23. $-\dfrac{1}{34}$ **25.** 2 **27.** -50

Problems, pages 86–87 **1.** $0.09 **3.** $5.20
5. 35 m **7.** 13 **9.** $54.75

Written Exercises, pages 90–91 **1.** -8
3. -108 **5.** 125 **7.** -60 **9.** $-11x$
11. -142 **13.** z **15.** $3x$ **17.** -5 **19.** -2
21. -3 **23.** 9 **25.** 15 **27.** 0 **29.** $-\dfrac{5}{7}$
31. (1) Rule for division   (2) Distributive
axiom of multiplication with respect to
addition   (3) Rule for division

Calculator Key-In, page 91 **1.** 0.25
3. -0.0625 **5.** 0.025 **7.** -0.12 **9.** 0.96875
11. 0.25 **13.** -0.0625 **15.** 0.025
17. -0.12 **19.** 0.96875

Just for Fun, page 91 (Answers may vary)
11, 23, 35

Written Exercises, page 93 **1.** 30 **3.** -16
5. -19 **7.** 26 **9.** 24 **11.** -43 **13.** 35
15. -11 **17.** 370 **19.** 680 **21.** -25
23. 26

Problems, page 93 **1.** -29 **3.** $21.50
5. $.59 **7.** $.24 **9.** $7840.40

Application, pages 94–95 **1.** 16.1 W
3. 120.05 V **5.** $5.12

Written Exercises, page 97 **1.** 3 **3.** -6
5. 24 **7.** -175 **9.** -2 **11.** -7 **13.** -4
15. 0 **17.** -21 **19.** -5 **21.** -1 **23.** -7
25. 4 **27.** -5 **29.** -1 **31.** -4 **33.** -5
35. -5 **37.** 3 **39.** 1 **41.** 4 **43.** -17
45. $-\dfrac{10}{3}$ **47.** 5 **49.** 6, -6

Problems, pages 98–99   **1.** 64   **3.** 8   **5.** 34
7. 11   **9.** 6   **11.** soft drink, \$.55; sandwich,
\$1.65   **13.** 9 years   **15.** 123 and 140
17. side of triangle, 12 cm; side of square,
24 cm   **19.** Juan, 9 subscriptions; Ingrid, 14
subscriptions   **21.** $-85.2°C$ **23.** 13 years
25. \$9.50

Just for Fun, page 99   \$8.75

Written Exercises, pages 101–102   **1.** 7
3. 17   **5.** 13   **7.** -9 **9.** 14   **11.** -5
13. -22 **15.** -6 **17.** no root   **19.** -6
21. 3   **23.** 17   **25.** -12 **27.** 3   **29.** 13
31. 0   **33.** identity   **35.** identity   **37.** -2
39. 1

Problems, pages 102–103   **1.** 12   **3.** 5
5. 19 and 57   **7.** 35 and 51   **9.** 10 g
11. \$15 on a three-speed; \$45 on a ten-
speed   **13.** Steve, 8 baskets; Mike, 24
baskets   **15.** 807 m; 57 m   **17.** Harry, 16
years; Tom, 24 years; Dick, 12 years
19. 10%; 25%; 62%

Written Exercises, pages 105–107
1. (1) Associative axiom for multiplication
(2) Axiom of reciprocals   (3) Identity axiom
for multiplication   (4) Commutative axiom
for multiplication   (5) Commutative axiom
for multiplication
3. (2) Addition property of equality
(3) Theorem proved on page 104
5. (1) Rule for subtraction   (2) Property of
the opposite of a sum   (3) Definition of the
opposite of a number   (4) Commutative
axiom for addition   (5) Rule for subtraction

Chapter Review, pages 108–109   **1.** c   **3.** b
5. b   **7.** a   **9.** b   **11.** c   **13.** b   **15.** b

Cumulative Review, page 110   **1.** 57
3. -23 **5.** 8   **7.** $r + 10$ **9.** $-9 - t$
11. -8 **13.** $-600z$ **15.** $-5m - n$ **17.** 3
19. -1 **21.** $-3.5, -2, 0, 1$ **23.** $\{0, 3\}$
25. $\{6, -6\}$ **27.** 9   **29.** 7   **31.** -8 **33.** 14
35. -53 **37.** -6 **39.** $\dfrac{6}{5}$ **41.** 11   **43.** \$2.49

Maintaining Skills, page 111   **1.** 0.74
3. 1.75   **5.** 0.83   **7.** $\dfrac{7}{25}$ **9.** $\dfrac{93}{100}$ **11.** $\dfrac{2}{125}$
13. 37%   **15.** 30%   **17.** 7.5%   **19.** 5.4
21. 2.25   **23.** 48.96   **25.** 60   **27.** 450
29. 5.8   **31.** 25%   **33.** 64%   **35.** 93.8%

CHAPTER 4   POLYNOMIALS AND PROBLEM SOLVING

Written Exercises, pages 115–116   **1.** x^3
3. z^3 **5.** $7b^2$ **7.** $-5r^2s$ **9.** $6y^3t^2$
11. $(a + b)^3$ **13.** $(c - 2)^2$ **15.** $17(m + p)^3$
17. $(d + e)^6$ **19.** 8   **21.** 5   **23.** 39   **25.** 18
27. 9   **29.** -13 **31.** 49   **33.** 1   **35.** -1
37. 0   **39.** 5

Calculator Key-In, page 116   **1.** 0.01
3. 0.16   **5.** 0.0144   **7.** 0.0009   **9.** 0.008
11. 0.125

Just for Fun, page 116   **1.** $4 = 1 + 3$;
$9 = 3 + 6$; $16 = 6 + 10$; $25 = 10 + 15$;
$36 = 15 + 21$; $49 = 21 + 28$;
$64 = 28 + 36$; $81 = 36 + 45$;
$100 = 45 + 55$

Written Exercises, pages 119–120
1. $3rt - 6$ **3.** $-x^2 + x$
5. $-4abc + 2bc - 3ac$
7. $2m^2n - 2mn^2 - 2mn$ **9.** $6x + 1$
11. $-2r + 5s$ **13.** $8s + 8t - 3$
15. $4x^2 + 3x + 1$ **17.** $n^2 + 4n - 7$
19. $8x^2 + 2x - 2$ **21.** $2x - 7$ **23.** $8r - 9s$
25. $-2s + 6t + 1$ **27.** $2x^2 + 7x + 3$
29. $3n^2 - 4n - 3$ **31.** $7a + 2b + 3$
33. $6a^2 - 2ab$ **35.** $x^3 + 2x^2 + 3x - 16$
37. $5b - 9$ **39.** $-4a + 4b - 3$
41. $-x^2 - 8x + 8$ **43.** $a^2 + ab - 2b^2$
45. 2   **47.** 6   **49.** 2   **51.** 2   **53.** -2
55. $-6a^4 + 4a^3 + 3$

Integer Problems, pages 120–121   **1.** 16, 17
3. 26, 28, 30, 32   **5.** 25   **7.** $-9, -8$
9. 7, 9, 11   **11.** 17, 18, 19, 20   **13.** 23 m by
25 m   **15.** 12, 16, 20

Written Exercises, pages 123–124 **1.** a^{10}
3. $15c^6$ **5.** $30c^{10}$ **7.** x^4y^3 **9.** $90n^3m^7$
11. $3x^6y^{12}$ **13.** n^4p^4 **15.** $6n^5m^5$ **17.** b^{6n}
19. 2^{2k+3} **21.** x^{3n+7} **23.** $(-x)^{10}$ **25.** $11a^5$
27. $44x^6$ **29.** $12a^6b^5$ **31.** $11a^3b^5$
33. $17a^2b^3c^4$ **35.** $12a^2b^2$ **37.** $19a^2$
39. $46x^2$ **41.** $6a^3$ **43.** $18a^3$

Extra, pages 124–125 **1.** 2×10^5
3. 4.08×10^{10} **5.** 1.9×10^{-7} **7.** 6×10^{14}
9. 3.6×10^{-9} **11.** 1.24×10^2
13. 2.4596×10^9 **15. a.** 10^2 **b.** 10^3 **c.** 10^5
d. 10^{-3} **e.** 10^3 **f.** 10^{-6}

Written Exercises, pages 127–128 **1.** x^8
3. $8b^3$ **5.** $16a^{12}$ **7.** $\frac{1}{32}x^{10}$ **9.** $-8b^6y^{15}$
11. $81t^8s^{16}$ **13.** $36a^3$ **15.** $125a^4$
17. $576n^5$ **19.** $r^{18}s^8$ **21.** 45 **23.** -28
25. -8 **27.** 1 **29.** $72c^9$ **31.** $16u^{10}v^{14}$
33. $16a^{7n}$ **35.** $x^{4n}y^{4n}$ **37.** $7a^8b^{12}$
39. $2x^5y^4$ **41. a.** $8x^3, 64x^3$ **b.** 8 times

Written Exercises, pages 129–130
1. $6x^2 + 15y + 12$ **3.** $-14x^3 + 7x^2 - 35x$
5. $3x^4 - 6x^3y + 3x^2y^2$ **7.** $a^3 + 2a^2b - 4ab^2$
9. $16n^3m - 6n^2m^2 + 2m^3$ **11.** $-6a^3b^3 +$
$14a^2b^4$ **13.** $8n^3 + 6n^2 + 14n$ **15.** $-8a^3b +$
$6a^2b^2 - 2ab^3$ **17.** $10x^2 - 2x$ **19.** $a^3 - 8a$
21. -9 **23.** $-a^4 - 3a^3 + 5a^2 + 4a$ **25.** 10
27. 14 **29.** -4 **31.** 1 **33.** $a - 1$
35. $-4pq - 5pqr - 6p^2q$
37. $6a^3 - 10a^2 - 3a$ **39.** 2 **41.** 7 **43.** -1
45. $2x^{2n} - 3x^{n+1} + 4x^n$ **47.** $2b^{2n+2} + 3b^{n+3}$

Written Exercises, pages 132–133
1. $n^2 + 7n + 12$ **3.** $y^2 - 4y - 21$
5. $2a^2 + 18a + 28$ **7.** $2c^2 - 7c - 4$
9. $3p^2 - 19p + 20$ **11.** $x^3 - x^2 - 5x + 2$
13. $6b^3 + 11b^2 + 8b + 2$ **15.** $3n^4 - 17n^3 +$
$27n^2 - 8n$ **17.** $6a^2 - 7a + 2$ **19.** $6x^3 +$
$17x^2 + x - 10$ **21.** $6r^2 + 7rs - 3s^2$
23. $2c^3 - 3c^2d + 2cd^2 - d^3$ **25.** $2n^3 -$
$11n^2 + n + 35$ **27.** $x^3 - 1$ **29.** $2p^4 -$
$11p^3q + p^2q^2 + 35pq^3$ **31.** $5x^3 - 6x^2y -$
$4xy^2 + y^3$ **33.** $12a^3 + a^2b - 5ab^2 + b^3$
35. $8x^3 + 22x^2 + 5x$ **37.** $3a^4 - a^3b -$
$4a^2b^2 - 3ab^3 - b^4$ **39.** 0 **41.** 2 **43.** 4
45. $4x^3 + 4x^2 - 13x + 5$ **47.** $a^{2n} - 1$
49. $b^{2m} - a^{2n}$

Just for Fun, page 133 **1.** $4^4 + 4$

Written Exercises, pages 136–138
1.

length	width	Area
$2x + 5$	x	$2x^2 + 5x$
$x + 4$	$x - 3$	$x^2 + x - 12$
$a + 1$	$\dfrac{24}{a + 1}$	24
$3n + 2$	$\dfrac{15}{3n + 2}$	15

3.

	number $\times$	value per coin $=$	Total value
nickels	x	5	$5x$
dimes	$x + 5$	10	$10x + 50$
quarters	$x + 8$	25	$25x + 200$

5.

	length $\times$	width $=$	Area
first rect.	$x + 12$	x	$x^2 + 12x$
second rect.	$x + 10$	$x + 5$	$x^2 + 15x + 50$

7. a.

	Age now	Age in 2 years
Woofie	x	$x + 2$
Janet	$7x$	$7x + 2$

b. $7x + 2 = 4(x + 2)$

9. a.

	number	× price	= Cost
Apples bought	n	10	$10n$
Apples sold	$n-2$	15	$(n-2)15$

b. $(n-2)15 - 10n = 20$

11. $x = a - c$ **13.** $z = a$ **15.** $y = \dfrac{a}{4}$

17. $t = \dfrac{I}{Pr}$ **19.** $a = \dfrac{2s}{t^2}$ **21.** $t = \dfrac{A-P}{Pr}$

23. $r = \dfrac{C}{2\pi}$ **25.** $h = \dfrac{T - 2\pi r^2}{2\pi r}$ **27. a.** 70

b. $R = \dfrac{4P - 100}{3}$ **c.** 76

Age Problems, pages 138–139 1. Juan, 21; Ben, 25 **3.** Bill, 20; father, 40 **5.** 15 years **7.** Ann, 19; Jill, 35 **9.** Jefferson, 7; Washington, 18 **11.** 1851

Problems, pages 140–141
1.

	number × price	= Cost
hot dogs	x	80	$80x$
lemonade	$\frac{1}{2}x$	50	$25x$

16 hot dogs
3. 27 covers **5.** 30 sets **7.** 5 nickels, 10 dimes, 3 quarters **9.** $3.80

Problems, pages 144–145 1. 3 h **3.** noon **5.** 2 h **7.** 4.5 km **9.** 50 m **11.** 1.2 km **13.** 45 km

Problems, pages 147–148 1. 6 cm by 12 cm **3.** 20 m by 28 m **5.** 10 cm by 16 cm **7.** 13 m **9.** 20 cm by 20 cm; 30 cm by 30 cm

Chapter Review, pages 149–150 1. d **3.** c **5.** d **7.** a **9.** a **11.** c **13.** d **15.** d **17.** c

Cumulative Review, page 152 1. 9 **3.** $\dfrac{1}{2}$

5. -23 **7.** 11 **9.** $-4m + 6n$ **11.** $-6b^2 + 19b - 8$ **13.** -0.5 **15.** -27

17. -1 **19.** -2 **21.** 3 **23.** -0.2 **25.** 0 **27.** no root **29.** identity **31.** identity **33.** 2 **35.** $-12, -10, -8$ **37.** Florence, 6.0 km; Trudy, 7.5 km

Maintaining Skills, page 153 1. $\dfrac{2}{3}$ **3.** $\dfrac{18}{49}$

5. $\dfrac{3}{4}$ **7.** $\dfrac{1}{3}$ **9.** $\dfrac{13}{15}$ **11.** $\dfrac{1}{2}$ **13.** $\dfrac{5}{9}$ **15.** $\dfrac{5}{6}$

17. $\dfrac{47}{40}$ **19.** $\dfrac{59}{189}$ **21.** $\dfrac{5}{8}$ **23.** $\dfrac{3}{11}$ **25.** $\dfrac{21}{170}$

27. $\dfrac{9}{20}$ **29.** $\dfrac{5}{7}$ **31.** $\dfrac{39}{44}$ **33.** 63 **35.** $\dfrac{3}{5}$

37. $\dfrac{25}{36}$

CHAPTER 5 FACTORING POLYNOMIALS

Written Exercises, page 157 1. 1, 2, 3, 6, 9, 18 **3.** 1, 37 **5.** 1, 2, 4, 8, 16, 32, 64 **7.** 1, 101 **9.** 1, 23 **11.** (1)(18), (2)(9), (3)(6), $(-1)(-18)$, $(-2)(-9)$, $(-3)(-6)$
13. (1)(37), $(-1)(-37)$ **15.** (1)(64), (2)(32), (4)(16), (8)(8), $(-1)(-64)$, $(-2)(-32)$, $(-4)(-16)$, $(-8)(-8)$ **17.** (1)(101), $(-1)(-101)$ **19.** (1)(23), $(-1)(-23)$
21. $(1)(-18)$, $(2)(-9)$, $(3)(-6)$, $(6)(-3)$, $(9)(-2)$, $(18)(-1)$ **23.** $(1)(-37)$, $(37)(-1)$
25. $(1)(-64)$, $(2)(-32)$, $(4)(-16)$, $(8)(-8)$, $(-1)(64)$, $(-2)(32)$, $(-4)(16)$ **27.** $(1)(-101)$, $(101)(-1)$ **29.** $(-1)(23)$, $(1)(-23)$
31. $2 \cdot 17$ **33.** $3^2 \cdot 7$ **35.** 2^7 **37.** $2^2 \cdot 7 \cdot 17$
39. $2^3 \cdot 3 \cdot 17$ **41.** 6 **43.** 6 **45.** 1

Calculator Key-In, page 157 1. 14 **3.** 12 **5.** 1240 **7.** 1011 **9.** 10

Written Exercises, pages 160–161 1. a^5

3. $-c^4$ **5.** $3a^3$ **7.** $\dfrac{1}{3y^2}$ **9.** $\dfrac{3x^2y^2}{4}$ **11.** $\dfrac{2}{3b^4}$

13. $\dfrac{1}{x}$ **15.** $\dfrac{1}{3y}$ **17.** 8 **19.** $\dfrac{-8}{y^3}$ **21.** $\dfrac{4b^2}{a^5}$

23. $\dfrac{c^5}{13d^4}$ **25.** $3a^4$ **27.** $-2c^2d$

29. $-8x^4y^2$ **31.** $7b^3$ **33.** $(a^2b)^2$ **35.** x^4y
37. $2a^3b^2$ **39.** $5x$ **41.** rs^2t^2 **43.** ab^2
45. (1) Rule for division (2) Property of the reciprocal of a product
(3) Commutative axiom for multiplication; Associative axiom for multiplication
(4) Rule for division

6 ANSWERS TO ODD-NUMBERED EXERCISES

Written Exercises, pages 163–164
1. $a + 2$ 3. $6x - 3$ 5. $x - 2y + 3$
7. $2y - 3x$ 9. $2 - 3y - y^2$ 11. $-4d^3 + 3cd + 2$ 13. $6s^3t^2 - 5$ 15. $3d^2k^2 - 5dk + 2d^2$ 17. 780 19. 380 21. 8100 23. 850
25. 770 27. $2(7a - 6b)$ 29. $4(x - 2y + 4)$
31. $6x(x + 2)$ 33. $6x(2x^2 - x + 4)$
35. $6a^2x(4a^2 - 3a + 2x)$ 37. $7y(s^2 - 3xy)$
39. $5cd(5c^2 - 3cd + d^2)$

41. $7k(3e^2 - 7e^2k + 12k^2)$ 43. $\dfrac{h}{2}(b - a)$

45. 3 47. $6a + 3b$ 49. $b^2 - b$

Problems, pages 164–165 1. $r^2(4 - \pi)$
3. $r^2(4 + \pi)$ 5. $r^2(4 - \pi)$ 7. $r^2(3\pi + 4)$

Written Exercises, page 167
1. $x^2 + 9x + 14$ 3. $a^2 - 9a + 20$
5. $c^2 + 10c + 21$ 7. $a^2 - 14a + 45$
9. $2a^2 + 11a + 5$ 11. $2a^2 + 3a - 27$
13. $x^2 - 2x - 63$ 15. $b^2 + 5b - 24$
17. $6k^2 + 17k + 5$ 19. $35a^3 - 74a^2 + 35a$
21. $12x^3 - 26x^2 - 10x$
23. $14k^3 - 27k^2 - 20k$ 25. $6x^2 + 16xy + 8y^2$ 27. $27a^2 - 51ab + 10b^2$
29. $2a^4 + a^2 - 21$ 31. $x^6 + 4x^4 - 21x^2$
33. $3a^8 - 11a^4b^2 + 10b^4$ 35. 26 37. 3
39. 1

Written Exercises, pages 169–170
1. $a^2 - 9$ 3. $9b^2 - 25$ 5. $81a^2 - 49$
7. $64a^2 - 25b^2$ 9. $9u^4 - v^2$ 11. $r^2s^2 - t^4$
13. 391 15. 3596 17. 2499 19. 39,984
21. $(5y + 3)(5y - 3)$ 23. $(12 + x)(12 - x)$
25. $(3a + bc)(3a - bc)$
27. $(x^3 + y^3)(x^3 - y^3)$
29. $(4x^2 + 3)(4x^2 - 3)$
31. $(15 - ab^2)(15 + ab^2)$
33. $(a^2b^2 + c^4)(ab + c^2)(ab - c^2)$
35. $(a^8 + 1)(a^4 + 1)(a^2 + 1)(a + 1)(a - 1)$
37. $3(2x + 3)$ 39. $4a$ 41. $2(x + 5)(x - 5)$
43. $5(3 + a)(3 - a)$ 45. $x(x + 3)(x - 3)$
47. $4(9 + k^2)(3 + k)(3 - k)$
49. $(x^n + y^n)(x^n - y^n)$
51. $(b^n + c^{2n})(b^n - c^{2n})$
53. $(a^{2n} + b^{3n})(a^{2n} - b^{3n})$
55. $y^3(y^n + 1)(y^n - 1)$

Extra, page 170 3. $(n + 3)(n^2 - 3n + 9)$
5. $(x + 4)(x^2 - 4x + 16)$

Written Exercises, pages 172–174
1. $x^2 + 4x + 4$ 3. $a^2 - 8a + 16$
5. $4x^2 + 12x + 9$ 7. $16k^2 - 40k + 25$

9. $16p^2 + 24pq + 9q^2$ 11. $9x^2 + 42xy + 49y^2$ 13. $a^2b^2 - 10ab + 25$
15. $y^4 - 14y^2 + 49$ 17. $25a^2 - 30a + 9$
19. $64x^4 - 16x^2 + 1$ 21. $(n - 1)^2$
23. $(r - 2)^2$ 25. $(b - 9)^2$ 27. $(2x + 1)^2$
29. $(6 - 5a)^2$ 31. $(8x - y)^2$ 33. $(x^2 + 1)^2$
35. $(ab - 6)^2$ 37. $(a^2 - 12)^2$
39. a. $25x^2 - 20x + 4$ b. $25x^2 - 20x + 4$
41. $x^4 - 18x^2 + 81 = (x^2 - 9)(x^2 - 9) = (x - 3)(x + 3)(x - 3)(x + 3) = (x - 3)^2(x + 3)^2$
43. 10 45. 0 47. $3(a + 3)^2$
49. $2(3x - 1)^2$ 51. $5(2x^2 + 3)^2$
53. $4k(2k - 3)^2$ 55. 2 57. 3 59. 4 cm by 16 cm 61. a. 1225, 3025, 7225
b. $(10t + 5)^2 = 100t^2 + 100t + 25 = 100t(t + 1) + 25 = t(t + 1) \times 100 + 25$

Written Exercises, pages 176–177
1. $(x + 5)(x + 1)$ 3. $(a - 3)(a - 1)$
5. $(r + 6)(r + 3)$ 7. $(k - 7)(k - 4)$
9. $(z - 7)(z - 6)$ 11. prime
13. $(y + 11)(y + 5)$ 15. $(p - 9)(p - 8)$
17. $(10 - c)(2 - c)$ 19. $(x - 5y)(x - 7y)$
21. $(s - 6t)(s - 5t)$ 23. $(b + 8c)(b + 5c)$
25. $(s - 7t)(s - 6t)$ 27. prime
29. $(d + 3e)(d + 9e)$ 31. $(a - 8)(a - 15)$
33. $(12 - a)(9 - a)$ 35. $(14n - x)(7n - x)$
37. 7, 11, -7, -11 39. 8, 16, -8, -16
41. 7, 8, 13, -7, -8, -13
43. $(x + 3)(x + 6)$
45. $(a + b - 4)(a + b - 2)$
47. $(a + 3)(a - 3)(a + 1)(a - 1)$
49. $(x^2 + 3)(x + 3)(x - 3)$

Written Exercises, page 179
1. $(a + 5)(a - 1)$ 3. $(y - 6)(y + 1)$
5. prime 7. prime 9. $(a + 7)(a - 5)$
11. $(z + 9)(z - 4)$ 13. $(p - 7)(p + 3)$
15. prime 17. $(a - 5b)(a + 4b)$
19. $(p - 10q)(p + 5q)$
21. $(k - 15d)(k + 4d)$
23. $(x - 11y)(x + 2y)$
25. $(1 - 10ab)(1 + 2ab)$
27. $(1 - 8ab)(1 + 7ab)$ 29. $(r - 24)(r + 6)$
31. $(40 + b)(20 - b)$ 33. $(40 + x)(8 - x)$
35. 1, 8, 19, -1, -8, -19
(Answers may vary for Exs. 37–41.)
37. -4, -10 39. -12, -5
41. -12, -26 43. $(x + 4)(x - 4)$
45. $(2x - y + 10)(2x - y + 6)$
47. $(x + 3)(x - 3)(x^2 + 1)$
49. $3(a - 5)(a + 5)(a^2 + 4)$

Written Exercises, pages 181–182
1. $(2x + 3)(x + 1)$ 3. $(5a + 1)(a + 1)$
5. $(7n - 1)(n - 1)$ 7. $(5y - 1)(y - 3)$
9. prime   11. $(2t + 3)(t - 2)$
13. $(4y + 3)(y - 1)$ 15. $(7k - 2)(k + 3)$
17. $(1 - 2b)(1 + 3b)$ 19. $(5 - 2y)(2 + y)$
21. $(a - b)(a + 2b)$ 23. $(9r + 2s)(r - 3s)$
25. $(5a - b)(5a + 3b)$
27. $(4x + 9y)(3x - 2y)$
29. $(6x + 7)(2x - 3)$
31. $(15 - 16c)(1 + 3c)$
33. $(3x + 1)(36x - 7)$
35. $(14y + 9)(3y + 1)$ 37. $(2y + 5)(y + 5)$
39. $x^2(x + 4)(x - 4)$
41. $((3x + 1)(2x - 5)(5x - 7))^2$

Written Exercises, page 184
1. $(a + b)(x - 5)$ 3. $(x^2 + 1)(5 - r)$
5. $(2a - b)(4 - y)$ 7. $(x + y)(a + b)$
9. $(x^2 + 1)(2d - e + f)$
11. $(3a - 7)(2 - y)$ 13. $(6c + 1)(z - 3)$
15. $(1 - x)(2a - b + 3c)$
17. $(p + q)(2 + a)$ 19. $(2r + p)(q + r)$
21. $(b + c)(a - 2)$ 23. $(x^2 + 4)(2x + 1)$
25. $(4x - 3)(x - 2y)$ 27. $(4y - 1)(y + 2a)$
29. $(2x + 7z)(2x - y)$
31. $(a + 2b + 3c)(a - 2b - 3c)$
33. $(6k + 2a - c)(6k - 2a + c)$
35. $(x - 4y - 3)(x - 4y + 3)$
37. $(x + 3 - y)(x + 3 + y)$
39. $(h - 6 + k)(h - 6 - k)$
41. $(5 + a + 2b)(5 - a - 2b)$
43. $(4y + 1 + 4z)(4y + 1 - 4z)$
45. $(a + 2b - 2)(a - 2b + 2)$
47. $(a + b + 5c)(a - b - 5c)$
49. $9(a - b + c)(a - b - c)$
51. $(a - b)(a - b - 3)$
53. $(2x^2 - 2x + 1)(2x^2 + 2x + 1)$

Written Exercises, page 186
1. $3a(b + 3a)(b - 3a)$ 3. $2(4x^2 - 4x - 1)$
5. $4(a - 4)(a + 2)$
7. $(x^2 + y^2)(x + y)(x - y)$
9. $2(x^2 + 9)(x + 3)(x - 3)$
11. $(a + 2b + 1)(a - 2b - 1)$
13. $(y + 2)(y - 2)(y + 1)(y - 1)$
15. $((b + 3)(b - 3))^2$
17. $5k(2k - 5)(k + 1)$
19. $2(x - 2y + 2)(x + 2y - 2)$
21. $4(a - 4)(a - 2)$

23. $(x - 1)(x + 2)(x - 2)$
25. $(m - k)(m + k + 1)$
27. $c(a - 2b - 3c)(a - 2b + 3c)$
29. $(x - a)(a^2 + ax - x)$
31. $(b - 3c)(a + 3b)(a - 3b)$
33. $2(1 + 2x + y)(1 - 2x - y)$
35. $(x + 1)^2(x - 2)$
37. $(x + 2y)(a - 3x + 6y)$
39. $2(p + 1)(p - 4)(p - 2)$
41. $(p - 2q + r - 2s)(p - 2q - r + 2s)$
43. $3(15x + y)(x - 4y)$
45. $(b + c + a)(b + c - a) \times$
$$(a + b - c)(a - b + c)$$
47. $(a + 3b)^2(1 + a - 3b)(1 - a + 3b)$
49. $(x + y + x^2 - 2y^2)(x + y - x^2 + 2y^2)$
51. $(x - 1)(x - 2)(x + 2)$

Written Exercises, page 188   1. $\{0, 7\}$
3. $\{7, 8\}$ 5. $\{15, 100\}$ 7. $\left\{\dfrac{1}{3}, -\dfrac{5}{2}\right\}$
9. $\left\{0, -\dfrac{5}{4}\right\}$ 11. $\left\{0, \dfrac{5}{2}, -\dfrac{2}{5}\right\}$
13. (2) Axiom of reciprocals
(3) Multiplication property of equality
(4) Multiplicative property of zero
(5) Associative axiom for multiplication
(6) Axiom of reciprocals   (7) Identity axiom
for multiplication

Written Exercises, page 190   1. $\{4, 9\}$
3. $\{2, -4\}$ 5. $\{3, -2\}$ 7. $\{8, -3\}$
9. $\{0, 16\}$ 11. $\left\{\dfrac{3}{2}, -\dfrac{3}{2}\right\}$ 13. $\left\{\dfrac{1}{3}, -1\right\}$
15. $\{2, 0, -2\}$ 17. $\left\{3, -\dfrac{1}{2}\right\}$ 19. $\{6, -6\}$
21. $\left\{\dfrac{1}{3}, -1\right\}$ 23. $\{0, 2\}$ 25. $\left\{\dfrac{7}{2}, -\dfrac{11}{3}\right\}$
27. $\left\{-\dfrac{3}{2}, -\dfrac{4}{3}\right\}$ 29. $\left\{5, -\dfrac{4}{3}\right\}$
31. $\{0, 4, 8\}$ 33. $\{2, 3, -2, -3\}$
35. $\{1, -1\}$ 37. $\{1, -1\}$ 39. $\{0, 5, -5\}$
41. $\{9, -2\}$ 43. $\{6, 0, -2\}$ 45. $\{3, -2\}$
47. $\{1, 3\}$ 49. $x^2 - 4x + 3 = 0$
51. $9x^2 - 3x - 2 = 0$ 53. $25x^2 - 16 = 0$
55. Since $a = b$, $a - b = 0$. Thus, division
by $a - b$ in Step 4 is not allowed.

Problems, pages 192–194   1. 8 or -9
3. -6 5. $-11, -10$ 7. 7 cm by 16 cm
9. 8 m by 13 m   11. 11 m by 11 m
13. 15, -2 15. 2 s, 3 s   17. 30 s

19. a. 3 s **b.** 44.1 m is the maximum height because this height is attained only at 3 s. If 44.1 m were less than the maximum height, it would be reached twice, once going up and once coming down. **21.** 6 cm **23.** 2 m **25.** 5 m **27.** 40 cm by 60 cm

Chapter Review, pages 195–197 1. b
3. b **5.** a **7.** c **9.** c **11.** b **13.** d **15.** d **17.** c **19.** b

Cumulative Review, page 198 1. -0.6
3. $2y - 28$ **5.** 0 **7.** $6b^3 - 18b^2 + 3b$
9. $2a^3 - a - 3$ **11.** $r^2s^2 - 49t^4$ **13.** 3
15. 19 **17.** $6s(2r^2s - 3rs^2 - 8)$ **19.** prime
21. $(9 - 7x)(1 + 2x)$ **23.** 0 **25.** 1 **27.** 4
29. -2 **31.** no root **33.** -2.5 **35.** $\frac{5}{3}$, $-\frac{4}{3}$
37. $0, \frac{1}{2}$ **39.** 15¢; 18¢ **41.** 8 m by 15 m

Maintaining Skills, page 199 1. $9\frac{5}{6}$ **3.** $8\frac{2}{9}$
5. $13\frac{7}{12}$ **7.** $\frac{21}{8}$ **9.** $\frac{123}{14}$ **11.** $\frac{41}{24}$ **13.** $12\frac{5}{12}$
15. $4\frac{11}{40}$ **17.** $\frac{11}{14}$ **19.** $\frac{10}{3}$ **21.** 90 **23.** $\frac{25}{12}$
25. 10 **27.** $\frac{1}{4}$ **29.** 9

CHAPTER 6 FRACTIONS

Written Exercises, pages 202–203
1. $2 \ (x \neq 2)$ **3.** $\dfrac{x - y}{x + y} \ (x \neq -y)$
5. $\dfrac{x - y}{x + y} \ (x \neq 0, x \neq -y)$
7. $\dfrac{2}{a - b} \ (a \neq 0, b \neq 0, a \neq b)$
9. $\dfrac{x + 6}{2} \ (x \neq 6)$
11. $\dfrac{4}{x - 5} \ (x \neq 5, x \neq -5)$
13. $\dfrac{b + 3}{b + 4} \ (b \neq -2, b \neq -4)$
15. $\dfrac{r}{r + 1} \ (r \neq 3, r \neq -1)$
17. $\dfrac{-1}{x + 3} \ (x \neq 3, x \neq -3)$
19. $\dfrac{1}{a - b} \ (a \neq b)$
21. $\dfrac{4c + 1}{1 - 4c} \left(c \neq \dfrac{1}{4}, c \neq -\dfrac{1}{4}\right)$

23. $\dfrac{-x}{x - 1} \ (x \neq 5, x \neq 1)$
25. $(6x - 4)$ cm $(x \neq 3)$
27. $\dfrac{2(x + 2)}{x + 6} \ (x \neq 2, x \neq -6)$
29. $\dfrac{4a + 7b}{4a - 7b} \left(a \neq \dfrac{7b}{4}\right)$
31. $\dfrac{s - 5}{s + 7} \ (s \neq -7, s \neq -3)$
33. $\dfrac{2(a + 2b)}{a + 3b} \ (a \neq b, a \neq -3b)$
35. $\dfrac{2x + 3y}{x - 2y} \left(x \neq 2y, x \neq -\dfrac{5y}{2}\right)$
37. $1 \ (x \neq y, x \neq -y)$
39. $2x + y$; cannot be evaluated
41. $\dfrac{c + 2d}{d(c - 2d)}$; $-\dfrac{8}{3}$
43. $\dfrac{5 - x}{x + 5} \left(x \neq 0, x \neq \dfrac{3}{2}, x \neq -5\right)$
45. $\dfrac{a - 3b}{a + 3b + 2} \ (a \neq 2 - 3b, a \neq -3b - 2)$
47. $\dfrac{a - 3b + 3}{3} \ (a \neq 3b + 3)$

Written Exercises, pages 205–207 1. $\dfrac{5}{3}$
3. $\dfrac{1}{15}$ **5.** $\dfrac{1}{2}$ **7.** 6 **9.** $\dfrac{a}{c}$ **11.** $\dfrac{3}{2c}$ **13.** $3pq$
15. $\dfrac{2y^3}{x^2}$ **17.** -2 **19.** $\dfrac{x}{x - 2}$
21. $\dfrac{1}{2xy(4 + y)}$ **23.** $2(1 - x)$ **25.** $\dfrac{3xy}{2}$ km
27. $\dfrac{nc}{3}$ cents **29.** $\dfrac{1}{b^3}$ **31.** $\dfrac{64d^3}{125}$ **33.** $\dfrac{d^4}{k^2}$
35. $\dfrac{x^{10}}{y^{15}}$ **37.** $\dfrac{8a^3n^3}{v^6}$ **39.** $\dfrac{x^2 + y^2}{2(x + y)}$ **41.** $\dfrac{y}{x}$
43. $\dfrac{2(x - 1)}{x + 2}$ **45.** $\dfrac{-2}{5y - 2x}$
47. $\dfrac{-2(2x + 1)(x - 3)}{x(x^2 - 3)}$ **49.** $8(2 - x^2)$
51. $\dfrac{-(z - 1)^2(z^2 - 1)^2}{z(1 + z^2)}$ **53.** $\dfrac{x^2 + 3}{6x}$

Application, page 207 1. $4.60 per kilogram **3.** The 1 L bottle

Written Exercises, pages 209–210 1. $\dfrac{3}{2}$
3. $\dfrac{6}{y}$ **5.** $\dfrac{a^3}{8}$ **7.** $2pq$ **9.** 1 **11.** $\dfrac{3a}{8b^2}$ **13.** 2
15. $\dfrac{y - 2}{2y}$ **17.** $(x - y)(x + y)$ **19.** $\dfrac{6}{a(a - b)}$

21. $\dfrac{x-y}{x+y}$ **23.** $\dfrac{x^2}{6}$ **25.** $\dfrac{9}{4z^6x^4y^5}$ **27.** $\dfrac{q^3}{p^3r^{10}}$

29. c **31.** $\dfrac{b-2a}{b^2}$ **33.** $\dfrac{2a-3}{a}$

35. $\dfrac{8(5-2x)}{3}$ **37.** $\dfrac{5(s-2)}{s-4}$ **39.** $\dfrac{2(a+3)}{a-2}$

Written Exercises, pages 214–215 **1.** 6
3. $24x$ **5.** $3(2a+3)$ **7.** $6(1-7x)$ **9.** x^3
11. $6a$ **13.** $2(x+2)$ **15.** -3 **17.** $x+1$
19. 10 **21.** $2x$ **23.** $-5a$ **25.** 18
27. $10xy$ **29.** $9cd^2$ **31.** $2(x+1)(x-1)$
33. $\dfrac{20}{72},\dfrac{27}{72}$ **35.** $\dfrac{4(2x-1)}{60},\dfrac{3(1+x)}{60}$
37. $\dfrac{24(2x-3)}{144},\dfrac{16(7+3y)}{144},\dfrac{9x}{144}$
39. $\dfrac{2y}{8x^2y^2},\dfrac{3x^3}{8x^2y^2}$
41. $\dfrac{4}{(3-x)(3+x)},\dfrac{3(3-x)}{(3-x)(3+x)}$
43. $\dfrac{x+2}{x(x-3)(x+2)},\dfrac{x-3}{x(x-3)(x+2)}$
45. $\dfrac{x}{4(x-5)(x+5)},\dfrac{8(x-5)}{4(x-5)(x+5)},$
$\dfrac{12(x+5)}{4(x-5)(x+5)}$ **47.** $\dfrac{4}{6(x+3)(x-3)},$
$\dfrac{3x(x-3)}{6(x+3)(x-3)},\dfrac{-6(x+3)^2}{6(x+3)(x-3)}$

Written Exercises, pages 217–218 **1.** $\dfrac{11}{a}$
3. $\dfrac{1}{c}$ **5.** 1 **7.** $y-2$ **9.** $\dfrac{(x-3)^2}{(x+3)^2}$ **11.** $\dfrac{a}{3}$
13. $\dfrac{3x+2}{x^2}$ **15.** $\dfrac{5a-6}{2a^2}$ **17.** $\dfrac{4-7y}{50}$
19. $\dfrac{8n+9}{15}$ **21.** $\dfrac{2(7y-x)}{45}$
23. $\dfrac{3y+2}{(y+2)(y-2)}$ **25.** $\dfrac{2}{3a-b}$
27. $\dfrac{3}{a(2a-3)}$ **29.** $\dfrac{8(2x+1)}{15}$ m; $\dfrac{x^2-4}{15}$ m²
31. $\dfrac{2x+1}{x(x+1)}$ **33.** $\dfrac{1}{4(x+1)}$
35. $\dfrac{x^2+y^2}{(x-y)(x+y)}$ **37.** $\dfrac{-a-b}{ab}$
39. $\dfrac{-2}{(a-3)(a+3)}$
41. $\dfrac{3c+5}{(c+1)(c-2)(c+2)}$

43. $\dfrac{2a}{(a+1)^2(a-1)}$ **45.** $\dfrac{3(3x+2)}{(x+1)(x+2)^2}$
47. $\dfrac{2x-1}{2x+1}$ **49.** $\dfrac{-2x^2-15x-9}{3(x+3)(x-3)}$ **51.** 0

Just for Fun, page 219 **1. a.** $\dfrac{2}{3};\dfrac{3}{4};\dfrac{4}{5}$
b. $\dfrac{100}{101}$ **c.** $\dfrac{n}{n+1}$

Written Exercises, page 221 **1.** $\dfrac{22}{7}$
3. $\dfrac{5x+2}{x}$ **5.** $\dfrac{4b+a}{b}$ **7.** $\dfrac{3+2n^2}{2n}$
9. $\dfrac{2x+7y}{3}$ **11.** $\dfrac{3(5x-8)}{2x-3}$ **13.** $\dfrac{x^2+4}{(x-2)^2}$
15. $\dfrac{4b+a-2ab}{ab}$ **17.** $\dfrac{18}{(x+3)(x-3)}$
19. $\dfrac{(x^2-3)(x^2+2)}{x^2}$ **21.** $\dfrac{x+y}{x}$
23. $x-1$ **25.** $\dfrac{a(a+b-c)}{c(c-a+b)}$ **27.** $A=-1,$
$B=1$

Just for Fun, page 221 Diophantus was 84 years old.

Written Exercises, pages 223–224
1. $x+4$ **3.** $x+4$ **5.** $a+1+\dfrac{5}{a+3}$
7. $z-2-\dfrac{7}{z-4}$ **9.** $x+12+\dfrac{29}{x-3}$
11. $x-1+\dfrac{5}{x+1}$ **13.** $x-2+\dfrac{1}{2x-1}$
15. $y-1+\dfrac{6}{5y-1}$ **17.** $2n+2+\dfrac{5}{3n-1}$
19. $3x-y-\dfrac{y^2}{2x+y}$ **21.** x^2-x+1
23. x^2-2x-3 **25.** $x^2+3x+15$
27. $a^2+5ab-7b^2$ **29.** $3a+2$
31. $(3n+2)(n-2)(n-1)$
33. $(2x+1)(2x+3)(x-5)$ **37.** -6 **39.** 1

Just for Fun, page 224 In 20 s; in 60 s

Extra, pages 225–227 **1.** $\dfrac{1}{3}$ **3.** ab **5.** $\dfrac{1}{3}$
7. 9 **9.** $\dfrac{1}{y}$ **11.** $\dfrac{a}{a-1}$ **13.** $\dfrac{a+3}{a-3}$
15. $x+1$ **17.** 1 **19.** $\dfrac{1-2y}{2(1-y)}$ **21.** $\dfrac{t}{2-t}$
25. $\dfrac{8n}{8+n}$ **27.** $\dfrac{-2-x}{x-6}$ **29.** a^2+1 **31.** 1

10 ANSWERS TO ODD-NUMBERED EXERCISES

Calculator Key-In, page 227   1. $0.\overline{5}$ 3. 1.125   5. $24.\overline{3}$ 7. 0.375

Chapter Review, pages 228–230   1. d   3. a   5. b   7. d   9. c   11. b   13. c   15. a   17. c

Just for Fun, page 231

^{1}6	3	▨	▨	^{2}3	^{3}6
2	▨	^{4}2	1	▨	4
^{5}5	^{6}2	8	▨	^{7}1	6
▨	^{8}4	0	^{9}3	2	▨
^{10}9	▨	^{11}8	1	▨	^{12}8
^{13}9	0	▨	▨	^{14}4	2

Cumulative Review, page 232   1. $2b - 3$
3. $21j^5k^4$ 5. $24z^3 + 11z^2 - 18z$ 7. $\dfrac{3s}{r^4}$
9. $49x^2 - 112xy + 64y^2$ 11. 3
13. $4(5a - b^2)(5a + b^2)$
15. $(x - 18y)(x - 3y)$
17. $k(3k + 2m)(2k + m)$ 19. 26   21. 5
23. 2   25. -7 27. $\dfrac{2}{5}, -8$ 29. $\dfrac{-1}{2y^3}$ 31. $\dfrac{r}{5}$
33. $\dfrac{4x^2 + 9x - 12}{(x + 4)(x + 3)}$ 35. $m^2 - 5m + 10$
37. 23, 25, 27   39. 11 cm by 12 cm
41. 40 km

Maintaining Skills, page 233   1. 14 dimes and 9 quarters   3. 12 cm by 14 cm

CHAPTER 7   APPLYING FRACTIONS

Written Exercises, page 237   1. 12:1
3. 1:10   5. 20:1   7. 26:1   9. 3:1   11. 3:5
13. 9:8   15. 20:1   17. 9:4   19. 2:5
21. 3:4   23. 2:1   25. 1:1

Problems, pages 238–239   1. 24, 40
3. 450   5. $960, $360, $480   7. $2,400,000
9. Marvin   11. 40 m, $4800; 50 m, $6000; 70 m, $8400   13. 56 quarters   15. 30, 80, 32

Written Exercises, pages 241–242   1. 21
3. $\dfrac{4}{15}$ 5. $\dfrac{28}{15}$ 7. $\dfrac{27}{2}$ 9. 0   11. $\dfrac{6}{7}$ 13. 34
15. 1   17. 5   19. 2.5   21. identity   23. no root   25. $\dfrac{ac}{b}$ 27. $na - b$ 29. $-\dfrac{3}{8}$ 31. $\dfrac{1}{18}$

Problems, pages 242–243   1. 3840 L
3. $560   5. 128 g   7. 960 shares   9. 40 ha
11. the cube of gold; 4.5384 g

Written Exercises, pages 244–245   1. 6
3. 1   5. 36   7. 15   9. $\dfrac{3}{2}$ 11. $-\dfrac{3}{4}$ 13. 2
15. -8 17. 7   19. -3 21. -1 23. 12
25. 4   27. 3   29. $-\dfrac{11}{4}$ 31. $\dfrac{4a}{3}$ 33. $-\dfrac{13c}{3}$

Problems, pages 245–246   1. 60   3. 12 cm by 18 cm   5. Sam, 2; Kathy, 4   7. Beverly, $20; Ann, $30   9. 3 km   11. 27 dimes

Written Exercises, page 248   1. 1   3. 6
5. 5   7. 2   9. 8   11. -6 13. 22
15. 20 km/h   17. 1   19. $\dfrac{16}{5}$ 21. $\dfrac{1}{4}, 2$
23. 2   25. $-4, 1$ 27. 9   29. 8   31. 4, 1
33. 4, -2

Application, pages 249–250   1. a. 180 mm
b. 2   3. a. 24.5 cm   b. 49

Written Exercises, pages 253–254   1. 88
3. 55   5. 4.4   7. 91   9. 11   11. 75%
13. 64%   15. 125%   17. 25%   19. 10%
21. 150%   23. 30   25. 42   27. 400   29. 18
31. 40   33. 9   35. 30   37. 4   39. $-64,000$
41. -13

Problems, pages 254–255   1. 4 mg
3. $425   5. 10.8 min   7. $1200
9. $8000 at 7% and $4000 at 9%   11. $9000

Problems, pages 257–258   1. 13%
3. $30.50   5. 5%   7. 125,000 subscribers
9. $75,000   11. 8%   13. 40%

Calculator Key-In, page 258   1. 1440.55
3. 682.5   5. 1275   7. $5382.73

Problems, pages 261–262 **1.** 25 kg of the $4.80 coffee and 15 kg of the $4.00 coffee
3. $\frac{1}{3}$, or 0.33, kg **5.** 150 kg of the $2.90 cheese and 50 kg of the $3.10 cheese
7. 60 g **9.** 150 g **11.** 3 kg **13.** 20 kg of oatmeal and 10 kg of bran flakes **15.** 300 discount tickets **17.** 11 pennies, 55 nickels, 20 dimes, 14 quarters **19.** 75 kg **21.** 4:7

Problems, pages 265–267 **1.** $1\frac{5}{7}$, or 1.71, h **3.** $\frac{4}{7}$, or 0.57, day **5.** $1\frac{5}{7}$, or 1.71, h **7.** $30\frac{10}{13}$, or 30.77, s **9.** 30 min
11. 22.5 min **13.** $12\frac{36}{47}$, or 12.766, min
15. $8\frac{4}{7}$, or 8.57, min **17.** 5 h **19.** 4.2 h

Application, page 268 **1.** 1.6:1

Chapter Review, pages 269–271 **1.** d **3.** c
5. b **7.** a **9.** d **11.** a **13.** d **15.** b
17. c

Cumulative Review, page 272 **1.** $2x + 4y$
3. $-7cd^4 + 14c^2d^3 + 21c^2d$ **5.** $\frac{b^6}{4}$
7. $16w^4 + 22w^2z - 3z^2$
9. $9g^2 - 41g + gh + 20 - 4h$ **11.** 92
13. $3(c + 14)(c - 5)$ **15.** $(2 - cd)(d - 1)$
17. prime **19.** 500 **21.** $-5r + 9s$
23. $\frac{-(m + 2)(m - 1)}{(m + 1)^2}$ **25.** $k + 1$
27. $\frac{(3a - b)(2a + b)}{(a - b)(a + b)}$ **29.** no root **31.** $\frac{7}{2}$, 1
33. $-\frac{2}{3}$ **35.** -6 **37.** 30.8 min **39.** $6000

Maintaining Skills, page 273 **1.** $-4m - 6$
3. $-2x + 9y$ **5.** $-w$ **7.** $-3h^2 - h + 2$
9. $14x^5y^3z^5$ **11.** $24t^{2n+2}$ **13.** $54c^{10}$
15. $-4m^7n^8$ **17.** $63c^7d^{12}$
19. $24b^5 - 8b^4 + 48b^3$
21. $-14p^3q^4 + 7p^2q^5 - 35pq^6$
23. $y^2 + 4y - 45$ **25.** $6k^2 + 17k - 28$
27. $4g^2 - 12g + 9$
29. $2r^3 - 11r^2 - 4r + 45$

CHAPTER 8 LINEAR EQUATIONS AND SYSTEMS

Written Exercises, pages 278–279
1–15.

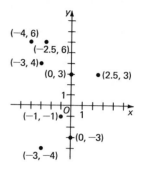

17. isosceles triangle

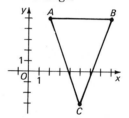

19. rectangle

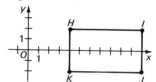

21. O **23.** A **25.** O, W **27.** W, A, Q
29. G, H **31.** $(-9, -5)$ **33.** $(5, -2)$,
$(3, -8)$ **35.** The points all lie on a line.

Written Exercises, pages 281–282 **1.** 5, 2,
0 **3.** 0, -1, -2 **5.** 1. $\frac{1}{2}$, -1 **7.** 4, 6, 11
9. -5, -4, -1 **11.** 0, 4, 2 **13.** $y = 6 - x$
15. $y = x - 6$ **17.** $y = -\frac{2}{3}x + 4$
19. $\{(-1, 2), (0, 1), (1, 0), (2, -1)\}$
21. $\{(-1, 0), (1, -1)\}$ **23.** $\{(1, 2), (2, -1)\}$
25. $\{(0, 8), (1, 7), (2, 6), (3, 5), (4, 4),$
$(5, 3), (6, 2), (7, 1), (8, 0)\}$
27. $\{(0, 5), (2, 4), (4, 3), (6, 2), (8, 1), (10, 0)\}$
29. $\{(0, 0), (1, 1), (2, 4)\}$ **31.** $\{(1, 0), (2, 3)\}$
33. $\{(3, 4), (4, 3)\}$ **35.** $\{(4, 0)\}$ **37.** $(1, 4)$
39. $(2, 6)$

Written Exercises, pages 285–286 **1.** 4, 8, 3 **3.** $-7, 7, 8$ **5. a.** $(4, 0)$ **b.** $(0, 3)$

7. a. $(0, 0)$ **b.** $(0, 0)$

9.

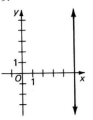

11.

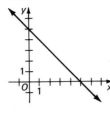

13.

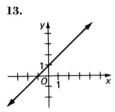

15.

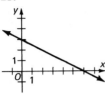

17.

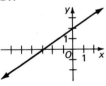

19.

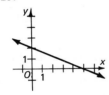

21. $x - y = 2$

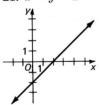

23. $x - y = -1$

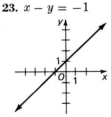

25. $5x - 2y = -3$

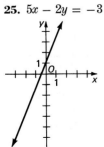

27.

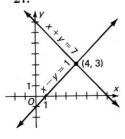

29.

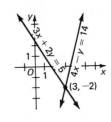

31. The lines are parallel.

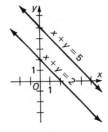

33. The lines are parallel.

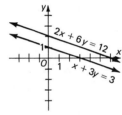

35. The lines are perpendicular.

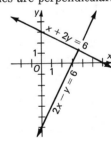

Written Exercises, page 289 **1.** $(3, -5)$ is a solution. **3.** $(0, 0)$ is not a solution.

5.

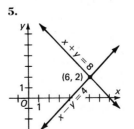

7.

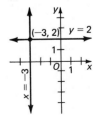

9.

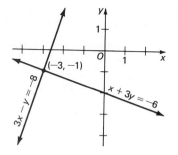

11.

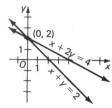

13.

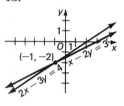

15. no solution

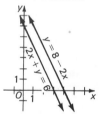

17. (0, 0)

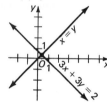

19. (4, 0)

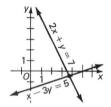

21. $A = 3, B = -2$ **23.** $A = 6, B = 6$
25. (5, 5) **27.** 27

Written Exercises, page 292 **1.** (6, 2)
3. (5, 1) **5.** (−3, −1) **7.** (4, 4) **9.** (3, 0)
11. (−1, 3) **13.** (−1, 2) **15.** $\left(\frac{5}{3}, \frac{1}{3}\right)$
17. $\left(-1, \frac{2}{3}\right)$ **19.** (−4, −3) **21.** (−10, 5)
23. (8, −2) **25.** $A = 3, B = -1$
27. (3, 5, −8) **29.** (3, 2, 4) **31.** (4, 0, −5)

Problems, pages 294–295 **1.** 86 and 92
3. 4000 trout; 8000 perch **5.** 213 adult; 426
student **7.** 432 people Friday; 658 people
Saturday **9.** 828 blue jays; 388 chickadees

11. a. 11 m by 14 m **b.** $280 **13.** engine
A, 280 L; engine B, 206 L

Written Exercises, page 297 **1.** (5, 2)
3. (0, −4) **5.** (6, 3) **7.** (3, 4) **9.** (0, 4)
11. (8, 6) **13.** (4, −3) **15.** (2, 0)
17. (1, −1) **19.** (1, −3) **21.** (−3, −1)
23. (−5, 0)

Problems, page 298 **1.** 72 and 98 **3.** first
car, 58 L; second car, 42 L **5.** 3 trout; 10
bass **7.** $10 for membership; $3 for each
session

Application, page 298 **1.** 14.8 **3.** 17.82
5. 41.51

Written Exercises, page 301 **1.** (3, 4)
3. (−3, −2) **5.** (2, 0) **7.** (0, −2)
9. (1, −1) **11.** (−2, 1) **13.** (0, −3)
15. (1, −1) **17.** (−3, −4) **19.** (2, −1)
21. (−4, −6) **23.** (3, 4) **25.** (5, 4)
27. (2, −3) **29.** $\left(\frac{1}{2}, -1\right)$ **31.** $\left(\frac{1}{3}, -\frac{1}{2}\right)$

Problems, page 302 **1.** 15 and 16 **3.** 22
and 38 **5.** membership fee, $25; monthly
dues, $2 **7.** father, 24; mother, 20 **9.** 50
cows

Calculator Key-In, page 303 **1.** (2, 3)

Problems, pages 306–308 **1.** Dixie, 16;
sister, 10 **3.** Joe, 23; Della, 20 **5.** Mary,
37; son, 7 **7.** 71 **9.** 28 **11.** 13 **13.** $\frac{2}{9}$
15. $\frac{7}{8}$ **17.** $\frac{3}{4}$ **19.** Grandmother, 21;
Grandfather, 24 **21.** 397 **23.** $\frac{458}{854}$
27. father, 39; son, 16

Problems, pages 310–312 **1.** 23 km/h;
7 km/h **3.** wind's speed, 40 km/h; plane's
speed, 280 km/h **5.** wind's rate,
120 m/min; robin's rate, 180 m/min
7. $128\frac{1}{3}$, or 128.33, km **9.** 175 km/h;
75 km/h **11.** 125 km/h; 50 km/h
13. glider's rate, 75 km/h; wind's rate,
5 km/h **15.** $s = 3w$, or $w = \frac{1}{3}s$ **17.** $s = 5c$,
or $c = \frac{1}{5}s$

Chapter Review, pages 313–315 **1.** d **3.** c
5. a **7.** c **9.** c **11.** d **13.** a **15.** c

Cumulative Review, page 316
1. $-2y^3 + 14y^2 + 18y$ **3.** $64r^4 - 9s^2$
5. $7d - 12$ **7.** $(1 - 9v)^2$
9. $(5 - m)(m - 3n)$ **11.** prime
13. $\dfrac{2x + 5y}{2x + 3y}$ **15.** $\dfrac{1}{4}$ **17.** $n^2 + 2n - 1$

19. 3 **21.** 15 **23.** 2250 **25.** 1, 3 **27.** $\dfrac{5}{2}$, -2

29. $(-1, -11)$ **31.** $(-2, 4)$ **33.** 84

Maintaining Skills, page 317
1. $2c^2(c + 2d)$ **3.** prime
5. $8a(8a^2 - 5a + 9)$ **7.** $a(8 - a)(8 + a)$
9. $(3p - 1)^2$ **11.** prime **13.** $(m^2 + 2n)^2$
15. $3(z - 6t)^2$ **17.** $(g - 10)(g + 4)$
19. $5(z - 6)(z - 4)$ **21.** $s(s + 9)(s - 8)$
23. $(c - 3d)(c - 11d)$ **25.** $(a - 6)(r - 5)$
27. prime **29.** $(4z + 3)(m - 2n)$
31. $(3a - 5)(4a - 1)$ **33.** $(5r + 9s)(r + 2s)$
35. $z(9z + 5)(3z - 2)$ **37.** prime
39. $(4x + v)(10x + 9v)$

CHAPTER 9 INTRODUCTION TO FUNCTIONS

Written Exercises, pages 322–323 **1.** $-\dfrac{1}{2}$

3. 1 **5.** $-\dfrac{1}{9}$ **7.** 1 **9.** no slope **11.** 0

13. 4 **15.** 2 **17.** 1 **19.** $\dfrac{2}{3}$ **21.** $\dfrac{4}{5}$ **23.** 0

25. same line, -2 **27.** not the same line

29. 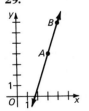 **31.**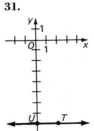

33.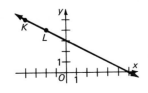

35. $\overline{AC}$, no slope; $\overline{AB}$, slope 0; $\overline{BC}$, slope $\dfrac{8}{9}$

37. Yes; if the slopes from $(-2, -4)$ to $(2, 8)$ and from $(2, 8)$ to $(0, 2)$ are the same, then all 3 points are on the same line.
39. $y = -2$ **41.** The slopes of $\overline{AC}$ and $\overline{AM}$ are both $-\dfrac{5}{3}$; so M is on $\overline{AC}$. The slopes of $\overline{BM}$ and $\overline{BD}$ are both $\dfrac{3}{5}$, so M is on $\overline{BD}$.

Written Exercises, page 326
1. $6x - 2y = -1$ **3.** $x - 4y = -12$
5. $15x - 3y = 2$ **7.** $x - 3y = -2$
9. $8x + 10y = 25$ **11.** $y = -3$

13. $y = -x + 8$ 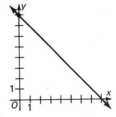 **15.** $y = x - 6$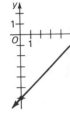

17. $y = \dfrac{1}{2}x - 4$ 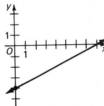 **19.** $y = -\dfrac{2}{3}x$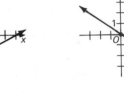

21. $y = \dfrac{5}{3}x + \dfrac{20}{3}$ 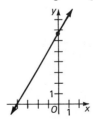 **23.** $y = \dfrac{2}{3}x - 4$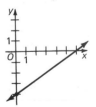

25. $y = 3x - 3$ **27.** $-3; 3$
29. slope $= -\dfrac{A}{B}$; y-intercept $= \dfrac{C}{B}$

Application, page 327 **1. a–d.** Answers may vary.

Written Exercises, page 329 **1.** 2 **3.** $-\frac{1}{3}$

5. $2x - y = 5$ **7.** $4x + y = -22$
9. $2x - 3y = 6$ **11.** $5x - 4y = 15$
13. $x + 2y = -7$ **15.** $y = -2$
17. $7x - 4y = 8$ **19.** $y = 0$
21. $2x + y = 7$ **23.** $8x - 3y = 22$
25. $5x - y = -3$ **27.** $3x + 4y = -13$
29. $2x - y = -6$ **31.** $3x - y = -4$
33. $x - 2y = -6$

Written Exercises, page 333 **1.** 4 **3.** 1

5. -5 **7.** 3 **9.** 0 **11.** 8 **13.** 0 **15.** $\frac{5}{4}$

17. $\{-1, 2, 5\}$ **19.** $\{3, -1, -13\}$
21. $\left\{-\frac{3}{2}, -6, 3\right\}$ **23.** $\{7, 3, -1\}$

25. $\{6, 3, 2\}$ **27.** $\{-2, 3, 1\}$ **29.** $\{8, -1\}$
31. $\{0, 2\}$ **33.** $\{-27, 0, 1\}$
35. $\{-8, -5, 4\}$ **37.** 24 **39.** 1 **41. a.** 3
b. 2 **c.** 6 **d.** 18 **43. a.** No **b.** 0

Written Exercises, page 336

1.

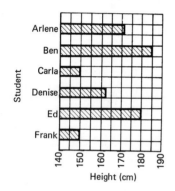

Height (cm)

3.

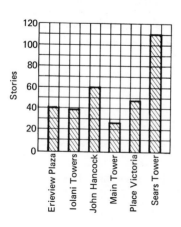

5. $\{(1967, 49{,}700{,}000),\ (1969, 53{,}200{,}000),$
$(1971, 59{,}800{,}000),\ (1973, 63{,}200{,}000),$
$(1975, 54{,}300{,}000),\ (1977, 63{,}700{,}000)\}$

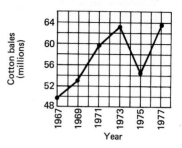

Application, page 337

1.

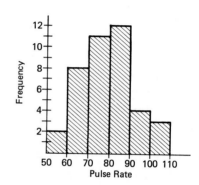

3. 8 **5.** 33

Written Exercises, page 341

1. $(0, 0)$

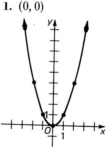

3. $(0, 0)$

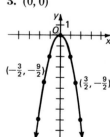

$\left(-\frac{3}{2}, -\frac{9}{2}\right)$ $\left(\frac{3}{2}, -\frac{9}{2}\right)$

5. $(0, 0)$

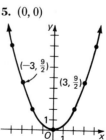

$\left(-3, \frac{9}{2}\right)$ $\left(3, \frac{9}{2}\right)$

7. $(-2, -4)$

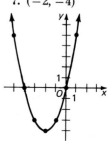

9. $(-1, 2)$

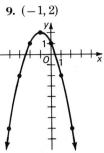

11. $(0, -2)$

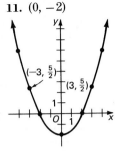

13. $-\dfrac{9}{4}$ **15.** $-\dfrac{25}{4}$ **17.** -6 **19.** $\dfrac{9}{4}$

21. -1 **23.** $\dfrac{1}{8}$

25. a.

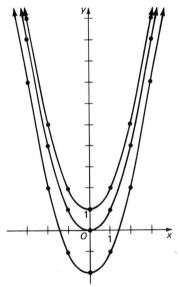

b. As c increases, the graph moves up; as c decreases, the graph moves down.

Written Exercises, page 345 **1.** $\dfrac{1}{6}$ **3.** 5

5. 25 **7.** 1000 **9.** 600 **11.** 21 **13.** 2.4

15. $\dfrac{1}{2}$ **17.** $M = kE$ or $\dfrac{M_1}{E_1} = \dfrac{M_2}{E_2}$

19. $m = kh$ or $\dfrac{m_1}{h_1} = \dfrac{m_2}{h_2}$ **21.** $P = kT$ or

$\dfrac{P_1}{T_1} = \dfrac{P_2}{T_2}$ **23.** $i = kn$ or $\dfrac{i_1}{n_1} = \dfrac{i_2}{n_2}$

Problems, pages 346–347 **1.** \$130 **3.** 15 min **5.** 4.5 cups **7.** 7.5 units **9.** 20 km

Calculator Key-In, page 347 9.4542×10^{15} m

Written Exercises, pages 350–351

1.

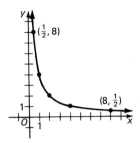

3.

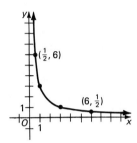

5. 125 **7.** 2.1 **9.** $ih = k$, or $i_1 h_1 = i_2 h_2$
11. $fl = k$, or $f_1 l_1 = f_2 l_2$ **13.** $fl = k$, or $f_1 l_1 = f_2 l_2$

Problems, pages 351–352 **1.** 2 m **3.** 7 people **5.** 800 km/h **7.** 8 m **9.** 0.75 h, or 45 min **11.** $\dfrac{1}{2}$ **13.** 0.4 m

Problems, pages 354–355 **1.** 25 cm^2 **3.** 1.6 min **5.** 144 km **7.** 5 cm **9.** The force is multiplied 256 times. **11. a.** 1 cm **b.** 27:8

Problems, pages 357–358 **1.** 57 cm^2
3. 36 cm **5.** 10 students **7.** 21 ohms
9. a. It is doubled. **b.** It is quadrupled.
c. It is multiplied by 18.

Chapter Review, pages 360–361 **1.** b
3. d **5.** a **7.** b **9.** c **11.** c **13.** d

Cumulative Review, page 362
1. $-16 + 5x$ **3.** $3p^2 + 5pq - p - 2q^2 - 2q$
5. $-3x + y$ **7.** $5a(5a + 6)(a - 2)$
9. $(4t^2 - 3v)(4t^2 + 3v)$ **11.** $\dfrac{2b - 1}{b - 1}$
13. $\dfrac{2c^2 + 6cd - 2d^2}{(c - 2d)(c + d)(c)}$ **15.** $r(7r + 4)$
17. $\{-3, 2, 3, 0, -7\}$

19. a. 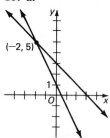 **b.**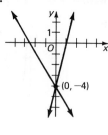

21. $\{28, -28\}$ **23.** -2.79 **25.** $\left\{2, -\dfrac{1}{3}\right\}$

27. $\dfrac{1}{2}$ **29.** $(2, -2)$ **31.** $\left(\dfrac{1}{3}, \dfrac{1}{2}\right)$

33. 36π cm^3

Maintaining Skills, page 363 1. $-\dfrac{1}{3y}$

3. $\dfrac{5a}{b}$ **5.** $\dfrac{28}{3(t-1)}$ **7.** $-\dfrac{4z^2}{5}$ **9.** $\dfrac{d+2}{d-7}$

11. $\dfrac{m-1}{m+1}$ **13.** $\dfrac{x^3(x-2y)}{(x+4y)^2}$ **15.** $4-g$

17. $\dfrac{-6r^2 - 2r + 8}{3r+1}$ **19.** $\dfrac{10x - 2x^3 + 3}{2x}$

21. $\dfrac{3a+8}{18a^2}$ **23.** $-\dfrac{x+3}{x+4}$

25. $\dfrac{-2p+1}{(p-3)(p-4)}$

CHAPTER 10 INEQUALITIES

Written Exercises, pages 367–368
1. $5 > -2$ **3.** $-15 \le -10$ **5.** $2 < 4 < 4.5$
7. $-20 < -12 < -10$ **9.** $8 > 1 > -2$
11. F **13.** T **15.** T
17. $\{-4, -3, -2, -1, 0, 1, 2\}$
19. $\{-4, -3\}$
21. $\{-4, -3, -2, -1, 0, 1, 2, 3, 4\}$
23. $\{-4, -3, -2, -1, 0, 1\}$

25. {the real numbers greater than 4}

27. $\{-4, -3, -2, -1, 0, 1\}$

29. {the real numbers greater than or equal to 0 and less than 5}

31. $\{-6, -5, -4, -3, -2, -1\}$

33. Answers may vary. **a.** $x = 6, y = -3$
b. $x = 6, y = -7$ **35.** Answers may vary.
a. $x = 4, y = 1$ **b.** $x = -2, y = -5$

Calculator Key-In, page 368 1. T **3.** F

Written Exercises, pages 372–373 1. d
3. c **5.** b **7.** e
9. {the real numbers greater than 15}

11. {the real numbers less than -24}

13. {the real numbers less than -48}

15. {the real numbers less than or equal to -1}

17. {the real numbers greater than -4}

19. {the real numbers less than or equal to -20}

21. {the real numbers less than 6}

23. {the real numbers greater than -15}

25. {the real numbers less than 6}

27. {the real numbers less than 8}
29. {the real numbers greater than -4}
31. {the real numbers less than or equal to 3} **33.** {the negative real numbers}
35. {the real numbers less than or equal to -1}

37. $\left\{\text{the real numbers less than } \dfrac{5}{2}\right\}$

39. {the real numbers greater than or equal to 6}

41. {the real numbers greater than or equal to 2}

43. {the real numbers less than −9}

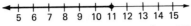

45. {the real numbers less than or equal to 11}

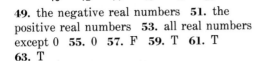

47. {the real numbers greater than 13}

[number line: 10, 12, 14, 16, 18, 20 with open circle at 13]

49. the negative real numbers **51.** the positive real numbers **53.** all real numbers except 0 **55.** 0 **57.** F **59.** T **61.** T **63.** T

Written Exercises, pages 375–376
1. $c - 12 < 75$ **3.** $k + 10k > 2800$

5. $\frac{1}{2}a + 12 < 100$

7. $9 < n + (n + 2) < 25$
9. $x - 2 \le 2x + 4$
11. $4(x + 2) - 2(x + 1) \ge 3x + 1$

Problems, pages 376–377 1. 15 **3.** 11 and 12 **5.** 38 and 39 **7.** 4.2 h, or 4 h 12 min **9.** 42 **11.** 9 quarters, 13 dimes **13.** 6, 8 **15.** 3, 5, 7, 9 **17.** 34 **19.** 19 km² **21.** 0, 1, 2

Extra, pages 380–381
1. {0, 1, 2, 3, 5, 6, 7, 8, 9} **3.** {6, 8} **5.** {6} **7.** {5, 6, 8} **9.** {5, 6, 7, 9} **11.** union: {0, 1, 2, 3, 4}; intersection: {2, 3} **13.** union: {1, 2, 3, 4, 5, 6}; intersection: ∅; disjoint **15.** union: {1, 2, 3, 5, 7, 9, 11}; intersection: {3, 5, 7} **17.** {the real numbers} **19.** {the real numbers between −2 and 3} **21.** {the real numbers less than 3} **23.** {the real numbers between −2 and 1}
25.

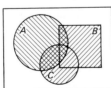

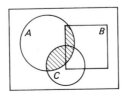

27. $A \cap (B \cup C) = (A \cap B) \cup (A \cap C)$

29.

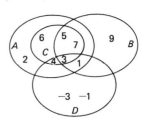

Written Exercises, pages 384–385
1.

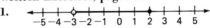

3. [number line: 0–10, closed dots at 4 and 8]

5. {the real numbers between −3 and 2}
[number line: −5 to 5, open circles at −3 and 2]

7. {5, and the real numbers between 0 and 5}
[number line: −3 to 7, open circle at 0, closed dot at 5]

9. {−1, and the real numbers between −1 and 2}
[number line: −5 to 5, closed dot at −1, open circle at 2]

11. {−2, and the real numbers between −2 and 1}
[number line: −5 to 5, closed dot at −2, open circle at 1]

13. {3, and the real numbers less than −1 or greater than 3}
[number line: −5 to 5, open circle at −1, closed dot at 3]

15. {−2, 2, and the real numbers less than −2 or greater than 2}
[number line: −5 to 5, closed dots at −2 and 2]

17. {−1, 2, and the real numbers less than −1 or greater than 2}
[number line: −5 to 5, closed dots at −1 and 2]

19. {−5, and the real numbers between −5 and 3}
[number line: −6 to 4, closed dot at −5, open circle at 3]

21. {−2, 3, and the real numbers between −2 and 3}
[number line: −5 to 5, closed dots at −2 and 3]

23. {the real numbers less than −2 or greater than 2}
[number line: −5 to 5, open circles at −2 and 2]

25. ∅

27. {5, and the real numbers between −2 and 5}

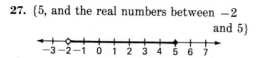

```
 -3 -2 -1  0  1  2  3  4  5  6  7
```

29. {the real numbers less than −1 or greater than 7}

```
 -2 -1  0  1  2  3  4  5  6  7  8
```

31. {the real numbers less than −1 or greater than 5}

```
 -3 -2 -1  0  1  2  3  4  5  6  7
```

33. {−2, 2, and the real numbers between −2 and 2}

```
 -5 -4 -3 -2 -1  0  1  2  3  4  5
```

35. {4, and the real numbers between 1 and 4}

```
 -5 -4 -3 -2 -1  0  1  2  3  4  5
```

37. {the real numbers less than or equal to 6}

```
  0  1  2  3  4  5  6  7  8  9 10
```

39. 5

Written Exercises, pages 387–388

1. $|x| = 4$ **3.** $|x| < 3$ **5.** $|x| \geq 2$

7. {3, −1}

```
 -5 -4 -3 -2 -1  0  1  2  3  4  5
```

9. {0, 2}

```
 -5 -4 -3 -2 -1  0  1  2  3  4  5
```

11. {the real numbers between −2 and 2}

```
 -5 -4 -3 -2 -1  0  1  2  3  4  5
```

13. {−4, 4, and the real numbers between −4 and 4}

```
 -5 -4 -3 -2 -1  0  1  2  3  4  5
```

15. {2, −2}

```
 -5 -4 -3 -2 -1  0  1  2  3  4  5
```

17. {−2, 2, and the real numbers between −2 and 2}

```
 -5 -4 -3 -2 -1  0  1  2  3  4  5
```

19. {the real numbers between −3 and 1}

```
 -5 -4 -3 -2 -1  0  1  2  3  4  5
```

21. {−1, 7, and the real numbers between −1 and 7}

```
 -3 -2 -1  0  1  2  3  4  5  6  7
```

23. {3, −2}

```
 -5 -4 -3 -2 -1  0  1  2  3  4  5
```

25. {2}

```
 -5 -4 -3 -2 -1  0  1  2  3  4  5
```

27. {the real numbers between −7 and 7}

```
 -9 -7 -5 -3 -1  1  3  5  7  9 11
```

29. {the real numbers less than −3 or greater than 4}

```
 -5 -4 -3 -2 -1  0  1  2  3  4  5
```

31. $\left\{-\dfrac{3}{2}, \dfrac{3}{2}\right.$, and the real numbers less than $-\dfrac{3}{2}$ or greater than $\left.\dfrac{3}{2}\right\}$

```
 -2    -1     0     1     2
```

33. {15, −3}

```
 -3 -1  1  3  5  7  9 11 13 15 17
```

35. {5, −1}

```
 -5 -4 -3 -2 -1  0  1  2  3  4  5
```

37. {the real numbers less than 2}

```
 -5 -4 -3 -2 -1  0  1  2  3  4  5
```

39. ∅

```
 -5 -4 -3 -2 -1  0  1  2  3  4  5
```

Written Exercises, pages 391–392

1.

3.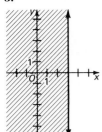

5.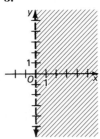

7.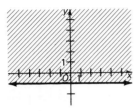

9.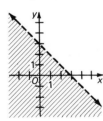

11.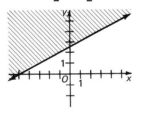

13. $y < 3 - x$

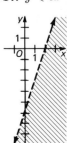

15. $y \geq \frac{1}{2}x + \frac{5}{2}$

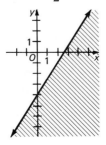

17. $y < 3x - 6$

19. $y \leq \frac{3}{2}x - 4$

21. $\frac{1}{3}x + \frac{2}{3} \leq y$

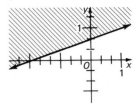

23. $y \leq -\frac{1}{2}x - \frac{5}{2}$

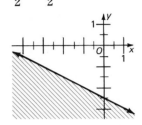

25. $y > -1$ **27.** $y \leq 0$ **29.** $y > \frac{1}{2}x - 3$

31. $y \leq 3x + 6$ **33.** $y > \frac{1}{2}x + 2$

35.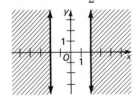

Written Exercises, pages 394–396

1.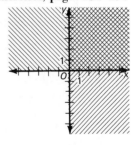

3.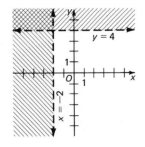

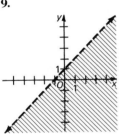

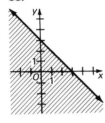

5.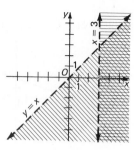

7.

9.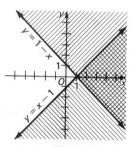

11.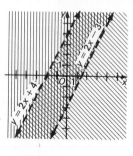

13.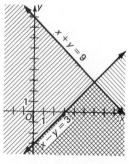

15.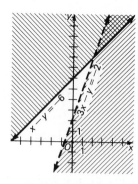

17.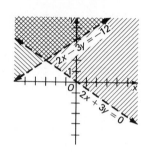

19. $x \geq -4$ **21.** $y \leq x - 3$
$y > x + 4$ $4y \geq -3x - 12$

23. $y \geq -3$
$y < -x + 1$
$y < 8x + 37$

25. $(0, 0)$; $(-1, -1)$; $(1, -1)$

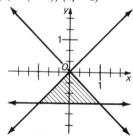

27. $(0, 3)$; $(6, 0)$; $\left(-\dfrac{3}{2}, 0\right)$

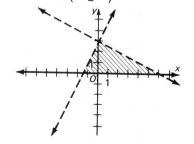

Just for Fun, page 396

1.

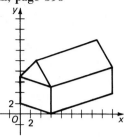

Application, page 397 1. 105% **3.** 12%

Chapter Review, pages 398–399 1. c
3. a **5.** d **7.** b **9.** a

Cumulative Review, page 400
1. $(5u - 3v)(3u - 7v)$ **3.** $(2 - 3h)(g - 1)$
5. $-16y$ **7.** $-4m^3 + 6$
9. $c^2 + 2cd + d^2 - 2c - 2d + 1$
11. $\dfrac{7x^2 - 112}{24x}$ **13.** $-\dfrac{c - 6}{c - 4}$, or $\dfrac{6 - c}{c - 4}$
15. $\dfrac{(z^2 + 9)(z + 3)}{2}$
17. 3, 33

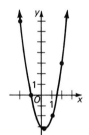

19. a.

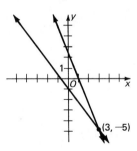

$(3, -5)$

b.

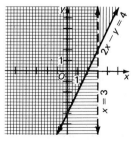

21. $\{9, -9\}$ **23.** $\{2.7\}$ **25.** $\{8, -3\}$
27. {the real numbers greater than or
equal to 14} **29.** $\{6, -3\}$ **31.** {the real
numbers less than or equal to 8} **33.** $\left(2, \dfrac{2}{3}\right)$
35. 2 km/h

Maintaining Skills, page 401
1. $n + 2 + \dfrac{-9}{n + 4}$ **3.** $r + 3 + \dfrac{3}{r + 5}$
5. $6s - 9 + \dfrac{7}{2s + 3}$
7. $c^2 - 2c + 2 - \dfrac{1}{c + 1}$ **9.** $\{-4\}$
11. $\{-5\}$ **13.** $\{21\}$ **15.** $\{10\}$ **17.** $\left\{-\dfrac{2}{3}\right\}$
19. $\left\{-\dfrac{8}{3}\right\}$ **21.** $\{0\}$ **23.** $\left\{\dfrac{35}{11}, -4\right\}$
25. $\{-1\}$

CHAPTER 11 RATIONAL AND IRRATIONAL NUMBERS

Written Exercises, pages 406–407 1. $<$
3. $<$ **5.** $>$ **7.** $>$ **9.** $>$ **11.** $-\dfrac{5}{7}, -\dfrac{3}{5}, \dfrac{2}{9}$
13. $\dfrac{91}{40}, \dfrac{57}{25}, 2.3$ **15.** $\dfrac{3}{7}, \dfrac{3}{5}, \dfrac{7}{9}, \dfrac{5}{6}$ **17.** $\dfrac{13}{24}$
19. $-\dfrac{27}{140}$ **21.** $\dfrac{28}{45}$ **23.** decreases
25. decreases **27.** $\dfrac{27}{32}$ **29.** $-\dfrac{41}{72}$ **31.** $\dfrac{5}{12}$,
for example **33.** $\dfrac{29a}{84}$
35. (2) Cancellation rule for fractions
(3) Multiplication axiom of order
(5) Multiplication axiom of order
(6) Cancellation rule for fractions

Written Exercises, pages 410–411 1. $0.\overline{4}$
3. 0.625 **5.** 0.6 **7.** 1.38 **9.** 0.5625
11. -0.55 **13.** $-0.\overline{45}$ **15.** -3.875
17. $\dfrac{33}{100}$ **19.** $\dfrac{2}{9}$ **21.** $\dfrac{7}{11}$ **23.** $-\dfrac{5}{12}$ **25.** $\dfrac{22}{15}$
27. $-\dfrac{139}{45}$ **29.** $\dfrac{1}{4}, \dfrac{1}{2}, \dfrac{1}{8}$ **31.** $\dfrac{4}{9}, \dfrac{3}{4}, \dfrac{1}{3}$
33. $\dfrac{9}{11}, \dfrac{22}{27}, \dfrac{2}{3}$ **35.** 0.008; 0.754, for
example **37.** $0.00\overline{6}$; 0.663, for example
39. $0.000\overline{2}$; 0.1137, for example

41. a. $\frac{1}{7} = 0.\overline{142857}$, $\frac{3}{7} = 0.\overline{428571}$ **b.** Each block contains the same digits, which would all be in the same order if arranged around a circle. **c.** $\frac{2}{7} = 0.\overline{285714}$, $\frac{4}{7} = 0.\overline{571428}$, $\frac{6}{7} = 0.\overline{857142}$ **43. a.** $\frac{7}{99} = 0.\overline{07}$, $\frac{15}{99} = 0.\overline{15}$, $\frac{86}{99} = 0.\overline{86}$ **b.** $1 = \frac{99}{99} = 0.\overline{99} = 0.\overline{9}$

Written Exercises, page 414 1. 16 **3.** 15 **5.** 19 **7.** -52 **9.** 72 **11.** $\frac{7}{60}$ **13.** $\frac{13}{8}$ **15.** $\frac{11}{25}$ **17.** $\frac{1}{5}$ **19.** $-\frac{22}{17}$ **21.** $\frac{1}{5}$ **23.** $-\frac{6}{5}$ **25.** $\frac{23}{10}$ **27.** $\pm\frac{27}{100}$ **29.** $\pm\frac{7}{100}$ **31.** -2 **33.** -8 **35.** $\frac{2}{5}$ **37.** $-\frac{1}{2}$ **39.** $\frac{9}{10}$ **41.** $\frac{3}{13}$ **43.** $\pm\frac{13}{20}$

Calculator Key-In, page 414 1. 2.236 **3.** 1.775 **5.** 0.673 **7.** 59.4390 **9.** 61.2372

Written Exercises, page 418 1. -22.4 **3.** 28.3 **5.** 99.5 **7.** 9.43 **9.** 0.76 **11.** 854 **13.** 510 **15.** 970 **17.** 3.61 **19.** -18.71

Written Exercises, page 420 1. $-0.6|t^3|$ **3.** $1.5a^2|b|$ **5.** $1.9|k^3n|$ **7.** $\frac{|n^3|}{13}$ **9.** $\frac{90}{|k^5|}$ **11.** $|x+5|$ **13.** $|k+9|$ **15.** $\{9, -9\}$ **17.** $\left\{\frac{3}{5}, -\frac{3}{5}\right\}$ **19.** $\{2, -2\}$ **21.** $\left\{\frac{1}{3}, -\frac{1}{3}\right\}$ **23.** $\{27.3, -27.3\}$ **25.** $\{2.6, -2.6\}$ **27.** $\{11.4, -11.4\}$ **29.** $\{11.1, -11.1\}$ **31.** $\{0.5, -0.5\}$ **33.** $\{2.7, -2.7\}$ **35.** $\{6.2, -6.2\}$

Problems, pages 420–421 1. 17.3 cm **3.** 7.1 cm by 28.4 cm **5.** 4.6 cm **7.** 42.4 cm **9.** 11.2 s **11.** 35.5 cm²

Computer Key-In, page 421 1. 3.87298

Written Exercises, pages 424–425 1. 10.00 **3.** 10.30 **5.** 18.38 **7.** 12.00 **9.** 2.24 **11.** no **13.** no **15.** no **17.** 15.56 **19.** 12.37 **21.** 21.63 **23.** 8.49 **25.** 8.94, 17.89

Problems, page 425 1. 9.43 cm **3.** 5 m **5.** 6, 8, 10 **7.** 34.64 cm **9.** 1.6 m

Just for Fun, page 425 13 peanuts

Extra, pages 426–427 1. 9.0 **3.** 10.0 **5.** 7.8 **7.** 8.5 **9.** 9.0 **11.** 14.2 **13.** For $A(0, 3)$, $B(3, 9)$, $C(6, 0)$, $D(9, 6)$: $AB = BD = DC = CA = 3\sqrt{5}$

Written Exercises, page 429 1. 6 **3.** 6 **5.** $3\sqrt{42}$ **7.** $12\sqrt{2}$ **9.** $36\sqrt{3}$ **11.** $\sqrt{2}$ **13.** 1 **15.** $\frac{1}{3}$ **17.** $\frac{\sqrt{2}}{12}$ **19.** $24\sqrt{3}$ **21.** $\frac{28\sqrt{2}}{3}$ **23.** $\frac{\sqrt{2}}{2}$ **25.** $-6|a|b$ **27.** $5\sqrt{m} + m$ **29.** -108 **31.** $4x^2\sqrt{22x}$ **33.** $45x$ **35.** $-2\sqrt{22}$ **37.** $2m\sqrt{3} - 12m\sqrt{3m}$ **39.** $24y^4\sqrt{3y}$

Written Exercises, pages 430–431 1. $3\sqrt{3}$ **3.** $-11\sqrt{21}$ **5.** $9\sqrt{3}$ **7.** $6\sqrt{3} - 5\sqrt{2}$ **9.** $12\sqrt{2}$ **11.** $14\sqrt{5}$ **13.** $4\sqrt{17} + 7\sqrt{6}$ **15.** $21\sqrt{5} + 6\sqrt{3}$ **17.** $\frac{2\sqrt{3}}{3}$ **19.** $\frac{47\sqrt{2}}{3}$ **21.** $\frac{\sqrt{6}}{12}$ **23.** $-\frac{23\sqrt{10}}{5}$ **25.** $\frac{55\sqrt{6} - 24\sqrt{3}}{30}$ **27.** $8\sqrt{3} + 48$ **29.** $\frac{5x}{24}$ **31.** $\frac{x}{ab} - \sqrt{a^2 + b^2}$ **33.** $7\sqrt{5}$

Just for Fun, page 431 The ant will reach the top on the eighth day.

Written Exercises, pages 432–433 1. 13 **3.** 42 **5.** 6 **7.** $19 + 8\sqrt{3}$ **9.** $67 + 16\sqrt{3}$ **11.** $169 + 24\sqrt{10}$ **13.** $21\sqrt{3} + 21$ **15.** $90\sqrt{2} - 18\sqrt{30}$ **17.** $50 + 8\sqrt{7}$ **19.** $163 - 26\sqrt{55}$ **21.** $742 + 79\sqrt{77}$ **23.** $\frac{-3 + 3\sqrt{3}}{2}$ **25.** $\frac{15 - 5\sqrt{5}}{4}$ **27.** $-4 - 2\sqrt{3} - \sqrt{15} - 2\sqrt{5}$ **29.** $\frac{18\sqrt{5} + 12}{41}$ **31.** $4 - 2\sqrt{2}$ **33.** 8 **39.** $x^2 - y$ **41.** $12m^2n - 19mp\sqrt{n} + 5p^2$

Written Exercises, page 435 1. 400 **3.** 27 **5.** $\frac{1}{48}$ **7.** 9 **9.** $\frac{16}{9}$ **11.** 100 **13.** 71 **15.** $\frac{32}{25}$ **17.** 45 **19.** $\frac{14}{3}$ **21.** $\frac{12}{5}$ **23.** $\frac{343}{9}$ **25.** 33 **27.** 61 **29.** 20 **31.** $\left\{\frac{5\sqrt{15}}{3}, -\frac{5\sqrt{15}}{3}\right\}$ **33.** $\{\sqrt{17}, -\sqrt{17}\}$ **35.** 4 **37.** $\{1, -4\}$ **39.** 1

24 *ANSWERS TO ODD-NUMBERED EXERCISES*

Problems, pages 435–436 1. 81 **3.** 80
5. 23 **7.** 100π cm² **9.** 54 and 56

Calculator Key-In, page 436 1. 0.618
3. 0.429 **5.** 1.754 **7.** 4.614

Chapter Review, pages 438–439 1. b **3.** c
5. a **7.** d **9.** d **11.** a **13.** b **15.** a

Cumulative Review, page 440
1. $(h - 3r^2)(h + 3r^2)(h^2 + 9r^4)$
3. $(3z - 5)(4z - 9)$ **5.** $x^5y^3 - x^3y^3 + 9x^3y$
7. $62 - 20\sqrt{6}$ **9.** $\dfrac{-5t^{13}}{4r}$ **11.** $15\sqrt{10}$
13. $\dfrac{2(r + 6)}{r(4r - 3)}$ **15.** $-\dfrac{b}{2}$
17. $\dfrac{16g - 5}{(g - 2)(4g + 1)}$
19. a.

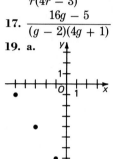

b.

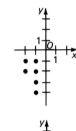

c.

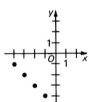

21. $f(-5) = 6, f(\sqrt{2} + 1) = 2 + 5\sqrt{2}$

$\left(-\frac{3}{2}, -\frac{25}{4}\right)$

23. $-\dfrac{43}{30}$ **25.** $\dfrac{5}{3}$ **27.** 25
29. $\{6\sqrt{3}, -6\sqrt{3}\}$ **31.** {the real numbers
greater than or equal to -3 and less than
$-\frac{1}{2}$} **33.** {the real numbers greater than
or equal to 7} **35.** {the real numbers less
than 3} **37.** $(7, -3)$ **39.** $\left(-1, \frac{3}{2}\right)$
41. 16.12 m

Maintaining Skills, page 441 1. $(-7, -2)$
3. $(0, 7)$ **5.** $(2, 6)$ **7.** $(-4, -6)$ **9.** $(0, 0)$
11. $\left(\dfrac{1}{4}, -\dfrac{1}{2}\right)$ **13.** no solution **15.** $(-6, 6)$
17. $\left(-7, -\dfrac{1}{3}\right)$ **19.** $(10, 2)$ **21.** $(16, 0)$

CHAPTER 12 QUADRATIC FUNCTIONS

Written Exercises, page 445 1. $\{10, -10\}$
3. $\left\{\dfrac{10}{11}, -\dfrac{10}{11}\right\}$ **5.** $\{9, -9\}$ **7.** $\{3, -3\}$
9. no solution **11.** $\{\sqrt{2}, -\sqrt{2}\}$
13. $\{2, -2\}$ **15.** $\{\sqrt{7}, -\sqrt{7}\}$ **17.** no
solution **19.** $\{4, -2\}$
21. $\{-4 + \sqrt{6}, -4 - \sqrt{6}\}$
23. $\{-3 + 3\sqrt{3}, -3 - 3\sqrt{3}\}$
25. $\{5 + \sqrt{5}, 5 - \sqrt{5}\}$
27. $\{-2 + \sqrt{10}, -2 - \sqrt{10}\}$ **29.** $\left\{\dfrac{3}{5}, -1\right\}$
31. $\{3, -1\}$ **33.** $\{1, -13\}$ **35.** $\left\{\dfrac{2}{3}, -\dfrac{2}{3}\right\}$
37. $\{\sqrt{11}, -\sqrt{11}\}$ **39.** $\left\{\dfrac{7}{11}, -\dfrac{7}{11}\right\}$
41. $\left\{\dfrac{7}{9}, -\dfrac{7}{9}\right\}$ **43.** $\left\{-\dfrac{37}{9}, -\dfrac{35}{9}\right\}$
45. $\left\{\dfrac{3 + \sqrt{10}}{5}, \dfrac{3 - \sqrt{10}}{5}\right\}$ **47.** $\{0, 3, -3\}$
49. $\{0, 5, -5\}$ **51.** $\{0, 7, -7\}$
53. $\{-1, -4\}$ **55.** no solution
57. $\{\sqrt{2} - \sqrt{7}, -\sqrt{2} - \sqrt{7}\}$

Written Exercises, page 448
1. $\{2 + \sqrt{26}, 2 - \sqrt{26}\}$ or $\{7.1, -3.1\}$
3. $\{-4 + 2\sqrt{3}, -4 - 2\sqrt{3}\}$ or
$\{-0.5, -7.5\}$ **5.** $\{3 + \sqrt{6}, 3 - \sqrt{6}\}$ or
$\{5.4, 0.6\}$ **7.** $\{1 + \sqrt{6}, 1 - \sqrt{6}\}$ or
$\{3.4, -1.4\}$ **9.** $\{8 + 2\sqrt{137}, 8 - 2\sqrt{137}\}$ or
$\{31.4, -15.4\}$ **11.** $\{-1 + \sqrt{5}, -1 - \sqrt{5}\}$
or $\{1.2, -3.2\}$ **13.** $\{1, -4\}$
15. $\left\{\dfrac{-11 + \sqrt{149}}{2}, \dfrac{-11 - \sqrt{149}}{2}\right\}$ or
$\{0.6, -11.6\}$ **17.** $\{37, -43\}$ **19.** $\{8, 5\}$
21. $\{-2, 20\}$ **23.** $\left\{\dfrac{3}{2}, -\dfrac{1}{2}\right\}$ **25.** $\{2, -4\}$
27. $\left\{\dfrac{1 + \sqrt{19}}{3}, \dfrac{1 - \sqrt{19}}{3}\right\}$
29. $\left\{\dfrac{5 + \sqrt{73}}{3}, \dfrac{5 - \sqrt{73}}{3}\right\}$
31. $\left\{\dfrac{11 + \sqrt{201}}{10}, \dfrac{11 - \sqrt{201}}{10}\right\}$

33. $\left\{\dfrac{-5 + \sqrt{313}}{12}, \dfrac{-5 - \sqrt{313}}{12}\right\}$

35. $\left\{\dfrac{-3 + \sqrt{137}}{8}, \dfrac{-3 - \sqrt{137}}{8}\right\}$

37. $\left\{\dfrac{-b + \sqrt{b^2 - 4}}{2}, \dfrac{-b - \sqrt{b^2 - 4}}{2}\right\}$;
$b \geq 2$ or $b \leq -2$

39. $\left\{\dfrac{-b + \sqrt{b^2 - 4ac}}{2a}, \dfrac{-b - \sqrt{b^2 - 4ac}}{2a}\right\}$;
$a \neq 0$ and $b^2 - 4ac \geq 0$

Written Exercises, pages 450–451
1. $\left\{-1 + \sqrt{2}, -1 - \sqrt{2}\right\}$ or $\{0.4, -2.4\}$
3. $\left\{-3 + \sqrt{5}, -3 - \sqrt{5}\right\}$ or $\{-0.8, -5.2\}$
5. $\{5, -1\}$ **7.** $\left\{-\dfrac{1}{2}, -2\right\}$ **9.** $\left\{4, -\dfrac{2}{3}\right\}$

11. $\left\{\dfrac{5}{4}, 1\right\}$ **13.** $\left\{\dfrac{-7 + \sqrt{89}}{20}, \dfrac{-7 - \sqrt{89}}{20}\right\}$

15. $\left\{\dfrac{3 + \sqrt{209}}{40}, \dfrac{3 - \sqrt{209}}{40}\right\}$ **17.** no

solution **19.** $\left\{\dfrac{7 + \sqrt{85}}{3}, \dfrac{7 - \sqrt{85}}{3}\right\}$

21. $\left\{\dfrac{-4 + \sqrt{26}}{4}, \dfrac{-4 - \sqrt{26}}{4}\right\}$ **23.** $-\dfrac{b}{a}$
25. $x^2 - 4x + 1 = 0$

Written Exercises, pages 454–455 **1.** 29;
two **3.** 37; two **5.** 17; two **7.** 25; two
9. -11; none **11.** 0; one **13.** two; below
15. two; above **17.** two; above **19.** 4

Just for Fun, page 455 **1.** 6

Written Exercises, pages 457–458
1. $\{-1, -2\}$ **3.** $\{17, -5\}$ **5.** $\{0, -3\}$

7. $\{3, -3\}$ **9.** $\left\{\dfrac{5 + \sqrt{37}}{3}, \dfrac{5 - \sqrt{37}}{3}\right\}$

11. $\left\{-3 + \sqrt{5}, -3 - \sqrt{5}\right\}$ **13.** $\{0, -4\}$

15. $\left\{\dfrac{1}{3}, -1\right\}$

17. $\left\{\dfrac{-3 + \sqrt{159}}{5}, \dfrac{-3 - \sqrt{159}}{5}\right\}$

19. $\left\{-9 + \sqrt{42}, -9 - \sqrt{42}\right\}$

21. $\left\{\dfrac{10 + \sqrt{118}}{6}, \dfrac{10 - \sqrt{118}}{6}\right\}$

23. $\left\{\dfrac{-13 + \sqrt{701}}{14}, \dfrac{-13 - \sqrt{701}}{14}\right\}$

25. $\left\{\dfrac{-29 + \sqrt{721}}{2}, \dfrac{-29 - \sqrt{721}}{2}\right\}$

27. $\left\{\dfrac{5}{3}, -\dfrac{1}{7}\right\}$ **29.** $\left\{\sqrt{7}, -\sqrt{7}\right\}$

31. $\left\{0, \dfrac{\sqrt{6}}{3}, -\dfrac{\sqrt{6}}{3}\right\}$

Problems, pages 460–461 **1.** 8 m by 5 m
3. 70 m by 120 m **5.** 8 cm **7.** 8.3 cm
9. 35 cm **11.** Dan, 3 h; Leah, 2 h
13. 90 km/h

Extra, page 462
1.

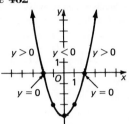

3.

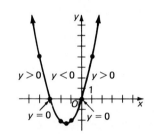

5.

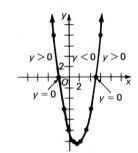

7. {all real numbers that are greater than
or equal to 6 or less than or equal to 0}

Application, page 463 **1.** 135,000 N
3. 6 m/s^2

Chapter Review, pages 464–465 **1.** b
3. a **5.** a **7.** d **9.** b

Cumulative Review, pages 466–467 **1.** 48
3. 197 **5.** $3z^3(-7z + 4 - 5z^5)$
7. $4(5b - 6y)(5b + 6y)$
9. $s(5s - 2t)(4s - 5t)$ **11.** 47 **13.** -39
15. $17c - 19$ **17.** $6t^5v^2 - 2t^4v^3$ **19.** $\dfrac{8}{3m^{10}}$

21. $27m^2 + 39m - 10$ **23.** $\dfrac{7c - d}{7c + 2d}$

25. $2m + 4$ **27.** z^3 **29.** $-\dfrac{3}{2}$

31. $\dfrac{-4t - 2}{(t + 3)(t - 2)}$ **33.** $-6\sqrt{10}$

35. $12a\sqrt{2}$ **37.** $\dfrac{1 - 3\sqrt{5}}{-2}$ **39.** $\dfrac{43}{55}$

41. a. $5x - y = -17$ **b.** $3x + 2y = 22$
43. $f(-4) = 42; f(2\sqrt{3}) = 22 - 6\sqrt{3}$

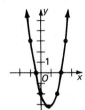

45. $-\dfrac{1}{2}$ **47.** 2.7 **49.** $\left\{\dfrac{4}{5}, -8\right\}$ **51.** {all

real numbers that are greater than $\dfrac{8}{3}$}

53. $\left\{-\dfrac{1}{3}, 2\right\}$ **55.** -3 **57.** $\left\{-\dfrac{1}{2}, 7\right\}$

59. {all real numbers that are greater than
or equal to 2, except for 3}
61. $\{3 + 2\sqrt{6}, 3 - 2\sqrt{6}\}$ **63.** $(-1, 2)$
65. $(-13, -9)$ **67.** 7 and 13 or -13 and
-7 **69.** 8 **71.** 640 cm^2 **73.** 9 min
75. 620 km/h

LOOKING AHEAD

Written Exercises, page 470 Answers may
vary for Exercises 1 and 3. **1.** any five of
$\overline{PQ}$, $\overline{QR}$, $\overline{RS}$, $\overline{PR}$, $\overline{QS}$, $\overline{PS}$ **3.** $\overline{XY}$, $\overline{YZ}$, $\overline{XZ}$,
$\overline{WY}$, $\overline{WZ}$ **5.** acute **7.** obtuse **9.** acute
11. obtuse

13. point

15. segment

17. line

19. segment

21. line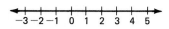

Written Exercises, pages 472–473
1. (Answers may vary.) $\angle EGF$, $\angle DCF$,
$\angle HGJ$ **3.** 140° **5.** 36° and 144° **7.** 55°
9. 90° **11.** 65°

Just for Fun, page 473 $x = 12$

Written Exercises, page 475 1. 69°
3. 125° **5.** 49° **7.** yes **9.** yes **11.** no
13. $US = 15$ **15.** $\angle R = 65°$
17. $AB = 2\sqrt{34}$ **19.** $BC = 2\sqrt{5}$
21. $AB = x\sqrt{2}$

Problems, page 476 1. 90°, 18°, 72°
3. 18°, 54°, 108° **5.** 70°, 35°, 75° **7.** 22°,
46°, 112° **9.** 32°, 78°, 70°

Just for Fun, page 476

Written Exercises, page 478 1. $\angle D$ and
$\angle K$, $\angle E$ and $\angle L$, $\angle F$ and $\angle J$, $\overline{DE}$ and
$\overline{KL}$, $\overline{EF}$ and $\overline{LJ}$, $\overline{DF}$ and $\overline{KJ}$ **3.** false
5. false **7.** $EF = 6$, $DF = 8$ **9.** $DE = 2$,
$DF = 4$ **11.** $DE = 5\dfrac{1}{3}$, $EF = 6\dfrac{2}{3}$

Problems, page 479 1. 12 cm **3.** 10 m
5. 3 m

Just for Fun, page 479 The reasoning for
the parallelogram is logical, but the
reasoning for the canaries is not. There
could be canaries in other parts of the
Canary Islands.

Written Exercises, page 482 1. $\cos A = \dfrac{3}{5}$,

$\sin A = \dfrac{4}{5}$, $\tan A = \dfrac{4}{3}$, $\cos B = \dfrac{4}{5}$,

$\sin B = \dfrac{3}{5}$, $\tan B = \dfrac{3}{4}$ **3.** $\cos A = \dfrac{5\sqrt{41}}{41}$,

$\sin A = \dfrac{4\sqrt{41}}{41}$, $\tan A = \dfrac{4}{5}$, $\cos B = \dfrac{4\sqrt{41}}{41}$,

$\sin B = \dfrac{5\sqrt{41}}{41}$, $\tan B = \dfrac{5}{4}$

5. $\cos A = \dfrac{2\sqrt{14}}{9}$, $\sin A = \dfrac{5}{9}$,

$\tan A = \dfrac{5\sqrt{14}}{28}$, $\cos B = \dfrac{5}{9}$, $\sin B = \dfrac{2\sqrt{14}}{9}$,

$\tan B = \dfrac{2\sqrt{14}}{5}$ **7.** $\cos A = \dfrac{b}{c} = \sin B$

9. $(\sin A)^2 + (\cos A)^2 = \left(\dfrac{a}{c}\right)^2 + \left(\dfrac{b}{c}\right)^2 =$

$\dfrac{a^2 + b^2}{c^2} = \dfrac{c^2}{c^2} = 1$ **11.** $\dfrac{8}{10}$ **13.** $\sin D = \dfrac{20}{29}$,

$\cos D = \dfrac{21}{29}$

Written Exercises, page 484 For Exercises 1–11, answers are given in the order $\sin A$, $\cos A$, $\tan A$ **1.** 0.3420, 0.9397, 0.3640 **3.** 0.5736, 0.8192, 0.7002 **5.** 0.2924, 0.9563, 0.3057 **7.** 0.6820, 0.7134, 0.9325 **9.** 0.8829, 0.4695, 1.8807 **11.** 0.9563, 0.2924, 3.2709 **13.** 28° **15.** 68° **17.** 23° **19.** 44° **21.** 21° **23.** 86°

Written Exercises, page 487 **1.** 16 **3.** 10 **5.** 53 **7.** $BC \approx 40$, $AC \approx 50$ **9.** $BC \approx 17$, $AB \approx 62$ **11.** $\angle M \approx 61°$, $\angle R \approx 29°$ **13.** $\angle M \approx 18°$, $\angle R \approx 72°$ **15.** $YZ \approx 39$, $XZ \approx 31$ **17.** $YZ \approx 19$, $XZ \approx 43$

Problems, pages 487–489 **1.** 98 m **3.** 15 m **5.** 3° **7.** 87 km **9.** 167 m **11.** 284 m **13.** 74° **15.** 8 m and 14 m

Review, page 490 **1.** a **3.** d **5.** c **7.** c **9.** a

EXTRA PRACTICE

Chapter 1, page 491 **1.** 22 **3.** 220 **5.** 2 **7.** 14 **9.** 1 **11.** 3 **13.** 2 **15.** 14 **17.** 1 **19.** no solution **21.** {4} **23.** {4} **25.** {2, 4, 6, 8, 10} **27.** no solution **29.** $n + 3$, or $3 + n$ **31.** $\dfrac{3}{n}$, or $3 \div n$ **33.** $2(n - 5)$ **35.** $x + 2$ **37.** $2r$ **39.** $22 - d$ **41.** $m - p$ **43–53.** Answers may vary. **43.** $4x = 32$ **45.** $12t = 8$ **47.** $m + (m + 1) + (m + 2) = 4224$ **49.** $x + 3x = x(3x)$ **51.** $7x = 175$ **53.** $r + (2r + 3) = 11.4$

Chapter 2, page 492 **1.** -5 **3.** 2 **5.** -5 **7.** 0 **9.** 6 **11.** -15 **13.** -2 **15.** 4 **17.** -6 **19.** -19 **21.** 17 **23.** -3

25. -21 **27.** -33 **29.** -30 **31.** 2 **33.** -7 **35.** -18 **37.** 0 **39.** {4} **41.** {2, 4} **43.** {-4, 4} **45.** {-2, 2} **47.** -14 **49.** 10 **51.** -3 **53.** -96 **55. a.** 3, -2, 7, 2 **b.** 10 **c.** 10 spaces **57. a.** 20, -8, 2, -1.5 **b.** 12.5 **c.** 12.5°C **59.** 7 **61.** 4 **63.** 2100 **65.** $4x$ **67.** $-20a$ **69.** x **71.** $12 + 14y$ **73.** $-8h$ **75.** $100x + 200$ **77.** $2.4x + 5.6$ **79.** $11k + 1 + 5m$ **81.** 8 **83.** 6 **85.** 0 **87.** -24 **89.** 0 **91.** -300 **93.** -1.8 **95.** 18 **97.** 14 **99.** -21 **101.** $-2x + (-6)$ **103.** $-16x + 6y$ **105.** -55 **107.** $\dfrac{1}{63}$ **109.** -5 **111.** 370 **113.** $11x + 22y$ **115.** $2x + 4y$

Chapter 3, page 495 **1.** 14 **3.** 9 **5.** -12 **7.** -14 **9.** -612 **11.** 12 **13.** 6 **15.** 30 **17.** 0 **19.** -59 **21.** -7 **23.** -1 **25.** -1 **27.** 0 **29.** z **31.** $9x$ **33.** $2m + 14$ **35.** -11 **37.** 5 **39.** -4 **41.** 15 **43.** -3 **45.** -7 **47.** 14 **49.** -14 **51.** -17 **53.** -34 **55.** 50 **57.** 11 **59.** -6 **61.** 1 **63.** 22 **65.** -4 **67.** -40 **69.** 15 **71.** -42 **73.** 63 **75.** -7 **77.** -7 **79.** 3 **81.** 1 **83.** 1134 **85.** -21 **87.** 9 **89.** -2 **91.** $\dfrac{5}{2}$ **93.** 0 **95.** $-\dfrac{12}{5}$ **97.** 4 **99.** 2 **101.** $\dfrac{3}{5}$ **103.** -1 **105.** 5 **107.** $\dfrac{3}{8}$ **109.** 2

Chapter 4, page 497 **1.** 25 **3.** 625 **5.** $\dfrac{1}{4}$ **7.** $\dfrac{1}{4}$ **9.** -25 **11.** -4000 **13.** 18 **15.** -78 **17.** -2 **19.** $3x^2 - 7x + 7$ **21.** $-4x - 2y - 10$ **23.** $5a + 5b + 5c + 5d$ **25.** 5 **27.** -9 **29.** a^{12} **31.** $60x^{18}$ **33.** $-8n^7 m^3$ **35.** $a^4 b^2$ **37.** $6xy^2$ **39.** 1 **41.** $8x^3$ **43.** x^{12} **45.** $4x^2 y^4$ **47.** $-27x^4$ **49.** $10a^4 b^4$ **51.** $8u^6 v^{10}$ **53.** -64 **55.** 0 **57.** 4 **59.** $-3x^3 - 15x^2 - 18x$ **61.** $-3x^4 - 15x^3 - 18x^2$ **63.** $-6x^2$ **65.** $-t^3 + 60t$ **67.** x **69.** 4 **71.** -3 **73.** -20 **75.** $m^2 - m - 6$ **77.** $m^2 - 5m + 6$ **79.** $2x^2 + 5x - 12$ **81.** $2x^2 - 11x + 12$ **83.** $9x^2 + 12x + 4$ **85.** $8x^3 - 1$

Chapter 5, page 498 **1.** 1, 2, 3, 4, 6, 11, 12 **3.** 1, 2, 3, 6, 11 **5.** 1, 2, 3, 6 **7.** 1, 2, 3, 4, 5,

6, 8, 10, 12 **9.** $2^3 \cdot 5 \cdot 7$ **11.** $2^2 \cdot 3^2 \cdot 7$ **13.** $\dfrac{x^3}{6}$

15. $2x^3$ **17.** $2r^3 - r$ **19.** $2r^2 - 4r$

21. $\dfrac{2}{y} - \dfrac{3}{x} + \dfrac{1}{2xy}$ **23.** 198,000 **25.** 144

27. $8xy(x - 1)$ **29.** $2\pi r(r - 1)$

31. $\pi rh\left(\dfrac{1}{3}r + 1\right)$ **33.** $-3x(x - 2)$, or

$3x(-x + 2)$ **35.** $5xy(2x - y)$

37. $5mr(2m^2 - 4r + 3)$ **39.** $2m^2 - m - 3$

41. $2m^2 + m - 3$ **43.** $16x^2 + 40x + 25$

45. $10w^2 - 11w + 3$ **47.** $(2x + 1)(2x - 1)$

49. $(b^2 + 40c)(b^2 - 40c)$ **51.** $(4a + b)^2$

53. $(k + 7)(k + 5)$ **55.** $(m - 6)(m - 1)$

57. $(p + 6)(p + 2)$ **59.** $(k + 10)(k + 2)$

61. $(y - 20)(y - 1)$ **63.** $(x - 3)(x - 2)$

65. $(x + 8)(x - 1)$ **67.** $(x + 4)(x - 2)$

69. $(y + 10)(y - 2)$ **71.** $(a + 4)(a - 3)$

73. $(r + 11)(r - 3)$ **75.** $(m + 20)(m - 1)$

77. $(p + 1)(8p - 7)$ **79.** $(8x + 7)(x - 1)$

81. $(2r + 1)(4r - 7)$ **83.** $(4y + 7)(2y - 1)$

85. $(6x + 1)(x - 2)$ **87.** $(2x + 1)(x - 3)$

89. $(4d + 1)(3d - 2)$ **91.** $(3x - 4)(2x - 3)$

93. $(x + 6)(3x - 4)$ **95.** $(a + 3)^2$

97. $(x + y)(x + 2)$ **99.** $(x + 1)^2(x - 3)$

101. $(a^4 + 64)(1 + a)(1 - a)$ **103.** $\{-1\}$

105. $\{5\}$ **107.** $\left\{-\dfrac{1}{2}, -7\right\}$

109. $\{0, -1, -2\}$ **111.** $\{12, -2\}$

113. $\left\{3, -\dfrac{1}{2}\right\}$ **115.** $\left\{5, -\dfrac{2}{3}\right\}$

117. $\left\{-\dfrac{1}{2}, 1\right\}$ **119, 121.** Answers may

vary. **119.** $x^2 - x - 2 = 0$

121. $x^2 - 49 = 0$

Chapter 6, page 500 **1.** 4 **3.** $\dfrac{2}{3}$; $x \neq -y$

5. $\dfrac{1 + b}{2}$; $a \neq 0$ **7.** $\dfrac{y + a}{xy + y}$; $x \neq 0, x \neq -1$,

$y \neq 0$ **9.** $\dfrac{4r + 1}{4r - 1}$; $r \neq \dfrac{1}{4}, r \neq -\dfrac{1}{4}$

11. $\dfrac{k - 4}{k - 5}$; $k \neq 4, k \neq 5$ **13.** -1; $x \neq \dfrac{1}{2}$

15. $-\dfrac{3x - 1}{3 - x}$, or $\dfrac{3x - 1}{x - 3}$; $x \neq \dfrac{5}{2}, x \neq 3$

17. $\dfrac{-2}{1 - 2a}$; $a \neq 0, a \neq \dfrac{1}{2}$ **19.** 2 **21.** $3m$

23. $10r$ **25.** $\dfrac{c}{c + 1}$ **27.** $\dfrac{x - 3}{(x + 3)(x + 2)}$

29. $3b^3$ **31.** $\dfrac{7}{a + b}$ **33.** $\dfrac{1}{3x + y}$ **35.** $\dfrac{2x}{a + b}$

37. $\dfrac{3}{2(3x + 5)}$ **39.** $\dfrac{1}{a - 1}$ **41.** $\dfrac{m^2}{m + r}$

43. $\dfrac{12x + 5}{(2x + 1)(3x + 1)}$ **45.** $-\dfrac{2r}{(r + 2)^2}$

47. 0 **49.** $\dfrac{2}{(x - 3)(x - 2)(x - 1)}$

51. $\dfrac{5a^2 - 2a - 32}{(a + 2)^2(a - 2)}$ **53.** $\dfrac{1}{2x - 1}$

55. $5x + 4$ **57.** $6a + 5$ **59.** $x^2 + 2x + 4$

61. $x^2 - 2x + 2$ **63.** $k - 1$

65. $p^2 + 3 - \dfrac{3p}{p^2 + p + 1}$

67. $-3m^3 - m^2 + m + 2$

Chapter 7, page 502 **1.** $5:8$ **3.** $7:32$

5. $3:200$ **7.** $\dfrac{1}{3}$ **9.** $\dfrac{10}{17}$ **11.** 19 **13.** -3

15. 15 **17.** 45 **19.** -5 **21.** 5 **23.** 2

25. 2 **27.** 7 **29.** $-\dfrac{1}{2}$ **31.** 2.97 **33.** 0.314

35. 80 **37.** 222 **39.** $57\dfrac{1}{7}$ **41.** 33

Chapter 8, page 503 **1.** $y = 8 - 2x$

3. $y = 6 - \dfrac{3}{2}x$ **5.** $y = \dfrac{1}{2}x - 2$

7. $y = 2x - 5$ **9.** $y = \dfrac{10}{3} - \dfrac{2}{3}x$ **11.** 1

13. 1 **15.** $-\dfrac{52}{5}$ **17. a.** $(20, 0)$ **b.** $(0, -5)$

19. a. $(10, 0)$ **b.** $(0, -2)$ **21. a.** $(100, 0)$

b. $(0, 30)$

23.

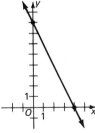

25.

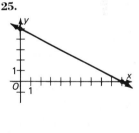

27.

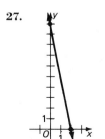

29.

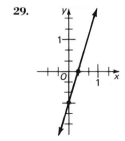

31.

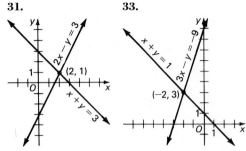

33.

35. $(9, -3)$ **37.** $s + a = 640$

39. $a = 2s + 160$ **41.** $\left(5, -\dfrac{25}{2}\right)$

43. $(5, -1)$ **45.** $(-3, -4)$ **47.** $n + 6$

49. $2(n + d)$ **51.** $20t + 2u$ **53.** $\dfrac{3n}{d - 7}$

55. $s - r$

Chapter 9, page 504 **1.** 2 **3.** -4 **5.** $\dfrac{1}{2}$

7. -2 **9.** -1 **11.** $\dfrac{5}{2}$ **13.** yes; $\dfrac{4}{3}$ **15.** yes;

$-\dfrac{3}{2}$

17.

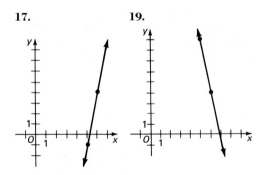

19.

21–25. Answers may vary.
21. $5x - y = -10$ **23.** $6x + 2y = 1$
25. $2x - y = -4$

27.

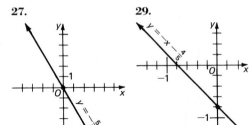

29.

31.

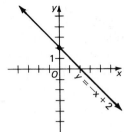

33–37. Answers may vary.
33. $2x - y = 2$ **35.** $4x - y = 0$ **37.** $y = 4$

39. **a.** 7 **b.** $5\dfrac{1}{2}$ **41.** **a.** 8 **b.** $\dfrac{9}{16}$ **43.** 2

and 3 **45.** $(2, -4)$ **47.** $(-1, 3)$

49. $\left(4\dfrac{1}{2}, 1\dfrac{1}{2}\right)$ **51.** 25 **53.** 13 **55.** 12

57. 2 **59.** 1 **61.** **a.** 3 **b.** 12 **63.** **a.** $\dfrac{1}{2}$

b. 2 **65.** $C = kd$; $\dfrac{C_1}{d_1} = \dfrac{C_2}{d_2}$ (Answers may

vary.) **67.** inverse; 3 **69.** direct; 3 or $\dfrac{1}{3}$

71. direct; 7.5 **73.** direct; cannot be

determined **75.** inverse; $\dfrac{1}{8}$ **77.** 2

79–85. Answers may vary. **79.** $bh = k$;
$b_1h_1 = b_2h_2$ **81.** $p = kv^2$ **83.** $V = klwd$
85. $F = \dfrac{kv^2}{r}$

Chapter 10, page 507

1.

3.

5. $\left\{\text{the real numbers less than } \dfrac{23}{3}\right\}$

7. $\left\{\text{the real numbers greater than } \dfrac{2}{3}\right\}$

9. $\left\{\text{the real numbers less than } \dfrac{2}{3}\right\}$

11. false **13.** true **15.** $\left\{\dfrac{1}{2}, -\dfrac{1}{2}\right\}$

17. $\{9, 7\}$ **19.** $\left\{3, -\dfrac{5}{3}\right\}$ **21.** {the real

numbers greater than 2 or less than -2}
23. {the real numbers between -5 and -3}
25. $\left\{\text{the real numbers between } -\dfrac{1}{2} \text{ and } \dfrac{9}{2}\right\}$
27–35. Answers may vary.

27. $n(n + 1) > 152$ **29.** $d \geq 42$ **31.** $p \leq 3$
33. $c \leq 28$ **35.** $6c \geq b + 4$ **37.** {2 and the
real numbers between 0 and 2} **39.** {4}
41. {the real numbers between -4 and 0}
43. {the real numbers} **45.** $\left\{\text{the real}\right.$
numbers greater than $\frac{1}{2}$ or less than $\left.-1\right\}$
47. $\left\{1 \text{ and the real numbers between}\right.$
$\frac{2}{3}$ and $\left.1\right\}$ **49.** no **51.** yes

53.

55.

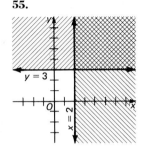

57.

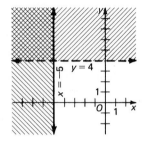

Chapter 11, page 508 1–5. Answers may
vary **1.** $\frac{13}{10}$ **3.** $\frac{3}{25}$ **5.** $-\frac{21}{8}$ **7.** $>$
9. $<$ **11.** $<$ **13.** $>$ **15.** $>$ **17.** 10
19. $\frac{7}{15}$ **21.** $-\frac{31}{39}$ **23.** $\frac{11}{7}$ **25.** $0.\overline{6}$
27. 28.1 **29.** 1.75 **31.** $0.\overline{135802469}$
33. 1.8 **35.** $7.\overline{36}$ **37.** $\frac{7}{50}$ **39.** $\frac{14}{5}$ **41.** $\frac{62}{99}$
43. $\frac{111}{90}$ **45.** 0.75, or $\frac{3}{4}$; 0.875, or $\frac{7}{8}$
47. 0.11; 0.165 **49.** 0.38; -2.31 **51.** 31
53. 42 **55.** 252 **57.** $\frac{4}{25}$ **59.** $\frac{3}{5}$ **61.** 0.9
63. 6.32 **65.** 91.10 **67.** 0.14 **69.** 6.16
71. 5.08 **73.** $9m^2$ **75.** $|a + 1|$
77. $m^{50}n^{100}$ **79.** $|4a - 1|$ **81.** {38, -38}
83. $\left\{\frac{1}{6}, -\frac{1}{6}\right\}$ **85.** {29, -29}
87. {3.3, -3.3} **89.** {2.7, -2.7} **91.** 10
93. 3.16 **95.** 25 **97.** $4\frac{1}{6}$ **99.** $6\sqrt{21}$

101. $10\sqrt{2}$ **103.** $\frac{\sqrt{26}}{13}$ **105.** $\frac{\sqrt{2}}{3}$
107. $6\sqrt{5}$ **109.** $32x$ **111.** $9x$ **113.** $\frac{1}{3}$
115. 3 **117.** $2\sqrt{2}$ **119.** $13\sqrt{7}$ **121.** $\frac{9}{2}\sqrt{2}$
123. $-\frac{4}{3}\sqrt{15}$ **125.** 0 **127.** $25\sqrt{2}$
129. $-8\sqrt{15}$ **131.** 23 **133.** 37 **135.** 7
137. $32 - 10\sqrt{7}$ **139.** $9 + 2\sqrt{14}$
141. $2\sqrt{3} + 3$ **143.** $25 + \frac{25}{2}\sqrt{3}$
145. $95 - 5\sqrt{21}$ **147.** $9\sqrt{3} - 11\sqrt{2}$
149. $\frac{4\sqrt{7} + 10}{3}$ **151.** 2 **153.** $14 + 2\sqrt{35}$
155. {-4} **157.** {30} **159.** $\left\{\frac{17}{2}\right\}$
161. {5}

Chapter 12, page 512 1. $(x + 3)^2$
3. $(x - 11)^2$ **5.** $\left\{\frac{1}{5}, -\frac{1}{5}\right\}$ **7.** {1, -17}
9. $\left\{\frac{\sqrt{42}}{6}, -\frac{\sqrt{42}}{6}\right\}$
11. $\{3 + \sqrt{7}, 3 - \sqrt{7}\}$ **13.** $\left\{1, \frac{1}{3}\right\}$
15. 36; 6 **17.** $\frac{49}{4}; \frac{7}{2}$ **19.** {2, -8}
21. $\{6 + \sqrt{46}, 6 - \sqrt{46}\}$
23. $\{4 + 9\sqrt{17}, 4 - 9\sqrt{17}\}$ **25.** {50, -32}
27. $\left\{\frac{-1 + \sqrt{5}}{2}, \frac{-1 - \sqrt{5}}{2}\right\}$ **29.** $\left\{\frac{1}{2}, -3\right\}$
31. $\{-1 + \sqrt{3}, -1 - \sqrt{3}\}$
33. $\{4 + \sqrt{15}, 4 - \sqrt{15}\}$
35. $\{5 + \sqrt{15}, 5 - \sqrt{15}\}$ **37.** $\left\{2, \frac{3}{2}\right\}$
39. $\left\{\frac{2 + \sqrt{22}}{6}, \frac{2 - \sqrt{22}}{6}\right\}$ **41.** 13; two
43. -36; none **45.** 4; two **47.** -104;
none **49.** $\left\{\frac{2 + \sqrt{19}}{3}, \frac{2 - \sqrt{19}}{3}\right\}$
51. {0, -2} **53.** $\{-3 + \sqrt{19}, -3 - \sqrt{19}\}$
55. $\{2 + 2\sqrt{3}, 2 - 2\sqrt{3}\}$

Problems, Chapter 3, page 514 1. -134
3. -23 **5.** 345 cm **7.** $12 - (-6) = 18$;
$18°$C **9.** $1230 - (-22) = 1252$; 1252 points
11. $-38.87 - (-78) = 39.13$; $39.13°$C
13. 18 **15.** 18 **17.** 94 **19.** 4 kg
21. \$4.50 **23.** 4 km **25.** -32 **27.** \$2.16
29. 11 **31.** soup, 85¢; salad, \$1.70
33. \$192 **35.** -4 **37.** 2

Problems, Chapter 4, page 516 **1.** 31, 32, 33
3. $-20, -19, -18$ **5.** 43, 45 **7.** 4, 5, 6
9. 6 years ago **11.** 14 student tickets
13. mathematics, 6 h; music, 4 h **15.** 11:12
A.M. **17.** 22 m by 15 m **19.** 20 m by 20 m

Problems, Chapter 5, page 517 **1.** 2 cm by
1 cm **3.** $-11, -9$ **5.** 11 m by 3 m **7.** 35 m
by 15 m

Problems, Chapter 7, page 517 **1.** 15 cm,
36 cm, 39 cm **3.** $11,250 **5.** 700 L **7.** 120
families **9.** 5 cm, 5 cm, 2 cm **11.** 3
13. 2, 5 **15.** 476 people **17.** $532
19. $7\frac{1}{2}\%$ **21.** $32.13 **23.** 30 kg

25. 10 kg of peppers; 5 kg of onions
27. about 3.4 h **29.** 4 d

Problems, Chapter 8, page 520 **1.** ninth-
grade, 45 bags; tenth-grade, 20 bags
3. engineer, $80; assistant, $60 **5.** first
number, 2; second number, 4 **7.** tape
player, $96; radio, $49 **9.** apples, $6;
apricots, $4 **11.** father, 36 years; son, 10
years **13.** 85 **15.** $\frac{16}{20}$ **17.** plane,

270 km/h; wind, 90 km/h

Problems, Chapter 9, page 521 **1.** 119 L of
oil **3.** 435 kg **5.** 63 r.p.m. **7.** $4900
9. 33.75 cm

Problems, Chapter 10, page 522 **1.** 4, 6
3. 38 km/h, 42 km/h

Problems, Chapter 11, page 522 **1.** 19.2 cm
by 6.4 cm **3.** 69.3 cm **5.** 3.32 m **7.** 100
9. 10

Problems, Chapter 12, page 523 **1.** 6 cm
3. 42, 44; $-42, -44$ **5.** 8 cm, 10 cm
7. 15 cm long, 10 cm wide, 11 cm high

Appendix, page 532 **1.** 45

3. -1 **5.** $6\frac{1}{2}$ **7.** 500 **9.** $\dfrac{u}{v^4}$

11. $\dfrac{q^2}{p}$ **13.** $\dfrac{n^3}{m^2}$ **15.** 1 **17.** $\dfrac{x^2}{4y^4}$

19. $\dfrac{a^2}{3}$ **21.** xy^{-3} **23.** $m^{-2}n^5$

25. $x^{-1}y^3w^{-1}z^2$ **27.** $7x^2$ **29.** c
31. $r^4s^4 + 3s^4$ **33.** $5uv^4 - 25u^4v^2$
35. $1 - 3c + d$

Appendix, page 535 **1.** $18x + 3y \geq 25$
3. Corner points are $(0, 8)$, $(2, 5)$, and $(12, 0)$.

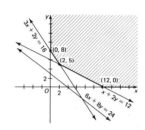

5. The most economical choice is to use
12 gallons of A and no gallons of B.
7. Corner points are $(0, 0)$, $(0, 200)$, $(100, 150)$, and $(300, 0)$.

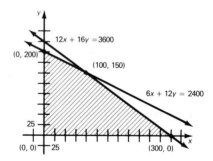